Improve Your Grade!

Access included with any new book.

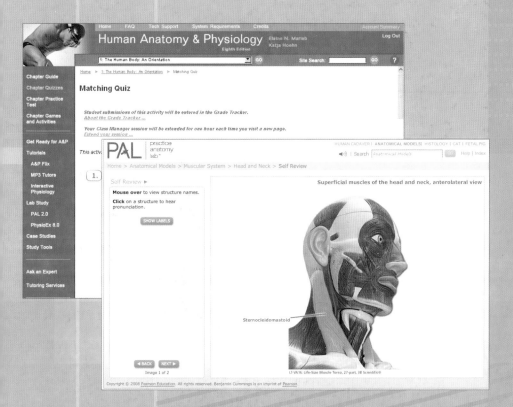

Registration will let you:

- Check your preparedness for A&P by taking *Get Ready for A&P* tests

- Prepare for exams by taking practice tests and quizzes

- Master tough concepts in A&P using interactive tutorials and animations

- Prepare for lab practicals by taking lab practicals in *Practice Anatomy Lab™* 2.0

www.myaandp.com

TO REGISTER

1. Go to www.myaandp.com

2. Click "Register."

3. Follow the on-screen instructions to create your login name and password.

Your Access Code is:

Note: If there is no silver foil covering the access code, it may already have been redeemed, and therefore may no longer be valid. In that case, you can purchase access online using a major credit card or PayPal account. To do so, go to www.myaandp.com, click "Buy Access," and follow the on-screen instructions.

TO LOG IN

1. Go to www.myaandp.com

2. Click "Log In."

3. Pick your book cover.

4. Enter your login name and password.

5. Click "Log In."

Hint:
Remember to bookmark the site after you log in.

Technical Support:
http://247pearsoned.custhelp.com

Human Anatomy & Physiology

Volume 1

CUSTOM EDITION FOR ARAPAHOE COMMUNITY COLLEGE

Elaine N. Marieb
Katja Hoehn

Taken from:
Human Anatomy & Physiology, Eighth Edition
by Elaine N. Marieb, R.N., Ph.D. and Katja Hoehn, M.D., Ph.D.

Custom Publishing

New York Boston San Francisco
London Toronto Sydney Tokyo Singapore Madrid
Mexico City Munich Paris Cape Town Hong Kong Montreal

Taken from:

Human Anatomy & Physiology, Eighth Edition
by Elaine N. Marieb, R.N., Ph. D. and Katja Hoehn, M.D., Ph.D.
Copyright © 2010 by Pearson Education, Inc.
Published by Benjamin Cummings
San Francisco, California 94111

This special edition published in cooperation with Pearson Custom Publishing.

Printed in the United States of America

10 9 8 7 6 5 4 3 2 1

2009640134

DM

Pearson
Custom Publishing
is a division of

www.pearsonhighered.com

ISBN 10: 0-558-36082-3
ISBN 13: 978-0-558-36082-5

About the Authors

*We dedicate this work to our students both present and past,
who always inspire us to "push the envelope."*

Elaine N. Marieb

For Elaine N. Marieb, taking the student's perspective into account has always been an integral part of her teaching style. Dr. Marieb began her teaching career at Springfield College, where she taught anatomy and physiology to physical education majors. She then joined the faculty of the Biological Science Division of Holyoke Community College in 1969 after receiving her Ph.D. in zoology from the University of Massachusetts at Amherst. While teaching at Holyoke Community College, where many of her students were pursuing nursing degrees, she developed a desire to better understand the relationship between the scientific study of the human body and the clinical aspects of the nursing practice. To that end, while continuing to teach full time, Dr. Marieb pursued her nursing education, which culminated in a Master of Science degree with a clinical specialization in gerontology from the University of Massachusetts. It is this experience, along with stories from the field—including those of former students now in health careers—that has informed the development of the unique perspective and accessibility for which her texts and laboratory manuals are known.

In her ongoing commitment to students and her realization of the challenges they face, Dr. Marieb has given generously to provide opportunities for students to further their education. She contributes to the New Directions, New Careers Program at Holyoke Community College by funding a staffed drop-in center and by providing several full-tuition scholarships each year for women who are returning to college after a hiatus or attending college for the first time and who would be unable to continue their studies without financial support. She funds the E. N. Marieb Science Research Awards at Mount Holyoke College, which promotes research by undergraduate science majors, and

has underwritten renovation and updating of one of the biology labs in Clapp Laboratory at that college. Dr. Marieb is also a contributor to the University of Massachusetts at Amherst where she generously provided funding for reconstruction and instrumentation of a cutting-edge cytology research laboratory that bears her name. Recognizing the severe national shortage of nursing faculty, she underwrites the Nursing Scholars of the Future Grant Program at the university.

In 1994, Dr. Marieb received the Benefactor Award from the National Council for Resource Development, American Association of Community Colleges, which recognizes her ongoing sponsorship of student scholarships, faculty teaching awards, and other academic contributions to Holyoke Community College. In May 2000, the science building at Holyoke Community College was named in her honor.

Dr. Marieb is an active member of the Human Anatomy and Physiology Society (HAPS) and the American Association for the Advancement of Science (AAAS). Additionally, while actively engaged as an author, Dr. Marieb serves as a consultant for the Benjamin Cummings *Interactive Physiology®* CD-ROM series. This text—*Human Anatomy & Physiology*, Eighth Edition—is the latest expression of her commitment to the needs of students in their pursuit of the study of A&P.

When not involved in academic pursuits, Dr. Marieb is a world traveler and has vowed to visit every country on this planet. Shorter term, she serves on the board of directors of the famed Marie Selby Botanical Gardens and on the scholarship committee of the Women's Resources Center of Sarasota County. She is an enthusiastic supporter of the local arts and enjoys a competitive match of doubles tennis.

Katja Hoehn

Dr. Katja Hoehn is an instructor in the Department of Chemical and Biological Sciences at Mount Royal College in Calgary, Canada. Dr. Hoehn's first love is teaching. Her teaching excellence has been recognized by several awards during her 14 years at Mount Royal College. These include a PanCanadian Educational Technology Faculty Award (1999), a Teaching Excellence Award from the Students' Association of Mount Royal College (2001), and the Mount Royal College Distinguished Faculty Teaching Award (2004).

Dr. Hoehn received her M.D. (with Distinction) from the University of Saskatchewan, and her Ph.D. in Pharmacology from Dalhousie University. In 1991, the Dalhousie Medical Research Foundation presented her with the Max Forman (Jr.) Prize for excellence in medical research. During her Ph.D. and postdoctoral studies, she also pursued her passion for teaching by presenting guest lectures to first- and second-year medical students at Dalhousie University and at the University of Calgary.

Dr. Hoehn has been a contributor to several books and has written numerous research papers in Neuroscience and Pharmacology. She oversaw the recent revision of the Benjamin Cummings *Interactive Physiology*® CD-ROM series modules, and coauthored the newest module, *The Immune System*.

Dr. Hoehn is also actively involved in the Human Anatomy and Physiology Society (HAPS). When not teaching, she likes to spend time outdoors with her husband and two boys, compete in triathlons, and play Irish flute.

To the Student: How to Use This Book

Introduce yourself to the chapter

Chapter outlines provide a preview of the chapter and let you know where you're going.

Focus on key concepts

Student objectives have been integrated into the chapter and give you a preview of what content is to come and what you are expected to learn.

NEW! Check Your Understanding questions ask you to stop, think, and to check your understanding of key concepts at the end of major sections.

Homeostatic Imbalance sections are integrated within the text and alert you to the consequences of body systems not functioning optimally. These pathological conditions are integrated with the text to clarify and illuminate normal functioning.

Regenerative Capacity of Different Tissues

The different tissues vary widely in their capacity for regeneration. Epithelial tissues, bone, areolar connective tissue, dense irregular connective tissue, and blood-forming tissue regenerate extremely well. Smooth muscle and dense regular connective tissue have a moderate capacity for regeneration, but skeletal muscle and cartilage have a weaker regenerative capacity. Cardiac muscle and the nervous tissue in the brain and spinal cord have virtually no *functional* regenerative capacity, and they are routinely replaced by scar tissue. However, recent studies have shown that some unexpected (and highly selective) cellular division occurs in both these tissues after damage, and efforts are under way to coax them to regenerate better.

In nonregenerating tissues and in exceptionally severe wounds, fibrosis totally replaces the lost tissue. Over a period of months, the fibrous mass shrinks and becomes more and more compact. The resulting scar appears as a pale, often shiny area composed mostly of collagen fibers. Scar tissue is strong, but it lacks the flexibility and elasticity of most normal tissues. Also, it cannot perform the normal functions of the tissue it has replaced.

HOMEOSTATIC IMBALANCE

Scar tissue that forms in the wall of the urinary bladder, heart, or other muscular organ may severely hamper the function of that organ. The normal shrinking of the scar reduces the internal volume of an organ and may hinder or even block movement of substances through a hollow organ. Scar tissue hampers muscle's ability to contract and may interfere with its normal excitation by the nervous system. In the heart, these problems may lead to progressive heart failure. In irritated visceral organs, particularly following abdominal surgery,

adjacent organs together. Such adhesions can prevent the normal shifting about (churning) of loops of the intestine, dangerously obstructing the flow of foodstuffs through. Adhesions can also restrict heart movements and immobilize joints. ■

CHECK YOUR UNDERSTANDING

21. What are the three main steps of tissue repair?
22. Why does a deep injury to the skin result in abundant scar tissue formation?

For answers, see Appendix G.

Developmental Aspects of Tissues

► Indicate the embryonic origin of each tissue class.
► Briefly describe tissue changes that occur with age.

One of the first events of embryonic development is the formation of the three **primary germ layers**, which lie one atop the next like a three-layered cellular pancake. From superficial to deep, these layers are the **ectoderm**, **mesoderm** (mez'o-derm), and **endoderm**. As shown in **Figure 4.13**, these primary germ layers then specialize to form the four primary tissues— epithelium, nervous tissue, muscle, and connective tissue—that make up all body organs.

By the end of the second month of development, the primary tissues have appeared, and all major organs are in place. In general, tissue cells remain mitotic and produce the rapid growth that occurs before birth. The division of nerve cells, however, stops or nearly stops during the fetal period. After birth, the cells of most other tissues continue to divide until adult body size is achieved. Cellular division then slows greatly

Illustrated tables summarize complex information and serve as a "one-stop shopping" study tool.

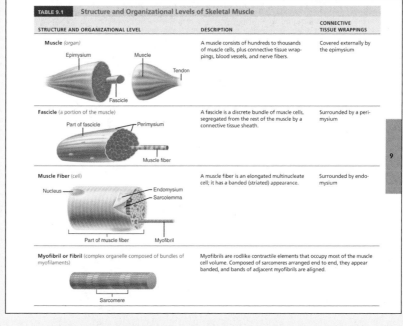

TABLE 9.1	Structure and Organizational Levels of Skeletal Muscle		
STRUCTURE AND ORGANIZATIONAL LEVEL		**DESCRIPTION**	**CONNECTIVE TISSUE WRAPPINGS**
Muscle *(organ)*		A muscle consists of hundreds to thousands of muscle cells, plus connective tissue wrappings, blood vessels, and nerve fibers.	Covered externally by the epimysium
Fascicle (a portion of the muscle)		A fascicle is a discrete bundle of muscle cells, segregated from the rest of the muscle by a connective tissue sheath.	Surrounded by a perimysium
Muscle Fiber (cell)		A muscle fiber is an elongated multinucleate cell; it has a banded (striated) appearance.	Surrounded by endomysium
Myofibril or Fibril (complex organelle composed of bundles of myofilaments)		Myofibrils are rodlike contractile elements that occupy most of the muscle cell volume. Composed of sarcomeres arranged end to end, they appear banded, and bands of adjacent myofibrils are aligned.	

Follow complex processes step-by-step

NEW! Focus figures help you grasp tough topics in A&P by walking you through carefully developed step-by-step illustrations that use a big-picture layout and dramatic art to provide a context for understanding the process.

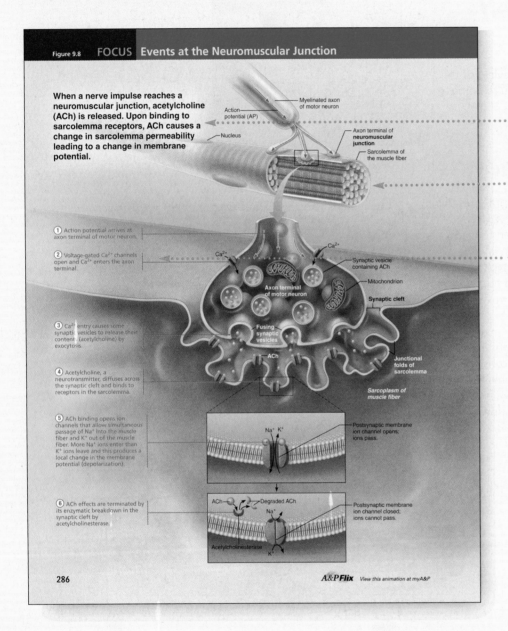

Figure 9.8 FOCUS **Events at the Neuromuscular Junction**

When a nerve impulse reaches a neuromuscular junction, acetylcholine (ACh) is released. Upon binding to sarcolemma receptors, ACh causes a change in sarcolemma permeability leading to a change in membrane potential.

Action potential (AP)

Myelinated axon of motor neuron

Nucleus

Axon terminal of neuromuscular junction

Sarcolemma of the muscle fiber

① Action potential arrives at axon terminal of motor neuron.

② Voltage-gated Ca²⁺ channels open and Ca²⁺ enters the axon terminal.

Ca²⁺

Synaptic vesicle containing ACh

Axon terminal of motor neuron

Mitochondrion

Synaptic cleft

③ Ca²⁺ entry causes some synaptic vesicles to release their content (acetylcholine) by exocytosis.

Fusing synaptic vesicles

ACh

Junctional folds of sarcolemma

④ Acetylcholine, a neurotransmitter, diffuses across the synaptic cleft and binds to receptors in the sarcolemma.

Sarcoplasm of muscle fiber

⑤ ACh binding opens ion channels that allow simultaneous passage of Na⁺ into the muscle fiber and K⁺ out of the muscle fiber. More Na⁺ ions enter than K⁺ ions leave and this produces a local change in the membrane potential (depolarization).

Na⁺ K⁺

Postsynaptic membrane ion channel opens; ions pass.

⑥ ACh effects are terminated by its enzymatic breakdown in the synaptic cleft by acetylcholinesterase.

ACh — Degraded ACh

Na⁺

Postsynaptic membrane ion channel closed; ions cannot pass.

Acetylcholinesterase

K⁺

286

A&P*Flix*   View this animation at myA&P

Overview provides a quick summary of the key idea of the figure.

Big picture orientation provides you with a concrete starting point for the process.

Step text walks you through the process step-by-step.

Visualize structures

NEW! Stunning 3-D anatomy art
is rendered in a dramatically more dynamic, realistic style with vibrant, saturated colors to help you visualize key anatomical structures.

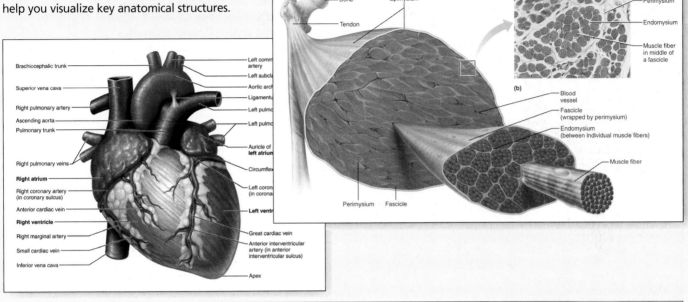

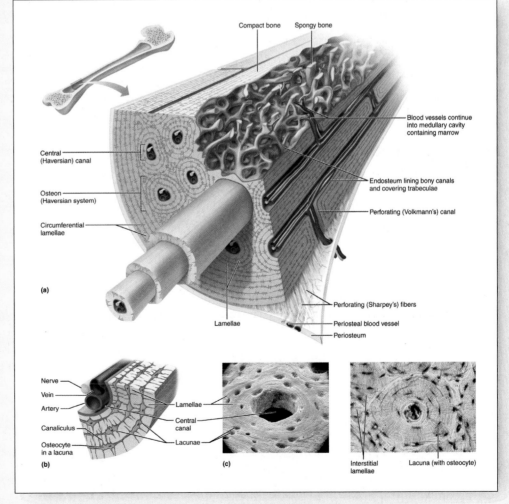

NEW! Bone art features
realistic bone color and texture with a consistent style from figure to figure.

Make connections

Making Connections at the end of each body system helps you understand the relationships between body systems with this three-tiered presentation:

- **System Connections** highlights the interrelationship between all of the body systems.
- **Closer Connections** focuses in greater depth on selected system interrelationships.
- **Clinical Connections** case study encourages you to apply chapter concepts to clinical situations.

MAKING CONNECTIONS

System Connections

Homeostatic Interrelationships Between the Integumentary System and Other Body Systems

5

Skeletal System
- Skin protects bones; skin synthesizes a vitamin D precursor needed for normal calcium absorption and deposit of bone (calcium) salts, which make bones hard
- Skeletal system provides support for skin

Muscular System
- Skin protects muscles
- Active muscles generate large amounts of heat, which increases blood flow to the skin and may promote activation of sweat glands of skin

Nervous System
- Skin protects nervous system organs; cutaneous sensory receptors for touch, pressure, pain, and temperature located in skin (see Figure 5.1)
- Nervous system regulates diameter of blood vessels in skin; activates sweat glands, contributing to thermoregulation; interprets cutaneous sensation; activates arrector pili muscles

Endocrine System
- Skin protects endocrine organs; converts some hormones to their active forms; synthesizes a vitamin D precursor
- Androgens produced by the endocrine system activate sebaceous glands and are involved in regulation of hair growth

Cardiovascular System
- Skin protects cardiovascular organs; prevents fluid loss from body; serves as blood reservoir
- Cardiovascular system transports oxygen and nutrients to skin and removes wastes from skin; provides substances needed by skin glands to make their secretions

Lymphatic System/Immunity
- Skin protects lymphatic organs; prevents pathogen invasion; dendritic cells and macrophages help activate the immune system
- Lymphatic system prevents edema by picking up excessive leaked fluid; immune system protects skin cells

Respiratory System
- Skin protects respiratory organs; hairs in nose help filter out dust from inhaled air
- Respiratory system furnishes oxygen to skin cells and removes carbon dioxide via gas exchange with blood

Digestive System
- Skin protects digestive organs; provides vitamin D needed for calcium absorption; performs some of the same chemical conversions as liver cells
- Digestive system provides needed nutrients to the skin

Urinary System
- Skin protects urinary organs; excretes salts and some nitrogenous wastes in sweat
- Urinary system activates vitamin D precursor made by keratinocytes; disposes of nitrogenous wastes of skin metabolism

Reproductive System
- Skin protects reproductive organs; cutaneous receptors respond to erotic stimuli; highly modified sweat glands (mammary glands) produce milk. During pregnancy, skin stretches to accommodate growing fetus; changes in skin pigmentation may occur

166

Closer Connections

The Integumentary System and Interrelationships with the Nervous, Cardiovascular, and Lymphatic/Immune Systems

First and foremost, our skin is a barrier. Like the skin of a grape, it keeps its contents juicy and whole. The skin is also a master at self (wound) repair, and interacts intimately with other body systems by making vitamin D (necessary for hard bones) and other potent molecules, all the while protecting deeper tissues from damaging external agents. Perhaps the most crucial roles of the skin in terms of overall body homeostasis are those it plays with the nervous, cardiovascular, and lymphatic systems. These interactions are detailed next.

Nervous System
The whole body benefits from the skin's interaction with the nervous system. The skin houses the tiny sensory receptors that provide a great deal of information about our external environment—its temperature, the pressure exerted by objects, and the presence of dangerous substances. What if we stepped on broken glass or hot pavement but did not have neural monitors in our skin? If we did not actually see, hear, taste, or smell such a damaging event, no reports would be sent to the nervous system. Consequently, the nervous system would be left "in the dark," unable to evaluate the need for a response and to order the steps needed to protect us from further damage or to get first aid.

Nervous and Cardiovascular System
Skin provides the site both for sensing external temperature and for responding to temperature changes. Dermal blood vessels (cardiovascular system organs) and sweat glands (controlled by the nervous system) play crucial roles in thermoregulation. So too do blood and the hot and cold receptors in the skin. When we are chilled, our blood loses heat to internal organs and cools. This loss alerts the nervous system to retain heat by constricting dermal blood vessels. When body and blood temperature rises, dermal vessels dilate and sweating begins.

Thermoregulation is vital: When the body overheats, life-threatening changes occur. Chemical reactions speed up, and as the temperature continues to rise vital proteins are destroyed and cells die. Cold has the opposite effect; cellular activity slows and ultimately stops.

Lymphatic System/Immunity
The role of the skin in immunity is complex. Keratinocytes in the skin manufacture interferons (proteins that block viral infection) and other proteins important to the immune response. Epidermal dendritic cells in the skin interact with antigens (foreign substances) that have penetrated the stratum corneum. The dendritic cells then migrate to lymphatic organs, where they present bits of the antigens to cells that will mount the immune response against them. This "messenger" function alerts the immune system early on to the presence of pathogens in the body.

Even a mild sunburn disrupts the normal immune response because UV radiation disables the skin's presenter cells. This effect may explain why many people infected by the cold sore virus tend to have a cold sore eruption after sun exposure.

5

Clinical Connections

Integumentary System

A terrible collision between a trailer truck and a bus has occurred on Route 91. Several of the passengers are rushed to area hospitals for treatment. We will follow a few of these people in clinical case studies that will continue through the book from one organ system to the next.

Case study: Examination of Mrs. DeStephano, a 45-year-old woman, reveals several impairments of homeostasis. Relative to her integumentary system, the following comments are noted on her chart:

- Epidermal abrasions of the right arm and shoulder
- Severe lacerations of the right cheek and temple
- Cyanosis apparent

The lacerated areas are cleaned, sutured, and bandaged by the emergency room (ER) personnel, and Mrs. DeStephano is admitted for further tests.

Relative to her signs:

1. What protective mechanisms are impaired or deficient in the abraded areas?
2. Assuming that bacteria are penetrating the dermis in these areas, what remaining skin defenses might act to prevent further bacterial invasion?
3. What benefit is conferred by suturing the lacerations? (Hint: See Chapter 4, p. 144.)
4. Mrs. DeStephano's cyanotic skin may hint at what additional problem (and impairment of what body systems or functions)?

(Answers in Appendix G)

167

Chapter 9 Muscles and Muscle Tissue 313

A CLOSER LOOK

Athletes Looking Good and Doing Better with Anabolic Steroids?

9

Society loves a winner and top athletes reap large social and monetary rewards. It is not surprising that some will grasp at anything that might increase their performance—including "juice," or anabolic steroids. These drugs are variants of the male sex hormone testosterone engineered by pharmaceutical companies. They were introduced in the 1950s to treat anemia and certain muscle-wasting diseases and to prevent muscle atrophy in patients immobilized after surgery. Testosterone is responsible for the increase in muscle and bone mass and other physical changes that occur during puberty and converts boys into men.

Convinced that megadoses of steroids could produce enhanced masculinizing effects in grown men, many athletes and bodybuilders were using them by the early 1960s. Investigations of the so-called Balco Scandal have stunned fans of major league baseball players with revelations in 2004 and since of rampant steroid use by Barry Bonds, of the San Francisco Giants, and many other elite athletes. It is still going on. In October of 2007, Marion Jones, one of the most celebrated of women athletes of all time, admitted that she was using performance-enhancing steroids when she won five gold medals in the 2000 Olympics. Furthermore, steroid use today is not confined to athletes. Indeed, it is estimated that nearly one in every 10 young men has tried them, and the practice is also spreading among young women.

It is difficult to determine the extent of anabolic steroid use because most international competitions ban the use of drugs. Users (and prescribing physicians or drug dealers) are naturally reluctant to talk about it, and users stop doping before the event, aware that evidence of drug use is hard to find a week after its use is stopped. Additionally, "underground" suppliers of performance-enhancing drugs keep producing new versions of designer steroids that evade standard antidoping tests. The Olympic Analytical Laboratory in Los Angeles rocked the sports world in November of 2003 when it revealed that a number of elite athletes tested positive for tetrahydrogestrinone (THG), a designer steroid not previously known or tested for. Nonetheless, there is little question that many professional bodybuilders and athletes competing in events that require muscle strength (e.g., shot put, discus throwing, and weight lifting) are heavy users. Sports figures such as football players have also admitted to using steroids as an adjunct to training, diet, and psychological preparation for games. These athletes claim that anabolic steroids enhance muscle mass and strength, and raise oxygen-carrying capability owing to greater red blood cell volume.

Typically, bodybuilders who use steroids combine high doses (up to 200 mg/day) via injection or transdermal skin patches with heavy resistance training. Intermittent use begins several months before an event, and commonly entails the use of many anabolic steroid supplements (a method called stacking). Doses are increased gradually as the competition nears.

Do the drugs do all that is claimed? Research studies report increased isometric strength and body weight in steroid users. While these are results weight lifters dream about, for runners and others requiring fine muscle coordination and endurance these changes may not translate into improved performance. The "jury is still out" on this question.

Do the alleged advantages of steroids outweigh their risks? Absolutely not. Physicians say they cause bloated faces (Cushingoid sign of steroid excess); acne and hair loss; shriveled testes and infertility; damage to the liver that promotes liver cancer; and changes in blood cholesterol levels that may predispose users to coronary heart disease. In addition, females can develop masculine characteristics such as smaller breasts, enlarged clitoris, excess body hair, and thinning scalp hair. The psychiatric hazards of anabolic steroid use may be equally threatening: Recent studies indicate that one-third of users suffer serious mental problems. Depression, delusions, and manic behavior—in which users undergo Jekyll-and-Hyde personality swings and become extremely violent (termed *'roid rage*)—are all common.

A more recent arrival on the scene, sold over the counter as a "nutritional performance-enhancer," is androstenedione, which is converted to testosterone in the body. Though it is taken orally (and much of it is destroyed by the liver soon after ingestion), the few milligrams that survive temporarily boost testosterone levels. Reports of its use by baseball great Mark McGwire before he retired, and of athletic wanna-bes from the fifth grade up sweeping the supplement off the drugstore shelves, are troubling, particularly since it is not regulated by the U.S. Food and Drug Administration (FDA) and its long-term effects are unpredictable and untested. A study at Massachusetts General Hospital found that males who took androstenedione developed higher levels of the female hormone estrogen as well as testosterone, raising their risk of feminizing effects such as enlarged breasts. Youths with elevated levels of estrogen or testosterone may enter puberty early, stunting bone growth and leading to shorter-than-normal adult height. Some people admit to a willingness to try almost anything to win, short of killing themselves. Are they unwittingly doing this as well?

Closer Look boxes on timely subjects such as medical technology, new discoveries in medical research, and important societal issues broaden your horizons and present scientific information that can be applied to your daily life.

Learn the language

Phonetic spellings are provided for words .... that may be unfamiliar to you to help you with pronunciation.

Color-coded chapter and unit tabs help you find information quickly and easily. ....

Word roots listed on the inside back cover will help you learn the special vocabulary of anatomy and physiology.

---

200   UNIT 2   Covering, Support, and Movement of the Body

trunk, and (3) protects the brain, spinal cord, and the organs in the thorax. As we will see later in this chapter, the bones of the appendicular skeleton, which allow us to interact with and manipulate our environment, are appended to the axial skeleton.

CHECK YOUR UNDERSTANDING

1. What are the three main parts of the axial skeleton?
2. Which part of the skeleton—axial or appendicular—is important in protecting internal organs?

For answers, see Appendix G.

The Skull

▶ Name, describe, and identify the skull bones. Identify their important markings.
▶ Compare and contrast the major functions of the cranium and the facial skeleton.

The **skull** is the body's most complex bony structure. It is formed by *cranial* and *facial bones*, 22 in all. The cranial bones, or **cranium** (kra'ne-um), enclose and protect the fragile brain and furnish attachment sites for head and neck muscles. The facial bones (1) form the framework of the face, (2) contain cavities for the special sense organs of sight, taste, and smell, (3) provide openings for air and food ...

sits snugly in these cranial fossae, completely enclosed by the cranial vault. Overall, the brain is said to occupy the *cranial cavity*.

In addition to the large cranial cavity, the skull has many smaller cavities. These include the middle and internal ear cavities (carved into the lateral side of its base) and, anteriorly, the nasal cavity and the orbits. The *orbits* house the eyeballs. Several bones of the skull contain air-filled sinuses, which lighten the skull.

The skull also has about 85 named openings (foramina, canals, fissures, etc.). The most important of these provide passageways for the spinal cord, the major blood vessels serving the brain, and the 12 pairs of cranial nerves (numbered I through XII), which transmit impulses to and from the brain.

As you read about the bones of the skull, locate each bone on the different skull views in Figures 7.4, 7.5, and 7.6. The skull bones and their important markings are also summarized in Table 7.1 (pp. 214–215). The color-coded boxes before a bone's name in the text and in Table 7.1 correspond to the color of that bone in the figures. For example, note the color of the frontal bone in Table 7.1 and see how you can easily find it in Figures 7.4 and 7.5.

Cranium

The eight cranial bones are the paired parietal and temporal bones and the unpaired frontal, occipital, sphenoid, and ethmoid bones. Together, these construct the brain's protective bony "helmet." Because its superior aspect is curved, the cranium is self-bracing. This allows the bones to be thin, and, like an eggshell, the cranium is remarkably strong for its weight.

Frontal Bone

The shell-shaped **frontal bone** (Figures 7.4a, 7.5, and 7.7) forms the anterior cranium. It articulates posteriorly with the paired parietal bones via the prominent *coronal suture*.

The most anterior part of the frontal bone is the vertical *squamous part*, commonly called the *forehead*. The frontal squamous region ends inferiorly at the **supraorbital margins**, the thickened superior margins of the orbits that lie under the eyebrows. From here, the frontal bone extends posteriorly, forming the superior wall of the *orbits* and most of the **anterior cranial fossa** (Figure 7.7a and b). This fossa supports the frontal lobes of the brain. Each supraorbital margin is pierced by a **supraorbital foramen (notch)**, which allows the supraorbital artery and nerve to pass to the forehead (Figure 7.4a).

The smooth portion of the frontal bone between the orbits is the **glabella** (glah-bel'ah). Just inferior to this the frontal bone meets the nasal bones at the *frontonasal suture* (Figure 7.4a). The areas lateral to the glabella are riddled internally with sinuses, called the **frontal sinuses** (Figures 7.5b and 7.3).

Parietal Bones and the Major Sutures

The two large **parietal bones** are curved, rectangular bones that form most of the superior and lateral aspects of the skull; hence they form the bulk of the cranial vault. The four largest sutures occur where the parietal bones articulate (form a joint) with other cranial bones:

Word Roots, Prefixes, Suffixes, and Combining Forms

(Prefixes and Combining Forms list — glossary of word roots)

Review what you've learned

Review questions at the end of each chapter, including multiple choice/matching, short answer, and Critical Thinking and Clinical Application questions, help you evaluate your progress.

Chapter summaries with page references provide excellent study aids.

Answers to Check Your Understanding, Clinical Connections, and end-of-chapter Multiple Choice and Matching Review Questions can be found in Appendix G.

---

170   UNIT 2   Covering, Support, and Movement of the Body

REVIEW QUESTIONS

Multiple Choice/Matching

(Some questions have more than one correct answer. Select the best answer or answers from the choices given.)

1. Which epidermal cell type is most numerous? (a) keratinocyte, (b) melanocyte, (c) epidermal dendritic cell, (d) tactile cell.
2. Which cell functions as part of the immune system? (a) a keratinocyte, (b) a melanocyte, (c) an epidermal dendritic cell, (d) a tactile cell.
3. The epidermis provides a physical barrier due largely to the presence of (a) melanin, (b) carotene, (c) collagen, (d) keratin.
4. Skin color is determined by (a) the amount of blood, (b) pigments, (c) oxygenation level of the blood, (d) all of these.
5. The sensations of touch and pressure are picked up by receptors located in (a) the stratum spinosum, (b) the dermis, (c) the hypodermis, (d) the stratum corneum.
6. Which is not a true statement about the papillary layer of the dermis? (a) It is largely areolar connective tissue, (b) it is most responsible for the toughness of the skin, (c) it contains nerve endings that respond to stimuli, (d) it is highly vascular.
7. Skin surface markings that reflect points of tight dermal attachment to underlying tissues are called (a) tension lines, (b) papillary ridges, (c) flexure lines, (d) dermal papillae.
8. Which of the following is not an epidermal derivative? (a) hair, (b) sweat gland, (c) sensory receptor, (d) sebaceous gland.
9. An arrector pili muscle (a) is associated with each sweat gland, (b) can cause a hair to stand up straight, (c) enables each hair to be stretched when wet, (d) provides new cells for continued growth of its associated hair.
10. The product of this type of sweat gland includes protein and lipid substances that become odoriferous as a result of bacterial action: (a) apocrine gland, (b) eccrine gland, (c) sebaceous gland, (d) pancreatic gland.
11. Sebum (a) lubricates the surface of the skin and hair, (b) consists of cell fragments and fatty substances, (c) in excess may cause seborrhea, (d) all of these.
12. The rule of nines is helpful clinically in (b) estimating the extent of a burn, (c) skin cancer is in, (d) preventing acne.

Short Answer Essay Questions

13. Which epidermal cells are also ...
14. Is a bald man really hairless? Ex ...
15. You go to the beach to swim one ...
16. Distinguish clearly between first ...
17. Describe the process of hair formation ...
18. What is cyanosis and what does ...
19. Why does skin wrinkle and wha ...

20. Explain each of these familiar phenomena in terms of what you learned in this chapter: (a) pimples, (b) dandruff, (c) greasy hair and "shiny nose," (d) stretch marks from gaining weight, (e) freckles.
21. Count Dracula, the most famous vampire, rumored to have killed at least 200,000 people, was based on a real person who lived in eastern Europe about 600 years ago. As said to have been a "monster," although he was not a real vampire. The historical Count Dracula may have suffered from which of the following? (a) porphyria, (b) EB, (c) halitosis, (d) vitiligo. Explain your answer.
22. Why are there no skin cancers that originate from stratum corneum cells?
23. A man put his finger caught in a machine at the factory. The damage was less serious than expected, but the entire nail was torn off his right index finger. The parts lost were the body, root, bed, matrix, and eponychium of the nail. First, define each of these parts. Then, tell if this nail is likely to grow back.
24. On an outline diagram of the human body, mark off various regions according to the rule of nines. What percentage of the total body surface is affected if the skin over the shoulder body parts is burned? (a) the entire posterior trunk and buttocks, (b) an entire lower limb, (c) the entire front of the left upper limb.
25. A common belief is that having your hair cut makes it become thicker. Explain why this belief is not true.

Critical Thinking and Clinical Application Questions

1. Dean, a 40-year-old aging beach boy, is complaining to you that although his suntan made him popular when he was young, now his face is all wrinkled, and he has several darkly pigmented moles that are growing rapidly and are as big as large coins. He shows you the moles, and immediately you think "ABCD." What does that mean and why should he be concerned?
2. Victims of third-degree burns demonstrate the loss of vital functions ...

CHAPTER SUMMARY

The Skin   (pp. 149–155)

1. The skin, or integument, is composed of two discrete tissue layers, an outer epidermis and a deeper dermis, resting on subcutaneous tissue, the hypodermis.

Epidermis   (pp. 150–152)

2. The epidermis is an avascular, keratinized sheet of stratified squamous epithelium. Most epidermal cells are keratinocytes. Scattered among the keratinocytes in the deepest epidermal layers are melanocytes, epidermal dendritic cells, and tactile cells.
3. From deep to superficial, the strata, or layers of the epidermis, are the basale, spinosum, granulosum, lucidum, and corneum. The stratum lucidum is absent in thin skin. The mitotically active stratum basale is the source of new cells for epidermal growth. The most superficial layers are increasingly keratinized and less viable.

Dermis   (pp. 152–153)

4. The dermis, composed mainly of dense, irregular connective tissue, is well supplied with blood vessels, lymphatic vessels, and nerves. Cutaneous receptors, glands, and hair follicles reside within the dermis.
5. The more superficial papillary layer exhibits dermal papillae that protrude into the epidermis above, as well as dermal ridges. Dermal ridges and epidermal ridges together form the friction ridges that produce fingerprints.
6. In the deeper, thicker reticular layer, the connective tissue fibers are much more densely interwoven. Less dense regions between the collagen bundles produce cleavage, or tension, lines in the skin. Points of tight dermal attachment to the hypodermis produce dermal folds, or flexure lines.

To the Student: How to Use myA&P

Check your readiness

Get Ready for A&P gets you prepared for your A&P course. Take the diagnostic test to see where you need review.

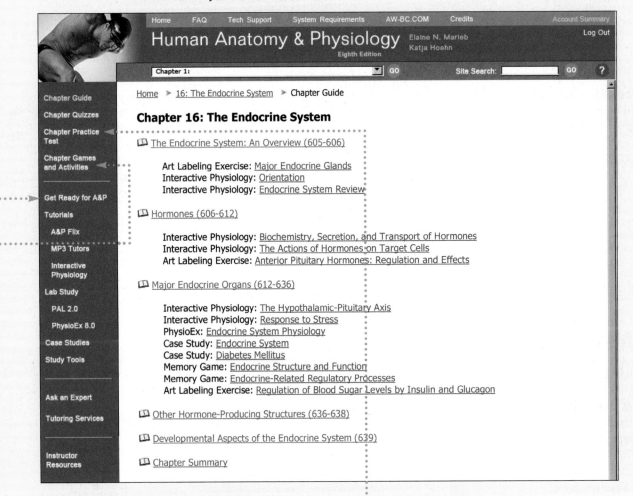

Prepare for exams

Chapter Quizzes and Practice Tests help you assess your understanding of the chapter and prepare for your exams.

Games and activities featuring Art Labeling Exercises, Memory Games, and Crossword Puzzles and Histology, Bone, and Muscle Reviews. Also included are new **MP3 Tutor Sessions** that carefully coach you through the most difficult A&P concepts including calcium regulation, the visual pathway, and gas exchange during respiration.

Chapter Guide

Chapter Quizzes

Chapter Practice
Test

Chapter Games
and Activities

Get Ready for A&P

Tutorials

A&P Flix

MP3 Tutors

Interactive
Physiology

Lab Study

PAL 2.0

PhysioEx 8.0

Case Studies

Study Tools

Ask an Expert

Tutoring Services

Instructor
Resources

Master tough concepts in A&P

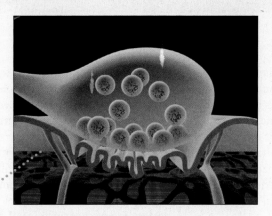

NEW! A&P Flix animations provide carefully developed step-by-step explanations with dramatic 3-D representations of structures that show action and movement of processes, thereby bringing difficult-to-teach A&P concepts to life. Each animation includes gradable quizzes as well as study sheets for practice and assessment.

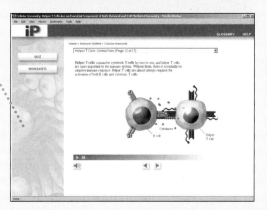

Interactive Physiology® **10-System Suite,** an award-winning tutorial program with a new module on the Immune System, tutors you in key physiological concepts and helps you advance beyond memorization to a genuine understanding of complex processes.

Access the A&P lab 24/7

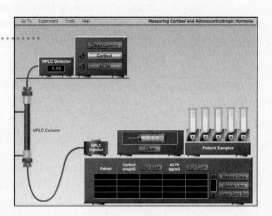

NEW! Practice Anatomy Lab™ 2.0 allows you to view hundreds of images of the human cadaver, anatomical models, histology slides, the cat, and the fetal pig and to take practice quizzes and simulated lab practical exams.

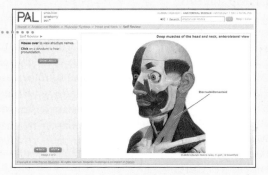

PhysioEx™ laboratory simulations allow you to conduct simulated experiments as part of your A&P lab.

Preface

As educators, clinically trained individuals, and perennial students, we are continually challenged by the learning mind. What works best to get students over conceptual hurdles and to help them apply new information to the world they personally understand? Our clinical backgrounds have served our teaching and writing purposes well. Perhaps even more important, our clinical experience has allowed us to view our presentations through our students' eyes and from the vantage points of their career interests.

Unifying Themes

Three integrating themes that organized, unified, and set the tone of the first edition of this text continue to be valid and are retained in this edition. These themes are:

Interrelationships of body organ systems. The fact that nearly all regulatory mechanisms require interaction of several organ systems is continually emphasized. For example, Chapter 25, which deals with the structure and function of the urinary system, discusses the vital importance of the kidneys not only in maintaining adequate blood volume to ensure normal blood circulation, but also in continually adjusting the chemical composition of blood so that all body cells remain healthy. The unique Making Connections feature is the culmination of this approach and should help students think of the body as a dynamic community of interdependent parts rather than as a number of isolated structural units.

Homeostasis. The normal and most desirable condition of body functioning is homeostasis. Its loss or destruction always leads to some type of pathology—temporary or permanent. Pathological conditions are integrated with the text to clarify and illuminate normal functioning, not as an end in and of themselves. For example, Chapter 19, which deals with the structure and function of blood vessels, explains how the ability of healthy arteries to expand and recoil ensures continuous blood flow and proper circulation. The chapter goes on to discuss the effects on homeostasis when arteries lose their elasticity: high blood pressure and all of its attendant problems. These homeostatic imbalances are indicated visually by a pink symbol with a fulcrum:

Whenever students see the imbalance symbol in text, the concept of disease as a loss of homeostasis is reinforced.

Complementarity of structure and function. Students are encouraged to understand the structure of an organ, a tissue, or a cell as a prerequisite to comprehending its function.

For this edition, as for those preceding it, feedback from both student and instructor reviews indicated areas of the text that needed to be revised for clarity, timeliness, and just plain reduction of verbal meatiness. Overall, feedback was positive, verifying that the approach of explaining fundamental principles and unifying themes first as a strong base for all that comes later is still viable. Furthermore, it is clear that backing up these explanations with comfortable analogies and familiar examples enhances the students' understanding of the workings of the human body.

Concepts of physiology are explained and related to structural characteristics that promote or allow the various functions to occur. For example, the lungs can act as a gas exchange site because the walls of their air sacs present an incredibly thin barrier between blood and air.

NEW TO THE EIGHTH EDITION

The Eighth Edition represents a monumental revision with an entirely new art program and text presentation that build upon the hallmark strengths of the previous seven editions. With every edition, our goal is powerful but simple—to make anatomy and physiology as engaging, accurate, and relevant as possible for both you and your students. The changes to the Eighth Edition are all driven by the needs of today's students, as we seek to make the learning of key concepts in A&P as easy as possible for them. Key concepts are important because of the overwhelming amount of material in this course. Mastering this material gives students an anchor and structure for managing this wealth of information. Below are the ways in which we've revised the Eighth Edition to make this book the one where learning happens most effectively, followed by a detailed list of specific chapter-by-chapter content changes.

A whole new art program. The drive for this revision began as a simple list. We sat down together and created a chapter-by-chapter list of the key concepts in A&P where students struggle the most. This list became the basis for our art revision plans. We first boiled it down to some of the toughest topics to get our list of Focus figures. This new Focus feature highlights tough topics in A&P and walks students step-by-step through complex processes that are difficult to teach and visualize. In each case, we scrutinized the process and worked through countless revisions to break it down in the most logical and easy-to-follow way possible for students. We hope you'll be as pleased with the results as we are.

We also revised and reconceptualized many of the process figures in the book to make them easier to follow and to learn from. Where appropriate we have added blue step text that serves as our author voice guiding students step-by-step through complex processes. The blue text clearly separates the process steps from the labels, making the figures easy to navigate.

Flipping through the Eighth Edition, you can see that our new art is dynamic, three-dimensional, and realistic, with dramatic views and perspectives that use vibrant, saturated colors. Using our list of key concepts, we targeted critical figures in anatomy and worked closely with the artistic team on making these figures superior in rendering and in conveying the key pedagogical information and structures that students need to learn from the figure, striking a perfect balance between realism and teaching effectiveness.

Finally, we've also added a wealth of new figures and photos to enhance learning, many of which are listed below.

Improved text presentation. New text features also serve to focus students on key concepts. We have integrated the student objectives to fall within the chapter, giving students a preview in smaller chunks of what they are expected to learn in a given section. We've also added new Check Your Understanding questions that ask students to stop, think, and check their understanding of key concepts at the end of major sections. These changes along with a brand-new design make the book easier than ever to study from and navigate. We have also edited the text throughout with a refined writing style that retains our hallmark analogies and accessible, friendly style while using simpler, more concise language and shorter paragraphs. These changes make the text easier for students to manage as they face the challenging amount of information in this course.

Factual updates and accuracy. As authors we pride ourselves on keeping our book as up-to-date and as accurate as possible in all areas—a monumental task that requires painstaking selectivity. Although information changes even as a textbook goes to press, be assured that our intent and responsibility to update was carried out to the best of our ability. We have incorporated updates from current research in the field as much as possible; many of these updates are included below in the chapter-by-chapter changes. A more complete list, along with references for selected updates, is available from your Pearson sales representative and in the Instructor Guide to Text and Media.

Chapter-by-Chapter Changes

Chapter 1 The Human Body: An Orientation
- New PET scan for A Closer Look on medical imaging

Chapter 2 Chemistry Comes Alive
- Updated information on molecular chaperones

Chapter 3 Cells: The Living Units
- New step art for exocytosis (Figure 3.14)
- Updated discussion of types of endocytosis accompanied by new endocytosis step art (Figure 3.12)

- New Figure 3.13 provides a comparison of three types of endocytosis
- New Figure 3.20 with step text on the signaling mechanism for targeting new proteins to the ER
- New Focus on Primary Active Transport: The Na^+-K^+ Pump (Figure 3.10)
- New Focus on G Proteins (Figure 3.16)
- New Focus on Mitosis (Figure 3.33)
- New diagrams accompany photos in figure showing the effects of varying tonicities on living red blood cells (Figure 3.9)
- New photomicrographs accompany all cell organelle illustrations, including new Figure 3.28 on microvilli
- Revised text and new figures for transcription (Figure 3.35) and translation (Figure 3.37).
- New information on the origin of peroxisomes based on recent research

Chapter 4 Tissue: The Living Fabric
- New Figure 4.1: Overview of four tissue types
- New photomicrographs for pseudostratified ciliated columnar epithelium (Figure 4.3d), goblet cells (Figure 4.4), and elastic connective tissue (Figure 4.8f)
- New Table 4.1 compares four main classes of connective tissue
- Updated A Closer Look on cancer

Chapter 5 The Integumentary System
- New Figure 5.3: Two regions of the dermis, with three new photomicrographs
- New Figure 5.4: Dermal modifications result in characteristic skin markings, with one new photomicrograph
- New photos: partial and full thickness burns (Figure 5.10)

Chapter 6 Bones and Skeletal Tissue
- New Figure 6.4 shows comparative morphology of bone cells
- New Figure 6.14 shows that vigorous exercise can lead to large increases in bone strength
- Updated information on homocysteine as a marker of low bone mass density and bone frailty; additional information on age-related bone changes and treatments

Chapter 7 The Skeleton
- New photo of midsagittal section of the skull (Figure 7.5c)
- New photos for inferior and superior views of the skull (Figures 7.6b, 7.7b)
- New photos of the sphenoid bone, superior and posterior views (Figure 7.9)
- New photo of right lateral view of the maxilla (Figure 7.11)
- New MRI of lumbar region in sagittal section showing herniated disc (Figure 7.17)
- New photo of midsagittal section of the thorax (Figure 7.22)
- New X ray of the foot (Figure 7.34)
- New Figure 7.37: The C-shaped spine of a newborn infant
- New Homeostatic Imbalance: xiphoid process projecting posteriorly

Chapter 8 Joints

- Figure 8.1 expanded to show a comparison of different types of fibrous joints; added gomphosis
- Added new views for knee, shoulder, and mandible joint

Chapter 9 Muscles and Muscle Tissue

- New Focus on Events at the Neuromuscular Junction (Figure 9.8)
- New Focus on Excitation-Contraction Coupling (Figure 9.11)
- New Focus on the Cross Bridge Cycle (Figure 9.12)
- New Figure 9.7: Phases leading to muscle fiber contraction
- New Figure 9.20: Comparison of energy sources used during short-duration and prolonged-duration exercise
- New Figure 9.24: Cross section of the three types of fibers in skeletal muscle
- New Figure 9.30: Formation of a multinucleate skeletal muscle fiber by fusion of myoblasts

Chapter 10 The Muscular System

- New cadaver photo of the anterior and lateral regions of the neck (Figure 10.9c)
- New cadaver photo of superficial muscles of the thorax (Figure 10.13b)
- New cadaver photo of muscles crossing the shoulder and elbow joint (Figure 10.14d)
- New cadaver photo of superficial muscles of the superior gluteal region (Figure 10.20b)

Chapter 11 Fundamentals of the Nervous System and Nervous Tissue

- New Focus on Resting Membrane Potential (Figure 11.8)
- New Focus on Action Potential (Figure 11.11)
- New Focus on Chemical Synapse (Figure 11.17)
- Updated role of satellite cells ·
- Updated discussion of nitric oxide and carbon dioxide; added paragraph on new class of neurotransmitter endo-cannabinoids
- Updated the roles of neurotropins in signaling the growth cone during neuronal development
- Updated information in A Closer Look on overcoming cocaine addiction
- Updated information on neurotransmitters (histamine, somatostatin, substance P, CCK) in Table 11.3
- New Figure 11.10: The spread and decay of a graded potential
- New Figure 11.15: Action potential propagation in unmyelinated and myelinated axons
- New photo, a neuronal growth cone (Figure 11.24)

Chapter 12 The Central Nervous System

- Updated location of cortex receiving vestibular input based on new fMRI studies
- New Homeostatic Imbalance on brain tumors in different regions of the brain: the anterior association area and the posterior parietal region

- Updated discussion of regulation of respiratory rhythm in the medulla
- Updated discussion of occurrence of theta waves in adult electroencephalogram
- Updated mechanisms of onset of sleep and wakefulness, the role of orexins (hypocretins) in narcolepsy, and recent finding that orexin antagonists promote sleep in humans
- Updated survival of strokes and stroke treatment
- Updated cause and treatment of Parkinson's disease
- Updated treatments for Alzheimer's disease
- New Figure 12.17 on the cerebellum with side-by-side illustration and photo showing a sagittal view
- New photo of frontal section of the brain (Figure 12.10)
- New photo of inferior view of the brain showing the regions of the brain stem (Figure 12.14)
- New EEG photo (Figure 12.20)

Chapter 13 The Peripheral Nervous System and Reflex Activity

- Updated axon regrowth and treating spinal cord injuries
- Updated Homeostatic Imbalance on cause and treatment of trigeminal neuralgia
- Updated origin and course of the accessory nerves (CN XI)
- New Focus on the Stretch Reflex (Figure 13.17)
- New cadaver photo of the brachial plexus (Figure 13.9)
- New cadaver photo of the sacral plexus (Figure 13.11)
- New Homeostatic Imbalance on hyperalgesia and phantom limb pain

Chapter 14 The Autonomic Nervous System

- New Homeostatic Imbalance on autonomic neuropathy

Chapter 15 The Special Senses

- Updated laser procedures to correct myopia
- Updated the mechanism of light adaptation in rods
- Updated odor signal processing
- Updated taste cell specificity
- Updated the mechanism of transduction for all five taste modalities
- Updated treatment of age-related macular degeneration

Chapter 16 The Endocrine System

- New Figure 16.7 on regulation of thyroid hormone secretion
- Updated hormones released by the thymus and by adipose tissue
- Added new information about incretins and osteocalcin
- Simplified and updated A Closer Look on diabetes mellitus

Chapter 17 Blood

- Updated discussion of erythropoietin—new understanding of how hypoxia induces erythropoiesis
- Updated treatment of sickle-cell anemia—new drug clotrimazole

Chapter 18 The Cardiovascular System: The Heart
- New cadaver photo of frontal section of the heart (Figure 18.4f)
- New photomicrograph of cardiac muscle (Figure 18.11)

Chapter 19 The Cardiovascular System: Blood Vessels
- Updated function of pericytes
- Updated relationship between obesity and hypertension
- Updated development of arteries and veins
- Updated systolic blood pressure as a better predictor of complications of hypertension in those older than 50
- Updated hypertension and its treatment—angiotensin II receptor blockers

Chapter 20 The Lymphatic System and Lymphoid Organs and Tissues
- Updated information on Hassall's corpuscles from current research

Chapter 21 The Immune System: Innate and Adaptive Body Defenses
- Added dermcidin—an important antimicrobial in human sweat
- Updated number of types of human TLRs
- Updated information that dendritic cells can obtain foreign antigens from infected cells through gap junctions
- Updated role of the T_H2 type of helper T cells in immunity
- Updated statistics on HIV/AIDS
- Updated treatments of autoimmune diseases and multiple sclerosis
- Added new type of T_H cell, T_H17
- New Figure 21.2 on phagocytosis
- New SEM of a dendritic cell (Figure 21.10)
- New computer-generated image of an antibody (Figure 21.14)
- New Homeostatic Imbalance on parasitic worms

Chapter 22 The Respiratory System
- Updated role of alveolar type II cells in innate immunity
- Updated mechanism for hypercapnia following administration of oxygen to patients with COPD
- Updated therapy for cystic fibrosis
- New photomicrograph showing a portion of the tracheal wall (Figure 22.6)

Chapter 23 The Digestive System
- New X ray of the mouth of a child showing the permanent incisors forming (Figure 23.10)
- New photomicrograph of small intestine villus (Figure 23.22)
- New photo of a peptic ulcer lesion and SEM of *H. pylori* bacteria (Figure 23.16)
- Updated discussion of the process of HCl formation within the parietal cells
- Expanded section on histology of the small intestine wall; added function of Paneth cells' secretions

Chapter 24 Nutrition, Metabolism, and Body Temperature Regulation
- Vitamin and mineral tables have been simplified for ease of student learning

- New sections and coverage of obesity, short- and long-term regulation of food intake, and additional regulatory factors
- New photo, atomic force microscopy, reveals the structure of energy-converting ATP synthase rotor rings (Figure 24.10)

Chapter 25 The Urinary System
- New photo of a frontal section of kidney (Figure 25.3)
- New photomicrograph of cut nephron tubules in new figure of renal cortical tissue and renal tubules (Figure 25.6)
- New intravenous pyelogram (Figure 25.19)
- Updated structure and possible function of extra-glomerular mesangial cells
- New Homeostatic Imbalance on chronic renal disease and renal failure

Chapter 26 Fluid, Electrolyte, and Acid-Base Balance
- Added clarification of difference between edema and hypotonic hydration
- New paragraph on angiotensin II

Chapter 27 The Reproductive System
- New SEM of sperm (Figure 27.8)
- New photomicrograph of the endometrium and its blood supply (Figure 27.13)
- New photo of mammogram procedure, plus new photos of a normal mammogram compared to one showing a tumor (Figure 27.16)
- New photomicrographs showing stages of follicular development (Figure 27.18)
- New section on erectile dysfunction
- Added new human papillomavirus vaccine
- Expanded discussion of interactions along the hypothalamic-pituitary-ovarian axis with reconceptualized figure
- Updated transmission of herpes virus
- Updated descent of the testes
- Updated hormone replacement therapy for women

Chapter 28 Pregnancy and Human Development
- New photomicrograph of a blastocyst that has just adhered to the uterine endometrium (Figure 28.5)
- New Figure 28.8 showing detailed anatomy of the vascular relationships in the mature decidua basalis
- New Figure 28.13, flowchart showing major derivatives of the embryonic germ layers
- Updated information on the initiation of labor and on contraception

Chapter 29 Heredity
- New photomicrograph of human sex chromosomes (Figure 29.5)
- New Figure 29.8 comparing amniocentesis and chorionic villus sampling
- Updated discussion of stem cells
- Updated discussion of epigenetics and nontraditional methods of gene regulation

Supplements for the Instructor

NEW! Instructor Resource DVD

(0-321-50704-5)

This media tool organizes all instructor media resources by chapter into one convenient package that allows you to easily and quickly pull together a lecture and to show animations, including brand-new A&P Flix, from your PowerPoint® presentations. The IRDVD contains:

- **NEW! A&P Flix**

  Movie-quality A&P Flix animations of key concepts invigorate classroom lectures. These animations provide carefully developed, step-by-step explanations with dramatic 3-D representations of structures that show action and movement of processes, bringing A&P concepts to life. Using the A&P Flix animations, you can help students visualize tough-to-teach A&P concepts such as muscle actions, excitation-contraction coupling, generation of an action potential, and more. These animations can be launched directly from your PowerPoint presentations.

  Note: *these animations are available on the myA&P™ companion website with gradable quizzes as well as printable study sheets for practice and assessment.*

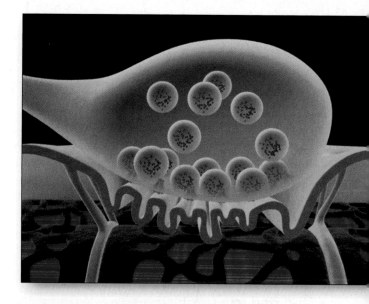

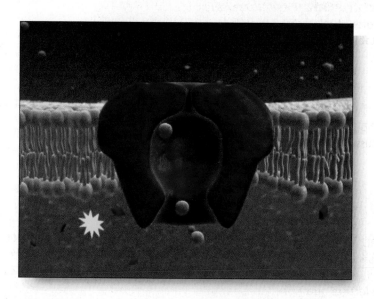

- **All art, photos, and tables** from the book in JPEG and PowerPoint format, as well as all photos from *A Brief Atlas of the Human Body,* Second Edition. Labels have been enlarged in easy-to-read type for optimal viewing in large lecture halls.

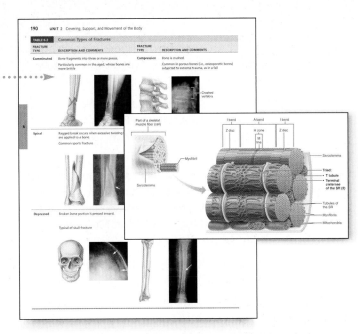

- **Instructor Guide to Text and Media**

- **Test Bank**

- **Illustrations offered in customizable PowerPoint formats,** including Label-Edit Art with editable leaders and labels and Step-Edit Art that walks through multistep figures step-by-step.

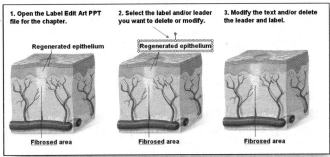

- **Quiz Show Game chapter reviews** that encourage student interaction

- **Updated, customizable PowerPoint Lecture Outline slides,** available for every chapter, that combine lecture notes, illustrations with editable labels, photos, tables, and animations.

- **Active Lecture Questions** (for use with or without clickers) that stimulate effective classroom discussions and check comprehension

Osteoarthritis (OA)

- Most common chronic arthritis; often called "wear-and-tear" arthritis
- Affects women more than men
- 85% of all Americans develop OA
- More prevalent in the aged, and is probably related to the normal aging process

The touch sensors of the epidermis are the _____.
a. keratinocytes
b. tactile cells
c. epidermal dendritic cells
d. melanocytes

BONUS!
IRDVD includes Practice Anatomy Lab 2.0 Instructor Resource DVD
PAL IRDVD includes customizable images from PAL 2.0 in JPEG and PowerPoint format. PowerPoint slides also include embedded links to relevant animations and PRS-enabled active lecture questions for use with or without clickers. Quizzes and lab practical are available in Microsoft Word and Computerized Test Bank formats.

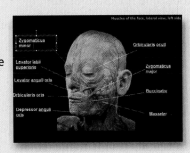

(For a description of PAL, please see page xix.)

myA&P™ Website now includes everything students need to practice, review, and self-assess for both the A&P lecture *and* lab.

- **NEW! *Get Ready for A&P*, Second Edition** helps students prepare for the A&P course through Pre-Tests, Post-Tests with Study Plans, tutorials, animations, activities, and an integrated E-Book.

- Chapter-specific resources include Chapter Quizzes and brand new Chapter Practice Tests; Games and Activities, featuring Art Labeling Exercises, Memory Games, and Crossword Puzzles; Histology, Bone, and Muscle Reviews; Flashcards; a Glossary; and more!

- *Interactive Physiology®* **10-System Suite** includes a new module on the immune system.

- **NEW! Practice Anatomy Lab™ 2.0** is an indispensable virtual anatomy practice tool that gives students 24/7 access to the most widely used lab specimens (includes self-study quizzes and gradable lab practicals).

- **PhysioEx™ 8.0** supplements traditional wet labs safely and cost-effectively (includes gradable quizzes and printable review sheets).

- **Instructor Gradebook** allows instructors to track student assessment.

- **Instructor Resource Section** includes IP Exercise Sheet Answer Key, and items from the IRDVD, including JPEG images (labeled and unlabeled sets), Label-Edit Art and Step-Edit Art, Active Lecture Questions, and Quiz Show Game Questions.

Course Management

CourseCompass™
This nationally hosted, dynamic, interactive online course management system is powered by Blackboard, the leading platform for Internet-based learning tools. This easy-to-use and customizable program enables professors to tailor content to meet individual course needs. Includes all of the content from myA&P™.

WebCT and Blackboard
These open-access cartridges are loaded with rich content, including assessment items, self-study quizzes, case studies, a histology tutorial, reference tools, and hundreds of fun games, animations, and anatomy labeling exercises.

NEW! New assessment items in the course management system of your choice, including CourseCompass, Blackboard, WebCT, and others. In addition to the Gradeable Quizzes from the myA&P™ Website and the Test Bank, you will now have access to Instructor Test Item assessments for:

- *Get Ready for A&P* (Diagnostic and Cumulative Tests and Chapter Pre- and Post-Tests).

- *Interactive Physiology®*
- PhysioEx™ 8.0
- Quizzes and lab practicals from Practice Anatomy Lab™ 2.0, including images and questions not available in the student product. Instructors can modify the questions to reflect the content they want their students to be quizzed and tested on.
- Post-Test versions of the new Chapter Practice Tests on the myA&P™ Website.

Instructor Guide to Text and Media
(0-321-55876-6)
This fully revised guide includes detailed objectives, lecture outlines, activities, online media resources, answers to end-of-chapter questions, and *Interactive Physiology®* exercise sheets and answer key. All the illustrations from the text are indexed as thumbnails in the Visual Resource Guide so you can easily locate and make the best use of the available media.

Printed Test Bank
(0-321-55884-7)
With more than 3600 test questions, this Test Bank has been updated with new and revised questions that cover all major topics at a range of difficulty levels. All questions in the printed Test Bank are available in Word and TestGen formats on the IRDVD. Both electronic options are cross-platform and allow instructors to easily generate and customize tests.

Transparency Acetates
(0-321-55888-X)
This package includes all illustrations, photos, and tables from the text—approximately 800 images—with labels that have been enlarged for easy viewing in the classroom or lecture hall.

Human Anatomy & Physiology Laboratory Manuals

Elaine N. Marieb's three widely used and acclaimed laboratory manuals complement this textbook and are designed to meet the varying needs of most laboratory courses: *Human Anatomy & Physiology Laboratory Manual: Cat Version*, Ninth Edition Update; *Main Version*, Eighth Edition Update; and *Pig Version*, Ninth Edition Update. Included with each laboratory manual is the PhysioEx™ 8.0 CD-ROM and a registration code for online access. PhysioEx™ 8.0 features 12 experiments and a Histology Tutorial.

Supplements for the Student

NEW! Practice Anatomy Lab™ 2.0 CD-ROM

(0-321-54725-X)

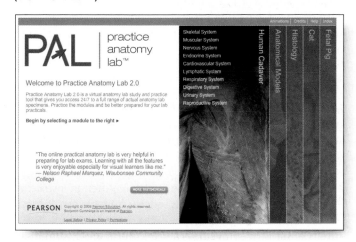

Interactive Physiology® 10-System Suite

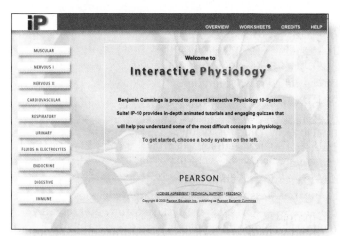

Practice Anatomy Lab™ 2.0 is a virtual anatomy study and practice tool that gives you 24/7 access to a full range of actual lab specimens, including:

- Human cadaver
- Anatomical models
- Histology slides
- Cat dissections
- Fetal pig dissections

Each module includes hundreds of images as well as interactive tools for reviewing the specimens, learning and hearing the names of anatomical structures, seeing animations, and taking multiple choice quizzes and fill-in-the-blank lab practical exams.

PAL 2.0 features include:

- All-new Human Cadaver module
- Fully rotatable human skull and 17 other rotatable skeletal structures
- 3-D animations of origins, insertions, actions, and innervations of over 65 individual muscles
- Greatly expanded Histology module

Interactive Physiology® will give you the help you need to grasp some of the most difficult concepts in A&P. This award-winning tutorial system features ten modules containing in-depth, fully narrated, animated tutorials and engaging quizzes covering key physiological processes and concepts. *Interactive Physiology*® is a highly effective program that provides the tools you need to advance beyond simple memorization to a genuine understanding of the most difficult concepts in A&P.

Modules

- Muscular System
- Nervous System I
- Nervous System II
- Cardiovascular System
- Respiratory System
- Urinary System
- Fluids & Electrolytes
- Endocrine System
- Digestive System
- **NEW!** Immune System

myA&P™

Please see How to Use myA&P for a description (p. x).

Get Ready for A&P, Second Edition

(0-321-55695-X)

This book and online component was created to help you be better prepared for your A&P course. This hands-on book helps you get up to speed in your knowledge of basic study skills, math review, basic chemistry, cell biology, anatomical terminology, and the human body. Features include pre-tests, guided explanations followed by interactive quizzes and exercises, and end-of-chapter

cumulative tests. The online component includes a gradable diagnostic pre-test and post-test, self-study quizzes with feedback, animations and links, a glossary, and flashcards. It is available via myA&P™.

New to the Second Edition

- New topics have been added, including coverage of pH, energy, and meiosis, as well as tips on how to minimize anxiety surrounding tests, and more.
- A more robust Companion Website includes new activities and tutorials on key topics and new myeBook content.
- A new preface for instructors explains how to use the book.
- All assessments are now available in course management platforms, including WebCT, Blackboard, and CourseCompass™. Separate Instructor Test Item versions of the Diagnostic Test, Cumulative Test, and the chapter Pre- and Post-Tests can now be easily imported into these course management systems.

A Brief Atlas of the Human Body, Second Edition

This full-color atlas is bundled with every new copy of the text, and includes 107 bone and 47 soft-tissue photographs with easy-to-read labels. This new edition of the atlas contains a brand-new, comprehensive histology photomicrograph section with more than 50 slides of basic tissue and organ systems. Featuring photos taken by renowned biomedical photographer Ralph Hutchings, this high-quality photographic atlas makes an excellent resource for the classroom and laboratory, and is referenced in appropriate figure legends throughout the text.

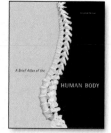

Study Guide

(0-321-55873-1)

Revised to accompany the Eighth Edition of *Human Anatomy & Physiology,* the study guide offers a wide variety of exercises that address different learning styles and call on students to develop their critical-thinking abilities. The three major sections, Building the Framework, Challenging Yourself, and Covering All Your Bases, help students build a base of knowledge using recall, reasoning, and imagination that can be applied to solving problems in both clinical and nonclinical situations.

The Tutor Center

Free tutoring is available to students with a valid myA&P™ course ID number from their instructor. The Tutor Center is staffed with qualified A&P instructors who can tutor students on all the materials covered in the text. Tutoring content is restricted to the text material, and tutors will discuss only answers that are provided in the textbook. After an instructor authorizes student access to this service, students can contact the Tutor Center by phone, email, fax, or the Internet. The Tutor Center is open five days a week. For more information, visit www.aw-bc.com/tutorcenter.

Additional Supplements Available from Benjamin Cummings

Anatomy & Physiology Coloring Workbook: A Complete Study Guide, Ninth Edition By Elaine N. Marieb

The Physiology Coloring Book, Second Edition By Wynn Kapit, Robert I. Macey, Esmail Meisami

The Anatomy Coloring Book, Third Edition By Wynn Kapit and Lawrence M. Elson

Human Cadaver Dissection Videos By Rose Leigh Vines, et al.

Student Video Series for Human Anatomy & Physiology, Volume 1

Student Video Series for Human Anatomy & Physiology, Volume 2

Acknowledgments

Harmonizing "Oh, happy day," we could hardly express our joy at coming to the end of this Eighth Edition update. This revision, like the ones that preceded it, is a major one. It has consumed most of our day and night hours for nearly two years. Text has been streamlined, rewritten for currency, or reorganized. As usual, it's been difficult to keep up to date in the very broad field of anatomy and physiology, and then a wrenching ordeal to decide how much of it to use in the new edition. We want our students to be informed intellectually, but how rich a diet that requires is a persistent question.

Though text revision is demanding, our task there was nothing compared to the Herculean effort of a whole new art program for the book. Literally every figure in the book has been touched in some way. These modifications ranged from light touches such as color changes or text editing for brevity, to art modifications for enhanced three-dimensionality (particularly in anatomy pieces), revisions for greater clarity, or a whole new conceptualization and rendering for better pedagogy. We are really excited about an entirely new feature—the Focus Feature. These one- to two-page displays showcase major concepts that students traditionally have trouble with, such as generation of an action potential, excitation-contraction coupling, or G protein mechanisms. In most cases the feature uses text that concisely states each step, accompanied by exceptionally instructive and evocative art. We are excited about this feature and hope that you will be too.

The sponsoring editor for this edition, Serina Beauparlant, has supported every aspect of this revision—sometimes too much! Serina is insightful and dedicated to producing the best educational product possible (both text and multimedia). She is a true human dynamo. Frank Ruggirello, publisher for this edition, has backed Serina up in the most effective way possible (with $). Thank you Frank. Project editor for this text is again the conscientious and competent Sabrina Larson. Wrestling with schedule deadlines, picking up manuscript loose ends, and trying to make overwhelmed authors work more quickly have made her life these many months a nightmare, we are sure. But she survived and still speaks to us. Derek Perrigo, our marketing manager, has efficiently kept us abreast of the pulse of the marketplace—keeping in touch with professors and students and providing feedback on what they do or don't like about the text and media products. Stacey Weinberger's expertise as manufacturing buyer has served us well. A resounding dollop of gratitude also goes to those on the editorial team with whom we have had little or no personal contact but who have provided valuable services for the revision: Erik Fortier, media producer, and Nicole Graziano, assistant editor, for the Eighth Edition.

We also want to thank the following reviewers who provided us with their expertise and constructive criticism to improve the art and text presentation. Their input resulted in the continued excellence and accuracy of this text.

Kurt Albertine, *University of Utah Medical School*
C. Thomas G. Appleton, *University of Western Ontario*
Barbie Baker, *Florida Community College–Jacksonville*
Sherry Bowen, *Indian River College*
Virginia Brooks, *Oregon Health and Science University*
Bruce Buttler, *Canadian University College*
Mary Beth Dawson, *Kingsborough Community College*
Trevor Day, *University of Calgary*
Randall Fameree, *Athens Technical College*
Patty Finkenstadt, *Phoenix College*
Lynn Gargan, *Tarrant County Community College*
Cynthia Gill, *Hampshire College*
William Hoover, *Bunker Hill Community College*
Mark Hubley, *Prince George's Community College*
Jody Johnson, *Arapahoe Community College*
John C. Koch, *John Tyler Community College*
John Lepri, *University of North Carolina–Greensboro*
Jane Marone, *University of Illinois at Chicago*
Justin Moore, *American River College*
Karen Payne, *Chattanooga State Technical Community College*
Louise Petroka, *Gateway Community College*
Brandon Poe, *Springfield Tech Community College*
David Quadagno, *Florida State University–Emeritus*
Saeed Rahmanian, *Roane State Community College*
Charles Roselli, *Oregon Health and Science University*
Pamela Siergiej, *Roane State Community College*
Tom Swensen, *Ithaca College*
Carol Veil, *Anne Arundel Community College*
Amy Way, *Lock Haven University*
Kelly Young, *California State University, Long Beach*

Additionally, we want to acknowledge Katja's colleagues at Mount Royal College (Trevor Day, Janice Meeking, Izak Paul, Michael Pollock, and Ruth Pickett-Seltner) for stimulating discussions of the text, which they embraced as their own cause, providing feedback on changes and options. We are also grateful to Yvonne Baptiste-Szymanski, Niagara County Community College, Mark Taylor, Baylor University, and Linda Porter, Midlands Technical College, for conducting student user diaries with their classes and gathering valuable feedback directly from our student users.

Once again Wendy Earl Productions handled the production of this text. As always, Wendy Earl, the managing editor, selects highly qualified people to work with her. Michele Mangelli, production supervisor extraordinaire, guided us through the schedule with an expert hand. Her efficient management style and excellent problem-solving skills headed off many a storm, which the whole team appreciated. Laura Southworth, the art development manager, was charged with being the developmental editor for all the art, ensuring the consistency of the art program to encourage automatic learning, helping to conceptualize and construct the Focus Features and all new pieces. All we had to say to Laura is "I don't like this piece of art; can't we do something to reconfigure it for more interest . . . more clarity . . . ?" Two days later there would be a mailer with a great new conceptualization of that figure. Laura is an enthusiastic, can-do woman and we love her! Recognition for a job well done is due Kristin Piljay, photo researcher, and David Novak, art coordinator. Jim Perkins helped us to reorganize key flowcharts in the book, for which we thank him. The talented artists at Imagineering and at Electronic Publishing Services generated the new art pieces conceived for this edition, and made changes requested on existing art. It is their art that puts the zing in the book. We'd also like to thank Precison Graphics who assisted in establishing the new art style for this edition. The new text design is the handiwork of Mark Ong, and the exciting cover image is a stunning photo of 16-time Olympic medalist, Michael Phelps. As always, a monumental thank-you goes to Anita Wagner, ultra-conscientious copyeditor. She edits with a light hand, all the while double-checking all statistics, drug names, and other technical data. Our text developmental editor, Annie Reid, did a great job helping us to rid the book of redundancies and unclear text. We are also fortunate to have Martha Ghent returning as proofreader for this edition. We thank Izak Paul for meticulously proofreading each chapter as well. In addition, Michael Wiley from the University of Toronto checked many pieces of anatomy art for accuracy. As has been the practice with this text, Aptara assembled the final pages with their customary expertise led by their extremely talented and organized Los Angeles Project Manager, Sandie Sigrist Allaway.

Once again, Dr. Marieb's husband, Harvey Howell, served as a sounding board for some of her ideas, manned the copy machine, and ran the manuscript to the FedEx box daily with nary a complaint during the unbelievably busy days. Thanks also to Katja's husband, Dr. Lawrence W. Haynes, who as a fellow physiologist has provided invaluable assistance to her during the course of the revision. She also thanks her children, Eric and Stefan Haynes, who are an inspiration and a joy.

Well, our tenure on this edition is over, but there will be another edition three years hence. We would really appreciate hearing from you concerning your opinion—suggestions and constructive criticisms—of this text. It is this type of feedback that provides the basis of each revision, and underwrites its improvement.

Elaine N. Marieb

Elaine N. Marieb

Katja Hoehn

Katja Hoehn

Elaine N. Marieb and Katja Hoehn
Anatomy and Physiology
Benjamin Cummings Science
1301 Sansome Street
San Francisco, CA 94111

Brief Contents

UNIT ONE **Organization of the Body**

1 **The Human Body: An Orientation** 1

2 **Chemistry Comes Alive** 23

3 **Cells: The Living Units** 61

4 **Tissue: The Living Fabric** 113

UNIT TWO **Covering, Support, and Movement of the Body**

5 **The Integumentary System** 148

6 **Bones and Skeletal Tissues** 172

7 **The Skeleton** 198

8 **Joints** 248

9 **Muscles and Muscle Tissue** 275

10 **The Muscular System** 320

UNIT THREE **Regulation and Integration of the Body**

11 **Fundamentals of the Nervous System and Nervous Tissue** 385

12 **The Central Nervous System** 429

13 **The Peripheral Nervous System and Reflex Activity** 484

14 **The Autonomic Nervous System** 525

15 **The Special Senses** 547

Contents

UNIT ONE Organization of the Body

1 The Human Body: An Orientation 1

An Overview of Anatomy and Physiology 2
Topics of Anatomy • Topics of Physiology • Complementarity of Structure and Function

Levels of Structural Organization 3

Maintaining Life 4
Necessary Life Functions • Survival Needs

Homeostasis 8
Homeostatic Control • Homeostatic Imbalance

The Language of Anatomy 11
Anatomical Position and Directional Terms • Regional Terms • Anatomical Variability • Body Planes and Sections • Body Cavities and Membranes

A CLOSER LOOK Medical Imaging: Illuminating the Body 18

2 Chemistry Comes Alive 23

PART 1: BASIC CHEMISTRY 24

Definition of Concepts: Matter and Energy 24
Matter • Energy

Composition of Matter: Atoms and Elements 25
Atomic Structure • Identifying Elements • Radioisotopes

How Matter Is Combined: Molecules and Mixtures 28
Molecules and Compounds • Mixtures • Distinguishing Mixtures from Compounds

Chemical Bonds 31
The Role of Electrons in Chemical Bonding • Types of Chemical Bonds

Chemical Reactions 35
Chemical Equations • Patterns of Chemical Reactions • Energy Flow in Chemical Reactions • Reversibility of Chemical Reactions • Factors Influencing the Rate of Chemical Reactions

PART 2: BIOCHEMISTRY 38

Inorganic Compounds 38
Water • Salts • Acids and Bases

Organic Compounds 42
Carbohydrates • Lipids • Proteins • Nucleic Acids (DNA and RNA) • Adenosine Triphosphate (ATP)

3 Cells: The Living Units 61

Overview of the Cellular Basis of Life 62

The Plasma Membrane: Structure 63
The Fluid Mosaic Model • Membrane Junctions

The Plasma Membrane: Membrane Transport 68
Passive Processes • Active Processes

The Plasma Membrane: Generation of a Resting Membrane Potential 79

The Plasma Membrane: Cell-Environment Interactions 80
Roles of Cell Adhesion Molecules • Roles of Membrane Receptors • Role of Voltage-Sensitive Membrane Channel Proteins

The Cytoplasm 81
Cytoplasmic Organelles • Cellular Extensions

The Nucleus 91
The Nuclear Envelope • Nucleoli • Chromatin

Cell Growth and Reproduction 95
The Cell Life Cycle • Protein Synthesis • Other Roles of DNA • Cytosolic Protein Degradation

Extracellular Materials 107

Developmental Aspects of Cells 108

4 Tissue: The Living Fabric   113

Preparing Human Tissue for Microscopy   114

Epithelial Tissue   115
Special Characteristics of Epithelium • Classification of Epithelia • Glandular Epithelia

Connective Tissue   124
Common Characteristics of Connective Tissue • Structural Elements of Connective Tissue • Types of Connective Tissue

Nervous Tissue   134

Muscle Tissue   136

Covering and Lining Membranes   138
Cutaneous Membrane • Mucous Membranes • Serous Membranes

Tissue Repair   139
Steps of Tissue Repair • Regenerative Capacity of Different Tissues

Developmental Aspects of Tissues   141

A CLOSER LOOK   Cancer—The Intimate Enemy   142

UNIT TWO   Covering, Support, and Movement of the Body

5 The Integumentary System   148

The Skin   149
Epidermis • Dermis • Skin Color

Appendages of the Skin   155
Sweat (Sudoriferous) Glands • Sebaceous (Oil) Glands • Hairs and Hair Follicles • Nails

Functions of the Integumentary System   160
Protection • Body Temperature Regulation • Cutaneous Sensation • Metabolic Functions • Blood Reservoir • Excretion

Homeostatic Imbalances of Skin   162
Skin Cancer • Burns

Developmental Aspects of the Integumentary System   165

MAKING CONNECTIONS   166

6 Bones and Skeletal Tissues   172

Skeletal Cartilages   173
Basic Structure, Types, and Locations • Growth of Cartilage

Classification of Bones   173

Functions of Bones   175

Bone Structure   176
Gross Anatomy • Microscopic Anatomy of Bone • Chemical Composition of Bone

Bone Development   182
Formation of the Bony Skeleton • Postnatal Bone Growth

Bone Homeostasis: Remodeling and Repair   185
Bone Remodeling • Bone Repair

Homeostatic Imbalances of Bone   189
Osteomalacia and Rickets • Osteoporosis • Paget's Disease

Developmental Aspects of Bones: Timing of Events   194

MAKING CONNECTIONS   192

7 The Skeleton   198

PART 1   THE AXIAL SKELETON   199

The Skull   200
Overview of Skull Geography • Cranium • Facial Bones • Special Characteristics of the Orbits and Nasal Cavity • The Hyoid Bone

The Vertebral Column   216
General Characteristics • General Structure of Vertebrae • Regional Vertebral Characteristics

The Thoracic Cage   223
Sternum • Ribs

PART 2:   THE APPENDICULAR SKELETON   225

The Pectoral (Shoulder) Girdle   225
Clavicles • Scapulae

The Upper Limb   228
Arm • Forearm • Hand

The Pelvic (Hip) Girdle   233
Ilium • Ischium • Pubis • Pelvic Structure and Childbearing

The Lower Limb   237
Thigh • Leg • Foot

Developmental Aspects of the Skeleton   242

8 Joints   248

Classification of Joints   248

Fibrous Joints   249
Sutures • Syndesmoses • Gomphoses

Cartilaginous Joints   250
Synchondroses • Symphyses

Synovial Joints   251
General Structure • Bursae and Tendon Sheaths • Factors Influencing the Stability of Synovial Joints • Movements Allowed by Synovial Joints • Types of Synovial Joints • Selected Synovial Joints

Homeostatic Imbalances of Joints 269
  Common Joint Injuries • Inflammatory and Degenerative
  Conditions

Developmental Aspects of Joints 272

A CLOSER LOOK **Joints: From Knights in Shining Armor
  to Bionic Humans 261**

9 Muscles and Muscle Tissue 275

Overview of Muscle Tissues 275
  Types of Muscle Tissue • Special Characteristics of Muscle
  Tissue • Muscle Functions

Skeletal Muscle 277
  Gross Anatomy of a Skeletal Muscle • Microscopic Anatomy
  of a Skeletal Muscle Fiber • Sliding Filament Model of
  Contraction • Physiology of Skeletal Muscle Fibers
  • Contraction of a Skeletal Muscle • Muscle Metabolism • Force
  of Muscle Contraction • Velocity and Duration of Contraction
  • Effect of Exercise on Muscles

Smooth Muscle 305
  Microscopic Structure of Smooth Muscle Fibers • Contraction
  of Smooth Muscle • Types of Smooth Muscle

Developmental Aspects of Muscles 311

A CLOSER LOOK **Athletes Looking Good and Doing
  Better with Anabolic Steroids? 313**

MAKING CONNECTIONS 314

10 The Muscular System 320

Interactions of Skeletal Muscles in the Body 321

Naming Skeletal Muscles 321

Muscle Mechanics: Importance of Fascicle Arrangement
and Leverage 322
  Arrangement of Fascicles • Lever Systems: Bone-Muscle
  Relationships

Major Skeletal Muscles of the Body 324

Table 10.1 Muscles of the Head, Part I: Facial
Expression 329

Table 10.2 Muscles of the Head, Part II: Mastication and
Tongue Movement 332

Table 10.3 Muscles of the Anterior Neck and Throat:
Swallowing 334

Table 10.4 Muscles of the Neck and Vertebral Column:
Head Movements and Trunk Extension 336

Table 10.5 Muscles of the Thorax: Breathing 340

Table 10.6 Muscles of the Abdominal Wall: Trunk
Movements and Compression of Abdominal
Viscera 342

Table 10.7 Muscles of the Pelvic Floor and Perineum:
Support of Abdominopelvic Organs 344

Table 10.8 Superficial Muscles of the Anterior and
Posterior Thorax: Movements of the Scapula 346

Table 10.9 Muscles Crossing the Shoulder Joint:
Movements of the Arm 350

Table 10.10 Muscles Crossing the Elbow Joint: Flexion
and Extension of the Forearm 353

Table 10.11 Muscles of the Forearm: Movements of the
Wrist, Hand, and Fingers 354

Table 10.12 Summary of Actions of Muscles Acting on
the Arm, Forearm, and Hand 358

Table 10.13 Intrinsic Muscles of the Hand: Fine
Movements of the Fingers 360

Table 10.14 Muscles Crossing the Hip and Knee Joints:
Movements of the Thigh and Leg 363

Table 10.15 Muscles of the Leg: Movements of the Ankle
and Toes 370

Table 10.16 Intrinsic Muscles of the Foot: Toe Movement
and Arch Support 376

Table 10.17 Summary of Actions of Muscles Acting on
the Thigh, Leg, and Foot 380

UNIT THREE **Regulation and Integration
  of the Body**

11 Fundamentals of the Nervous System and Nervous Tissue 385

Functions and Divisions of the Nervous System 386

Histology of Nervous Tissue 388
  Neuroglia • Neurons

Membrane Potentials 395
  Basic Principles of Electricity • The Resting Membrane
  Potential • Membrane Potentials That Act as Signals

The Synapse 406
  Electrical Synapses • Chemical Synapses • Postsynaptic
  Potentials and Synaptic Integration

Neurotransmitters and Their Receptors 413
  Classification of Neurotransmitters by Chemical Structure
  • Classification of Neurotransmitters by Function
  • Neurotransmitter Receptors

Basic Concepts of Neural Integration 421
  Organization of Neurons: Neuronal Pools • Types of Circuits
  • Patterns of Neural Processing

Developmental Aspects of Neurons 423

A CLOSER LOOK **Pleasure Me, Pleasure Me! 414**

12 The Central Nervous System 429

The Brain 430
Embryonic Development • Regions and Organization
• Ventricles • Cerebral Hemispheres • Diencephalon • Brain Stem
• Cerebellum • Functional Brain Systems

Higher Mental Functions 453
Brain Wave Patterns and the EEG • Consciousness • Sleep and
Sleep-Wake Cycles • Language • Memory

Protection of the Brain 460
Meninges • Cerebrospinal Fluid • Blood-Brain Barrier
• Homeostatic Imbalances of the Brain

The Spinal Cord 466
Embryonic Development • Gross Anatomy and Protection
• Cross-Sectional Anatomy • Spinal Cord Trauma and Disorders

Diagnostic Procedures for Assessing CNS
Dysfunction 477

Developmental Aspects of the Central Nervous
System 477

13 The Peripheral Nervous System and Reflex Activity 484

PART 1: SENSORY RECEPTORS AND SENSATION 485

Sensory Receptors 485
Classification by Stimulus Type • Classification by Location
• Classification by Structural Complexity

Sensory Integration: From Sensation to Perception 488
General Organization of the Somatosensory System
• Perception of Pain

PART 2: TRANSMISSION LINES: NERVES AND THEIR
STRUCTURE AND REPAIR 491

Nerves and Associated Ganglia 491
Structure and Classification • Regeneration of Nerve Fibers

Cranial Nerves 493

Spinal Nerves 502
Innervation of Specific Body Regions

PART 3: MOTOR ENDINGS AND MOTOR ACTIVITY 512

Peripheral Motor Endings 512
Innervation of Skeletal Muscle • Innervation of Visceral Muscle
and Glands

Motor Integration: From Intention to Effect 512
Levels of Motor Control

PART 4: REFLEX ACTIVITY 514

The Reflex Arc 514
Components of a Reflex Arc

Spinal Reflexes 514
Stretch and Golgi Tendon Reflexes • The Flexor and
Crossed-Extensor Reflexes • Superficial Reflexes

Developmental Aspects of the Peripheral Nervous
System 520

14 The Autonomic Nervous System 525

Introduction 526
Comparison of the Somatic and Autonomic Nervous Systems
• ANS Divisions

ANS Anatomy 528
Parasympathetic (Craniosacral) Division • Sympathetic
(Thoracolumbar) Division • Visceral Reflexes

ANS Physiology 535
Neurotransmitters and Receptors • The Effects of Drugs
• Interactions of the Autonomic Divisions • Control of
Autonomic Functioning

Homeostatic Imbalances of the ANS 540

Developmental Aspects of the ANS 541

MAKING CONNECTIONS 542

15 The Special Senses 547

The Eye and Vision 548
Accessory Structures of the Eye • Structure of the Eyeball
• Physiology of Vision

The Chemical Senses: Taste and Smell 569
The Olfactory Epithelium and the Sense of Smell • Taste Buds
and the Sense of Taste • Homeostatic Imbalances of the
Chemical Senses

The Ear: Hearing and Balance 574
Structure of the Ear • Physiology of Hearing • Homeostatic
Imbalances of Hearing • Equilibrium and Orientation

Developmental Aspects of the Special Senses 588
Taste and Smell • Vision • Hearing and Balance

Appendices

A The Metric System A-1
B Functional Groups in Organic Molecules A-3
C The Amino Acids A-4
D Two Important Metabolic Pathways A-5
E Periodic Table of the Elements A-8
F Reference Values for Selected Blood and Urine
   Studies A-9
G Answers to Check Your Understanding, Clinical
   Connections, Multiple Choice, and Matching
   Questions A-14

Glossary G-1
Photo and Illustration Credits C-1
Index I-1

1

An Overview of Anatomy and Physiology (pp. 2–3)

Topics of Anatomy (p. 2)

Topics of Physiology (pp. 2–3)

Complementarity of Structure and Function (p. 3)

Levels of Structural Organization (pp. 3–4)

Maintaining Life (pp. 4–8)

Necessary Life Functions (pp. 4–8)

Survival Needs (p. 8)

Homeostasis (pp. 8–11)

Homeostatic Control (pp. 9–11)

Homeostatic Imbalance (p. 11)

The Language of Anatomy (pp. 11–20)

Anatomical Position and Directional Terms (p. 13)

Regional Terms (p. 14)

Anatomical Variability (p. 14)

Body Planes and Sections (p. 14)

Body Cavities and Membranes (pp. 14–20)

The Human Body: An Orientation

Welcome to the study of one of the most fascinating subjects possible—your own body. Such a study is not only highly personal, but timely as well. We get news of some medical advance almost daily. To appreciate emerging discoveries in genetic engineering, to understand new techniques for detecting and treating disease, and to make use of published facts on how to stay healthy, you'll find it helpful to learn about the workings of your body. If you are preparing for a career in the health sciences, the study of anatomy and physiology has added rewards because it provides the foundation needed to support your clinical experiences.

In this chapter we define and contrast anatomy and physiology and discuss how the human body is organized. Then we review needs and functional processes common to all living organisms. Three essential concepts—*the complementarity of structure and function, the hierarchy of structural organization,* and *homeostasis*—will unify and form the bedrock for your study of the human body. The final section of the chapter deals with the language of anatomy—terminology that anatomists use to describe the body or its parts.

An Overview of Anatomy and Physiology

▶ Define anatomy and physiology and describe their subdivisions.

▶ Explain the principle of complementarity.

Two complementary branches of science—anatomy and physiology—provide the concepts that help us to understand the human body. **Anatomy** studies the *structure* of body parts and their relationships to one another. Anatomy has a certain appeal because it is concrete. Body structures can be seen, felt, and examined closely. You don't need to imagine what they look like.

Physiology concerns the *function* of the body, in other words, how the body parts work and carry out their life-sustaining activities. When all is said and done, physiology is explainable only in terms of the underlying anatomy.

To simplify the study of the body, when we refer to body structures and/or physiological values (body temperature, heart rate, and the like), we will assume that we are talking about a healthy young (22-year-old) male weighing about 155 lb (the *reference man*) or a healthy young female weighing about 125 lb (the *reference woman*).

Topics of Anatomy

Anatomy is a broad field with many subdivisions, each providing enough information to be a course in itself. **Gross**, or **macroscopic**, **anatomy** is the study of large body structures visible to the naked eye, such as the heart, lungs, and kidneys. Indeed, the term *anatomy* (derived from the Greek words meaning "to cut apart") relates most closely to gross anatomy because in such studies preserved animals or their organs are dissected (cut up) to be examined.

Gross anatomy can be approached in different ways. In **regional anatomy**, all the structures (muscles, bones, blood vessels, nerves, etc.) in a particular region of the body, such as the abdomen or leg, are examined at the same time.

In **systemic anatomy** (sis-tem′ik),* body structure is studied system by system. For example, when studying the cardiovascular system, you would examine the heart and the blood vessels of the entire body.

*For the pronunciation guide rules, see the Preface to the Student.

Another subdivision of gross anatomy is **surface anatomy**, the study of internal structures as they relate to the overlying skin surface. You use surface anatomy when you identify the bulging muscles beneath a bodybuilder's skin, and clinicians use it to locate appropriate blood vessels in which to feel pulses and draw blood.

Microscopic anatomy deals with structures too small to be seen with the naked eye. For most such studies, exceedingly thin slices of body tissues are stained and mounted on glass slides to be examined under the microscope. Subdivisions of microscopic anatomy include **cytology** (si-tol′o-je), which considers the cells of the body, and **histology** (his-tol′o-je), the study of tissues.

Developmental anatomy traces structural changes that occur in the body throughout the life span. **Embryology** (em″bre-ol′o-je), a subdivision of developmental anatomy, concerns developmental changes that occur before birth.

Some highly specialized branches of anatomy are used primarily for medical diagnosis and scientific research. For example, *pathological anatomy* studies structural changes caused by disease. *Radiographic anatomy* studies internal structures as visualized by X-ray images or specialized scanning procedures.

Subjects of interest to anatomists range from easily seen structures down to the smallest molecule. In *molecular biology*, for example, the structure of biological molecules (chemical substances) is investigated. Molecular biology is actually a separate branch of biology, but it falls under the anatomy umbrella when we push anatomical studies to the subcellular level.

One essential tool for studying anatomy is a mastery of anatomical terminology. Others are observation, manipulation, and, in a living person, *palpation* (feeling organs with your hands) and *auscultation* (listening to organ sounds with a stethoscope). A simple example illustrates how some of these tools work together in an anatomical study.

Let's assume that your topic is freely movable joints of the body. In the laboratory, you will be able to *observe* an animal joint, noting how its parts fit together. You can work the joint (*manipulate* it) to determine its range of motion. Using *anatomical terminology*, you can name its parts and describe how they are related so that other students (and your instructor) will have no trouble understanding you. The list of word roots (at the back of the book) and the glossary will help you with this special vocabulary.

Although you will make most of your observations with the naked eye or with the help of a microscope, medical technology has developed a number of sophisticated tools that can peer into the body without disrupting it. Read about these exciting medical imaging techniques in *A Closer Look* on pp. 18–19.

Topics of Physiology

Like anatomy, physiology has many subdivisions. Most of them consider the operation of specific organ systems. For example, **renal physiology** concerns kidney function and urine production. **Neurophysiology** explains the workings of the nervous system. **Cardiovascular physiology** examines the operation of the heart and blood vessels. While anatomy provides us with a static image of the body's architecture, physiology reveals the body's dynamic and animated workings.

Physiology often focuses on events at the cellular or molecular level. This is because the body's abilities depend on those of its individual cells, and cells' abilities ultimately depend on the chemical reactions that go on within them. Physiology also rests on principles of physics, which help to explain electrical currents, blood pressure, and the way muscles use bones to cause body movements, among other things. We present basic chemical and physical principles in Chapter 2 and throughout the book as needed to explain physiological topics.

Complementarity of Structure and Function

Although it is possible to study anatomy and physiology individually, they are really inseparable because function always reflects structure. That is, what a structure can do depends on its specific form. This key concept is called the **principle of complementarity of structure and function**.

For example, bones can support and protect body organs because they contain hard mineral deposits. Blood flows in one direction through the heart because the heart has valves that prevent backflow. Throughout this book, we accompany a description of a structure's anatomy with an explanation of its function, and we emphasize structural characteristics contributing to that function.

CHECK YOUR UNDERSTANDING

1. In what way does physiology depend on anatomy?
2. Would you be studying anatomy or physiology if you investigated how muscles shorten? If you explored the location of the lungs in the body?

For answers, see Appendix G.

Levels of Structural Organization

▶ Name the different levels of structural organization that make up the human body, and explain their relationships.

▶ List the 11 organ systems of the body, identify their components, and briefly explain the major function(s) of each system.

The human body has many levels of structural organization **(Figure 1.1)**. The simplest level of the structural hierarchy is the **chemical level**, which we study in Chapter 2. At this level, *atoms*, tiny building blocks of matter, combine to form *molecules* such as water and proteins. Molecules, in turn, associate in specific ways to form *organelles*, basic components of the microscopic cells. *Cells* are the smallest units of living things. We examine the **cellular level** in Chapter 3. All cells have some common functions, but individual cells vary widely in size and shape, reflecting their unique functions in the body.

The simplest living creatures are single cells, but in complex organisms such as human beings, the hierarchy continues on to the **tissue level**. *Tissues* are groups of similar cells that have a common function. The four basic tissue types in the human body are epithelium, muscle, connective tissue, and nervous tissue.

Each tissue type has a characteristic role in the body, which we explore in Chapter 4. Briefly, epithelium covers the body surface and lines its cavities. Muscle provides movement. Connective tissue supports and protects body organs. Nervous tissue provides a means of rapid internal communication by transmitting electrical impulses.

An *organ* is a discrete structure composed of at least two tissue types (four is more common) that performs a specific function for the body. The liver, the brain, and a blood vessel are very different from the stomach, but each is an organ. You can think of each organ of the body as a specialized functional center responsible for a necessary activity that no other organ can perform.

At the **organ level**, extremely complex functions become possible. Let's take the stomach for an example. Its lining is an epithelium that produces digestive juices. The bulk of its wall is muscle, which churns and mixes stomach contents (food). Its connective tissue reinforces the soft muscular walls. Its nerve fibers increase digestive activity by stimulating the muscle to contract more vigorously and the glands to secrete more digestive juices.

The next level of organization is the **organ system level**. Organs that work together to accomplish a common purpose make up an *organ system*. For example, the heart and blood vessels of the cardiovascular system circulate blood continuously to carry oxygen and nutrients to all body cells. Besides the cardiovascular system, the other organ systems of the body are the integumentary, skeletal, muscular, nervous, endocrine, lymphatic, respiratory, digestive, urinary, and reproductive systems. (Note that the immune system is closely associated with the lymphatic system.) Look ahead to Figure 1.3 on pp. 6 and 7 for an overview of the 11 organ systems, which we discuss in the next section and study in more detail in Units 2–5.

The highest level of organization is the *organism*, the living human being. The **organismal level** represents the sum total of all structural levels working together to keep us alive.

CHECK YOUR UNDERSTANDING

3. What level of structural organization is typical of a cytologist's field of study?
4. What is the correct structural order for the following terms: tissue, organism, organ, cell?
5. Which organ system includes the bones and cartilages? Which includes the nasal cavity, lungs, and trachea?

For answers, see Appendix G.

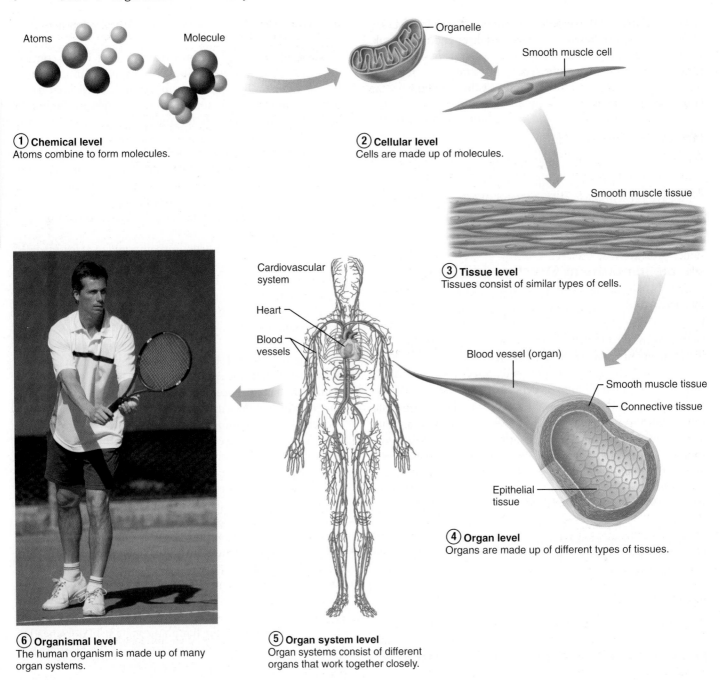

① **Chemical level**
Atoms combine to form molecules.

② **Cellular level**
Cells are made up of molecules.

③ **Tissue level**
Tissues consist of similar types of cells.

④ **Organ level**
Organs are made up of different types of tissues.

⑤ **Organ system level**
Organ systems consist of different organs that work together closely.

⑥ **Organismal level**
The human organism is made up of many organ systems.

Atoms

Molecule

Organelle

Smooth muscle cell

Smooth muscle tissue

Cardiovascular system

Heart

Blood vessels

Blood vessel (organ)

Smooth muscle tissue

Connective tissue

Epithelial tissue

Figure 1.1 Levels of structural organization. Components of the cardiovascular system are used to illustrate the levels of structural organization in a human being.

Maintaining Life

▶ List the functional characteristics necessary to maintain life in humans.

▶ List the survival needs of the body.

Necessary Life Functions

Now that you know the structural levels of the human body, the question that naturally follows is: What does this highly organized human body do?

Like all complex animals, humans maintain their boundaries, move, respond to environmental changes, take in and digest nutrients, carry out metabolism, dispose of wastes, reproduce themselves, and grow. We will introduce these necessary life functions here and discuss them in more detail in later chapters.

We cannot emphasize too strongly that all body cells are interdependent. This interdependence is due to the fact that humans are multicellular organisms and our vital body functions are parceled out among different organ systems. Organ systems, in turn, work cooperatively to promote the well-being of the entire body. This theme is repeated throughout the book. Figure 1.2 identifies some of the organ systems making major contributions to necessary life functions. Also, as you read this section, check Figure 1.3 for more detailed descriptions of the body's organ systems.

Maintaining Boundaries

Every living organism must **maintain its boundaries** so that its internal environment (its inside) remains distinct from the external environment surrounding it (its outside). In single-celled organisms, the external boundary is a limiting membrane that encloses its contents and lets in needed substances while restricting entry of potentially damaging or unnecessary substances. Similarly, all the cells of our body are surrounded by a selectively permeable membrane.

Additionally, the body as a whole is enclosed and protected by the integumentary system, or skin (Figure 1.3a). This system protects our internal organs from drying out (a fatal change), bacteria, and the damaging effects of heat, sunlight, and an unbelievable number of chemicals in the external environment.

Movement

Movement includes the activities promoted by the muscular system, such as propelling ourselves from one place to another by running or swimming, and manipulating the external environment with our nimble fingers (Figure 1.3c). The skeletal system provides the bony framework that the muscles pull on as they work (Figure 1.3b). Movement also occurs when substances such as blood, foodstuffs, and urine are propelled through internal organs of the cardiovascular, digestive, and urinary systems, respectively. On the cellular level, the muscle cell's ability to move by shortening is more precisely called **contractility**.

Responsiveness

Responsiveness, or **irritability**, is the ability to sense changes (which serve as stimuli) in the environment and then respond to them. For example, if you cut your hand on broken glass, a withdrawal reflex occurs—you involuntarily pull your hand away from the painful stimulus (the broken glass). You don't have to think about it—it just happens! Likewise, when carbon dioxide in your blood rises to dangerously high levels, chemical sensors respond by sending messages to brain centers controlling respiration, and you breathe more rapidly.

Because nerve cells are highly irritable and communicate rapidly with each other via electrical impulses, the nervous system is most involved with responsiveness (Figure 1.3d). However, all body cells are irritable to some extent.

Digestion

Digestion is the breaking down of ingested foodstuffs to simple molecules that can be absorbed into the blood. The nutrient-rich blood is then distributed to all body cells by the cardiovascular system. In a simple, one-celled organism such as an

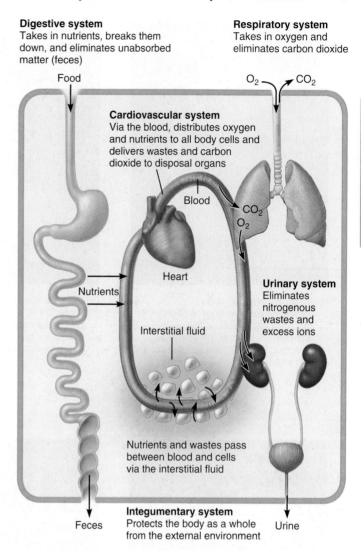

Digestive system
Takes in nutrients, breaks them down, and eliminates unabsorbed matter (feces)

Respiratory system
Takes in oxygen and eliminates carbon dioxide

Food

O_2 — CO_2

Cardiovascular system
Via the blood, distributes oxygen and nutrients to all body cells and delivers wastes and carbon dioxide to disposal organs

Blood

CO_2
O_2

Heart

Nutrients

Urinary system
Eliminates nitrogenous wastes and excess ions

Interstitial fluid

Nutrients and wastes pass between blood and cells via the interstitial fluid

Feces

Integumentary system
Protects the body as a whole from the external environment

Urine

Figure 1.2 Examples of interrelationships among body organ systems.

amoeba, the cell itself is the "digestion factory," but in the multicellular human body, the digestive system performs this function for the entire body (Figure 1.3i).

Metabolism

Metabolism (mĕ-tab′o-lizm; "a state of change") is a broad term that includes all chemical reactions that occur within body cells. It includes breaking down substances into their simpler building blocks (more specifically, the process of *catabolism*), synthesizing more complex cellular structures from simpler substances (*anabolism*), and using nutrients and oxygen to produce (via *cellular respiration*) ATP, the energy-rich molecules that power cellular activities. Metabolism depends on the digestive and respiratory systems to make nutrients and oxygen available to the blood and on the cardiovascular system to distribute them throughout the body (Figure 1.3i, h, and f, respectively). Metabolism is regulated largely by hormones secreted by endocrine system glands (Figure 1.3e).

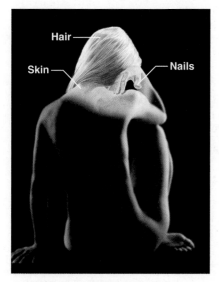

(a) Integumentary System
Forms the external body covering, and
protects deeper tissues from injury.
Synthesizes vitamin D, and houses
cutaneous (pain, pressure, etc.) receptors
and sweat and oil glands.

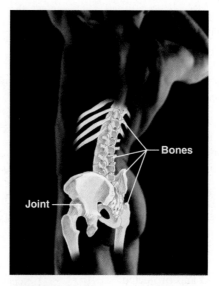

(b) Skeletal System
Protects and supports body organs, and
provides a framework the muscles use
to cause movement. Blood cells are
formed within bones. Bones store minerals.

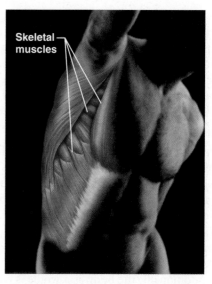

(c) Muscular System
Allows manipulation of the environment,
locomotion, and facial expression. Maintains posture, and produces heat.

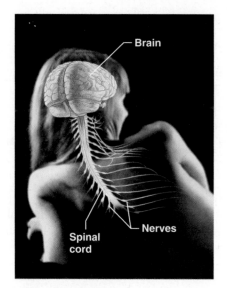

(d) Nervous System
As the fast-acting control system of the
body, it responds to internal and external
changes by activating appropriate
muscles and glands.

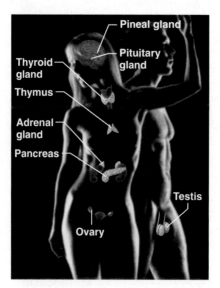

(e) Endocrine System
Glands secrete hormones that regulate
processes such as growth, reproduction,
and nutrient use (metabolism) by body
cells.

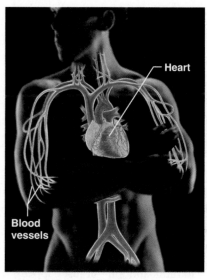

(f) Cardiovascular System
Blood vessels transport blood, which
carries oxygen, carbon dioxide,
nutrients, wastes, etc. The heart pumps
blood.

Figure 1.3 The body's organ systems and their major functions.

Excretion

Excretion is the process of removing wastes, or *excreta*
(ek-skre'tah), from the body. If the body is to operate as we
expect it to, it must get rid of nonuseful substances produced
during digestion and metabolism.

Several organ systems participate in excretion. For example,
the digestive system rids the body of indigestible food residues
in feces, and the urinary system disposes of nitrogen-containing
metabolic wastes, such as urea, in urine (Figure 1.3i and j). Carbon dioxide, a by-product of cellular respiration, is carried in

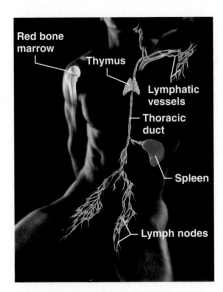

(g) Lymphatic System/Immunity
Picks up fluid leaked from blood vessels and returns it to blood. Disposes of debris in the lymphatic stream. Houses white blood cells (lymphocytes) involved in immunity. The immune response mounts the attack against foreign substances within the body.

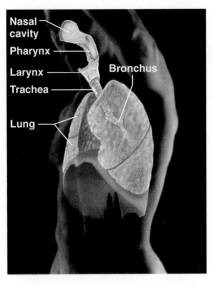

(h) Respiratory System
Keeps blood constantly supplied with oxygen and removes carbon dioxide. The gaseous exchanges occur through the walls of the air sacs of the lungs.

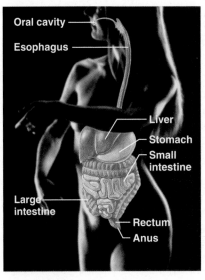

(i) Digestive System
Breaks down food into absorbable units that enter the blood for distribution to body cells. Indigestible foodstuffs are eliminated as feces.

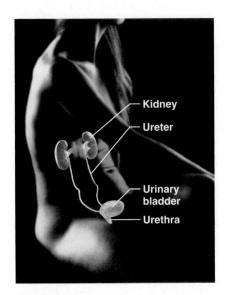

(j) Urinary System
Eliminates nitrogenous wastes from the body. Regulates water, electrolyte and acid-base balance of the blood.

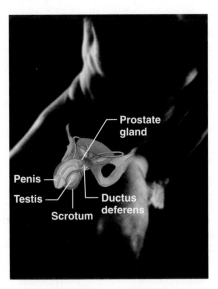

(k) Male Reproductive System

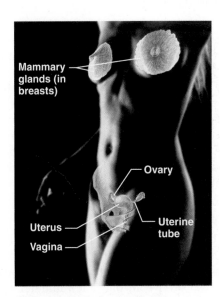

(l) Female Reproductive System
Overall function is production of offspring. Testes produce sperm and male sex hormone, and male ducts and glands aid in delivery of sperm to the female reproductive tract. Ovaries produce eggs and female sex hormones. The remaining female structures serve as sites for fertilization and development of the fetus. Mammary glands of female breasts produce milk to nourish the newborn.

the blood to the lungs, where it leaves the body in exhaled air (Figure 1.3h).

Reproduction

Reproduction occurs at the cellular and the organismal level. In cellular reproduction, the original cell divides, producing two identical daughter cells that may then be used for body growth or repair. Reproduction of the human organism, or making a whole new person, is the major task of the reproductive system. When a sperm unites with an egg, a fertilized egg forms and develops into a baby within the mother's body. The reproductive system is directly responsible for producing offspring, but its function is exquisitely regulated by hormones of the endocrine system (Figure 1.3e).

Because males produce sperm and females produce eggs (ova), there is a division of labor in reproduction, and the reproductive organs of males and females are different (Figure 1.3k, l). Additionally, the female's reproductive structures provide the site for fertilization of eggs by sperm, and then protect and nurture the developing fetus until birth.

Growth

Growth is an increase in size of a body part or the organism. It is usually accomplished by increasing the number of cells. However, individual cells also increase in size when not dividing. For true growth to occur, constructive activities must occur at a faster rate than destructive ones.

Survival Needs

The ultimate goal of all body systems is to maintain life. However, life is extraordinarily fragile and requires several factors. These factors, which we will call *survival needs*, include nutrients (food), oxygen, water, and appropriate temperature and atmospheric pressure.

Nutrients

Nutrients, taken in via the diet, contain the chemical substances used for energy and cell building. Most plant-derived foods are rich in carbohydrates, vitamins, and minerals, whereas most animal foods are richer in proteins and fats.

Carbohydrates are the major energy fuel for body cells. Proteins, and to a lesser extent fats, are essential for building cell structures. Fats also provide a reserve of energy-rich fuel. Selected minerals and vitamins are required for the chemical reactions that go on in cells and for oxygen transport in the blood. The mineral calcium helps to make bones hard and is required for blood clotting.

Oxygen

All the nutrients in the world are useless unless **oxygen** is also available. Because the chemical reactions that release energy from foods are *oxidative* reactions that require oxygen, human cells can survive for only a few minutes without oxygen. Approximately 20% of the air we breathe is oxygen. The cooperative efforts of the respiratory and cardiovascular systems make oxygen available to the blood and body cells.

Water

Water accounts for 60–80% of our body weight and is the single most abundant chemical substance in the body. It provides the watery environment necessary for chemical reactions and the fluid base for body secretions and excretions. We obtain water chiefly from ingested foods or liquids. We lose it from the body by evaporation from the lungs and skin and in body excretions.

Normal Body Temperature

If chemical reactions are to continue at life-sustaining rates, **normal body temperature** must be maintained. As body temperature drops below 37°C (98.6°F), metabolic reactions become slower and slower, and finally stop. When body temperature is too high, chemical reactions occur at a frantic pace and body proteins lose their characteristic shape and stop functioning. At either extreme, death occurs. The activity of the muscular system generates most body heat.

Appropriate Atmospheric Pressure

Atmospheric pressure is the force that air exerts on the surface of the body. Breathing and gas exchange in the lungs depend on *appropriate* atmospheric pressure. At high altitudes, where atmospheric pressure is lower and the air is thin, gas exchange may be inadequate to support cellular metabolism.

The mere presence of these survival factors is not sufficient to sustain life. They must be present in *appropriate* amounts. Excesses and deficits may be equally harmful. For example, oxygen is essential, but excessive amounts are toxic to body cells. Similarly, the food we eat must be of high quality and in proper amounts. Otherwise, nutritional disease, obesity, or starvation is likely. Also, while the needs listed above are the most crucial, they do not even begin to encompass all of the body's needs. For example, we can live without gravity if we must, but the quality of life suffers.

CHECK YOUR UNDERSTANDING

6. What separates living beings from nonliving objects?
7. What name is given to all chemical reactions that occur within body cells?
8. Why is it necessary to be in a pressurized cabin when flying at 30,000 feet?

For answers, see Appendix G.

Homeostasis

▶ Define homeostasis and explain its significance.

▶ Describe how negative and positive feedback maintain body homeostasis.

▶ Describe the relationship between homeostatic imbalance and disease.

When you think about the fact that your body contains trillions of cells in nearly constant activity, and that remarkably little usually goes wrong with it, you begin to appreciate what a marvelous machine your body is. Walter Cannon, an American physiologist of the early twentieth century, spoke of the "wisdom of the body," and he coined the word **homeostasis** (ho″me-o-sta′sis) to describe its ability to maintain relatively stable internal conditions even though the outside world changes continuously.

Although the literal translation of homeostasis is "unchanging," the term does not really mean a static, or unchanging, state.

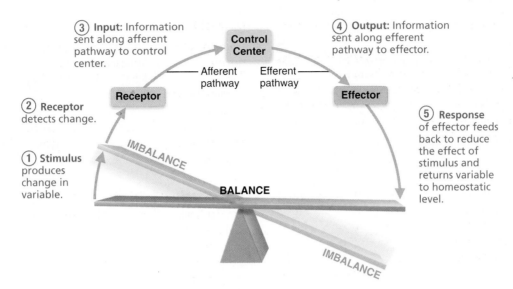

Figure 1.4 **Interaction among the elements of a homeostatic control system.**

Rather, it indicates a *dynamic* state of equilibrium, or a balance, in which internal conditions vary, but always within relatively narrow limits. In general, the body is in homeostasis when its needs are adequately met and it is functioning smoothly.

Maintaining homeostasis is more complicated than it appears at first glance. Virtually every organ system plays a role in maintaining the constancy of the internal environment. Adequate blood levels of vital nutrients must be continuously present, and heart activity and blood pressure must be constantly monitored and adjusted so that the blood is propelled to all body tissues. Also, wastes must not be allowed to accumulate, and body temperature must be precisely controlled. A wide variety of chemical, thermal, and neural factors act and interact in complex ways—sometimes helping and sometimes hindering the body as it works to maintain its "steady rudder."

Homeostatic Control

Communication within the body is essential for homeostasis. Communication is accomplished chiefly by the nervous and endocrine systems, which use neural electrical impulses or bloodborne hormones, respectively, as information carriers. We cover the details of how these two great regulating systems operate in later chapters, but here we explain the basic characteristics of control systems that promote homeostasis.

Regardless of the factor or event being regulated—the **variable**—all homeostatic control mechanisms are processes involving at least three components that work together (Figure 1.4). The first component, the **receptor**, is some type of sensor that monitors the environment and responds to changes, called *stimuli*, by sending information (input) to the second component, the *control center*. Input flows from the receptor to the control center along the so-called *afferent pathway*.

The **control center** determines the *set point*, which is the level or range at which a variable is to be maintained. It also analyzes the input it receives and determines the appropriate response or course of action. Information (output) then flows from the control center to the third component, the *effector*, along the *efferent pathway*. (To help you remember the difference between "afferent" and "efferent," you might note that information traveling along the afferent pathway **approaches** the control center and efferent information **exits** from the control center.)

The **effector** provides the means for the control center's response (output) to the stimulus. The results of the response then *feed back* to influence the effect of the stimulus, either reducing it (in negative feedback) so that the whole control process is shut off, or enhancing it (in positive feedback) so that the whole process continues at an even faster rate.

Negative Feedback Mechanisms

Most homeostatic control mechanisms are **negative feedback mechanisms**. In these systems, the output shuts off the original effect of the stimulus or reduces its intensity. These mechanisms cause the variable to change in a direction *opposite* to that of the initial change, returning it to its "ideal" value; thus the name "negative" feedback mechanisms.

Let's start with an example of a nonbiological negative feedback system: a home heating system connected to a temperature-sensing thermostat. The thermostat houses both the receptor (thermometer) and the control center. If the thermostat is set at 20°C (68°F), the heating system (effector) is triggered ON when the house temperature drops below that setting. As the furnace produces heat and warms the air, the temperature rises, and when it reaches 20°C or slightly higher, the thermostat triggers the furnace OFF. This process results in a cycling of "furnace-ON" and "furnace-OFF" so that the temperature in the house stays very near the desired temperature of 20°C.

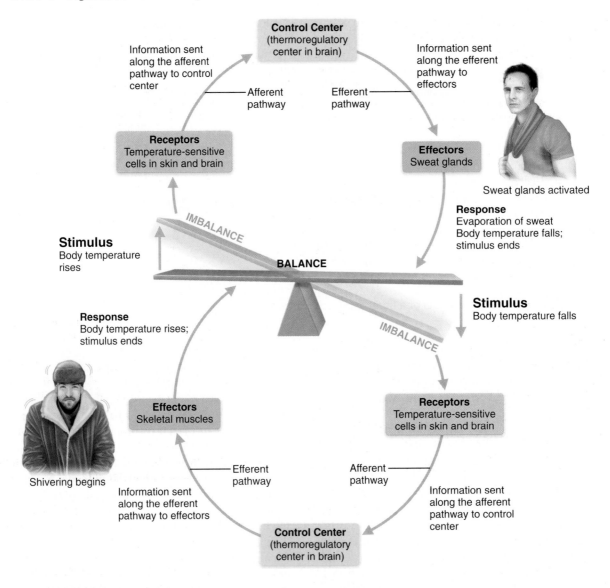

Figure 1.5 Regulation of body temperature by a negative feedback mechanism.

Your body "thermostat," located in a part of your brain called the hypothalamus, operates in a similar fashion (**Figure 1.5**). Regulation of body temperature is only one of the many ways the nervous system maintains the constancy of the internal environment. Another type of neural control mechanism is seen in the *withdrawal reflex* mentioned earlier, in which the hand is jerked away from a painful stimulus such as broken glass.

The endocrine system is equally important in maintaining homeostasis. A good example of a hormonal negative feedback mechanism is the control of blood volume by antidiuretic hormone (ADH). As blood volume drops, receptors in the body sense this change, and the hypothalamus of the brain (the control center) stimulates the release of ADH to the blood. This change in turn prompts the kidneys to reabsorb more water and return it to the bloodstream. The rising blood volume then ends the stimulus for ADH release.

The body's ability to regulate its internal environment is fundamental. All negative feedback mechanisms have the same goal: preventing sudden severe changes within the body. Body temperature and blood volume are only two of the variables that need to be regulated. There are hundreds! Other negative feedback mechanisms regulate heart rate, blood pressure, the rate and depth of breathing, and blood levels of oxygen, carbon dioxide, and minerals. Now, let's take a look at the other type of feedback control mechanism—positive feedback.

Positive Feedback Mechanisms

In **positive feedback mechanisms**, the result or response enhances the original stimulus so that the response is accelerated. This feedback mechanism is "positive" because the change that results proceeds in the *same* direction as the initial change, causing the variable to deviate further and further from its original value or range.

In contrast to negative feedback controls, which maintain some physiological function or keep blood chemicals within narrow ranges, positive feedback mechanisms usually control infrequent events that do not require continuous adjustments. Typically, they set off a series of events that may be self-perpetuating and that, once initiated, have an amplifying or waterfall effect. Because of these characteristics, positive feedback mechanisms are often referred to as *cascades* (from the Italian word meaning "to fall").

Positive feedback mechanisms are likely to race out of control, so they are rarely used to promote the moment-to-moment well-being of the body. However, two familiar examples of their use as homeostatic mechanisms are the enhancement of labor contractions during birth and blood clotting.

Chapter 28 describes the positive feedback mechanism in which oxytocin, a hypothalamic hormone, intensifies labor contractions during the birth of a baby (see Figure 28.17). Oxytocin causes the contractions to become both more frequent and more powerful. The increased contractions cause more oxytocin to be released, which causes more contractions, and so on until the baby is finally born. The birth ends the stimulus for oxytocin release and shuts off the positive feedback mechanism.

Blood clotting is a normal response to a break in the wall of a blood vessel and is an excellent example of an important body function controlled by positive feedback. Basically, once a vessel has been damaged, blood elements called platelets immediately begin to cling to the injured site and release chemicals that attract more platelets. This rapidly growing pileup of platelets temporarily "plugs" the tear and initiates the sequence of events that finally forms a clot (Figure 1.6).

Homeostatic Imbalance

Homeostasis is so important that most disease can be regarded as a result of its disturbance, a condition called **homeostatic imbalance**. As we age, our body's control systems become less efficient, and our internal environment becomes less and less stable. These events increase our risk for illness and produce the changes we associate with aging.

Another important source of homeostatic imbalance occurs when the usual negative feedback mechanisms are overwhelmed and destructive positive feedback mechanisms take over. Some instances of heart failure reflect this phenomenon.

Examples of homeostatic imbalance appear throughout this book to enhance your understanding of normal physiological mechanisms. This symbol ⚖ introduces the homeostatic imbalance sections and alerts you to the fact that we are describing an abnormal condition.

CHECK YOUR UNDERSTANDING

9. What process allows us to adjust to either extreme heat or extreme cold?

10. When we begin to get dehydrated, we usually get thirsty, which causes us to drink fluids. Is thirst part of a negative or a positive feedback control system? Defend your choice.

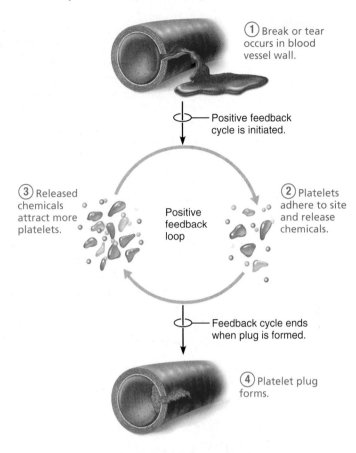

① Break or tear occurs in blood vessel wall.

Positive feedback cycle is initiated.

③ Released chemicals attract more platelets.

Positive feedback loop

② Platelets adhere to site and release chemicals.

Feedback cycle ends when plug is formed.

④ Platelet plug forms.

Figure 1.6 Summary of the positive feedback mechanism regulating formation of a platelet plug.

11. Why is the control mechanism shown in Figure 1.6 called a positive feedback system? What event ends it?

For answers, see Appendix G.

The Language of Anatomy

▶ Describe the anatomical position.

▶ Use correct anatomical terms to describe body directions, regions, and body planes or sections.

Most of us are naturally curious about our bodies, but our interest sometimes dwindles when we are confronted with the terminology of anatomy and physiology. Let's face it—you can't just pick up an anatomy and physiology book and read it as though it were a novel.

Unfortunately, confusion is likely without precise, specialized terminology. To prevent misunderstanding, anatomists use universally accepted terms to identify body structures precisely and with a minimum of words. We present and explain the language of anatomy next.

TABLE 1.1	Orientation and Directional Terms		
TERM	**DEFINITION**	**EXAMPLE**	
Superior (cranial)	Toward the head end or upper part of a structure or the body; above		The head is superior to the abdomen.
Inferior (caudal)	Away from the head end or toward the lower part of a structure or the body; below		The navel is inferior to the chin.
Ventral (anterior)*	Toward or at the front of the body; in front of		The breastbone is anterior to the spine.
Dorsal (posterior)*	Toward or at the back of the body; behind		The heart is posterior to the breastbone.
Medial	Toward or at the midline of the body; on the inner side of		The heart is medial to the arm.
Lateral	Away from the midline of the body; on the outer side of		The arms are lateral to the chest.
Intermediate	Between a more medial and a more lateral structure		The collarbone is intermediate between the breastbone and shoulder.
Proximal	Closer to the origin of the body part or the point of attachment of a limb to the body trunk		The elbow is proximal to the wrist.
Distal	Farther from the origin of a body part or the point of attachment of a limb to the body trunk		The knee is distal to the thigh.
Superficial (external)	Toward or at the body surface		The skin is superficial to the skeletal muscles.
Deep (internal)	Away from the body surface; more internal		The lungs are deep to the skin.

*The terms *ventral* and *anterior* are synonymous in humans, but this is not the case in four-legged animals. *Anterior* refers to the leading portion of the body (abdominal surface in humans, head in a cat), but *ventral* specifically refers to the "belly" of a vertebrate animal, so it is the inferior surface of four-legged animals. Likewise, although the dorsal and posterior surfaces are the same in humans, the term *dorsal* specifically refers to an animal's back. Thus, the dorsal surface of four-legged animals is their superior surface.

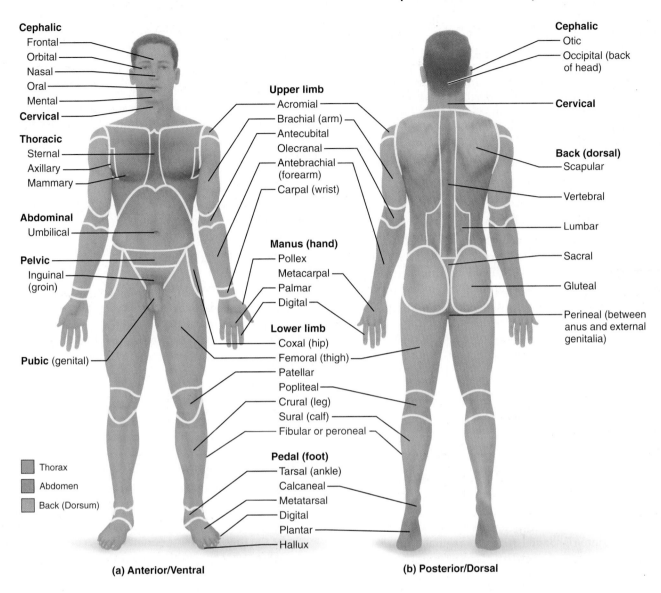

Figure 1.7 Regional terms used to designate specific body areas. (a) The anatomical position. **(b)** The heels are raised to show the plantar surface of the foot, which is actually on the inferior surface of the body.

Anatomical Position and Directional Terms

To describe body parts and position accurately, we need an initial reference point, and we must indicate direction. The anatomical reference point is a standard body position called the **anatomical position**. In the anatomical position, the body is erect with feet slightly apart. This position is easy to remember because it resembles "standing at attention," except that the palms face forward and the thumbs point away from the body. You can see the anatomical position in **Table 1.1** (top) and **Figure 1.7a**.

It is essential to understand the anatomical position because most of the directional terms used in this book refer to the body *as if it were in this position, regardless of its actual position.* Another point to remember is that the terms "right" and "left" refer to those sides of the person or the cadaver (body of a deceased person) being viewed—not those of the observer.

Directional terms allow us to explain where one body structure is in relation to another. For example, we could describe the relationship between the ears and the nose informally by stating, "The ears are located on each side of the head to the right and left of the nose." Using anatomical terminology, we can condense this to "The ears are lateral to the nose." Using anatomical terms saves words and is less ambiguous.

Commonly used orientation and directional terms are defined and illustrated in Table 1.1. Many of these terms are also used in everyday conversation, but keep in mind as you study them that their anatomical meanings are very precise.

Regional Terms

The two fundamental divisions of our body are its *axial* and *appendicular* (ap″en-dik′u-lar) parts. The **axial part**, which makes up the main *axis* of our body, includes the head, neck, and trunk. The **appendicular part** consists of the *appendages*, or *limbs*, which are attached to the body's axis. **Regional terms** used to designate specific areas within these major body divisions are indicated in Figure 1.7. The figure also gives the common term for each of these body regions (in parentheses).

Anatomical Variability

Although we use common directional and regional terms to refer to all human bodies, you know from observing the faces and body shapes of people around you that humans differ in their external anatomy. The same kind of variability holds for internal organs as well. In some bodies, for example, a nerve or blood vessel may be somewhat out of place, or a small muscle may be missing. Nonetheless, well over 90% of all structures present in any human body match the textbook descriptions. We seldom see extreme anatomical variations because they are incompatible with life.

Body Planes and Sections

For anatomical studies, the body is often cut, or *sectioned*, along a flat surface called a *plane*. The most frequently used body planes are *sagittal*, *frontal*, and *transverse* planes, which lie at right angles to one another (Figure 1.8). A section is named for the plane along which it is cut. Thus, a cut along a sagittal plane produces a sagittal section.

A **sagittal plane** (saj′ĭ-tal; "arrow") is a vertical plane that divides the body into right and left parts. A sagittal plane that lies exactly in the midline is the **median plane**, or **midsagittal plane** (Figure 1.8c). All other sagittal planes, offset from the midline, are **parasagittal planes** (*para* = near).

Frontal planes, like sagittal planes, lie vertically. Frontal planes, however, divide the body into anterior and posterior parts (Figure 1.8a). A frontal plane is also called a **coronal plane** (kŏ-ro′nal; "crown").

A **transverse**, or **horizontal**, **plane** runs horizontally from right to left, dividing the body into superior and inferior parts (Figure 1.8b). Of course, many different transverse planes exist, at every possible level from head to foot. A transverse section is also called a **cross section**.

Oblique sections are cuts made diagonally between the horizontal and the vertical planes. Because oblique sections are often confusing and difficult to interpret, they are seldom used.

At the bottom of Figure 1.8, you can see examples of magnetic resonance imaging (MRI) scans that correspond to the three different sections shown in the figure. In the clinical sciences, the ability to interpret sections made through the body, especially transverse sections, is important. Additionally,

the new medical imaging devices (*A Closer Look*, pp. 18–19) produce sectional images rather than three-dimensional images.

It takes practice to decipher an object's overall shape from sectioned material. A cross section of a banana, for example, looks like a circle and gives no indication of the whole banana's crescent shape. Likewise, sectioning the body or an organ along different planes often results in very different views. For example, a transverse section of the body trunk at the level of the kidneys would show kidney structure in cross section very nicely. A frontal section of the body trunk would show a different view of kidney anatomy, and a midsagittal section would miss the kidneys completely. With experience, you will gradually learn to relate two-dimensional sections to three-dimensional shapes.

CHECK YOUR UNDERSTANDING

12. What is the anatomical position? Why is it important that *you* learn this position?

13. The axillary and acromial regions are both in the general area of the shoulder. Where specifically is each located?

14. What type of cut would separate the brain into anterior and posterior parts?

For answers, see Appendix G.

Body Cavities and Membranes

▶ Locate and name the major body cavities and their subdivisions and associated membranes, and list the major organs contained within them.

▶ Name the four quadrants or nine regions of the abdominopelvic cavity and list the organs they contain.

Anatomy and physiology textbooks typically describe two sets of internal body cavities called the dorsal and ventral body cavities. These cavities are closed to the outside and provide different degrees of protection to the organs contained within them. Because these two cavities differ in their mode of embryonic development, and their lining membranes, the dorsal body cavity is not recognized as such in many anatomical references. However, the idea of two sets of internal body cavities is a useful learning concept and we use it here.

Dorsal Body Cavity

The **dorsal body cavity**, which protects the fragile nervous system organs, has two subdivisions (Figure 1.9, gold areas). The **cranial cavity**, in the skull, encases the brain. The **vertebral**, or **spinal**, **cavity**, which runs within the bony vertebral column, encloses the delicate spinal cord. The spinal cord is essentially a continuation of the brain, and the cranial and spinal cavities are continuous with one another.

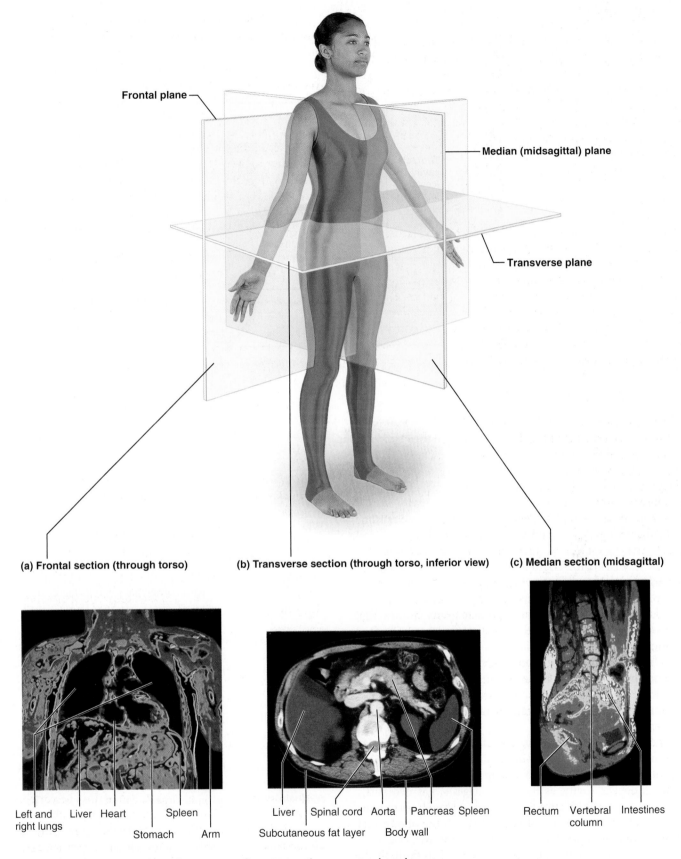

Frontal plane

Median (midsagittal) plane

Transverse plane

(a) Frontal section (through torso)

(b) Transverse section (through torso, inferior view)

(c) Median section (midsagittal)

Left and right lungs Liver Heart Spleen Stomach Arm

Liver Spinal cord Aorta Pancreas Spleen Subcutaneous fat layer Body wall

Rectum Vertebral column Intestines

Figure 1.8 **Planes of the body with corresponding magnetic resonance imaging (MRI) scans.**

1

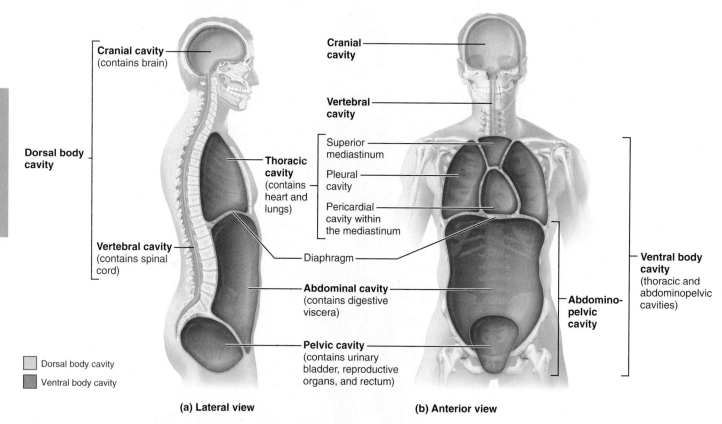

Cranial cavity
(contains brain)

Dorsal body
cavity

Thoracic
cavity
(contains
heart and
lungs)

Vertebral cavity
(contains spinal
cord)

Cranial
cavity

Vertebral
cavity

Superior
mediastinum

Pleural
cavity

Pericardial
cavity within
the mediastinum

Diaphragm

Abdominal cavity
(contains digestive
viscera)

Pelvic cavity
(contains urinary
bladder, reproductive
organs, and rectum)

Ventral body
cavity
(thoracic and
abdominopelvic
cavities)

Abdomino-
pelvic
cavity

☐ Dorsal body cavity

■ Ventral body cavity

(a) Lateral view

(b) Anterior view

Figure 1.9 Dorsal and ventral body cavities and their subdivisions.

Ventral Body Cavity

The more anterior and larger of the closed body cavities is the **ventral body cavity** (Figure 1.9, rust-red areas). Like the dorsal cavity, it has two major subdivisions, the *thoracic cavity* and the *abdominopelvic cavity*. The ventral body cavity houses internal organs collectively called the **viscera** (vis′er-ah; *viscus* = an organ in a body cavity), or visceral organs.

The superior subdivision, the **thoracic cavity** (tho-ras′ik), is surrounded by the ribs and muscles of the chest. The thoracic cavity is further subdivided into lateral **pleural cavities** (ploo′ral), each enveloping a lung, and the medial **mediastinum** (me″de-ah-sti′num). The mediastinum contains the **pericardial cavity** (per″ĭ-kar′de-al), which encloses the heart, and it also surrounds the remaining thoracic organs (esophagus, trachea, and others).

The thoracic cavity is separated from the more inferior **abdominopelvic cavity** (ab-dom′ĭ-no-pel′-vic) by the diaphragm, a dome-shaped muscle important in breathing. The abdominopelvic cavity, as its name suggests, has two parts. However, these regions are not physically separated by a muscular or membrane wall. Its superior portion, the **abdominal cavity**, contains the stomach, intestines, spleen, liver, and other organs. The inferior part, the **pelvic cavity**, lies in the bony pelvis and contains the urinary bladder, some reproductive organs, and the rectum. The abdominal and pelvic cavities are not aligned with each other. Instead, the bowl-shaped pelvis tips away from the perpendicular.

HOMEOSTATIC IMBALANCE

When the body is subjected to physical trauma (as in an automobile accident), the abdominopelvic organs are most vulnerable. Why? This is because the walls of the abdominal cavity are formed only by trunk muscles and are not reinforced by bone. The pelvic organs receive a somewhat greater degree of protection from the bony pelvis. ■

Membranes in the Ventral Body Cavity The walls of the ventral body cavity and the outer surfaces of the organs it contains are covered by a thin, double-layered membrane, the **serosa** (se-ro′sah), or **serous membrane**. The part of the membrane lining the cavity walls is called the **parietal serosa** (pah-ri′ĕ-tal; *parie* = wall). It folds in on itself to form the **visceral serosa**, covering the organs in the cavity.

You can visualize the relationship between the serosal layers by pushing your fist into a limp balloon **(Figure 1.10a)**. The part of the balloon that clings to your fist can be compared to the visceral serosa clinging to an organ's external surface. The outer wall of the balloon then represents the parietal serosa that lines the walls of the cavity. (However, unlike the balloon, the parietal serosa is never exposed but is always fused to the cavity wall.) In the body, the serous membranes are separated not by air but by a thin layer of lubricating fluid, called **serous fluid**, which is

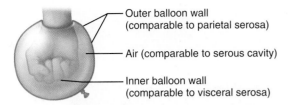

Outer balloon wall
(comparable to parietal serosa)

Air (comparable to serous cavity)

Inner balloon wall
(comparable to visceral serosa)

(a) A fist thrust into a flaccid balloon demonstrates the relationship between the parietal and visceral serous membrane layers.

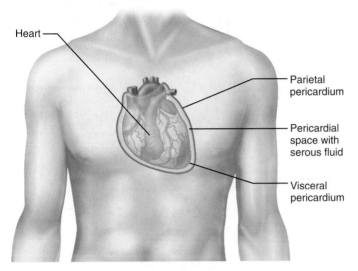

Heart

Parietal pericardium

Pericardial space with serous fluid

Visceral pericardium

(b) The serosae associated with the heart.

Figure 1.10 Serous membrane relationships.

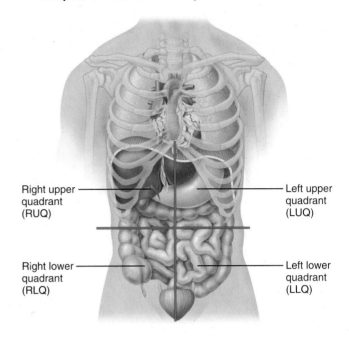

Right upper quadrant (RUQ)

Left upper quadrant (LUQ)

Right lower quadrant (RLQ)

Left lower quadrant (LLQ)

Figure 1.11 The four abdominopelvic quadrants. In this scheme, the abdominopelvic cavity is divided into four quadrants by two planes.

secreted by both membranes. Although there is a potential space between the two membranes, the barely present, slitlike cavity is filled with serous fluid.

The slippery serous fluid allows the organs to slide without friction across the cavity walls and one another as they carry out their routine functions. This freedom of movement is especially important for mobile organs such as the pumping heart and the churning stomach.

The serous membranes are named for the specific cavity and organs with which they are associated. For example, as shown in Figure 1.10b, the *parietal pericardium* lines the pericardial cavity and folds back as the *visceral pericardium*, which covers the heart. Likewise, the *parietal pleurae* (ploo′re) line the walls of the thoracic cavity, and the *visceral pleurae* cover the lungs. The *parietal peritoneum* (per″ĭ-to-ne′um) is associated with the walls of the abdominopelvic cavity, while the *visceral peritoneum* covers most of the organs within that cavity. (The pleural and peritoneal serosae are illustrated in Figure 4.11c on p. 139.)

HOMEOSTATIC IMBALANCE

When serous membranes are inflamed, their normally smooth surfaces become roughened. This roughness causes the organs to stick together and drag across one another, leading to excruciating pain, as anyone who has experienced *pleurisy* (inflammation of the pleurae) or *peritonitis* (inflammation of the peritonea) knows. ■

Abdominopelvic Regions and Quadrants Because the abdominopelvic cavity is large and contains several organs, it helps to divide it into smaller areas for study. Medical personnel usually use a simple scheme to locate the abdominopelvic cavity organs **(Figure 1.11)**. In this scheme, a transverse and a median plane pass through the umbilicus at right angles. The four resulting quadrants are named according to their positions from the subject's point of view: the **right upper quadrant (RUQ)**, **left upper quadrant (LUQ)**, **right lower quadrant (RLQ)**, and **left lower quadrant (LLQ)**. (See Figure 1.12 for organs located in different areas of the abdomen.)

Another division method, used primarily by anatomists, uses two transverse and two parasagittal planes. These planes, positioned like a tic-tac-toe grid on the abdomen, divide the cavity into nine regions **(Figure 1.12)**:

- The **umbilical region** is the centermost region deep to and surrounding the umbilicus (navel).
- The **epigastric region** is located superior to the umbilical region (*epi* = upon, above; *gastri* = belly).
- The **hypogastric (pubic) region** is located inferior to the umbilical region (*hypo* = below).
- The **right** and **left iliac**, or **inguinal**, **regions** (ing′gwĭ-nal) are located lateral to the hypogastric region (*iliac* = superior part of the hip bone).
- The **right** and **left lumbar regions** lie lateral to the umbilical region (*lumbus* = loin).
- The **right** and **left hypochondriac regions** lie lateral to the epigastric region (*chondro* = cartilage).

(*Text continues on p. 20.*)

A CLOSER LOOK
Medical Imaging: Illuminating the Body

Until 50 years ago, the magical but murky X ray was the only nonsurgical means to extract information from within a living body. Produced by directing *X rays*, electromagnetic waves of very short wavelength, at the body, an **X ray** or **radiograph** is essentially a shadowy negative image of internal structures. Dense structures absorb the X rays most and so appear as light areas. Hollow air-containing organs and fat, which absorb the X rays less, show up as dark areas. What X rays do best is visualize hard, bony structures and locate abnormally dense structures (tumors, tuberculosis nodules) in the lungs.

The 1950s saw the advent of nuclear medicine, which uses radioisotopes to scan the body, and ultrasound techniques, which use sound waves. The 1970s brought CT, PET, and MRI scans. These technologies not only reveal the structure of our "insides" but also wring out information about the hidden workings of their molecules.

Computed tomography (**CT**, formerly called **computerized axial tomography, CAT**) uses a refined version of X-ray equipment. As the patient is slowly moved through the doughnut-shaped CT machine, its X-ray tube rotates around the body and sends beams from all directions to a specific level of the patient's body. Because at any moment its beam is confined to a "slice" of the body about as thick as a dime, CT ends the confusion resulting from overlapping structures seen in conventional X rays. The device's computer translates this information into a detailed, cross-sectional picture of each body region scanned. CT scans are at the forefront for evaluating most problems that affect the brain and abdomen. Their clarity, illustrated in photo (a), has all but eliminated exploratory surgery.

Xenon CT is a CT brain scan enhanced with radioactive xenon gas to quickly trace blood flow. Inhaled xenon rapidly enters the bloodstream and distributes to different body tissues in proportion to their blood flow. Absence of xenon from part of the brain indicates that a stroke is occurring there, information that aids treatment.

Dynamic spatial reconstruction (DSR) uses ultrafast CT scanners to provide three-dimensional images of body organs from any angle, and scrutinize their movements and changes in their internal

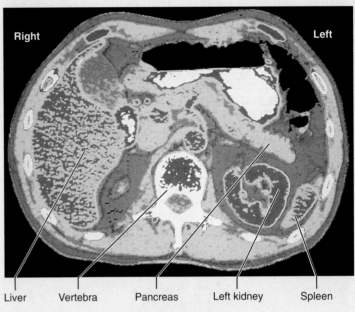

(a) **A CT scan through the superior abdomen.**

Liver   Vertebra   Pancreas   Left kidney   Spleen

volumes at normal speed, in slow motion, and at a specific moment. DSR's greatest value has been to visualize the heart beating and blood flowing through blood vessels. This information allows clinicians to evaluate heart defects, constricted or blocked blood vessels, and the status of coronary bypass grafts.

Another computer-assisted X-ray technique, **digital subtraction angiography (DSA)** (*angiography* = vessel pictures), provides an unobstructed view of small arteries. Conventional radiographs are taken before and after a contrast medium is injected into an artery. The computer subtracts the "before" image from the "after" image, eliminating all traces of body structures that obscure the vessel. DSA is often used to identify blockages in the arteries that supply the heart wall, as in photo (b), and in the brain.

Just as the X ray spawned related technologies, so too did nuclear medicine in the form of **positron emission tomography (PET)**. PET excels in observing *metabolic processes*. The patient is given an injection of radioisotopes tagged to biological molecules (such as glucose) and is then positioned in the PET scanner. As the radioisotopes are absorbed by the most active brain cells, high-energy gamma rays are produced. The computer analyzes the gamma-ray emission and produces a live-action picture of the

brain's biochemical activity in vivid colors. PET's greatest value has been its ability to provide insights into brain activity in people affected by mental illness, stroke, Alzheimer's disease, and epilepsy. One of its most exciting uses has been to determine which areas of the healthy brain are most active during certain tasks (e.g., speaking, listening to music, or figuring out a mathematical problem), providing direct evidence of the functions of specific brain regions. Currently PET can reveal signs of trouble in those with undiagnosed Alzheimer's disease (AD) because regions of beta-amyloid accumulation (a defining characteristic of AD) show up in brilliant red and yellow, as in photo (c). PET scans can also help to predict who may develop AD in the future by identifying areas of decreased metabolism in crucial memory areas of the brain.

Sonography, or **ultrasound imaging**, has some distinct advantages over the approaches examined so far. The equipment is inexpensive, and the ultrasound used as its energy source seems to be safer than the ionizing forms of radiation used in nuclear medicine. The body is probed with pulses of sound waves that cause echoes when reflected and scattered by body tissues. A computer analyzes these echoes to construct somewhat blurry outlines of body organs. A single easy-to-use handheld device

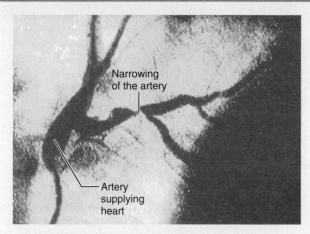

(b) A DSA image of the arteries that supply the heart.

Narrowing
of the artery

Artery
supplying
heart

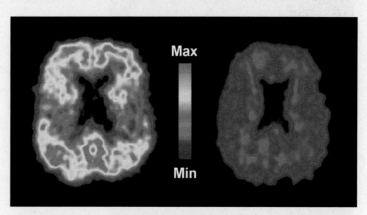

Max

Min

(c) In a PET scan, regions of beta-amyloid accumulation "light up" (red-yellow) in an Alzheimer's patient (*left*) but not in a healthy person (*right*).

emits the sound and picks up the echoes, so sections can be scanned from many different body planes.

Because of its safety, ultrasound is the imaging technique of choice in obstetrics for determining fetal age and position and locating the placenta. However, sound waves have low penetrating power and rapidly dissipate in air, so sonography is of little value for looking at air-filled structures (the lungs) or those surrounded by bone (the brain and spinal cord).

Magnetic resonance imaging (MRI) produces high-contrast images of our soft tissues, an area in which X rays and CT scans are weak. As initially developed, MRI primarily maps the body's content of hydrogen, most of which is in water. The technique subjects the body to magnetic fields up to 60,000 times stronger than that of the earth to pry information from the body's molecules. The patient lies in a chamber within a huge magnet. Hydrogen molecules act like tiny magnets, spinning like tops in the magnetic field. Their energy is further enhanced by radio waves, and when the radio waves are turned off, the energy released is translated into a visual image.

MRI distinguishes body tissues based on their water content, so it can differentiate between the fatty white matter and the more watery gray matter of the brain. Because dense structures do not show up at all in MRI, it peers easily into the skull and vertebral column, enabling the delicate nerve fibers of the spinal cord to be seen. MRI is also particularly good at detecting tumors and degenerative disease. Multiple sclerosis plaques do not show up well in CT scans, but are daz-

zlingly clear in MRI scans. MRI can also tune in on metabolic reactions, such as processes that generate energy-rich ATP molecules.

Until recently, trying to diagnose asthma and other lung problems has been off limits to MRI scans because the lungs have a low water content. However, an alternate tack—filling the lungs with a gas that can be magnetized (hyperpolarized helium-3 or xenon-129)—has yielded spectacular pictures of the lungs in just the few seconds it takes the patient to inhale, hold the breath briefly, and then exhale. This technique offers a distinct improvement over the hours required for conventional MRI and it has the additional advantage of using a magnetic field as little as one-tenth that of the conventional MRI.

Newer variations of MRI include **magnetic resonance spectroscopy (MRS)**, which maps the distribution of elements other than hydrogen to reveal more about how disease changes body chemistry. Other advances in computer techniques display MRI scans in three dimensions to guide laser surgery.

The **functional MRI** tracks blood flow into the brain in real time. Matching thoughts, deeds, and disease to brain activity has been the sole domain of PET. Because functional MRI does not require injections of tracers and can pinpoint much smaller brain areas than PET, it may provide a desirable alternative. Clinical studies are also using functional MRI to determine if a patient in the vegetative state has conscious thought.

Despite its advantages, the powerful magnets of the clanging, claustrophobia-

inducing MRI present some thorny problems. For example, they can "suck" metal objects, such as implanted pacemakers and loose tooth fillings, through the body. Moreover, although such strong magnetic fields are currently considered safe, there is no convincing evidence that they are risk free.

Although stunning, medical images other than straight X rays are abstractions assembled within the "mind" of a computer. They are artificially enhanced for sharpness and artificially colored to increase contrast (all their colors are "phony"). The images are several steps removed from direct observation.

As you can see, medical science offers remarkable diagnostic tools. Consider the M2A Swallowable Imaging Capsule, a tiny camera that a patient swallows like a pill, and then excretes normally 8–72 hours later. As the M2A travels through the digestive tract, it photographs the small intestine and beams the color images to a Walkman-sized receiver. A study found the device to be 60% effective at detecting intestinal problems, compared to a 35% success rate with other imaging techniques. At present the M2A can provide images only of the small intestine because the battery gives out before it enters the large intestine.

New imaging technologies also make long-distance surgery possible. Visual images of a diseased organ travel via fiber-optic cable to surgeons at another location (even a different country), who manipulate delicate robotic instruments to remove the organ.

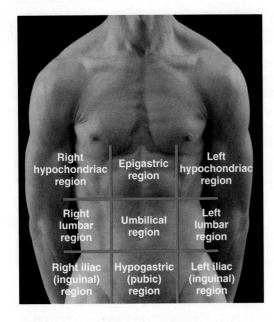

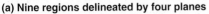

(a) Nine regions delineated by four planes

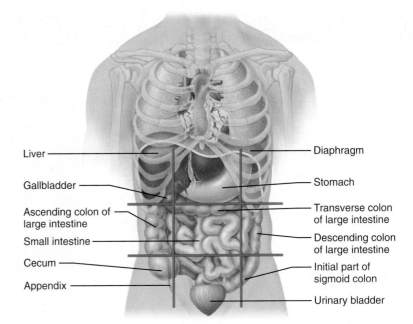

(b) Anterior view of the nine regions showing the superficial organs

Figure 1.12 The nine abdominopelvic regions. In **(a)** the superior transverse plane is just inferior to the ribs; the inferior transverse plane is just superior to the hip bones; and the parasagittal planes lie just medial to the nipples.

Other Body Cavities

In addition to the large closed body cavities, there are several smaller body cavities. Most of these are in the head and most open to the body exterior. Figure 1.7 provides the terms that will help you locate all but the last two cavities mentioned here.

1. **Oral and digestive cavities**. The oral cavity, commonly called the mouth, contains the teeth and tongue. This cavity is part of and continuous with the cavity of the digestive organs, which opens to the exterior at the anus.
2. **Nasal cavity**. Located within and posterior to the nose, the nasal cavity is part of the respiratory system passageways.
3. **Orbital cavities**. The orbital cavities (orbits) in the skull house the eyes and present them in an anterior position.
4. **Middle ear cavities**. The middle ear cavities in the skull lie just medial to the eardrums. These cavities contain tiny bones that transmit sound vibrations to the hearing receptors in the inner ears.
5. **Synovial cavities**. Synovial (sǐ-no′ve-al) cavities are joint cavities. They are enclosed within fibrous capsules that surround freely movable joints of the body (such as the elbow and knee joints). Like the serous membranes, membranes lining synovial cavities secrete a lubricating fluid that reduces friction as the bones move across one another.

CHECK YOUR UNDERSTANDING

15. Joe went to the emergency room where he complained of severe pains in the lower right quadrant of his abdomen. What might be his problem?
16. Of the uterus, small intestine, spinal cord, and heart, which is/are in the dorsal body cavity?
17. When you rub your cold hands together, the friction between them results in heat that warms your hands. Why doesn't warming friction result during movements of the heart, lungs, and digestive organs?

For answers, see Appendix G.

CHAPTER SUMMARY

An Overview of Anatomy and Physiology   (pp. 2–3)

1. Anatomy is the study of body structures and their relationships. Physiology is the science of how body parts function.

Topics of Anatomy   (p. 2)

2. Major subdivisions of anatomy include gross anatomy, microscopic anatomy, and developmental anatomy.

Topics of Physiology   (pp. 2–3)

3. Typically, physiology concerns the functioning of specific organs or organ systems. Examples include cardiac physiology, renal physiology, and muscle physiology.
4. Physiology is explained by chemical and physical principles.

Complementarity of Structure and Function   (p. 3)

5. Anatomy and physiology are inseparable: What a body can do depends on the unique architecture of its parts. This principle is called the complementarity of structure and function.

Levels of Structural Organization   (pp. 3–4)

1. The levels of structural organization of the body, from simplest to most complex, are: chemical, cellular, tissue, organ, organ system, and organismal.
2. The 11 organ systems of the body are the integumentary, skeletal, muscular, nervous, endocrine, cardiovascular, lymphatic, respiratory, digestive, urinary, and reproductive systems. The immune system is a functional system closely associated with the lymphatic system. (For functions of these systems see pp. 6–7.)

Maintaining Life   (pp. 4–8)
Necessary Life Functions   (pp. 4–8)

1. All living organisms carry out certain vital functional activities necessary for life, including maintenance of boundaries, movement, responsiveness, digestion, metabolism, excretion, reproduction, and growth.

Survival Needs   (p. 8)

2. Survival needs include nutrients, water, oxygen, and appropriate temperature and atmospheric pressure.

Homeostasis   (pp. 8–11)

1. Homeostasis is a dynamic equilibrium of the internal environment. All body systems contribute to homeostasis, but the nervous and endocrine systems are most important. Homeostasis is necessary for health.

Homeostatic Control   (pp. 9–11)

2. Control mechanisms of the body contain at least three elements that work together: receptor(s), control center, and effector(s).
3. Negative feedback mechanisms reduce the effect of the original stimulus, and are essential for maintaining homeostasis. Body temperature, heart rate, breathing rate and depth, and blood levels of glucose and certain ions are regulated by negative feedback mechanisms.
4. Positive feedback mechanisms intensify the initial stimulus, leading to an enhancement of the response. They rarely contribute to homeostasis, but blood clotting and labor contractions are regulated by such mechanisms.

Homeostatic Imbalance   (p. 11)

5. With age, the efficiency of negative feedback mechanisms declines, and positive feedback mechanisms occur more frequently. These changes underlie certain disease conditions.

The Language of Anatomy   (pp. 11–20)
Anatomical Position and Directional Terms   (pp. 12–13)

1. In the anatomical position, the body is erect, facing forward, feet slightly apart, arms at sides with palms forward.
2. Directional terms allow body parts to be located precisely. Terms that describe body directions and orientation include: superior/inferior; anterior/posterior; ventral/dorsal; medial/lateral; intermediate; proximal/distal; and superficial/deep.

Regional Terms   (p. 14)

3. Regional terms are used to designate specific areas of the body (see Figure 1.7).

Anatomical Variability   (p. 14)

4. People vary internally as well as externally, but extreme variations are rare.

Body Planes and Sections   (p. 14)

5. The body or its organs may be cut along planes, or imaginary lines, to produce different types of sections. Frequently used planes are sagittal, frontal, and transverse.

Body Cavities and Membranes   (pp. 14–20)

6. The body contains two major closed cavities. The dorsal cavity, subdivided into the cranial and spinal cavities, contains the brain and spinal cord. The ventral cavity is subdivided into the thoracic cavity, which houses the heart and lungs, and the abdominopelvic cavity, which contains the liver, digestive organs, and reproductive structures.
7. The walls of the ventral cavity and the surfaces of the organs it contains are covered with thin membranes, the parietal and visceral serosae, respectively. The serosae produce a thin fluid that decreases friction during organ functioning.
8. The abdominopelvic cavity may be divided by four planes into nine abdominopelvic regions (epigastric, umbilical, hypogastric, right and left iliac, right and left lumbar, and right and left hypochondriac), or by two planes into four quadrants. (For boundaries and organs contained, see Figures 1.11 and 1.12.)
9. There are several smaller body cavities. Most of these are in the head and open to the exterior.

REVIEW QUESTIONS

Multiple Choice/Matching

(Some questions have more than one correct answer. Select the best answer or answers from the choices given.)

1. The correct sequence of levels forming the structural hierarchy is
   (a) organ, organ system, cellular, chemical, tissue, organismal;
   (b) chemical, cellular, tissue, organismal, organ, organ system;
   (c) chemical, cellular, tissue, organ, organ system, organismal;
   (d) organismal, organ system, organ, tissue, cellular, chemical.

2. The structural and functional unit of life is (a) a cell, (b) an organ, (c) the organism, (d) a molecule.

3. Which of the following is a *major* functional characteristic of all organisms? (a) movement, (b) growth, (c) metabolism, (d) responsiveness, (e) all of these.

4. Two of these organ systems bear the *major* responsibility for ensuring homeostasis of the internal environment. Which two? (a) nervous system, (b) digestive system, (c) cardiovascular system, (d) endocrine system, (e) reproductive system.

5. In (a)–(e), a directional term [e.g., distal in (a)] is followed by terms indicating different body structures or locations (e.g., the elbow/the wrist). In each case, choose the structure or organ that matches the given directional term.
   (a) distal: the elbow/the wrist
   (b) lateral: the hip bone/the umbilicus
   (c) superior: the nose/the chin
   (d) anterior: the toes/the heel
   (e) superficial: the scalp/the skull

6. Assume that the body has been sectioned along three planes: (1) a median plane, (2) a frontal plane, and (3) a transverse plane made at the level of each of the organs listed below. Which organs would not be visible in all three cases? (a) urinary bladder, (b) brain, (c) lungs, (d) kidneys, (e) small intestine, (f) heart.

7. Relate each of the following conditions or statements to either the dorsal body cavity or the ventral body cavity.
   (a) surrounded by the bony skull and the vertebral column
   (b) includes the thoracic and abdominopelvic cavities
   (c) contains the brain and spinal cord
   (d) contains the heart, lungs, and digestive organs

8. Which of the following relationships is *incorrect*?
   (a) visceral peritoneum/outer surface of small intestine
   (b) parietal pericardium/outer surface of heart
   (c) parietal pleura/wall of thoracic cavity

9. Which ventral cavity subdivision has no bony protection? (a) thoracic cavity, (b) abdominal cavity, (c) pelvic cavity.

10. Terms that apply to the backside of the body in the anatomical position include:
    (a) ventral; anterior
    (b) back; rear
    (c) posterior; dorsal
    (d) medial; lateral

Short Answer Essay Questions

11. According to the principle of complementarity, how does anatomy relate to physiology?

12. Construct a table that lists the 11 systems of the body, names two organs of each system (if appropriate), and describes the overall or major function of each system.

13. List and describe briefly five external factors that must be present or provided to sustain life.

14. Define homeostasis.

15. Compare and contrast the operation of negative and positive feedback mechanisms in maintaining homeostasis. Provide two examples of variables controlled by negative feedback mechanisms and one example of a process regulated by a positive feedback mechanism.

16. Why is an understanding of the anatomical position important?

17. Define plane and section.

18. Provide the anatomical term that correctly names each of the following body regions: (a) arm, (b) thigh, (c) chest, (d) fingers and toes, (e) anterior aspect of the knee.

19. Use as many directional terms as you can to describe the relationship between the elbow's olecranal region and your palm.

20. (a) Make a diagram showing the nine abdominopelvic regions, and name each region. Name two organs (or parts of organs) that could be located in each of the named regions. (b) Make a similar sketch illustrating how the abdominopelvic cavity may be divided into quadrants, and name each quadrant.

Critical Thinking and Clinical Application Questions

1. John has been suffering agonizing pain with each breath and has been informed by the physician that he has pleurisy. (a) Specifically, what membranes are involved in this condition? (b) What is their usual role in the body? (c) Explain why John's condition is so painful.

2. At the clinic, Harry was told that blood would be drawn from his antecubital region. What body part was Harry asked to hold out? Later, the nurse came in and gave Harry a shot of penicillin in the area just distal to his acromial region. Did Harry take off his shirt or drop his pants to receive the injection? Before Harry left, the nurse noticed that Harry had a nasty bruise on his gluteal region. What part of his body was black and blue?

3. A man is behaving abnormally, and his physician suspects that he has a brain tumor. Which of the following medical imaging techniques would best localize the tumor in the man's brain (and why)? Conventional X ray, DSA, PET, sonography, MRI.

4. Calcium levels in Mr. Gallariani's blood are dropping to dangerously low levels. The hormone PTH is released and soon blood calcium levels begin to rise. Shortly after, PTH release slows. Is this an example of a positive or negative feedback mechanism? What is the initial stimulus? What is the result?

5. Mr. Harvey, a computer programmer, has been complaining of numbness and pain in his right hand. The nurse practitioner diagnosed his problem as carpal tunnel syndrome and prescribed use of a splint. Where will Mr. Harvey apply the splint?

2

Chemistry Comes Alive

PART 1
BASIC CHEMISTRY

Definition of Concepts: Matter and Energy (pp. 24–25)

Composition of Matter: Atoms and Elements (pp. 25–28)

How Matter Is Combined: Molecules and Mixtures (pp. 28–30)

Chemical Bonds (pp. 31–35)

Chemical Reactions (pp. 35–38)

PART 2
BIOCHEMISTRY

Inorganic Compounds (pp. 38–41)

Organic Compounds (pp. 42–56)

Why study chemistry in an anatomy and physiology course? The answer is simple. Your entire body is made up of chemicals, thousands of them, continuously interacting with one another at an incredible pace. Although it is possible to study anatomy without much reference to chemistry, chemical reactions underlie all physiological processes—movement, digestion, the pumping of your heart, and even your thoughts. This chapter presents the basic chemistry and biochemistry (the chemistry of living material) you need to understand body functions.

PART 1

BASIC CHEMISTRY

Definition of Concepts: Matter and Energy

▶ Differentiate between matter and energy and between potential energy and kinetic energy.

▶ Describe the major energy forms.

Matter

Matter is the "stuff" of the universe. More precisely, **matter** is anything that occupies space and has mass. With some exceptions, it can be seen, smelled, and felt.

For all practical purposes, we can consider mass to be the same as weight. However, this usage is not quite accurate. The *mass* of an object is equal to the actual amount of matter in the object, and it remains constant wherever the object is. In contrast, weight varies with gravity. So while your mass is the same at sea level and on a mountaintop, you weigh just slightly less on that mountaintop. The science of chemistry studies the nature of matter, especially how its building blocks are put together and interact.

States of Matter

Matter exists in *solid, liquid,* and *gaseous states.* Examples of each state are found in the human body. Solids, like bones and teeth, have a definite shape and volume. Liquids such as blood plasma have a definite volume, but they conform to the shape of their container. Gases have neither a definite shape nor a definite volume. The air we breathe is a gas.

Energy

Compared with matter, energy is less tangible. It has no mass, does not take up space, and we can measure it only by its effects on matter. **Energy** is defined as the capacity to do work, or to put matter into motion. The greater the work done, the more energy is used doing it. A baseball player who has just hit the ball over the fence uses much more energy than a batter who bunts the ball back to the pitcher.

Kinetic Versus Potential Energy

Energy exists in two forms, or work capacities, and each can be transformed to the other. **Kinetic energy** (ki-net′ik) is energy in action. We see evidence of kinetic energy in the constant movement of the tiniest particles of matter (atoms) as well as in larger objects (a bouncing ball). Kinetic energy does work by moving objects, which in turn can do work by moving or pushing on other objects. For example, a push on a swinging door sets it into motion.

Potential energy is stored energy, that is, inactive energy that has the *potential,* or capability, to do work but is not presently doing so. The batteries in an unused toy have potential energy, as does water confined behind a dam. Your leg muscles have potential energy when you sit still on the couch. When potential energy is released, it becomes kinetic energy and so is capable of doing work. For example, dammed water becomes a rushing torrent when the dam is opened, and that rushing torrent can move a turbine at a hydroelectric plant, or charge a battery.

Actually, energy is a topic of physics, but matter and energy are inseparable. Matter is the substance, and energy is the mover of the substance. All living things are composed of matter and they all require energy to grow and function. The release and use of energy by living systems gives us the elusive quality we call life. Now let's consider the forms of energy used by the body as it does its work.

Forms of Energy

■ **Chemical energy** is the form stored in the bonds of chemical substances. When chemical reactions occur that rearrange the atoms of the chemicals in a certain way, the potential energy is unleashed and becomes kinetic energy, or energy in action.

For example, some of the energy in the foods you eat is eventually converted into the kinetic energy of your moving arm. However, food fuels cannot be used to energize body activities directly. Instead, some of the food energy is captured temporarily in the bonds of a chemical called *adenosine triphosphate (ATP)* (ah-den′o-sēn tri″fos′fāt). Later, ATP's bonds are broken and the stored energy is released as needed to do cellular work. Chemical energy in the form of ATP is the most useful form of energy in living systems because it is used to run almost all functional processes.

■ **Electrical energy** results from the movement of charged particles. In your home, electrical energy is found in the flow of electrons along the household wiring. In your body, electrical currents are generated when charged particles called *ions* move along or across cell membranes. The nervous system uses electrical currents, called *nerve impulses,* to transmit messages from one part of the body to another. Electrical currents traveling across the heart stimulate it to contract (beat) and pump blood. (This is why a strong electrical shock, which interferes with such currents, can cause death.)

■ **Mechanical energy** is energy *directly* involved in moving matter. When you ride a bicycle, your legs provide the mechanical energy that moves the pedals.

■ **Radiant energy,** or **electromagnetic energy** (e-lek″tro-mag-net′ik), is energy that travels in waves. These waves, which vary in length, are collectively called the *electromagnetic spectrum.* They include visible light, infrared waves, radio waves, ultraviolet waves, and X rays. Light energy, which stimulates the retinas of our eyes, is important in vision. Ultraviolet waves cause sunburn, but they also stimulate our body to make vitamin D.

Energy Form Conversions

With few exceptions, energy is easily converted from one form to another. For example, the chemical energy (in gasoline) that powers the motor of a speedboat is converted into the mechanical energy of the whirling propeller that makes the boat skim across the water.

Energy conversions are quite inefficient. Some of the initial energy supply is always "lost" to the environment as heat. (It is not really lost because energy cannot be created or destroyed, but that portion given off as heat is at least partly *unusable*.) It is easy to demonstrate this principle. Electrical energy is converted into light energy in a lightbulb. But if you touch a lit bulb, you will soon discover that some of the electrical energy is producing heat instead.

Likewise, all energy conversions in the body liberate heat. This heat helps to maintain our relatively high body temperature, which influences body functioning. For example, when matter is heated, the kinetic energy of its particles increases and they begin to move more quickly. The higher the temperature, the faster the body's chemical reactions occur. We will learn more about this later.

CHECK YOUR UNDERSTANDING

1. What form of energy is found in the food we eat?
2. What form of energy is used to transmit messages from one part of the body to another?
3. What type of energy is available when we are still? When we are exercising?

For answers, see Appendix G.

Composition of Matter: Atoms and Elements

▶ Define chemical element and list the four elements that form the bulk of body matter.

▶ Define atom. List the subatomic particles, and describe their relative masses, charges, and positions in the atom.

▶ Define atomic number, atomic mass, atomic weight, isotope, and radioisotope.

All matter is composed of **elements**, unique substances that cannot be broken down into simpler substances by ordinary chemical methods. Among the well-known elements are oxygen, carbon, gold, silver, copper, and iron.

At present, 112 elements are known with certainty (and numbers 113, 114, 115, 116, and most recently 118 are alleged). Of these, 92 occur in nature. The rest are made artificially in particle accelerator devices.

Four elements—carbon, oxygen, hydrogen, and nitrogen— make up about 96% of body weight, and 20 others are present in the body, some in trace amounts. **Table 2.1** lists the elements contributing to body mass and gives their importance. In Appendix E, an oddly shaped checkerboard called the **periodic table** provides a more complete listing of the known elements.

Each element is composed of more or less identical particles or building blocks, called **atoms**. The smallest atoms are less than 0.1 nanometer (nm) in diameter, and the largest are only about five times as large. [1 nm = 0.0000001 (or 10^{-7}) centimeter (cm), or 40 billionths of an inch!]

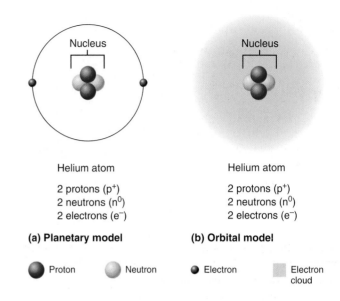

Helium atom
2 protons (p^+)
2 neutrons (n^0)
2 electrons (e^-)

(a) Planetary model

Helium atom
2 protons (p^+)
2 neutrons (n^0)
2 electrons (e^-)

(b) Orbital model

● Proton   ● Neutron   ● Electron   ▪ Electron cloud

Figure 2.1 Two models of the structure of an atom.

Every element's atoms differ from those of all other elements and give the element its unique physical and chemical properties. *Physical properties* are those we can detect with our senses (such as color and texture) or measure (such as boiling point and freezing point). *Chemical properties* pertain to the way atoms interact with other atoms (bonding behavior) and account for the facts that iron rusts, animals can digest their food, and so on.

We designate each element by a one- or two-letter chemical shorthand called an **atomic symbol**, usually the first letter(s) of the element's name. For example, C stands for carbon, O for oxygen, and Ca for calcium. In a few cases, the atomic symbol is taken from the Latin name for the element. For example, sodium is indicated by Na, from the Latin word *natrium*.

Atomic Structure

The word *atom* comes from the Greek word meaning "indivisible." However, we now know that atoms are clusters of even smaller particles called protons, neutrons, and electrons and that even those subatomic particles can be subdivided with high-technology tools. Still, the old idea of atomic indivisibility is useful because an atom loses the unique properties of its element when it is split into its subatomic particles.

An atom's subatomic particles differ in mass, electrical charge, and position in the atom. An atom has a central **nucleus** containing protons and neutrons tightly bound together. The nucleus, in turn, is surrounded by orbiting electrons (**Figure 2.1**). **Protons** (p^+) bear a positive electrical charge, and **neutrons** (n^0) are neutral, so the nucleus is positively charged overall. Protons and neutrons are heavy particles and have approximately the same mass, arbitrarily designated as 1 **atomic mass unit** (1 amu). Since all of the heavy subatomic particles are concentrated in the nucleus, the nucleus is fantastically dense. It accounts for nearly the entire mass (99.9%) of the atom.

TABLE 2.1		**Common Elements Composing the Human Body***	
ELEMENT	**ATOMIC SYMBOL**	**APPROX. % BODY MASS†**	**FUNCTIONS**
Major (96.1%)			
Oxygen	O	65.0	A major component of both organic (carbon-containing) and inorganic (non-carbon-containing) molecules. As a gas, it is needed for the production of cellular energy (ATP).
Carbon	C	18.5	A primary component of all organic molecules, which include carbohydrates, lipids (fats), proteins, and nucleic acids.
Hydrogen	H	9.5	A component of all organic molecules. As an ion (proton), it influences the pH of body fluids.
Nitrogen	N	3.2	A component of proteins and nucleic acids (genetic material).
Lesser (3.9%)			
Calcium	Ca	1.5	Found as a salt in bones and teeth. Its ionic (Ca^{2+}) form is required for muscle contraction, conduction of nerve impulses, and blood clotting.
Phosphorus	P	1.0	Part of calcium phosphate salts in bones and teeth. Also present in nucleic acids, and part of ATP.
Potassium	K	0.4	Its ion (K^+) is the major positive ion (cation) in cells. Necessary for conduction of nerve impulses and muscle contraction.
Sulfur	S	0.3	Component of proteins, particularly muscle proteins.
Sodium	Na	0.2	As an ion (Na^+), sodium is the major positive ion found in extracellular fluids (fluids outside of cells). Important for water balance, conduction of nerve impulses, and muscle contraction.
Chlorine	Cl	0.2	Its ion (chloride, Cl^-) is the most abundant negative ion (anion) in extracellular fluids.
Magnesium	Mg	0.1	Present in bone. Also an important cofactor in a number of metabolic reactions.
Iodine	I	0.1	Needed to make functional thyroid hormones.
Iron	Fe	0.1	Component of hemoglobin (which transports oxygen within red blood cells) and some enzymes.
Trace (less than 0.01%)			
Chromium (Cr); cobalt (Co); copper (Cu); fluorine (F); manganese (Mn); molybdenum (Mo); selenium (Se); silicon (Si); tin (Sn); vanadium (V); zinc (Zn)			
These elements are referred to as *trace elements* because they are required in very minute amounts; many are found as part of enzymes or are required for enzyme activation.			

*A listing of the elements by ascending order of atomic number appears in the periodic table, Appendix E.
†Percentage of "wet" body mass; includes water.

The tiny **electrons** (e⁻) bear a negative charge equal in strength to the positive charge of the proton. However, an electron has only about 1/2000 the mass of a proton, and the mass of an electron is usually designated as 0 amu.

All atoms are electrically neutral because the number of protons in an atom is precisely balanced by its number of electrons (the + and − charges will then cancel the effect of each other). For example, hydrogen has one proton and one electron, and iron has 26 protons and 26 electrons. For any atom, the number of protons and electrons is always equal.

The **planetary model** of the atom, illustrated in Figure 2.1a, is a simplified (and now outdated) model of atomic structure. As you can see, it depicts electrons moving around the nucleus in fixed, generally circular orbits. But we can never determine the exact location of electrons at a particular time because they jump around following unknown trajectories. So, instead of speaking of specific orbits, chemists talk about **orbitals**—regions around the nucleus in which a given electron or electron pair is likely to be found most of the time. This more modern model of atomic structure, called the **orbital model**, is more useful for predicting the chemical behavior of atoms. As illustrated in Figure 2.1b, the orbital model depicts *probable* regions of greatest electron density by denser shading (this haze is called the *electron cloud*). However, the planetary model is simpler to depict, so we will use that model in most illustrations of atomic structure in this text.

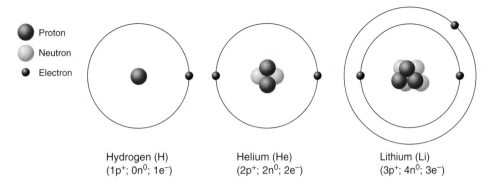

Figure 2.2 Atomic structure of the three smallest atoms.

Hydrogen, with just one proton and one electron, is the simplest atom. You can visualize the spatial relationships in the hydrogen atom by imagining it as a sphere enlarged until its diameter equals the length of a football field. In that case, the nucleus could be represented by a lead ball the size of a gumdrop in the exact center of the sphere. Its lone electron could be pictured as a fly buzzing about unpredictably within the sphere. Though not completely accurate, this mental image demonstrates that most of the volume of an atom is empty space, and nearly all of its mass is concentrated in the central nucleus.

Identifying Elements

All protons are alike, regardless of the atom considered. The same is true of all neutrons and all electrons. So what determines the unique properties of each element? The answer is that atoms of different elements are composed of *different numbers* of protons, neutrons, and electrons.

The simplest and smallest atom, hydrogen, has one proton, one electron, and no neutrons (**Figure 2.2**). Next in size is the helium atom, with two protons, two neutrons, and two orbiting electrons. Lithium follows with three protons, four neutrons, and three electrons. If we continued this step-by-step progression, we would get a graded series of atoms containing from 1 to 112 protons, an equal number of electrons, and a slightly larger number of neutrons at each step.

All we really need to know to identify a particular element, however, are its atomic number, mass number, and atomic weight. Taken together, these provide a fairly complete picture of each element.

Atomic Number

The **atomic number** of any atom is equal to the number of protons in its nucleus and is written as a subscript to the left of its atomic symbol. Hydrogen, with one proton, has an atomic number of 1 ($_1$H). Helium, with two protons, has an atomic number of 2 ($_2$He), and so on. The number of protons is always equal to the number of electrons in an atom, so the atomic number *indirectly* tells us the number of electrons in the atom as well. As we will see shortly, this information is important

indeed, because electrons determine the chemical behavior of atoms.

Mass Number and Isotopes

The **mass number** of an atom is the sum of the masses of its protons and neutrons. (The mass of the electrons is so small that it is ignored.) Recall that protons and neutrons have a mass of 1 amu. Hydrogen has only one proton in its nucleus, so its atomic and mass numbers are the same: 1. Helium, with two protons and two neutrons, has a mass number of 4.

The mass number is usually indicated by a superscript to the left of the atomic symbol. For example, helium is $_2^4$He. This simple notation allows us to deduce the total number and kinds of subatomic particles in any atom because it indicates the number of protons (the atomic number), the number of electrons (equal to the atomic number), and the number of neutrons (mass number minus atomic number). In our example, we can do the subtraction to find that $_2^4$He has two neutrons.

From what we have said so far, it may appear as if each element has one, and only one, type of atom representing it. This is not the case. Nearly all known elements have two or more structural variations called **isotopes** (i'so-tōps), which have the same number of protons (and electrons), but differ in the number of neutrons they contain. Earlier, when we said that hydrogen has a mass number of 1, we were speaking of ^{1}H, its most abundant isotope. Some hydrogen atoms have a mass of 2 or 3 amu (atomic mass units), which means that they have one proton and, respectively, one or two neutrons (**Figure 2.3**).

Carbon has several isotopes. The most abundant of these are ^{12}C, ^{13}C, and ^{14}C. Each of the carbon isotopes has six protons (otherwise it would not be carbon), but ^{12}C has six neutrons, ^{13}C has seven, and ^{14}C has eight. Isotopes can also be written with the mass number following the symbol: C-14, for example.

Atomic Weight

You might think that atomic weight should be the same as atomic mass, and this would be so if atomic weight referred to the weight of a single atom. However, **atomic weight** is an average of the relative weights (mass numbers) of *all* the isotopes of an element, taking into account their relative abundance in

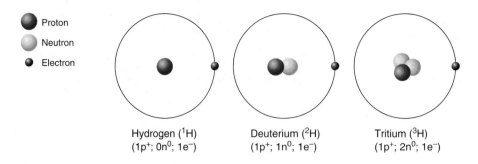

Figure 2.3 **Isotopes of hydrogen.**

nature. As a rule, the atomic weight of an element is approximately equal to the mass number of its most abundant isotope. For example, the atomic weight of hydrogen is 1.008, which reveals that its lightest isotope (^{1}H) is present in much greater amounts in our world than its ^{2}H or ^{3}H forms.

Radioisotopes

The heavier isotopes of many elements are unstable, and their atoms decompose spontaneously into more stable forms. This process of atomic decay is called *radioactivity*, and isotopes that exhibit this behavior are called **radioisotopes** (ra″de-o-i′so-tōps). The disintegration of a radioactive nucleus may be compared to a tiny explosion. It occurs when subatomic *alpha* (α) *particles* (packets of 2p + 2n), *beta* (β) *particles* (electron-like negative particles), or *gamma* (γ) *rays* (electromagnetic energy) are ejected from the atomic nucleus.

Why does this happen? The answer is complex, but for our purposes, the important point to know is that the dense nuclear particles are composed of even smaller particles called *quarks* that associate in one way to form protons and in another way to form neutrons. Apparently, the "glue" that holds these nuclear particles together is weaker in the heavier isotopes. When radioisotopes disintegrate, the element may transform to a different element.

Because we can detect radioactivity with scanners, and radioactive isotopes share the same chemistry as their more stable isotopes, radioisotopes are valuable tools for biological research and medicine. Most radioisotopes used in the clinical setting are used for diagnosis, that is, to localize and illuminate damaged or cancerous tissues. For example, iodine-131 is used to determine the size and activity of the thyroid gland and to detect thyroid cancer. The sophisticated PET scans described in *A Closer Look* in Chapter 1 use radioisotopes to probe the workings of molecules deep within our bodies. All radioisotopes, regardless of the purpose for which they are used, damage living tissue, and all radioisotopes gradually lose their radioactive behavior. The time required for a radioisotope to lose one-half of its activity is called its *half-life*. The half-lives of radioisotopes vary dramatically from hours to thousands of years.

Alpha emission has the lowest penetrating power and is least damaging to living tissue. Nonetheless, inhaled alpha particles from decaying radon are second only to smoking as a cause of lung cancer. (Radon results naturally from decay of uranium in the ground.) Gamma emission has the greatest penetrating

power. Radium-226, cobalt-60, and certain other radioisotopes that decay by gamma emission are used to destroy localized cancers.

Contrary to what some believe, ionizing radiation does not damage organic molecules directly. Instead, it knocks electrons out of other atoms and sends them flying, like bowling balls smashing through pins all along their path. It is the electron energy and the unstable molecules left behind that do the damage.

CHECK YOUR UNDERSTANDING

4. What two elements besides H and N make up the bulk of living matter?
5. An element has a mass of 207 and has 125 neutrons in its nucleus. How many protons and electrons does it have and where are they located?
6. How do the terms atomic mass and atomic weight differ?

For answers, see Appendix G.

How Matter Is Combined: Molecules and Mixtures

▶ Define molecule, and distinguish between a compound and a mixture.

▶ Compare solutions, colloids, and suspensions.

Molecules and Compounds

Most atoms do not exist in the free state, but instead are chemically combined with other atoms. Such a combination of two or more atoms held together by chemical bonds is called a **molecule**.

If two or more atoms of the *same* element combine, the resulting substance is called a *molecule of that element*. When two hydrogen atoms bond, the product is a molecule of hydrogen gas and is written as H_2. Similarly, when two oxygen atoms combine, a molecule of oxygen gas (O_2) is formed. Sulfur atoms commonly combine to form sulfur molecules containing eight sulfur atoms (S_8).

When two or more *different* kinds of atoms bind, they form molecules of a **compound**. Two hydrogen atoms combine with one oxygen atom to form the compound water (H_2O). Four hydrogen atoms combine with one carbon atom to form the compound methane (CH_4). Notice again that molecules of

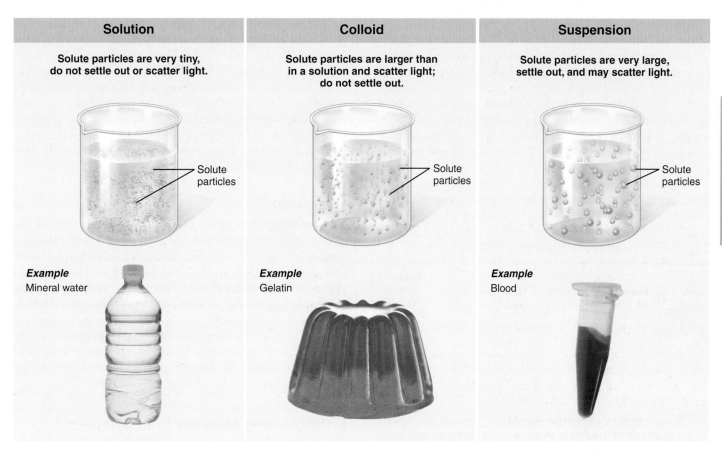

Solution	Colloid	Suspension
Solute particles are very tiny, do not settle out or scatter light.	Solute particles are larger than in a solution and scatter light; do not settle out.	Solute particles are very large, settle out, and may scatter light.
Solute particles	Solute particles	Solute particles
Example Mineral water	*Example* Gelatin	*Example* Blood

Figure 2.4 The three basic types of mixtures.

methane and water are compounds, but molecules of hydrogen gas are not, because compounds always contain atoms of at least two different elements.

Compounds are chemically pure, and all of their molecules are identical. So, just as an atom is the smallest particle of an element that still has the properties of the element, a molecule is the smallest particle of a compound that still has the specific characteristics of the compound. This concept is important because the properties of compounds are usually very different from those of the atoms they contain. Water, for example, is very different from the elements hydrogen and oxygen. Indeed, it is next to impossible to tell what atoms are in a compound without analyzing it chemically.

Mixtures

Mixtures are substances composed of two or more components *physically intermixed*. Most matter in nature exists in the form of mixtures, but there are only three basic types: *solutions, colloids*, and *suspensions* (Figure 2.4).

Solutions

Solutions are homogeneous mixtures of components that may be gases, liquids, or solids. *Homogeneous* means that the mixture has exactly the same composition or makeup throughout—a sample taken from any part of the mixture has the same composition (in terms of the atoms or molecules it contains) as a sample taken from any other part of the mixture. Examples include the air we breathe (a mixture of gases) and seawater (a mixture of salts, which are solids, and water). The substance present in the greatest amount is called the **solvent** (or dissolving medium). Solvents are usually liquids. Substances present in smaller amounts are called **solutes**.

Water is the body's chief solvent. Most solutions in the body are *true solutions* containing gases, liquids, or solids dissolved in water. True solutions are usually transparent. Examples are saline solution [table salt (NaCl) and water], a mixture of glucose and water, and mineral water. The solutes of true solutions are minute, usually in the form of individual atoms and molecules. Consequently, they are not visible to the naked eye, do not settle out, and do not scatter light. In other words, if a beam of light is passed through a true solution, you will not see the path of light.

Concentration of Solutions We describe true solutions in terms of their *concentration*, which may be indicated in various ways. Solutions used in a college laboratory or a hospital are often described in terms of the **percent** (parts per 100 parts) of the solute in the total solution. This designation always refers to the solute percentage, and unless otherwise noted, water is assumed to be the solvent.

Milligrams per deciliter (mg/dl) is another common concentration measurement. (A deciliter is 100 milliliters or 0.1 liter.)

Still another way to express the concentration of a solution is in terms of its **molarity** (mo-lar′ĭ-te), or moles per liter, indicated by *M*. This method is more complicated but much more useful. To understand molarity, you must understand what a mole is. A **mole** of any element or compound is equal to its atomic weight or **molecular weight** (sum of the atomic weights) weighed out in grams. This concept is easier than it seems, as illustrated by the following example.

Glucose is $C_6H_{12}O_6$, which indicates that it has 6 carbon atoms, 12 hydrogen atoms, and 6 oxygen atoms. To compute the molecular weight of glucose, you would look up the atomic weight of each of its atoms in the periodic table (see Appendix E) and compute its molecular weight as follows:

Atom	Number of Atoms		Atomic Weight		Total Atomic Weight
C	6	×	12.011	=	72.066
H	12	×	1.008	=	12.096
O	6	×	15.999	=	95.994
					180.156

Then, to make a *one-molar* solution of glucose, you would weigh out 180.156 grams (g), called a *gram molecular weight*, of glucose and add enough water to make 1 liter (L) of solution. In short, a one-molar solution (abbreviated 1.0 *M*) of a chemical substance is one gram molecular weight of the substance (or one gram atomic weight in the case of elemental substances) in 1 L (1000 milliliters) of solution.

The beauty of using the mole as the basis of preparing solutions is its precision. One mole of any substance always contains exactly the same number of solute particles, that is, 6.02×10^{23}. This number is called **Avogadro's number** (av″o-gad′rōz). So whether you weigh out 1 mole of glucose (180 g) or 1 mole of water (18 g) or 1 mole of methane (16 g), in each case you will have 6.02×10^{23} molecules of that substance.* This allows almost mind-boggling precision to be achieved.

Because solute concentrations in body fluids tend to be quite low, those values are usually reported in terms of millimoles (m*M*; 1/1000 mole).

Colloids

Colloids (kol′oidz), also called *emulsions*, are *heterogeneous* mixtures, which means that their composition is dissimilar in different areas of the mixture. Colloids often appear translucent or milky and although the solute particles are larger than those in true solutions, they still do not settle out. However, they do scatter light, so the path of a light beam shining through a colloidal mixture is visible.

Colloids have many unique properties, including the ability of some to undergo **sol-gel transformations**, that is, to change reversibly from a fluid (sol) state to a more solid (gel) state. Jell-O, or any gelatin product (Figure 2.4), is a familiar example of a nonliving colloid that changes from a sol to a gel when refrigerated (and that gel will liquefy again if placed in the sun). Cytosol, the semifluid material in living cells, is also a colloid, largely because of its dispersed proteins. Its sol-gel transformations underlie many important cell activities, such as cell division and changes in cell shape.

Suspensions

Suspensions are *heterogeneous* mixtures with large, often visible solutes that tend to settle out. An example of a suspension is a mixture of sand and water. So is blood, in which the living blood cells are suspended in the fluid portion of blood (blood plasma). If left to stand, the suspended cells will settle out unless some means—mixing, shaking, or circulation in the body—keeps them in suspension.

As you can see, all three types of mixtures are found in both living and nonliving systems. In fact, living material is the most complex mixture of all, since it contains all three kinds of mixtures interacting with one another.

Distinguishing Mixtures from Compounds

Now let's zero in on how to distinguish mixtures and compounds from one another. Mixtures differ from compounds in several important ways:

1. The chief difference between mixtures and compounds is that no chemical bonding occurs between the components of a mixture. The properties of atoms and molecules are not changed when they become part of a mixture. Remember they are only physically intermixed.
2. Depending on the mixture, its components can be separated by physical means—straining, filtering, evaporation, and so on. Compounds, by contrast, can be separated into their constituent atoms only by chemical means (breaking bonds).
3. Some mixtures are homogeneous, whereas others are heterogeneous. A bar of 100% pure (elemental) iron is homogeneous, as are all compounds. As already mentioned, heterogeneous substances vary in their makeup from place to place. For example, iron ore is a heterogeneous mixture that contains iron and many other elements.

CHECK YOUR UNDERSTANDING

7. What is the meaning of the term "molecule"?
8. Why is sodium chloride (NaCl) considered a compound, but oxygen gas is not?
9. Blood contains a liquid component and living cells. Would it be classified as a compound or a mixture? Why?

For answers, see Appendix G.

___

*The important exception to this rule concerns molecules that ionize and break up into charged particles (ions) in water, such as salts, acids, and bases (see p. 39). For example, simple table salt (sodium chloride) breaks up into two types of charged particles. Therefore, in a 1.0*M* solution of sodium chloride, *2 moles* of solute particles are actually in solution.

Chemical Bonds

▶ Explain the role of electrons in chemical bonding and in relation to the octet rule.

▶ Differentiate among ionic, covalent, and hydrogen bonds.

▶ Compare and contrast polar and nonpolar compounds.

As noted earlier, when atoms combine with other atoms, they are held together by **chemical bonds**. A chemical bond is not a physical structure like a pair of handcuffs linking two people together. Instead, it is an energy relationship between the electrons of the reacting atoms, and it is made or broken in less than a trillionth of a second.

The Role of Electrons in Chemical Bonding

Electrons forming the electron cloud around the nucleus of an atom occupy regions of space called **electron shells** that consecutively surround the atomic nucleus. The atoms known so far can have electrons in seven shells (numbered 1 to 7 from the nucleus outward), but the actual number of electron shells occupied in a given atom depends on the number of electrons that atom has. Each electron shell contains one or more orbitals. (Recall from our earlier discussion that *orbitals* are regions around the nucleus in which a given electron is likely to be found most of the time.)

It is important to understand that each electron shell represents a different **energy level**, because this prompts you to think of electrons as particles with a certain amount of potential energy. In general, the terms *electron shell* and *energy level* are used interchangeably.

How much potential energy does an electron have? The answer depends on the energy level that an electron occupies. The attraction between the positively charged nucleus and negatively charged electrons is greatest when electrons are closest to the nucleus and falls off with increasing distance. This statement explains why electrons farthest from the nucleus (1) have the greatest potential energy (it takes more energy for them to overcome the nuclear attraction and reach the more distant energy levels) and (2) are most likely to interact chemically with other atoms. (They are the least tightly held by their own atomic nucleus and the most easily influenced by other atoms and molecules.)

Each electron shell can hold a specific number of electrons. Shell 1, the shell immediately surrounding the nucleus, accommodates only 2 electrons. Shell 2 holds a maximum of 8, and shell 3 has room for 18. Subsequent shells hold larger and larger numbers of electrons, and the shells tend to be filled with electrons consecutively. For example, shell 1 fills completely before any electrons appear in shell 2.

Which electrons are involved in chemical bonding? When we consider bonding behavior, the only electrons that are important are those in the atom's outermost energy level. Inner electrons usually do not take part in bonding because they are more tightly held by the atomic nucleus.

When the outermost energy level of an atom is filled to capacity or contains eight electrons, the atom is stable. Such atoms

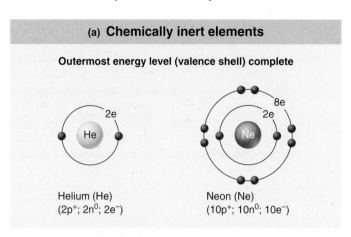

(a) Chemically inert elements

Outermost energy level (valence shell) complete

Helium (He)
($2p^+$; $2n^0$; $2e^-$)

Neon (Ne)
($10p^+$; $10n^0$; $10e^-$)

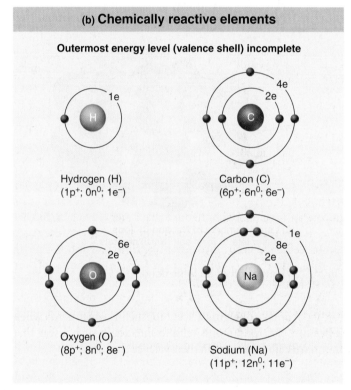

(b) Chemically reactive elements

Outermost energy level (valence shell) incomplete

Hydrogen (H)
($1p^+$; $0n^0$; $1e^-$)

Carbon (C)
($6p^+$; $6n^0$; $6e^-$)

Oxygen (O)
($8p^+$; $8n^0$; $8e^-$)

Sodium (Na)
($11p^+$; $12n^0$; $11e^-$)

Figure 2.5 Chemically inert and reactive elements. (*Note*: For simplicity, each atomic nucleus is shown as a sphere with the atom's symbol; individual protons and neutrons are not shown.)

are *chemically inert*, that is, unreactive. A group of elements called the *noble gases*, which include helium and neon, typify this condition **(Figure 2.5a)**. On the other hand, atoms in which the outermost energy level contains fewer than eight electrons tend to gain, lose, or share electrons with other atoms to achieve stability (Figure 2.5b).

What about atoms that have more than 20 electrons, in which the energy levels beyond shell 2 can contain *more* than eight electrons? The number of electrons that can participate in bonding is still limited to a total of eight. The term **valence shell** (va′lens) specifically indicates an atom's outermost energy level *or that portion of it* containing the electrons that are chemically reactive. Hence, the key to chemical reactivity is the **octet rule**

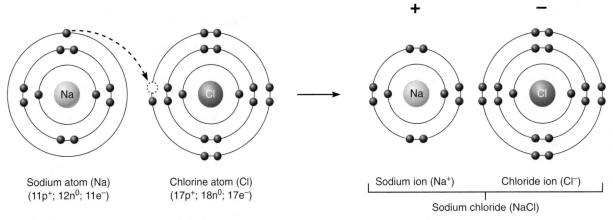

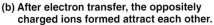

Sodium atom (Na)
(11p$^+$; 12n^0; 11e$^-$)

Chlorine atom (Cl)
(17p$^+$; 18n^0; 17e$^-$)

(a) Sodium gains stability by losing one electron, and chlorine becomes stable by gaining one electron.

Sodium ion (Na$^+$)

Chloride ion (Cl$^-$)

Sodium chloride (NaCl)

(b) After electron transfer, the oppositely charged ions formed attract each other.

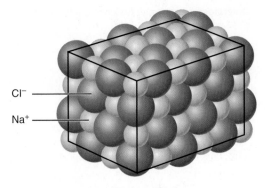

Cl$^-$

Na$^+$

(c) Large numbers of Na$^+$ and Cl$^-$ ions associate to form salt (NaCl) crystals.

Figure 2.6 **Formation of an ionic bond.**

(ok-tet′), or **rule of eights**. Except for shell 1, which is full when it has two electrons, atoms tend to interact in such a way that they have eight electrons in their valence shell.

Types of Chemical Bonds

Three major types of chemical bonds—*ionic, covalent,* and *hydrogen bonds*—result from attractive forces between atoms.

Ionic Bonds

Recall that atoms are electrically neutral. However, electrons can be transferred from one atom to another, and when this happens, the precise balance of + and − charges is lost so that charged particles called **ions** are formed. An **ionic bond** (i-on′ik) is a chemical bond between atoms formed by the transfer of one or more electrons from one atom to the other. The atom that gains one or more electrons is the *electron acceptor*. It acquires a net negative charge and is called an **anion** (an′i-on). The atom that loses electrons is the *electron donor*. It acquires a net positive charge and is called a **cation** (kat′i-on). (To remember this term, think of the "t" in "cation" as a + sign.) Both anions and cations are formed whenever electron transfer between atoms occurs. Because opposite charges attract, these ions tend to stay close together, resulting in an ionic bond.

One example of ionic bonding is the formation of table salt, or sodium chloride (NaCl), by interaction of sodium and chlorine atoms **(Figure 2.6)**. Sodium, with an atomic number of 11, has only one electron in its valence shell. It would be very difficult to attempt to fill this shell by adding seven more. However, if this single electron is lost, shell 2 with eight electrons becomes the valence shell (outermost energy level containing electrons) and is full. Thus, by losing the lone electron in its third energy level, sodium achieves stability and becomes a cation (Na$^+$). On the other hand, chlorine, atomic number 17, needs only one electron to fill its valence shell. By accepting an electron, chlorine achieves stability and becomes an anion.

When sodium and chlorine atoms interact, this is exactly what happens. Sodium donates an electron to chlorine (Figure 2.6a), and the oppositely charged ions created in this exchange attract each other, forming sodium chloride (Figure 2.6b). Ionic bonds are commonly formed between atoms with one or two valence shell electrons (the metallic elements, such as sodium, calcium, and potassium) and atoms with seven valence shell electrons (such as chlorine, fluorine, and iodine).

Most ionic compounds fall in the chemical category called *salts*. In the dry state, salts such as sodium chloride do not exist as individual molecules. Instead, they form **crystals**, large arrays of cations and anions held together by ionic bonds (Figure 2.6c).

Sodium chloride is an excellent example of the difference in properties between a compound and its constituent atoms. Sodium is a silvery white metal, and chlorine in its molecular state is a poisonous green gas used to make bleach. However, sodium chloride is a white crystalline solid that we sprinkle on our food.

Covalent Bonds

Electrons do not have to be completely transferred for atoms to achieve stability. Instead, they may be *shared* so that each atom is able to fill its outer electron shell at least part of the time. Electron sharing produces molecules in which the shared electrons occupy a single orbital common to both atoms, which constitutes a **covalent bond** (ko-va′lent).

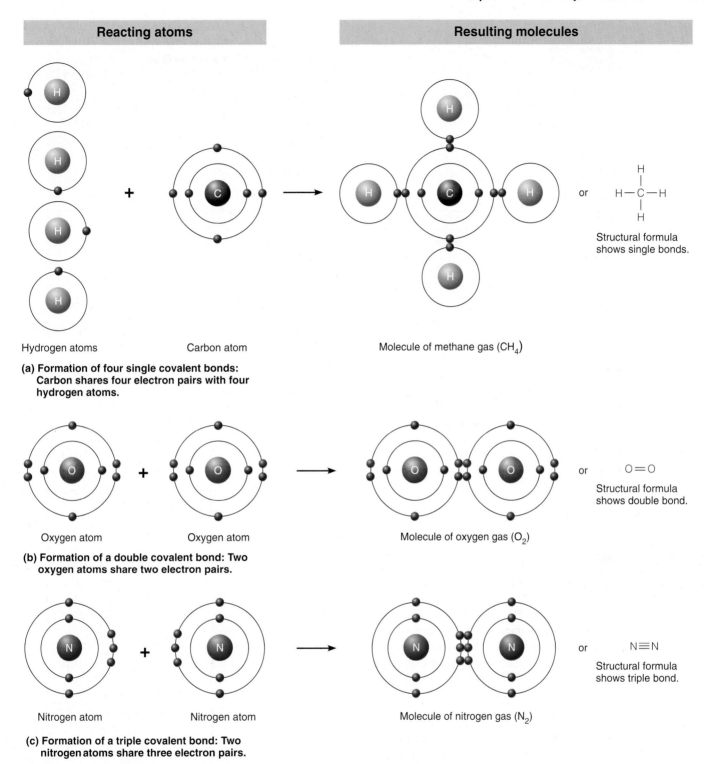

Reacting atoms	Resulting molecules

Hydrogen atoms   Carbon atom

Molecule of methane gas (CH_4)

or

Structural formula shows single bonds.

(a) Formation of four single covalent bonds: Carbon shares four electron pairs with four hydrogen atoms.

Oxygen atom   Oxygen atom

Molecule of oxygen gas (O_2)

or $O = O$

Structural formula shows double bond.

(b) Formation of a double covalent bond: Two oxygen atoms share two electron pairs.

Nitrogen atom   Nitrogen atom

Molecule of nitrogen gas (N_2)

or $N \equiv N$

Structural formula shows triple bond.

(c) Formation of a triple covalent bond: Two nitrogen atoms share three electron pairs.

Figure 2.7 **Formation of covalent bonds.**

Hydrogen with its single electron can fill its only shell (shell 1) by sharing a pair of electrons with another atom. When it shares with another hydrogen atom, a molecule of hydrogen gas is formed. The shared electron pair orbits around the molecule as a whole, satisfying the stability needs of each atom.

Hydrogen can also share an electron pair with different kinds of atoms to form a compound (Figure 2.7a). Carbon has four electrons in its outermost shell, but needs eight to achieve stability. Hydrogen has one electron, but needs two. When a methane molecule (CH_4) is formed, carbon shares four pairs of electrons

$O{=}C{=}O$

(a) Carbon dioxide (CO₂) molecules are linear and symmetrical. They are nonpolar.

δ^-

δ^+ δ^+

(b) V-shaped water (H₂O) molecules have two poles of charge—a slightly more negative oxygen end (δ^-) and a slightly more positive hydrogen end (δ^+).

Figure 2.8 Carbon dioxide and water molecules have different shapes, as illustrated by molecular models.

Ionic bond	Polar covalent bond	Nonpolar covalent bond
Complete transfer of electrons	Unequal sharing of electrons	Equal sharing of electrons
Separate ions (charged particles) form	Slight negative charge (δ^-) at one end of molecule, slight positive charge (δ^+) at other end	Charge balanced among atoms
Na⁺ Cl⁻ Sodium chloride	Water	O=C=O Carbon dioxide

Figure 2.9 Ionic, polar covalent, and nonpolar covalent bonds compared along a continuum.

with four hydrogen atoms (one pair with each hydrogen). Again, the shared electrons orbit and "belong to" the whole molecule, ensuring the stability of each atom.

When two atoms share one pair of electrons, a *single covalent bond* is formed (indicated by a single line connecting the atoms, such as H—H). In some cases, atoms share two or three electron pairs, resulting in *double* or *triple covalent bonds* (Figure 2.7b and c). (These bonds are indicated by double or triple connecting lines such as O=O or N≡N.)

Polar and Nonpolar Molecules   In the covalent bonds we have discussed, the shared electrons are shared equally between the atoms of the molecule for the most part. The molecules formed are electrically balanced and are called **nonpolar molecules** (because they do not have separate + and − poles of charge).

Such electrical balance is not always the case. When covalent bonds are formed, the resulting molecule always has a specific three-dimensional shape, with the bonds formed at definite angles. A molecule's shape helps determine what other molecules or atoms it can interact with. It may also result in unequal electron pair sharing, creating a **polar molecule**, especially in nonsymmetrical molecules containing atoms with different electron-attracting abilities.

In general, *small* atoms with six or seven valence shell electrons, such as oxygen, nitrogen, and chlorine, are electron-hungry and attract electrons very strongly, a capability called **electronegativity**. On the other hand, most atoms with only one or two valence shell electrons tend to be **electropositive**. In other words, their electron-attracting ability is so low that they usually lose *their* valence shell electrons to other atoms. Potassium and sodium, each with one valence shell electron, are good examples of electropositive atoms.

Carbon dioxide and water illustrate how molecular shape and the relative electron-attracting abilities of atoms determine whether a covalently bonded molecule is nonpolar or polar. In carbon dioxide (CO₂), carbon shares four electron pairs with two oxygen atoms (two pairs are shared with each oxygen). Oxy-

gen is very electronegative and so attracts the shared electrons much more strongly than does carbon. However, because the carbon dioxide molecule is linear and symmetrical (Figure 2.8a), the electron-pulling ability of one oxygen atom offsets that of the other, like a standoff between equally strong teams in a game of tug-of-war. As a result, the shared electrons orbit the entire molecule and carbon dioxide is a nonpolar compound.

In contrast, a water molecule (H₂O) is bent, or V shaped (Figure 2.8b). The two electropositive hydrogen atoms are located at the same end of the molecule, and the very electronegative oxygen is at the opposite end. This arrangement allows oxygen to pull the shared electrons toward itself and away from the two hydrogen atoms. In this case, the electron pairs are *not* shared equally, but spend more time in the vicinity of oxygen. Because electrons are negatively charged, the oxygen end of the molecule is slightly more negative (the charge is indicated with a delta and minus as δ^-) and the hydrogen end slightly more positive (indicated by δ^+). Because water has two poles of charge, it is a *polar molecule*, or **dipole** (di′pōl).

Polar molecules orient themselves toward other dipoles or toward charged particles (such as ions and some proteins), and they play essential roles in chemical reactions in body cells. The polarity of water is particularly significant, as you will see later in this chapter.

Different molecules exhibit different degrees of polarity, and we can see a gradual change from ionic to nonpolar covalent bonding as summarized in **Figure 2.9**. Ionic bonds (complete electron transfer) and nonpolar covalent bonds (equal electron sharing) are the extremes of a continuum, with various degrees of unequal electron sharing in between.

Hydrogen Bonds

Unlike the stronger ionic and covalent bonds, hydrogen bonds are more like attractions than true bonds. Hydrogen bonds form when a hydrogen atom, already covalently linked to one electronegative atom (usually nitrogen or oxygen), is attracted by another electron-hungry atom, so that a "bridge" forms between them.

Hydrogen bonding is common between dipoles such as water molecules, because the slightly negative oxygen atoms of one molecule attract the slightly positive hydrogen atoms of other molecules **(Figure 2.10a)**. Hydrogen bonding is responsible for the tendency of water molecules to cling together and form films, referred to as *surface tension*. This tendency helps explain why water beads up into spheres when it sits on a hard surface and why water striders can walk on a pond's surface (Figure 2.10b).

Although hydrogen bonds are too weak to bind atoms together to form molecules, they are important *intramolecular bonds* (literally, bonds within molecules), which hold different parts of a single large molecule in a specific three-dimensional shape. Some large biological molecules, such as proteins and DNA, have numerous hydrogen bonds that help maintain and stabilize their structures.

CHECK YOUR UNDERSTANDING

10. What kinds of bonds form between water molecules?

11. Oxygen ($_8$O) and argon ($_{18}$A) are both gases. Oxygen combines readily with other elements, but argon does not. What accounts for this difference?

12. Assume imaginary compound XY has a polar covalent bond. How does its charge distribution differ from that of XX molecules?

For answers, see Appendix G.

Chemical Reactions

▶ Define the three major types of chemical reactions: synthesis, decomposition, and exchange. Comment on the nature of oxidation-reduction reactions and their importance.

▶ Explain why chemical reactions in the body are often irreversible.

▶ Describe factors that affect chemical reaction rates.

As we noted earlier, all particles of matter are in constant motion because of their kinetic energy. Movement of atoms or molecules in a solid is usually limited to vibration because the particles are united by fairly rigid bonds. But in liquids or gases, particles dart about randomly, sometimes colliding with one another and interacting to undergo chemical reactions. A **chemical reaction** occurs whenever chemical bonds are formed, rearranged, or broken.

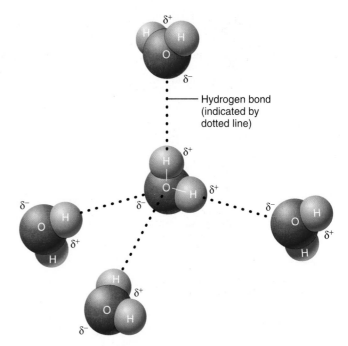

(a) The slightly positive ends (δ^+) of the water molecules become aligned with the slightly negative ends (δ^-) of other water molecules.

(b) A water strider can walk on a pond because of the high surface tension of water, a result of the combined strength of its hydrogen bonds.

Figure 2.10 **Hydrogen bonding between polar water molecules.**

Chemical Equations

We can write chemical reactions in symbolic form as **chemical equations**. For example, we indicate the joining of two hydrogen atoms to form hydrogen gas as

$$H + H \rightarrow H_2 \text{ (hydrogen gas)}$$

reactants   product

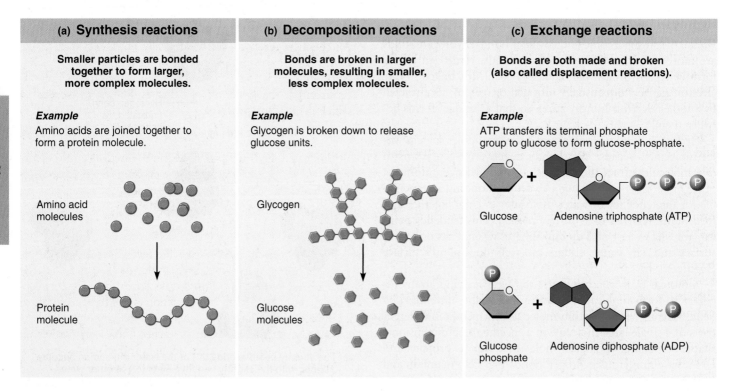

Figure 2.11 Patterns of chemical reactions.

and the combining of four hydrogen atoms and one carbon atom to form methane as

$$4H + C \rightarrow CH_4 \text{ (methane)}$$
$$\underset{\text{reactants}}{} \qquad \underset{\text{product}}{}$$

Notice that in equations, a number written as a *subscript* indicates that the atoms are joined by chemical bonds. But a number written as a *prefix* denotes the number of *unjoined* atoms or molecules. For example, CH_4 reveals that four hydrogen atoms are bonded together with carbon to form the methane molecule, but 4H signifies four unjoined hydrogen atoms.

A chemical equation is like a sentence describing what happens in a reaction. It contains the following information: the number and kinds of reacting substances, or **reactants**; the chemical composition of the **product(s)**; and in balanced equations, the relative proportion of each reactant and product.

In the equations above, the reactants are atoms, as indicated by their atomic symbols (H, C). The product in each case is a molecule, as represented by its **molecular formula** (H_2, CH_4). The equation for the formation of methane may be read in terms of molecules or moles—as *either* "four hydrogen atoms plus one carbon atom yield one molecule of methane" *or* "four moles of hydrogen atoms plus one mole of carbon yield one mole of methane." Using moles is more practical because it is impossible to measure out one atom or one molecule of anything!

Patterns of Chemical Reactions

Most chemical reactions exhibit one of three recognizable patterns: They are either *synthesis, decomposition,* or *exchange reactions.*

When atoms or molecules combine to form a larger, more complex molecule, the process is a **synthesis**, or **combination**, **reaction**. A synthesis reaction always involves bond formation. It can be represented (using arbitrary letters) as

$$A + B \rightarrow AB$$

Synthesis reactions are the basis of constructive, or **anabolic**, activities in body cells, such as joining small molecules called amino acids into large protein molecules **(Figure 2.11a)**. Synthesis reactions are conspicuous in rapidly growing tissues.

A **decomposition reaction** occurs when a molecule is broken down into smaller molecules or its constituent atoms:

$$AB \rightarrow A + B$$

Essentially, decomposition reactions are reverse synthesis reactions: Bonds are broken. Decomposition reactions underlie all degradative, or **catabolic**, processes in body cells. For example, the bonds of glycogen molecules are broken to release simpler molecules of glucose sugar (Figure 2.11b).

Exchange, or **displacement**, **reactions** involve both synthesis and decomposition. Bonds are both made and broken. In an exchange reaction, parts of the reactant molecules change partners, so to speak, producing different product molecules:

$$AB + C \rightarrow AC + B \quad \text{and} \quad AB + CD \rightarrow AD + CB$$

An exchange reaction occurs when ATP reacts with glucose and transfers its end phosphate group (indicated by a circled P in Figure 2.11c) to glucose, forming glucose-phosphate. At the same time, the ATP becomes ADP. This important reaction occurs whenever glucose enters a body cell, and it effectively traps the glucose fuel molecule inside the cell.

Another group of important chemical reactions in living systems is **oxidation-reduction reactions**, called **redox reactions** for short. Oxidation-reduction reactions are decomposition reactions in that they are the basis of all reactions in which food fuels are broken down for energy (that is, in which ATP is produced). They are also a special type of exchange reaction because electrons are exchanged between the reactants. The reactant losing the electrons is referred to as the *electron donor* and is said to be **oxidized**. The reactant taking up the transferred electrons is called the *electron acceptor* and is said to become **reduced**.

Redox reactions also occur when ionic compounds are formed. Recall that in the formation of NaCl (see Figure 2.6), sodium loses an electron to chlorine. Consequently, sodium is oxidized and becomes a sodium ion, and chlorine is reduced and becomes a chloride ion. However, not all oxidation-reduction reactions involve *complete transfer* of electrons—some simply change the pattern of electron sharing in covalent bonds. For example, a substance is oxidized both by losing hydrogen atoms and by combining with oxygen. The common factor in these events is that electrons that formerly "belonged" to the reactant molecule are lost. The electrons are lost either entirely (as hydrogen is removed and takes its electron with it) or relatively (as the shared electrons spend more time in the vicinity of the very electronegative oxygen atom).

To understand the importance of oxidation-reduction reactions in living systems, take a look at the overall equation for *cellular respiration*, which represents the major pathway by which glucose is broken down for energy in body cells:

$$C_6H_{12}O_6 + 6O_2 \rightarrow 6CO_2 + 6H_2O + ATP$$

glucose   oxygen   carbon   water   cellular
dioxide   energy

As you can see, it is an oxidation-reduction reaction. Consider what happens to the hydrogen atoms (and their electrons). Glucose is oxidized to carbon dioxide as it loses hydrogen atoms, and oxygen is reduced to water as it accepts the hydrogen atoms. This reaction is described in detail in Chapter 24, along with other topics of cellular metabolism.

Energy Flow in Chemical Reactions

Because all chemical bonds represent stored chemical energy, all chemical reactions ultimately result in net absorption or release of energy. Reactions that release energy are called **exergonic reactions**. These reactions yield products with less energy than the initial reactants, along with energy that can be harvested for other uses. With a few exceptions, catabolic and oxidative reactions are exergonic.

In contrast, the products of energy-absorbing, or **endergonic**, reactions contain more potential energy in their chemical bonds than did the reactants. Anabolic reactions are typically energy-absorbing endergonic reactions. Essentially this is a case of "one hand washing the other"—the energy released when fuel molecules are broken down (oxidized) is captured in ATP molecules and then used to synthesize the complex biological molecules the body needs to sustain life.

Reversibility of Chemical Reactions

All chemical reactions are theoretically reversible. If chemical bonds can be made, they can be broken, and vice versa. Reversibility is indicated by a double arrow. When the arrows differ in length, the longer arrow indicates the major direction in which the reaction proceeds:

$$A + B \rightleftharpoons AB$$

In this example, the forward reaction (reaction going to the right) predominates. Over time, the product (AB) accumulates and the reactants (A and B) decrease in amount.

When the arrows are of equal length, as in

$$A + B \rightleftharpoons AB$$

neither the forward reaction nor the reverse reaction is dominant. In other words, for each molecule of product (AB) formed, one product molecule breaks down, releasing the reactants A and B. Such a chemical reaction is said to be in a state of **chemical equilibrium**.

Once chemical equilibrium is reached, there is no further *net change* in the amounts of reactants and products unless more of either are added to the mix. Product molecules are still formed and broken down, but the balance established when equilibrium was reached (such as greater numbers of product molecules) remains unchanged.

Chemical equilibrium is analogous to the admission scheme used by many large museums in which tickets are sold according to time of entry. If 300 tickets are issued for the 9 AM admission, 300 people will be admitted when the doors open. Thereafter, when 6 people leave, 6 are admitted, and when another 15 people leave, 15 more are allowed in. There is a continual turnover, but the museum contains about 300 art lovers throughout the day.

All chemical reactions are reversible, but many biological reactions show so little tendency to go in the reverse direction that they are irreversible for all practical purposes. Chemical reactions that release energy will not go in the opposite direction unless energy is put back into the system. For example, when our cells break down glucose via the reactions of cellular respiration to yield carbon dioxide and water, some of the energy released is trapped in the bonds of ATP. Because the cells then use ATP's energy for various functions (and more glucose will be along with the next meal), this particular reaction is never reversed in our cells. Furthermore, if a product of a reaction is continuously removed from the reaction site, it is unavailable to take part in the reverse reaction. This situation occurs when the carbon dioxide that is released during glucose breakdown leaves the cell, enters the blood, and is eventually removed from the body by the lungs.

Factors Influencing the Rate of Chemical Reactions

What influences how quickly chemical reactions go? For atoms and molecules to react chemically in the first place, they must *collide* with enough force to overcome the repulsion between their electrons. Interactions between valence shell electrons—the basis of bond making and breaking—cannot occur long distance. The force of collisions depends on how fast the particles are moving. Solid, forceful collisions between rapidly moving particles in which valence shells overlap are much more likely to cause reactions than are collisions in which the particles graze each other lightly.

Temperature Increasing the temperature of a substance increases the kinetic energy of its particles and the force of their collisions. For this reason, chemical reactions proceed more quickly at higher temperatures.

Concentration Chemical reactions progress most rapidly when the reacting particles are present in high numbers, because the chance of successful collisions is greater. As the concentration of the reactants declines, the reaction slows. Chemical equilibrium eventually occurs unless additional reactants are added or products are removed from the reaction site.

Particle Size Smaller particles move faster than larger ones (at the same temperature) and tend to collide more frequently and more forcefully. Hence, the smaller the reacting particles, the faster a chemical reaction goes at a given temperature and concentration.

Catalysts Many chemical reactions in nonliving systems can be speeded up simply by heating, but drastic increases in body temperature are life threatening because important biological molecules are destroyed. Still, at normal body temperatures, most chemical reactions would proceed far too slowly to maintain life were it not for the presence of catalysts. **Catalysts** (kat′ah-lists) are substances that increase the rate of chemical reactions without themselves becoming chemically changed or part of the product. Biological catalysts are called *enzymes* (en′zīmz). Later in this chapter we describe how enzymes work.

CHECK YOUR UNDERSTANDING

13. Which reaction type—synthesis, decomposition, or exchange—occurs when fats are digested in your small intestine?

14. Why are many reactions that occur in living systems irreversible for all intents and purposes?

15. What specific name is given to decomposition reactions in which food fuels are broken down for energy?

For answers, see Appendix G.

PART 2

BIOCHEMISTRY

Biochemistry is the study of the chemical composition and reactions of living matter. All chemicals in the body fall into one of two major classes: organic or inorganic compounds. **Organic compounds** contain carbon. All organic compounds are covalently bonded molecules, and many are large.

All other chemicals in the body are considered **inorganic compounds**. These include water, salts, and many acids and bases. Organic and inorganic compounds are equally essential for life. Trying to decide which is more valuable is like trying to decide whether the ignition system or the engine is more essential to run your car!

Inorganic Compounds

▶ Explain the importance of water and salts to body homeostasis.

▶ Define acid and base, and explain the concept of pH.

Water

Water is the most abundant and important inorganic compound in living material. It makes up 60–80% of the volume of most living cells. What makes water so vital to life? The answer lies in several properties:

1. **High heat capacity.** Water has a high heat capacity. In other words, it absorbs and releases large amounts of heat before changing appreciably in temperature itself. This property of water prevents sudden changes in temperature caused by external factors, such as sun or wind exposure, or by internal conditions that release heat rapidly, such as vigorous muscle activity. As part of blood, water redistributes heat among body tissues, ensuring temperature homeostasis.

2. **High heat of vaporization.** When water evaporates, or vaporizes, it changes from a liquid to a gas (water vapor). This transformation requires that large amounts of heat be absorbed to break the hydrogen bonds that hold water molecules together. This property is extremely beneficial when we sweat. As perspiration (mostly water) evaporates from our skin, large amounts of heat are removed from the body, providing efficient cooling.

3. **Polar solvent properties.** Water is an unparalleled solvent. Indeed, it is often called the **universal solvent**. Biochemistry is "wet chemistry." Biological molecules do not react chemically unless they are in solution, and virtually all chemical reactions occurring in the body depend on water's solvent properties.

   Because water molecules are polar, they orient themselves with their slightly negative ends toward the positive ends of the solutes, and vice versa, first attracting the solute molecules, and then surrounding them. This polarity of water explains why ionic compounds and other small reactive molecules (such as acids and bases) *dissociate* in water, their ions separating from each other and becoming evenly scattered in the water, forming true solutions (**Figure 2.12**).

   Water also forms layers of water molecules, called **hydration layers**, around large charged molecules such as proteins, shielding them from the effects of other charged substances in the vicinity and preventing them from settling out of solution. Such protein-water mixtures are *biological colloids*. Blood plasma and cerebrospinal fluid (which surrounds the brain and spinal cord) are examples of colloids.

   Water is the body's major transport medium because it is such an excellent solvent. Nutrients, respiratory gases, and metabolic wastes carried throughout the body are dissolved in blood plasma, and many metabolic wastes are excreted from the body in urine, another watery fluid. Specialized molecules that lubricate the body (e.g., mucus) also use water as their dissolving medium.

4. **Reactivity.** Water is an important *reactant* in many chemical reactions. For example, foods are digested to their building blocks by adding a water molecule to each bond to be broken. Such decomposition reactions are more specifically called **hydrolysis reactions** (hi-drol′ĭ-sis; "water splitting"). Conversely, when large carbohydrate or protein molecules are synthesized from smaller molecules, a water molecule is removed for every bond formed, a reaction called **dehydration synthesis**.

5. **Cushioning.** By forming a resilient cushion around certain body organs, water helps protect them from physical trauma. The cerebrospinal fluid surrounding the brain exemplifies water's cushioning role.

Salts

A **salt** is an ionic compound containing cations other than H^+ and anions other than the hydroxyl ion (OH^-). As already noted, when salts are dissolved in water, they dissociate into their component ions (Figure 2.12). For example, sodium sulfate (Na_2SO_4) dissociates into two Na^+ ions and one SO_4^{2-} ion. It dissociates easily because the ions are already formed. All that remains is for water to overcome the attraction between the oppositely charged ions.

All ions are **electrolytes** (e-lek′tro-līts), substances that conduct an electrical current in solution. (Note that groups of atoms that bear an overall charge, such as sulfate, are called *polyatomic ions.*)

Salts commonly found in the body include NaCl, $CaCO_3$ (calcium carbonate), and KCl (potassium chloride). However, the most plentiful salts are the calcium phosphates that make bones and teeth hard. In their ionized form, salts play vital roles in body function. For instance, the electrolyte properties of sodium and potassium ions are essential for nerve impulse transmission and muscle contraction. Ionic iron forms part of the hemoglobin molecules that transport oxygen within red blood cells, and zinc and copper ions are important to the activity of some enzymes. Other important functions of the elements found in body salts are summarized in Table 2.1 on p. 26.

HOMEOSTATIC IMBALANCE

Maintaining proper ionic balance in our body fluids is one of the most crucial homeostatic roles of the kidneys. When this balance is severely disturbed, virtually nothing in the body works. All the physiological activities listed above and thousands of others are disrupted and grind to a stop. ■

Acids and Bases

Like salts, acids and bases are electrolytes. They ionize and dissociate in water and can then conduct an electrical current.

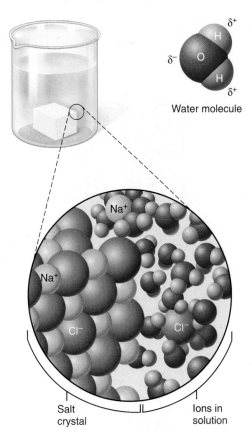

Water molecule

Salt crystal | Ions in solution

Figure 2.12 Dissociation of salt in water.

Acids

Acids have a sour taste, can react with (dissolve) many metals, and "burn" a hole in your rug. But for our purposes the most useful definition of an acid is a substance that releases **hydrogen ions** (H^+) in detectable amounts. Because a hydrogen ion is just a hydrogen nucleus, or "naked" proton, acids are also defined as **proton donors**.

When acids dissolve in water, they release hydrogen ions (protons) and anions. It is the concentration of protons that determines the acidity of a solution. The anions have little or no effect on acidity. For example, hydrochloric acid (HCl), an acid produced by stomach cells that aids digestion, dissociates into a proton and a chloride ion:

$$HCl \rightarrow H^+ + Cl^-$$
$$\text{proton} \quad \text{anion}$$

Other acids found or produced in the body include acetic acid ($HC_2H_3O_2$, commonly abbreviated as HAc), which is the acidic portion of vinegar; and carbonic acid (H_2CO_3). The molecular formula for an acid is easy to recognize because the hydrogen is written first.

Bases

Bases have a bitter taste, feel slippery, and are **proton acceptors**—that is, they take up hydrogen ions (H^+) in detectable amounts. Common inorganic bases include the *hydroxides* (hi-drok′sīds), such as magnesium hydroxide (milk of magnesia) and sodium

Concentration (moles/liter)

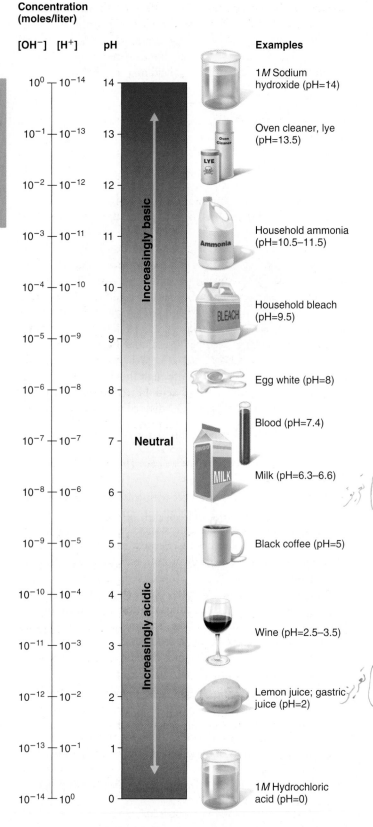

Figure 2.13 The pH scale and pH values of representative substances. The pH scale is based on the number of hydrogen ions in solution. The actual concentrations of hydrogen ions, [H⁺], and hydroxyl ions, [OH⁻], in moles per liter are indicated for each pH value noted. At a pH of 7, [H⁺] = [OH⁻] and the solution is neutral.

hydroxide (lye). Like acids, hydroxides dissociate when dissolved in water, but in this case **hydroxyl ions (OH⁻)** (hi-drok′sil) and cations are liberated. For example, ionization of sodium hydroxide (NaOH) produces a hydroxyl ion and a sodium ion, and the hydroxyl ion then binds to (accepts) a proton present in the solution. This reaction produces water and simultaneously reduces the acidity (hydrogen ion concentration) of the solution:

$$NaOH \rightarrow \underset{\text{cation}}{Na^+} + \underset{\substack{\text{hydroxyl} \\ \text{ion}}}{OH^-}$$

and then

$$\underset{\text{water}}{OH^- + H^+ \rightarrow H_2O}$$

Bicarbonate ion (HCO₃⁻), an important base in the body, is particularly abundant in blood. **Ammonia (NH₃)**, a common waste product of protein breakdown in the body, is also a base. It has one pair of unshared electrons that strongly attracts protons. By accepting a proton, ammonia becomes an ammonium ion:

$$NH_3 + H^+ \rightarrow \underset{\substack{\text{ammonium} \\ \text{ion}}}{NH_4^+}$$

pH: Acid-Base Concentration

The more hydrogen ions in a solution, the more acidic the solution is. Conversely, the greater the concentration of hydroxyl ions (the lower the concentration of H⁺), the more basic, or *alkaline* (al′kuh-līn), the solution becomes. The relative concentration of hydrogen ions in various body fluids is measured in concentration units called **pH units** (pe-āch′).

The idea for a pH scale was devised by a Danish biochemist and part-time beer brewer named Sören Sörensen in 1909. He was searching for a convenient means of checking the acidity of his alcoholic product to prevent its spoilage by bacterial action. (Acidic conditions inhibit many bacteria.) The pH scale that resulted is based on the concentration of hydrogen ions in a solution, expressed in terms of moles per liter, or molarity. The pH scale runs from 0 to 14 and is *logarithmic*. In other words, each successive change of one pH unit represents a tenfold change in hydrogen ion concentration **(Figure 2.13)**. The pH of a solution is thus defined as the negative logarithm of the hydrogen ion concentration [H⁺] in moles per liter, or $-\log[H^+]$. (Note that brackets [ ] indicate concentration of a substance.)

At a pH of 7 (at which [H⁺] is 10^{-7} *M*), the solution is *neutral*—neither acidic nor basic. The number of hydrogen ions exactly equals the number of hydroxyl ions (pH = pOH). Absolutely pure (distilled) water has a pH of 7.

Solutions with a pH below 7 are acidic—the hydrogen ions outnumber the hydroxyl ions. The lower the pH, the more acidic the solution. A solution with a pH of 6 has ten times as many hydrogen ions as a solution with a pH of 7.

Solutions with a pH higher than 7 are alkaline, and the relative concentration of hydrogen ions decreases by a factor of 10 with each higher pH unit. Thus, solutions with pH values of 8 and 12 have, respectively, 1/10 and 1/100,000 (1/10 × 1/10 × 1/10 × 1/10 × 1/10) as many hydrogen ions as a solution of pH 7.

The approximate pH of several body fluids and of a number of common substances appears in Figure 2.13. Notice that as the hydrogen ion concentration decreases, the hydroxyl ion concentration rises, and vice versa.

Neutralization

What happens when acids and bases are mixed? They react with each other in displacement reactions to form water and a salt. For example, when hydrochloric acid and sodium hydroxide interact, sodium chloride (a salt) and water are formed.

$$HCl + NaOH \rightarrow NaCl + H_2O$$
acid   base   salt   water

This type of reaction is called a **neutralization reaction**, because the joining of H^+ and OH^- to form water neutralizes the solution. Although the salt produced is written in molecular form (NaCl), remember that it actually exists as dissociated sodium and chloride ions when dissolved in water.

Buffers

Living cells are extraordinarily sensitive to even slight changes in the pH of the environment. In high concentrations, acids and bases are extremely damaging to living tissue. Imagine what would happen to all those hydrogen bonds in biological molecules with large numbers of free H^+ running around. (Can't you just hear those molecules saying "Why share hydrogen when I can have my own?")

Homeostasis of acid-base balance is carefully regulated by the kidneys and lungs and by chemical systems (proteins and other types of molecules) called **buffers**. Buffers resist abrupt and large swings in the pH of body fluids by releasing hydrogen ions (acting as acids) when the pH begins to rise and by binding hydrogen ions (acting as bases) when the pH drops. Because blood comes into close contact with nearly every body cell, regulation of its pH is particularly critical. Normally, blood pH varies within a very narrow range (7.35 to 7.45). If blood pH varies from these limits by more than a few tenths of a unit, it may be fatal.

To comprehend how chemical buffer systems operate, you must thoroughly understand strong and weak acids and bases. The first important concept is that the acidity of a solution reflects *only* the free hydrogen ions, not those still bound to anions. Consequently, acids that dissociate completely and irreversibly in water are called **strong acids**, because they can dramatically change the pH of a solution. Examples are hydrochloric acid and sulfuric acid. If we could count out 100 hydrochloric acid molecules and place them in 1 milliliter (ml) of water, we could expect to end up with 100 H^+, 100 Cl^-, and no undissociated hydrochloric acid molecules in that solution.

Acids that do not dissociate completely, like carbonic acid (H_2CO_3) and acetic acid (HAc), are **weak acids**. If we were to place 100 acetic acid molecules in 1 ml of water, the reaction would be something like this:

$$100\ HAc \rightarrow 90\ HAc + 10\ H^+ + 10\ Ac^-$$

Because undissociated acids do not affect pH, the acetic acid solution is much less acidic than the HCl solution. Weak acids dissociate in a predictable way, and molecules of the intact acid are in dynamic equilibrium with the dissociated ions. Consequently, the dissociation of acetic acid may also be written as

$$HAc \rightleftharpoons H^+ + Ac^-$$

This viewpoint allows us to see that if H^+ (released by a strong acid) is added to the acetic acid solution, the equilibrium will shift to the left and some H^+ and Ac^- will recombine to form HAc. On the other hand, if a strong base is added and the pH begins to rise, the equilibrium shifts to the right and more HAc molecules dissociate to release H^+. This characteristic of weak acids allows them to play important roles in the chemical buffer systems of the body.

The concept of strong and weak bases is more easily explained.. Remember that bases are proton acceptors. Thus, **strong bases** are those, like hydroxides, that dissociate easily in water and quickly tie up H^+. On the other hand, sodium bicarbonate (commonly known as baking soda) ionizes incompletely and reversibly. Because it accepts relatively few protons, its released bicarbonate ion is considered a **weak base**.

Now let's examine how one buffer system helps to maintain pH homeostasis of the blood. Although there are other chemical blood buffers, the **carbonic acid–bicarbonate system** is a major one. Carbonic acid (H_2CO_3) dissociates reversibly, releasing bicarbonate ions (HCO_3^-) and protons (H^+):

Response to rise in pH

$$H_2CO_3 \rightleftharpoons HCO_3^- + H^+$$

H^+ donor   Response to drop in pH H^+ acceptor   proton
(weak acid)   (weak base)

The chemical equilibrium between carbonic acid (a weak acid) and bicarbonate ion (a weak base) resists changes in blood pH by shifting to the right or left as H^+ ions are added to or removed from the blood. As blood pH rises (becomes more alkaline due to the addition of a strong base), the equilibrium shifts to the right, forcing more carbonic acid to dissociate. Similarly, as blood pH begins to drop (becomes more acidic due to the addition of a strong acid), the equilibrium shifts to the left as more bicarbonate ions begin to bind with protons. As you can see, strong bases are replaced by a weak base (bicarbonate ion) and protons released by strong acids are tied up in a weak one (carbonic acid). In either case, the blood pH changes much less than it would in the absence of the buffering system. We discuss acid-base balance and buffers in more detail in Chapter 26.

CHECK YOUR UNDERSTANDING

16. Water makes up 60–80% of living matter. What property makes it an excellent solvent?

17. Salts are electrolytes. What does that mean?

18. Which ion is responsible for increased acidity?

19. To minimize the sharp pH shift that occurs when a strong acid is added to a solution, is it better to add a weak base or a strong base? Why?

For answers, see Appendix G.

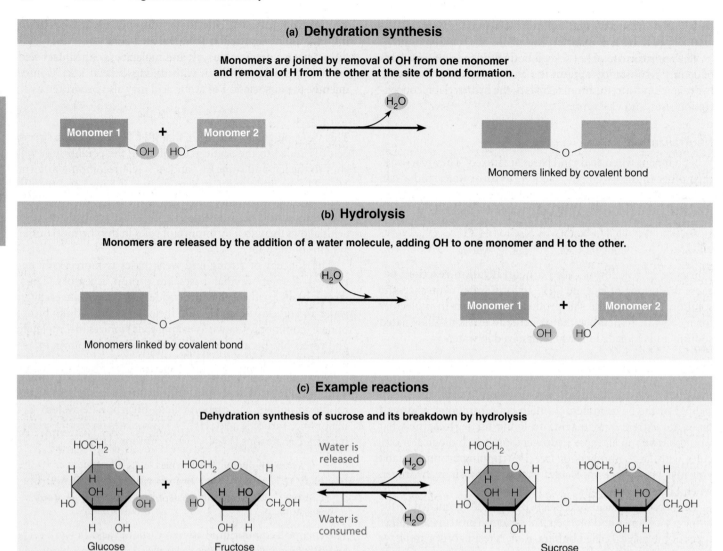

Figure 2.14 Biological molecules are formed from their monomers or units by dehydration synthesis and broken down to the monomers by hydrolysis reactions.

Organic Compounds

▶ Describe and compare the building blocks, general structures, and biological functions of carbohydrates and lipids.

▶ Explain the role of dehydration synthesis and hydrolysis in the formation and breakdown of organic molecules.

Molecules unique to living systems—carbohydrates, lipids (fats), proteins, and nucleic acids—all contain carbon and hence are organic compounds. Organic compounds are generally distinguished by the fact that they contain carbon, and inorganic compounds are defined as compounds that lack carbon. You should be aware of a few irrational exceptions to this generalization: Carbon dioxide and carbon monoxide, for example, contain carbon but are considered inorganic compounds.

For the most part, organic molecules are very large molecules, but their interactions with other molecules typically involve only small, reactive parts of their structure called *functional groups* (acid groups, amines, and others). The most important functional groups involved in biochemical reactions are illustrated in Appendix B.

What makes carbon so special that "living" chemistry depends on its presence? To begin with, no other *small* atom is so precisely **electroneutral**. The consequence of its electroneutrality is that carbon never loses or gains electrons. Instead, it always shares them. Furthermore, with four valence shell electrons, carbon forms four covalent bonds with other elements, as well as with other carbon atoms. As a result, carbon can help form long, chainlike molecules (common in fats), ring structures (typical of carbohydrates and steroids), and many other structures that are uniquely suited for specific roles in the body.

As you will see shortly, many biological molecules (carbohydrates and proteins for example) are polymers. **Polymers** are chainlike molecules made of many similar or repeating units (**monomers**), which are joined together by dehydration synthesis (**Figure 2.14**). During dehydration synthesis, a hydrogen atom is removed from one monomer and a hydroxyl group is removed from the monomer it is to be joined with. As a covalent bond unites the monomers, a water molecule is released. This removal of a water molecule at the bond site occurs each time a monomer is added to the growing polymer chain.

Carbohydrates

Carbohydrates, a group of molecules that includes sugars and starches, represent 1–2% of cell mass. Carbohydrates contain carbon, hydrogen, and oxygen, and generally the hydrogen and oxygen atoms occur in the same 2:1 ratio as in water. This ratio is reflected in the word *carbohydrate* ("hydrated carbon").

A carbohydrate can be classified according to size and solubility as a monosaccharide ("one sugar"), disaccharide ("two sugars"), or polysaccharide ("many sugars"). Monosaccharides are the monomers, or building blocks, of the other carbohydrates. In general, the larger the carbohydrate molecule, the less soluble it is in water.

Monosaccharides

Monosaccharides (mon″o-sak′ah-rīdz), or *simple sugars*, are single-chain or single-ring structures containing from three to seven carbon atoms (Figure 2.15a). Usually the carbon, hydrogen, and oxygen atoms occur in the ratio 1:2:1, so a general formula for a monosaccharide is $(CH_2O)n$, where *n* is the number of carbons in the sugar. Glucose, for example, has six carbon atoms, and its molecular formula is $C_6H_{12}O_6$. Ribose, with five carbons, is $C_5H_{10}O_5$.

Monosaccharides are named generically according to the number of carbon atoms they contain. Most important in the body are the pentose (five-carbon) and hexose (six-carbon) sugars. For example, the pentose *deoxyribose* (de-ok″sĭ-ri′bōs) is part of DNA, and *glucose*, a hexose, is blood sugar.

Two other hexoses, *galactose* and *fructose*, are **isomers** (i′so-mers) of glucose. That is, they have the same molecular formula $(C_6H_{12}O_6)$, but as you can see in Figure 2.15a, their atoms are arranged differently, giving them different chemical properties.

Disaccharides

A **disaccharide** (di-sak′ah-rīd), or *double sugar*, is formed when two monosaccharides are joined by *dehydration synthesis* (Figure 2.14a). In this synthesis reaction, a water molecule is lost as the bond is made, as illustrated by the synthesis of sucrose (soo′krōs):

$$2C_6H_{12}O_6 \rightarrow C_{12}H_{22}O_{11} + H_2O$$
glucose + fructose   sucrose   water

Notice that the molecular formula for sucrose contains two hydrogen atoms and one oxygen atom less than the total number of hydrogen and oxygen atoms in glucose and fructose, because a water molecule is released during bond formation.

Important disaccharides in the diet are *sucrose* (glucose + fructose), which is cane or table sugar; *lactose* (glucose + galactose), found in milk; and *maltose* (glucose + glucose), also called malt sugar (Figure 2.15b). Disaccharides are too large to pass through cell membranes, so they must be digested to their

simple sugar units to be absorbed from the digestive tract into the blood. This decomposition process is *hydrolysis*, essentially the reverse of dehydration synthesis (Figure 2.14a, b). A water molecule is added to each bond, breaking the bonds and releasing the simple sugar units.

Polysaccharides

Polysaccharides (pol″e-sak′ah-rīdz) are polymers of simple sugars linked together by dehydration synthesis. Because polysaccharides are large, fairly insoluble molecules, they are ideal storage products. Another consequence of their large size is that they lack the sweetness of the simple and double sugars.

Only two polysaccharides are of major importance to the body: starch and glycogen. Both are polymers of glucose. Only their degree of branching differs.

Starch is the storage carbohydrate formed by plants. The number of glucose units composing a starch molecule is high and variable. When we eat starchy foods such as grain products and potatoes, the starch must be digested for its glucose units to be absorbed. We are unable to digest *cellulose*, another polysaccharide found in all plant products. However, it is important in providing the *bulk* (one form of fiber) that helps move feces through the colon.

Glycogen (gli′ko-jen), the storage carbohydrate of animal tissues, is stored primarily in skeletal muscle and liver cells. Like starch, it is highly branched and is a very large molecule (Figure 2.15c). When blood sugar levels drop sharply, liver cells break down glycogen and release its glucose units to the blood. Since there are many branch endings from which glucose can be released simultaneously, body cells have almost instant access to glucose fuel.

Carbohydrate Functions

The major function of carbohydrates in the body is to provide a ready, easily used source of cellular fuel. Most cells can use only a few types of simple sugars, and glucose is at the top of the "cellular menu." As described in our earlier discussion of oxidation-reduction reactions (p. 37), glucose is broken down and oxidized within cells. During these chemical reactions, electrons are transferred. This relocation of electrons releases the bond energy stored in glucose, and this energy is used to synthesize ATP. When ATP supplies are sufficient, dietary carbohydrates are converted to glycogen or fat and stored. Those of us who have gained weight from eating too many carbohydrate-rich snacks have personal experience with this conversion process!

Only small amounts of carbohydrates are used for structural purposes. For example, some sugars are found in our genes. Others are attached to the external surfaces of cells where they act as "road signs" to guide cellular interactions.

Lipids

Lipids are insoluble in water but dissolve readily in other lipids and in organic solvents such as alcohol and ether. Like carbohydrates, all lipids contain carbon, hydrogen, and oxygen, but the proportion of oxygen in lipids is much lower. In addition,

2

(a) Monosaccharides

Monomers of carbohydrates

Example
Hexose sugars (the hexoses shown here are isomers)

Example
Pentose sugars

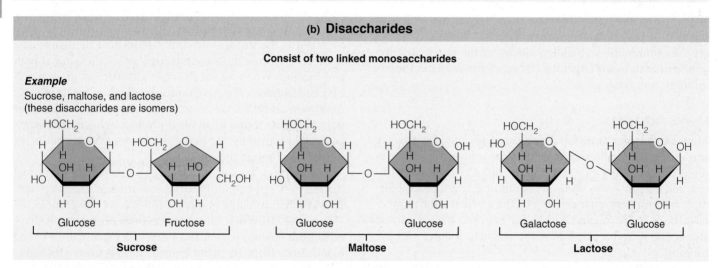

Glucose	Fructose	Galactose	Deoxyribose	Ribose

(b) Disaccharides

Consist of two linked monosaccharides

Example
Sucrose, maltose, and lactose
(these disaccharides are isomers)

Glucose	Fructose	Glucose	Glucose	Galactose	Glucose
Sucrose		**Maltose**		**Lactose**	

(c) Polysaccharides

Long branching chains (polymers) of linked monosaccharides

Example
This polysaccharide is a simplified representation of glycogen, a polysaccharide formed from glucose units.

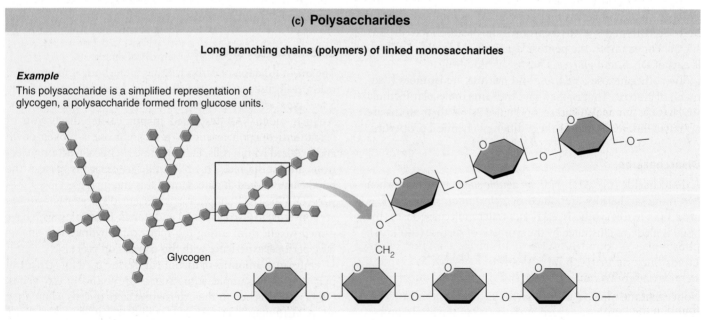

Glycogen

Figure 2.15 Carbohydrate molecules important to the body.*

*Notice that in Figure 2.15 the carbon (C) atoms present at the angles of the carbohydrate ring structures are not illustrated and in Figure 2.15c only the oxygen atoms and one CH_2 group are shown. The illustrations at right give an example of this shorthand style: The full structure of glucose is on the left and the shorthand structure on the right. This style is used for nearly all organic ringlike structures illustrated in this chapter.

TABLE 2.2	Representative Lipids Found in the Body
LIPID TYPE	**LOCATION/FUNCTION**
Triglycerides (Neutral Fats)	
	Fat deposits (in subcutaneous tissue and around organs) protect and insulate body organs, and are the major source of *stored* energy in the body.
Phospholipids (phosphatidylcholine; cephalin; others)	
	Chief components of cell membranes. Participate in the transport of lipids in plasma. Prevalent in nervous tissue.
Steroids	
Cholesterol	The structural basis for manufacture of all body steroids. A component of cell membranes.
Bile salts	These breakdown products of cholesterol are released by the liver into the digestive tract, where they aid fat digestion and absorption.
Vitamin D	A fat-soluble vitamin produced in the skin on exposure to UV radiation. Necessary for normal bone growth and function.
Sex hormones	Estrogen and progesterone (female hormones) and testosterone (a male hormone) are produced in the gonads. Necessary for normal reproductive function.
Adrenocortical hormones	Cortisol, a glucocorticoid, is a metabolic hormone necessary for maintaining normal blood glucose levels. Aldosterone helps to regulate salt and water balance of the body by targeting the kidneys.
Other Lipoid Substances	
Fat-soluble vitamins:	
A	Ingested in orange-pigmented vegetables and fruits. Converted in the retina to retinal, a part of the photoreceptor pigment involved in vision.
E	Ingested in plant products such as wheat germ and green leafy vegetables. Claims have been made (but not proved in humans) that it promotes wound healing, contributes to fertility, and may help to neutralize highly reactive particles called free radicals believed to be involved in triggering some types of cancer.
K	Made available to humans largely by the action of intestinal bacteria. Also prevalent in a wide variety of foods. Necessary for proper clotting of blood.
Eicosanoids (prostaglandins; leukotrienes; thromboxanes)	Group of molecules derived from fatty acids found in all cell membranes. The potent prostaglandins have diverse effects, including stimulation of uterine contractions, regulation of blood pressure, control of gastrointestinal tract motility, and secretory activity. Both prostaglandins and leukotrienes are involved in inflammation. Thromboxanes are powerful vasoconstrictors.
Lipoproteins	Lipoid and protein-based substances that transport fatty acids and cholesterol in the bloodstream. Major varieties are high-density lipoproteins (HDLs) and low-density lipoproteins (LDLs).

phosphorus is found in some of the more complex lipids. Lipids include *triglycerides, phospholipids* (fos″fo-lip′idz), *steroids* (stĕ′roidz), and a number of other lipoid substances. **Table 2.2** gives the locations and functions of some lipids found in the body.

Triglycerides (Neutral Fats)

Triglycerides (tri-glis′er-īdz), also called **neutral fats**, are commonly known as *fats* when solid or *oils* when liquid. A triglyceride is composed of two types of building blocks, **fatty acids** and **glycerol** (glis′er-ol), in a 3:1 ratio of fatty acids to glycerol **(Figure 2.16a)**. Fatty acids are linear chains of carbon and hydro-

gen atoms (hydrocarbon chains) with an organic acid group (—COOH) at one end. Glycerol is a modified simple sugar (a sugar alcohol).

Fat synthesis involves attaching three fatty acid chains to a single glycerol molecule by dehydration synthesis. The result is an E-shaped molecule. The glycerol backbone is the same in all triglycerides, but the fatty acid chains vary, resulting in different kinds of fats and oils.

These are large molecules, often consisting of hundreds of atoms, and ingested fats and oils must be broken down to their building blocks before they can be absorbed. Their hydrocarbon chains make the triglycerides nonpolar molecules. Because polar and nonpolar molecules do not interact, oil (or

2

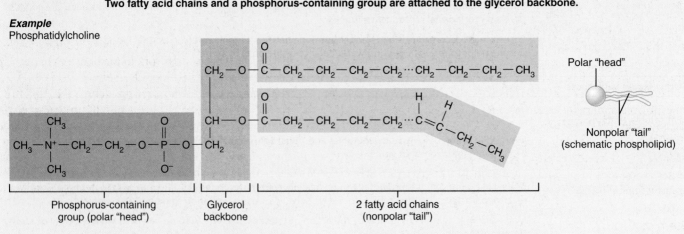

(a) Triglyceride formation

Three fatty acid chains are bound to glycerol by dehydration synthesis.

Glycerol   3 fatty acid chains   Triglyceride, or neutral fat   3 water molecules

(b) "Typical" structure of a phospholipid molecule

Two fatty acid chains and a phosphorus-containing group are attached to the glycerol backbone.

Example
Phosphatidylcholine

Polar "head"

Nonpolar "tail"
(schematic phospholipid)

Phosphorus-containing group (polar "head")   Glycerol backbone   2 fatty acid chains (nonpolar "tail")

(c) Simplified structure of a steroid

Four interlocking hydrocarbon rings form a steroid.

Example
Cholesterol (cholesterol is the
basis for all steroids formed in the body)

Figure 2.16 Lipids. The general structure of **(a)** triglycerides, or neutral fats, **(b)** phospholipids, and **(c)** cholesterol.

Triglycerides are found mainly beneath the skin, where they insulate the deeper body tissues from heat loss and protect them from mechanical trauma. For example, women are usually more successful English Channel swimmers than men. Their success is due partly to their thicker subcutaneous fatty layer, which helps insulate them from the bitterly cold water of the Channel.

The length of a triglyceride's fatty acid chains and their degree of *saturation* with H atoms determine how solid the molecule is at a given temperature. Fatty acid chains with only single covalent bonds between carbon atoms are referred to as **saturated**. Their fatty acid chains are straight and, at room temperature, the molecules of a saturated fat are packed closely together, forming a solid. Fatty acids that contain one or more double bonds between carbon atoms are said to be **unsaturated** (**monounsaturated** and **polyunsaturated**, re-

fats) and water do not mix. Consequently, triglycerides provide the body's most efficient and compact form of stored energy, and when they are oxidized, they yield large amounts of energy.

spectively). The double bonds cause the fatty acid chains to kink so that they cannot be packed closely enough to solidify. Hence, triglycerides with short fatty acid chains or unsaturated fatty acids are oils (liquid at room temperature) and are typical of plant lipids. Examples include olive and peanut oils (rich in monounsaturated fats) and corn, soybean, and safflower oils, which contain a high percentage of polyunsaturated fatty acids. Longer fatty acid chains and more saturated fatty acids are common in animal fats such as butterfat and the fat of meats, which are solid at room temperature. Of the two types of fatty acids, the unsaturated variety, especially olive oil, is said to be more "heart healthy."

Trans fats, common in many margarines and baked products, are oils that have been solidified by addition of H atoms at sites of double carbon bonds. They have recently been branded as increasing the risk of heart disease even more than the solid animal fats. Conversely, the **omega-3 fatty acids**, found naturally in cold-water fish, appear to decrease the risk of heart disease and some inflammatory diseases.

Phospholipids

Phospholipids are modified triglycerides. Specifically, they are diglycerides with a phosphorus-containing group and two, rather than three, fatty acid chains (Figure 2.16b). The phosphorus-containing group gives phospholipids their distinctive chemical properties. Although the hydrocarbon portion (the "tail") of the molecule is nonpolar and interacts only with nonpolar molecules, the phosphorus-containing part (the "head") is polar and attracts other polar or charged particles, such as water or ions. This unique characteristic of phospholipids allows them to be used as the chief material for building cellular membranes. Some biologically important phospholipids and their functions are listed in Table 2.2.

Steroids

Structurally, steroids differ quite a bit from fats and oils. **Steroids** are basically flat molecules made of four interlocking hydrocarbon rings. Like triglycerides, steroids are fat soluble and contain little oxygen. The single most important molecule in our steroid chemistry is *cholesterol* (ko-les'ter-ol) (Figure 2.16c). We ingest cholesterol in animal products such as eggs, meat, and cheese, and our liver produces some.

Cholesterol has earned bad press because of its role in arteriosclerosis, but it is essential for human life. Cholesterol is found in cell membranes and is the raw material for synthesis of vitamin D, steroid hormones, and bile salts. Although steroid hormones are present in the body in only small quantities, they are vital to homeostasis. Without sex hormones, reproduction would be impossible, and a total lack of the corticosteroids produced by the adrenal glands is fatal.

Eicosanoids

The **eicosanoids** (i-ko'sah-noyds) are diverse lipids chiefly derived from a 20-carbon fatty acid (arachidonic acid) found in all cell membranes. Most important of these are the *prostaglandins* and their relatives, which play roles in various body processes including blood clotting, regulation of blood pressure, inflammation, and labor contractions (Table 2.2). Their synthesis and inflammatory actions are blocked by NSAIDs (nonsteroidal anti-inflammatory drugs) and the newer COX inhibitors.

CHECK YOUR UNDERSTANDING

20. What are the monomers of carbohydrates called? Which monomer is blood sugar?

21. What is the animal form of stored carbohydrate called?

22. How do triglycerides differ from phospholipids in body function and location?

23. What is the result of hydrolysis reactions and how are these reactions accomplished in the body?

For answers, see Appendix G.

Proteins

▶ Describe the four levels of protein structure.

▶ Indicate the function of molecular chaperones.

▶ Describe enzyme action.

The full set of proteins made by the body, called the *proteome*, and the way those proteins network in the body or change with disease, is a matter of intense biotech research.

Protein composes 10–30% of cell mass and is the basic structural material of the body. However, not all proteins are construction materials. Many play vital roles in cell function. Proteins, which include enzymes (biological catalysts), hemoglobin of the blood, and contractile proteins of muscle, have the most varied functions of any molecules in the body. All proteins contain carbon, oxygen, hydrogen, and nitrogen, and many contain sulfur and phosphorus as well.

Amino Acids and Peptide Bonds

The building blocks of proteins are molecules called **amino acids**, of which there are 20 common types (see Appendix C). All amino acids have two important functional groups: a basic group called an *amine* (ah'mēn) *group* ($-NH_2$), and an organic *acid group* ($-COOH$). An amino acid may therefore act either as a base (proton acceptor) or an acid (proton donor). All amino acids are identical except for a single group of atoms called their *R group*. Hence, it is differences in the R group that make each amino acid chemically unique, as the examples in **Figure 2.17** show.

Proteins are long chains of amino acids joined together by dehydration synthesis, with the amine end of one amino acid linked to the acid end of the next. The resulting bond produces a characteristic arrangement of linked atoms called a **peptide bond** (**Figure 2.18**). Two united amino acids form a *dipeptide*, three a *tripeptide*, and ten or more a *polypeptide*. Although polypeptides containing more than 50 amino acids are called proteins, most proteins are **macromolecules**, large, complex molecules containing from 100 to over 10,000 amino acids.

Because each type of amino acid has distinct properties, the sequence in which they are bound together produces proteins that vary widely in both structure and function. We can think of

2

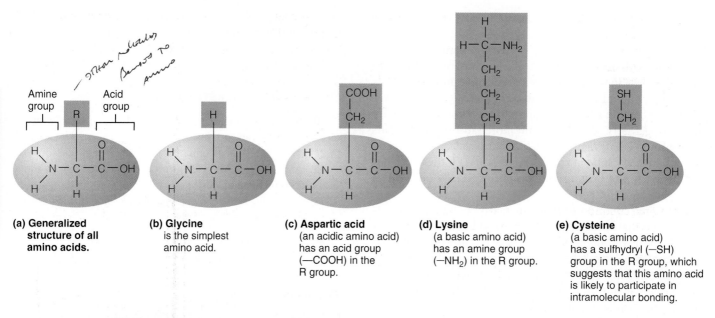

(a) Generalized structure of all amino acids.

(b) Glycine is the simplest amino acid.

(c) Aspartic acid (an acidic amino acid) has an acid group (—COOH) in the R group.

(d) Lysine (a basic amino acid) has an amine group (—NH₂) in the R group.

(e) Cysteine (a basic amino acid) has a sulfhydryl (—SH) group in the R group, which suggests that this amino acid is likely to participate in intramolecular bonding.

Figure 2.17 Amino acid structures. All amino acids have both an amine group (—NH₂) and an acid group (—COOH). They differ only in their R groups (green). Differences in their R groups allow them to function differently in the body.

the 20 amino acids as a 20-letter "alphabet" used in specific combinations to form "words" (proteins). Just as a change in one letter can produce a word with an entirely different meaning (flour → floor) or that is nonsensical (flour → fllur), changes in the kinds or positions of amino acids can yield proteins with different functions or proteins that are nonfunctional. Nevertheless, there are thousands of different proteins in the body, each with distinct functional properties, and all constructed from different combinations of the 20 common amino acids.

Structural Levels of Proteins

Proteins can be described in terms of four structural levels. The linear sequence of amino acids composing the polypeptide chain is called the *primary structure* of a protein. This structure, which resembles a strand of amino acid "beads," is the backbone of the protein molecule **(Figure 2.19a)**.

Proteins do not normally exist as simple, linear chains of amino acids. Instead, they twist or bend upon themselves to form a more complex *secondary structure*. The most common type of secondary structure is the **alpha (α)-helix**, which resembles a Slinky toy or the coils of a telephone cord (Figure 2.19b). The α-helix is formed by coiling of the primary chain and is stabilized by hydrogen bonds formed between NH and CO groups in amino acids in the primary chain which are approximately four amino acids apart. Hydrogen bonds in α-helices always link different parts of the *same* chain together.

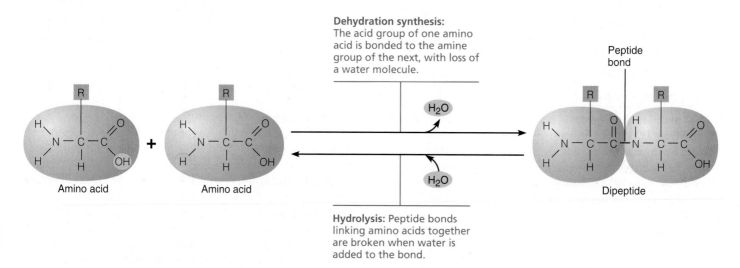

Dehydration synthesis: The acid group of one amino acid is bonded to the amine group of the next, with loss of a water molecule.

Peptide bond

Amino acid + Amino acid

H_2O

H_2O

Hydrolysis: Peptide bonds linking amino acids together are broken when water is added to the bond.

Dipeptide

Figure 2.18 Amino acids are linked together by peptide bonds. Peptide bonds are formed by dehydration synthesis and broken by hydrolysis reactions.

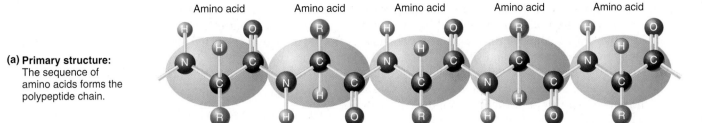

Amino acid   Amino acid   Amino acid   Amino acid   Amino acid

(a) Primary structure:
The sequence of
amino acids forms the
polypeptide chain.

2

(b) Secondary structure:
The primary chain forms
spirals (α-helices) and
sheets (β-sheets).

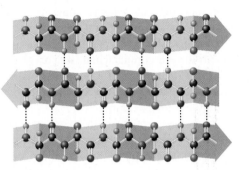

α-Helix: The primary chain is coiled
to form a spiral structure, which is
stabilized by hydrogen bonds.

β-Sheet: The primary chain "zig-zags" back
and forth forming a "pleated" sheet. Adjacent
strands are held together by hydrogen bonds.

(c) Tertiary structure:
Superimposed on secondary structure.
α-Helices and/or β-sheets are folded up
to form a compact globular molecule
held together by intramolecular bonds.

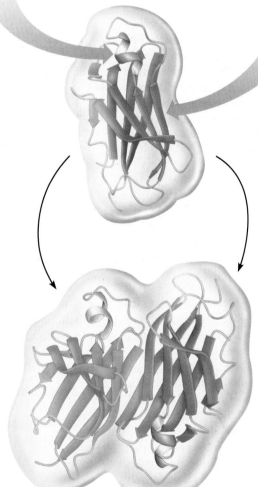

Tertiary structure of prealbumin
(transthyretin), a protein that
transports the thyroid hormone
thyroxine in serum and cerebrospinal fluid.

(d) Quaternary structure:
Two or more polypeptide chains, each
with its own tertiary structure, combine
to form a functional protein.

Quaternary structure of a
functional prealbumin molecule.
Two identical prealbumin subunits
join head to tail to form the dimer.

Figure 2.19 **Levels of protein structure.**

In another type of secondary structure, the **beta (β)-pleated sheet**, the primary polypeptide chains do not coil, but are linked side by side by hydrogen bonds to form a pleated, ribbonlike structure that resembles an accordion (Figure 2.19b). Notice that in this type of secondary structure, the hydrogen bonds may link together *different polypeptide chains* as well as *different parts* of the same chain that has folded back on itself. A single polypeptide chain may exhibit both types of secondary structure at various places along its length.

Many proteins have *tertiary structure* (ter′she-a″re), the next higher level of complexity, which is superimposed on secondary structure. Tertiary structure is achieved when α-helical or β-pleated regions of the polypeptide chain fold upon one another to produce a compact ball-like, or *globular*, molecule (Figure 2.19c). The unique structure is maintained by both covalent and hydrogen bonds between amino acids that are often far apart in the primary chain.

When two or more polypeptide chains aggregate in a regular manner to form a complex protein, the protein has *quaternary structure* (kwah′ter-na″re). Prealbumin, a protein that transports thyroid hormone in the blood, exhibits this structural level (Figure 2.19d).

How do these different levels of structure arise? Although a protein with tertiary or quaternary structure looks a bit like a clump of congealed pasta, the ultimate overall structure of any protein is very specific and is dictated by its primary structure. In other words, the types and relative positions of amino acids in the protein backbone determine where bonds can form to produce the complex coiled or folded structures that keep water-loving amino acids near the surface and water-fleeing amino acids buried in the protein's core. In addition, cells decorate many proteins by attaching sugars or fatty acids to them in ways that are difficult to imagine or predict.

Fibrous and Globular Proteins

The overall structure of a protein determines its biological function. In general, proteins are classified according to their overall appearance and shape as either fibrous or globular.

Fibrous proteins are extended and strandlike. Some exhibit only secondary structure, but most have tertiary or even quaternary structure as well. For example, *collagen* (kol′ah-jen) is a composite of the helical tropocollagen molecules packed together side by side to form a strong ropelike structure. Fibrous proteins are insoluble in water, and very stable—qualities ideal for providing mechanical support and tensile strength to the body's tissues. Besides collagen, which is the single most abundant protein in the body, the fibrous proteins include keratin, elastin, and certain contractile proteins of muscle **(Table 2.3)**. Because fibrous proteins are the chief building materials of the body, they are also known as **structural proteins**.

Globular proteins are compact, spherical proteins that have at least tertiary structure. Some also exhibit quaternary structure. The globular proteins are water-soluble, chemically active molecules, and they play crucial roles in virtually all biological processes. Consequently, this group is also called **functional proteins**. Some (antibodies) help to provide immunity, others (protein-based hormones) regulate growth and development, and still others (enzymes) are catalysts that oversee just about every chemical reaction in the body. The roles of these and selected other proteins found in the body are summarized in Table 2.3.

Protein Denaturation

Fibrous proteins are stable, but globular proteins are quite the opposite. The activity of a protein depends on its specific three-dimensional structure, and intramolecular bonds, particularly hydrogen bonds, are important in maintaining that structure. However, hydrogen bonds are fragile and easily broken by many chemical and physical factors, such as excessive acidity or temperature. Although individual proteins vary in their sensitivity to environmental conditions, hydrogen bonds begin to break when the pH drops or the temperature rises above normal (physiological) levels, causing proteins to unfold and lose their specific three-dimensional shape. In this condition, a protein is said to be **denatured**.

Fortunately, the disruption is reversible in most cases, and the "scrambled" protein regains its native structure when desirable conditions are restored. However, if the temperature or pH change is so extreme that protein structure is damaged beyond repair, the protein is *irreversibly denatured*. The coagulation of egg white (primarily albumin protein) that occurs when you boil or fry an egg is an example of irreversible protein denaturation. There is no way to restore the white, rubbery protein to its original translucent form.

When globular proteins are denatured, they can no longer perform their physiological roles because their function depends on the presence of specific arrangements of atoms, called **active sites**, on their surfaces. The active sites are regions that fit and interact chemically with other molecules of complementary shape and charge. Because atoms contributing to an active site may actually be far apart in the primary chain, disruption of intramolecular bonds separates them and destroys the active site. For example, hemoglobin becomes totally unable to bind and transport oxygen when blood pH is too acidic, because the structure needed for its function has been destroyed.

We will describe most types of body proteins in conjunction with the organ systems or functional processes to which they are closely related. However, two groups of proteins—*molecular chaperones* and *enzymes*—are intimately involved in the normal functioning of all cells, so we will consider these incredibly complex molecules here.

CHECK YOUR UNDERSTANDING

24. What does the name "amino acid" tell you about the structure of this molecule?

25. What is the primary structure of proteins?

26. What are the two types of secondary structure in proteins?

For answers, see Appendix G.

Molecular Chaperones

In addition to enzymes, all cells contain a class of unrelated globular proteins called **molecular chaperones** which, among

TABLE 2.3	Representative Types of Proteins in the Body	

CLASSIFICATION ACCORDING TO

OVERALL STRUCTURE	GENERAL FUNCTION	EXAMPLES FROM THE BODY
Fibrous		
	Structural framework/ mechanical support	*Collagen*, found in all connective tissues, is the single most abundant protein in the body. It is responsible for the tensile strength of bones, tendons, and ligaments.
		Keratin is the structural protein of hair and nails and a water-resistant material of skin.
		Elastin is found, along with collagen, where durability and flexibility are needed, such as in the ligaments that bind bones together.
		Spectrin internally reinforces and stabilizes the surface membrane of some cells, particularly red blood cells. *Dystrophin* reinforces and stabilizes the surface membrane of muscle cells. *Titin* helps organize the intracellular structure of muscle cells and accounts for the elasticity of skeletal muscles.
	Movement	*Actin* and *myosin*, contractile proteins, are found in substantial amounts in muscle cells, where they cause muscle cell shortening (contraction); they also function in cell division in all cell types. Actin is important in intracellular transport, particularly in nerve cells.
Globular		
	Catalysis	Protein enzymes are essential to virtually every biochemical reaction in the body; they increase the rates of chemical reactions by at least a millionfold. Examples include salivary amylase (in saliva), which catalyzes the breakdown of starch, and oxidase enzymes, which act to oxidize food fuels.
	Transport	*Hemoglobin* transports oxygen in blood, and *lipoproteins* transport lipids and cholesterol. Other transport proteins in the blood carry iron, hormones, or other substances. Some globular proteins in plasma membranes are involved in membrane transport (as carriers or channels).
	Regulation of pH	Many plasma proteins, such as *albumin*, function reversibly as acids or bases, thus acting as buffers to prevent wide swings in blood pH.
	Regulation of metabolism	*Peptide* and *protein hormones* help to regulate metabolic activity, growth, and development. For example, *growth hormone* is an anabolic hormone necessary for optimal growth; *insulin* helps regulate blood sugar levels.
	Body defense	*Antibodies* (immunoglobulins) are specialized proteins released by immune cells that recognize and inactivate foreign substances (bacteria, toxins, some viruses).
		Complement proteins, which circulate in blood, enhance both immune and inflammatory responses.
	Protein management	*Molecular chaperones* aid folding of new proteins in both healthy and damaged cells and transport of metal ions into and within the cell. They also promote breakdown of damaged proteins.

other things, help proteins to achieve their functional three-dimensional structure. Although its amino acid sequence determines the precise way a protein folds, the folding process also requires the help of molecular chaperones to ensure that the folding is quick and accurate. Apparently, molecular chaperones have numerous protein-related roles to play. For example, specific molecular chaperones

- Prevent accidental, premature, or incorrect folding of polypeptide chains or their association with other polypeptides
- Aid the desired folding and association process
- Help to translocate proteins and certain metal ions (copper, iron, zinc) across cell membranes
- Promote the breakdown of damaged or denatured proteins
- Interact with other cells to trigger the immune response to diseased cells in the body

The first such proteins discovered were called *heat shock proteins (hsp)* because they seemed to protect cells from the destructive effects of heat. It was later found that these proteins are produced in response to a variety of traumatizing stimuli—for example, in the oxygen-deprived cells of a heart attack patient—and the name *stress proteins* replaced hsp for that particular group of molecular chaperones. It is now clear that these proteins are vitally important to cell function in all types of stressful circumstances.

Enzymes and Enzyme Activity

Enzymes are globular proteins that act as biological catalysts. *Catalysts* are substances that regulate and accelerate the rate of biochemical reactions but are not used up or changed in those reactions. More specifically, enzymes can be thought of as chemical

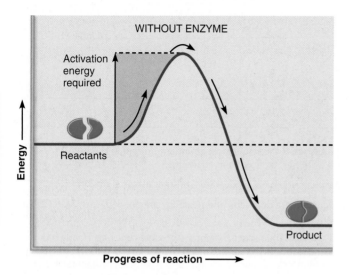
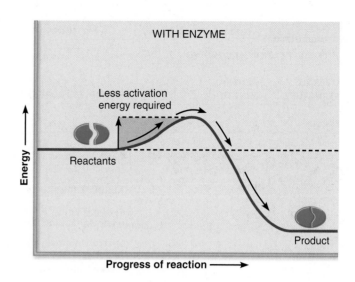

Figure 2.20 Enzymes lower the activation energy required for a reaction to proceed rapidly.

traffic cops that keep our metabolic pathways flowing. Enzymes cannot force chemical reactions to occur between molecules that would not otherwise react; they can only increase the speed of reaction. Without enzymes, biochemical reactions proceed so slowly that for practical purposes they do not occur at all.

Characteristics of Enzymes   Some enzymes are purely protein. In other cases, the functional enzyme consists of two parts, collectively called a **holoenzyme**: an **apoenzyme** (the protein portion) and a **cofactor**. Depending on the enzyme, the cofactor may be an ion of a metal element such as copper or iron, or an organic molecule needed to assist the reaction in some particular way. Most organic cofactors are derived from vitamins (especially the B complex vitamins). This type of cofactor is more precisely called a **coenzyme**.

Each enzyme is chemically specific. Some enzymes control only a single chemical reaction. Others exhibit a broader specificity in that they can bind with similar (but not identical) molecules and thus regulate a small group of related reactions. The substance on which an enzyme acts is called a **substrate**.

The presence of specific enzymes determines not only which reactions will be speeded up, but also which reactions will occur—no enzyme, no reaction. This also means that unwanted or unnecessary chemical reactions do not occur.

Most enzymes are named for the type of reaction they catalyze. *Hydrolases* (hi′druh-lās-es) add water during hydrolysis reactions, *oxidases* (ok′sĭ-dās-es) add oxygen, and so on. You can recognize most enzyme names by the suffix *-ase*.

In many cases, enzymes are part of cellular membranes in a bucket-brigade type of arrangement. The product of one enzyme-catalyzed reaction becomes the substrate of the neighboring enzyme, and so on. Some enzymes are produced in an inactive form and must be activated in some way before they can function, often by a change in the pH of their surroundings. For example, digestive enzymes produced in the pancreas are activated in the small intestine, where they actually do their

work. If they were produced in active form, the pancreas would digest itself.

Sometimes, enzymes are inactivated immediately after they have performed their catalytic function. This is true of enzymes that promote blood clot formation when the wall of a blood vessel is damaged. Once clotting is triggered, those enzymes are inactivated. Otherwise, you would have blood vessels full of solid blood instead of one protective clot. (Eek!)

Enzyme Action   How do enzymes perform their catalytic role? Every chemical reaction requires that a certain amount of energy, called **activation energy**, be absorbed to prime the reaction. The activation energy is the amount of energy needed to break the bonds of the reactants so that they can rearrange themselves and become the product. It is present when kinetic energy pushes the reactants to an energy level where their random collisions are forceful enough to ensure interaction. Activation energy is needed regardless of whether the overall reaction is ultimately energy absorbing or energy releasing.

One way to increase kinetic energy is to increase the temperature, but higher temperatures denature proteins. (This is why a high fever can be a serious event.) Enzymes allow reactions to occur at normal body temperature by decreasing the amount of activation energy required **(Figure 2.20)**.

Exactly how do enzymes accomplish this remarkable feat? The answer is not fully understood. However, we know that, due to structural and electrostatic factors, they decrease the randomness of reactions by binding to the reacting molecules temporarily and presenting them to each other in the proper position for chemical interaction to occur.

Three basic steps appear to be involved in enzyme action **(Figure 2.21)**.

① **The enzyme's active site binds to the substrate(s) on which it acts, temporarily forming an enzyme-substrate complex.** Substrate binding causes the active site to change shape so that the substrate and the active site fit together

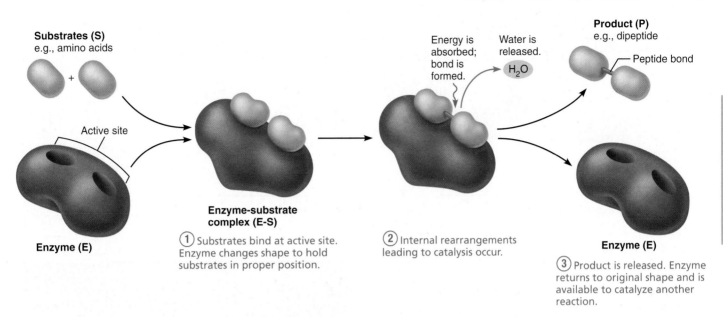

Figure 2.21 Mechanism of enzyme action. In this example, the enzyme catalyzes the formation of a dipeptide from specific amino acids. *Summary:* E + S → E-S → P + E

precisely. Although enzymes are specific for particular substrates, other (nonsubstrate) molecules may act as *enzyme inhibitors* if their structure is similar enough to occupy or block the enzyme's active site.

② **The enzyme-substrate complex undergoes internal rearrangements that form the product(s).** This step shows the catalytic role of an enzyme.

③ **The enzyme releases the product(s) of the reaction.** The enzyme is not changed. If the enzyme became part of the product, it would be a reactant and not a catalyst.

Because enzymes are unchanged by their catalytic role and can act again and again, cells need only small amounts of each enzyme. Catalysis occurs with incredible speed. Most enzymes can catalyze millions of reactions per minute.

CHECK YOUR UNDERSTANDING

27. What is the main event that molecular chaperones prevent?

28. How do enzymes reduce the amount of activation energy needed to make a chemical reaction go?

For answers, see Appendix G.

Nucleic Acids (DNA and RNA)

▶ Compare and contrast DNA and RNA.

The **nucleic acids** (nu-kle′ic), composed of carbon, oxygen, hydrogen, nitrogen, and phosphorus, are the largest molecules in the body. The nucleic acids include two major classes of molecules, **deoxyribonucleic acid (DNA)** (de-ok″sĭ-ri″bo-nu-kle′ik) and **ribonucleic acid (RNA)**.

The structural units of nucleic acids, called **nucleotides**, are quite complex. Each nucleotide consists of three components: a nitrogen-containing base, a pentose sugar, and a phosphate group **(Figure 2.22a)**. Five major varieties of nitrogen-containing bases can contribute to nucleotide structure: **adenine**, abbreviated **A** (ad′ĕ-nēn); **guanine**, **G** (gwan′ēn); **cytosine**, **C** (si′to-sēn); **thymine**, **T** (thi′mēn); and **uracil**, **U** (u′rah-sil). Adenine and guanine are large, two-ring bases (called purines), whereas cytosine, thymine, and uracil are smaller, single-ring bases (called pyrimidines).

The stepwise synthesis of a nucleotide involves the attachment of a base to the pentose sugar to form first a *nucleoside*, named for the nitrogenous base it contains. The nucleotide is formed when a phosphate group is bonded to the sugar of the nucleoside.

Although DNA and RNA are both composed of nucleotides, they differ in many respects, as summarized in **Table 2.4**. Typically, DNA is found in the nucleus (control center) of the cell, where it constitutes the *genetic material*, also called the *genes*, or more recently the *genome*. DNA has two fundamental roles: It replicates (reproduces) itself before a cell divides, ensuring that the genetic information in the descendant cells is identical, and it provides the basic instructions for building every protein in the body. Although we have said that enzymes govern all chemical reactions, remember that enzymes, too, are proteins formed at the direction of DNA.

By providing the information for protein synthesis, DNA determines what type of organism you will be—frog, human, oak tree—directs your growth and development, and accounts for your uniqueness. A technique called DNA fingerprinting can help solve forensic mysteries (for example, verify one's presence at a crime scene), identify badly burned or mangled bodies at a disaster scene, and establish or disprove paternity. DNA fingerprinting analyzes tiny samples of DNA taken from blood, semen, or other body tissues and shows the results as a "genetic barcode" that distinguishes each of us from all others.

2

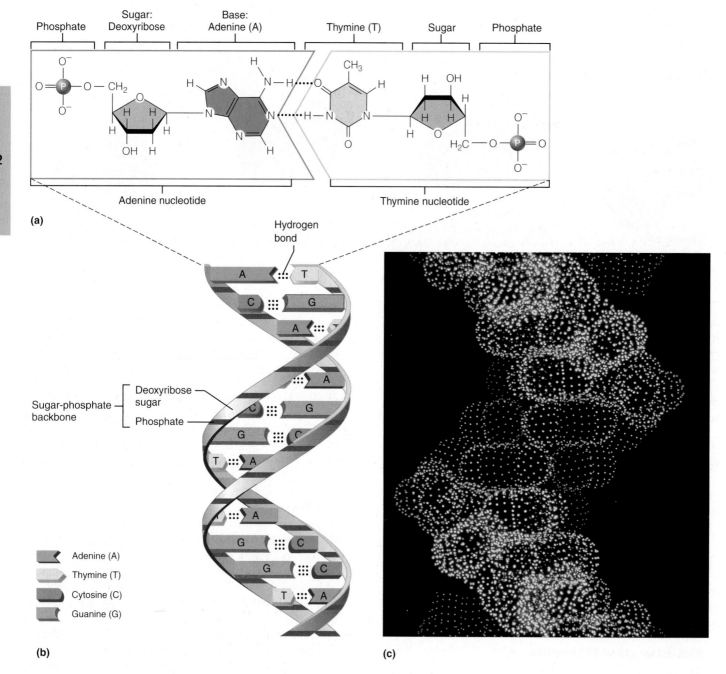

(a)

(b)   **(c)**

Figure 2.22 Structure of DNA. (a) The unit of DNA is the nucleotide, which is composed of a deoxyribose sugar molecule linked to a phosphate group, with a base attached to the sugar. Two nucleotides, linked by hydro-gen bonds between their complementary bases, are illustrated. **(b)** DNA is a coiled dou-ble polymer of nucleotides (a double helix). The backbones of the ladderlike molecule are formed by alternating sugar and phosphate units. The rungs are formed by the binding together of complementary bases (A-T and G-C) by hydrogen bonds (shown by dotted lines). **(c)** Computer-generated image of a DNA molecule.

DNA is a long, double-stranded polymer—a double chain of nucleotides (Figure 2.22b and c). The bases in DNA are A, G, C, and T, and its pentose sugar is *deoxyribose* (as reflected in its name). Its two nucleotide chains are held together by hydrogen bonds between the bases, so that a ladderlike molecule is formed. Alternating sugar and phosphate components of each chain form the *backbones* or "uprights" of the "ladder," and the joined bases form the "rungs." The whole molecule is coiled into a spiral staircase–like structure called a **double helix**.

Bonding of the bases is very specific: A always bonds to T, and G always bonds to C. A and T are therefore called **complementary bases**, as are C and G. According to these base-pairing rules, ATGA on one DNA nucleotide strand would nec-essarily be bonded to TACT (a complementary base sequence) on the other strand.

TABLE 2.4	Comparison of DNA and RNA	
CHARACTERISTIC	**DNA**	**RNA**
Major cellular site	Nucleus	Cytoplasm (cell area outside the nucleus)
Major functions	Is the genetic material; directs protein synthesis; replicates itself before cell division	Carries out the genetic instructions for protein synthesis
Sugar	Deoxyribose	Ribose
Bases	Adenine, guanine, cytosine, thymine	Adenine, guanine, cytosine, uracil
Structure	Double strand coiled into a double helix	Single strand, straight or folded

RNA is located chiefly outside the nucleus and can be considered a "molecular slave" of DNA. That is, RNA carries out the orders for protein synthesis issued by DNA. [Viruses in which RNA (rather than DNA) is the genetic material are an exception to this generalization.]

RNA molecules are single strands of nucleotides. RNA bases include A, G, C, and U (U replaces the T found in DNA), and its sugar is *ribose* instead of deoxyribose. The three major varieties of RNA (messenger RNA, ribosomal RNA, and transfer RNA) are distinguished by their relative size and shape, and each has a specific role to play in carrying out DNA's instructions for protein synthesis. In addition to these three RNAs, small RNA molecules called *microRNAs* (*miRNAs*) appear to control genetic expression by shutting down genes or altering their expression. We discuss DNA replication and the relative roles of DNA and RNA in protein synthesis in Chapter 3.

CHECK YOUR UNDERSTANDING

29. How do DNA and RNA differ in the bases and sugars they contain?

30. What are two important roles of DNA?

For answers, see Appendix G.

Adenosine Triphosphate (ATP)

▶ Explain the role of ATP in cell metabolism.

Glucose is the most important cellular fuel, but none of the chemical energy contained in its bonds is used directly to power cellular work. Instead, energy released during glucose catabolism is coupled to the synthesis of **adenosine triphosphate** (**ATP**). In other words, some of this energy is captured and stored as small packets of energy in the bonds of ATP. ATP is the primary energy-transferring molecule in cells and it provides a form of energy that is immediately usable by all body cells.

Structurally, ATP is an adenine-containing RNA nucleotide to which two additional phosphate groups have been added (Figure 2.23). Chemically, the triphosphate tail of ATP can be compared to a tightly coiled spring ready to uncoil with tremendous energy when the catch is released. Actually, ATP is a very unstable energy-storing molecule because its three negatively charged phosphate groups are closely packed and repel each

other. When its terminal high-energy phosphate bonds are broken (hydrolyzed), the chemical "spring" relaxes and the molecule as a whole becomes more stable.

Cells tap ATP's bond energy during coupled reactions by using enzymes to transfer the terminal phosphate groups from ATP to other compounds. These newly *phosphorylated* molecules are said to be "primed" and temporarily become more energetic and capable of performing some type of cellular work. In the process of doing their work, they lose the phosphate group. The amount of energy released and transferred during ATP hydrolysis corresponds closely to that needed to drive most biochemical reactions. As a result, cells are protected from excessive energy release that might be damaging, and energy squandering is kept to a minimum.

Cleaving the terminal phosphate bond of ATP yields a molecule with two phosphate groups—*adenosine diphosphate*

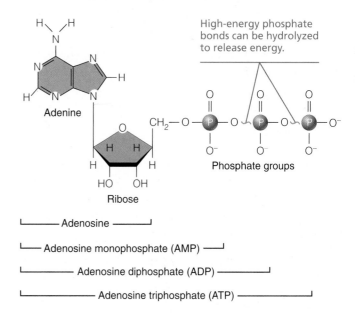

Figure 2.23 Structure of ATP (adenosine triphosphate). ATP is an adenine nucleotide to which two additional phosphate groups have been attached during breakdown of food fuels. When the terminal phosphate group is cleaved off, energy is released to do useful work and ADP (adenosine diphosphate) is formed. When the terminal phosphate group is cleaved off ADP, a similar amount of energy is released and AMP (adenosine monophosphate) is formed.

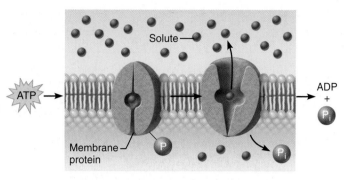

(a) Transport work: ATP phosphorylates transport proteins, activating them to transport solutes (ions, for example) across cell membranes.

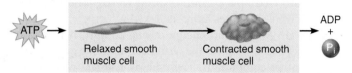

(b) Mechanical work: ATP phosphorylates contractile proteins in muscle cells so the cells can shorten.

(c) Chemical work: ATP phosphorylates key reactants, providing energy to drive energy-absorbing chemical reactions.

Figure 2.24 **Three examples of cellular work driven by energy from ATP.**

(*ADP*)—and an inorganic phosphate group, indicated by Pi, accompanied by a transfer of energy:

$$ATP \rightleftarrows ADP + P_i + energy$$
(with H_2O shown above and below the reaction arrows)

As ATP is hydrolyzed to provide energy for cellular needs, ADP accumulates. Cleavage of the terminal phosphate bond of ADP liberates a similar amount of energy and produces adenosine monophosphate (AMP).

The cell's ATP supplies are replenished as glucose and other fuel molecules are oxidized and their bond energy is released. The same amount of energy that is liberated when ATP's terminal phosphates are cleaved off must be captured and used to reverse the reaction to reattach phosphates and re-form the energy-transferring phosphate bonds. Without ATP, molecules cannot be made or degraded, cells cannot transport substances across their membrane boundaries, muscles cannot shorten to tug on other structures, and life processes cease **(Figure 2.24)**.

CHECK YOUR UNDERSTANDING

31. Glucose is an energy-rich molecule. So why do body cells need ATP?

32. What change occurs in ATP when it releases energy?

For answers, see Appendix G.

RELATED CLINICAL TERMS

Acidosis (as″ĭ-do′sis; *acid* = sour, sharp) A condition of acidity or low pH (below 7.35) of the blood; high hydrogen ion concentration.

Alkalosis (al″kah-lo′sis) A condition of basicity or high pH (above 7.45) of the blood; low hydrogen ion concentration.

Heavy metals Metals with toxic effects on the body, including arsenic, mercury, and lead. Iron, also included in this group, is toxic in high concentrations.

Ionizing radiation Radiation that causes atoms to ionize; for example, radioisotope emissions and X rays.

Ketosis (ke-to′sis) A condition resulting from excessive ketones (breakdown products of fats) in the blood; common during starvation and acute attacks of diabetes mellitus.

Radiation sickness Disease resulting from exposure of the body to radioactivity; digestive system organs are most affected.

CHAPTER SUMMARY

Media study tools that could provide you additional help in reviewing specific key topics of Chapter 2 are referenced below.

iP = *Interactive Physiology*

PART 1: BASIC CHEMISTRY

Definition of Concepts: Matter and Energy (pp. 24–25)
Matter (p. 24)
1. Matter is anything that takes up space and has mass.

Energy (pp. 24–25)
2. Energy is the capacity to do work or put matter into motion.
3. Energy exists as potential energy (stored energy or energy of position) and kinetic energy (active or working energy).
4. Forms of energy involved in body functioning are chemical, electrical, radiant, and mechanical. Of these, chemical (bond) energy is most important.
5. Energy may be converted from one form to another, but some energy is always unusable (lost as heat) in such transformations.

Composition of Matter: Atoms and Elements (pp. 25–28)
1. Elements are unique substances that cannot be decomposed into simpler substances by ordinary chemical methods. Four elements (carbon, hydrogen, oxygen, and nitrogen) make up 96% of body weight.

Atomic Structure (pp. 25–27)
2. The building blocks of elements are atoms.
3. Atoms are composed of positively charged protons, negatively charged electrons, and uncharged neutrons. Protons and neutrons are located in the atomic nucleus, constituting essentially the atom's total mass. Electrons are outside the nucleus in the electron shells. In any atom, the number of electrons equals the number of protons.

Identifying Elements (pp. 27–28)
4. Atoms may be identified by their atomic number (p^+) and mass number ($p^+ + n^0$). The notation $^4_2$He means that helium (He) has an atomic number of 2 and a mass number of 4.
5. Isotopes of an element differ in the number of neutrons they contain. The atomic weight of any element is approximately equal to the mass number of its most abundant isotope.

Radioisotopes (p. 28)
6. Many heavy isotopes are unstable (radioactive). These so-called radioisotopes decompose to more stable forms by emitting alpha or beta particles or gamma rays. Radioisotopes are useful in medical diagnosis and treatment and in biochemical research.

How Matter Is Combined: Molecules and Mixtures (pp. 28–30)
Molecules and Compounds (pp. 28–29)
1. A molecule is the smallest unit resulting from the chemical bonding of two or more atoms. If the atoms are different, they form a molecule of a compound.

Mixtures (pp. 29–30)
2. Mixtures are physical combinations of solutes in a solvent. Mixture components retain their individual properties.
3. The types of mixtures, in order of increasing solute size, are solutions, colloids, and suspensions.
4. Solution concentrations are typically designated in terms of percent or molarity.

Distinguishing Mixtures from Compounds (p. 30)
5. Compounds are homogeneous; their elements are chemically bonded. Mixtures may be homogeneous or heterogeneous; their components are physically combined and separable.

Chemical Bonds (pp. 31–35)
The Role of Electrons in Chemical Bonding (pp. 31–32)
1. Electrons of an atom occupy areas of space called electron shells or energy levels. Electrons in the shell farthest from the nucleus (valence shell) are most energetic.
2. Chemical bonds are energy relationships between valence shell electrons of the reacting atoms. Atoms with a full valence shell or eight valence shell electrons are chemically unreactive (inert). Those with an incomplete valence shell interact with other atoms to achieve stability.

Types of Chemical Bonds (pp. 32–35)
3. Ionic bonds are formed when valence shell electrons are completely transferred from one atom to another.
4. Covalent bonds are formed when atoms share electron pairs. If the electron pairs are shared equally, the molecule is nonpolar. If they are shared unequally, it is polar (a dipole).
5. Hydrogen bonds are weak bonds formed between one hydrogen atom, already covalently linked to an electronegative atom, and another electronegative atom (such as nitrogen or hydrogen and oxygen). They bind together different molecules (e.g., water molecules) or different parts of the same molecule (as in protein molecules).

Chemical Reactions (pp. 35–38)
Chemical Equations (pp. 35–36)
1. Chemical reactions involve the formation, breaking, or rearrangement of chemical bonds.

Patterns of Chemical Reactions (pp. 36–37)
2. Chemical reactions are either anabolic (constructive) or catabolic (destructive). They include synthesis, decomposition, and exchange reactions. Oxidation-reduction reactions may be considered a special type of exchange (or decomposition) reaction.

Energy Flow in Chemical Reactions (p. 37)
3. Bonds are energy relationships and there is a net loss or gain of energy in every chemical reaction.
4. In exergonic reactions, energy is liberated. In endergonic reactions, energy is absorbed.

Reversibility of Chemical Reactions (p. 37)
5. If reaction conditions remain unchanged, all chemical reactions eventually reach a state of chemical equilibrium in which the reaction proceeds in both directions at the same rate.

2

6. All chemical reactions are theoretically reversible, but many biological reactions go in only one direction because of energy requirements or the removal of reaction products.

Factors Influencing the Rate of Chemical Reactions   (pp. 37–38)

7. Chemical reactions occur only when particles collide and valence shell electrons interact.
8. The smaller the reacting particles, the greater their kinetic energy and the faster the reaction rate. Higher temperature or reactant concentration, as well as the presence of catalysts, increases chemical reaction rates.

PART 2: BIOCHEMISTRY

Inorganic Compounds   (pp. 38–41)

1. Most inorganic compounds do not contain carbon. Those found in the body include water, salts, and inorganic acids and bases.

Water   (pp. 38–39)

2. Water is the single most abundant compound in the body. It absorbs and releases heat slowly, acts as a universal solvent, participates in chemical reactions, and cushions body organs.

Salts   (p. 39)

3. Salts are ionic compounds that dissolve in water and act as electrolytes. Calcium and phosphorus salts contribute to the hardness of bones and teeth. Ions of salts are involved in many physiological processes.

Acids and Bases   (pp. 39–41)

4. Acids are proton donors; in water, they ionize and dissociate, releasing hydrogen ions (which account for their properties) and anions.

iP **Fluid, Electrolyte and Acid/Base Balance; Topic: Acid Base Homeostasis, pp. 1–12, 16, 17.**

5. Bases are proton acceptors. The most common inorganic bases are the hydroxides; bicarbonate ion and ammonia are important bases in the body.
6. pH is a measure of hydrogen ion concentration of a solution (in moles per liter). A pH of 7 is neutral; a higher pH is alkaline, and a lower pH is acidic. Normal blood pH is 7.35–7.45. Buffers help to prevent excessive changes in the pH of body fluids.

iP **Fluid, Electrolyte and Acid/Base Balance; Topic: Introduction to Body Fluids, pp. 1–8.**

Organic Compounds   (pp. 42–56)

1. Organic compounds contain carbon. Those found in the body include carbohydrates, lipids, proteins, and nucleic acids, all of which are synthesized by dehydration synthesis and digested by hydrolysis. All of these biological molecules contain C, H, and O. Proteins and nucleic acids also contain N.

Carbohydrates   (pp. 43–44)

2. Carbohydrate building blocks are monosaccharides, the most important of which are hexoses (glucose, fructose, galactose) and pentoses (ribose, deoxyribose).
3. Disaccharides (sucrose, lactose, maltose) and polysaccharides (starch, glycogen) are composed of linked monosaccharide units.

4. Carbohydrates, particularly glucose, are the major energy fuel for forming ATP. Excess carbohydrates are stored as glycogen or converted to fat for storage.

Lipids   (pp. 43–47)

5. Lipids dissolve in fats or organic solvents, but not in water.
6. Triglycerides are composed of fatty acid chains and glycerol. They are found chiefly in fatty tissue where they provide insulation and reserve body fuel. Unsaturated fatty acid chains produce oils. Saturated fatty acids produce solid fats typical of animal fats.
7. Phospholipids are modified phosphorus-containing triglycerides that have polar and nonpolar portions. They are found in all plasma membranes.
8. The steroid cholesterol is found in cell membranes and is the basis of steroid hormones, bile salts, and vitamin D.

Proteins   (pp. 47–53)

9. The unit of proteins is the amino acid, and 20 common amino acids are found in the body.
10. Many amino acids joined by peptide bonds form a polypeptide. A protein (one or more polypeptides) is distinguished by the number and sequence of amino acids in its chain(s) and by the complexity of its three-dimensional structure.
11. Fibrous proteins, such as keratin and collagen, have secondary (α-helix or β-pleated sheet) and perhaps tertiary and quaternary structure. Fibrous proteins are used as structural materials.
12. Globular proteins achieve tertiary and sometimes quaternary structure and are generally spherical, soluble molecules. Globular proteins (e.g., enzymes, some hormones, antibodies, hemoglobin) perform special functional roles for the cell (e.g., catalysis, molecule transport).
13. Proteins are denatured by extremes of temperature or pH. Denatured globular proteins are unable to perform their usual function.
14. Molecular chaperones assist in folding proteins into their functional 3-D shape. They are synthesized in greater amounts when cells are stressed by environmental factors.
15. Enzymes are biological catalysts. They increase the rate of chemical reactions by decreasing the amount of activation energy needed. They do this by combining with the reactants and holding them in the proper position to interact. Many enzymes require cofactors to function.

Nucleic Acids (DNA and RNA)   (pp. 53–55)

16. Nucleic acids include deoxyribonucleic acid (DNA) and ribonucleic acid (RNA). The structural unit of nucleic acids is the nucleotide, which consists of a nitrogenous base (adenine, guanine, cytosine, thymine, or uracil), a sugar (ribose or deoxyribose), and a phosphate group.
17. DNA is a double-stranded helix. It contains deoxyribose and the bases A, G, C, and T. DNA specifies protein structure and replicates itself exactly before cell division.
18. RNA is single stranded. It contains ribose and the bases A, G, C, and U. RNAs involved in carrying out DNA's instructions for protein synthesis include messenger, ribosomal, and transfer RNA.

Adenosine Triphosphate (ATP)   (pp. 55–56)

19. ATP is the universal energy compound of body cells. Some of the energy liberated by the breakdown of glucose and other food fuels is captured in the bonds of ATP molecules and transferred via coupled reactions to energy-consuming reactions.

REVIEW QUESTIONS

Multiple Choice/Matching

(Some questions have more than one correct answer. Select the best answer or answers from the choices given.)

1. Which of the following forms of energy is the stimulus for vision? (a) chemical, (b) electrical, (c) mechanical, (d) radiant.

2. All of the following are examples of the four major elements contributing to body mass except (a) hydrogen, (b) carbon, (c) nitrogen, (d) sodium, (e) oxygen.

3. The mass number of an atom is (a) equal to the number of protons it contains, (b) the sum of its protons and neutrons, (c) the sum of all of its subatomic particles, (d) the average of the mass numbers of all of its isotopes.

4. A deficiency in this element can be expected to reduce the hemoglobin content of blood: (a) Fe, (b) I, (c) F, (d) Ca, (e) K.

5. Which set of terms best describes a proton? (a) negative charge, massless, in the orbital; (b) positive charge, 1 amu, in the nucleus; (c) uncharged, 1 amu, in the nucleus.

6. The subatomic particles responsible for the chemical behavior of atoms are (a) electrons, (b) ions, (c) neutrons, (d) protons.

7. In the body, carbohydrates are stored in the form of (a) glycogen, (b) starch, (c) cholesterol, (d) polypeptides.

8. Which of the following does *not* describe a mixture? (a) properties of its components are retained, (b) chemical bonds are formed, (c) components can be separated physically, (d) includes both heterogeneous and homogeneous examples.

9. In a beaker of water, the water-water bonds can properly be called (a) ionic bonds, (b) polar covalent bonds, (c) nonpolar covalent bonds, (d) hydrogen bonds.

10. When a pair of electrons is shared between two atoms, the bond formed is called (a) a single covalent bond, (b) a double covalent bond, (c) a triple covalent bond, (d) an ionic bond.

11. Molecules formed when electrons are shared unequally are (a) salts, (b) polar molecules, (c) nonpolar molecules.

12. Which of the following covalently bonded molecules are polar?

(a)   (b)   (c)   (d)

13. Identify each reaction as one of the following: (a) a synthesis reaction (b) a decomposition reaction (c) an exchange reaction
    _____(1) $2Hg + O_2 \longrightarrow 2HgO$
    _____(2) $HCl + NaOH \longrightarrow NaCl + H_2O$

14. Factors that accelerate the rate of chemical reactions include all but (a) the presence of catalysts, (b) increasing the temperature, (c) increasing the particle size, (d) increasing the concentration of the reactants.

15. Which of the following molecules is an inorganic molecule? (a) sucrose, (b) cholesterol, (c) collagen, (d) sodium chloride.

16. Water's importance to living systems reflects (a) its polarity and solvent properties, (b) its high heat capacity, (c) its high heat of vaporization, (d) its chemical reactivity, (e) all of these.

17. Acids (a) release hydroxyl ions when dissolved in water, (b) are proton acceptors, (c) cause the pH of a solution to rise, (d) release protons when dissolved in water.

18. A chemist, during the course of an analysis, runs across a chemical composed of carbon, hydrogen, and oxygen in the proportion 1:2:1 and having a six-sided molecular shape. It is probably (a) a pentose, (b) an amino acid, (c) a fatty acid, (d) a monosaccharide, (e) a nucleic acid.

19. A triglyceride consists of (a) glycerol plus three fatty acids, (b) a sugar-phosphate backbone to which two amino groups are attached, (c) two to several hexoses, (d) amino acids that have been thoroughly saturated with hydrogen.

20. A chemical has an amine group and an organic acid group. It does not, however, have any peptide bonds. It is (a) a monosaccharide, (b) an amino acid, (c) a protein, (d) a fat.

21. The lipid(s) used as the basis of vitamin D, sex hormones, and bile salts is/are (a) triglycerides, (b) cholesterol, (c) phospholipids, (d) prostaglandin.

22. Enzymes are organic catalysts that (a) alter the direction in which a chemical reaction proceeds, (b) determine the nature of the products of a reaction, (c) increase the speed of a chemical reaction, (d) are essential raw materials for a chemical reaction that are converted into some of its products.

Short Answer Essay Questions

23. Define or describe energy, and explain the relationship between potential and kinetic energy.

24. Some energy is lost in every energy conversion. Explain the meaning of this statement. (Direct your response to answering the question: Is it really lost? If not, what then?)

25. Provide the atomic symbol for each of the following elements: (a) calcium, (b) carbon, (c) hydrogen, (d) iron, (e) nitrogen, (f) oxygen, (g) potassium, (h) sodium.

26. Consider the following information about three atoms:

$$^{12}_{6}C \qquad ^{13}_{6}C \qquad ^{14}_{6}C$$

(a) How are they similar to one another? (b) How do they differ from one another? (c) What are the members of such a group of atoms called? (d) Using the planetary model, draw the atomic configuration of $^{12}_{6}C$ showing the relative position and numbers of its subatomic particles.

27. How many moles of aspirin, $C_9H_8O_4$, are in a bottle containing 450 g by weight? (*Note:* The approximate atomic weights of its atoms are C = 12, H = 1, and O = 16.)

28. Given the following types of atoms, decide which type of bonding, ionic or covalent, is most likely to occur: (a) two oxygen atoms; (b) four hydrogen atoms and one carbon atom; (c) a potassium atom ($^{39}_{19}K$) and a fluorine atom ($^{19}_{9}F$).

29. What are hydrogen bonds and how are they important in the body?

30. The following equation, which represents the oxidative breakdown of glucose by body cells, is a reversible reaction.

Glucose + oxygen $\longrightarrow$ carbon dioxide + water + ATP

(a) How can you indicate that the reaction is reversible? (b) How can you indicate that the reaction is in chemical equilibrium? (c) Define chemical equilibrium.

31. Differentiate clearly between primary, secondary, and tertiary protein structure.

32. Dehydration and hydrolysis reactions are essentially opposite reactions. How are they related to the synthesis and degradation (breakdown) of biological molecules?

33. Describe the mechanism of enzyme action.

34. Explain the importance of molecular chaperones.

35. Explain why, if you pour water into a glass very carefully, you can "stack" the water slightly above the rim of the glass.

Critical Thinking and Clinical Application Questions

1. As Ben jumped on his bike and headed for the freshwater lake, his mother called after him, "Don't swim if we have an electrical storm—it looks threatening." This was a valid request. Why?

2. Some antibiotics act by binding to certain essential enzymes in the target bacteria. (**a**) How might these antibiotics influence the chemical reactions controlled by the enzymes? (**b**) What is the anticipated effect on the bacteria? On the person taking the antibiotic prescription?

3. Mrs. Roberts, in a diabetic coma, has just been admitted to Noble Hospital. Her blood pH indicates that she is in severe acidosis, and measures are quickly instituted to bring her blood pH back within normal limits. (**a**) Define pH and note the normal pH of blood. (**b**) Why is severe acidosis a problem?

4. Jimmy, a 12-year-old boy, was awakened suddenly by a loud crash. As he sat up in bed, straining to listen, his fright was revealed by his rapid breathing (hyperventilation), a breathing pattern effective in ridding the blood of CO_2. At this point, was his blood pH rising or falling?

5. After you eat a protein bar, which chemical reactions introduced in this chapter must occur for the amino acids in the protein bar to be converted into proteins in your body cells?

Access everything you need to practice, review, and self-assess for both your A&P lecture and lab courses at **myA&P** (www.myaandp.com). There, you'll find powerful online resources, including chapter quizzes and tests, games, A&P Flix animations with quizzes, *Interactive Physiology*® with quizzes, MP3 Tutor Sessions, Practice Anatomy Lab™, and more to help you get a better grade in your course.

3

Overview of the Cellular Basis of Life (pp. 62–63)

The Plasma Membrane: Structure (pp. 63–67)

The Fluid Mosaic Model (pp. 63–66)

Membrane Junctions (pp. 66–67)

The Plasma Membrane: Membrane Transport (pp. 68–77)

Passive Processes (pp. 68–72)

Active Processes (pp. 72–77)

The Plasma Membrane: Generation of a Resting Membrane Potential (pp. 79–80)

The Plasma Membrane: Cell-Environment Interactions (pp. 80–81)

Roles of Cell Adhesion Molecules (pp. 80–81)

Roles of Membrane Receptors (p. 81)

Role of Voltage-Sensitive Membrane Channel Proteins (p. 81)

The Cytoplasm (pp. 81–91)

Cytoplasmic Organelles (pp. 83–89)

Cellular Extensions (pp. 90–91)

The Nucleus (pp. 91–95)

The Nuclear Envelope (pp. 91–93)

Nucleoli (p. 93)

Chromatin (pp. 93–95)

Cell Growth and Reproduction (pp. 95–107)

The Cell Life Cycle (pp. 95–100)

Protein Synthesis (pp. 100–105)

Other Roles of DNA (pp. 105–106)

Cytosolic Protein Degradation (pp. 106–107)

Extracellular Materials (p. 107)

Developmental Aspects of Cells (pp. 108–109)

Cells:
The Living
Units

Just as bricks and timbers are the structural units of a house, **cells** are the structural units of all living things, from one-celled "generalists" like amoebas to complex multicellular organisms such as humans, dogs, and trees. The human body has 50 to 100 trillion of these tiny building blocks.

This chapter focuses on structures and functions shared by all cells. We address specialized cells and their unique functions in later chapters.

Overview of the Cellular Basis of Life

▶ Define cell.

▶ List the three major regions of a generalized cell and indicate the function of each.

The English scientist Robert Hooke first observed plant cells with a crude microscope in the late 1600s. However, it was not until the 1830s that two German scientists, Matthias Schleiden and Theodor Schwann, were bold enough to insist that all living things are composed of cells. The German pathologist Rudolf Virchow extended this idea by contending that cells arise only from other cells. Virchow's proclamation was revolutionary because it openly challenged the widely accepted *theory of spontaneous generation*, which held that organisms arise spontaneously from garbage or other nonliving matter.

Since the late 1800s, cell research has been exceptionally fruitful and provided us with four concepts collectively known as the **cell theory**:

1. A *cell* is the basic structural and functional unit of living organisms. So when you define cell properties you are in fact defining the properties of life.
2. The activity of an organism depends on both the individual and the collective activities of its cells.
3. According to the *principle of complementarity of structure and function*, the biochemical activities of cells are dictated by the relative number of their specific subcellular structures.
4. Continuity of life from one generation to another has a cellular basis.

We will expand on all of these concepts as we progress. Let us begin with the idea that the cell is the smallest living unit. Whatever its form, however it behaves, the cell is the microscopic package that contains all the parts necessary to survive in an ever-changing world. It follows then that loss of cellular homeostasis underlies virtually every disease.

The trillions of cells in the human body include over 200 different cell types that vary greatly in shape, size, and function (Figure 3.1). The spherical fat cells, disc-shaped red blood cells, branching nerve cells, and cubelike cells of kidney tubules are just a few examples of the shapes cells take. Depending on type, cells also vary greatly in length—ranging from 2 micrometers (1/12,000 of an inch) in the smallest cells to over a meter in the nerve cells that cause you to wiggle your toes. A cell's shape reflects its function. For example, the flat, tilelike epithelial cells that line the inside of your cheek fit closely together, forming a living barrier that protects underlying tissues from bacterial invasion.

Regardless of type, all cells are composed chiefly of carbon, hydrogen, nitrogen, oxygen, and trace amounts of several other elements. In addition, all cells have the same basic parts and some common functions. For this reason, it is possible to speak of a **generalized**, or **composite**, **cell** (Figure 3.2).

Human cells have three main parts: the plasma membrane, the cytoplasm, and the nucleus. The *plasma membrane*, a fragile

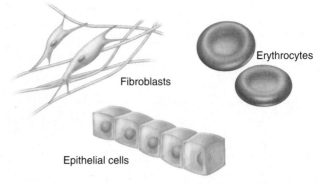

Erythrocytes

Fibroblasts

Epithelial cells

(a) Cells that connect body parts, form linings, or transport gases

Skeletal muscle cell

Smooth muscle cells

(b) Cells that move organs and body parts

Macrophage

Fat cell

(c) Cell that stores nutrients   **(d) Cell that fights disease**

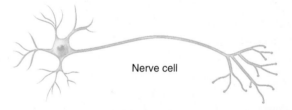

Nerve cell

(e) Cell that gathers information and controls body functions

Sperm

(f) Cell of reproduction

Figure 3.1 **Cell diversity.** (Note that cells are not drawn to the same scale.)

barrier, is the outer boundary of the cell. Internal to this membrane is the *cytoplasm* (si′to-plazm), the intracellular fluid that is packed with organelles, small structures that perform specific cell functions. The *nucleus* (nu′kle-us) controls cellular activities and typically it lies near the cell's center. We use these three main parts of the cell to organize the summary in Table 3.3 (pp. 94–95), and we describe them in greater detail next.

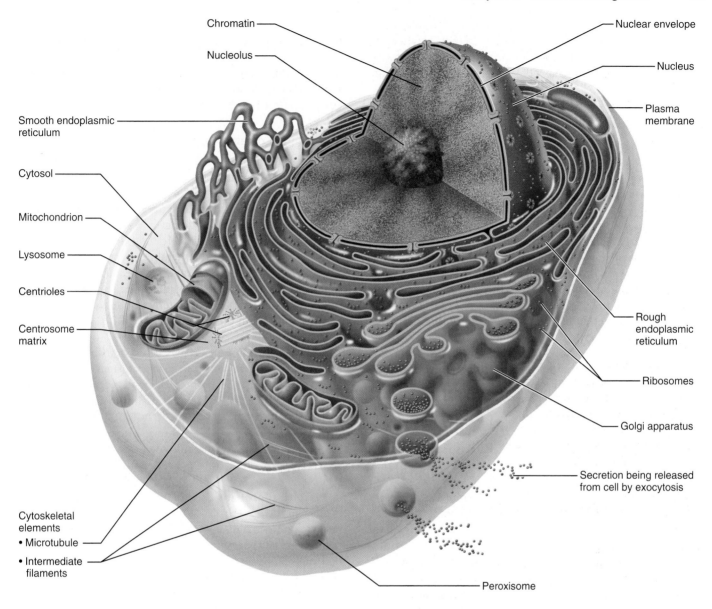

Figure 3.2 **Structure of the generalized cell.** No cell is exactly like this one, but this composite illustrates features common to many human cells. Note that not all of the organelles are drawn to the same scale in this illustration.

CHECK YOUR UNDERSTANDING

1. Name the three basic parts of a cell and describe the function of each.
2. How would you explain the meaning of a "generalized cell" to a classmate?

For answers, see Appendix G.

The Plasma Membrane: Structure

▶ Describe the chemical composition of the plasma membrane and relate it to membrane functions.

▶ Compare the structure and function of tight junctions, desmosomes, and gap junctions.

The flexible **plasma membrane** defines the extent of a cell, thereby separating two of the body's major fluid compartments—the *intracellular* fluid within cells and the *extracellular* fluid outside cells. The term *cell membrane* is commonly used as a synonym for plasma membrane, but because nearly all cellular organelles are enclosed in a membrane, in this book we will always refer to the cell's surface, or outer limiting membrane, as the plasma membrane. The plasma membrane is much more than a passive envelope. As you will see, its unique structure allows it to play a dynamic role in many cellular activities.

The Fluid Mosaic Model

The **fluid mosaic model** of membrane structure depicts the plasma membrane as an exceedingly thin (7–10 nm) structure composed of a double layer, or bilayer, of lipid molecules with protein molecules "plugged into" or dispersed in it **(Figure 3.3)**. The proteins, many of which float in the fluid *lipid bilayer*, form a constantly changing mosaic pattern. The model is named for this characteristic.

Membrane Lipids

The lipid bilayer forms the basic "fabric" of the membrane. It is constructed largely of *phospholipids*, with smaller amounts of *cholesterol* and *glycolipids*. Each lollipop-shaped phospholipid molecule has a polar "head" that is charged and is **hydrophilic** (*hydro* = water, *philic* = loving), and an uncharged, nonpolar "tail" that is made of two fatty acid chains and is **hydrophobic** (*phobia* = fear). The polar heads are attracted to water—the main constituent of both the intracellular and extracellular fluids—and so they lie on both the inner and outer surfaces of the membrane. The nonpolar tails, being hydrophobic, avoid water and line up in the center of the membrane.

The result is that all biological membranes share a common sandwich-like structure: They are composed of two parallel sheets of phospholipid molecules lying tail to tail, with their polar heads exposed to water both inside and outside the cell. This self-orienting property of phospholipids encourages biological membranes to self-assemble into closed, generally spherical, structures and to reseal themselves quickly when torn.

The plasma membrane is a dynamic fluid structure that is in constant flux. Its consistency is like that of olive oil. The lipid molecules of the bilayer move freely from side to side, parallel to the membrane surface, but their polar-nonpolar interactions prevent them from flip-flopping or moving from one phospholipid layer (half of the bilayer) to the other. The inward-facing and outward-facing surfaces of the plasma membrane differ in the kinds and amounts of lipids they contain, and these variations are important in determining local membrane structure and function. The majority of membrane phospholipids are unsaturated, a condition which kinks their tails (increasing the space between them) and increases membrane fluidity. (See the illustration of phosphatidylcholine in Figure 2.16b, p. 46.)

Glycolipids (gli″ko-lip′idz) are lipids with attached sugar groups. They are found only on the outer plasma membrane surface and account for about 5% of the total membrane lipid. Their sugar groups, like the phosphate-containing groups of phospholipids, make that end of the glycolipid molecule polar, whereas the fatty acid tails are nonpolar.

Some 20% of membrane lipid is cholesterol. Like phospholipids, cholesterol has a polar region (its hydroxyl group) and a nonpolar region (its fused ring system). It wedges its platelike hydrocarbon rings between the phospholipid tails, stabilizing the membrane, while increasing the mobility of the phospholipids and the fluidity of the membrane.

About 20% of the outer membrane surface contains **lipid rafts**, dynamic assemblies of saturated phospholipids (which pack together tightly) associated with unique lipids called sphingolipids and lots of cholesterol. These quiltlike patches are more stable and orderly and less fluid than the rest of the membrane, and they can include or exclude specific proteins to various extents. Because of these qualities, lipid rafts are assumed to be concentrating platforms for certain receptor molecules or for molecules needed for cell signaling. (Cell signaling will be discussed on pp. 81–82.)

Membrane Proteins

Proteins make up about half of the plasma membrane by mass and are responsible for most of the specialized membrane functions. There are two distinct populations of membrane proteins, integral and peripheral (Figure 3.3). **Integral proteins** are firmly inserted into the lipid bilayer. Some protrude from one membrane face only, but most are *transmembrane proteins* that span the entire width of the membrane and protrude on both sides. Whether transmembrane or not, all integral proteins have both hydrophobic and hydrophilic regions. This structural feature allows them to interact both with the nonpolar lipid tails buried in the membrane and with water inside and outside the cell.

Although some are enzymes, most transmembrane proteins are involved in transport. Some cluster together to form *channels*, or pores, through which small, water-soluble molecules or ions can move, thus bypassing the lipid part of the membrane. Others act as *carriers* that bind to a substance and then move it through the membrane. Still others are receptors for hormones or other chemical messengers and relay messages to the cell interior (a process called *signal transduction*) **(Figure 3.4a, b)**.

Peripheral proteins (Figure 3.3), in contrast, are not embedded in the lipid. Instead, they attach rather loosely only to integral proteins and are easily removed without disrupting the membrane. Peripheral proteins include a network of filaments that helps support the membrane from its cytoplasmic side (Figure 3.4c). Some peripheral proteins are enzymes. Others are motor proteins involved in mechanical functions, such as changing cell shape during cell division and muscle cell contraction. Still others link cells together.

Some of the proteins float freely. Others, particularly the peripheral proteins, are restricted in their movements because they are "tethered" to intracellular structures that make up the *cytoskeleton*. Many of the proteins that abut the extracellular fluid are glycoproteins with branching sugar groups. The term **glycocalyx** (gli″ko-kal′iks; "sugar covering") is used to describe the fuzzy, sticky, carbohydrate-rich area at the cell surface. You can think of your cells as sugar-coated. The glycocalyx that clings to each cell's surface is enriched both by glycolipids and by glycoproteins secreted by the cell.

Because every cell type has a different pattern of sugars in its glycocalyx, the glycocalyx provides highly specific biological markers by which approaching cells recognize each other (Figure 3.4f). For example, a sperm recognizes an ovum (egg cell) by the ovum's unique glycocalyx. Cells of the immune system identify a bacterium by binding to certain membrane glycoproteins in the bacterial glycocalyx.

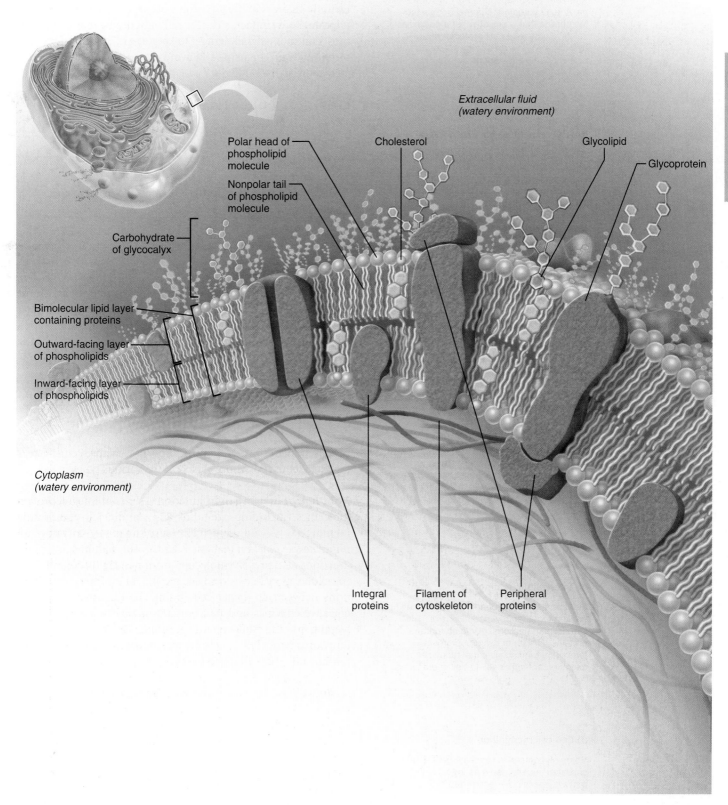

Extracellular fluid
(watery environment)

Polar head of
phospholipid
molecule

Cholesterol

Glycolipid

Glycoprotein

Nonpolar tail
of phospholipid
molecule

Carbohydrate
of glycocalyx

Bimolecular lipid layer
containing proteins

Outward-facing layer
of phospholipids

Inward-facing layer
of phospholipids

Cytoplasm
(watery environment)

Integral
proteins

Filament of
cytoskeleton

Peripheral
proteins

Figure 3.3 Structure of the plasma membrane according to the fluid mosaic model. The
lipid bilayer forms the basic structure of the membrane. The associated proteins are involved in
membrane functions such as membrane transport, catalysis, and cell-to-cell recognition.

3

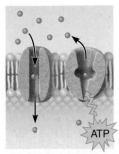

(a) Transport

A protein (left) that spans the membrane may provide a hydrophilic channel across the membrane that is selective for a particular solute. Some transport proteins (right) hydrolyze ATP as an energy source to actively pump substances across the membrane.

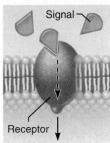

(b) Receptors for signal transduction

A membrane protein exposed to the outside of the cell may have a binding site with a specific shape that fits the shape of a chemical messenger, such as a hormone. The external signal may cause a change in shape in the protein that initiates a chain of chemical reactions in the cell.

(c) Attachment to the cytoskeleton and extracellular matrix (ECM)

Elements of the cytoskeleton (cell's internal supports) and the extracellular matrix (fibers and other substances outside the cell) may be anchored to membrane proteins, which help maintain cell shape and fix the location of certain membrane proteins. Others play a role in cell movement or bind adjacent cells together.

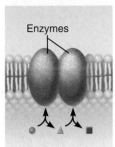

(d) Enzymatic activity

A protein built into the membrane may be an enzyme with its active site exposed to substances in the adjacent solution. In some cases, several enzymes in a membrane act as a team that catalyzes sequential steps of a metabolic pathway as indicated (left to right) here.

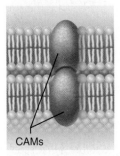

(e) Intercellular joining

Membrane proteins of adjacent cells may be hooked together in various kinds of intercellular junctions. Some membrane proteins (CAMs) of this group provide temporary binding sites that guide cell migration and other cell-to-cell interactions.

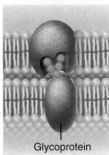

(f) Cell-cell recognition

Some glycoproteins (proteins bonded to short chains of sugars) serve as identification tags that are specifically recognized by other cells.

Figure 3.4 Membrane proteins perform many tasks. A single protein may perform some combination of these tasks.

HOMEOSTATIC IMBALANCE

Definite changes in the glycocalyx occur in a cell that is becoming cancerous. In fact, a cancer cell's glycocalyx may change almost continuously, allowing it to keep ahead of immune system recognition mechanisms and avoid destruction. (Cancer is discussed on pp. 142–143.) ∎

CHECK YOUR UNDERSTANDING

3. What basic structure do all cellular membranes share?
4. Why do phospholipids, which form the greater part of cell membranes, organize into a bilayer—tail-to-tail—in a watery environment?
5. What is the importance of the glycocalyx in cell interactions?

For answers, see Appendix G.

Membrane Junctions

Although certain cell types—blood cells, sperm cells, and some phagocytic cells (which ingest and destroy bacteria and other substances)—are "footloose" in the body, many other types, particularly epithelial cells, are knit into tight communities. Typically, three factors act to bind cells together:

1. Glycoproteins in the glycocalyx act as an adhesive.
2. Wavy contours of the membranes of adjacent cells fit together in a tongue-and-groove fashion.
3. Special membrane junctions are formed (**Figure 3.5**).

Because junctions are the most important factor securing cells together, let us look more closely at the various types.

Tight Junctions In a **tight junction**, a series of integral protein molecules (including occludins and claudins) in the plasma membranes of adjacent cells fuse together, forming an *impermeable junction* that encircles the cell (Figure 3.5a). Tight junctions help prevent molecules from passing through the extracellular space between adjacent cells. For example, tight junctions between epithelial cells lining the digestive tract keep digestive enzymes and microorganisms in the intestine from seeping into the bloodstream. (Although called "impermeable" junctions, some tight junctions are somewhat leaky and may allow certain types of ions to pass.)

Desmosomes Desmosomes (des′mo-sōmz; "binding bodies") are *anchoring junctions*—mechanical couplings scattered like rivets along the sides of abutting cells that prevent their separation (Figure 3.5b). On the cytoplasmic face of each plasma membrane is a buttonlike thickening called a *plaque.* Adjacent cells are held together by thin linker protein filaments (cadherins) that extend from the plaques and fit together like the teeth of a zipper in the intercellular space. Thicker keratin filaments (intermediate filaments, which form part of the cytoskeleton) extend from the cytoplasmic side of the plaque across the width of the cell to anchor to the plaque on the cell's opposite side. In this way, desmosomes not only bind neighboring cells together,

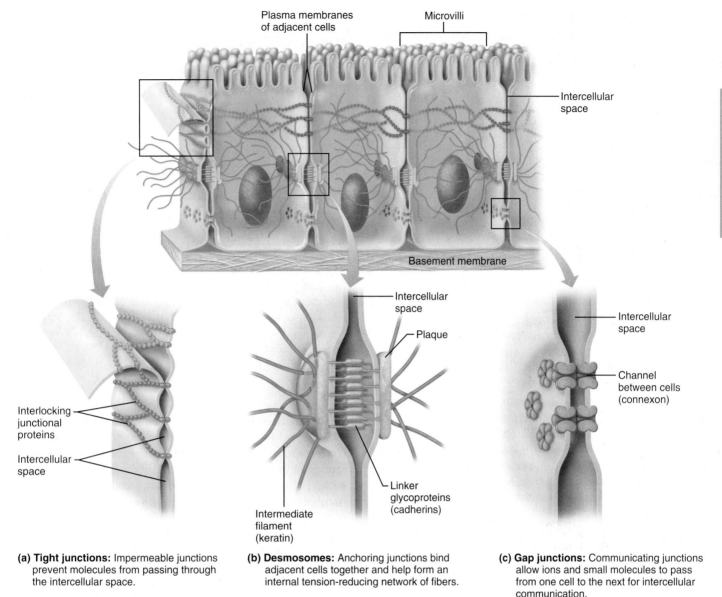

(a) **Tight junctions:** Impermeable junctions prevent molecules from passing through the intercellular space.

(b) **Desmosomes:** Anchoring junctions bind adjacent cells together and help form an internal tension-reducing network of fibers.

(c) **Gap junctions:** Communicating junctions allow ions and small molecules to pass from one cell to the next for intercellular communication.

Figure 3.5 Cell junctions. An epithelial cell is shown joined to adjacent cells by three common types of cell junctions. (Note: Except for epithelia, it is unlikely that a single cell will have all three junction types.)

but they also contribute to a continuous internal network of strong "guy-wires."

This arrangement distributes tension throughout a cellular sheet and reduces the chance of tearing when it is subjected to pulling forces. Desmosomes are abundant in tissues subjected to great mechanical stress, such as skin and heart muscle.

Gap Junctions A **gap junction**, or *nexus* (nek′sus; "bond"), is a communicating junction between adjacent cells. At gap junctions the adjacent plasma membranes are very close, and the cells are connected by hollow cylinders called *connexons* (kŏ-nek′sonz), composed of transmembrane proteins. The many different types of connexon proteins vary the selectivity of the

gap junction channels. Ions, simple sugars, and other small molecules pass through these water-filled channels from one cell to the next (Figure 3.5c).

Gap junctions are present in electrically excitable tissues, such as the heart and smooth muscle, where ion passage from cell to cell helps synchronize their electrical activity and contraction.

CHECK YOUR UNDERSTANDING

6. What two types of membrane junctions would you expect to find between muscle cells of the heart?

For answer, see Appendix G.

3

Figure 3.6 Diffusion. Molecules in solution move continuously and collide constantly with other molecules, causing them to move away from areas of their highest concentration and become evenly distributed. From left to right, molecules from a dye pellet diffuse into the surrounding water down their concentration gradient.

The Plasma Membrane: Membrane Transport

▶ Relate plasma membrane structure to active and passive transport processes.

▶ Compare and contrast simple diffusion, facilitated diffusion, and osmosis relative to substances transported, direction, and mechanism.

Our cells are bathed in an extracellular fluid called **interstitial fluid** (in″ter-stish′al) that is derived from the blood. Interstitial fluid is like a rich, nutritious "soup." It contains thousands of ingredients, including amino acids, sugars, fatty acids, vitamins, regulatory substances such as hormones and neurotransmitters, salts, and waste products. To remain healthy, each cell must extract from this mix the exact amounts of the substances it needs at specific times.

Although there is continuous traffic across the plasma membrane, it is a **selectively**, or **differentially**, **permeable** barrier, meaning that it allows some substances to pass while excluding others. It allows nutrients to enter the cell, but keeps many undesirable substances out. At the same time, it keeps valuable cell proteins and other substances in the cell, but allows wastes to exit.

Substances move through the plasma membrane in essentially two ways—passively or actively. In **passive processes**, substances cross the membrane without any energy input from the cell. In **active processes**, the cell provides the metabolic energy (ATP) needed to move substances across the membrane. The various transport processes that occur in cells are summarized in Table 3.1 on p. 72 and Table 3.2 on p. 80. Let's examine each of these types of membrane transport.

HOMEOSTATIC IMBALANCE

Selective permeability is a characteristic of healthy, intact cells. When a cell (or its plasma membrane) is severely damaged, the membrane becomes permeable to virtually everything, and substances flow into and out of the cell freely. This phenomenon is evident when someone has been severely burned. Precious fluids, proteins, and ions "weep" from the dead and damaged cells. ■

Passive Processes

The two main types of passive transport are *diffusion* (di-fu′zhun) and *filtration*. Diffusion is an important means of passive membrane transport for every cell of the body. Because filtration generally occurs only across capillary walls, that topic is more properly covered in conjunction with capillary transport processes later in the book.

Diffusion

Diffusion is the tendency of molecules or ions to move from an area where they are in higher concentration to an area where they are in lower concentration, that is, down or along their **concentration gradient**. The constant random and high-speed motion of molecules and ions (a result of their intrinsic kinetic energy) results in collisions. With each collision, the particles ricochet off one another and change direction. The overall effect of this erratic movement is the scattering or dispersion of the particles throughout the environment (Figure 3.6). The greater the difference in concentration of the diffusing molecules and ions between the two areas, the more collisions occur and the faster the net diffusion of the particles.

Because the driving force for diffusion is the kinetic energy of the molecules themselves, the speed of diffusion is influenced by molecular *size* (the smaller, the faster) and by *temperature* (the warmer, the faster). In a closed container, diffusion eventually produces a uniform mixture of molecules. In other words, the system reaches equilibrium, with molecules moving equally in all directions (no *net* movement).

Diffusion is occurring all around us, but obvious examples of pure diffusion are almost impossible to see. The reason is that any diffusion process that occurs over an easily observable distance takes a long time, and is often accompanied by other processes (convection, for example) that affect the movement of molecules and ions. In fact, one should suspect any readily observable "example" of diffusion. Nonetheless, diffusion is immensely important in physiological systems and it occurs rapidly because the distances molecules are moving are very short, perhaps 1/1000 (or less) the thickness of this page! Examples include the movement of ions across cell membranes and the movement of neurotransmitters between two nerve cells.

The plasma membrane is a physical barrier to free diffusion because of its hydrophobic core. However, a molecule *will* diffuse

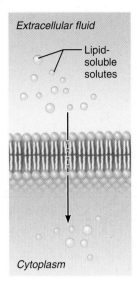

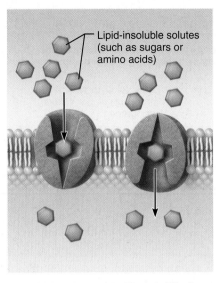

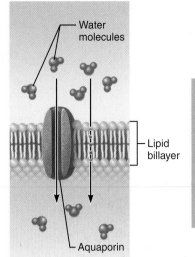

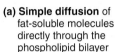

(a) Simple diffusion of fat-soluble molecules directly through the phospholipid bilayer

(b) Carrier-mediated facilitated diffusion via a protein carrier specific for one chemical; binding of substrate causes shape change in transport protein

(c) Channel-mediated facilitated diffusion through a channel protein; mostly ions selected on basis of size and charge

(d) Osmosis, diffusion of a solvent such as water through a specific channel protein (aquaporin) or through the lipid bilayer

Figure 3.7 Diffusion through the plasma membrane.

through the membrane if the molecule is (1) lipid soluble, (2) small enough to pass through membrane channels, or (3) assisted by a carrier molecule. The unassisted diffusion of lipid-soluble or very small particles is called *simple diffusion*. A special name, *osmosis*, is given to the unassisted diffusion of a solvent (usually water) through a membrane. Assisted diffusion is known as *facilitated diffusion*.

Simple Diffusion In **simple diffusion**, nonpolar and lipid-soluble substances diffuse directly through the lipid bilayer **(Figure 3.7a)**. Such substances include oxygen, carbon dioxide, and fat-soluble vitamins. Because oxygen concentration is always higher in the blood than in tissue cells, oxygen continuously diffuses from the blood into the cells. Carbon dioxide, on the other hand, is in higher concentration within the cells, so it diffuses from tissue cells into the blood.

Facilitated Diffusion Certain molecules, notably glucose and other sugars, some amino acids, and ions are transported passively even though they are unable to pass through the lipid bilayer. Instead they move through the membrane by a passive transport process called **facilitated diffusion** in which the transported substance either (1) binds to protein carriers in the membrane and is ferried across or (2) moves through water-filled protein channels.

■ **Carriers** are transmembrane integral proteins that show specificity for molecules of a certain polar substance or class of substances that are too large to pass through membrane channels, such as sugars and amino acids. The most popular model for the action of carriers indicates that changes in the shape of the carrier allow it to first envelop and then release the transported substance, shielding it en route from the

nonpolar regions of the membrane. Essentially, the binding site is moved from one face of the membrane to the other by changes in the conformation of the carrier protein (Figure 3.7b and Table 3.1).

Note that a substance transported by carrier-mediated facilitated diffusion, such as glucose, moves down its concentration gradient, just as in simple diffusion. Glucose is normally in higher concentrations in the blood than in the cells, where it is rapidly used for ATP synthesis. So, glucose transport within the body is *typically* unidirectional—into the cells. However, carrier-mediated transport is limited by the number of protein carriers present. For example, when all the glucose carriers are "engaged," they are said to be *saturated*, and glucose transport is occurring at its maximum rate.

■ **Channels** are transmembrane proteins that serve to transport substances, usually ions or water, through aqueous channels from one side of the membrane to the other (Figure 3.7c and d). Binding or association sites exist within the channels, and the channels are selective due to pore size and the charges of the amino acids lining the channel. Some channels, the so-called *leakage channels*, are always open and simply allow ion or water fluxes according to concentration gradients. Others are gated and are controlled (opened or closed) by various chemical or electrical signals.

Like carriers, many channels can be inhibited by certain molecules, show saturation, and tend to be specific. Substances moving through them also follow the concentration gradient (always moving down the gradient). When a substance crosses the membrane by simple diffusion, the rate of diffusion is not controllable because the lipid solubility of the membrane is not immediately changeable. By contrast, the rate of facilitated diffusion *is* controllable because the

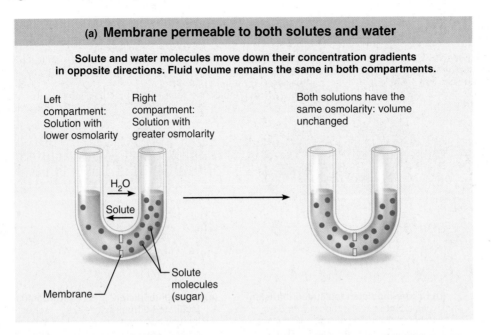

(a) Membrane permeable to both solutes and water

Solute and water molecules move down their concentration gradients in opposite directions. Fluid volume remains the same in both compartments.

Left compartment: Solution with lower osmolarity

Right compartment: Solution with greater osmolarity

Both solutions have the same osmolarity: volume unchanged

H_2O

Solute

Membrane

Solute molecules (sugar)

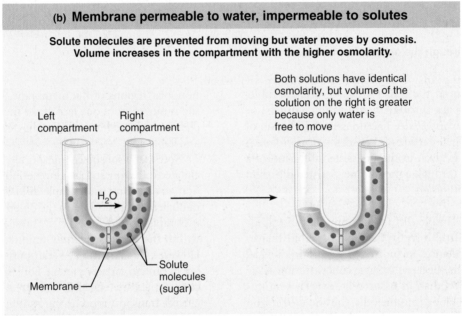

(b) Membrane permeable to water, impermeable to solutes

Solute molecules are prevented from moving but water moves by osmosis. Volume increases in the compartment with the higher osmolarity.

Left compartment

Right compartment

Both solutions have identical osmolarity, but volume of the solution on the right is greater because only water is free to move

H_2O

Solute molecules (sugar)

Membrane

Figure 3.8 Influence of membrane permeability on diffusion and osmosis.

permeability of the membrane can be altered by regulating the activity or number of individual carriers or channels.

Oxygen, water, glucose, and various ions are vitally important to cellular homeostasis. Their passive transport by diffusion (either simple or facilitated) represents a tremendous saving of cellular energy. Indeed, if these substances had to be transported actively, cell expenditures of ATP would increase exponentially!

Osmosis The diffusion of a solvent, such as water, through a selectively permeable membrane is **osmosis** (oz-mo′sis; *osmos* = pushing). Even though water is highly polar, it passes via osmosis through the lipid bilayer (Figure 3.7d). This is surprising because you'd expect water to be repelled by the hydrophobic lipid tails. Although still hypothetical, one explanation is that

random movements of the membrane lipids open small gaps between their wiggling tails, allowing water to slip and slide its way through the membrane by moving from gap to gap.

Water also moves freely and reversibly through water-specific channels constructed by transmembrane proteins called **aquaporins (AQPs)**. Although aquaporins are believed to be present in all cell types, they are particularly abundant in red blood cells and in cells involved in water balance such as kidney tubule cells.

Osmosis occurs whenever the water concentration differs on the two sides of a membrane. If distilled water is present on both sides of a selectively permeable membrane, no *net* osmosis occurs, even though water molecules move in both directions through the membrane. If the solute concentration on the two sides of

(a) **Isotonic solutions**	(b) **Hypertonic solutions**	(c) **Hypotonic solutions**
Cells retain their normal size and shape in isotonic solutions (same solute/water concentration as inside cells; water moves in and out).	Cells lose water by osmosis and shrink in a hypertonic solution (contains a higher concentration of solutes than are present inside the cells).	Cells take on water by osmosis until they become bloated and burst (lyse) in a hypotonic solution (contains a lower concentration of solutes than are present in cells).

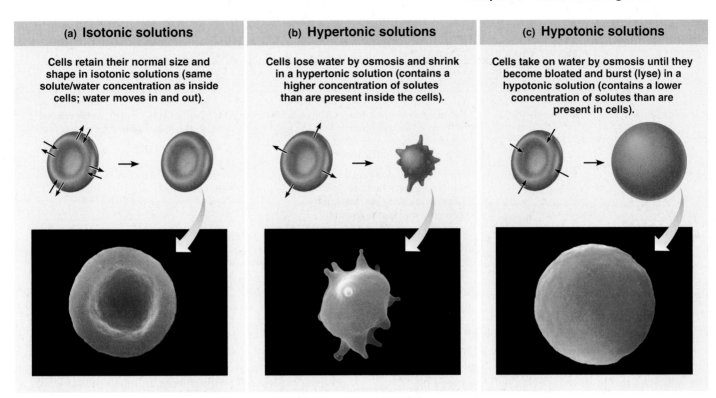

Figure 3.9 The effect of solutions of varying tonicities on living red blood cells.

the membrane differs, water concentration differs as well (as solute concentration increases, water concentration decreases).

The extent to which water's concentration is decreased by solutes depends on the *number*, not the *type*, of solute particles, because one molecule or one ion of solute (theoretically) displaces one water molecule. The total concentration of all solute particles in a solution is referred to as the solution's **osmolarity** (oz″mo-lar′ĭ-te). When equal volumes of aqueous solutions of different osmolarity are separated by a membrane that is *permeable to all molecules* in the system, net diffusion of both solute and water occurs, each moving down its own concentration gradient. Eventually, equilibrium is reached when the water concentration on the left equals that on the right, and the solute concentration on both sides is the same **(Figure 3.8a)**.

If we consider the same system, but make the membrane *impermeable to solute molecules*, we see quite a different result (Figure 3.8b). Water quickly diffuses from the left to the right compartment and continues to do so until its concentration is the same on the two sides of the membrane. Notice that in this case equilibrium results from the movement of water alone (the solutes are prevented from moving). Notice also that the movement of water leads to dramatic changes in the volumes of the two compartments.

The last example mimics osmosis across plasma membranes of living cells, with one major difference. In our examples, the volumes of the compartments are infinitely expandable and the effect of pressure exerted by the added weight of the higher fluid column is not considered. In living plant cells, which have rigid cell walls external to their plasma membranes, this is not the case. As water diffuses into the cell, the point is finally reached where the **hydrostatic pressure** (the back pressure exerted by water against the membrane) within the cell is equal to its **osmotic pressure** (the tendency of water to move into the cell by osmosis). At this point, there is no further (net) water entry. As a rule, the higher the amount of nondiffusible, or *nonpenetrating*, solutes in a cell, the higher the osmotic pressure and the greater the hydrostatic pressure that must be developed to resist further net water entry.

However, such major changes in hydrostatic (and osmotic) pressures do not occur in living animal cells, which lack rigid cell walls. Osmotic imbalances cause animal cells to swell or shrink (due to net water gain or loss) until either the solute concentration is the same on both sides of the plasma membrane, or the membrane is stretched to its breaking point.

Such changes in animal cells lead us to the important concept of *tonicity* (to-nis′ĭ-te). As noted, many molecules, particularly intracellular proteins and selected ions, are prevented from diffusing through the plasma membrane. Consequently, any change in their concentration alters the water concentration on the two sides of the membrane and results in a net loss or gain of water by the cell.

The ability of a solution to change the shape or tone of cells by altering their internal water volume is called **tonicity** (*tono* = tension). Solutions with the same concentrations of nonpenetrating solutes as those found in cells (0.9% saline or 5% glucose) are **isotonic** ("the same tonicity"). Cells exposed to such solutions retain their normal shape, and exhibit no net loss or gain of water **(Figure 3.9a)**. As you might expect, the body's extracellular fluids and most intravenous solutions (solutions infused into the body via a vein) are isotonic.

TABLE 3.1	Passive Membrane Transport Processes			
PROCESS	ENERGY SOURCE	DESCRIPTION		EXAMPLES
Diffusion				
Simple diffusion	Kinetic energy	Net movement of molecules from an area of their higher concentration to an area of their lower concentration, that is, along their concentration gradient		Movement of fats, oxygen, carbon dioxide through the lipid portion of the membrane
Facilitated diffusion	Kinetic energy	Same as simple diffusion, but the diffusing substance is attached to a lipid-soluble membrane carrier protein or moves through a membrane channel		Movement of glucose and some ions into cells
Osmosis	Kinetic energy	Simple diffusion of water through a selectively permeable membrane		Movement of water into and out of cells directly through the lipid phase of the membrane or via membrane channels (aquaporins)

Solutions with a higher concentration of nonpenetrating solutes than seen in the cell (for example, a strong saline solution) are **hypertonic**. Cells immersed in hypertonic solutions lose water and shrink, or *crenate* (kre′nat) (Figure 3.9b).

Solutions that are more dilute (contain a lower concentration of nonpenetrating solutes) than cells are called **hypotonic**. Cells placed in a hypotonic solution plump up rapidly as water rushes into them (Figure 3.9c). Distilled water represents the most extreme example of hypotonicity. Because it contains *no* solutes, water continues to enter cells until they finally burst or *lyse*.

Notice that osmolarity and tonicity are not the same thing. A solution's osmolarity is based solely on its total solute concentration. In contrast, its tonicity is based on how the solution affects cell volume, which depends on (1) solute concentration and (2) solute permeability of the plasma membrane. Osmolarity is expressed as osmoles per liter (osmol/L) where 1 osmol is equal to 1 mole of nonionizing molecules.* A 0.3-osmol/L solution of NaCl is isotonic because sodium ions are usually prevented from diffusing through the plasma membrane. But if the cell is immersed in a 0.3-osmol/L solution of a penetrating solute, the solute will enter the cell and water will follow. The cell will swell and burst, just as if it had been placed in pure water.

Osmosis is extremely important in determining distribution of water in the various fluid-containing compartments of the body (in cells, in blood, and so on). In general, osmosis continues until osmotic and hydrostatic pressures acting at the membrane are equal. For example, water is forced out of capillary blood by the hydrostatic pressure of the blood against the capillary wall, but the presence in blood of solutes that are too large to cross the capillary membrane draws water back into the bloodstream. As a result, very little net loss of plasma fluid occurs.

Simple diffusion and osmosis occurring directly through the plasma membrane are not selective processes. In those processes, whether a molecule can pass through the membrane depends chiefly on its size or its solubility in lipid, not on its unique structure. Facilitated diffusion, on the other hand, is often highly selective. The carrier for glucose, for example, combines specifically with glucose, in much the same way an enzyme binds to its specific substrate and ion channels allow only selected ions to pass.

HOMEOSTATIC IMBALANCE

Hypertonic solutions are sometimes infused intravenously into the bloodstream of edematous patients (those swollen because water is retained in their tissues) to draw excess water out of the extracellular space and move it into the bloodstream so that it can be eliminated by the kidneys. Hypotonic solutions may be used (with care) to rehydrate the tissues of extremely dehydrated patients. In less extreme cases of dehydration, drinking hypotonic fluids (colas, apple juice, and sports drinks) usually does the trick. ■

Table 3.1 summarizes passive membrane transport processes.

CHECK YOUR UNDERSTANDING

7. What is the energy source for all types of diffusion?
8. What determines the direction of any diffusion process?
9. What are the two types of facilitated diffusion and how do they differ?

For answers, see Appendix G.

Active Processes

▶ Differentiate between primary and secondary active transport.

▶ Compare and contrast endocytosis and exocytosis in terms of function and direction.

▶ Compare and contrast pinocytosis, phagocytosis, and receptor-mediated endocytosis.

*Osmolarity (Osm) is determined by multiplying molarity (moles per liter, or *M*) by the number of particles resulting from ionization. For example, since NaCl ionizes to $Na^+ + Cl^-$, a $1M$ solution of NaCl is a 2-Osm solution. For substances that do not ionize (e.g., glucose), molarity and osmolarity are the same.

Whenever a cell uses the bond energy of ATP to move solutes across the membrane, the process is referred to as *active*. Substances moved actively across the plasma membrane are usually unable to pass in the necessary direction by passive transport processes. The substance may be too large to pass through the channels, incapable of dissolving in the lipid bilayer, or unable to move down its concentration gradient. There are two major means of active membrane transport: active transport and vesicular transport.

Active Transport

Active transport, like carrier-mediated facilitated diffusion, requires carrier proteins that combine *specifically* and *reversibly* with the transported substances. However, facilitated diffusion always follows concentration gradients because its driving force is kinetic energy. In contrast, the active transporters or **solute pumps** move solutes, most importantly ions (such as Na^+, K^+, and Ca^{2+}), "uphill" *against* a concentration gradient. To do this work, cells must expend the energy of ATP.

Active transport processes are distinguished according to their source of energy. In *primary active transport*, the energy to do work comes *directly from hydrolysis of ATP*. In *secondary active transport*, transport is driven indirectly *by energy stored in ionic gradients* created by operation of primary active transport pumps. Secondary active transport systems are all *coupled systems*; that is, they move more than one substance at a time. If the two transported substances are moved in the same direction, the system is a **symport system** (*sym* = same). If the transported substances "wave to each other" as they cross the membrane in opposite directions, the system is an **antiport system** (*anti* = opposite, against). Let's examine these processes more carefully.

Primary Active Transport In **primary active transport**, hydrolysis of ATP results in the phosphorylation of the transport protein. This step causes the protein to change its shape in such a manner that it "pumps" the bound solute across the membrane.

Primary active transport systems include calcium and hydrogen pumps, but the most investigated example of a primary active transport system is the operation of the **sodium-potassium pump**, for which the carrier, or "pump," is an enzyme called **Na^+-K^+ ATPase**. In the body, the concentration of K^+ inside the cell is some 10 times higher than that outside, and the reverse is true of Na^+. These ionic concentration differences are essential for excitable cells like muscle and nerve cells to function normally and for all body cells to maintain their normal fluid volume. Because Na^+ and K^+ leak slowly but continuously through leakage channels in the plasma membrane along their concentration gradient (and cross more rapidly in stimulated muscle and nerve cells), the Na^+-K^+ pump operates more or less continuously as an antiporter. It simultaneously drives Na^+ out of the cell against a steep concentration gradient and pumps K^+ back in.

The electrochemical gradients maintained by the Na^+-K^+ pump underlie most primary and secondary active transport of nutrients and ions, and are crucial for cardiac and skeletal muscle and neuron function.

The step-by-step operation of the Na^+-K^+ pump is described in *Focus on Primary Active Transport: The Na^+-K^+ Pump* (Figure 3.10) on p. 74. Make sure you understand this process thoroughly before moving on to the topic of secondary active transport.

Secondary Active Transport A single ATP-powered pump, such as the Na^+-K^+ pump, can indirectly drive the **secondary active transport** of several other solutes. By moving sodium across the plasma membrane against its concentration gradient, the pump stores energy (in the ion gradient). Then, just as water pumped uphill can do work as it flows back down (to turn a turbine or water wheel), a substance pumped across a membrane can do work as it leaks back, propelled "downhill" along its concentration gradient. In this way, as sodium moves back into the cell with the help of a carrier protein (facilitated diffusion), other substances are "dragged along," or cotransported, by a common carrier protein (Figure 3.11). A carrier moving two substances in the same direction is a symport system.

For example, some sugars, amino acids, and many ions are cotransported in this way into cells lining the small intestine. Both cotransported substances move passively because the energy for this type of transport is the concentration gradient of the ion (in this case Na^+). Na^+ has to be pumped back out into the lumen (cavity) of the intestine to maintain its diffusion gradient. Ion gradients can also be used to drive antiport systems such as those that help to regulate intracellular pH by using the sodium gradient to expel hydrogen ions.

Regardless of whether the energy is provided directly (primary active transport) or indirectly (secondary active transport), each membrane pump or cotransporter transports only specific substances. For this reason, active transport systems provide a way for the cell to be very selective in cases where substances cannot pass by diffusion. (No pump—no transport.)

Vesicular Transport

In **vesicular transport**, fluids containing large particles and macromolecules are transported across cellular membranes inside membranous sacs called *vesicles*. Vesicular transport processes that eject substances from the cell interior into the extracellular fluid are called **exocytosis** (ek″so-si-to′sis; "out of the cell"). Those in which the cell ingests small patches of the plasma

Figure 3.10 **FOCUS** Primary Active Transport: The Na⁺-K⁺ Pump

Primary active transport is the process in which ions are moved across cell membranes against electrochemical gradients using energy supplied directly by ATP. The action of the Na⁺-K⁺ pump is an important example of primary active transport.

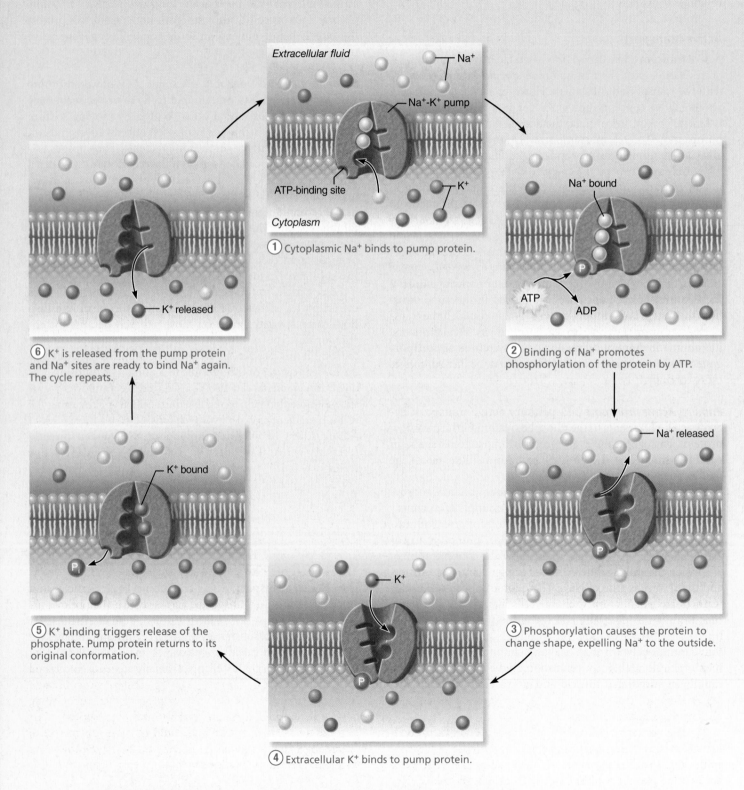

① Cytoplasmic Na⁺ binds to pump protein.

② Binding of Na⁺ promotes phosphorylation of the protein by ATP.

③ Phosphorylation causes the protein to change shape, expelling Na⁺ to the outside.

④ Extracellular K⁺ binds to pump protein.

⑤ K⁺ binding triggers release of the phosphate. Pump protein returns to its original conformation.

⑥ K⁺ is released from the pump protein and Na⁺ sites are ready to bind Na⁺ again. The cycle repeats.

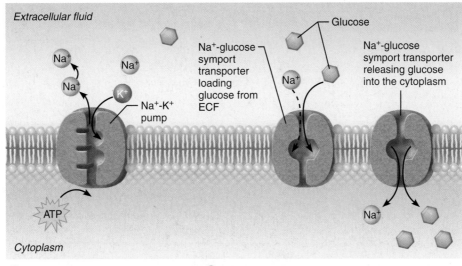

① The ATP-driven Na⁺-K⁺ pump stores energy by creating a steep concentration gradient for Na⁺ entry into the cell.

② As Na⁺ diffuses back across the membrane through a membrane cotransporter protein, it drives glucose against its concentration gradient into the cell. (ECF = extracellular fluid)

Figure 3.11 Secondary active transport.

membrane and moves substances from the cell exterior to the cell interior are called **endocytosis** (en″do-si-to′sis; "within the cell").

Vesicular transport is also used for combination processes such as *transcytosis*, moving substances into, across, and then out of the cell, and *substance*, or *vesicular*, *trafficking*, moving substances from one area (or organelle) in the cell to another.

Like solute pumping, vesicular transport processes are energized by ATP (or in some cases another energy-rich compound, *GTP*—guanosine triphosphate).

Endocytosis, Transcytosis, and Vesicular Trafficking

Virtually all forms of vesicular transport involve an assortment of protein-coated vesicles of three types and, with some exceptions, all are mediated by membrane receptors. Before we get specific about each type of coated vesicular transport, let's look at the general scheme of endocytosis.

Protein-coated vesicles provide the main route for endocytosis and transcytosis of bulk solids, most macromolecules, and fluids. On occasion, these vesicles are also hijacked by pathogens seeking entry into a cell.

Figure 3.12 shows the basic steps in endocytosis and transcytosis. ① The substance to be taken into the cell by endocytosis is progressively enclosed by an infolding portion of the plasma membrane called a *coated pit*. The coating is most often the bristlelike **clathrin** (kla′thrin; "lattice clad") protein coating found on the cytoplasmic face of the pit. The clathrin coat (clathrin and some accessory proteins) acts both in cargo selection and in deforming the membrane to produce the vesicle. ② The vesicle detaches, and ③ the coat proteins are recycled back to the plasma membrane.

④ The uncoated vesicle then typically fuses with a processing and sorting vesicle called an *endosome*. ⑤ Some membrane components and receptors of the fused vesicle may be recycled back to the plasma membrane in a transport vesicle. ⑥ The

remaining contents of the vesicle may (a) combine with a *lysosome* (li′so-sōm), a specialized cell structure containing digestive enzymes, where the ingested substance is degraded or released (if iron or cholesterol), or (b) be transported completely across the cell and released by exocytosis on the opposite side (*transcytosis*). Transcytosis is common in the endothelial cells lining blood vessels because it provides a quick means to get substances from the blood to the interstitial fluid.

Based on the nature and quantity of material taken up and the means of uptake, three types of endocytosis that use clathrin-coated vesicles are recognized: phagocytosis, pinocytosis, and receptor-mediated endocytosis.

Phagocytosis (fag″o-si-to′sis; "cell eating") is the type of endocytosis in which the cell engulfs some relatively large or solid material, such as a clump of bacteria, cell debris, or inanimate particles (asbestos fibers or glass, for example) **(Figure 3.13a)**. When a particle binds to receptors on the cell's surface, cytoplasmic extensions called pseudopods (soo′do-pahdz; *pseudo* = false, *pod* = foot) form and flow around the particle and engulf it. The endocytotic vesicle formed in this way is called a **phagosome** (fag′o-sōm; "eaten body"). In most cases, the phagosome then fuses with a lysosome and its contents are digested. Any indigestible contents are ejected from the cell by exocytosis.

In the human body, only macrophages and certain white blood cells are "experts" at phagocytosis. Commonly referred to as *phagocytes*, these cells help police and protect the body by ingesting and disposing of bacteria, other foreign substances, and dead tissue cells. The disposal of dying cells is crucial, because dead cell remnants trigger inflammation in the surrounding area or may stimulate an undesirable immune response. Most phagocytes move about by **amoeboid motion** (ah-me′boyd; "changing shape"); that is, the flowing of their cytoplasm into temporary pseudopods allows them to creep along.

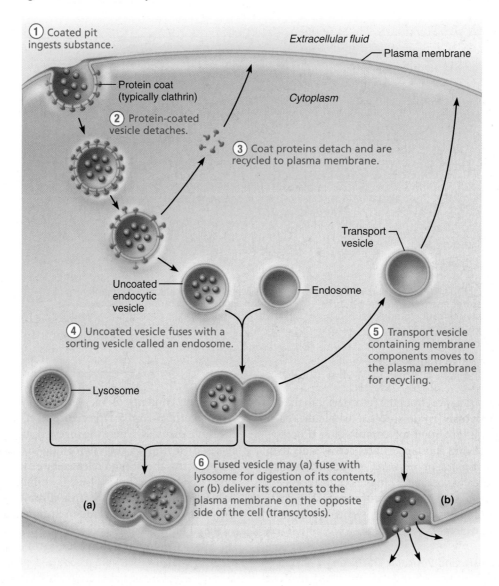

① Coated pit ingests substance.

Protein coat (typically clathrin)

② Protein-coated vesicle detaches.

③ Coat proteins detach and are recycled to plasma membrane.

Extracellular fluid

Plasma membrane

Cytoplasm

Transport vesicle

Uncoated endocytic vesicle

Endosome

④ Uncoated vesicle fuses with a sorting vesicle called an endosome.

⑤ Transport vesicle containing membrane components moves to the plasma membrane for recycling.

Lysosome

⑥ Fused vesicle may (a) fuse with lysosome for digestion of its contents, or (b) deliver its contents to the plasma membrane on the opposite side of the cell (transcytosis).

(a)

(b)

Figure 3.12 Events of endocytosis mediated by protein-coated pits. Note the three possible fates for a vesicle and its contents, shown in ⑤ and ⑥.

In **pinocytosis** ("cell drinking"), also called **fluid-phase endocytosis**, a bit of infolding plasma membrane (which begins as a clathrin-coated pit) surrounds a very small volume of extracellular fluid containing dissolved molecules (Figure 3.13b). This droplet enters the cell and fuses with an endosome. Unlike phagocytosis, pinocytosis is a routine activity of most cells, affording them a nonselective way of sampling the extracellular fluid. It is particularly important in cells that absorb nutrients, such as cells that line the intestines.

As mentioned, bits of the plasma membrane are removed when the membranous sacs are internalized. However, these membranes are recycled back to the plasma membrane by exocytosis as described shortly, so the surface area of the plasma membrane remains remarkably constant.

Receptor-mediated endocytosis is the main mechanism for the specific endocytosis and transcytosis of most macromolecules by body cells, and it is exquisitely selective (Figure 3.13c). It is also the mechanism that allows cells to concentrate material

that is present only in very small amounts in the extracellular fluid. The receptors for this process are plasma membrane proteins that bind only certain substances. Both the receptors and attached molecules are internalized in a clathrin-coated pit and then dealt with in one of the ways discussed above. Substances taken up by receptor-mediated endocytosis include enzymes, insulin (and some other hormones), low-density lipoproteins (such as cholesterol attached to a transport protein), and iron. Unfortunately, flu viruses, diphtheria, and cholera toxins use this route to enter and attack our cells.

Other coat proteins are also used for certain types of vesicular transport. **Caveolae** (ka″ve-o′le; "little caves"), tubular or flask-shaped inpocketings of the plasma membrane seen in many cell types, are involved in a unique kind of receptor-mediated endocytosis called **potosis**. Like clathrin-coated pits, caveolae capture specific molecules (folic acid, tetanus toxin) from the extracellular fluid in coated vesicles and participate in some forms of transcytosis. However, caveolae are smaller than clathrin-coated

TABLE 3.2	**Active Membrane Transport Processes**			
PROCESS	**ENERGY SOURCE**	**DESCRIPTION**		**EXAMPLES**
Active Transport				
Primary active transport	ATP	Transport of substances against a concentration (or electrochemical) gradient. Performed across the plasma membrane by a solute pump, directly using energy of ATP hydrolysis.		Ions (Na^+, K^+, H^+, Ca^{2+}, and others)
Secondary active transport	Ion concentration gradient maintained with ATP	Cotransport (coupled transport) of two solutes across the membrane. Energy is supplied indirectly by the ion gradient created by primary active transport. Symporters move the transported substances in the same direction; antiporters move transported substances in opposite directions across the membrane.		Movement of polar or charged solutes, e.g., amino acids (into cell by symporters); Ca^{2+}, H^+ (out of cells via antiporters)
Vesicular Transport				
Exocytosis	ATP	Secretion or ejection of substances from a cell. The substance is enclosed in a membranous vesicle, which fuses with the plasma membrane and ruptures, releasing the substance to the exterior.		Secretion of neurotransmitters, hormones, mucus, etc.; ejection of cell wastes
Endocytosis ▪ Via clathrin-coated vesicles	ATP			
Phagocytosis	ATP	"Cell eating": A large external particle (proteins, bacteria, dead cell debris) is surrounded by a "seizing foot" and becomes enclosed in a vesicle (phagosome).		In the human body, occurs primarily in protective phagocytes (some white blood cells and macrophages)
Pinocytosis (fluid-phase endocytosis)	ATP	Plasma membrane sinks beneath an external fluid droplet containing small solutes. Membrane edges fuse, forming a fluid-filled vesicle.		Occurs in most cells; important for taking in dissolved solutes by absorptive cells of the kidney and intestine
Receptor-mediated endocytosis	ATP	Selective endocytosis and transcytosis. External substance binds to membrane receptors.		Means of intake of some hormones, cholesterol, iron, and most macromolecules
▪ Via caveolin-coated vesicles (caveolae)	ATP	Selective endocytosis (and transcytosis). External substance binds to membrane receptors (often associated with lipid rafts).		Roles not fully known; proposed roles include cholesterol regulation and trafficking, and platforms for signal transduction
Intracellular vesicular trafficking				
▪ Via coatomer-coated vesicles	ATP	Vesicles pinch off from organelles and travel to other organelles to deliver their cargo.		Accounts for nearly all intracellular trafficking between certain organelles (endoplasmic reticulum and Golgi apparatus). Exceptions include vesicles budding from the trans face of the Golgi apparatus, which are clathrin-coated.

vesicles. Additionally, their cage-like protein coat is thinner and composed of a different protein called **caveolin.**

Caveolae are closely associated with lipid rafts that are platforms for G proteins, receptors for hormones (for example, insulin), and enzymes involved in cell regulation. These vesicles appear to provide sites for cell signaling and cross talk between signaling pathways. Their precise role in the cell is still being worked out.

Vesicles coated with **coatomer (COP1** and **COP2) proteins** are used in most types of intracellular *vesicular trafficking,* in which vesicles transport substances between organelles.

3

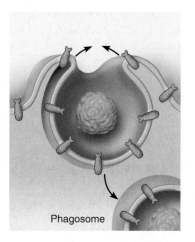

(a) Phagocytosis
The cell engulfs a large particle by forming projecting pseudopods ("false feet") around it and enclosing it within a membrane sac called a phagosome. The phagosome is combined with a lysosome. Undigested contents remain in the vesicle (now called a residual body) or are ejected by exocytosis. Vesicle may or may not be protein-coated but has receptors capable of binding to microorganisms or solid particles.

Phagosome

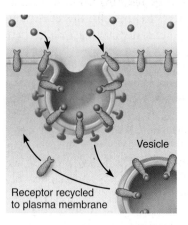

(b) Pinocytosis
The cell "gulps" drops of extracellular fluid containing solutes into tiny vesicles. No receptors are used, so the process is nonspecific. Most vesicles are protein-coated.

Vesicle

(c) Receptor-mediated endocytosis
Extracellular substances bind to specific receptor proteins in regions of coated pits, enabling the cell to ingest and concentrate specific substances (ligands) in protein-coated vesicles. Ligands may simply be released inside the cell, or combined with a lysosome to digest contents. Receptors are recycled to the plasma membrane in vesicles.

Vesicle

Receptor recycled to plasma membrane

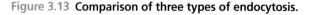

Figure 3.13 Comparison of three types of endocytosis.

Exocytosis The process of exocytosis, typically stimulated by a cell-surface signal such as binding of a hormone to a membrane receptor or a change in membrane voltage, accounts for hormone secretion, neurotransmitter release, mucus secretion, and in some cases, ejection of wastes. The substance to be removed from the cell is first enclosed in a protein-coated membranous sac called a **vesicle**. In most cases, the vesicle migrates to the plasma membrane, fuses with it, and then ruptures, spilling the sac contents out of the cell **(Figure 3.14)**.

Exocytosis, like other cases in which vesicles are targeted to their destinations, involves a "docking" process in which transmembrane proteins on the vesicles, fancifully called v-SNAREs (*v* for vesicle), recognize certain plasma membrane proteins,

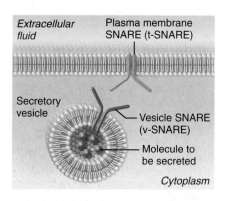

Extracellular fluid · Plasma membrane SNARE (t-SNARE)

Secretory vesicle

Vesicle SNARE (v-SNARE)

Molecule to be secreted

Cytoplasm

(a) The process of exocytosis

① The membrane-bound vesicle migrates to the plasma membrane.

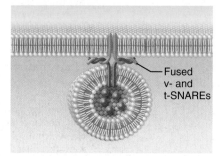

② There, proteins at the vesicle surface (v-SNAREs) bind with t-SNAREs (plasma membrane proteins).

Fused v- and t-SNAREs

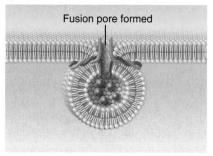

Fusion pore formed

③ The vesicle and plasma membrane fuse and a pore opens up.

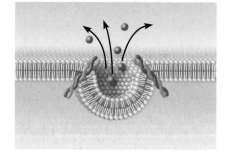

④ Vesicle contents are released to the cell exterior.

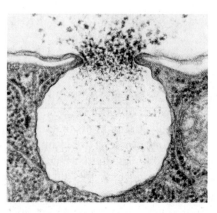

(b) Photomicrograph of a secretory vesicle releasing its contents by exocytosis (100,000×)

Figure 3.14 Exocytosis.

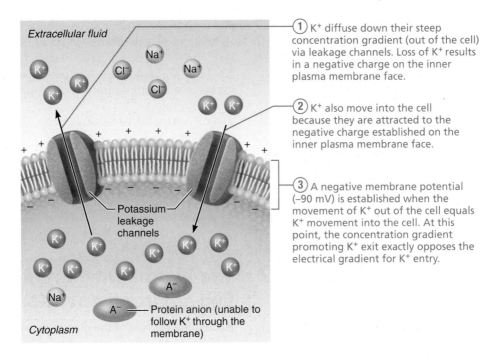

① K⁺ diffuse down their steep concentration gradient (out of the cell) via leakage channels. Loss of K⁺ results in a negative charge on the inner plasma membrane face.

② K⁺ also move into the cell because they are attracted to the negative charge established on the inner plasma membrane face.

③ A negative membrane potential (–90 mV) is established when the movement of K⁺ out of the cell equals K⁺ movement into the cell. At this point, the concentration gradient promoting K⁺ exit exactly opposes the electrical gradient for K⁺ entry.

Figure 3.15 The key role of K⁺ in generating the resting membrane potential. The resting membrane potential is largely determined by K⁺ because the membrane is much more permeable to K⁺ than Na⁺ at rest. The active transport of sodium and potassium ions (in a ratio of 3:2) by the Na⁺-K⁺ pump maintains these conditions.

called t-SNAREs (*t* for target), and bind with them. This binding causes the membranes to "corkscrew" together and fuse, rearranging the lipid monolayers without mixing them (Figure 3.14a). As described, membrane material added by exocytosis is removed by endocytosis—the reverse process.

Table 3.2 summarizes active membrane transport processes.

CHECK YOUR UNDERSTANDING

10. What happens when the Na⁺-K⁺ pump is phosphorylated? When K⁺ binds to the pump protein?
11. As a cell grows, its plasma membrane expands. Does this membrane expansion involve endocytosis or exocytosis?
12. Phagocytic cells gather in the lungs, particularly in the lungs of smokers. What is the connection?
13. What vesicular transport process allows a cell to take in cholesterol from the extracellular fluid?

For answers, see Appendix G.

The Plasma Membrane: Generation of a Resting Membrane Potential

▶ Define membrane potential and explain how the resting membrane potential is established and maintained.

As you're now aware, the selective permeability of the plasma membrane can lead to dramatic osmotic flows, but that is not its only consequence. An equally important result is the generation of a **membrane potential**, or voltage, across the membrane. A

voltage is electrical potential energy resulting from the separation of oppositely charged particles. In cells, the oppositely charged particles are ions, and the barrier that keeps them apart is the plasma membrane.

In their resting state, all body cells exhibit a **resting membrane potential** that typically ranges from –50 to –100 millivolts (mV), depending on cell type. For this reason, all cells are said to be **polarized**. The minus sign before the voltage indicates that the *inside* of the cell is negative compared to its outside. This voltage (or charge separation) exists *only at the membrane*. If we were to add up all the negative and positive charges in the cytoplasm, we would find that the cell interior is electrically neutral. Likewise, the positive and negative charges in the extracellular fluid balance each other exactly.

So how does the resting membrane potential come about, and how is it maintained? The short answer is that diffusion causes ionic imbalances that polarize the membrane, and active transport processes *maintain* that membrane potential. First, let's look at how diffusion polarizes the membrane.

Many kinds of ions are found both inside cells and in the extracellular fluid, but the resting membrane potential is determined mainly by the concentration gradient of potassium (K⁺) and by the differential permeability of the plasma membrane to K⁺ and other ions **(Figure 3.15)**. Recall that K⁺ and protein anions predominate inside body cells, and the extracellular fluid contains relatively more Na⁺, which is largely balanced by Cl⁻. The unstimulated plasma membrane is somewhat permeable to K⁺ because of leakage channels, but impermeable to the protein anions. Consequently, K⁺ diffuses out of the cell along its concentration gradient but the protein anions are unable to follow, and this loss of positive charges makes the membrane interior more negative (Figure 3.15). As more and more K^+ leaves the cell, the negativity of the inner membrane face becomes great enough to attract K^+ back toward and even into the cell. At this point (−90 mV), potassium's concentration gradient is exactly balanced by the electrical gradient (membrane potential), and one K^+ enters the cell as one leaves.

In many cells, sodium (Na^+) also contributes to the resting membrane potential. Sodium is strongly attracted to the cell interior by its concentration gradient, bringing the resting membrane potential to −70 mV. However, potassium still largely determines the resting membrane potential because the membrane is much more permeable to K^+ than to Na^+. Even though the membrane is permeable to Cl^-, in most cells Cl^- does not contribute to the resting membrane potential, because its entry is resisted by the negative charge of the interior. We may be tempted to believe that massive flows of K^+ ions are needed to generate the resting potential, but this is not the case. Surprisingly, the number of ions producing the membrane potential is so small that it does not change ion concentrations in any significant way.

In a cell at rest, very few ions cross its plasma membrane. However, Na^+ and K^+ are not at equilibrium and there is some net movement of K^+ out of the cell and of Na^+ into the cell. Na^+ is strongly pulled into the cell by both its concentration gradient and the interior negative charge. If only passive forces were at work, these ion concentrations would eventually become equal inside and outside the cell.

Now let's look at how active transport processes *maintain* the membrane potential that diffusion has established, with the result that the cell exhibits a *steady state*. The rate of active transport is equal to, and depends on, the rate of Na^+ diffusion into the cell. If more Na^+ enters, more is pumped out. (This is like being in a leaky boat. The more water that comes in, the faster you bail!) The Na^+-K^+ pump couples sodium and potassium transport and, on average, each "turn" of the pump ejects $3Na^+$ out of the cell and carries $2K^+$ back in (see Figure 3.10). Because the membrane is always 50 to 100 times more permeable to K^+, the ATP-dependent Na^+-K^+ pump maintains both the membrane potential (the charge separation) and the osmotic balance. Indeed, if Na^+ was not continuously removed from cells, in time so much would accumulate intracellularly that the osmotic gradient would draw water into the cells, causing them to burst.

Now that we've introduced the membrane potential, we can add a detail or two to our discussion of diffusion. Earlier we said that solutes diffuse down their concentration gradient. This is true for uncharged solutes, but only partially true for ions. The negatively and positively charged faces of the plasma membrane can help or hinder diffusion of ions driven by a concentration gradient. It is more correct to say that ions diffuse according to **electrochemical gradients**, thereby recognizing the effect of both electrical and concentration (chemical) forces.

Consequently, although diffusion of K^+ across the plasma membrane is aided by the membrane's greater permeability to it and by the ion's concentration gradient, its diffusion is resisted somewhat by the positive charge on the cell exterior. In contrast, Na^+ is drawn into the cell by a steep electrochemical gradient,

and the limiting factor is the membrane's relative impermeability to it. As we will describe in detail in later chapters, "upsetting" the resting membrane potential by transient opening of Na^+ and K^+ channels in the plasma membrane is a normal means of activating neurons and muscle cells.

CHECK YOUR UNDERSTANDING

14. What event or process establishes the resting membrane potential?
15. Is the inside of the plasma membrane negative or positive relative to its outside in a polarized membrane?

For answers, see Appendix G.

The Plasma Membrane: Cell-Environment Interactions

▶ Describe the role of the glycocalyx when cells interact with their environment.

▶ List several roles of membrane receptors and that of voltage-sensitive membrane channel proteins.

Cells are biological minifactories and, like other factories, they receive and send orders from and to the outside community. But *how* does a cell interact with its environment, and what activates it to carry out its homeostatic functions?

Although cells sometimes interact directly with other cells, this is not always the case. In many cases cells respond to extracellular chemicals, such as hormones and neurotransmitters distributed in body fluids. Cells also interact with extracellular molecules that act as signposts to guide cell migration during development and repair.

Whether cells interact directly or indirectly, however, the glycocalyx is always involved. The best understood of the participating glycocalyx molecules fall into two large families—cell adhesion molecules and plasma membrane receptors (see Figure 3.4). Another group of membrane proteins, the voltage-sensitive channel proteins, are important in cells that respond to electrical signals.

Roles of Cell Adhesion Molecules

Thousands of **cell adhesion molecules (CAMs)** are found on almost every cell in the body. They play key roles in embryonic development and wound repair (situations where cell mobility is important) and in immunity. These sticky glycoproteins (*cadherins* and *integrins*) act as

1. The molecular "Velcro" that cells use to anchor themselves to molecules in the extracellular space and to each other (see desmosome discussion on pp. 66–67)
2. The "arms" that migrating cells use to haul themselves past one another
3. SOS signals sticking out from the blood vessel lining that rally protective white blood cells to a nearby infected or injured area

4. Mechanical sensors that respond to local tension at the cell surface by stimulating synthesis or degradation of adhesive membrane junctions

5. Transmitters of intracellular signals that direct cell migration, proliferation, and specialization

Roles of Membrane Receptors

A huge and diverse group of integral proteins and glycoproteins that serve as binding sites are collectively known as **membrane receptors**. Some function in contact signaling, and others in chemical signaling. Let's take a look.

Contact Signaling   *Contact signaling* is the actual coming together and touching of cells, and it is the means by which cells recognize one another. It is particularly important for normal development and immunity. Some bacteria and other infectious agents use contact signaling to identify their "preferred" target tissues or organs.

Chemical Signaling   Most plasma membrane receptors are involved in *chemical signaling*, and this group will receive the bulk of our attention. Signaling chemicals that bind specifically to plasma membrane receptors are called **ligands**. Among these ligands are most *neurotransmitters* (nervous system signals), *hormones* (endocrine system signals), and *paracrines* (chemicals that act locally and are rapidly destroyed).

Different cells respond in different ways to the same ligand. Acetylcholine, for instance, stimulates skeletal muscle cells to contract, but inhibits heart muscle. Why do different cells have such different responses? The reason is that a target cell's response depends on the internal machinery that the receptor is linked to, not the specific ligand that binds to it.

Though cell responses to receptor binding vary widely, there is a fundamental similarity. When a ligand binds to a membrane receptor, the receptor's structure changes, and cell proteins are altered in some way. For example, muscle proteins change shape to generate force. Some membrane receptor proteins are *catalytic proteins* that function as enzymes. Others, such as the *chemically gated channel-linked receptors* common in muscle and nerve cells, respond to ligands by transiently opening or closing ion gates, which in turn changes the excitability of the cell.

Still other receptors are coupled to enzymes or ion channels by a regulatory molecule called a G protein. Because nearly every cell in the body displays at least some of these receptors, we will spend a bit more time with them. The lipid rafts mentioned earlier group together many receptor-mediated elements, thus facilitating cell signaling.

G protein–linked receptors exert their effect indirectly through a **G protein**, which acts as a middleman or relay to activate (or inactivate) a membrane-bound enzyme or ion channel. As a result, one or more intracellular chemical signals, commonly called **second messengers**, are generated and connect plasma membrane events to the internal metabolic machinery of the cell. Two very important second messengers are **cyclic AMP** and ionic calcium, both of which typically activate *protein kinase enzymes*, which transfer phosphate groups from

ATP to other proteins. In this way, the protein kinases can activate a whole series of enzymes that bring about the desired cellular activity. Because a single enzyme can catalyze hundreds of reactions, the amplification effect of such a chain of events is tremendous. *Focus on G Proteins* (Figure 3.16) on p. 82 describes how a G protein signaling system works. Take a moment to study this carefully because this key signaling pathway is involved in neurotransmission, smell, vision, and hormone action (Chapters 11, 15, and 16).

One important signaling molecule must be mentioned even though it doesn't act in any of the ways we have already described. *Nitric oxide* (*NO*), one of nature's simplest molecules, is made of a single atom of nitrogen and one of oxygen. It is also an environmental pollutant and the first gas known to act as a biological messenger. Because of its tiny size, it slips into and out of cells easily. Its unpaired electron makes it highly reactive and it reacts with head-spinning speed with other key molecules to spur cells into a broad array of activities. You will be hearing more about NO later (in the neural, cardiovascular, and immune system chapters).

Role of Voltage-Sensitive Membrane Channel Proteins

Electrical Signaling   In the process known as *electrical signaling*, certain plasma membrane proteins are channel proteins that respond to changes in membrane potential by opening or closing the channel. Such voltage-gated channels are common in excitable tissues like neural and muscle tissues, and are indispensable to their normal functioning.

CHECK YOUR UNDERSTANDING

16. What term is used to indicate signaling chemicals that bind to membrane receptors? Which type of membrane receptor is most important in directing intracellular events by promoting formation of second messengers?

For answer, see Appendix G.

The Cytoplasm

▶ Describe the composition of the cytosol. Define inclusions and list several types.

▶ Discuss the structure and function of mitochondria.

▶ Discuss the structure and function of ribosomes, the endoplasmic reticulum, and the Golgi apparatus, including functional interrelationships among these organelles.

▶ Compare the functions of lysosomes and peroxisomes.

Cytoplasm ("cell-forming material") is the cellular material between the plasma membrane and the nucleus. It is the site where most cellular activities are accomplished. Although early microscopists thought that the cytoplasm was a structureless gel, the electron microscope reveals that it consists of three major elements: the cytosol, organelles, and inclusions.

Figure 3.16 **FOCUS G Proteins**

G proteins act as middlemen or relays between extracellular first messengers and intracellular second messengers that cause responses within the cell.

The sequence described here is like a molecular relay race. Instead of a baton passed from runner to runner, the message is passed from molecule to molecule as it makes its way across the cell membrane from outside to inside the cell.

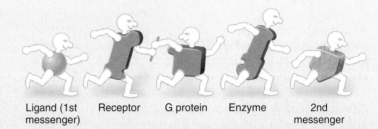

Ligand (1st messenger)   Receptor   G protein   Enzyme   2nd messenger

① **Ligand (1st messenger) binds to the receptor. The** receptor is activated and changes shape.

② **The activated receptor binds to a G protein and activates it.** During activation, a G protein changes shape (turns "on") causing it to release GDP and bind GTP.

③ **Activated G protein activates (or inactivates) effector protein (e.g., an enzyme) by causing its shape to change.**

Extracellular fluid

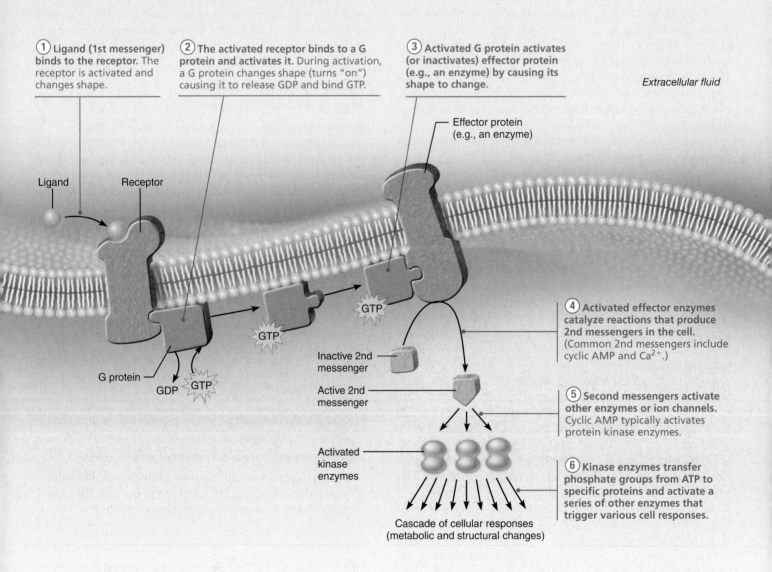

Effector protein (e.g., an enzyme)

Ligand   Receptor

G protein

GDP   GTP

GTP

GTP

Inactive 2nd messenger

Active 2nd messenger

Activated kinase enzymes

④ **Activated effector enzymes catalyze reactions that produce 2nd messengers in the cell.** (Common 2nd messengers include cyclic AMP and Ca^{2+}.)

⑤ **Second messengers activate other enzymes or ion channels.** Cyclic AMP typically activates protein kinase enzymes.

⑥ **Kinase enzymes transfer phosphate groups from ATP to specific proteins and activate a series of other enzymes that trigger various cell responses.**

Cascade of cellular responses (metabolic and structural changes)

Intracellular fluid

The **cytosol** (si′to-sol) is the viscous, semitransparent fluid in which the other cytoplasmic elements are suspended. It is a complex mixture with properties of both a colloid and a true solution. Dissolved in the cytosol, which is largely water, are proteins, salts, sugars, and a variety of other solutes.

The **cytoplasmic organelles** are the metabolic machinery of the cell. Each type of organelle carries out a specific function for the cell—some synthesize proteins, others package those proteins, and so on.

Inclusions are chemical substances that may or may not be present, depending on cell type. Examples include stored nutrients, such as the glycogen granules abundant in liver and muscle cells; lipid droplets common in fat cells; pigment (melanin) granules seen in certain cells of skin and hair; water-containing vacuoles; and crystals of various types.

Cytoplasmic Organelles

The cytoplasmic organelles ("little organs") are specialized cellular compartments, each performing its own job to maintain the life of the cell. Some organelles, the *nonmembranous organelles*, lack membranes. Examples are the cytoskeleton, centrioles, and ribosomes.

Most organelles, however, are bounded by a membrane similar in composition to the plasma membrane. This membrane enables such *membranous organelles* to maintain an internal environment different from that of the surrounding cytosol. This compartmentalization is crucial to cell functioning. Without it, thousands of enzymes would be randomly mixed and biochemical activity would be chaotic. The cell's membranous organelles include the mitochondria, peroxisomes, lysosomes, endoplasmic reticulum, and Golgi apparatus.

Besides providing "splendid isolation," an organelle's membrane often unites it with the rest of an interactive intracellular system called the *endomembrane system* (see p. 87) and the lipid makeup of its membrane allows it to recognize and interact with other organelles. Now, let us consider what goes on in each of the workshops of our cellular factory.

Mitochondria

Mitochondria (mi″to-kon′dre-ah) are threadlike (*mitos =* thread) or lozenge-shaped membranous organelles. In living cells they squirm, elongate, and change shape almost continuously. They are the power plants of a cell, providing most of its ATP supply. The density of mitochondria in a particular cell reflects that cell's energy requirements, and mitochondria are generally clustered where the action is. Busy cells like kidney and liver cells have hundreds of mitochondria, whereas relatively inactive cells (such as unchallenged lymphocytes) have just a few.

Mitochondria are enclosed by *two* membranes, each with the general structure of the plasma membrane **(Figure 3.17)**. The *outer membrane* is smooth and featureless, but the *inner membrane* folds inward, forming shelflike **cristae** (krī′ste; "crests") that protrude into the *matrix*, the gel-like substance within the mitochondrion. Intermediate products of food fuels (glucose and others) are broken down to water and carbon dioxide by

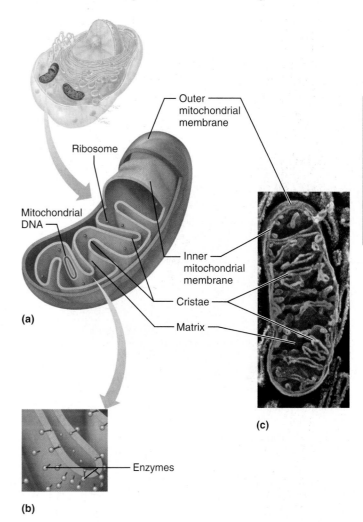

(a)

(b)

(c)

Figure 3.17 Mitochondrion. (a) Diagrammatic view of a longitudinally sectioned mitochondrion. **(b)** Close-up view of a crista showing enzymes (stalked particles). **(c)** Electron micrograph of a mitochondrion (50,000×).

teams of enzymes, some dissolved in the mitochondrial matrix and others forming part of the crista membrane.

As the metabolites are broken down and oxidized, some of the energy released is captured and used to attach phosphate groups to ADP molecules to form ATP. This multistep mitochondrial process (described in Chapter 24) is generally referred to as *aerobic cellular respiration* (a-er-o′bik) because it requires oxygen.

Mitochondria are complex organelles: They contain their own DNA, RNA, and ribosomes and are able to reproduce themselves. Mitochondrial genes (some 37 of them) direct the synthesis of 1% of the proteins required for mitochondrial function, and the DNA of the cell's nucleus encodes the remaining proteins needed to carry out cellular respiration. When cellular requirements for ATP increase, the mitochondria synthesize more cristae or simply pinch in half (a process called *fission*) to increase their number, then grow to their former size.

Intriguingly, mitochondria are similar to a specific group of bacteria (the purple bacteria phylum), and mitochondrial DNA

3

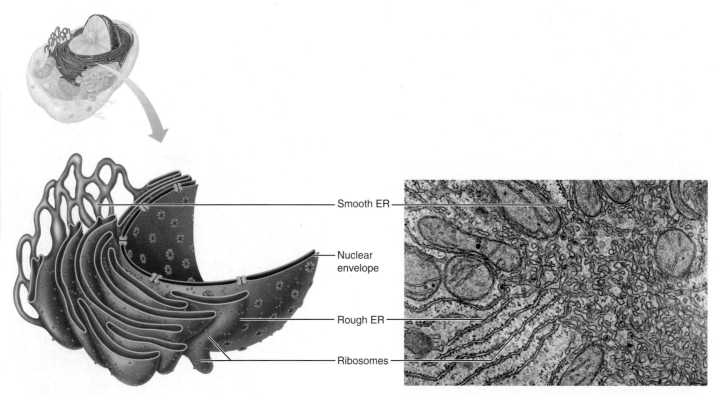

(a) Diagrammatic view of smooth and rough ER

Smooth ER

Nuclear envelope

Rough ER

Ribosomes

(b) Electron micrograph of smooth and rough ER (10,000×)

Figure 3.18 **The endoplasmic reticulum.**

is bacteria-like. It is widely believed that mitochondria arose from bacteria that invaded the ancient ancestors of plant and animal cells, and that this unique merger gave rise to all complex cells.

Ribosomes

Ribosomes (ri′bo-sōmz) are small, dark-staining granules composed of proteins and a variety of RNAs called *ribosomal RNAs*. Each ribosome has two globular subunits that fit together like the body and cap of an acorn. Ribosomes are sites of protein synthesis, a function we discuss in detail later in this chapter.

Some ribosomes float freely in the cytoplasm. Others are attached to membranes, forming a complex called the *rough endoplasmic reticulum* (**Figure 3.18**). These two ribosomal populations appear to divide the chore of protein synthesis. *Free ribosomes* make soluble proteins that function in the cytosol, as well as those imported into mitochondria and some other organelles. *Membrane-bound ribosomes* synthesize proteins destined either for incorporation into cell membranes or for export from the cell. Ribosomes can switch back and forth between these two functions, attaching to and detaching from the membranes of the endoplasmic reticulum, according to the type of protein they are making at a given time.

Endoplasmic Reticulum

The **endoplasmic reticulum (ER)** (en″do-plaz′mik re-tik′u-lum; "network within the cytoplasm") is an extensive system of interconnected tubes and parallel membranes enclosing fluid-filled

cavities, or **cisternae** (sis-ter′ne). Coiling and twisting through the cytosol, the ER is continuous with the nuclear membrane and accounts for about half of the cell's membranes. There are two distinct varieties of ER: rough ER and smooth ER.

Rough Endoplasmic Reticulum The external surface of the **rough ER** is studded with ribosomes (Figure 3.18a, b). Proteins assembled on these ribosomes thread their way into the fluid-filled interior of the ER cisternae, where various fates await them (as described on p. 106). When complete, the newly made proteins are enclosed in coatomer-coated vesicles for their journey to the Golgi apparatus where they undergo further processing.

The rough ER has several functions. Its ribosomes manufacture all proteins secreted from cells. For this reason, the rough ER is particularly abundant and well developed in most secretory cells, antibody-producing plasma cells, and liver cells, which produce most blood proteins. It is also the cell's "membrane factory" because integral proteins and phospholipids that form part of all cellular membranes are manufactured there. The enzymes needed to catalyze lipid synthesis have their active sites on the external (cytosolic) face of the ER membrane, where the needed substrates are readily available.

Smooth Endoplasmic Reticulum The **smooth ER** (see Figures 3.2 and 3.18a, b) is continuous with the rough ER and consists of tubules arranged in a looping network. Its enzymes (all integral proteins forming part of its membranes) play no role in

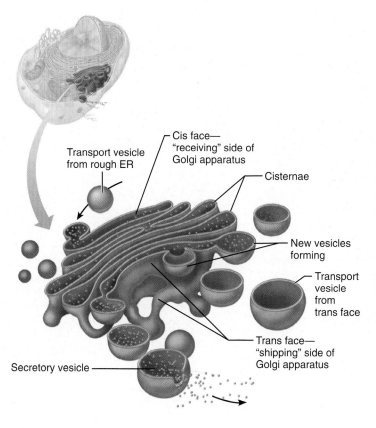

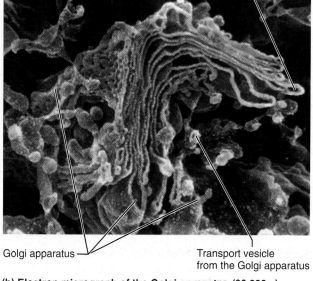

(a) Many vesicles in the process of pinching off from the membranous Golgi apparatus.

(b) Electron micrograph of the Golgi apparatus (90,000×)

Figure 3.19 Golgi apparatus. Note: In **(a)**, the various and abundant vesicles shown in the process of pinching off from the membranous Golgi apparatus would have a protein coating on their external surfaces. These proteins are omitted from the diagram for simplicity.

protein synthesis. Instead, they catalyze reactions involved with the following processes:

1. Lipid metabolism, cholesterol synthesis, and synthesis of the lipid components of lipoproteins (in liver cells)
2. Synthesis of steroid-based hormones such as sex hormones (testosterone-synthesizing cells of the testes are full of smooth ER)
3. Absorption, synthesis, and transport of fats (in intestinal cells)
4. Detoxification of drugs, certain pesticides, and carcinogens (in liver and kidneys)
5. Breakdown of stored glycogen to form free glucose (in liver cells especially)

Additionally, skeletal and cardiac muscle cells have an elaborate smooth ER (called the sarcoplasmic reticulum) that plays an important role in calcium ion storage and release during muscle contraction. Except for the examples given above, most body cells contain little, if any, true smooth ER.

Golgi Apparatus

The **Golgi apparatus** (gol′je) consists of stacked and flattened membranous sacs, shaped like hollow dinner plates, associated with swarms of tiny membranous vesicles **(Figure 3.19)**. The Golgi apparatus is the principal "traffic director" for cellular proteins. Its major function is to modify, concentrate, and package the proteins and lipids made at the rough ER.

The transport vesicles that bud off from the rough ER move to and fuse with the membranes at the convex *cis face*, the "receiving" side, of the Golgi apparatus. Inside the apparatus, the proteins are modified: Some sugar groups are trimmed while others are added, and in some cases, phosphate groups are added. The various proteins are "tagged" for delivery to a specific address, sorted, and packaged in at least three types of vesicles that bud from the concave *trans face* (the "shipping" side) of the Golgi stack.

Vesicles containing proteins destined for export pinch off from the trans face as **secretory vesicles**, or **granules**, which migrate to the plasma membrane and discharge their contents from the cell by exocytosis (pathway A, **Figure 3.20**). Specialized secretory cells, such as the enzyme-producing cells of the pancreas, have a very prominent Golgi apparatus. Besides its packaging-for-release function, the Golgi apparatus pinches off vesicles containing lipids and transmembrane proteins destined for a "home" in the plasma membrane (pathway B, Figure 3.20) or other membranous organelles. It also packages digestive

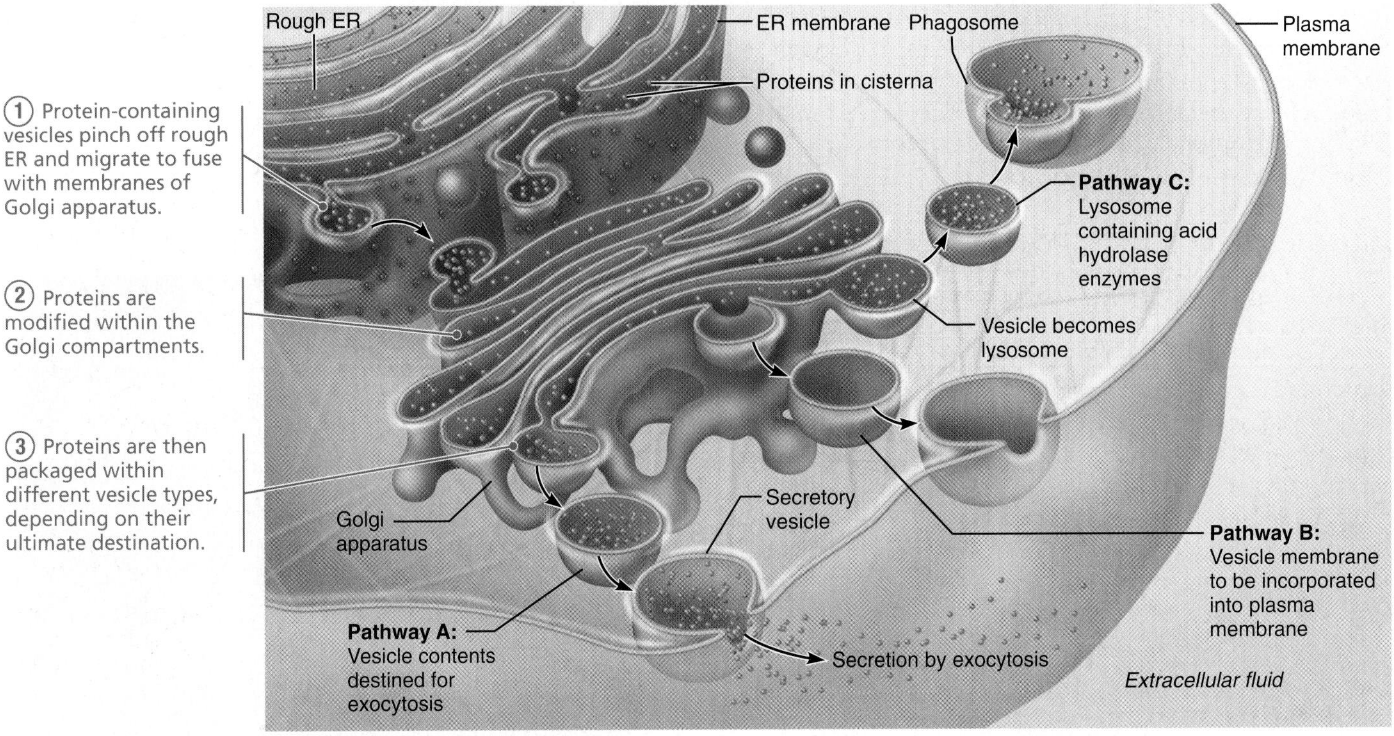

3

Rough ER

ER membrane   Phagosome

Plasma membrane

Proteins in cisterna

① Protein-containing vesicles pinch off rough ER and migrate to fuse with membranes of Golgi apparatus.

Pathway C: Lysosome containing acid hydrolase enzymes

② Proteins are modified within the Golgi compartments.

Vesicle becomes lysosome

③ Proteins are then packaged within different vesicle types, depending on their ultimate destination.

Golgi apparatus

Secretory vesicle

Pathway B: Vesicle membrane to be incorporated into plasma membrane

Pathway A: Vesicle contents destined for exocytosis

Secretion by exocytosis

Extracellular fluid

Figure 3.20 The sequence of events from protein synthesis on the rough ER to the final distribution of those proteins. The protein coats on the transport vesicles are not illustrated.

enzymes into membranous lysosomes that remain in the cell (pathway C in Figure 3.20, and discussed next).

Lysosomes

Born as endosomes which contain inactive enzymes, **lysosomes** ("disintegrator bodies") are spherical membranous organelles containing activated digestive enzymes (Figure 3.21). As you might guess, lysosomes are large and abundant within phagocytes, the cells that dispose of invading bacteria and cell debris. Lysosomal enzymes can digest almost all kinds of biological molecules. They work best in acidic conditions and so are called *acid hydrolases*.

The lysosomal membrane is adapted to serve lysosomal functions in two important ways. First, it contains H^+ (proton) "pumps," which are ATPases that gather hydrogen ions from the surrounding cytosol to maintain the organelle's acidic pH. Second, it retains the dangerous acid hydrolases while permitting the final products of digestion to escape so that they can be used by the cell or excreted. In this way, lysosomes provide sites where digestion can proceed *safely* within a cell.

Lysosomes function as a cell's "demolition crew" by

1. Digesting particles taken in by endocytosis, particularly ingested bacteria, viruses, and toxins
2. Degrading worn-out or nonfunctional organelles
3. Performing metabolic functions, such as glycogen breakdown and release
4. Breaking down nonuseful tissues, such as the webs between the fingers and toes of a developing fetus and the uterine lining during menstruation
5. Breaking down bone to release calcium ions into the blood

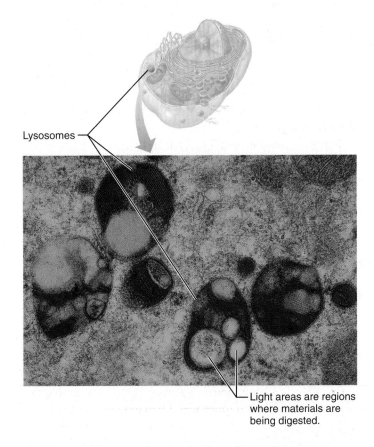

Lysosomes

Light areas are regions where materials are being digested.

Figure 3.21 Electron micrograph of a cell containing lysosomes (12,000×).

The lysosomal membrane is ordinarily quite stable, but it becomes fragile when the cell is injured or deprived of oxygen and when excessive amounts of vitamin A are present. When lysosomes rupture, the cell digests itself, a process called **autolysis** (aw″tol′ĭ-sis). Autolysis is the basis for desirable destruction of cells, as in the fourth point listed above.

HOMEOSTATIC IMBALANCE

Glycogen and certain lipids in the brain are degraded by lysosomes at a relatively constant rate. In *Tay-Sachs disease*, an inherited condition seen mostly in Jews from Central Europe, the lysosomes lack an enzyme needed to break down a glycolipid abundant in nerve cell membranes. As a result, the nerve cell lysosomes swell with the undigested lipids, which interfere with nervous system functioning. Affected infants typically have doll-like features and pink translucent skin. At 3 to 6 months of age, the first signs of disease appear (listlessness, motor weakness). These symptoms progress to mental retardation, seizures, blindness, and ultimately death within 18 months. ■

Summary of Interactions in the Endomembrane System

The **endomembrane system** is a system of organelles (most described above) that work together mainly (1) to produce, store, and export biological molecules, and (2) to degrade potentially harmful substances (**Figure 3.22**). It includes the ER, Golgi apparatus, secretory vesicles, and lysosomes, as well as the nuclear membrane—that is, all of the membranous organelles or elements that are either structurally continuous or arise via forming or fusing transport vesicles. There are continuities between the nuclear envelope (itself an extension of the rough ER) and the rough and smooth ER (Figure 3.18). The plasma membrane, though not actually an *endo*membrane, is also functionally part of this system.

Besides these direct structural relationships, a wide variety of indirect interactions (indicated by arrows in Figure 3.22) occur among the members of the system. Some of the vesicles "born" in the ER migrate to and fuse with the Golgi apparatus or the plasma membrane, and vesicles arising from the Golgi apparatus can become part of the plasma membrane, secretory vesicles, or lysosomes.

Peroxisomes

Peroxisomes (pĕ-roks′ĭ-sōmz; "peroxide bodies") are membranous sacs containing a variety of powerful enzymes, the most important of which are oxidases and catalases. Oxidases use molecular oxygen (O_2) to detoxify harmful substances, including alcohol and formaldehyde. Their most important function is to neutralize dangerous **free radicals**, highly reactive chemicals with unpaired electrons that can scramble the structure of biological molecules. Oxidases convert free radicals to hydrogen peroxide, which is also reactive and dangerous but is quickly converted to water by catalase enzymes. Free radicals and hydrogen peroxide are normal by-products of cellular metabolism, but they have devastating effects on cells if allowed to accumulate. Peroxisomes are especially

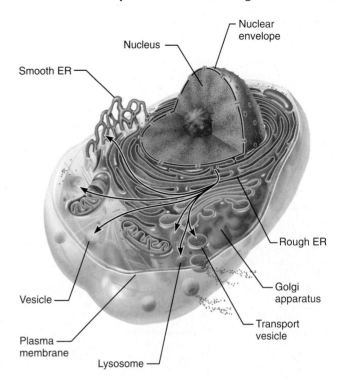

Figure 3.22 The endomembrane system.

numerous in liver and kidney cells, which are very active in detoxification. A significant amount of fatty acid oxidation also occurs in peroxisomes. Hence, they also play a role in energy metabolism.

Peroxisomes look like small lysosomes (see Figure 3.2), and for many years it was thought that they were self-replicating organelles formed when existing peroxisomes simply pinch in half. Recent evidence, however, suggests that most new peroxisomes form by budding off of the endoplasmic reticulum.

CHECK YOUR UNDERSTANDING

17. What organelle is the major site of ATP synthesis?

18. What are three organelles involved in protein synthesis and how do these organelles interact in that process?

19. How does the function of lysosomes compare to that of peroxisomes?

For answers, see Appendix G.

Cytoskeleton

▶ Name and describe the structure and function of cytoskeletal elements.

The **cytoskeleton**, literally, "cell skeleton," is an elaborate network of rods running through the cytosol. It acts as a cell's "bones," "muscles," and "ligaments" by supporting cellular structures and providing the machinery to generate various cell movements. The three types of rods in order of increasing size in the cytoskeleton are *microfilaments, intermediate filaments,* and *microtubules.* None of these is membrane covered.

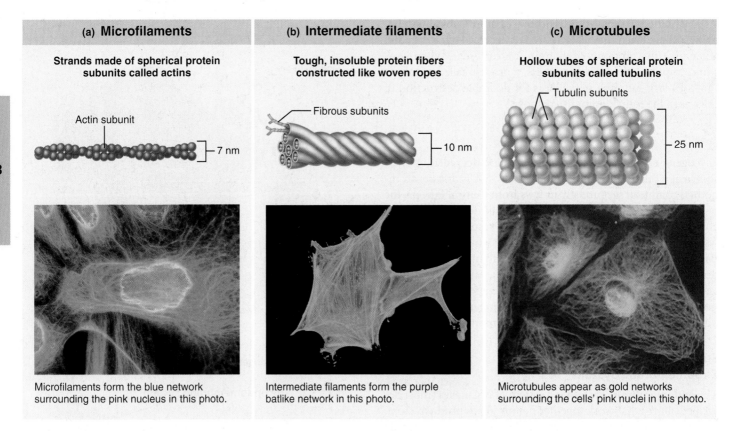

(a) Microfilaments	(b) Intermediate filaments	(c) Microtubules
Strands made of spherical protein subunits called actins	**Tough, insoluble protein fibers constructed like woven ropes**	**Hollow tubes of spherical protein subunits called tubulins**

Microfilaments form the blue network surrounding the pink nucleus in this photo.

Intermediate filaments form the purple batlike network in this photo.

Microtubules appear as gold networks surrounding the cells' pink nuclei in this photo.

Figure 3.23 Cytoskeletal elements support the cell and help to generate movement. Diagrammatic views (above) and photos (below). The photos are of fibroblasts treated to fluorescently tag the structure of interest.

Microtubules (mi″kro-tu′būlz), the elements with the largest diameter, are hollow tubes made of spherical protein subunits called *tubulins* (Figure 3.23c). Most microtubules radiate from a small region of cytoplasm near the nucleus called the *centrosome* or *cell center* (see Figures 3.2, 3.25). Microtubules are remarkably dynamic organelles, constantly growing out from the centrosome, disassembling, and then reassembling at the same or different sites. The stiff but bendable microtubules determine the overall shape of the cell, as well as the distribution of cellular organelles.

Mitochondria, lysosomes, and secretory vesicles attach to the microtubules like ornaments hanging from tree branches. They are continually moved along the microtubules and repositioned by tiny protein machines called **motor proteins** (*kinesins, dyneins,* and others) or **motor molecules**. The various motor proteins work by changing their shapes. Powered by ATP, some motor proteins appear to act like train engines moving substances along on the microtubular "railroad tracks." No one analogy completely captures their action, but the most common analogy has these motor molecules moving "hand over hand" somewhat like an orangutan—gripping, releasing, and then gripping again at a new site further along the microtubule (Figure 3.24a).

Microfilaments (mi″kro-fil′ah-ments), the thinnest elements of the cytoskeleton, are strands of the protein *actin* ("ray") (Figure 3.23a). Each cell has its own unique arrangement of mi-crofilaments, so no two cells are alike. However, nearly all cells have a fairly dense cross-linked network of microfilaments, called the *terminal web*, attached to the cytoplasmic side of their plasma membrane. The web strengthens the cell surface and resists compression.

Most microfilaments are involved in cell motility or changes in cell shape. You could say that cells move "when they get their act(in) together." For example, actin filaments interact with another protein, *unconventional myosin* (mi′o-sin), to generate contractile forces in a cell (Figure 3.24b). This interaction also forms the cleavage furrow that pinches one cell into two during cell division. Microfilaments attached to CAMs (see Figure 3.4e) are responsible for the crawling movements of amoeboid motion, and for the membrane changes that accompany endocytosis and exocytosis. Except in muscle cells, where they are highly developed, stable, and long-lived, actin filaments are constantly breaking down and re-forming from smaller subunits whenever and wherever their services are needed.

Intermediate filaments are tough, insoluble protein fibers that have a diameter between those of microfilaments and microtubules (Figure 3.23b). Constructed like woven ropes, intermediate filaments are the most stable and permanent of the cytoskeletal elements and have high tensile strength. Unlike microtubules and microfilaments, intermediate filaments do not bind ATP or serve as "tracks" for molecular motors to transport intracellular substances. Instead, they attach to desmosomes,

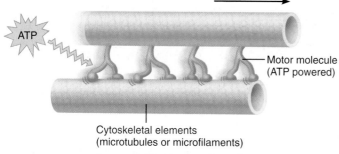

(a) Motor molecules can attach to receptors on vesicles or organelles, and "walk" the organelles along the microtubules of the cytoskeleton.

(b) In some types of cell motility, motor molecules attached to one element of the cytoskeleton can cause it to slide over another element, as in muscle contraction and cilia movement.

Figure 3.24 Microtubules and microfilaments function in cell motility by interacting with motor molecules. The various motor molecules, all powered by ATP, work by changing their shapes, moving back or forth on something like microscopic legs. With each cycle of shape changes, the motor molecule releases its free end and grips at a site farther along the microtubule or microfilament.

and their main job is to act as internal guy-wires to resist pulling forces exerted on the cell. Because the protein composition of intermediate filaments varies in different cell types, there are numerous names for these cytoskeletal elements—for example, they are called neurofilaments in nerve cells and keratin filaments in epithelial cells.

Centrosome and Centrioles

▶ Describe the roles of centrioles in mitosis and in formation of cilia and flagella.

As mentioned, microtubules are anchored at one end in an inconspicuous region near the nucleus called the **centrosome** or *cell center*. The centrosome acts as a *microtubule organizing center*. It has few distinguishing marks other than a granular-looking

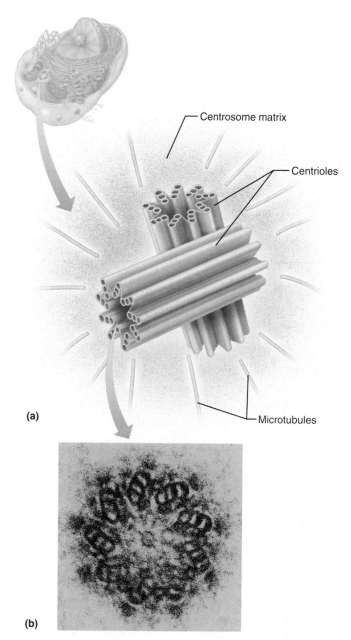

(a)

(b)

Figure 3.25 Centrioles. (a) Three-dimensional view of a centriole pair oriented at right angles, as they are usually seen in the cell. The centrioles are located in an inconspicuous region to one side of the nucleus called the centrosome, or cell center. **(b)** An electron micrograph showing a cross section of a centriole (120,000×). Notice that it is composed of nine microtubule triplets.

matrix that contains paired **centrioles**, small, barrel-shaped organelles oriented at right angles to each other **(Figure 3.25)**. The centrosome matrix is best known for generating microtubules and organizing the mitotic spindle in cell division (see Figure 3.33). Each centriole consists of a pinwheel array of nine *triplets* of microtubules, each connected to the next by nontubulin proteins and arranged to form a hollow tube. Centrioles also form the bases of cilia and flagella, our next topics.

3

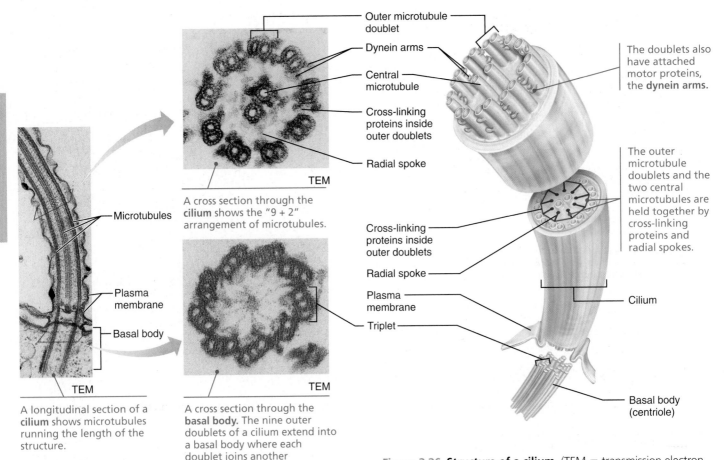

Outer microtubule doublet

Dynein arms

Central microtubule

Cross-linking proteins inside outer doublets

Radial spoke

TEM

A cross section through the **cilium** shows the "9 + 2" arrangement of microtubules.

Microtubules

Plasma membrane

Basal body

TEM

A longitudinal section of a **cilium** shows microtubules running the length of the structure.

Cross-linking proteins inside outer doublets

Radial spoke

Plasma membrane

Triplet

TEM

A cross section through the **basal body**. The nine outer doublets of a cilium extend into a basal body where each doublet joins another microtubule to form a ring of nine triplets.

The doublets also have attached motor proteins, the **dynein arms**.

The outer microtubule doublets and the two central microtubules are held together by cross-linking proteins and radial spokes.

Cilium

Basal body (centriole)

Figure 3.26 Structure of a cilium. (TEM = transmission electron micrograph.)

Cellular Extensions

▶ Describe how the two main types of cell extensions, cilia and microvilli, differ in structure and function.

Cilia and Flagella

Cilia (sil′e-ah; "eyelashes") are whiplike, motile cellular extensions that occur, typically in large numbers, on the exposed surfaces of certain cells **(Figure 3.26)**. Ciliary action moves substances in one direction across cell surfaces. For example, ciliated cells that line the respiratory tract propel mucus laden with dust particles and bacteria upward away from the lungs.

When a cell is about to form cilia, the centrioles multiply and line up beneath the plasma membrane at the free cell surface. Microtubules then begin to "sprout" from each centriole, forming the ciliary projections by exerting pressure on the plasma membrane.

When the projections formed by centrioles are substantially longer, they are called **flagella** (flah-jel′ah). The single example of a flagellated cell in the human body is a sperm, which has one propulsive flagellum, commonly called a tail. Notice that cilia *propel other substances* across a cell's surface, whereas a flagellum *propels the cell itself.*

Centrioles forming the bases of cilia and flagella are commonly referred to as **basal bodies** (ba′sal) (Figure 3.26). They were given a separate name because they were thought to be

different from the structures seen in the centrosome. We now know that centrioles and basal bodies are modifications of the same structure. The "9 + 2" pattern of microtubules in the cilium or flagellum itself (nine *doublets,* or pairs, of microtubules encircling one central pair) differs slightly from that of a centriole (nine microtubule *triplets*). Additionally, the cilium has flexible "wagon wheels" of cross-linking proteins (purple in Figure 3.26), and motor proteins (green dynein arms in Figure 3.26) that promote movement of the cilium or flagellum.

Just how ciliary activity is coordinated is not fully understood, but microtubules are definitely involved. Extending from the microtubule doublets are arms composed of the motor protein dynein (Figure 3.26). The dynein side arms of one doublet grip the adjacent doublet, and powered by ATP, push it up, release, and then grip again. Because the doublets are physically restricted by other proteins, they cannot slide far and instead are forced to bend. The collective bending action of all the doublets causes the cilium to bend.

As a cilium moves, it alternates rhythmically between a propulsive *power stroke,* when it is nearly straight and moves in an arc, and a *recovery stroke,* when it bends and returns to its initial position **(Figure 3.27a)**. With these two strokes, the cilium produces a pushing motion in a single direction that is repeated some 10 to 20 times per second. The activity of cilia in a particular region is coordinated so that the bending of one cilium is

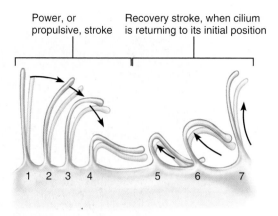

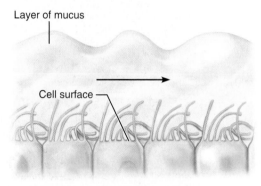

Power, or propulsive, stroke

Recovery stroke, when cilium is returning to its initial position

1 2 3 4 5 6 7

(a) Phases of ciliary motion.

Layer of mucus

Cell surface

(b) Traveling wave created by the activity of many cilia acting together propels mucus across cell surfaces.

Figure 3.27 Ciliary function.

quickly followed by the bending of the next and then the next, creating a current at the cell surface that brings to mind the traveling waves that pass across a field of grass on a windy day (Figure 3.27b).

Microvilli

Microvilli (mi″kro-vil′i; "little shaggy hairs") are minute, fingerlike extensions of the plasma membrane that project from a free, or exposed, cell surface (Figure 3.5 top and **Figure 3.28**). They increase the plasma membrane surface area tremendously and are most often found on the surface of absorptive cells such as intestinal and kidney tubule cells. Microvilli have a core of bundled actin filaments that extend into the so-called *terminal web* of the cytoskeleton of the cell. Actin is sometimes a contractile protein, but in microvilli it appears to function as a mechanical "stiffener."

CHECK YOUR UNDERSTANDING

20. How are microtubules and microfilaments related functionally?

21. Of microfilaments, microtubules, or intermediate filaments, which is most important in maintaining cell shape?

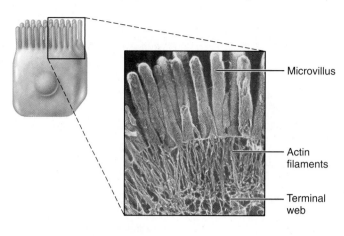

Microvillus

Actin filaments

Terminal web

Figure 3.28 Microvilli.

22. The major function of cilia is to move substances across the free cell surface. What is the major role of microvilli?

For answers, see Appendix G.

The Nucleus

▶ Outline the structure and function of the nuclear envelope, nucleolus, and chromatin.

Anything that works, works best when it is controlled. For cells, the control center is the gene-containing **nucleus** (*nucle* = pit, kernel). The nucleus can be compared to a computer, design department, construction boss, and board of directors—all rolled into one. As the genetic library, it contains the instructions needed to build nearly all the body's proteins. Additionally, it dictates the kinds and amounts of proteins to be synthesized at any one time in response to signals acting on the cell.

Most cells have only one nucleus, but some, including skeletal muscle cells, bone destruction cells, and some liver cells, are **multinucleate** (mul″tĭ-nu′kle-āt), that is, they have many nuclei. The presence of more than one nucleus usually signifies that a larger-than-usual cytoplasmic mass must be regulated.

With one exception, all of our body cells are nucleated. The exception is mature red blood cells, whose nuclei are ejected before the cells enter the bloodstream. These **anucleate** (a-nu′kle-āt; *a* = without) cells cannot reproduce and therefore live in the bloodstream for only three to four months before they begin to deteriorate. Without a nucleus, a cell cannot produce mRNA to make proteins, and when its enzymes and cell structures start to break down (as all eventually do), they cannot be replaced.

The nucleus, averaging 5 μm in diameter, is larger than any of the cytoplasmic organelles. Although most often spherical or oval, its shape usually conforms to the shape of the cell. The nucleus has three recognizable regions or structures: the *nuclear envelope* (*membrane*), *nucleoli*, and *chromatin* (**Figure 3.29a**). Besides these structures, there are several distinct compartments (a splicing factor compartment and others) rich in specific sets of proteins. These are not limited by membranes and

3

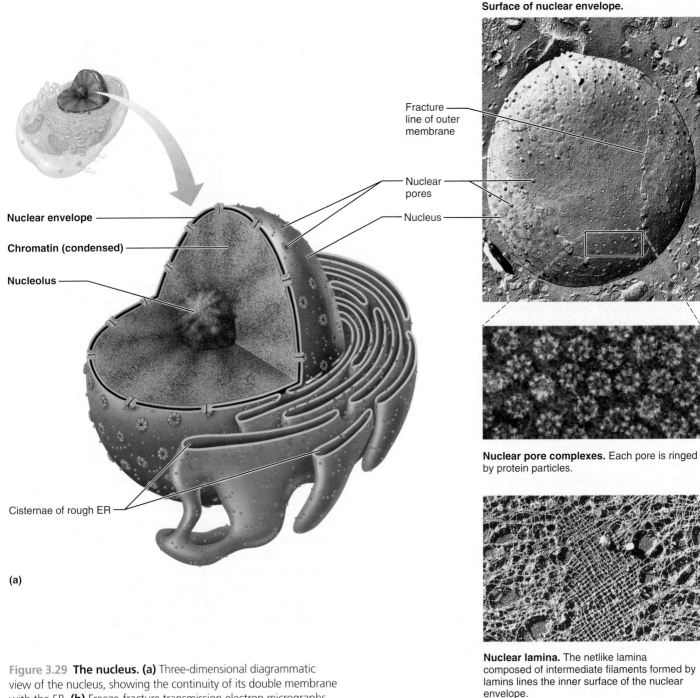

Surface of nuclear envelope.

Fracture line of outer membrane

Nuclear pores

Nucleus

Nuclear envelope

Chromatin (condensed)

Nucleolus

Cisternae of rough ER

(a)

Nuclear pore complexes. Each pore is ringed by protein particles.

Nuclear lamina. The netlike lamina composed of intermediate filaments formed by lamins lines the inner surface of the nuclear envelope.

(b)

Figure 3.29 The nucleus. (a) Three-dimensional diagrammatic view of the nucleus, showing the continuity of its double membrane with the ER. **(b)** Freeze-fracture transmission electron micrographs (TEMs).

are in a constant state of dynamic flux. Much remains to be learned about them.

The Nuclear Envelope

The nucleus is bounded by the **nuclear envelope**, a *double* membrane barrier separated by a fluid-filled space (similar to the mitochondrial membrane). The outer nuclear membrane is continuous with the rough ER of the cytoplasm and is studded with ribosomes on its external face. The inner nuclear membrane is lined by the *nuclear lamina*, a network of *lamins* (rod-

shaped proteins that assemble to form intermediate filaments) that maintains the shape of the nucleus and acts as a scaffold to organize DNA in the nucleus (Figure 3.29b, bottom).

At various points, the two layers of the nuclear envelope interconnect to form the edges of **nuclear pores**. An intricate complex of proteins, called a *nuclear pore complex* (NPC), lines each pore, forming an aqueous transport channel and regulating entry and exit of molecules (e.g., mRNAs) and large particles into and out of the nucleus (see Figure 3.29b, middle).

Like other cell membranes, the nuclear envelope is selectively permeable, but here passage of substances is much freer than elsewhere. Small molecules pass through the relatively large nuclear pore complexes unimpeded. Protein molecules imported from the cytoplasm and RNA molecules exported from the nucleus are transported through the central channel of the pores in an energy-dependent process by soluble transport proteins (importins and others).

The nuclear envelope encloses a jellylike fluid called *nucleoplasm* (nu'kle-o-plazm) in which other nuclear elements are suspended. Like the cytosol, the nucleoplasm contains dissolved salts, nutrients, and other essential solutes.

Nucleoli

Nucleoli (nu-kle′o-li; "little nuclei") are the dark-staining spherical bodies found within the nucleus. They are not membrane bounded. Typically, there are one or two nucleoli per nucleus, but there may be more. Because they are sites where ribosomal subunits are assembled, nucleoli are usually large in growing cells that are making large amounts of tissue proteins.

Nucleoli are associated with *nucleolar organizer regions*, which contain the DNA that issues genetic instructions for synthesizing ribosomal RNA (rRNA). As molecules of rRNA are synthesized, they are combined with proteins to form the two kinds of ribosomal subunits. (The proteins are manufactured on ribosomes in the cytoplasm and "imported" into the nucleus.) Most of these subunits leave the nucleus through the nuclear pores and enter the cytoplasm, where they join to form functional ribosomes.

Chromatin

Seen through a light microscope, **chromatin** (kro′mah-tin) appears as a fine, unevenly stained network, but special techniques reveal it as a system of bumpy threads weaving their way through the nucleoplasm. Chromatin is composed of about 30% **DNA**, which is traditionally called our genetic material, about 60% globular **histone proteins** (his′tōn), and about 10% RNA chains, newly formed or forming. The fundamental units of chromatin are **nucleosomes** (nu′kle-o-sōmz; "nuclear bodies"), which consist of flattened disc-shaped cores or clusters of eight histone proteins connected like beads on a string by a DNA molecule. The DNA winds (like a ribbon of Velcro) twice around each nucleosome and continues on to the next cluster via *linker DNA* segments (**Figure 3.30**, top).

Histones provide a physical means for packing the very long DNA molecules in a compact, orderly way, but they also play an important role in gene regulation. In a nondividing cell, for example, the presence of methyl groups on histone proteins shuts down the nearby DNA, and attachment of a phosphate group to a particular histone protein may indicate that the cell is about to commit suicide. On the other hand, addition of acetyl groups to histone exposes different DNA segments, or genes, so that they can dictate the specifications for protein synthesis or for various small RNA species. Such active chromatin segments, referred to as *extended chromatin*, are not usually visible under the light microscope. The generally inactive *condensed chromatin* segments are darker staining and so are more easily detected. Understandably, the most active body cells have much larger amounts of extended chromatin. Interestingly, particular chromatin strands

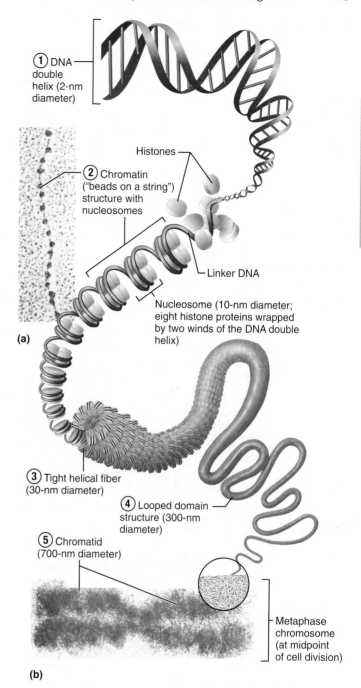

(a)

(b)

Figure 3.30 Chromatin and chromosome structure. (a) Electron micrograph of chromatin fiber (125,000×). **(b)** DNA packing in a chromosome. The levels of increasing structural complexity (coiling) from the DNA helix to the metaphase chromosome are indicated in order from the smallest (① DNA double helix) to the largest and most complex (⑤ chromosome).

occupy discrete regions in the nucleus called *chromosome territories*. Depending on the specific genes contained, and the cell and tissue type, the chromosome territory patterns change during development. At the simplest level, active and inactive genetic regions can be separated from each other or genetic expression can be enhanced or repressed by such chromatin separation.

When a cell is preparing to divide, the chromatin threads coil and condense enormously to form short, barlike bodies called

TABLE 3.3	Parts of the Cell: Structure and Function	
CELL PART	**STRUCTURE**	**FUNCTIONS**
Plasma Membrane (Figure 3.3)		
	Membrane made of a double layer of lipids (phospholipids, cholesterol, and so on) within which proteins are embedded. Proteins may extend entirely through the lipid bilayer or protrude on only one face. Externally facing proteins and some lipids have attached sugar groups.	Serves as an external cell barrier, and acts in transport of substances into or out of the cell. Maintains a resting potential that is essential for functioning of excitable cells. Externally facing proteins act as receptors (for hormones, neurotransmitters, and so on) and in cell-to-cell recognition.
Cytoplasm		
	Cellular region between the nuclear and plasma membranes. Consists of fluid **cytosol** containing dissolved solutes, **organelles** (the metabolic machinery of the cytoplasm), and **inclusions** (stored nutrients, secretory products, pigment granules).	
Cytoplasmic Organelles		
▪ Mitochondria (Figure 3.17)	Rodlike, double-membrane structures; inner membrane folded into projections called cristae.	Site of ATP synthesis; powerhouse of the cell.
▪ Ribosomes (Figures 3.18, 3.37–3.39)	Dense particles consisting of two subunits, each composed of ribosomal RNA and protein. Free or attached to rough endoplasmic reticulum.	The sites of protein synthesis.
▪ Rough endoplasmic reticulum (Figures 3.18, 3.39)	Membrane system enclosing a cavity, the cisterna, and coiling through the cytoplasm. Externally studded with ribosomes.	Sugar groups are attached to proteins within the cisternae. Proteins are bound in vesicles for transport to the Golgi apparatus and other sites. External face synthesizes phospholipids.
▪ Smooth endoplasmic reticulum (Figure 3.18)	Membranous system of sacs and tubules; free of ribosomes.	Site of lipid and steroid (cholesterol) synthesis, lipid metabolism, and drug detoxification.
▪ Golgi apparatus (Figures 3.19, 3.20)	A stack of smooth membrane sacs and associated vesicles close to the nucleus.	Packages, modifies, and segregates proteins for secretion from the cell, inclusion in lysosomes, and incorporation into the plasma membrane.
▪ Lysosomes (Figure 3.21)	Membranous sacs containing acid hydrolases.	Sites of intracellular digestion.
▪ Peroxisomes (Figure 3.2)	Membranous sacs of oxidase enzymes.	The enzymes detoxify a number of toxic substances. The most important enzyme, catalase, breaks down hydrogen peroxide.
▪ Microtubules (Figures 3.23–3.25)	Cylindrical structures made of tubulin proteins.	Support the cell and give it shape. Involved in intracellular and cellular movements. Form centrioles and cilia and flagella, if present.
▪ Microfilaments (Figures 3.23, 3.24)	Fine filaments composed of the protein actin.	Involved in muscle contraction and other types of intracellular movement, help form the cell's cytoskeleton.
▪ Intermediate filaments (Figure 3.23)	Protein fibers; composition varies.	The stable cytoskeletal elements; resist mechanical forces acting on the cell.
▪ Centrioles (Figure 3.25)	Paired cylindrical bodies, each composed of nine triplets of microtubules.	Organize a microtubule network during mitosis to form the spindle and asters. Form the bases of cilia and flagella.
Inclusions	Varied; includes stored nutrients such as lipid droplets and glycogen granules, protein crystals, pigment granules.	Storage for nutrients, wastes, and cell products.

TABLE 3.3	(continued)	
CELL PART	**STRUCTURE**	**FUNCTIONS**
Cellular Extensions		
▪ Cilia (Figure 3.26, 3.27)	Short cell-surface projections; each cilium composed of nine pairs of microtubules surrounding a central pair.	Coordinated movement creates a unidirectional current that propels substances across cell surfaces.
▪ Flagella	Like a cilium, but longer; only example in humans is the sperm tail.	Propel the cell.
▪ Microvilli (Figure 3.28)	Tubular extensions of the plasma membrane; contain a bundle of actin filaments.	Increase surface area for absorption.
Nucleus (Figure 3.2, 3.29)		
	Largest organelle. Surrounded by the nuclear envelope; contains fluid nucleoplasm, nucleoli, and chromatin.	Control center of the cell; responsible for transmitting genetic information and providing the instructions for protein synthesis.
▪ Nuclear envelope (Figure 3.29)	Double-membrane structure pierced by pores. Outer membrane continuous with the endoplasmic reticulum.	Separates the nucleoplasm from the cytoplasm and regulates passage of substances to and from the nucleus.
▪ Nucleoli (Figure 3.29)	Dense spherical (non-membrane-bounded) bodies, composed of ribosomal RNA and proteins.	Site of ribosome subunit manufacture.
▪ Chromatin (Figure 3.30)	Granular, threadlike material composed of DNA and histone proteins.	DNA constitutes the genes.

chromosomes ("colored bodies") (Figure 3.30, bottom). Chromosome compactness prevents the delicate chromatin strands from tangling and breaking during the movements that occur during cell division. We describe the functions of DNA and the events of cell division in the next section.

Table 3.3 summarizes the parts of the cell.

CHECK YOUR UNDERSTANDING

23. If a cell ejects or loses its nucleus, what is its fate and why?

24. What is the role of nucleoli?

25. What is the importance of the histone proteins present in the nucleus?

For answers, see Appendix G.

Cell Growth and Reproduction

The Cell Life Cycle

▶ List the phases of the cell life cycle and describe the key events of each phase.

▶ Describe the process of DNA replication.

The **cell life cycle** is the series of changes a cell goes through from the time it is formed until it reproduces. The outer ring of Figure 3.31 shows the two major periods of the cell cycle:

interphase (in green), in which the cell grows and carries on its usual activities, and *cell division* or the *mitotic phase* (in yellow), during which it divides into two cells.

Interphase

Interphase is the period from cell formation to cell division. Early cytologists, unaware of the constant molecular activity in cells and impressed by the obvious movements of cell division, called interphase the resting phase of the cell cycle. (The term *interphase* reflects this idea of a stage *between* cell divisions.) However, this image is grossly misleading because during interphase a cell is carrying out all its routine activities and is "resting" only from dividing. Perhaps a more accurate name for this phase would be *metabolic phase* or *growth phase*.

Subphases In addition to carrying on its life-sustaining reactions, an interphase cell prepares for the next cell division. Interphase is divided into G_1, S, and G_2 subphases (the Gs stand for *gaps* before and after the S phase, and S is for *synthetic*). In all three subphases, the cell grows by producing proteins and organelles, but chromatin is reproduced only during the S subphase.

During G_1 (**gap 1**), the cell is metabolically active, synthesizing proteins rapidly and growing vigorously (Figure 3.31, light green area). This is the most variable phase in terms of length. In cells that divide rapidly, G_1 typically lasts several minutes to hours, but in those that divide slowly, it may last for days or even

3

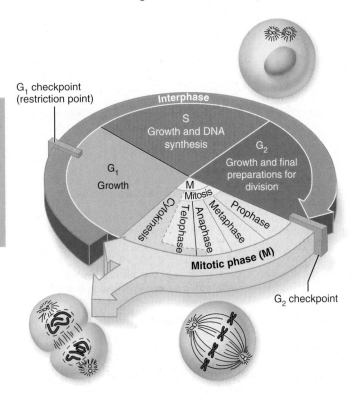

Figure 3.31 The cell cycle. During G₁, cells grow rapidly and carry out their routine functions. The S phase is the period of DNA synthesis. In G₂, materials needed for cell division are synthesized and growth continues. During the M phase (cell division), mitosis and cytokinesis occur, producing two daughter cells. Important checkpoints at which mitosis may be prevented from occurring are found throughout interphase; two are shown on the diagram.

years. Cells that permanently cease dividing are said to be in the **G₀ phase**. For most of G₁, virtually no activities directly related to cell division occur. However, as G₁ ends, the centrioles start to replicate in preparation for cell division.

During the **S phase**, DNA is replicated, ensuring that the two future cells being created will receive identical copies of the genetic material (Figure 3.31, blue area). New histones are made and assembled into chromatin. One thing is sure: Without a proper S phase, there can be no correct mitotic phase. (We will describe DNA replication next.)

The final phase of interphase, called G₂, is brief (Figure 3.31, dark green area). Enzymes and other proteins needed for division are synthesized and moved to their proper sites. By the end of G₂, centriole replication (begun in G₁) is complete. The cell is now ready to divide. Throughout S and G₂, the cell continues to grow and carries on with business as usual.

DNA Replication   Before a cell can divide, its DNA must be replicated exactly, so that identical copies of the cell's genes can be passed on to each of its offspring. During the S phase, replication begins simultaneously on several chromatin threads and continues until all the DNA has been replicated.

Replication is still being studied but appears to involve the following events:

1. The DNA helices begin unwinding from the histones of the nucleosomes.
2. In an ATP-requiring process, a *helicase* enzyme untwists the double helix and gradually separates the DNA molecule into two complementary nucleotide chains, exposing the nitrogenous bases. The Y-shaped site of separation, where active DNA replication will soon begin, is called the *replication fork* (Figure 3.32).
3. Each nucleotide strand then serves as a *template*, or set of instructions, for building a new complementary nucleotide strand from free DNA precursors dissolved in the nucleoplasm.
4. At sites where DNA synthesis is to occur, the needed "machinery" gradually accumulates until several different proteins (mostly enzymes) are present in a large complex called a **replisome**. Primase enzymes, which are part of the replisome, catalyze the formation of short (about ten bases long) **RNA primers**, which actually initiate DNA synthesis.
5. Once the primer is in place, the enzyme **DNA polymerase** comes into the picture. Continuing from the primer, it positions complementary nucleotides along the template strand and then covalently links them together. So, if the DNA polymerase encounters the sequence of bases GCT on the template strand, it assembles the bases CGA to bind to it. DNA polymerase works only in one direction. Consequently, one strand, the *leading strand*, is synthesized continuously (once primed by the RNA primer) following the movement of the replication fork. The other strand, called the *lagging strand*, is constructed in segments in the opposite direction and requires that a primer initiate replication of each segment. These primers are eventually replaced with DNA nucleotides by DNA polymerases.
6. The short segments of DNA are then spliced together by **DNA ligase**. The end result is that two DNA molecules are formed from the original DNA helix and are identical to it. Because each new molecule consists of one old and one new nucleotide strand, this mechanism of DNA replication is called **semiconservative replication** (Figure 3.32). Replication also involves the generation of two new *telomeres* (*tel* = end; *mer* = piece), snugly fitting nucleoprotein caps that prevent degradation of the ends of the chromatin strands.

As soon as replication ends, histones (synthesized in the cytoplasm and imported into the nucleus) associate with the DNA, completing the formation of two new chromatin strands. The chromatin strands, united by a buttonlike centromere (a stretch of repetitive DNA), remain attached, held together by the centromere and a protein complex called *cohesin*, until the cell enters the anaphase stage of mitotic cell division (see p. 99). They are then distributed to the daughter cells as described next, ensuring that each cell has identical genetic information.

The progression from DNA synthesis into the events of cell division presumes that the newly synthesized DNA is not damaged or broken in any way. If damage occurs, progress through

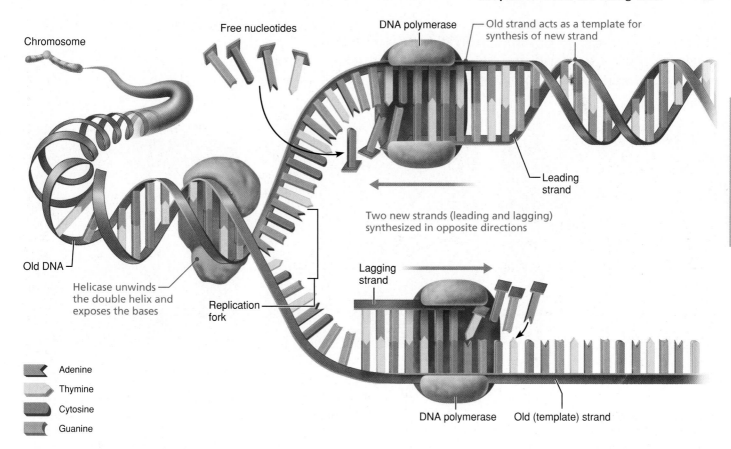

Figure 3.32 Replication of DNA. The DNA helix uncoils, and the hydrogen bonds between its base pairs are broken. Then, each nucleotide strand of the DNA acts as a template for constructing a complementary strand, as illustrated on the right-hand side of the diagram. DNA polymerases work in one direction only, so the two new strands (leading and lagging) are synthesized in opposite directions. (The DNA ligase enzymes that join the DNA fragments on the lagging strand are not illustrated.) Each DNA molecule formed consists of one old (template) strand and one newly assembled strand and constitutes a chromatid of a chromosome.

the cell cycle is arrested until the DNA repair mechanism has fixed the problem.

Cell Division

Cell division is essential for body growth and tissue repair. Cells that continually wear away, such as cells of the skin and intestinal lining, reproduce themselves almost continuously. Others, such as liver cells, divide more slowly (to maintain the particular size of the organ they compose) but retain the ability to reproduce quickly if the organ is damaged. Most cells of nervous tissue, skeletal muscle, and heart muscle lose their ability to divide when they are fully mature, and repairs are made with scar tissue (a fibrous type of connective tissue).

Events of Cell Division In most body cells, cell division, which is called the **M (mitotic) phase** of the cell life cycle, involves two distinct events: **mitosis** (mi-to′sis; *mit* = thread; *osis* = process), or division of the nucleus, and **cytokinesis** (si-to-kĭ-ne′sis; *kines* = movement), or division of the cytoplasm (see Figure 3.31, yellow area). A somewhat different process of nuclear division called *meiosis* (mi-o′sis) produces sex cells (ova

and sperm) with only half the number of genes found in other body cells. We discuss the details of meiosis in Chapter 27. Here we concentrate on mitotic cell division.

Mitosis Mitosis is the series of events that parcel out the replicated DNA of the mother cell to two daughter cells. It is described in terms of four phases: **prophase**, **metaphase**, **anaphase**, and **telophase**, but it is actually a continuous process, with one phase merging smoothly into the next. Its duration varies according to cell type, but in human cells it typically lasts about an hour or less from start to finish. *Focus on Mitosis* **(Figure 3.33)**, pp. 98–99, describes the phases of mitosis in detail.

Cytokinesis Cytokinesis, or the division of the cytoplasm, begins during late anaphase and is completed after mitosis ends. The plasma membrane over the center of the cell (the spindle equator) is drawn inward to form a **cleavage furrow** by the activity of a *contractile ring* (Figure 3.33) made of actin filaments. The furrow deepens until the cytoplasmic mass is pinched into two parts, so that at the end of cytokinesis there are two daughter cells. Each is smaller and has less cytoplasm than the mother

Figure 3.33 FOCUS Mitosis

Mitosis is the process of nuclear division in which the chromosomes are distributed to two daughter nuclei. Together with cytokinesis, it produces two identical daughter cells.

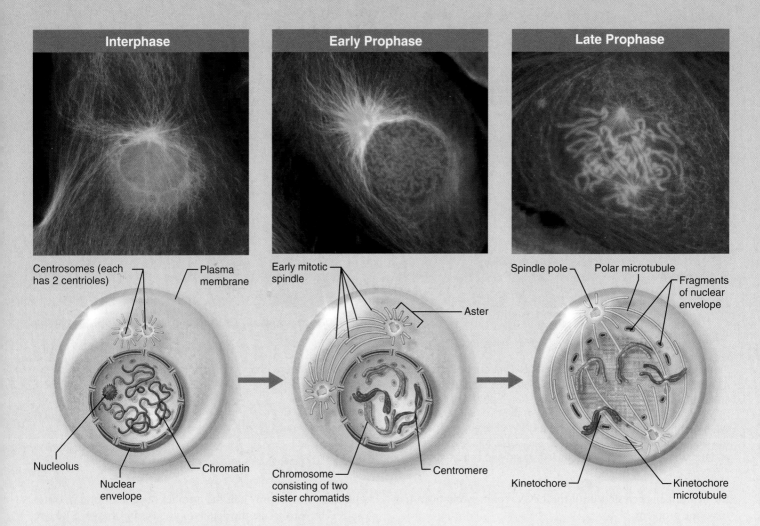

Interphase

Centrosomes (each has 2 centrioles) — Plasma membrane

Nucleolus

Nuclear envelope — Chromatin

Early Prophase

Early mitotic spindle — Aster

Chromosome consisting of two sister chromatids — Centromere

Late Prophase

Spindle pole — Polar microtubule — Fragments of nuclear envelope

Kinetochore — Kinetochore microtubule

Interphase

Interphase is the period of a cell's life when it carries out its normal metabolic activities and grows.

• During interphase, the DNA-containing material is in the form of chromatin. The nuclear envelope and one or more nucleoli are intact and visible.

• There are three distinct periods of this phase:
G_1: The centrioles begin replicating.
S: DNA is replicated.
G_2: Final preparations for mitosis are completed and centrioles finish replicating.

The light micrographs show dividing lung cells from a newt. The chromosomes appear blue and the microtubules green. (The red fibers are intermediate filaments.) The schematic drawings show details not visible in the micrographs. For simplicity, only four chromosomes are drawn.

Early Prophase

• The chromatin condenses, forming barlike *chromosomes* that are visible with a light microscope.

• Each duplicated chromosome appears as two identical threads, now called *sister chromatids*, held together at a small, constricted region called a *centromere*. (After the chromatids separate, each is considered a new chromosome.)

• As the chromosomes appear, the nucleoli disappear, and the two centrosomes separate from one another.

• The centrosomes act as focal points for growth of a microtubule assembly called the **mitotic spindle**. As these microtubules lengthen, they propel the centrosomes toward opposite ends (poles) of the cell.

• Microtubule arrays called *asters* ("stars") are seen extending from the matrix around the centrosomes.

Late Prophase

• While the centrosomes are still moving apart, the nuclear envelope fragments, allowing the spindle to interact with the chromosomes.

• Some of the growing spindle microtubules attach to *kinetochores* (ki-ne´-to-korz), special protein structures at each chromosome's centromere. Such microtubules are called *kinetochore microtubules*.

• The remaining spindle microtubules (not attached to any chromosomes) are called *polar microtubules*. The microtubules slide past each other, forcing the poles apart.

• The kinetochore microtubules pull on each chromosome from both poles in a kind of tug-of-war that ultimately draws the chromosomes to the exact center or equator of the cell.

A&P Flix View this animation at myA&P

Metaphase	**Anaphase**	**Telophase and Cytokinesis**

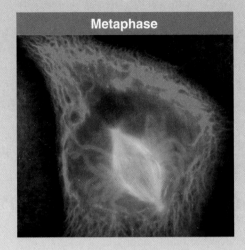

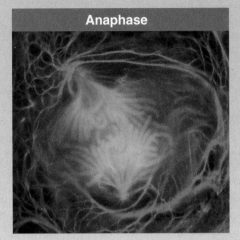

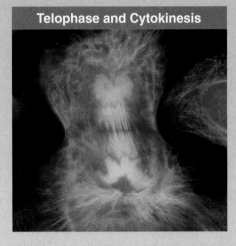

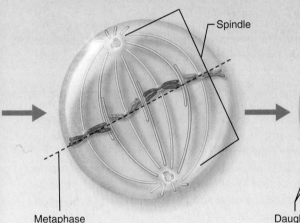

Spindle

Metaphase plate

Daughter chromosomes

Nuclear envelope forming

Nucleolus forming

Contractile ring at cleavage furrow

Metaphase

Metaphase is the second phase of mitosis.

• The two centrosomes are at opposite poles of the cell.

• The chromosomes cluster at the middle of the cell, with their centromeres precisely aligned at the *equator* of the spindle. This imaginary plane midway between the poles is called the *metaphase plate*.

Anaphase

Anaphase is the third and shortest phase of mitosis. Anaphase begins abruptly as the centromeres of the chromosomes split simultaneously. Each chromatid now becomes a chromosome in its own right.

• The kinetochore microtubules, moved along by motor proteins in the kinetochores, gradually pull each chromosome toward the pole it faces.

• At the same time, the polar microtubules slide past each other, lengthen, and push the two poles of the cell apart.

• Anaphase is easy to recognize because the moving chromosomes look V shaped. The centromeres lead the way, and the chromosomal "arms" dangle behind them.

• This process of moving and separating the chromosomes is helped by the fact that the chromosomes are short, compact bodies. Diffuse threads of chromatin would tangle, trail, and break, resulting in imprecise "parceling out" to the daughter cells.

Telophase

Telophase begins as soon as chromosomal movement stops. This final phase is like prophase in reverse.

• The identical sets of chromosomes at the opposite poles of the cell uncoil and resume their threadlike chromatin form.

• A new nuclear envelope forms around each chromatin mass, nucleoli reappear within the nuclei, and the spindle breaks down and disappears.

• Mitosis is now ended. The cell, for just a brief period, is binucleate (has two nuclei) and each new nucleus is identical to the original mother nucleus.

Cytokinesis

• As a rule, as mitosis draws to a close, cytokinesis completes the division of the cell into two identical daughter cells. Cytokinesis occurs as a contractile ring of actin microfilaments forms the *cleavage furrow* and pinches the cell apart. It begins during late anaphase and continues through and beyond telophase.

cell, but is genetically identical to it. The daughter cells then enter the interphase portion of the life cycle until it is their turn to divide.

Control of Cell Division   The signals that prod cells to divide are incompletely understood, but we know that the ratio of cell surface area to cell volume is important. The amount of nutrients a growing cell requires is directly related to its volume. Volume increases with the cube of cell radius, whereas surface area increases more slowly with the square of the radius. For example, a 64-fold (4^3) increase in cell volume is accompanied by only a 16-fold (4^2) increase in surface area. Consequently, the surface area of the plasma membrane becomes inadequate for nutrient and waste exchange when a cell reaches a certain critical size. Cell division solves this problem because the smaller daughter cells have a favorable ratio of surface area to volume. These surface-volume relationships help explain why most cells are microscopic in size.

Two other factors that influence when cells divide are chemical signals (growth factors, hormones, and others) released by other cells and the availability of space. Normal cells stop proliferating when they begin touching, a phenomenon called *contact inhibition*. The cell life cycle is controlled by a system that has been compared to an automatic washer's timer control. Like that timer, the control system for the cell cycle is driven by a built-in clock. However, just as the washer's cycle is subject to adjustments (by regulating the flow from the faucet, say, or by an internal water-level sensor), the cell cycle is regulated by both internal and external factors.

Two groups of proteins are crucial to the ability of a cell to accomplish the S phase and enter mitosis. They are **cyclins** (regulatory proteins whose levels rise and fall during each life cycle) and **Cdks (cyclin-dependent kinases)**, which are present in a constant concentration in the cell and are activated by binding to particular cyclins. In response to specific signals, a new batch of cyclins accumulates during each interphase. Subsequent joining of specific Cdk and cyclin proteins initiates enzymatic cascades that phosphorylate histones and other proteins needed for the various stages of cell division. At the end of mitosis, the cyclins are abruptly destroyed by enzymes.

A number of "switches" and crucial checkpoints for cell division occur throughout interphase. These built-in stop signals halt the cell cycle until overridden by internal or external go-ahead signals. In many cells, a G_1 checkpoint, called the *restriction point*, seems to be most important (see Figure 3.31). If the cell is diverted from dividing at this checkpoint, it enters the nondividing state (G_0). Another important checkpoint, and the first to be understood, occurs late in G_2, when a threshold amount of a protein complex called **MPF (M-phase promoting factor)** is required to give the okay signal to pass the G_2 checkpoint and enter the M phase. Later in M phase, MPF is inactivated.

Besides these "go" signals, there are a number of so-called repressor genes that inhibit cell division. One example is the *p53* gene that initiates a series of enzymatic events that produce growth-inhibiting factors. Roughly half of all cancers have abnormal *p53* genes. These cancers are not inhibited by contact with other cells and divide wildly, making them dangerous to their host.

CHECK YOUR UNDERSTANDING

26. If one of the DNA strands being replicated "reads" CGAATG, what will be the base sequence of the corresponding DNA strand?

27. During what phase of the cell cycle is DNA synthesized?

28. What are three events occurring in prophase that are undone in telophase?

For answers, see Appendix G.

Protein Synthesis

▶ Define gene and genetic code and explain the function of genes.

▶ Name the two phases of protein synthesis and describe the roles of DNA, mRNA, tRNA, and rRNA in each phase.

▶ Contrast triplets, codons, and anticodons.

In addition to directing its own replication, DNA serves as the master blueprint for protein synthesis. Although cells also make lipids and carbohydrates, DNA does not dictate their structure. Historically, DNA is said to specify *only* the structure of protein molecules, including the enzymes that catalyze the synthesis of all classes of biological molecules. Most of the metabolic machinery of the cell is concerned in some way with protein synthesis. This is not surprising, seeing as structural proteins constitute most of the dry cell material, and functional proteins direct almost all cellular activities. Essentially, cells are miniature protein factories that synthesize the huge variety of proteins that determine the chemical and physical nature of cells—and therefore of the whole body.

Proteins, as you will recall from Chapter 2, are composed of polypeptide chains, which in turn are made up of amino acids. For purposes of this discussion, we can define a **gene** as a segment of a DNA molecule that carries instructions for creating one polypeptide chain. (Note, however, that some genes specify the structure of certain varieties of RNA as their final product.)

The four nucleotide bases (A, G, T, and C) are the "letters" used in the genetic dictionary, and the information of DNA is found in the sequence of these bases. Each sequence of three bases, called a **triplet**, can be thought of as a "word" that specifies a particular amino acid. For example, the triplet AAA calls for the amino acid phenylalanine, and CCT calls for glycine. The sequence of triplets in each gene forms a "sentence" that tells exactly how a particular polypeptide is to be made: It specifies the number, kinds, and order of amino acids needed to build a particular polypetide.

Variations in the arrangement of A, T, C, and G allow our cells to make all the different kinds of proteins needed. Even an unusually "small" gene has an estimated 210 base pairs in sequence. The ratio between DNA bases in the gene and amino acids in the polypeptide is 3:1 (because each triplet stands for one amino acid), so we would expect the polypeptide specified by such a gene to contain 70 amino acids.

Most genes of higher organisms contain **exons**, which are amino acid–specifying informational sequences. These exons are often separated by **introns**, which are noncoding, often repetitive, segments that range from 60 to 100,000 nucleotides. Once considered a type of "junk DNA," intron DNA is now believed to represent a genome scrapyard that provides a reservoir of ready-to-use DNA segments for genome evolution, as well as a rich source of a large variety of small RNA molecules. The rest of the DNA (the great majority of it) is essentially "dark matter" whose function is a mystery. It is in these regions that *pseudogenes* (false genes) are found. Pseudogenes "look like" real genes but have deficits that render them apparently functionless.

The Role of RNA

By itself, DNA is like a CD recording: The information it contains cannot be used without a decoding mechanism (a CD player). Furthermore, most polypeptides are manufactured at ribosomes in the cytoplasm, but in interphase cells, DNA never leaves the nucleus. So, DNA requires not only a decoder, but a messenger as well. The decoding and messenger functions are carried out by RNA, the second type of nucleic acid.

As you learned in Chapter 2, RNA differs from DNA in being single stranded and in having the sugar ribose instead of deoxyribose and the base uracil (U) in place of thymine (T). Three forms of RNA typically act together to carry out DNA's instructions for polypeptide synthesis:

1. **Messenger RNA (mRNA)**, relatively long nucleotide strands resembling "half-DNA" molecules (one of the two strands of a DNA molecule coding for protein structure)
2. **Ribosomal RNA (rRNA)**, part of the ribosomes
3. **Transfer RNA (tRNA)**, small, roughly L-shaped molecules

All types of RNA are formed on the DNA in the nucleus in much the same way as DNA replicates itself: The DNA helix separates and one of its strands serves as a template for synthesizing a complementary RNA strand. Once formed, the RNA molecule is released from the DNA template and migrates into the cytoplasm. Its job done, the DNA simply recoils into its helical, inactive form.

Approximately 2% of the nuclear DNA codes for the synthesis of short-lived mRNA, so named because it carries, from gene to ribosome, the "message" containing the instructions for building a polypeptide. (Kind of a genetic memo for protein structure.) DNA in the nucleolar organizer regions (mentioned previously) codes for the synthesis of rRNA, which is long-lived and stable, as is tRNA coded by other DNA sequences. Because rRNA and tRNA do not transport codes for synthesizing other molecules, they are the final products of the genes that code for them. Ribosomal RNA and tRNA act together to "translate" the message carried by mRNA.

Essentially, polypeptide synthesis involves two major steps: (1) *transcription*, in which DNA's information is encoded

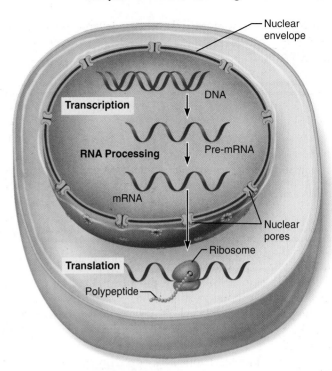

Figure 3.34 Simplified scheme of information flow from the DNA gene to mRNA to protein structure during transcription and translation. (Note that mRNA is first synthesized as pre-mRNA, which is processed by enzymes before leaving the nucleus.)

in mRNA, and (2) *translation*, in which the information carried by mRNA is decoded and used to assemble polypeptides. **Figure 3.34** shows an overview of the information flow in these two major steps. The figure also indicates the "RNA processing" that removes introns from mRNA before this molecule leaves the nucleus and moves into the cytoplasm.

Transcription

A transcriptionist converts a message from a recording or short-hand notes into a word-processed or electronic copy. In other words, information is transformed, or transferred, from one form or format to another. In cells, **transcription** involves the transfer of information from a DNA's base sequence to the complementary base sequence of an mRNA molecule. The form is different, but the same information is being conveyed. Once the mRNA molecule is made, it detaches and leaves the nucleus via a nuclear pore.

Essentially, three basic phases are involved in transcription: (1) initiation, (2) elongation, and (3) termination. In addition to looking at the synthesis of mRNA, we will also examine the editing and further processing needed to clean up the mRNA transcript.

How does transcription get started? Transcription cannot begin until gene-activating chemicals called *transcription factors* stimulate loosening of the histones at the site-to-be of gene

3

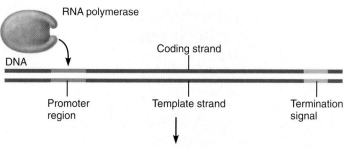

RNA polymerase

DNA

Coding strand

Promoter region Template strand Termination signal

① **Initiation:** With the help of transcription factors, RNA polymerase binds to the promoter, pries apart the two DNA strands, and initiates mRNA synthesis at the start point on the template strand.

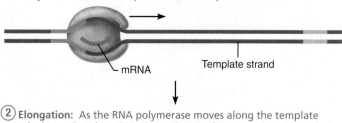

mRNA

Template strand

② **Elongation:** As the RNA polymerase moves along the template strand, elongating the mRNA transcript one base at a time, it unwinds the DNA double helix before it and rewinds the double helix behind it.

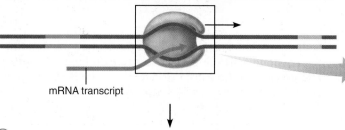

mRNA transcript

③ **Termination:** mRNA synthesis ends when the termination signal is reached. RNA polymerase and the completed mRNA transcript are released.

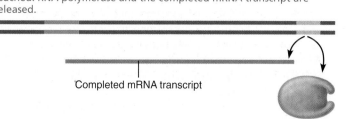

Completed mRNA transcript

RNA polymerase

Figure 3.35 Overview of stages of transcription.

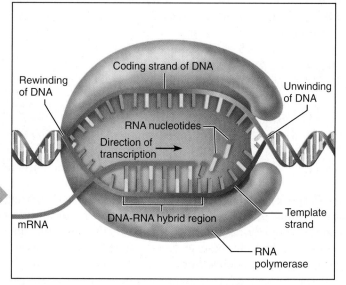

Rewinding of DNA

Coding strand of DNA

Unwinding of DNA

RNA nucleotides

Direction of transcription

mRNA

DNA-RNA hybrid region

Template strand

RNA polymerase

The DNA-RNA hybrid: At any given moment, 16–18 base pairs of DNA are unwound and the most recently made RNA is still bound to DNA. This small region is called the DNA-RNA hybrid.

transcription and then bind to the promoter. The **promoter** is a special DNA sequence that contains the *start point* (beginning of the structural gene to be transcribed). It specifies where mRNA synthesis starts and which DNA strand is going to serve as the *template strand* (Figure 3.35, top). The uncoiled DNA strand not used as a template is called the *coding strand* because it has the same (coded) sequence as the mRNA to be built (except for the use of U in mRNA in place of T in DNA). The transcription factors also help position **RNA polymerase**, the enzyme that oversees the synthesis of mRNA, correctly at the promoter. Once these preparations are made, RNA polymerase can initiate transcription.

Figure 3.35 illustrates the following steps in transcription:

① **Initiation.** Once bound with the help of the transcription factors, RNA polymerase pulls apart the strands of the

DNA double helix so that transcription can begin at the start point in the promoter.

② **Elongation.** Using incoming RNA nucleotides as substrates, the RNA polymerase aligns them with complementary DNA bases on the template strand and then links them together. As RNA polymerase elongates the mRNA strand one base at a time, it unwinds the DNA helix in front of it, and rewinds the helix behind it. At any given moment, 16 to 18 base pairs of DNA are unwound and the most recently made mRNA is still hydrogen-bonded (H-bonded) to the template DNA. This small region—called the **DNA-RNA hybrid**—is up to 12 base pairs long.

③ **Termination.** When the polymerase reaches a special base sequence called a **termination signal**, transcription ends and the newly formed mRNA pulls off the DNA template.

Processing of mRNA Although it would appear that translation can begin as soon as the mRNA is made, that is not the case. The process is a bit more complex. Recall that mammalian DNA like ours has coding regions (exons) separated by non-protein-coding regions (introns). Because the DNA is transcribed sequentially, the mRNA initially made, called *pre-mRNA* or *primary transcript*, is littered with intron "junk" or "nonsense." Before the newly formed RNA can be used as a messenger, it must be processed, or edited—that is, sections corresponding to introns must be removed. This job is done by *spliceosomes*. These large RNA-protein complexes snip out the introns and splice together the remaining exon-coded sections in the order in which they occurred in the DNA, producing the functional mRNA that directs translation at the ribosome.

Although many introns naturally degrade, some contain active segments (such as microRNAs) that can function to control, interfere with, or silence other genes. Additionally, before the edited mRNA can function in protein synthesis, a number of specific RNA-binding proteins, called *mRNA complex proteins*, must become associated with it. These mRNA complex proteins guide its export from the nucleus, determine its localization, translation, and stability, and check it for premature termination codons.

Translation

A translator takes a message in one language and restates it in another. In the **translation** step of protein synthesis, the language of nucleic acids (base sequence) is translated into the language of proteins (amino acid sequence).

The rules by which the base sequence of a gene is translated into an amino acid sequence are called the **genetic code**. For each triplet, or three-base sequence on DNA, the corresponding three-base sequence on mRNA is called a **codon**. Since there are four kinds of RNA (or DNA) nucleotides, there are 4^3, or 64, possible codons. Three of these 64 codons are "stop signs" that call for termination of polypeptide synthesis. All the rest code for amino acids. Because there are only about 20 amino acids, some are specified by more than one codon. This redundancy in the genetic code helps protect against problems due to transcription (and translation) errors. The genetic code and a complete codon list are provided in **Figure 3.36**.

The process of translation occurs in the cytoplasm and involves the mRNAs, tRNAs, and rRNAs mentioned above, and occurs in the sequence of events described next and illustrated in **Figure 3.37**.

When it reaches the cytoplasm after processing in the nucleus, the mRNA molecule carrying instructions for a particular protein binds to a small ribosomal subunit (Figure 3.37, ①). Then tRNA comes into the picture, its job being to *transfer* amino acids, dissolved in the cytosol, to the ribosome.

Shaped like a handheld drill, tRNA is well suited to its dual function of binding to both an amino acid and an mRNA codon. The amino acid is bound to one end of tRNA, at a region called the stem. At the other end, the head, is its **anticodon** (an″ti-ko′don), a three-base sequence complementary to the mRNA codon calling for the amino acid carried by that partic-

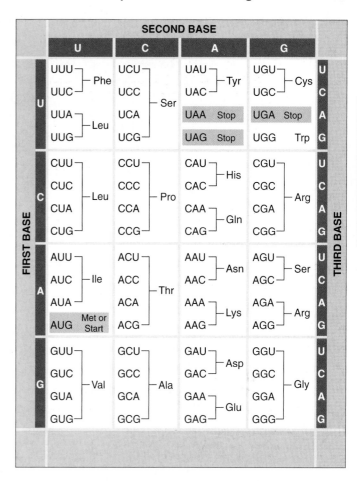

Figure 3.36 The genetic code. The three bases in an mRNA codon are designated as the first, second, and third. Each set of three specifies a particular amino acid, represented here by an abbreviation (see list below). The codon AUG (which specifies the amino acid methionine) is the usual start signal for protein synthesis. The word *stop* indicates the codons that serve as signals to terminate protein synthesis.

Abb.*	Amino acid	Abb.*	Amino acid
Ala	alanine	Leu	leucine
Arg	arginine	Lys	lysine
Asn	asparagine	Met	methionine
Asp	aspartic acid	Phe	phenylalanine
Cys	cysteine	Pro	proline
Glu	glutamic acid	Ser	serine
Gln	glutamine	Thr	threonine
Gly	glycine	Trp	tryptophan
His	histidine	Tyr	tyrosine
Ile	isoleucine	Val	valine

*Abbreviation for the amino acid

ular tRNA. Because anticodons form hydrogen bonds with complementary codons, tRNA is the link between the language of nucleic acids and the language of proteins. For example, if the mRNA codon is AUA, which specifies isoleucine, the tRNAs carrying isoleucine will have the anticodon UAU, which can bind to the AUA codons.

There are approximately 45 different types of tRNA, each capable of binding with a specific amino acid. The attachment

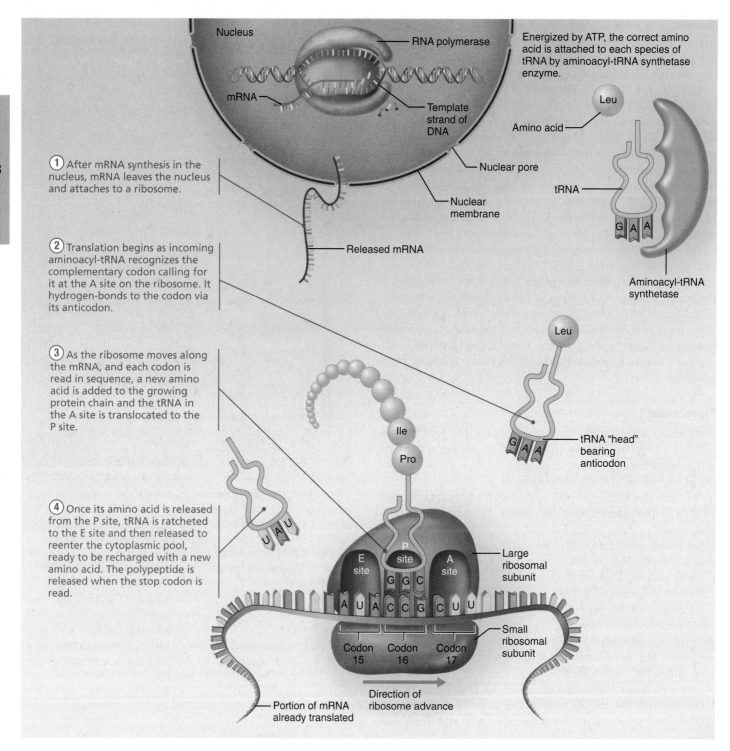

① After mRNA synthesis in the nucleus, mRNA leaves the nucleus and attaches to a ribosome.

② Translation begins as incoming aminoacyl-tRNA recognizes the complementary codon calling for it at the A site on the ribosome. It hydrogen-bonds to the codon via its anticodon.

③ As the ribosome moves along the mRNA, and each codon is read in sequence, a new amino acid is added to the growing protein chain and the tRNA in the A site is translocated to the P site.

④ Once its amino acid is released from the P site, tRNA is ratcheted to the E site and then released to reenter the cytoplasmic pool, ready to be recharged with a new amino acid. The polypeptide is released when the stop codon is read.

Figure 3.37 The basic steps of translation. The diagram presumes that initiation was accomplished and the 17th amino acid as dictated by the mRNA codons is being brought to the ribosome.

process is controlled by an aminoacyl-tRNA synthetase enzyme and is activated by ATP (see the top right side of Figure 3.37). Once its amino acid is loaded, the tRNA (now called an *aminoacyl-tRNA* because of its amino acid cargo) migrates to the ribosome, where it maneuvers the amino acid into the proper position, as specified by the mRNA codons (Figure 3.37, ②).

The ribosome is more than just a passive attachment site for mRNA and tRNA. Like a vise, the ribosome holds the tRNA and mRNA close together to coordinate the coupling of codons and anticodons, and positions the next (incoming) amino acid for addition to the growing polypeptide chain. To do its job, the ribosome has a binding site for mRNA and three binding sites for tRNA: an A (aminoacyl) site for an incoming aminoacyl-tRNA, a P (peptidyl) site for the tRNA holding the growing polypeptide chain, and an E (exit) site for an outgoing tRNA (Figure 3.37).

How does translation get started? When a special methionine-charged **initiator tRNA** binds to the middle (P) site on the small ribosomal subunit, the translation process officially begins. The newly formed mRNA has an initial base sequence, called a *leader sequence*, that allows it to attach to its binding site on the small ribosomal subunit. With the initiator tRNA still in tow, the small ribosomal subunit scans along the mRNA until it encounters the *start codon* (the first AUG triplet it meets). When the initiator tRNA's UAC anticodon "recognizes" and binds to the start codon, a large ribosomal subunit unites with the small one, forming a functional ribosome. With the mRNA firmly positioned in the "groove" between the two ribosomal subunits, translation begins in earnest. This initiation process requires the help of a number of initiation factors and is energized by GTP.

Now the ribosome slides the mRNA strand along, bringing the next codon into position to be "read" by an aminoacyl-tRNA coming into the A site (Figure 3.37, ②). It is at this point that the ribosome does a little "proofreading" to make sure of the codon-anticodon match. That accomplished, an enzymatic component in the large ribosomal particle peptide-bonds the amino acid of the initiator tRNA in the P site to that of the tRNA at the A site. The ribosome then translocates the tRNA that is now carrying two amino acids to the P site (as in Figure 3.37, ③). At the same time, it ratchets the initiator tRNA to the E site, from which it leaves the ribosome (as in Figure 3.37, ④).

This orderly "musical chairs" process continues: the peptidyl-tRNAs transferring their polypeptide cargo to the aminoacyl-tRNAs, and then the P-site-to-E-site and A-site-to-P-site movements of the tRNAs (see again Figure 3.37, ③ and ④). As the ribosome "chugs" along the mRNA track and the mRNA is progressively read, its initial portion passes through the ribosome and may ultimately become attached successively to several other ribosomes, all reading the same message simultaneously and sequentially. Such a multiple ribosome–mRNA complex is called a *polyribosome*, and it provides an efficient system for producing many copies of the same protein (Figure 3.38).

The mRNA strand continues to be read sequentially until its last codon, the *stop codon* (one of UGA, UAA, or UAG) enters the ribosomal groove. The stop codon is the "period" at the end of the mRNA sentence that tells the ribosome that translation of that mRNA is finished. The completed polypeptide chain is then released from the ribosome, and the ribosome separates into its two subunits (Figure 3.38a). The released protein folds into a complex 3-D structure and floats off, ready to work. When the message of the mRNA that directed its formation becomes outdated, it is degraded in structures called *processing* (P) *bodies*.

As noted earlier in the chapter, ribosomes attach to and detach from the rough ER. When a short "leader" peptide called an **ER signal sequence** is present in a protein being synthesized, the associated ribosome attaches to the membrane of the rough ER. This signal sequence, with its attached cargo of a ribosome and mRNA, is guided to appropriate receptor sites on the ER membrane by a signal-recognition particle (SRP), a molecular

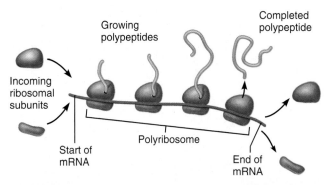

(a) Each polyribosome consists of one strand of mRNA being read by several ribosomes simultaneously. In this diagram, the mRNA is moving to the left and the "oldest" functional ribosome is farthest to the right.

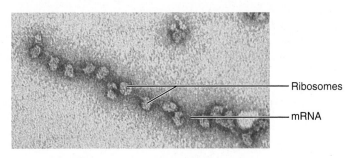

(b) This transmission electron micrograph shows a large polyribosome (400,000×).

Figure 3.38 Polyribosome arrays allow a single strand of mRNA to be translated into hundreds of the same polypeptide molecules in a short time.

chaperone that cycles between the ER and the cytosol. The subsequent events occurring at the ER are detailed in **Figure 3.39**.

In summary, the genetic information of a cell is translated into the production of proteins via a sequence of information transfer that is completely directed by complementary base pairing. The transfer of information goes from DNA base sequence (triplets) to the complementary base sequence of mRNA (codons) and then to the tRNA base sequence (anticodons), which is identical to the DNA sequence except for the substitution of uracil (U) for thymine (T) **(Figure 3.40)**.

Other Roles of DNA

The story of DNA doesn't end with the production of proteins encoded by exons. Scientists are finding that other intron or "junk" DNA actually codes for a surprising variety of active RNA species, including the following:

- **Antisense RNAs**, made on the DNA strand complementary to the template strand for mRNA, can intercept and bind to the protein-coding mRNA strand and prevent it from being translated into protein.
- **MicroRNAs** are small RNAs that can use RNA interference machinery to interfere with and suppress mRNAs made by certain exons, thus effectively silencing them.
- **Riboswitches** are folded RNAs that code, like mRNA, for a particular protein. What sets them apart from other mRNAs is

3

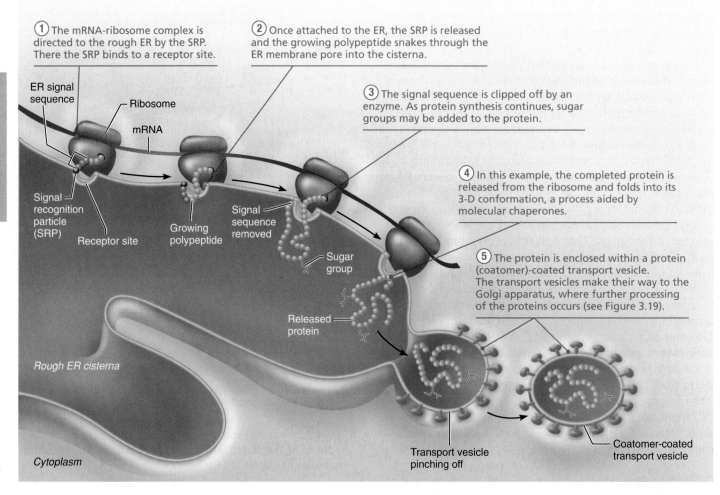

① The mRNA-ribosome complex is directed to the rough ER by the SRP. There the SRP binds to a receptor site.

② Once attached to the ER, the SRP is released and the growing polypeptide snakes through the ER membrane pore into the cisterna.

③ The signal sequence is clipped off by an enzyme. As protein synthesis continues, sugar groups may be added to the protein.

④ In this example, the completed protein is released from the ribosome and folds into its 3-D conformation, a process aided by molecular chaperones.

⑤ The protein is enclosed within a protein (coatomer)-coated transport vesicle. The transport vesicles make their way to the Golgi apparatus, where further processing of the proteins occurs (see Figure 3.19).

ER signal sequence
Ribosome
mRNA
Signal recognition particle (SRP)
Receptor site
Growing polypeptide
Signal sequence removed
Sugar group
Released protein
Rough ER cisterna
Cytoplasm
Transport vesicle pinching off
Coatomer-coated transport vesicle

Figure 3.39 Presence of an endoplasmic reticulum (ER) signal sequence in a newly forming protein causes the signal recognition particle (SRP) to direct the mRNA-ribosome complex to the rough ER.

a region that acts as a switch to turn protein synthesis on or off in response to specific metabolic changes in the environment, such as changes in the concentration of vitamins, amino acids, nucleotides, or other small molecules in the cell. When it senses these changes, the riboswitch changes shape, thereby stopping or starting production of the protein it specifies.

We still have much to learn about these versatile RNA species that arise from intron and "junk" DNA and appear to play a role in heredity. Other areas of research focus on the consequences of the triplet code being degenerate (that is, having several codons code for a single amino acid), and on the multitasking of DNA segments. For example, a sequence can code for structure of a protein and also manage to guide positioning of a nucleosome.

CHECK YOUR UNDERSTANDING

29. Codons and anticodons are both three-base sequences. How do they differ?

30. How do the A, P, and E ribosomal sites differ functionally during protein synthesis?

31. What is the role of DNA in transcription?

For answers, see Appendix G.

Cytosolic Protein Degradation

▶ Describe the importance of ubiquitin-dependent degradation of soluble proteins.

What happens to proteins that are no longer useful? To carry out their physiological roles, proteins must be in the right place at the right time and in the right amounts. Like everything else, proteins outlive their usefulness and are eventually degraded. Organelle proteins are digested by lysosomes, but lysosomal enzymes do not have access to misfolded, damaged, or unneeded soluble proteins in the cytosol that need to be disposed of. For example, these proteins might include some used only in cell division, or short-lived transcription factors.

So, how does the cell prevent such proteins from accumulating while avoiding wholesale destruction of virtually all soluble proteins by the cytosolic enzymes? Doomed proteins are marked for attack (proteolysis) by attachment of proteins called **ubiquitins** (u-bĭ′kwĭ-tinz) in an ATP-dependent reaction. The tagged proteins are then hydrolyzed to small peptides by soluble enzymes or by **proteasomes**, giant "waste disposal" complexes composed of protein-digesting enzymes and the ubiquitin is

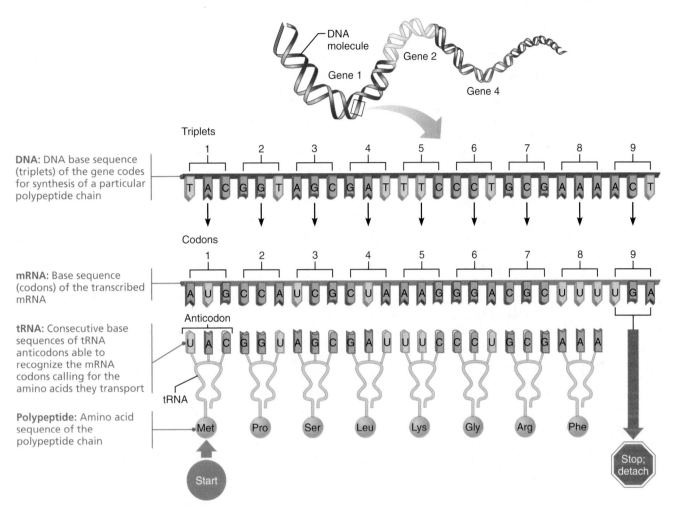

Figure 3.40 Information transfer from DNA to RNA to polypeptide. Information is transferred from the DNA of the gene to the complementary messenger RNA molecule, whose codons are then "read" by transfer RNA anticodons. Notice that the "reading" of the mRNA by tRNA anticodons reestablishes the base (triplet) sequence of the DNA genetic code (except that T is replaced by U).

recycled. Proteasome activity is critical during starvation when these complexes degrade preexisting proteins to provide amino acids for synthesis of new and needed proteins.

Extracellular Materials

▶ Name and describe the composition of extracellular materials.

Extracellular materials are any substances contributing to body mass that are found outside the cells. One class of extracellular materials is *body fluids*, mainly interstitial fluid, blood plasma, and cerebrospinal fluid. These fluids are important transport and dissolving media. *Cellular secretions* are also extracellular materials and include substances that aid in digestion (intestinal and gastric fluids) and some that act as lubricants (saliva, mucus, and serous fluids).

By far the most abundant extracellular material is the *extracellular matrix*. Most body cells are in contact with a jelly-like substance composed of proteins and polysaccharides. These molecules are secreted by the cells and self-assemble into an organized mesh in the extracellular space, where they serve as a universal "cell glue" that helps to hold body cells together. As described in Chapter 4, the extracellular matrix is particularly abundant in connective tissues—in some cases so abundant that it (rather than living cells) accounts for the bulk of that tissue type. Depending on the structure to be formed, the extracellular matrix in connective tissue ranges from soft to rock-hard.

CHECK YOUR UNDERSTANDING

32. What is the importance of ubiquitin in the life of a cell?

33. What are two body fluids that inhabit the extracellular space and what role does each play in the body?

For answers, see Appendix G.

Developmental Aspects of Cells

▶ Discuss some theories of cell differentiation and aging.

▶ Indicate the value of apoptosis to the body.

We all begin life as a single cell, the fertilized egg, and all the cells of our body arise from it. Very early in development, cells begin to specialize. Some become liver cells, some nerve cells, and so on. All our cells carry the same genes, so how can one cell become so different from another? This is a fascinating question.

Apparently, cells in various regions of the embryo are exposed to different chemical signals that channel them into specific pathways of development. When the embryo consists of just a few cells (these are the embryonic *stem cells* you keep hearing about), the major signals may be nothing more than slight differences in oxygen and carbon dioxide concentrations between the more superficial and the deeper cells. But as development continues, cells release chemicals that influence development of neighboring cells by triggering processes that switch some genes "off." Some genes are active in all cells. For example, genes for rRNA and ATP synthesis are "on" in all cells, but genes for synthesizing the enzymes needed to produce thyroxine are "on" only in cells that are going to be part of the thyroid gland. Hence, the secret of cell specialization lies in the kinds of proteins made and reflects the activation of different genes in different cell types.

Cell specialization leads to *structural* variation—different organelles come to predominate in different cells. For example, muscle cells make large amounts of actin and myosin, and their cytoplasm fills with microfilaments. Liver and phagocytic cells produce more lysosomes. The development of specific and distinctive features in cells is called **cell differentiation**.

During early development, cell death and destruction are normal events. Nature takes few chances. More cells than needed are produced, and excesses are eliminated later in a type of programmed cell death called **apoptosis** (ap″o-to′sis; "falling away"). This process of controlled cellular suicide also eliminates cells that are stressed, no longer needed, injured, or aged.

How does apoptosis work? In response to damaged macromolecules within the cell or to some extracellular signal, mitochondrial membranes become permeable, allowing cytochrome c and other factors to leak into the cytosol. These chemicals, in turn, trigger apoptosis by causing activation of a series of intracellular enzymes called *caspases*. These enzymes are normally dormant, but when they are activated, they unleash a torrent of protein digestion activity within the cell, destroying the cell's DNA, cytoskeleton, and so on, producing a quick, neat death. The apoptotic cell shrinks without leaking its contents into the surrounding tissue, detaches from other cells, and rounds up. Because the dying cell releases a chemical (lysophosphatidylcholine) that attracts macrophages, and sprouts "eat me" signals, it is immediately phagocytized.

Cancer cells do not undergo apoptosis, but oxygen-starved cells do so excessively (heart-muscle and brain cells during heart attacks and strokes, for example). Apoptosis is particularly common in the developing nervous system. It is also responsible for "carving out" fingers and toes from their embryonic precursors.

Most organs are well formed and functional long before birth, but the body continues to grow and enlarge by forming new cells throughout childhood and adolescence. Once we reach adult size, cell division is important mainly to replace short-lived cells and repair wounds.

During young adulthood, cell numbers remain fairly constant. However, local changes in the rate of cell division are common. For example, when a person is anemic, his or her bone marrow undergoes **hyperplasia** (hi″per-pla′ze-ah), or accelerated growth (*hyper* = over; *plas* = grow), so that red blood cells are produced at a faster rate. If the anemia is remedied, the excessive marrow activity ceases. **Atrophy** (at′ro-fe), a decrease in size of an organ or body tissue, can result from loss of normal stimulation. Muscles that lose their nerve supply atrophy and waste away, and lack of exercise leads to thinned, brittle bones.

Cell aging occurs and it accounts for most problems associated with old age. Cell aging is a complicated process with many causes. The *wear-and-tear theory* attributes aging to little chemical insults and formation of free radicals, both of which have cumulative effects. For example, environmental toxins such as pesticides, alcohol, and bacterial toxins may damage cell membranes, poison enzyme systems, or cause "mistakes" in DNA replication. Temporary lack of oxygen, which occurs increasingly with age as our blood vessels clog with fatty materials, leads to accelerated rates of cell death throughout the body.

Most free radicals are produced in the mitochondria, because these organelles have the highest metabolic rate. This finding implies that diminished energy production by radical-damaged mitochondria, due perhaps to an increasing burden of mutations in mitochondrial DNA, weakens (and ages) cells. X rays and other types of radiation, and some chemicals, also generate huge numbers of free radicals, which can overwhelm the peroxisomal enzymes. Vitamins C and E act as antioxidants in the body and may help to prevent excessive free radical formation. With age, glucose (blood sugar) becomes party to cross-linking proteins together, a condition that severely disrupts protein function and accelerates the course of arteriosclerosis.

Another theory attributes cell aging to progressive disorders in the immune system. According to this theory, cell damage results from (1) autoimmune responses, which means the immune system turns against one's own tissues, and (2) a progressive weakening of the immune response, so that the body is less and less able to get rid of cell-damaging pathogens.

Perhaps the most widely accepted theory of cell aging is the *genetic theory*, which suggests that cessation of mitosis and cell aging are "programmed into our genes." One interesting notion here is that a *telomere clock* determines the number of times a cell can divide. **Telomeres** (*telo* = end; *mer* = piece) are strings of nucleotides that cap the ends of chromosomes, protecting them from fraying or fusing with other chromosomes, much like plastic caps preserve the ends of shoelaces. In human telomeres, the base sequence TTAGGG is repeated a thousand times or more (like a DNA stutter). Though telomeres carry no genes, they appear to be vital for chromosomal survival, because each time DNA is replicated, 50 to 100 of the end nucleotides are lost and the telomeres get a bit shorter. When telomeres reach a certain minimum length, the stop-division signal is given.

The idea that cell longevity depends on telomere integrity was supported by the discovery of *telomerase*, an enzyme that protects telomeres from degrading. Pegged as the "immortality enzyme," telomerase is found in germ line cells (cells that give rise to sperm and ova), but it is barely detectable or absent in other adult cell types.

CHECK YOUR UNDERSTANDING

34. What is apoptosis and what is its importance in the body?

35. What is the wear-and-tear theory of aging?

For answers, see Appendix G.

In this chapter we have described the structure and function of the generalized cell. One of the wonders of the cell is the disparity between its minute size and its extraordinary activity, which reflects the diversity of its organelles. The evidence for division of labor and functional specialization among organelles is inescapable. Only ribosomes synthesize proteins, while protein packaging is the bailiwick of the Golgi apparatus. Membranes compartmentalize most organelles, allowing them to work without hindering or being hindered by other cell activities, and the plasma membrane regulates molecular traffic across the cell's boundary. Now that you know what cells have in common, you are ready to explore how they differ in the various body tissues, the topic of Chapter 4.

RELATED CLINICAL TERMS

Anaplasia (an'ah-pla'ze-ah; *an* = without, not; *plas* = to grow) Abnormalities in cell structure and loss of differentiation; for example, cancer cells typically lose the appearance of the parent cells and come to resemble undifferentiated or embryonic cells.

Dysplasia (dis-pla'ze-ah; *dys* = abnormal) A change in cell size, shape, or arrangement due to chronic irritation or inflammation (infections, etc.).

Hypertrophy (hi-per'tro-fe) Growth of an organ or tissue due to an increase in the size of its cells. Hypertrophy is a normal response of skeletal muscle cells when they are challenged to lift excessive weight; differs from hyperplasia, which is an increase in size due to an increase in cell number.

Liposomes (lip'o-sōmz) Hollow microscopic sacs formed of phospholipids that can be filled with a variety of drugs. Serve as multipurpose vehicles for drugs, genetic material, and cosmetics.

Mutation A change in DNA base sequence that may lead to incorporation of incorrect amino acids in particular positions in the resulting protein; the affected protein may remain unimpaired or may function abnormally or not at all, leading to disease.

Necrosis (nĕ-kro'sis; *necros* = death; *osis* = process) Death of a cell or group of cells due to injury or disease. Acute injury causes the cells to swell and burst, and induces the inflammatory response. (This is *uncontrolled* cell death, in contrast to apoptosis described in the text.)

CHAPTER SUMMARY

Media study tools that could provide you additional help in reviewing specific key topics of Chapter 3 are referenced below.

iP = *Interactive Physiology*

Overview of the Cellular Basis of Life (pp. 62–63)

1. All living organisms are composed of cells—the basic structural and functional units of life. Cells vary widely in both shape and size.

2. The principle of complementarity states that the biochemical activity of cells reflects the operation of their organelles.

3. The generalized cell is a concept that typifies all cells. The generalized cell has three major regions—the nucleus, cytoplasm, and plasma membrane.

The Plasma Membrane: Structure (pp. 63–67)

1. The plasma membrane encloses cell contents, mediates exchanges with the extracellular environment, and plays a role in cellular communication.

The Fluid Mosaic Model (pp. 63–66)

2. The fluid mosaic model depicts the plasma membrane as a fluid bilayer of lipids (phospholipids, cholesterol, and glycolipids) within which proteins are inserted.

3. The lipids have both hydrophilic and hydrophobic regions that organize their aggregation and self-repair. The lipids form the structural part of the plasma membrane.

4. Most proteins are integral transmembrane proteins that extend entirely through the membrane. Some, appended to the integral proteins, are peripheral proteins.

5. Proteins are responsible for most specialized membrane functions: Some are enzymes, some are receptors, and others mediate membrane transport functions. Externally facing glycoproteins contribute to the glycocalyx.

Membrane Junctions (p. 66–67)

6. Membrane junctions join cells together and may aid or inhibit movement of molecules between or past cells.

7. Tight junctions are impermeable junctions. Desmosomes mechanically couple cells into a functional community. Gap junctions allow joined cells to communicate.

The Plasma Membrane: Membrane Transport (pp. 68–77)

1. The plasma membrane acts as a selectively permeable barrier. Substances move across the plasma membrane by passive processes, which depend on the kinetic energy of molecules, and by active processes, which depend on the use of cellular energy (ATP).

Passive Processes (pp. 68–72)

2. Diffusion is the movement of molecules (driven by kinetic energy) down a concentration gradient. Fat-soluble solutes can diffuse directly through the membrane by dissolving in the lipid.

3. Facilitated diffusion is the passive movement of certain solutes across the membrane either by their binding with a membrane carrier protein or by their moving through a membrane channel. As with other diffusion processes, it is driven by kinetic energy, but the carriers and channels are selective.

4. Osmosis is the diffusion of a solvent, such as water, through a selectively permeable membrane. Water diffuses through membrane channels (aquaporins) or directly through the lipid portion of the membrane from a solution of lesser osmolarity (total concentration of all solute particles) to a solution of greater osmolarity.

5. The presence of solutes unable to permeate the plasma membrane leads to changes in cell tone that may cause the cell to swell or shrink. Net osmosis ceases when the solute concentration on both sides of the plasma membrane reaches equilibrium.

6. Solutions that cause a net loss of water from cells are hypertonic. Those causing net water gain are hypotonic. Those causing neither gain nor loss of water are isotonic.

Active Processes (pp. 72–77)

7. Active transport (solute pumping) depends on a carrier protein and ATP. Substances transported move against concentration or electrical gradients. In primary active transport, such as that provided by the Na^+-K^+ pump, ATP directly provides the energy.

8. In secondary active transport, the energy of an ion gradient (produced by a primary active transport process) is used to transport a substance passively. Many active transport systems are coupled, and cotransported substances move in either the same (symport) or opposite (antiport) directions across the membrane.

9. Vesicular transport also requires ATP. Endocytosis brings substances into the cell, typically in protein-coated vesicles. If the substance is particulate, the process is called phagocytosis. If the substance is dissolved molecules, the process is pinocytosis. Receptor-mediated endocytosis is selective: Engulfed molecules attach to receptors on the membrane before endocytosis occurs. Exocytosis, which uses SNAREs to anchor the vesicles to the plasma membrane, ejects substances (hormones, wastes, secretions) from the cell.

10. Most endocytosis (and transcytosis) is mediated by clathrin-coated vesicles. Caveolin-coated vesicles engulf some substances but appear to be more important as sites that accumulate receptors involved in cell signaling. Coatomer-coated vesicles mediate most types of substance (vesicular) trafficking within the cell.

The Plasma Membrane: Generation of a Resting Membrane Potential (pp. 79–80)

1. All cells in the resting stage exhibit a voltage across their membrane, called the resting membrane potential. Because of the membrane potential, both concentration and electrical gradients determine the ease of an ion's diffusion.

2. The resting membrane potential is generated by concentration gradients of ions and the differential permeability of the plasma membrane to ions, particularly potassium ions. Sodium is in high extracellular concentration and low intracellular concentration, and the membrane is poorly permeable to it. Potassium is in high concentration in the cell and low concentration in the extracellular fluid. The membrane is more permeable to potassium than to sodium. Protein anions in the cell are too large to cross the membrane and Cl^-, the main anion in extracellular fluid, is repelled by the negative charge on the inner membrane face.

3. Essentially, a negative membrane potential is established when the movement of K^+ out of the cell equals K^+ movement into the cell. Na^+ movements across the membrane contribute minimally to establishing the membrane potential. The greater outward diffusion of potassium (than inward diffusion of sodium) leads to a charge separation at the membrane (inside negative). This charge separation is maintained by the operation of the sodium-potassium pump.

iP Nervous System I; Topics: Ion Channels, pp. 3, 8, 9; The Membrane Potential, pp. 1–17.

The Plasma Membrane: Cell-Environment Interactions (pp. 80–81)

1. Cells interact directly and indirectly with other cells. Indirect interactions involve extracellular chemicals carried in body fluids or forming part of the extracellular matrix.

2. Molecules of the glycocalyx are intimately involved in cell-environment interactions. Most are cell adhesion molecules or membrane receptors.

3. Activated membrane receptors act as catalysts, regulate channels, or, like G protein–linked receptors, act through second messengers such as cyclic AMP and Ca^{2+}. Ligand binding results in changes in protein structure or function within the targeted cell.

The Cytoplasm (pp. 81–91)

1. The cytoplasm, the cellular region between the nuclear and plasma membranes, consists of the cytosol (fluid cytoplasmic environment), inclusions (nonliving nutrient stores, pigment granules, crystals, etc.), and cytoplasmic organelles.

Cytoplasmic Organelles (pp. 83–89)

2. The cytoplasm is the major functional area of the cell. These functions are mediated by cytoplasmic organelles.

3. Mitochondria, organelles limited by a double membrane, are sites of ATP formation. Their internal enzymes carry out the oxidative reactions of cellular respiration.

4. Ribosomes, composed of two subunits containing ribosomal RNA and proteins, are the sites of protein synthesis. They may be free or attached to membranes.

5. The rough endoplasmic reticulum is a ribosome-studded membrane system. Its cisternae act as sites for protein modification. Its external face acts in phospholipid synthesis. Vesicles pinched off from the ER transport the proteins to other cell sites.

6. The smooth endoplasmic reticulum synthesizes lipid and steroid molecules. It also acts in fat metabolism and in drug detoxification. In muscle cells, it is a calcium ion depot.

7. The Golgi apparatus is a membranous system close to the nucleus that packages protein secretions for export, packages enzymes into lysosomes for cellular use, and modifies proteins destined to become part of cellular membranes.

8. Lysosomes are membranous sacs of acid hydrolases packaged by the Golgi apparatus. Sites of intracellular digestion, they degrade worn-out organelles and tissues that are no longer useful, and they release ionic calcium from bone.

9. Peroxisomes are membranous sacs containing oxidase enzymes that protect the cell from the destructive effects of free radicals and other toxic substances by converting them first to hydrogen peroxide and then water.

10. The cytoskeleton includes microtubules, intermediate filaments, and microfilaments. Microtubules organize the cytoskeleton and

are important in intracellular transport. Microfilaments are important in cell motility or movement of cell parts. Motility functions involve motor proteins. Intermediate filaments help cells resist mechanical stress and connect other elements.

Cellular Extensions (pp. 90–91)

11. Centrioles organize the mitotic spindle and are the bases of cilia and flagella.
12. Microvilli are extensions of the plasma membrane that increase its surface area for absorption.

The Nucleus (pp. 91–95)

1. The nucleus is the control center of the cell. Most cells have a single nucleus. Without a nucleus, a cell cannot divide or synthesize more proteins, and is destined to die.
2. The nucleus is surrounded by the nuclear envelope, a double membrane penetrated by fairly large pores.
3. Nucleoli are nuclear sites of ribosome subunit synthesis.
4. Chromatin is a complex network of slender threads containing histone proteins and DNA. The chromatin units are called nucleosomes. When a cell begins to divide, the chromatin coils and condenses, forming chromosomes.

Cell Growth and Reproduction (pp. 95–107)

The Cell Life Cycle (pp. 95–100)

1. The cell life cycle is the series of changes that a cell goes through from the time it is formed until it divides.
2. Interphase is the nondividing phase of the cell life cycle. Interphase consists of G_1, S, and G_2 subphases. During G_1, the cell grows and centriole replication begins. During the S phase, DNA replicates. During G_2, the final preparations for division are made. Many checkpoints occur during interphase at which the cell gets the go-ahead signal to go through mitosis or is prevented from continuing to mitosis.
3. DNA replication occurs before cell division, ensuring that both daughter cells have identical genes. The DNA helix uncoils, and each DNA nucleotide strand acts as a template for the formation of a complementary strand. Base pairing provides the guide for the proper positioning of nucleotides.
4. The semiconservative replication of a DNA molecule produces two DNA molecules identical to the parent molecule, each formed of one "old" and one "new" strand.
5. Cell division, essential for body growth and repair, occurs during the M phase. Cell division consists of two distinct phases: mitosis (nuclear division) and cytokinesis (division of the cytoplasm).
6. Mitosis, consisting of prophase, metaphase, anaphase, and telophase, parcels out the replicated chromosomes to two daughter nuclei, each genetically identical to the mother nucleus. Cytokinesis, which begins late in mitosis, divides the cytoplasmic mass into two parts.

7. Cell division is stimulated by certain chemicals (including growth factors and some hormones) and increasing cell size. Lack of space and inhibitory chemicals deter cell division. Cell division is regulated by cyclin-Cdk complexes.

Protein Synthesis (pp. 100–105)

8. A gene is defined as a DNA segment that provides the instructions for the synthesis of one polypeptide chain. Since the major structural materials of the body are proteins, and all enzymes are proteins, this amply covers the synthesis of all biological molecules.
9. The base sequence of exon DNA provides the information for protein structure. Each three-base sequence (triplet) calls for a particular amino acid to be built into a polypeptide chain.
10. The RNA molecules acting in protein synthesis are synthesized on single strands of the DNA template. RNA nucleotides are joined according to base-pairing rules.
11. Messenger RNA carries instructions for making a polypeptide chain from the DNA to the ribosomes. Ribosomal RNA forms part of the protein synthesis sites. A transfer RNA ferries each amino acid to the ribosome and binds to a codon on the mRNA strand specifying its amino acid.
12. Protein synthesis involves (a) transcription, synthesis of a complementary mRNA, and (b) translation, "reading" of the mRNA by tRNA and peptide bonding of the amino acids into the polypeptide chain. Ribosomes coordinate translation.

Other Roles of DNA (pp. 105–106)

13. Intron and other "junk" DNA encodes many RNA species that may interfere with or promote the function of specific genes.

Cytosolic Protein Degradation (pp. 106–107)

14. Soluble proteins that are damaged or no longer needed are targeted for destruction by attachment of ubiquitin. Cytosolic enzymes or proteasomes then degrade these proteins.

Extracellular Materials (p. 107)

1. Extracellular materials are substances found outside the cells. They include body fluids, cellular secretions, and extracellular matrix. Extracellular matrix is particularly abundant in connective tissues.

Developmental Aspects of Cells (pp. 108–109)

1. The first cell of an organism is the fertilized egg. Early in development, cell specialization begins and reflects differential gene activation.
2. Apoptosis is programmed cell death. Its function is to dispose of damaged or unnecessary cells.
3. During adulthood, cell numbers remain fairly constant. Cell division occurs primarily to replace lost cells.
4. Cellular aging may reflect chemical insults, progressive disorders of immunity, or a genetically programmed decline in the rate of cell division with age.

REVIEW QUESTIONS

Multiple Choice/Matching

(Some questions have more than one correct answer. Select the best answer or answers from the choices given.)

1. The smallest unit capable of life by itself is (**a**) the organ, (**b**) the organelle, (**c**) the tissue, (**d**) the cell, (**e**) the nucleus.

2. The major types of lipid found in the plasma membranes are (choose two) (**a**) cholesterol, (**b**) triglycerides, (**c**) phospholipids, (**d**) fat-soluble vitamins.
3. Membrane junctions that allow nutrients or ions to flow from cell to cell are (**a**) desmosomes, (**b**) gap junctions, (**c**) tight junctions, (**d**) all of these.

4. The term used to describe the type of solution in which cells will lose water to their environment is (**a**) isotonic, (**b**) hypertonic, (**c**) hypotonic, (**d**) catatonic.

5. Osmosis always involves (**a**) a selectively permeable membrane, (**b**) a difference in solvent concentration, (**c**) diffusion, (**d**) active transport, (**e**) a, b, and c.

6. A physiologist observes that the concentration of sodium inside a cell is decidedly lower than that outside the cell. Sodium diffuses easily across the plasma membrane of such cells when they are dead, but *not* when they are alive. What cellular function that is lacking in dead cells explains the difference? (**a**) osmosis, (**b**) diffusion, (**c**) active transport (solute pumping), (**d**) dialysis.

7. The solute-pumping type of active transport is accomplished by (**a**) exocytosis, (**b**) phagocytosis, (**c**) electrical forces in the cell membrane, (**d**) changes in shape and position of carrier molecules in the plasma membrane.

8. The endocytotic process in which a sampling of particulate matter is engulfed and brought into the cell is called (**a**) phagocytosis, (**b**) fluid-phase endocytosis, (**c**) exocytosis.

9. Which is *not* true of centrioles? (**a**) they start to duplicate in G$_1$, (**b**) they lie in the centrosome, (**c**) they are made of microtubules, (**d**) they are membrane-walled barrels lying parallel to each other.

10. The nuclear substance composed of histone proteins and DNA is (**a**) chromatin, (**b**) the nucleolus, (**c**) nuclear sap, or nucleoplasm, (**d**) nuclear pores.

11. The information sequence that determines the nature of a protein is the (**a**) nucleotide, (**b**) gene, (**c**) triplet, (**d**) codon.

12. Mutations may be caused by (**a**) X rays, (**b**) certain chemicals, (**c**) radiation from ionizing radioisotopes, (**d**) all of these.

13. The phase of mitosis during which centrioles reach the poles and chromosomes attach to the spindle is (**a**) anaphase, (**b**) metaphase, (**c**) prophase, (**d**) telophase.

14. Final preparations for cell division are made during the life cycle subphase called (**a**) G$_1$, (**b**) G$_2$, (**c**) M, (**d**) S.

15. The RNA synthesized on one of the DNA strands is (**a**) mRNA, (**b**) tRNA, (**c**) rRNA, (**d**) all of these.

16. The RNA species that carries the coded message, specifying the sequence of amino acids in the protein to be made, from the nucleus to the cytoplasm is (**a**) mRNA, (**b**) tRNA, (**c**) rRNA, (**d**) all of these.

17. If DNA has a sequence of AAA, then a segment of mRNA synthesized on it will have a sequence of (**a**) TTT, (**b**) UUU, (**c**) GGG, (**d**) CCC.

18. A nerve cell and a lymphocyte are presumed to differ in their (**a**) specialized structure, (**b**) suppressed genes and embryonic history, (**c**) genetic information, (**d**) a and b, (**e**) a and c.

19. A pancreas cell makes proteins (enzymes) which it releases to the small intestine. Which of the following best describes the path of these proteins from synthesis to exocytosis at the pancreatic cell's plasma membrane (PM)? (**a**) Golgi → rough ER → PM, (**b**) smooth ER → Golgi → lysosome → PM, (**c**) rough ER → Golgi → PM, (**d**) nucleus → Golgi → PM.

Short Answer Essay Questions

20. Which organelle is responsible for a newborn having distinctive toes and fingers instead of webbed digits?

21. Explain why mitosis can be thought of as cellular immortality.

22. Contrast the roles of ER-bound ribosomes with those free in the cytosol.

23. Cells lining the trachea have whiplike motile extensions on their free surfaces. What are these extensions, what is their source, and what is their function?

24. Name the three phases of interphase and describe an activity unique to each phase.

25. Comment on the role of the sodium-potassium pump in maintaining a cell's resting membrane potential.

26. Differentiate clearly between primary and secondary active transport processes.

27. Cell division typically yields two daughter cells, each with one nucleus. How is the occasional binucleate condition of liver cells explained?

Critical Thinking and Clinical Application Questions

1. Explain why limp celery becomes crisp and the skin of your fingertips wrinkles when placed in tap water. (The principle is exactly the same.)

2. A "red-hot" bacterial infection of the intestinal tract irritates the intestinal cells and interferes with digestion. Such a condition is often accompanied by diarrhea, which causes loss of body water. On the basis of what you have learned about osmotic water flows, explain why diarrhea may occur.

3. Two examples of chemotherapeutic drugs (drugs used to treat cancer) and their cellular actions are listed below. Explain why each drug could be fatal to a cell.
   - Vincristine (Oncovin): damages the mitotic spindle
   - Doxorubicin (Adriamycin): binds to DNA and blocks mRNA synthesis

4. The normal function of one tumor suppressor gene is to prevent cells with damaged chromosomes and DNA from "progressing from G$_1$ to S," whereas another tumor suppressor gene prevents "passage from G$_2$ to M." When these tumor suppressor genes fail to work, cancer can result. Explain what the phrases in quotations mean.

5. In their anatomy lab, many students are exposed to the chemical preservatives phenol, formaldehyde, and alcohol. Our cells break down these toxins very effectively. What cellular organelle is responsible for this?

6. Dynein is missing from the cilia and flagella of individuals with a specific inherited disorder. These individuals have severe respiratory problems and, if males, are sterile. What is the structural connection between these two symptoms?

7. Explain why alcoholics are likely to have much more smooth ER than teetotalers.

8. Water is a precious natural resource in Florida and it is said that supplies are dwindling. Desalinizing (removing salt from) ocean water has been recommended as a solution to the problem. Why shouldn't we drink salt water?

PEARSON **myA&P** place

Access everything you need to practice, review, and self-assess for both your A&P lecture and lab courses at **myA&P** (www.myaandp.com). There, you'll find powerful online resources, including chapter quizzes and tests, games, A&P Flix animations with quizzes, *Interactive Physiology*® with quizzes, MP3 Tutor Sessions, Practice Anatomy Lab™, and more to help you get a better grade in your course.

reparing Human Tissue for Microscopy
pp. 114–115)

pithelial Tissue (pp. 115–124)

Special Characteristics of Epithelium
(pp. 115–116)

Classification of Epithelia (pp. 116–121)

Glandular Epithelia (pp. 121–124)

onnective Tissue (pp. 124–135)

Common Characteristics of Connective Tissue
(p. 124)

Structural Elements of Connective Tissue
(pp. 124–126)

Types of Connective Tissue (pp. 126–135)

lervous Tissue (pp. 134–136)

luscle Tissue (pp. 136–138)

Covering and Lining Membranes
pp. 138–139)

Cutaneous Membrane (pp. 138–139)

Mucous Membranes (pp. 138–139)

Serous Membranes (pp. 138–139)

issue Repair (pp. 139–141)

Steps of Tissue Repair (pp. 139–140)

Regenerative Capacity of Different Tissues
(p. 141)

Developmental Aspects of Tissues
pp. 141–144)

Tissue: The Living Fabric

Amoebas and other unicellular (one-cell) organisms are rugged individualists. Each cell alone obtains and digests its food, ejects its wastes, and carries out all the other activities necessary to keep itself alive and "buzzin' around on all cylinders." But in the multicellular human body, cells do not operate independently. Instead, they form tight cell communities that live and work together.

Individual body cells are specialized, with each type performing specific functions that help maintain homeostasis and benefit the body as a whole. Cell specialization is obvious: How muscle cells look and act

4

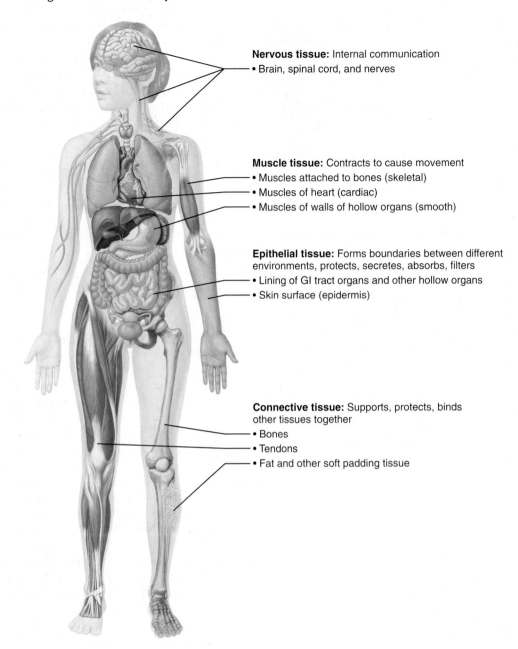

Nervous tissue: Internal communication
• Brain, spinal cord, and nerves

Muscle tissue: Contracts to cause movement
• Muscles attached to bones (skeletal)
• Muscles of heart (cardiac)
• Muscles of walls of hollow organs (smooth)

Epithelial tissue: Forms boundaries between different
environments, protects, secretes, absorbs, filters
• Lining of GI tract organs and other hollow organs
• Skin surface (epidermis)

Connective tissue: Supports, protects, binds
other tissues together
• Bones
• Tendons
• Fat and other soft padding tissue

**Figure 4.1 Overview of four tissue types: epithelial, connective, muscle,
and nervous tissues.**

differs greatly from skin cells, which in turn are easy to distinguish from brain cells. Cell specialization allows the body to function in sophisticated ways, but division of labor has certain hazards. When a particular group of cells is indispensable, its loss or injury can severely disable or even destroy the body.

Groups of cells that are similar in structure and perform a common or related function are called **tissues** (*tissu* = woven). Four primary tissue types interweave to form the "fabric" of the body. These basic tissues are epithelial (ep″i-the′le-ul), connective, muscle, and nervous tissue, and each has numerous subclasses or varieties. If we had to describe the general role of each primary tissue type in a single word, the words would most likely be *covering* (epithelial), *support* (connective), *movement* (muscle), and *control* (nervous). However, these words reveal only a fraction of the functions that each tissue performs **(Figure 4.1)**.

As we explained in Chapter 1, tissues are organized into organs such as the kidneys and the heart. Most organs contain all four tissue types, and their arrangement determines the organ's structure and capabilities. The study of tissues, or **histology**, complements the study of gross anatomy. Together they provide the structural basis for understanding organ physiology.

Preparing Human Tissue for Microscopy

▶ List the steps involved in preparing animal tissue for microscopic viewing.

Elaborate steps are taken to prepare human or animal tissue for microscopic viewing. The specimen must be **fixed** (preserved) and then cut into **sections** (slices) thin enough to transmit light or electrons. Finally the specimen must be **stained** to enhance contrast.

The stains used in light microscopy are beautifully colored organic dyes, most of which were originally developed by clothing manufacturers in the mid-1800s. Many dyes consist of negatively or positively charged molecules (acidic and basic stains, respectively) that bind within the tissue to macromolecules of the opposite charge. The stains distinguish different anatomical structures because different parts of cells and tissues take up different dyes.

For transmission electron microscopy (TEM), tissue sections are "stained" with heavy metal salts. These metals deflect electrons in the beam to different extents, providing contrast in the image. Electron-microscope images are in shades of gray because color is a property of light, not of electron waves, but the image may be artificially colored to enhance contrast. Another kind of electron microscopy, scanning electron microscopy (SEM), provides three-dimensional pictures of an unsectioned tissue surface. These striking images are scattered throughout this book.

Preserved tissue we see under the microscope has been exposed to many procedures that alter its original condition and introduce minor distortions called **artifacts**. For this reason, keep in mind that most microscopic structures we view are not exactly like those in living tissue.

CHECK YOUR UNDERSTANDING

1. What is the purpose of fixing tissue for microscopic viewing?

2. What types of stains are used to stain tissues to be viewed with an electron microscope?

For answers, see Appendix G.

Epithelial Tissue

▶ List several structural and functional characteristics of epithelial tissue.

▶ Name, classify, and describe the various types of epithelia, and indicate their chief function(s) and location(s).

Epithelial tissue, or an **epithelium** (plural: epithelia), is a sheet of cells that covers a body surface or lines a body cavity (*epithe* = laid on, covering). It occurs in the body as (1) *covering and lining epithelium* and (2) *glandular epithelium*. Covering and lining epithelium forms the outer layer of the skin, dips into and lines the open cavities of the cardiovascular, digestive, and respiratory systems, and covers the walls and organs of the closed ventral body cavity. Glandular epithelium fashions the glands of the body.

Epithelia form boundaries between different environments, and nearly all substances received or given off by the body must pass through an epithelium. For example, the epidermis of the skin lies between the inside and the outside of the body. Epithelium

lining the urinary bladder separates underlying cells of the bladder wall from urine.

In its role as an interface tissue, epithelium accomplishes many functions, including (1) protection, (2) absorption, (3) filtration, (4) excretion, (5) secretion, and (6) sensory reception. We describe each of these functions in detail later, but here we illustrate these functions briefly: The epithelium of the skin protects underlying tissues from mechanical and chemical injury and bacterial invasion and contains nerve endings that respond to various stimuli acting at the skin surface (pressure, heat, etc.). The epithelium lining the digestive tract is specialized to absorb substances. That found in the kidneys performs nearly the whole functional "menu"—excretion, absorption, secretion, and filtration. Secretion is the specialty of glands.

Special Characteristics of Epithelium

Epithelial tissues have many characteristics that distinguish them from other tissue types.

1. **Polarity**. All epithelia have an **apical surface**, an upper free surface exposed to the body exterior or the cavity of an internal organ, and a lower attached **basal surface**. For this reason, all epithelia exhibit *apical-basal polarity*, meaning that cell regions near the apical surface differ from those near the basal surface in both structure and function. This situation is maintained, at least in part, by the highly ordered cytoskeleton of epithelial cells.

   Although some apical surfaces are smooth and slick, most have **microvilli**, fingerlike extensions of the plasma membrane. Microvilli tremendously increase the exposed surface area. In epithelia that absorb or secrete substances (those lining the intestine or kidney tubules, for instance), the microvilli are often so dense that the cell apices have a fuzzy appearance called a *brush border*. Some epithelia, such as that lining the trachea, have motile **cilia** (tiny hairlike projections) that propel substances along their free surface.

   Lying adjacent to the basal surface of an epithelium is a thin supporting sheet called the **basal lamina** (lam′ĭ-nah; "sheet"). This noncellular, adhesive sheet consists largely of glycoproteins secreted by the epithelial cells plus some fine collagen fibers. The basal lamina acts as a selective filter that determines which molecules diffusing from the underlying connective tissue are allowed to enter the epithelium. The basal lamina also acts as a scaffolding along which epithelial cells can migrate to repair a wound.

2. **Specialized contacts**. Except for glandular epithelia (discussed on pp. 121–124), epithelial cells fit close together to form continuous sheets. Adjacent cells are bound together at many points by lateral contacts, including *tight junctions* and *desmosomes* (see Chapter 3). The tight junctions help keep proteins in the apical region of the plasma membrane from diffusing into the basal region, and thus help to maintain epithelial polarity.

3. **Supported by connective tissue**. All epithelial sheets rest upon and are supported by connective tissue. Just deep to the basal lamina is the **reticular lamina**, a layer of

4

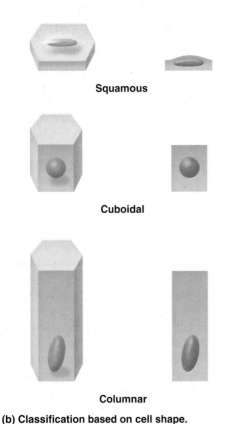

Simple

Apical surface

Basal surface

Stratified

Apical surface

Basal surface

(a) Classification based on number of cell layers.

Squamous

Cuboidal

Columnar

(b) Classification based on cell shape.

Figure 4.2 **Classification of epithelia.**

extracellular material containing a fine network of collagen protein fibers that "belongs to" the underlying connective tissue. Together the two laminae form the **basement membrane**. The basement membrane reinforces the epithelial sheet, helping it to resist stretching and tearing forces, and defines the epithelial boundary.

HOMEOSTATIC IMBALANCE

An important characteristic of cancerous epithelial cells is their failure to respect the basement membrane boundary, which they penetrate to invade the tissues beneath. ■

4. **Avascular but innervated**. Although epithelium is *innervated* (supplied by nerve fibers), it is *avascular* (contains no blood vessels). Epithelial cells are nourished by substances diffusing from blood vessels in the underlying connective tissue.

5. **Regeneration**. Epithelium has a high regenerative capacity. Some epithelia are exposed to friction and their surface cells rub off. Others are damaged by hostile substances in the external environment (bacteria, acids, smoke). If and when their apical-basal polarity and lateral contacts are destroyed, epithelial cells begin to reproduce themselves rapidly. As long as epithelial cells receive adequate nutrition, they can replace lost cells by cell division.

CHECK YOUR UNDERSTANDING

3. Epithelial tissue is the only tissue type that has polarity, that is, an apical and a basal surface. Why is this important?

4. Which of the following properties apply to epithelial tissue? Has blood vessels, can repair itself (regenerates), cells joined by lateral contacts.

For answers, see Appendix G.

Classification of Epithelia

Each epithelium is given two names. The first name indicates the number of cell layers present, and the second describes the shape of its cells. Based on the number of cell layers, there are simple and stratified epithelia **(Figure 4.2a)**. **Simple epithelia** consist of a single cell layer. They are typically found where absorption, secretion, and filtration occur and a thin epithelial barrier is desirable. **Stratified epithelia**, composed of two or more cell layers stacked one on top of the other, are common in high-abrasion areas where protection is important, such as the skin surface and the lining of the mouth.

In cross section, all epithelial cells have six (somewhat irregular) sides, and an apical surface view of an epithelial sheet looks like a honeycomb. This polyhedral shape allows the cells to be closely packed. However, epithelial cells vary in height, and on that basis, there are three common shapes of epithelial cells (Figure 4.2b). **Squamous cells** (skwa′mus) are flattened and scalelike (*squam* = scale). **Cuboidal cells** (ku-boi′dahl) are boxlike, approximately as tall as they are wide, and **columnar cells** (kŏ-lum′nar) are tall and column shaped.

In each case, the shape of the nucleus conforms to that of the cell. The nucleus of a squamous cell is a flattened disc; that of a cuboidal cell is spherical; and a columnar cell nucleus is elongated from top to bottom and usually located close to the cell base. Keep nuclear shape in mind when you attempt to identify epithelial types.

Simple epithelia are easy to classify by cell shape because all cells in the layer usually have the same shape. In stratified epithelia, however, the cell shapes usually differ among the different cell layers. To avoid ambiguity, stratified epithelia are named according to the shape of the cells in the *apical* layer. This naming system will become clearer as we explore the specific epithelial types.

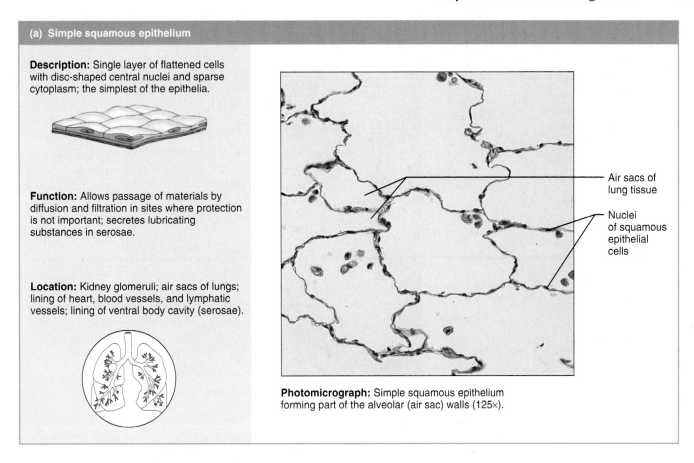

(a) Simple squamous epithelium

Description: Single layer of flattened cells with disc-shaped central nuclei and sparse cytoplasm; the simplest of the epithelia.

Function: Allows passage of materials by diffusion and filtration in sites where protection is not important; secretes lubricating substances in serosae.

Location: Kidney glomeruli; air sacs of lungs; lining of heart, blood vessels, and lymphatic vessels; lining of ventral body cavity (serosae).

Air sacs of lung tissue

Nuclei of squamous epithelial cells

Photomicrograph: Simple squamous epithelium forming part of the alveolar (air sac) walls (125×).

Figure 4.3 Epithelial tissues. (a) Simple epithelium. (See *A Brief Atlas of the Human Body*, Plates 1 and 2.)

As you read about the epithelial classes, study **Figure 4.3**. Using the photomicrographs, try to pick out the individual cells within each epithelium. This is not always easy, because the boundaries between epithelial cells often are indistinct. Furthermore, the nucleus of a particular cell may or may not be visible, depending on the precise plane of the cut made to prepare the tissue slides.

Simple Epithelia

The simple epithelia are most concerned with absorption, secretion, and filtration. Because they consist of a single cell layer and are usually very thin, protection is not one of their specialties.

Simple Squamous Epithelium The cells of a **simple squamous epithelium** are flattened laterally, and their cytoplasm is sparse (Figure 4.3a). In a surface view, the close-fitting cells resemble a tiled floor. When the cells are cut perpendicular to their free surface, they resemble fried eggs seen from the side, with their cytoplasm wisping out from the slightly bulging nucleus. Thin and often permeable, this epithelium is found where filtration or the exchange of substances by rapid diffusion is a priority. In the kidneys, simple squamous epithelium forms part of the filtration membrane. In the lungs, it forms the walls of the air sacs across which gas exchange occurs.

Two simple squamous epithelia in the body have special names that reflect their location. **Endothelium** (en″do-the′le-um; "inner covering") provides a slick, friction-reducing lining in lymphatic vessels and in all hollow organs of the cardiovascular system—blood vessels and the heart. Capillaries consist exclusively of endothelium, and its exceptional thinness encourages the efficient exchange of nutrients and wastes between the bloodstream and surrounding tissue cells. **Mesothelium** (mez″o-the′le-um; "middlecovering") is the epithelium found in serous membranes lining the ventral body cavity and covering its organs.

Simple Cuboidal Epithelium Simple cuboidal epithelium consists of a single layer of cells as tall as they are wide (Figure 4.3b). The spherical nuclei stain darkly, causing the cell layer to look like a string of beads when viewed microscopically. Important functions of simple cuboidal epithelium are secretion and absorption. This epithelium forms the walls of the smallest ducts of glands and of many kidney tubules.

Simple Columnar Epithelium Simple columnar epithelium is seen as a single layer of tall, closely packed cells, aligned like soldiers in a row (Figure 4.3c). It lines the digestive tract from the stomach through the rectum. Columnar cells are mostly associated with absorption and secretion, and the digestive tract lining has two distinct modifications that make it ideal for that

4

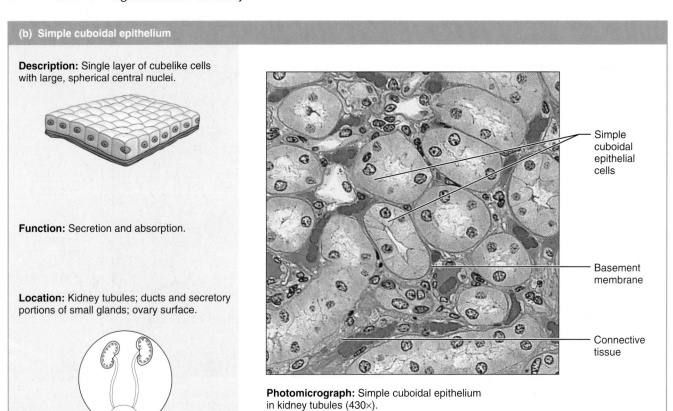

(b) Simple cuboidal epithelium

Description: Single layer of cubelike cells with large, spherical central nuclei.

Function: Secretion and absorption.

Location: Kidney tubules; ducts and secretory portions of small glands; ovary surface.

Simple cuboidal epithelial cells

Basement membrane

Connective tissue

Photomicrograph: Simple cuboidal epithelium in kidney tubules (430×).

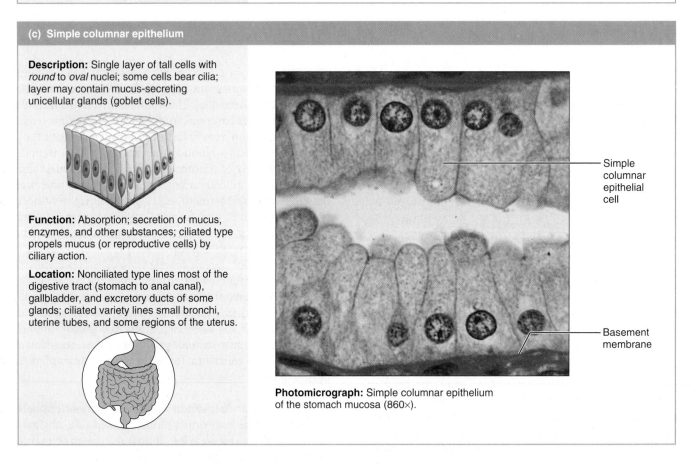

(c) Simple columnar epithelium

Description: Single layer of tall cells with *round* to *oval* nuclei; some cells bear cilia; layer may contain mucus-secreting unicellular glands (goblet cells).

Function: Absorption; secretion of mucus, enzymes, and other substances; ciliated type propels mucus (or reproductive cells) by ciliary action.

Location: Nonciliated type lines most of the digestive tract (stomach to anal canal), gallbladder, and excretory ducts of some glands; ciliated variety lines small bronchi, uterine tubes, and some regions of the uterus.

Simple columnar epithelial cell

Basement membrane

Photomicrograph: Simple columnar epithelium of the stomach mucosa (860×).

Figure 4.3 *(continued)* **Epithelial tissues. (b)** and **(c)** Simple epithelium. (See *A Brief Atlas of the Human Body*, Plates 3, 4, and 5.)

4

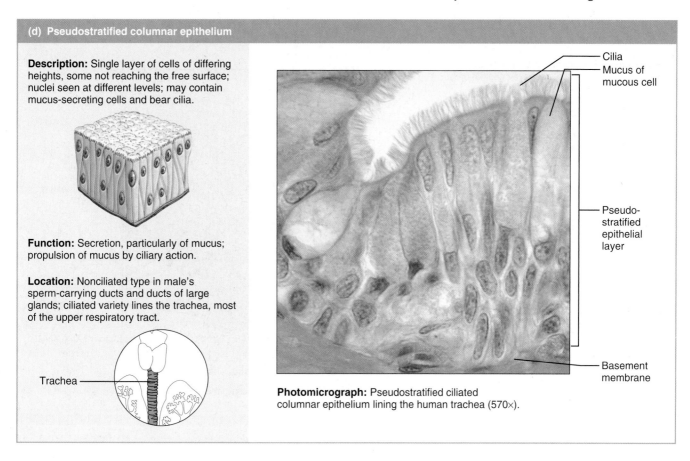

(d) Pseudostratified columnar epithelium

Description: Single layer of cells of differing heights, some not reaching the free surface; nuclei seen at different levels; may contain mucus-secreting cells and bear cilia.

Function: Secretion, particularly of mucus; propulsion of mucus by ciliary action.

Location: Nonciliated type in male's sperm-carrying ducts and ducts of large glands; ciliated variety lines the trachea, most of the upper respiratory tract.

Trachea

Cilia
Mucus of mucous cell
Pseudo-stratified epithelial layer
Basement membrane

Photomicrograph: Pseudostratified ciliated columnar epithelium lining the human trachea (570×).

Figure 4.3 *(continued)* **(d)** Simple epithelium. (See *A Brief Altas of the Human Body,* Plate 6.)

dual function: (1) dense microvilli on the apical surface of absorptive cells and (2) cells that secrete a protective lubricating mucus. Some simple columnar epithelia display cilia on their free surfaces, which help to move substances or cells through an internal passageway.

Pseudostratified Columnar Epithelium The cells of **pseudostratified columnar epithelium** (soo″do-stră′tĭ-fīd) vary in height (Figure 4.3d). All of its cells rest on the basement membrane, but only the tallest reach the free surface of the epithelium. Because the cell nuclei lie at different levels above the basement membrane, the tissue gives the false (pseudo) impression that several cell layers are present; hence "pseudostratified." The short cells are relatively unspecialized and give rise to the taller cells. This epithelium, like the simple columnar variety, secretes or absorbs substances. A ciliated version containing mucus-secreting cells lines most of the respiratory tract. Here the motile cilia propel sheets of dust-trapping mucus superiorly away from the lungs.

Stratified Epithelia

Stratified epithelia contain two or more cell layers. They regenerate from below; that is, the basal cells divide and push apically to replace the older surface cells. Stratified epithelia are considerably more durable than the simple epithelia, and protection is their major role (but not their only role).

Stratified Squamous Epithelium Stratified squamous epithelium is the most widespread of the stratified epithelia (Figure 4.3e). Composed of several layers, it is thick and well suited for its protective role in the body. Its free surface cells are squamous, and cells of the deeper layers are cuboidal or columnar. This epithelium is found in areas subjected to wear and tear, and its surface cells are constantly being rubbed away and replaced by division of its basal cells. Because epithelium depends on diffusion of nutrients from a deeper connective tissue layer, the epithelial cells farther from the basement membrane are less viable and those at the apical surface are often flattened and atrophied.

To avoid memorizing all its locations, simply remember that this epithelium forms the external part of the skin and extends a short distance into every body opening that is directly continuous with the skin. The outer layer, or *epidermis*, of the skin is *keratinized* (ker′ah-tin″īzd), meaning its surface cells contain *keratin,* a tough protective protein. (We discuss the epidermis in Chapter 5.) The other stratified squamous epithelia of the body are *nonkeratinized.*

Stratified Cuboidal and Columnar Epithelia Stratified cuboidal epithelium is quite rare in the body, mostly found in the ducts of some of the larger glands (sweat glands, mammary glands). It typically has two layers of cuboidal cells.

(e) Stratified squamous epithelium

Description: Thick membrane composed of several cell layers; basal cells are cuboidal or columnar and metabolically active; surface cells are flattened (squamous); in the keratinized type, the surface cells are full of keratin and dead; basal cells are active in mitosis and produce the cells of the more superficial layers.

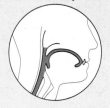

Function: Protects underlying tissues in areas subjected to abrasion.

Location: Nonkeratinized type forms the moist linings of the esophagus, mouth, and vagina; keratinized variety forms the epidermis of the skin, a dry membrane.

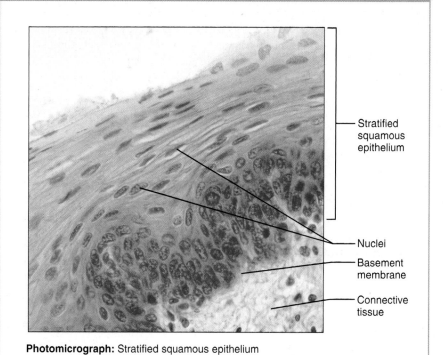

Stratified squamous epithelium

Nuclei

Basement membrane

Connective tissue

Photomicrograph: Stratified squamous epithelium lining the esophagus (285×).

(f) Transitional epithelium

Description: Resembles both stratified squamous and stratified cuboidal; basal cells cuboidal or columnar; surface cells dome shaped or squamouslike, depending on degree of organ stretch.

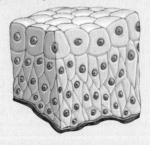

Function: Stretches readily and permits distension of urinary organ by contained urine.

Location: Lines the ureters, urinary bladder, and part of the urethra.

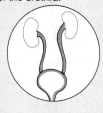

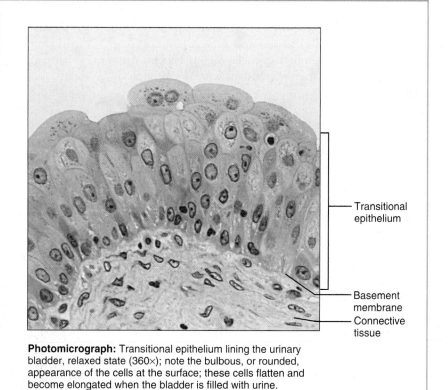

Transitional epithelium

Basement membrane

Connective tissue

Photomicrograph: Transitional epithelium lining the urinary bladder, relaxed state (360×); note the bulbous, or rounded, appearance of the cells at the surface; these cells flatten and become elongated when the bladder is filled with urine.

Figure 4.3 *(continued)* **Epithelial tissues. (e)** and **(f)** Stratified epithelium. (See *A Brief Atlas of the Human Body*, Plates 7 and 10.)

Stratified columnar epithelium also has a limited distribution in the body. Small amounts are found in the pharynx, the male urethra, and lining some glandular ducts. This epithelium also occurs at transition areas or junctions between two other types of epithelia. Only its apical layer of cells is columnar. Because of their relative scarcity in the body, these two stratified epithelia are not illustrated in Figure 4.3, but are illustrated in *A Brief Atlas of the Human Body*, Plates 8 and 9, respectively.

Transitional Epithelium **Transitional epithelium** forms the lining of hollow urinary organs, which stretch as they fill with urine (Figure 4.3f). Cells of its basal layer are cuboidal or columnar. The apical cells vary in appearance, depending on the degree of distension of the organ. When the organ is distended with urine, the transitional epithelium thins from about six cell layers to three, and its domelike apical cells flatten and become squamouslike. The ability of transitional cells to change their shape (undergo "transitions") allows a greater volume of urine to flow through a tubelike organ. In the bladder, it allows more urine to be stored.

CHECK YOUR UNDERSTANDING

5. Stratified epithelia are "built" for protection or to resist abrasion. What are the simple epithelia better at?
6. Some epithelia are pseudostratified. What does this mean?
7. Where is transitional epithelium found and what is its importance at those sites?

For answers, see Appendix G.

Glandular Epithelia

▶ Define gland.

▶ Differentiate between exocrine and endocrine glands, and between multicellular and unicellular glands.

▶ Describe how multicellular exocrine glands are classified structurally and functionally.

A **gland** consists of one or more cells that make and secrete (export) a particular product. This product, called a **secretion**, is an aqueous (water-based) fluid that usually contains proteins, but there is variation. For example, some glands release a lipid- or steroid-rich secretion.

Secretion is an active process. Glandular cells obtain needed substances from the blood and transform them chemically into a product that is then discharged from the cell. Notice that the term *secretion* can refer to both the gland's *product* and the *process* of making and releasing that product.

Glands are classified as *endocrine* ("internally secreting") or *exocrine* ("externally secreting") depending on where they release their product, and as *unicellular* ("one-celled") or *multicellular* ("many-celled") based on the relative cell number making up the gland. Unicellular glands are scattered

within epithelial sheets. By contrast, most multicellular epithelial glands form by invagination (inward growth) or evagination (outward growth) from an epithelial sheet and, at least initially, most have *ducts*, tubelike connections to the epithelial sheets.

Endocrine Glands

Because **endocrine glands** eventually lose their ducts, they are often called *ductless glands*. They produce **hormones**, regulatory chemicals that they secrete by exocytosis directly into the extracellular space. From there the hormones enter the blood or lymphatic fluid and travel to specific target organs. Each hormone prompts its target organ(s) to respond in some characteristic way. For example, hormones produced by certain intestinal cells cause the pancreas to release enzymes that help digest food in the digestive tract.

Endocrine glands are structurally diverse, so one description does not fit all. Most endocrine glands are compact multicellular organs, but some individual hormone-producing cells are scattered in the digestive tract mucosa and in the brain, giving rise to their collective description as the *diffuse endocrine system*. Their secretions are also varied, ranging from modified amino acids to peptides, glycoproteins, and steroids. Since not all endocrine glands are epithelial derivatives, we defer consideration of their structure and function to Chapter 16.

Exocrine Glands

Exocrine glands are numerous, and many of their products are familiar. All exocrine glands secrete their products onto body surfaces (skin) or into body cavities. The unicellular glands do so directly (by exocytosis), whereas the multicellular glands do so via an epithelium-walled duct that transports the secretion to the epithelial surface. Exocrine glands are a diverse lot. They include mucous, sweat, oil, and salivary glands, the liver (which secretes bile), the pancreas (which synthesizes digestive enzymes), and many others.

Unicellular Exocrine Glands The only important examples of **unicellular** (or one-celled) **glands** are *mucous cells* and *goblet cells*. Unicellular glands are sprinkled in the epithelial linings of the intestinal and respiratory tracts amid columnar cells with other functions (see **Figure 4.4** and Figure 4.3d). In humans, all such glands produce **mucin** (mu′sin), a complex glycoprotein that dissolves in water when secreted. Once dissolved, mucin forms **mucus**, a slimy coating that both protects and lubricates surfaces. In **goblet cells** the cuplike accumulation of mucin distends the top of the cell, making the cells look like a glass with a stem (thus "goblet" cell). This distortion does not occur in **mucous cells**.

Multicellular Exocrine Glands Compared to the unicellular glands, **multicellular exocrine glands** are structurally more complex. They have two basic parts: an epithelium-derived *duct* and a *secretory unit* (*acinus*) consisting of secretory cells. In all but the simplest glands, *supportive*

4

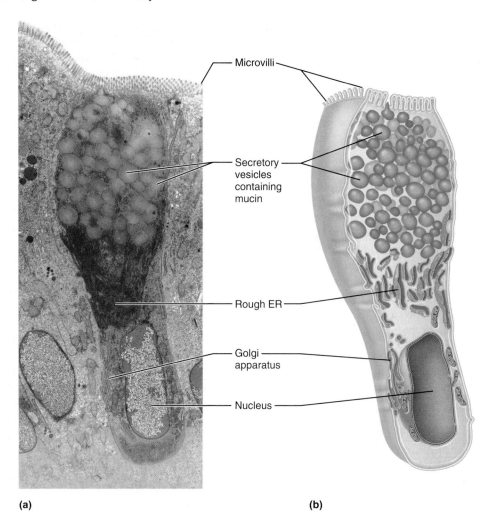

Microvilli

Secretory vesicles containing mucin

Rough ER

Golgi apparatus

Nucleus

(a)   **(b)**

Figure 4.4 Goblet cell (unicellular exocrine gland). (a) Photomicrograph of a goblet cell in the simple columnar epithelium lining the small intestine (1640×). **(b)** Corresponding diagram. Notice the secretory vesicles and well-developed rough ER and Golgi apparatus.

connective tissue surrounds the secretory unit and supplies it with blood vessels and nerve fibers, and forms a *fibrous capsule* that extends into the gland proper and divides the gland into *lobes*.

- **Structural classification**. On the basis of their duct structures, multicellular exocrine glands are either simple or compound **(Figure 4.5)**. **Simple glands** have an unbranched duct, whereas **compound glands** have a branched duct. The glands are further categorized by their secretory units as (1) **tubular** if the secretory cells form tubes; (2) **alveolar** (al-ve′o-lar) if the secretory cells form small, flasklike sacs (*alveolus* = "small hollow cavity"); and (3) **tubuloalveolar** if they have both types of secretory units. Note that the term **acinar** (as′ĭ-nar; "berrylike") is used interchangeably with alveolar.

- **Modes of secretion**. Multicellular exocrine glands secrete their products in different ways, so they can also be described functionally. Most are **merocrine glands** (mer′o-krin), which secrete their products by exocytosis as they are pro-

duced. The secretory cells are not altered in any way. The pancreas, most sweat glands, and salivary glands belong to this class **(Figure 4.6a)**.

Secretory cells of **holocrine glands** (hol′o-krin) accumulate their products within them until they rupture. (They are replaced by the division of underlying cells.) Because holocrine gland secretions include the synthesized product plus dead cell fragments (*holos* = all), you could say that their cells "die for their cause." Sebaceous (oil) glands of the skin are the only true example of holocrine glands (Figure 4.6b).

Although *apocrine glands* (ap′o-krin) are definitely present in other animals, there is some controversy over whether humans have this third gland type. Like holocrine glands, apocrine glands accumulate their products, but in this case only just beneath the free surface. Eventually, the apex of the cell pinches off (*apo* = from, off), releasing the secretory granules and a small amount of cytoplasm. The cell repairs its damage and the process repeats again and again. The best

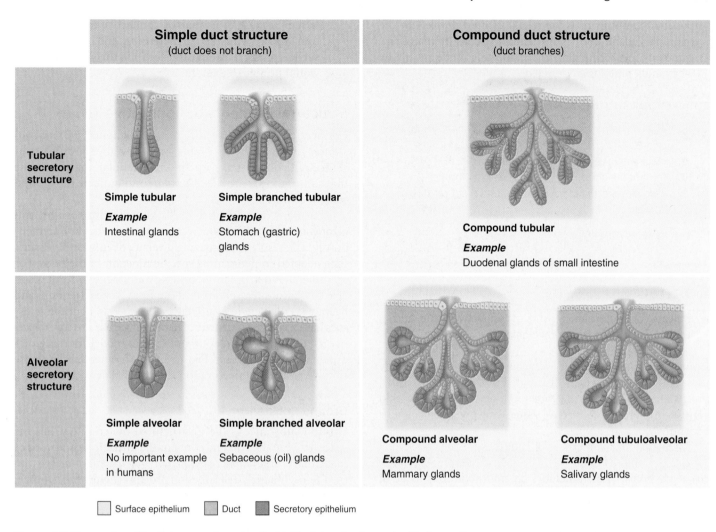

Simple duct structure (duct does not branch)		Compound duct structure (duct branches)	
Tubular secretory structure	**Simple tubular**	**Compound tubular**	
Simple branched tubular			
Example Intestinal glands	*Example* Stomach (gastric) glands	*Example* Duodenal glands of small intestine	
Alveolar secretory structure	**Simple alveolar**	**Simple branched alveolar**	**Compound alveolar**
Example No important example in humans	*Example* Sebaceous (oil) glands	*Example* Mammary glands	**Compound tubuloalveolar** *Example* Salivary glands

☐ Surface epithelium   ☐ Duct   ■ Secretory epithelium

Figure 4.5 Types of multicellular exocrine glands. Multicellular glands are classified according to duct type (simple or compound) and the structure of their secretory units (tubular, alveolar, or tubuloalveolar).

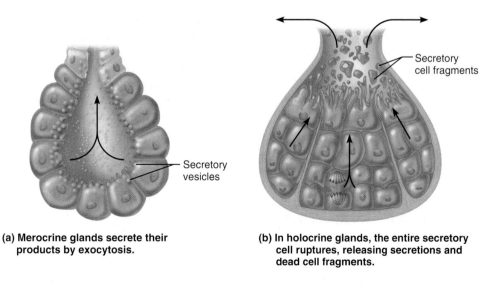

(a) Merocrine glands secrete their products by exocytosis.

Secretory vesicles

Secretory cell fragments

(b) In holocrine glands, the entire secretory cell ruptures, releasing secretions and dead cell fragments.

Figure 4.6 Chief modes of secretion in human exocrine glands.

possibility in humans is the release of lipid droplets by the mammary glands, but most histologists classify mammary glands as merocrine glands because this is the means by which milk proteins are secreted.

CHECK YOUR UNDERSTANDING

8. What common secretion is produced by all unicellular exocrine glands?

9. How are multicellular exocrine glands classified?

10. Which of the gland types—merocrine or holocrine—would be expected to have the highest rate of cell division and why?

For answers, see Appendix G.

Connective Tissue

▶ Indicate common characteristics of connective tissue, and list and describe its structural elements.

Connective tissue is found everywhere in the body. It is the most abundant and widely distributed of the primary tissues, but its amount in particular organs varies. For example, skin consists primarily of connective tissue, while the brain contains very little.

There are four main classes of connective tissue and several subclasses (**Table 4.1** on p. 134). The main classes are (1) *connective tissue proper* (which includes fat and the fibrous tissue of ligaments), (2) *cartilage*, (3) *bone tissue*, and (4) *blood*.

Connective tissue does much more than just *connect* body parts. It has many forms and functions. Its major functions include (1) *binding and support*, (2) *protection*, (3) *insulation*, and as blood, (4) *transportation* of substances within the body. For example, bone and cartilage support and protect body organs by providing the hard underpinnings of the skeleton, and cushions of fat insulate and protect body organs and provide reserve energy fuel.

Common Characteristics of Connective Tissue

Despite their many and diverse functions in the body, connective tissues have some common characteristics that set them apart from other primary tissues:

1. **Common origin.** All connective tissues arise from *mesenchyme* (an embryonic tissue) and hence have a kinship.

2. **Degrees of vascularity.** Connective tissues run the entire gamut of vascularity. Cartilage is avascular. Dense connective tissue is poorly vascularized, and the other types of connective tissue have a rich supply of blood vessels.

3. **Extracellular matrix.** All other primary tissues are composed mainly of cells, but connective tissues are largely nonliving **extracellular matrix** (ma′triks; "womb"), which separates, often widely, the living cells of the

tissue. Because of its matrix, connective tissue is able to bear weight, withstand great tension, and endure abuses, such as physical trauma and abrasion that no other tissue would be able to tolerate.

Structural Elements of Connective Tissue

Connective tissues have three main elements: *ground substance*, *fibers*, and *cells* (Table 4.1). Together ground substance and fibers make up the extracellular matrix. (Note that some authors use the term *matrix* to indicate the ground substance only.)

The characteristics of the cells and the composition and arrangement of extracellular matrix elements vary tremendously. The result is an amazing diversity of connective tissues, each adapted to perform its specific function in the body. For example, the matrix can be delicate and fragile to form a soft "packing" around an organ, or it can form "ropes" (tendons and ligaments) of incredible strength. Nonetheless, connective tissues have a common structural plan, and we use *areolar connective tissue* (ah-re′o-lar) as our *prototype*, or model, for this group of tissues (**Figure 4.7** and Figure 4.8a). All other subclasses are simply variants of this common structural plan.

Ground Substance

Ground substance is the unstructured material that fills the space between the cells and contains the fibers. It is composed of *interstitial* (*tissue*) *fluid*, *cell adhesion proteins*, and *proteoglycans* (pro″te-o-gli′kanz). Cell adhesion proteins (*fibronectin, laminin,* and others) serve mainly as a connective tissue glue that allows connective tissue cells to attach themselves to matrix elements. The proteoglycans consist of a protein core to which *glycosaminoglycans* (GAGs) (gli″kos-ah-me″no-gli′kanz) are attached. The strandlike GAGs, most importantly *chondroitin sulfate* and *hyaluronic acid* (hi″ah-lu-ron′ik), are large, negatively charged polysaccharides that stick out from the core protein like the fibers of a bottle brush. The proteoglycans tend to form huge aggregates in which the GAGs intertwine and trap water, forming a substance that varies from a fluid to a viscous gel. In general, the higher the GAG content, the more viscous the ground substance.

The ground substance holds large amounts of fluid and functions as a molecular sieve, or medium, through which nutrients and other dissolved substances can diffuse between the blood capillaries and the cells. The fibers embedded in the ground substance make it less pliable and hinder diffusion somewhat.

Fibers

The fibers of connective tissue provide support. Three types of fibers are found in connective tissue matrix: collagen, elastic, and reticular fibers. Of these, collagen fibers are by far the strongest and most abundant.

Collagen fibers are constructed primarily of the fibrous protein *collagen*. Collagen molecules are secreted into the extracellular

Cell types

Extracellular matrix

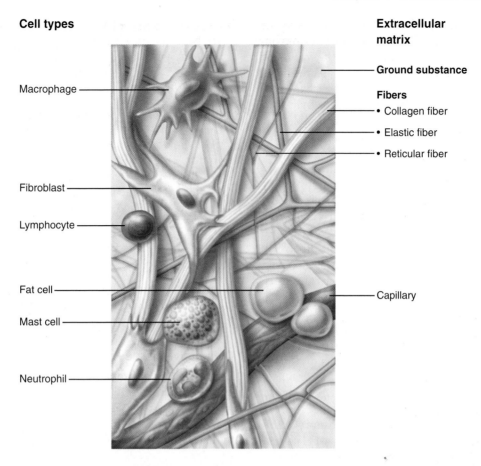

Macrophage

Fibroblast

Lymphocyte

Fat cell

Mast cell

Neutrophil

Ground substance

Fibers

• Collagen fiber

• Elastic fiber

• Reticular fiber

Capillary

Figure 4.7 Areolar connective tissue: A prototype (model) connective tissue. This tissue underlies epithelia and surrounds capillaries. Notice the various cell types and three classes of fibers (collagen, reticular, elastic) embedded in the ground substance. (See Figure 4.8a for a less idealized version.)

space, where they assemble spontaneously into cross-linked fibrils, which in turn are bundled together into the thick collagen fibers seen with a microscope. Because of the cross-linking of their fibrils, collagen fibers are extremely tough and provide high tensile strength (that is, the ability to resist longitudinal stress) to the matrix. Indeed, stress tests show that collagen fibers are stronger than steel fibers of the same size! When fresh, they have a glistening white appearance, and for this reason, they are also called *white fibers*. (See the large lavender-white fibers in Figure 4.7.)

Elastic fibers are long, thin fibers that form branching networks in the extracellular matrix. These fibers contain a rubberlike protein, *elastin*, that allows them to stretch and recoil like rubber bands. Connective tissue can stretch only so much before its thick, ropelike collagen fibers become taut. Then, when the tension lets up, elastic fibers snap the connective tissue back to its normal length and shape. Elastic fibers are found where greater elasticity is needed, for example, in the skin, lungs, and blood vessel walls. Because fresh elastic fibers appear yellow, they are sometimes called *yellow fibers*. (See the thin orange fibers in Figure 4.7.)

Reticular fibers are short, fine, collagenous fibers with a slightly different chemistry and form. They are continuous with

collagen fibers, and they branch extensively, forming delicate networks (*reticul* = network) that surround small blood vessels and support the soft tissue of organs. They are particularly abundant where connective tissue abuts other tissue types, for example, in the basement membrane of epithelial tissues, and around capillaries, where they form fuzzy "nets" that allow more "give" than the larger collagen fibers. (See the thin, dark blue fibers in Figure 4.7.)

Cells

Each major class of connective tissue has a fundamental or resident cell type that exists in immature and mature forms (see Table 4.1). The undifferentiated cells, indicated by the suffix *blast* (literally, "bud" or "sprout," but the suffix means "forming"), are actively mitotic cells that secrete the ground substance and the fibers characteristic of their particular matrix. As listed in the third column of Table 4.1, the primary blast cell types by connective tissue class are (1) connective tissue proper: **fibroblast**; (2) cartilage: **chondroblast** (kon'dro-blast"); and (3) bone: **osteoblast** (os'te-o-blast"). The **hematopoietic stem cell** (hem"ah-to-poy-et'ik), which is the undifferentiated blast cell that produces blood cells, is not included in Table 4.1

because it is not located in "its" tissue (blood) and does not make the fluid matrix (plasma) of that tissue. Blood formation is considered in Chapter 17.

Once they synthesize the matrix, the blast cells assume their less active, mature mode, indicated by the suffix *cyte*, also shown in Table 4.1, third column. The mature cells maintain the health of the matrix. However, if the matrix is injured, they can easily revert to their more active state to repair and regenerate the matrix. (The blood-forming hematopoietic stem cells found in bone marrow are always actively mitotic.)

Additionally, connective tissue is home to an assortment of other cell types, such as nutrient-storing *fat cells* and mobile cells that migrate into the connective tissue matrix from the bloodstream. These mobile cells include defensive **white blood cells** (neutrophils, eosinophils, lymphocytes) and other cell types concerned with tissue response to injury, such as *mast cells* and *macrophages* (mak′ro-fāj-es). This wide variety of cells is particularly obvious in our prototype, areolar connective tissue (Figure 4.7).

We describe all of these accessory cell types in later chapters, but mast cells and macrophages are so important to overall body defense that they deserve a brief mention here. The oval **mast cells** typically cluster along blood vessels. These cells act as sensitive sentinels to detect foreign microorganisms (e.g., bacteria, fungi) and initiate local inflammatory responses against them.

In the mast cell cytoplasm are conspicuous secretory granules (*mast* = stuffed full of granules) containing several chemicals that mediate inflammation, especially in severe allergies. These chemicals include (1) *heparin* (hep′ah-rin), an anticoagulant chemical that prevents blood clotting when free in the bloodstream (but in human mast cells it appears to bind to and regulate the action of other mast cell chemicals); (2) *histamine* (his′tah-mēn), a substance that makes capillaries leaky; and (3) *proteases* (protein-degrading enzymes) and various other enzymes.

Macrophages (*macro* = large; *phago* = eat) are large, irregularly shaped cells that avidly phagocytize a broad variety of foreign materials, ranging from foreign molecules to entire bacteria to dust particles. These "big eaters" also dispose of dead tissue cells, and they are central actors in the immune system. In connective tissues, they may be attached to connective tissue fibers (fixed) or may migrate freely through the matrix.

Macrophages are peppered throughout loose connective tissue, bone marrow, and lymphatic tissue. Those in certain sites are given specific names. For example, those in the liver are called Kupffer cells. Some macrophages have selective appetites. For example, those of the spleen primarily dispose of aging red blood cells, but they will not turn down other "delicacies" that come their way.

CHECK YOUR UNDERSTANDING

11. What are four functions of connective tissue?

12. What are the three types of fibers found in connective tissues?

For answers, see Appendix G.

Types of Connective Tissue

▶ Describe the types of connective tissue found in the body, and indicate their characteristic functions.

As noted, all classes of connective tissue consist of living cells surrounded by a matrix. Their major differences reflect cell type, and fiber types and relative amounts, as summarized in Table 4.1.

As mentioned earlier, mature connective tissues arise from a common embryonic tissue, called **mesenchyme** (meh′zin-kīm), derived from embryonic mesoderm (see Figure 4.13, p. 141). Mesenchyme has a fluid ground substance containing fine sparse fibers and star-shaped *mesenchymal cells*. It arises during the early weeks of embryonic development and eventually differentiates (specializes) into all other connective tissue cells. However, some mesenchymal cells remain and provide a source of new cells in mature connective tissues.

The connective tissues that we describe in the next sections are illustrated in **Figure 4.8**. Study the parts of this figure as you read along.

Connective Tissue Proper—Loose Connective Tissues

Connective tissue proper has two subclasses: the **loose connective tissues** (areolar, adipose, and reticular) and **dense connective tissues** (dense regular, dense irregular, and elastic). Except for bone, cartilage, and blood, all mature connective tissues belong to this class. Let's look first at the loose variety.

Areolar Connective Tissue The functions of **areolar connective tissue**, shared by some but not all connective tissues, include (1) supporting and binding other tissues (the job of the fibers); (2) holding body fluids (the ground substance's role); (3) defending against infection (via the activity of white blood cells and macrophages); and (4) storing nutrients as fat (in fat cells) (Figure 4.8a).

Fibroblasts, flat, branching cells that appear spindle shaped in profile, predominate, but numerous macrophages are also seen and present a formidable barrier to invading microorganisms. Fat cells appear singly or in clusters, and occasional mast cells are identified easily by the large, darkly stained cytoplasmic granules that often obscure their nuclei. Other cell types are scattered throughout.

The most obvious structural feature of this tissue is the loose arrangement of its fibers. For this reason, its classification as a *loose* connective tissue is fitting. The rest of the matrix, occupied by ground substance, appears to be empty space when viewed through the microscope, and in fact, the Latin term *areola* means "a small open space." Because of its loose nature, areolar connective tissue provides a reservoir of water and salts for surrounding body tissues, always holding approximately as much fluid as there is in the entire bloodstream. Essentially all body cells obtain their nutrients from and release their wastes into this "tissue fluid."

The high content of hyaluronic acid makes its ground substance quite viscous, like molasses, which may hinder the movement of cells through it. Some white blood cells, which protect the body from disease-causing microorganisms, secrete the enzyme hyaluronidase to liquefy the ground substance and ease their passage. (Unhappily, some potentially harmful bacteria have the same

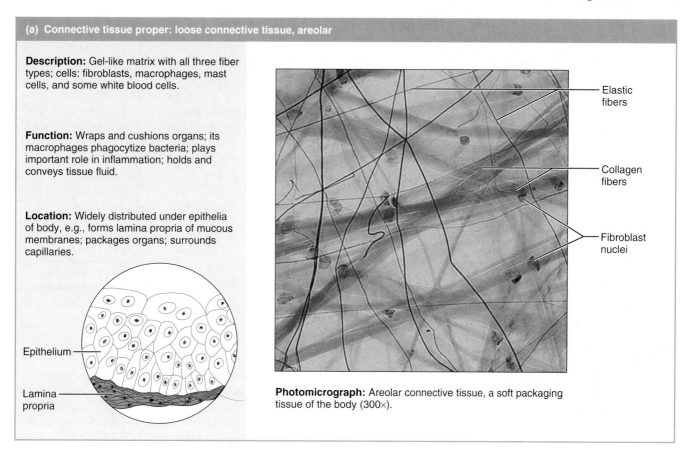

(a) Connective tissue proper: loose connective tissue, areolar

Description: Gel-like matrix with all three fiber types; cells: fibroblasts, macrophages, mast cells, and some white blood cells.

Function: Wraps and cushions organs; its macrophages phagocytize bacteria; plays important role in inflammation; holds and conveys tissue fluid.

Location: Widely distributed under epithelia of body, e.g., forms lamina propria of mucous membranes; packages organs; surrounds capillaries.

Epithelium

Lamina propria

Elastic fibers

Collagen fibers

Fibroblast nuclei

Photomicrograph: Areolar connective tissue, a soft packaging tissue of the body (300×).

Figure 4.8 Connective tissues. (a) Connective tissue proper. (See *A Brief Atlas of the Human Body*, Plate 11.)

ability.) When a body region is inflamed, the areolar tissue in the area soaks up excess fluids like a sponge, and the affected area swells and becomes puffy, a condition called **edema** (ĕ-de′mah).

Areolar connective tissue is the most widely distributed connective tissue in the body, and it serves as a kind of universal packing material between other tissues. It binds body parts together while allowing them to move freely over one another; wraps small blood vessels and nerves; surrounds glands; and forms the subcutaneous tissue, which cushions and attaches the skin to underlying structures. It is present in all mucous membranes as the *lamina propria*. (Mucous membranes line body cavities open to the exterior.)

Adipose (Fat) Tissue **Adipose tissue** (ad′ĭ-pōs) is similar to areolar tissue in structure and function, but its nutrient-storing ability is much greater. Consequently, **adipocytes** (ad′ĭ-po-sītz), commonly called *adipose* or *fat cells*, predominate and account for 90% of this tissue's mass. The matrix is scanty and the cells are packed closely together, giving a chicken-wire appearance to the tissue. A glistening oil droplet (almost pure triglyceride) occupies most of a fat cell's volume and displaces the nucleus to one side so that only a thin rim of surrounding cytoplasm is seen (Figure 4.8b). Mature adipocytes are among the largest cells in the body. As they take up or release fat, they become plumper or more wrinkled looking, respectively.

Adipose tissue is richly vascularized, indicating its high metabolic activity. Without the fat stores in our adipose tissue,

we could not live for more than a few days without eating. Adipose tissue is certainly abundant: It constitutes 18% of an average person's body weight, and a chubby person's body can be 50% fat without being considered morbidly obese.

Adipose tissue may develop almost anywhere areolar tissue is plentiful, but it usually accumulates in subcutaneous tissue, where it acts as a shock absorber, as insulation, and as an energy storage site. Because fat is a poor conductor of heat, it helps prevent heat loss from the body. Other sites where fat accumulates include surrounding the kidneys, behind the eyeballs, and at genetically determined fat depots such as the abdomen and hips.

The abundant fat beneath the skin serves the general nutrient needs of the entire body, and smaller depots of fat serve the local nutrient needs of highly active organs. Such depots occur around the hard-working heart and around lymph nodes (where cells of the immune system are furiously fighting infection), within some muscles, and as individual fat cells in the bone marrow, where new blood cells are produced at a rapid rate. Many of these local depots are highly enriched in special lipids.

The adipose tissue just described is sometimes called *white fat*, or *white adipose tissue*, to distinguish it from **brown fat**, or **brown adipose tissue**. White fat stores nutrients (mainly for other cells), but brown fat adipose cells contain abundant mitochondria, which use the lipid fuels to heat the bloodstream to warm the body (rather than to produce ATP molecules). The richly vascular brown fat occurs only in babies who (as yet) lack

4

(b) Connective tissue proper: loose connective tissue, adipose

Description: Matrix as in areolar, but very sparse; closely packed adipocytes, or fat cells, have nucleus pushed to the side by large fat droplet.

Function: Provides reserve food fuel; insulates against heat loss; supports and protects organs.

Location: Under skin in the hypodermis; around kidneys and eyeballs; within abdomen; in breasts.

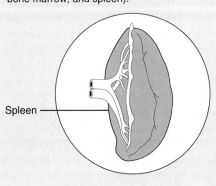

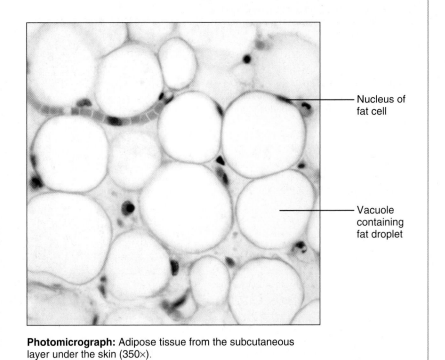

Nucleus of fat cell

Vacuole containing fat droplet

Photomicrograph: Adipose tissue from the subcutaneous layer under the skin (350×).

(c) Connective tissue proper: loose connective tissue, reticular

Description: Network of reticular fibers in a typical loose ground substance; reticular cells lie on the network.

Function: Fibers form a soft internal skeleton (stroma) that supports other cell types including white blood cells, mast cells, and macrophages.

Location: Lymphoid organs (lymph nodes, bone marrow, and spleen).

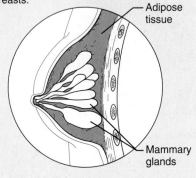

Spleen

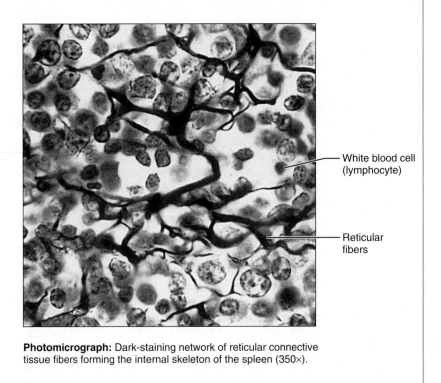

White blood cell (lymphocyte)

Reticular fibers

Photomicrograph: Dark-staining network of reticular connective tissue fibers forming the internal skeleton of the spleen (350×).

Figure 4.8 *(continued)* **Connective tissues. (b)** and **(c)** Connective tissue proper. (See *A Brief Atlas of the Human Body*, Plates 12 and 13.)

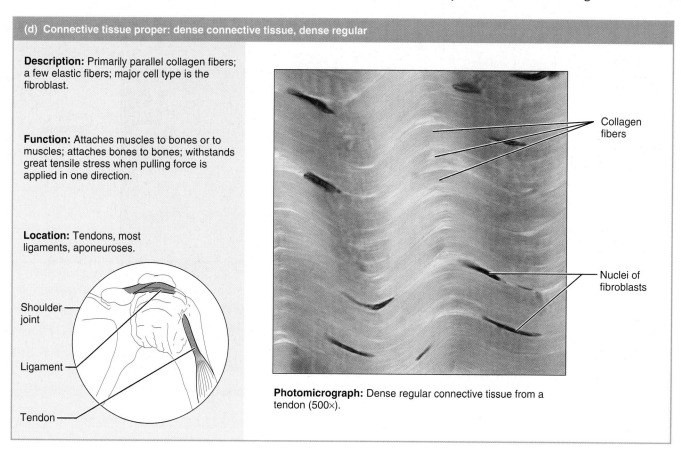

(d) Connective tissue proper: dense connective tissue, dense regular

Description: Primarily parallel collagen fibers; a few elastic fibers; major cell type is the fibroblast.

Function: Attaches muscles to bones or to muscles; attaches bones to bones; withstands great tensile stress when pulling force is applied in one direction.

Location: Tendons, most ligaments, aponeuroses.

Shoulder joint

Ligament

Tendon

Collagen fibers

Nuclei of fibroblasts

Photomicrograph: Dense regular connective tissue from a tendon (500×).

Figure 4.8 *(continued)* **(d)** Connective tissue proper. (See *A Brief Atlas of the Human Body,* Plate 15.)

the ability to produce body heat by shivering. Most such deposits are located between the shoulder blades, on the anterolateral neck, and on the anterior abdominal wall.

Reticular Connective Tissue   **Reticular connective tissue** resembles areolar connective tissue, but the only fibers in its matrix are reticular fibers, which form a delicate network along which fibroblasts called **reticular cells** are scattered (Figure 4.8c). Although reticular *fibers* are widely distributed in the body, reticular *tissue* is limited to certain sites. It forms a labyrinth-like **stroma** (literally, "bed" or "mattress"), or internal framework, that can support many free blood cells (largely lymphocytes) in lymph nodes, the spleen, and bone marrow.

Connective Tissue Proper—Dense Connective Tissues

The three varieties of dense connective tissue have fibers as their prominent element. For this reason, the dense connective tissues are often referred to as **fibrous connective tissues**.

Dense Regular Connective Tissue   **Dense regular connective tissue** contains closely packed bundles of collagen fibers running in the same direction, parallel to the direction of pull (Figure 4.8d). This arrangement results in white, flexible structures with great resistance to tension (pulling forces) where the tension is exerted in a single direction. Crowded between the

collagen fibers are rows of fibroblasts that continuously manufacture the fibers and scant ground substance.

As seen in Figure 4.8d, collagen fibers are slightly wavy. This allows the tissue to stretch a little, but once the fibers are straightened out by a pulling force, there is no further "give" to this tissue. Unlike our model (areolar) connective tissue, this tissue has few cells other than fibroblasts and is poorly vascularized.

With its enormous tensile strength, dense regular connective tissue forms the *tendons*, which are cords that attach muscles to bones, and flat, sheetlike tendons called *aponeuroses* (ap″o-nu-ro′sēz) that attach muscles to other muscles or to bones. It also forms fascia (fash′e-ah; "a bond"), a fibrous membrane that wraps around muscles, groups of muscles, blood vessels, and nerves, binding those structures together like plastic sandwich wrap; and the ligaments that bind bones together at joints. Ligaments contain more elastic fibers than tendons and are slightly more stretchy.

Dense Irregular Connective Tissue   **Dense irregular connective tissue** has the same structural elements as the regular variety. However, the bundles of collagen fibers are much thicker and they are arranged irregularly; that is, they run in more than one plane (Figure 4.8e). This type of tissue forms sheets in body areas where tension is exerted from many different directions. It is found in the skin as the leathery *dermis*, and it forms fibrous joint capsules and the fibrous coverings that surround some organs (kidneys, bones, cartilages, muscles, and nerves).

(e) Connective tissue proper: dense connective tissue, dense irregular

Description: Primarily irregularly arranged collagen fibers; some elastic fibers; major cell type is the fibroblast.

Function: Able to withstand tension exerted in many directions; provides structural strength.

Location: Fibrous capsules of organs and of joints; dermis of the skin; submucosa of digestive tract.

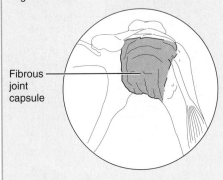

Fibrous joint capsule

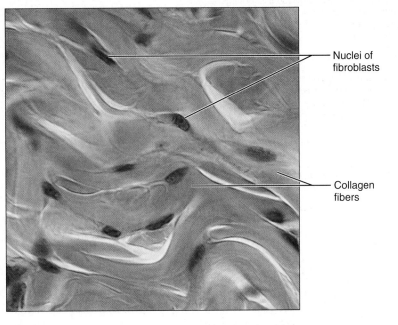

Nuclei of fibroblasts

Collagen fibers

Photomicrograph: Dense irregular connective tissue from the dermis of the skin (400×).

(f) Connective tissue proper: dense connective tissue, elastic

Description: Dense regular connective tissue containing a high proportion of elastic fibers.

Function: Allows recoil of tissue following stretching; maintains pulsatile flow of blood through arteries; aids passive recoil of lungs following inspiration.

Location: Walls of large arteries; within certain ligaments associated with the vertebral column; within the walls of the bronchial tubes.

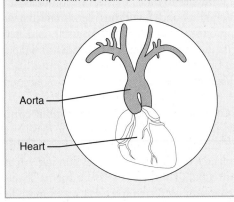

Aorta

Heart

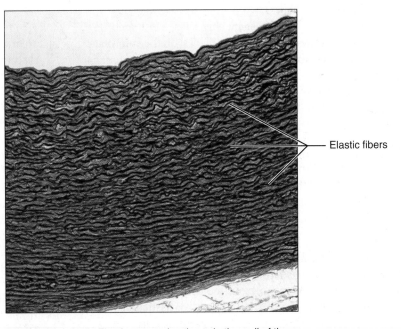

Elastic fibers

Photomicrograph: Elastic connective tissue in the wall of the aorta (250×).

Figure 4.8 *(continued)* **Connective tissues. (e)** and **(f)** Connective tissue proper. (See *A Brief Atlas of the Human Body*, Plates 14 and 16.)

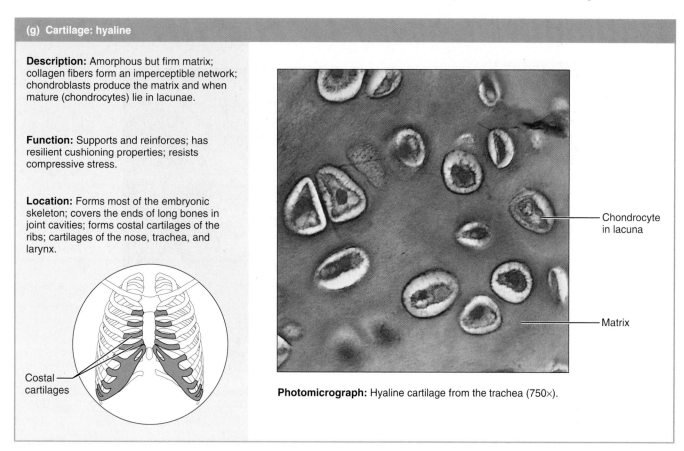

(g) Cartilage: hyaline

Description: Amorphous but firm matrix; collagen fibers form an imperceptible network; chondroblasts produce the matrix and when mature (chondrocytes) lie in lacunae.

Function: Supports and reinforces; has resilient cushioning properties; resists compressive stress.

Location: Forms most of the embryonic skeleton; covers the ends of long bones in joint cavities; forms costal cartilages of the ribs; cartilages of the nose, trachea, and larynx.

Costal cartilages

Chondrocyte in lacuna

Matrix

Photomicrograph: Hyaline cartilage from the trachea (750×).

Figure 4.8 *(continued)* **(g)** Cartilage. (See *A Brief Atlas of the Human Body,* Plate 17.)

Elastic Connective Tissue A few ligaments, such as the *ligamenta nuchae* and *flava* connecting adjacent vertebrae, are very elastic, so much so that the dense regular connective tissue in those structures is referred to more specifically as **elastic connective tissue** (Figure 4.8f).

Cartilage

Cartilage (kar′tĭ-lij), which stands up to both tension *and* compression, has qualities intermediate between dense connective tissue and bone. It is tough but flexible, providing a resilient rigidity to the structures it supports. Cartilage lacks nerve fibers and is avascular. It receives its nutrients by diffusion from blood vessels located in the connective tissue membrane (perichondrium) surrounding it. Its ground substance contains large amounts of the GAGs chrondroitin sulfate and hyaluronic acid, firmly bound collagen fibers (and in some cases elastic fibers), and is quite firm. Cartilage matrix also contains an exceptional amount of tissue fluid. In fact, cartilage is up to 80% water! The movement of tissue fluid in its matrix enables cartilage to rebound after being compressed and also helps to nourish the cartilage cells.

Chondroblasts, the predominant cell type in growing cartilage, produce new matrix until the skeleton stops growing at the end of adolescence. The firmness of the cartilage matrix prevents the cells from becoming widely separated, so **chondrocytes**, or mature cartilage cells, are typically found in small groups within cavities called *lacunae* (lah-ku′ne; "pits").

HOMEOSTATIC IMBALANCE

Because cartilage is avascular and aging cartilage cells lose their ability to divide, injured cartilages heal slowly. This phenomenon is excruciatingly familiar to those who have experienced sports injuries. During later life, cartilages tend to calcify or even ossify (become bony). In such cases, the chondrocytes are poorly nourished and die. ■

There are three varieties of cartilage: *hyaline cartilage, elastic cartilage,* and *fibrocartilage,* each dominated by a particular fiber type.

Hyaline Cartilage Hyaline cartilage (hi′ah-līn), or *gristle,* is the most abundant cartilage type in the body. Although it contains large numbers of collagen fibers, they are not apparent and the matrix appears amorphous and glassy (*hyalin* = glass) blue-white when viewed by the unaided eye (Figure 4.8g). Chondrocytes account for only 1–10% of the cartilage volume.

Hyaline cartilage provides firm support with some pliability. It covers the ends of long bones as *articular cartilage,* providing springy pads that absorb compression at joints. Hyaline cartilage also supports the tip of the nose, connects the ribs to the sternum, and supports most of the respiratory system passages. Most of the embryonic skeleton is formed of hyaline cartilage before bone is formed. Skeletal hyaline cartilage persists during childhood as the *epiphyseal plates* (e″pĭ-fis′e-ul), actively growing

4

(h) Cartilage: elastic

Description: Similar to hyaline cartilage, but more elastic fibers in matrix.

Function: Maintains the shape of a structure while allowing great flexibility.

Location: Supports the external ear (pinna); epiglottis.

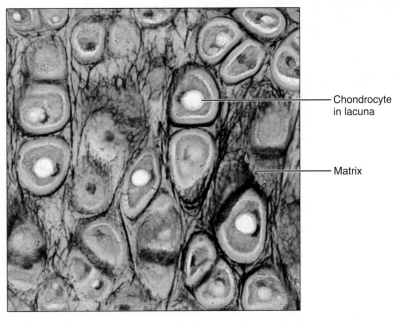

Chondrocyte in lacuna

Matrix

Photomicrograph: Elastic cartilage from the human ear pinna; forms the flexible skeleton of the ear (800×).

(i) Cartilage: fibrocartilage

Description: Matrix similar to but less firm than that in hyaline cartilage; thick collagen fibers predominate.

Function: Tensile strength with the ability to absorb compressive shock.

Location: Intervertebral discs; pubic symphysis; discs of knee joint.

Intervertebral discs

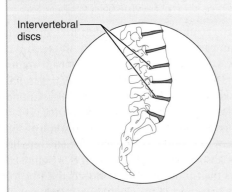

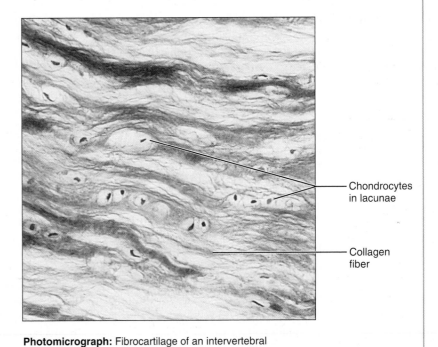

Chondrocytes in lacunae

Collagen fiber

Photomicrograph: Fibrocartilage of an intervertebral disc (125×). Special staining produced the blue color seen.

Figure 4.8 *(continued)* **Connective tissues. (h)** and **(i)** Cartilage. (See *A Brief Atlas of the Human Body*, Plates 18 and 19.)

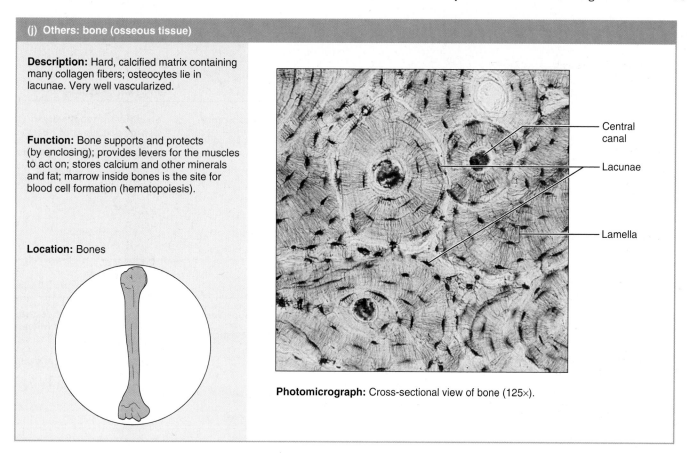

(j) Others: bone (osseous tissue)

Description: Hard, calcified matrix containing many collagen fibers; osteocytes lie in lacunae. Very well vascularized.

Function: Bone supports and protects (by enclosing); provides levers for the muscles to act on; stores calcium and other minerals and fat; marrow inside bones is the site for blood cell formation (hematopoiesis).

Location: Bones

Central canal — Lacunae — Lamella

Photomicrograph: Cross-sectional view of bone (125×).

Figure 4.8 *(continued)* **(j)** Bone. (See *A Brief Atlas of the Human Body*, Plate 20.)

regions near the ends of long bones that provide for continued growth in length.

Elastic Cartilage Histologically, **elastic cartilage** (Figure 4.8h) is nearly identical to hyaline cartilage. However, there are many more elastic fibers in elastic cartilage. Found where strength and exceptional stretchability are needed, elastic cartilage forms the "skeletons" of the external ear and the epiglottis. (The epiglottis is the flap that covers the opening to the respiratory passageway when we swallow, preventing food or fluids from entering the lungs.)

Fibrocartilage **Fibrocartilage** is a perfect structural intermediate between hyaline cartilage and dense regular connective tissues. Its rows of chondrocytes (a cartilage feature) alternate with rows of thick collagen fibers (a feature of dense regular connective tissue) (Figure 4.8i). Because it is compressible and resists tension well, fibrocartilage is found where strong support and the ability to withstand heavy pressure are required. For example, the intervertebral discs (resilient cushions between the bony vertebrae) and the spongy cartilages of the knee (menisci) are fibrocartilage structures (see Figure 6.1, p. 174).

Bone (Osseous Tissue)

Because of its rocklike hardness, **bone**, or **osseous tissue** (os′e-us), has an exceptional ability to support and protect body structures. Bones of the skeleton also provide cavities for fat storage

and synthesis of blood cells. Bone matrix is similar to that of cartilage but is harder and more rigid because, in addition to its more abundant collagen fibers, bone has an added matrix element—inorganic calcium salts (bone salts).

Osteoblasts produce the organic portion of the matrix, and then bone salts are deposited on and between the fibers. Mature bone cells, or **osteocytes**, reside in the lacunae within the matrix they have made (Figure 4.8j). In cross section, bone tissue is seen as closely packed structural units called *osteons* formed of concentric rings of bony matrix (lamellae) surrounding central canals containing the blood vessels and nerves serving the bone. Unlike cartilage, the next firmest connective tissue, bone is well supplied by invading blood vessels.

Blood

Blood, the fluid within blood vessels, is the most atypical connective tissue. It does *not* connect things or give mechanical support. It is classified as a connective tissue because it develops from mesenchyme and consists of *blood cells*, surrounded by a nonliving fluid matrix called *blood plasma* (Figure 4.8k). The vast majority of blood cells are red blood cells or erythrocytes, but scattered white blood cells (neutrophils, lymphocytes, monocytes, eosinophils, basophils) are also seen. The "fibers" of blood are soluble protein molecules that precipitate, forming visible fiberlike structures during blood clotting. Blood functions as the transport vehicle for the cardiovascular system, carrying nutrients, wastes, respiratory gases, and many other substances throughout the body.

| TABLE 4.1 | Comparison of Classes of Connective Tissues | | | |

COMPONENTS

TISSUE CLASS AND EXAMPLE	SUBCLASSES	CELLS	MATRIX	GENERAL FEATURES

Connective Tissue Proper
 	
Dense regular connective tissue
	1. Loose connective tissue
	  ▪ Areolar
	  ▪ Adipose
	  ▪ Reticular
	2. Dense connective tissue
	  ▪ Regular
	  ▪ Irregular
	  ▪ Elastic
		Fibroblasts
		Fibrocytes
		Defense cells
		Fat cells
			Gel-like ground substance
			All three fiber types: collagen, reticular, elastic
				Six different types; vary in density and types of fibers
				Functions as a binding tissue
				Resists mechanical stress, particulary tension

Cartilage *Hyaline cartilage*	1. Hyaline cartilage 2. Elastic cartilage 3. Fibrocartilage	Chondroblasts found in growing cartilage Chondrocytes	Gel-like ground substance Fibers: collagen, elastic fibers in some	Resists compression because of the large amounts of water held in the matrix Functions to cushion and support body structures
Bone Tissue *Compact bone*	1. Compact bone 2. Spongy bone	Osteoblasts Osteocytes	Gel-like ground substance calcified with inorganic salts Fibers: collagen	Hard tissue that resists both compression and tension Functions in support
Blood	Blood cell formation and differentiation are quite complex. Details are provided in Chapter 17.	Erythrocytes (RBC) Leukocytes (WBC) Platelets	Plasma No fibers	A fluid tissue Functions to carry O_2, CO_2, nutrients, wastes, and other substances (hormones, for example)

CHECK YOUR UNDERSTANDING

13. Which connective tissue has a soft weblike matrix capable of serving as a fluid reservoir?

14. What type of connective tissue is damaged when you lacerate your index finger tendon?

15. John wants to become a professional basketball player. Unfortunately he is short for his age and his epiphyseal plates have already fused. What type of connective tissue forms the epiphyseal plates?

For answers, see Appendix G.

Nervous Tissue

▶ Indicate the general characteristics of nervous tissue.

Nervous tissue is the main component of the nervous system—the brain, spinal cord, and nerves—which regulates and controls body functions. It contains two major cell types. **Neurons** are highly specialized nerve cells that generate and conduct nerve impulses **(Figure 4.9)**. Typically, they are branching cells with cytoplasmic extensions or processes. Their processes allow them to (1) respond to stimuli (a role of the processes called *dendrites*) and (2) to transmit electrical impulses over substantial distances within the body (the job of *axons*, which may be very long and myelinated, that is,

(k) Others: blood

Description: Red and white blood cells in a fluid matrix (plasma).

Function: Transport of respiratory gases, nutrients, wastes, and other substances.

Location: Contained within blood vessels.

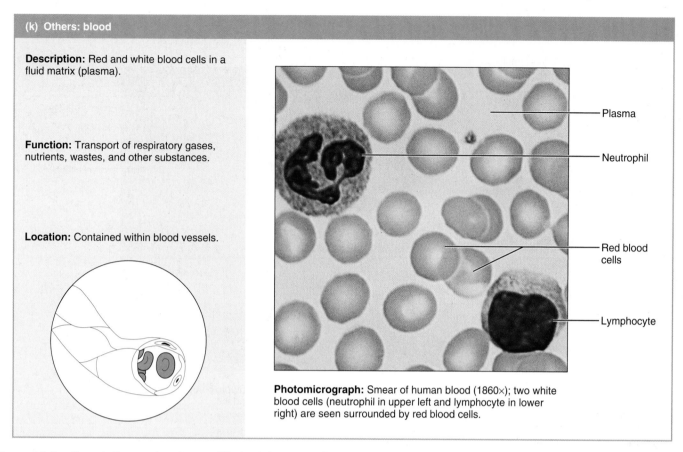

Photomicrograph: Smear of human blood (1860×); two white blood cells (neutrophil in upper left and lymphocyte in lower right) are seen surrounded by red blood cells.

Plasma

Neutrophil

Red blood cells

Lymphocyte

Figure 4.8 *(continued)* **Connective tissues. (k)** Blood. (See *A Brief Atlas of the Human Body,* Plates 22–27.)

Nervous tissue

Description: Neurons are branching cells; cell processes that may be quite long extend from the nucleus-containing cell body; also contributing to nervous tissue are nonirritable supporting cells (not illustrated).

Neuron processes — Cell body
Axon   Dendrites

Function: Transmit electrical signals from sensory receptors and to effectors (muscles and glands) which control their activity.

Location: Brain, spinal cord, and nerves.

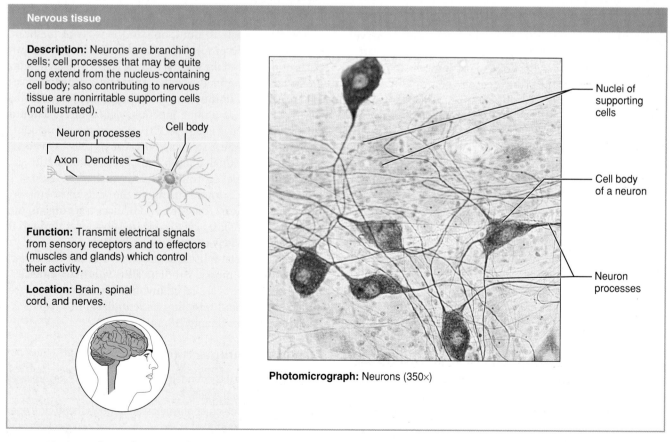

Photomicrograph: Neurons (350×)

Nuclei of supporting cells

Cell body of a neuron

Neuron processes

Figure 4.9 **Nervous tissue.** (See *A Brief Atlas of the Human Body,* Plate 33.)

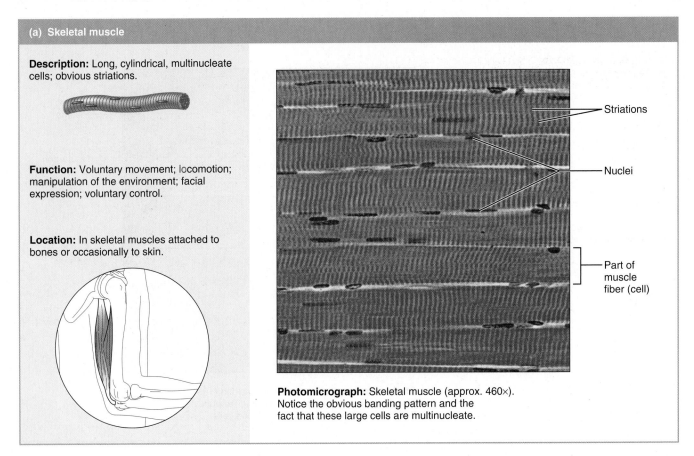

(a) Skeletal muscle

Description: Long, cylindrical, multinucleate cells; obvious striations.

Function: Voluntary movement; locomotion; manipulation of the environment; facial expression; voluntary control.

Location: In skeletal muscles attached to bones or occasionally to skin.

Striations

Nuclei

Part of muscle fiber (cell)

Photomicrograph: Skeletal muscle (approx. 460×). Notice the obvious banding pattern and the fact that these large cells are multinucleate.

Figure 4.10 Muscle tissues. (a) Skeletal muscle tissue. (See *A Brief Atlas of the Human Body,* Plate 28.)

covered with a fatty sheath that increases the speed of nerve transmission). The balance of nervous tissue consists of various types of supporting cells, nonconducting cells that support, insulate, and protect the delicate neurons. A more complete discussion of nervous tissue appears in Chapter 11.

Muscle Tissue

▶ Compare and contrast the structures and body locations of the three types of muscle tissue.

Muscle tissues are highly cellular, well-vascularized tissues that are responsible for most types of body movement. Muscle cells possess **myofilaments**, elaborate versions of the *actin* and *myosin* filaments that bring about movement or contraction in all cell types. There are three kinds of muscle tissue: skeletal, cardiac, and smooth.

Skeletal muscle tissue is packaged by connective tissue sheets into organs called *skeletal muscles* that are attached to the bones of the skeleton. These muscles form the flesh of the body, and as they contract, they pull on bones or skin, causing body movements. Skeletal muscle cells, also called **muscle fibers**, are long, cylindrical cells that contain many nuclei. Their obvious banded, or *striated*, appearance reflects the precise alignment of their myofilaments **(Figure 4.10a)**.

Cardiac muscle is found only in the walls of the heart. Its contractions help propel blood through the blood vessels to all parts of the body. Like skeletal muscle cells, cardiac muscle cells are striated. However, they differ structurally in that cardiac cells (1) are generally uninucleate and (2) are branching cells that fit together tightly at unique junctions called **intercalated discs** (in-ter′kah-la″ted) (Figure 4.10b).

Smooth muscle is so named because its cells have no visible striations. Individual smooth muscle cells are spindle shaped and contain one centrally located nucleus (Figure 4.10c). Smooth muscle is found mainly in the walls of hollow organs other than the heart (digestive and urinary tract organs, uterus, and blood vessels). It acts to squeeze substances through these organs by alternately contracting and relaxing.

Because skeletal muscle contraction is under our conscious control, skeletal muscle is often called **voluntary muscle**, and the other two types are called **involuntary muscle**. We describe skeletal muscle and smooth muscle in detail in Chapter 9, and cardiac muscle in Chapter 18.

CHECK YOUR UNDERSTANDING

16. How does the extended length of a neuron's processes aid its function in the body?

17. You are looking at muscle tissue through the microscope and you see striped branching cells that connect with one another. What type of muscle are you viewing?

(Text continues on p. 138.)

(b) Cardiac muscle

Description: Branching, striated, generally uninucleate cells that interdigitate at specialized junctions (intercalated discs).

Function: As it contracts, it propels blood into the circulation; involuntary control.

Location: The walls of the heart.

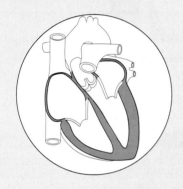

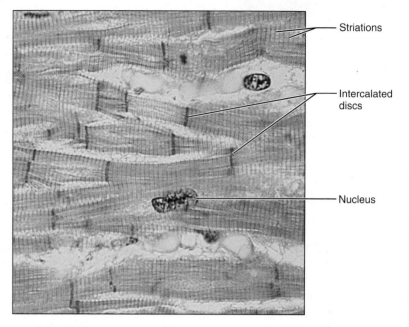

Striations

Intercalated discs

Nucleus

Photomicrograph: Cardiac muscle (500×); notice the striations, branching of cells, and the intercalated discs.

(c) Smooth muscle

Description: Spindle-shaped cells with central nuclei; no striations; cells arranged closely to form sheets.

Function: Propels substances or objects (foodstuffs, urine, a baby) along internal passageways; involuntary control.

Location: Mostly in the walls of hollow organs.

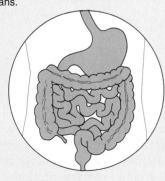

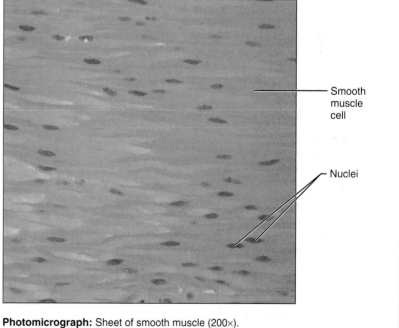

Smooth muscle cell

Nuclei

Photomicrograph: Sheet of smooth muscle (200×).

Figure 4.10 *(continued)* **(b)** Cardiac muscle tissue. (See *A Brief Atlas of the Human Body*, Plate 31.) **(c)** Smooth muscle tissue. (See *A Brief Atlas of the Human Body*, Plate 32.)

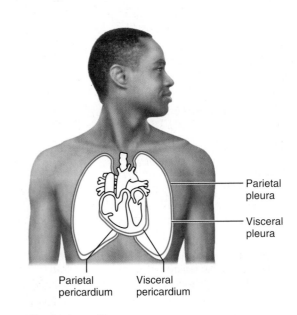

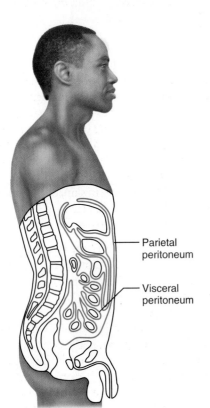

(a) Cutaneous membrane (the skin) covers the body surface.

Cutaneous membrane (skin)

Mucosa of nasal cavity

Mucosa of mouth

Esophagus lining

Mucosa of lung bronchi

(b) Mucous membranes line body cavities open to the exterior.

Parietal peritoneum

Visceral peritoneum

Parietal pleura

Visceral pleura

Parietal pericardium   Visceral pericardium

(c) Serous membranes line body cavities closed to the exterior.

Figure 4.11 **Classes of membranes.**

18. Which muscle type(s) is voluntary? Injured when you pull a muscle while exercising?

For answers, see Appendix G.

Covering and Lining Membranes

▶ Describe the structure and function of cutaneous, mucous, and serous membranes.

Now that we have described all four primary tissues, we can consider the body's membranes that incorporate more than one type of tissue. The covering and lining membranes are of three types: *cutaneous, mucous,* or *serous*. Essentially they all are continuous multicellular sheets composed of at least two primary tissue types: an epithelium bound to an underlying layer of connective tissue proper. Hence, these membranes are simple organs. We describe the *synovial membranes*, which line joint cavities and consist of connective tissue only, in Chapter 8.

Cutaneous Membrane

The **cutaneous membrane** (ku-ta′ne-us; *cutis* = skin) is your skin **(Figure 4.11a)**. It is an organ system consisting of a keratinized stratified squamous epithelium (epidermis) firmly attached to a thick layer of dense irregular connective tissue (dermis). Unlike other epithelial membranes, the cutaneous membrane is exposed to the air and is a dry membrane. Chapter 5 is devoted to this unique organ system.

Mucous Membranes

Mucous membranes, or **mucosae** (mu-ko′se), line body cavities that open to the exterior, such as those of the hollow organs of the digestive, respiratory, and urogenital tracts (Figure 4.11b). In all cases, they are "wet," or moist, membranes bathed by secretions or, in the case of the urinary mucosa, urine. Notice that the term *mucosa* refers to the location of the membrane, *not* its cell composition, which varies. However, most mucosae contain either stratified squamous or simple columnar epithelia. The epithelial sheet is directly underlain by a layer of loose connective tissue called the **lamina propria** (lam′ĭ-nah pro′pre-ah; "one's own layer"). In some mucosae, the lamina propria rests on a third (deeper) layer of smooth muscle cells.

Mucous membranes are often adapted for absorption and secretion. Although many mucosae secrete mucus, this is not a requirement. The mucosae of both the digestive and respiratory tracts secrete copious amounts of lubricating mucus, but that of the urinary tract does not.

Serous Membranes

Serous membranes, or **serosae** (se-ro′se), introduced in Chapter 1, are the moist membranes found in closed ventral body cavities (Figure 4.11c). A serous membrane consists of simple squamous epithelium (a mesothelium) resting on a thin layer of loose connective (areolar) tissue. The mesothelial cells add hyaluronic acid to the fluid that filters from the capillaries in the associated connective tissue. The result is the thin, clear *serous fluid* that lubricates the facing surfaces of the parietal and visceral layers, so that they slide across each other easily.

The serosae are named according to their site and specific organ associations. For example, the serosa lining the thoracic wall and covering the lungs is the **pleura**; that enclosing the heart is the **pericardium**; and those of the abdominopelvic cavity and viscera are the **peritoneums**.

CHECK YOUR UNDERSTANDING

19. What type of membrane consists of epithelium and connective tissue, and lines body cavities open to the exterior?

20. What type of membrane lines the thoracic walls and covers the lungs, and what is it called?

For answers, see Appendix G.

Tissue Repair

▶ Outline the process of tissue repair involved in normal healing of a superficial wound.

The body has many techniques for protecting itself from uninvited "guests" or injury. Intact mechanical barriers such as the skin and mucosae, the cilia of epithelial cells lining the respiratory tract, and the strong acid (chemical barrier) produced by stomach glands represent three defenses exerted at the body's external boundaries.

When tissue injury occurs, these barriers are penetrated. This stimulates the body's inflammatory and immune responses, which wage their battles largely in the connective tissues of the body. The *inflammatory response* is a relatively nonspecific reaction that develops quickly wherever tissues are injured, while the *immune response* is extremely specific, but takes longer to swing into action. We consider the inflammatory and immune responses in detail in Chapter 21.

Steps of Tissue Repair

Tissue repair requires that cells divide and migrate, activities that are initiated by growth factors (wound hormones) released by injured cells. Repair occurs in two major ways: by regeneration and by fibrosis. Which of these occurs depends on (1) the type of tissue damaged and (2) the severity of the injury. **Regeneration** is replacement of destroyed tissue with the same kind of tissue, whereas **fibrosis** involves proliferation of fibrous connective tissue called **scar tissue**. In skin, the tissue we will use as our example, repair involves both activities. **Figure 4.12** illustrates the following steps in tissue repair.

① **Inflammation sets the stage.** Tissue injury sets inflammatory events into motion. First, the tissue trauma causes injured tissue cells, macrophages, mast cells, and others to release inflammatory chemicals, which cause the capillaries to dilate and become very permeable. This allows white blood cells (neutrophils, monocytes) and plasma fluid rich in clotting proteins, antibodies, and other substances to seep into the injured area. The leaked clotting proteins construct a clot, which stops the loss of blood, holds the edges of the wound together, and effectively walls in, or isolates, the injured area, preventing bacteria, toxins, or other harmful substances from spreading to surrounding tissues. The part of the clot exposed to air quickly dries and hardens, forming a *scab*. The inflammatory events leave behind excess fluid, bits of destroyed cells, and other debris, which are eventually removed via lymphatic vessels or phagocytized by macrophages.

② **Organization restores the blood supply.** Even while the inflammatory process is going on, the first phase of tissue repair, called **organization**, begins. During organization the blood clot is replaced by granulation tissue. **Granulation tissue** is a delicate pink tissue composed of several elements. It contains capillaries that grow in from nearby areas and lay down a new capillary bed. Granulation tissue is actually named for these capillaries, which protrude nublike from its surface, giving it a granular appearance. These capillaries are

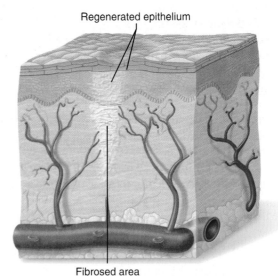

Scab — Blood clot in incised wound

Epidermis

Vein

Inflammatory chemicals — Migrating white blood cell — Artery

Regenerating epithelium

Area of granulation tissue ingrowth

Fibroblast

Macrophage

Regenerated epithelium

Fibrosed area

① **Inflammation sets the stage:**
- Severed blood vessels bleed and inflammatory chemicals are released.
- Local blood vessels become more permeable, allowing white blood cells, fluid, clotting proteins and other plasma proteins to seep into the injured area.
- Clotting occurs; surface dries and forms a scab.

② **Organization restores the blood supply:**
- The clot is replaced by granulation tissue, which restores the vascular supply.
- Fibroblasts produce collagen fibers that bridge the gap.
- Macrophages phagocytize cell debris.
- Surface epithelial cells multiply and migrate over the granulation tissue.

fragile and bleed freely, as we see when someone picks at a scab. Proliferating fibroblasts in granulation tissue produce growth factors as well as new collagen fibers to bridge the gap. Some of these fibroblasts have contractile properties that pull the margins of the wound together. As organization proceeds, macrophages digest the original blood clot and collagen fiber deposit continues. The granulation tissue, destined to become scar tissue (a permanent fibrous patch), is highly resistant to infection because it produces bacteria-inhibiting substances. As a rule, wound healing is a self-limited response. Once enough matrix has accumulated in the injured area, the fibroblasts either revert to the resting stage or undergo apoptosis.

③ **Regeneration and fibrosis effect permanent repair.** During organization, the surface epithelium begins to *regenerate,* growing under the scab, which soon detaches. As the fibrous tissue beneath matures and contracts, the regenerating epithelium thickens until it finally resembles that of the adjacent skin. The end result is a fully regenerated epithelium, and an underlying area of scar tissue. The scar may be invisible, or visible as a thin white line, depending on the severity of the wound.

The repair process that we have just described follows healing of a wound (cut, scrape, puncture) that breaches an epithelial barrier. In simple *infections* (a pimple or sore throat), healing is solely by regeneration. There is usually no clot formation or scarring. Only severe (destructive) infections lead to scarring.

③ **Regeneration and fibrosis effect permanent repair:**
- The fibrosed area matures and contracts; the epithelium thickens.
- A fully regenerated epithelium with an underlying area of scar tissue results.

Figure 4.12 Tissue repair of a nonextensive skin wound: regeneration and fibrosis.

Regenerative Capacity of Different Tissues

The different tissues vary widely in their capacity for regeneration. Epithelial tissues, bone, areolar connective tissue, dense irregular connective tissue, and blood-forming tissue regenerate extremely well. Smooth muscle and dense regular connective tissue have a moderate capacity for regeneration, but skeletal muscle and cartilage have a weak regenerative capacity. Cardiac muscle and the nervous tissue in the brain and spinal cord have virtually no *functional* regenerative capacity, and they are routinely replaced by scar tissue. However, recent studies have shown that some unexpected (and highly selective) cellular division occurs in both these tissues after damage, and efforts are under way to coax them to regenerate better.

In nonregenerating tissues and in exceptionally severe wounds, fibrosis totally replaces the lost tissue. Over a period of months, the fibrous mass shrinks and becomes more and more compact. The resulting scar appears as a pale, often shiny area composed mostly of collagen fibers. Scar tissue is strong, but it lacks the flexibility and elasticity of most normal tissues. Also, it cannot perform the normal functions of the tissue it has replaced.

HOMEOSTATIC IMBALANCE

Scar tissue that forms in the wall of the urinary bladder, heart, or other muscular organ may severely hamper the function of that organ. The normal shrinking of the scar reduces the internal volume of an organ and may hinder or even block movement of substances through a hollow organ. Scar tissue hampers muscle's ability to contract and may interfere with its normal excitation by the nervous system. In the heart, these problems may lead to progressive heart failure. In irritated visceral organs, particularly following abdominal surgery, *adhesions* may form as the newly forming scar tissue connects adjacent organs together. Such adhesions can prevent the normal shifting about (churning) of loops of the intestine, dangerously obstructing the flow of foodstuffs through it. Adhesions can also restrict heart movements and immobilize joints. ■

CHECK YOUR UNDERSTANDING

21. What are the three main steps of tissue repair?

22. Why does a deep injury to the skin result in abundant scar tissue formation?

For answers, see Appendix G.

Developmental Aspects of Tissues

▶ Indicate the embryonic origin of each tissue class.

▶ Briefly describe tissue changes that occur with age.

One of the first events of embryonic development is the formation of the three **primary germ layers**, which lie one atop the next like a three-layered cellular pancake. From superficial to deep, these layers are the **ectoderm**, **mesoderm** (mez′o-derm), and **endoderm**. As shown in **Figure 4.13**, these primary germ layers then specialize to form the four primary tissues—epithelium, nervous tissue, muscle, and connective tissues—that make up all body organs.

By the end of the second month of development, the primary tissues have appeared, and all major organs are in place. In general, tissue cells remain mitotic and produce the rapid growth that occurs before birth. The division of nerve cells, however, stops or nearly stops during the fetal period. After birth, the cells of most other tissues continue to divide until adult body size is achieved. Cellular division then slows greatly,

(Text continues on p. 144.)

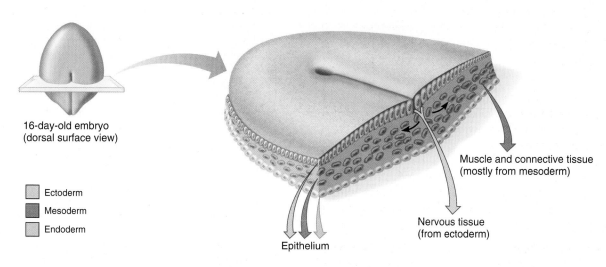

16-day-old embryo
(dorsal surface view)

☐ Ectoderm
■ Mesoderm
☐ Endoderm

Muscle and connective tissue
(mostly from mesoderm)

Nervous tissue
(from ectoderm)

Epithelium

Figure 4.13 Embryonic germ layers and the primary tissue types they produce. The three embryonic layers collectively form the very early embryonic body.

A CLOSER LOOK
Cancer—The Intimate Enemy

The word *cancer* elicits dread in everyone. Why does cancer strike some and not others?

Although once perceived as disorganized cell growth, this disease is now known to be a logical, coordinated process in which a precise sequence of tiny alterations changes a normal cell into a killer. Let's take a closer look at what cancer really is.

When cells fail to follow normal controls of cell division and multiply excessively, an abnormal mass of proliferating cells called a **neoplasm** (ne'o-plazm, "new growth") results. Neoplasms are classified as **benign** ("kindly") or **malignant** ("bad"). A benign neoplasm is strictly a local affair. Its cells remain compacted, are often encapsulated, tend to grow slowly, and seldom kill their hosts if removed before they compress vital organs.

In contrast, cancers are malignant neoplasms, nonencapsulated masses that grow relentlessly and may become killers. Their cells resemble immature cells, and they invade their surroundings rather than pushing them aside, as reflected in the name *cancer*, from the Latin word for "crab." Whereas normal cells become fatally "homesick" and die when they lose contact with the surrounding matrix, malignant cells tend to break away from the parent mass, the primary tumor, and travel via blood or lymph to other body organs, where they form *secondary cancer masses*.

This capability for traveling to other parts of the body, called **metastasis** (mĕ-tas'tah-sis), probably has a lot to do with signaling molecules and the cell-surface glycoproteins the cancer cells bear. Metastasis and invasiveness distinguish cancer cells from the cells of benign neoplasms. Cancer cells consume an exceptional amount of the body's nutrients, leading to weight loss and tissue wasting that contribute to death.

Carcinogenesis

Autopsies on individuals aged 50–70 who died of another cause have revealed that most of us have microscopic (but dormant) in situ neoplasms. So what causes a normal cell to **transform** or change into a cancerous one? Some physical factors (radiation, mechanical trauma), certain viral infections, chronic inflammations, and many chemicals (tobacco tars, saccharine, some natural food chemicals) can act as

carcinogens (cancer-causers). What do these factors have in common? They all cause *mutations*—changes in DNA that alter the expression of certain genes. However, not all carcinogens do damage because most are eliminated by peroxisomal or lysosomal enzymes or by the immune system. Furthermore, one mutation usually isn't enough. It takes several genetic changes to transform a normal cell into a cancerous cell.

A clue to the role of genes in cancer was provided by the discovery of **oncogenes** (Greek *onco* = tumor), or cancer-causing genes, in rapidly spreading cancers. **Proto-oncogenes**, benign forms of oncogenes in normal cells, were discovered later. Proto-oncogenes code for proteins that are essential for cell division, growth, and cellular adhesion, among other things. Many have fragile sites that break when exposed to carcinogens, converting them to oncogenes. Failure to code for certain proteins may lead to loss of an enzyme that controls an important metabolic process. Oncogenes may also "switch on" dormant genes that allow cells to become invasive and metastasize. Known oncogenes now number over 100.

Oncogenes have been detected in only 15–20% of human cancers, so investigators were not too surprised by the discovery of **tumor suppressor genes**, or **anti-oncogenes**, which suppress cancer by inactivating carcinogens, aiding DNA repair, or enhancing the immune system's counterattack. In fact, over half of all cancers involve malfunction or loss of just 2 of the 15 identified tumor suppressor genes—*p53* and *p16*. This is not surprising when you learn that *p53* prompts most cells to make proteins that stop cell division in stressed cells by promoting apoptosis or cell cycle arrest. Its impairment invites uncontrolled division and cancer.

Furthermore, although each type of cancer is genetically distinct, human cancers appear to share a common master set of genes—an activated group of 67 genes—and almost all cancer cells have gained or lost entire chromosomes. Whatever genetic factors are at work, the "seeds" of cancer do appear to be in our own genes. Cancer is an intimate enemy indeed.

The illustration depicts some of the mutations involved in colorectal cancer, one of the best-understood human cancers.

As with most cancers, a metastasis develops gradually. One of the first signs is a polyp, a small benign growth consisting of apparently normal mucosa cells. As cell division continues, the growth enlarges, becoming an adenoma (a term for any neoplasm of glandular epithelium). As various tumor suppressor genes are inactivated and the *K-ras* oncogene is mobilized, the mutations pile up and the adenoma becomes increasingly abnormal. The final consequence is colon carcinoma, a form of cancer that metastasizes quickly.

Cancer Prevalence

Almost half of all Americans develop cancer in their lifetime and a fifth of us will die of it. Cancer can arise from almost any cell type, but the most common cancers originate in the skin, lung, colon, breast, and prostate gland. Although stomach and colon cancer incidence is down, skin and lymphoid cancer rates are up.

Many cancers are preceded by observable lumps or other structural changes in tissue—for instance, *leukoplakia*, white patches in the mouth caused by the chronic irritation of ill-fitting dentures or heavy smoking. Although these lesions sometimes progress to cancer, in many cases they remain stable or even revert to normal if the environmental stimulus is removed.

Diagnosis and Staging

Screening procedures are vital for early detection. Examples include *mammography* (X-ray examination of the breasts), examining breasts or testicles for lumps, and checking fecal samples for blood. Unfortunately, most cancers are diagnosed only after symptoms have already appeared. In this case the diagnostic method is usually a **biopsy**: removing a tissue sample surgically and examining it microscopically for malignant cells. Increasingly, diagnosis is made by chemical or genetic analysis of the sample. Typing cancer cells by what genes are switched on or off tells clinicians which drugs to use. For example, taxol, quite successful with breast and ovarian cancer, works only against tumors with a specific genetic makeup.

Several techniques (physical and histological examinations, lab tests, and imaging techniques [MR, CT]) are used to determine the extent of the disease (size

4

of the neoplasm, degree of metastasis, etc.). Then, the cancer is assigned a **stage** from 1 to 4 according to the probability of cure (stage 1 has the best probability, stage 4 the worst).

Cancer Treatments

Most cancers are removed surgically if possible. To destroy metastasized cells, surgery is commonly followed by radiation therapy (X irradiation and/or treatment with radioisotopes) and chemotherapy (treatment with cytotoxic drugs). Recently, some oncologists have been using heat therapy (just a slight upward temperature change) to put the cancer cells on the "cliff's edge," so that they are sensitized and much more vulnerable to chemotherapy or radiation.

Chemotherapy is beset with the problem of resistance. Some cancer cells can eject the drugs in tiny bubbles or flattened vesicles dubbed exosomes, and these cells proliferate, forming new tumors that are invulnerable to chemotherapy. Furthermore, anticancer drugs have unpleasant side effects—nausea, vomiting, hair loss—because they kill all rapidly dividing cells, including normal tissue cells. The anticancer drugs also can severely damage the brain, producing a phenomenon called chemobrain—a mental fuzziness and memory loss reported by many cancer patients. X rays also have side effects because, in passing through the body, they destroy healthy tissue in their path as well as cancer cells.

Promising New Therapies

Traditional cancer treatments—"cut, burn, and poison"—are widely recognized as crude and painful. Promising new therapies focus on

- *Targeted drugs that interrupt the signaling pathways that fuel the cancer's growth.* Examples include imatinib (Gleevec), which incapacitates a mutated enzyme that triggers uncontrolled division of cells in two rare blood and digestive system cancers, and trastuzumab (Herceptin), used to treat breast cancer patients. These drugs have been strikingly successful in providing a few extra weeks of life, before their protective effects wear off and the disease progresses again.

- *Delivering drugs or radiation more precisely to the cancer while sparing normal tissue.* One approach is to inject the patient with tiny drug-coated metal beads, which are guided to the tumor by a powerful magnet positioned over the body site. Or, a patient might take light-sensitive drugs that are drawn naturally into rapidly dividing cancer cells. Then, exposure to certain frequencies of laser light sets off reactions that kill the malignant cells. Another new procedure, proton therapy, delivers highly targeted killing doses of protons (radiation) that strike at cancer cells with incredible precision and with greater effectiveness than traditional X rays. Unlike X rays, which pass through the cancer and onward through the patient's body, protons can be slowed down and even directed to stop in the neoplasm.

- *Using genetically modified immune cells to target cancer cells.* One promising technique harvests a patient's most aggressive cancer-killing immune cells (T lymphocytes), inserts modified genes into them that make them even more efficient killers, multiplies the cells in the lab, and then infuses the immune cells back into the patient.

- *Using drugs that target cancer cell bioenergetics.* The fact that many cancers use glucose as their energy fuel almost exclusively has suggested a pharmaceutical approach that limits glucose use. In theory, this approach would kill cancer cells while sparing normal cells, which can also use amino acids and fats as energy fuels.

Other experimental treatments seek to starve cancer cells by cutting off their blood supply, fix defective tumor suppressor genes and oncogenes, destroy cancer cells with viruses, or signal cancer cells to commit suicide by apoptosis. Additionally, a cancer vaccine (TRICOM) contains genetically engineered viruses carrying genes for a cancer protein called carcinoembryonic antigen (CEA). When these proteins are delivered into the patient's body, they stimulate an immune response that orchestrates an attack on all CEA-bearing cancer cells.

At present, about half of all cancer cases are cured. Although average survival rates have not increased, the quality of life of cancer patients has improved in the last decade. We can offer better treatments for cancer-associated pain, and antinausea drugs and other helpful medicines can soothe the side effects of chemotherapy.

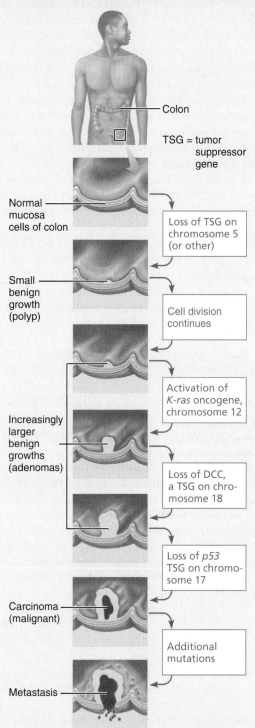

Some of the mutations involved in the development of colon cancer.

although many tissues retain the ability to regenerate. In adults, only epithelia and blood-forming tissues are highly mitotic. Some tissues that regenerate through life, such as the glandular cells of the liver, do so through division of their mature (specialized) cells. Others, like the epidermis of the skin and cells lining the intestine, have abundant *stem cells,* relatively undifferentiated cells that divide as necessary to produce new cells.

Given good nutrition, good circulation, and relatively infrequent wounds and infections, our tissues normally function efficiently through youth and middle age. But with increasing age, epithelia thin and are more easily breached. Tissue repair is less efficient, and bone, muscle, and nervous tissues begin to atrophy, particularly when a person is not physically active. These events are due partly to decreased circulatory efficiency, which reduces delivery of nutrients to the tissues, but in some cases, diet is a contributing factor. As income declines or as chewing becomes more difficult, older people tend to eat soft foods, which may be low in protein and vitamins. As a result, tissue health suffers.

Another problem of aging tissues is the likelihood of DNA mutations in the most actively mitotic cells, which increases the risk of cancer (as indicated in *A Closer Look* on p. 142).

CHECK YOUR UNDERSTANDING

23. What are the names of the three embryonic germ layers?
24. Which germ layer gives rise to the nervous system?
25. Which two tissue types remain highly mitotic throughout life?

For answers, see Appendix G.

As we have seen, body cells combine to form four discrete tissue types: epithelial, connective, muscle, and nervous tissues. The cells making up each of these tissues share certain features but are by no means identical. They "belong" together because they have basic functional similarities. The connective tissues assume many guises, but perhaps the most versatile cells are those of epithelium: They protect our outer and inner surfaces, permit us to obtain oxygen, absorb vital nutrients into the blood, and allow our kidneys to excrete wastes. The important concept to carry away with you is that tissues, despite their unique abilities, cooperate to keep the body safe, healthy, and whole.

RELATED CLINICAL TERMS

Adenoma (ad″ĕ-no′mah; *aden* = gland, *oma* = tumor) Any neoplasm of glandular epithelium, benign or malignant. The malignant type is more specifically called *adenocarcinoma.*

Autopsy (aw′top-se) Examination of the body, its organs, and its tissues after death to determine the actual cause of death; also called postmortem examination and necropsy.

Carcinoma (kar″sĭ-no′mah; *karkinos* = crab, cancer) Cancer arising in an epithelium; accounts for 90% of human cancers.

Healing by first intention The simplest type of healing; occurs when the edges of the wound are brought together by sutures, staples, or other means used to close surgical incisions. Only small amounts of granulation tissue need be formed.

Healing by second intention The wound edges remain separated, and the gap is bridged by relatively large amounts of granulation tissue; the manner in which unattended wounds heal. Healing is slower than in wounds in which the edges are brought together, and larger scars result.

Keloid (ke′loid) Abnormal proliferation of connective tissue during healing of skin wounds; results in large, unsightly mass of scar tissue at the skin surface.

Lesion (le′zhun; "wound") Any injury, wound, or infection that affects tissue over an area of a definite size (as opposed to being widely spread throughout the body).

Marfan's syndrome Genetic disease resulting in abnormalities of connective tissues due to a defect in fibrillin, a protein that is associated with elastin in elastic fibers. Clinical signs include loose-jointedness, long limbs and spiderlike fingers and toes, visual problems, and weakened blood vessels (especially the aorta) due to poor connective tissue reinforcement.

Pathology (pah-thol′o-je) Scientific study of changes in organs and tissues produced by disease.

Pus A collection of tissue fluid, bacteria, dead and dying tissue cells, white blood cells, and macrophages in an inflamed area.

Sarcoma (sar-ko′mah; *sarkos* = flesh; *oma* = tumor) Cancer arising in the mesenchyme-derived tissues, that is, in connective tissues and muscle.

Scurvy A nutritional deficiency caused by lack of adequate vitamin C needed to synthesize collagen; signs and symptoms include blood vessel disruption, delay in wound healing, weakness of scar tissue, and loosening of teeth.

VAC (vacuum-assisted closure) Innovative healing process for open-skin wounds and skin ulcers. Often induces healing when all other methods fail. Involves covering the wound with a special sponge, and then applying suction through the sponge. In response to the subsequent skin stretching, fibroblasts in the wound form more collagen tissue and new blood vessels proliferate, bringing more blood into the injured area, which also promotes healing.

CHAPTER SUMMARY

Media study tools that could provide you additional help in reviewing specific key topics of Chapter 4 are referenced below.

iP = *Interactive Physiology*

Tissues are collections of structurally similar cells with related functions. The four primary tissues are epithelial, connective, muscle, and nervous tissues.

Preparing Human Tissue for Microscopy (pp. 114–115)

1. Preparation of tissues for microscopic examination involves cutting thin sections of the tissue and using dyes to stain the tissue. Minor distortions called artifacts can be introduced by the tissue preparation process.

Epithelial Tissue (pp. 115–124)

1. Epithelial tissue is the covering, lining, and glandular tissue of the body. Its functions include protection, absorption, excretion, filtration, secretion, and sensory reception.

Special Characteristics of Epithelium (pp. 115–116)

2. Epithelial tissues exhibit specialized contacts, polarity, avascularity, support from connective tissue, and high regenerative capacity.

Classification of Epithelia (pp. 116–121)

3. Epithelium is classified by arrangement as simple (one layer) or stratified (more than one layer) and by cell shape as squamous, cuboidal, or columnar. The terms denoting cell shape and arrangement are combined to describe the epithelium fully.
4. Simple squamous epithelium is a single layer of squamous cells. Highly adapted for filtration and exchange of substances, it forms walls of air sacs of the lungs and lines blood vessels. It contributes to serosae as mesothelium and lines all hollow circulatory system organs as endothelium.
5. Simple cuboidal epithelium, commonly active in secretion and absorption, is found in glands and in kidney tubules.
6. Simple columnar epithelium, specialized for secretion and absorption, consists of a single layer of tall columnar cells that exhibit microvilli and often mucus-producing cells. It lines most of the digestive tract.
7. Pseudostratified columnar epithelium is a simple columnar epithelium that appears stratified. Its ciliated variety, rich in mucus-secreting cells, lines most of the upper respiratory passages.
8. Stratified squamous epithelium is multilayered; cells at the free surface are squamous. It is adapted to resist abrasion. It lines the esophagus and vagina; its keratinized variety forms the skin epidermis.
9. Stratified cuboidal epithelia are rare in the body, and are found chiefly in ducts of large glands. Stratified columnar epithelium has a very limited distribution, found mainly in the male urethra and at transition areas between other epithelia types.
10. Transitional epithelium is a modified stratified squamous epithelium, adapted for responding to stretch. It lines hollow urinary system organs.

Glandular Epithelia (pp. 121–124)

11. A gland is one or more cells specialized to secrete a product.
12. On the basis of site of product release, glands are classified as exocrine or endocrine. Glands are classified structurally as multicellular or unicellular.
13. Unicellular glands, typified by goblet cells and mucous cells, are mucus-secreting single-celled glands.
14. Multicellular exocrine glands are classified according to duct structure as simple or compound, and according to the structure of their secretory parts as tubular, alveolar, or tubuloalveolar.
15. Multicellular exocrine glands of humans are classified functionally as merocrine or holocrine.

Connective Tissue (pp. 124–135)

1. Connective tissue is the most abundant and widely distributed tissue of the body. Its functions include support, protection, binding, insulation, and transportation (blood).

Common Characteristics of Connective Tissue (p. 124)

2. Connective tissues originate from embryonic mesenchyme and exhibit matrix. Depending on type, a connective tissue may be well vascularized (most), poorly vascularized (dense connective tissue), or avascular (cartilage).

Structural Elements of Connective Tissue (pp. 124–126)

3. The structural elements of all connective tissues are extracellular matrix and cells.
4. The extracellular matrix consists of ground substance and fibers (collagen, elastic, and reticular). It may be fluid, gel-like, or firm.
5. Each connective tissue type has a primary cell type that can exist as a mitotic, matrix-secreting cell (blast) or as a mature cell (cyte) responsible for maintaining the matrix. The undifferentiated cell type of connective tissue proper is the fibroblast; that of cartilage is the chondroblast; that of bone is the osteoblast; and that of blood-forming tissue is the hematopoietic stem cell.

Types of Connective Tissue (pp. 126–135)

6. Embryonic connective tissue is called mesenchyme.
7. Connective tissue proper consists of loose and dense varieties. The loose connective tissues are
   - Areolar: gel-like ground substance; all three fiber types loosely interwoven; a variety of cells; forms the lamina propria and soft packing around body organs; the prototype.
   - Adipose: consists largely of adipocytes; scant matrix; insulates and protects body organs; provides reserve energy fuel. Brown fat, present only in infants, is more important for generating body heat.
   - Reticular: finely woven reticular fibers in soft ground substance; the stroma of lymphoid organs and bone marrow.
8. Dense connective tissue proper includes
   - Dense regular: dense parallel bundles of collagen fibers; few cells, little ground substance; high tensile strength; forms tendons, ligaments, aponeuroses; in cases where this tissue also contains numerous elastic fibers it is called elastic connective tissue.
   - Dense irregular: like regular variety, but fibers are arranged in different planes; resists tension exerted from many different directions; forms the dermis of the skin and organ capsules.
9. Cartilage exists as
   - Hyaline: firm ground substance containing collagen fibers; resists compression well; found in fetal skeleton, at articulating surfaces of bones, and trachea; most abundant type.
   - Elastic cartilage: elastic fibers predominate; provides flexible support of the external ear and epiglottis.

■ Fibrocartilage: coarse parallel collagen fibers; provides support with compressibility; forms intervertebral discs and knee cartilages.

10. Bone (osseous tissue) consists of a hard, collagen-containing matrix embedded with calcium salts; forms the bony skeleton.

11. Blood consists of blood cells in a fluid matrix (plasma).

Nervous Tissue (pp. 134–136)

1. Nervous tissue forms organs of the nervous system. It is composed of neurons and supporting cells.

2. Neurons are branching cells that receive and transmit electrical impulses. They are involved in body regulation.

iP Nervous System I; Topic: Anatomy Review, pp. 1, 3.

Muscle Tissue (pp. 136–138)

1. Muscle tissue consists of elongated cells specialized to contract and cause movement.

2. Based on structure and function, the muscle tissues are
   ■ Skeletal muscle: attached to and moves the bony skeleton; cells are cylindrical and striated.
   ■ Cardiac muscle: forms the walls of the heart; pumps blood; cells are branched and striated.
   ■ Smooth muscle: in the walls of hollow organs; propels substances through the organs; cells are spindle shaped and lack striations.

Covering and Lining Membranes (pp. 138–139)

1. Membranes are simple organs, consisting of an epithelium bound to an underlying connective tissue layer. They include mucosae, serosae, and the cutaneous membrane.

Tissue Repair (pp. 139–141)

1. Inflammation is the body's response to injury. Tissue repair begins during the inflammatory process. It may lead to regeneration, fibrosis, or both.

2. Tissue repair begins with organization, during which the blood clot is replaced by granulation tissue. If the wound is small and the damaged tissue is actively mitotic, the tissue will regenerate and cover the fibrous tissue. When a wound is extensive or the damaged tissue amitotic, it is repaired only by fibrous connective (scar) tissue.

Developmental Aspects of Tissues (pp. 141, 144)

1. Epithelium arises from all three primary germ layers (ectoderm, mesoderm, endoderm); muscle and connective tissue from mesoderm; and nervous tissue from ectoderm.

2. The decrease in mass and viability seen in most tissues during old age often reflects circulatory deficits or poor nutrition.

REVIEW QUESTIONS

Multiple Choice/Matching

(Some questions have more than one correct answer. Select the best answer or answers from the choices given.)

1. Use the key to classify each of the following described tissue types into one of the four major tissue categories.
   Key: (a) connective tissue   (c) muscle
        (b) epithelium   (d) nervous tissue

   _____ (1) Tissue type composed largely of nonliving extracellular matrix; important in protection and support

   _____ (2) The tissue immediately responsible for body movement

   _____ (3) The tissue that enables us to be aware of the external environment and to react to it

   _____ (4) The tissue that lines body cavities and covers surfaces

2. An epithelium that has several layers, with an apical layer of flattened cells, is called (choose all that apply): (a) ciliated, (b) columnar, (c) stratified, (d) simple, (e) squamous.

3. Match the epithelial types named in column B with the appropriate description(s) in column A.

Column A	Column B
_____ (1) Lines most of the digestive tract	(a) pseudostratified ciliated columnar
_____ (2) Lines the esophagus	(b) simple columnar
_____ (3) Lines much of the respiratory tract	(c) simple cuboidal
_____ (4) Forms the walls of the air sacs of the lungs	(d) simple squamous
_____ (5) Found in urinary tract organs	(e) stratified columnar
_____ (6) Endothelium and mesothelium	(f) stratified squamous
	(g) transitional

4. The gland type that secretes products such as milk, saliva, bile, or sweat through a duct is (a) an endocrine gland, (b) an exocrine gland.

5. The membrane which lines body cavities that open to the exterior is a(n) (a) endothelium, (b) cutaneous membrane, (c) mucous membrane, (d) serous membrane.

6. Scar tissue is a variety of (a) epithelium, (b) connective tissue, (c) muscle tissue, (d) nervous tissue, (e) all of these.

Short Answer Essay Questions

7. Define tissue.

8. Name four important functions of epithelial tissue and provide at least one example of a tissue that exemplifies each function.

9. Describe the criteria used to classify covering and lining epithelia.

10. Explain the functional classification of multicellular exocrine glands and supply an example for each class.

11. Provide examples from the body that illustrate four of the major functions of connective tissue.

12. Name the primary cell type in connective tissue proper; in cartilage; in bone.

13. Name the two major components of matrix and, if applicable, subclasses of each component.

14. Matrix is extracellular. How does the matrix get to its characteristic position?

15. Name the specific connective tissue type found in the following body locations: (a) forming the soft packing around organs, (b) supporting the ear pinna, (c) forming "stretchy" ligaments, (d) first connective tissue in the embryo, (e) forming the intervertebral discs, (f) covering the ends of bones at joint surfaces, (g) main component of subcutaneous tissue.

16. What is the function of macrophages?

17. Differentiate clearly between the roles of neurons and the supporting cells of nervous tissue.

18. Compare and contrast skeletal, cardiac, and smooth muscle tissue relative to structure, body location, and specific function.

19. Describe the process of tissue repair, making sure you indicate factors that influence this process.

20. Indicate which primary tissue classes derive from each embryonic germ layer.

21. In what ways are adipose tissue and bone similar? How are they different?

Critical Thinking and Clinical Application Questions

1. John has sustained a severe injury during football practice and is told that he has a torn knee cartilage. Can he expect a quick, uneventful recovery? Explain your response.

2. The epidermis (epithelium of the cutaneous membrane or skin) is a keratinized stratified squamous epithelium. Explain why that epithelium is much better suited for protecting the body's external surface than a mucosa consisting of a simple columnar epithelium would be.

3. Your friend is trying to convince you that if the ligaments binding the bones together at your freely movable joints (such as your knee, shoulder, and hip joints) contained more elastic fibers, you would be much more flexible. Although there is *some* truth to this statement, such a condition would present serious problems. Why?

4. In adults, over 90% of all cancers are either adenomas (adenocarcinomas) or carcinomas. (See Related Clinical Terms for this chapter.) In fact, cancers of the skin, lung, colon, breast, and prostate are all in these categories. Which one of the four basic tissue types gives rise to most cancers? Why do you think this is so?

5. Cindy, an overweight high school student, is overheard telling her friend that she's going to research how she can transform some of her white fat to brown fat. What is her rationale here (assuming it is possible)?

6. Mrs. Delancy went to the local meat market and bought a beef tenderloin (cut from the loin, the region along the steer's vertebral column) and some tripe (cow's stomach). What type of muscle was she preparing to eat in each case?

5

The Skin (pp. 149–155)

    Epidermis (pp. 150–152)

    Dermis (pp. 152–153)

    Skin Color (pp. 154–155)

Appendages of the Skin (pp. 155–160)

    Sweat (Sudoriferous) Glands (pp. 155–156)

    Sebaceous (Oil) Glands (pp. 156–157)

    Hairs and Hair Follicles (pp. 157–159)

    Nails (p. 160)

Functions of the Integumentary System (pp. 160–162)

    Protection (pp. 160–161)

    Body Temperature Regulation (p. 161)

    Cutaneous Sensation (p. 161)

    Metabolic Functions (p. 161)

    Blood Reservoir (pp. 161–162)

    Excretion (p. 162)

Homeostatic Imbalances of Skin (pp. 162–165)

    Skin Cancer (pp. 162–163)

    Burns (pp. 163–165)

Developmental Aspects of the Integumentary System (p. 165)

The Integumentary System

Would you be enticed by an advertisement for a coat that is waterproof, stretchable, washable, and permanent-press, that automatically repairs small cuts, rips, and burns, and that is guaranteed to last a lifetime with reasonable care? Sounds too good to be true, but you already have such a coat—your skin. The skin and its derivatives (sweat and oil glands, hairs, and nails) make up a complex set of organs that serves several functions, mostly protective. Together, these organs form the **integumentary system** (in-teg″u-men′tar-e).

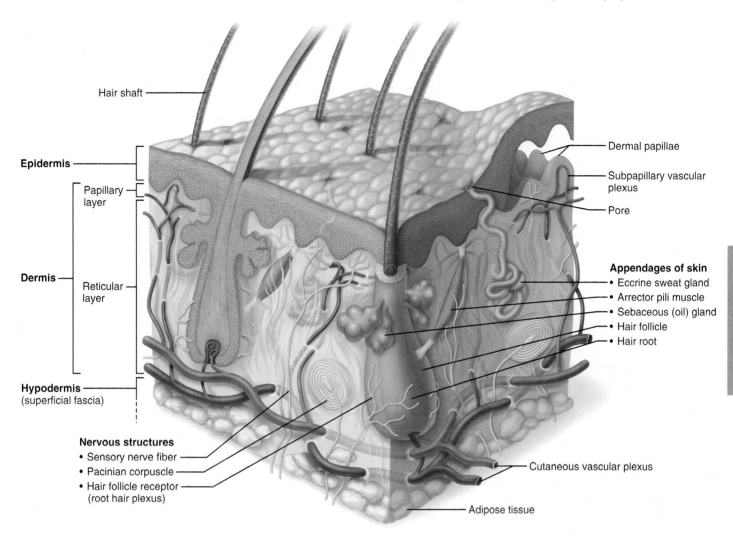

Figure 5.1 Skin structure. Three-dimensional view of the skin and underlying subcutaneous tissue. The epidermal and dermal layers have been pulled apart at the right corner to reveal the dermal papillae.

The Skin

▶ Name the tissue types composing the epidermis and dermis. List the major layers of each and describe the functions of each layer.

▶ Describe the factors that normally contribute to skin color. Briefly describe how changes in skin color may be used as clinical signs of certain disease states.

The skin ordinarily receives little respect from its inhabitants, but architecturally it is a marvel. It covers the entire body, has a surface area of 1.2 to 2.2 square meters, weighs 4 to 5 kilograms (4–5 kg = 9–11 lb), and accounts for about 7% of total body weight in the average adult. Also called the integument, which simply means "covering," the skin multitasks. Its functions go well beyond serving as a large, opaque bag for the body contents. It is pliable yet tough, allowing it to take constant punishment from external agents. Without our skin, we would quickly fall prey to bacteria and perish from water and heat loss.

The skin, which varies in thickness from 1.5 to 4.0 millimeters (mm) or more in different parts of the body, is composed of two distinct regions, the *epidermis* (ep″ĭ-der′mis) and the *dermis* **(Figure 5.1)**. The epidermis (*epi* = upon), composed of epithelial cells, is the outermost protective shield of the body. The underlying dermis, making up the bulk of the skin, is a tough, leathery layer composed mostly of fibrous connective tissue. Only the dermis is vascularized. Nutrients reach the epidermis by diffusing through the tissue fluid from blood vessels in the dermis.

The subcutaneous tissue just deep to the skin is known as the **hypodermis** (Figure 5.1). Strictly speaking, the hypodermis is not part of the skin, but it shares some of the skin's protective functions. The hypodermis, also called **superficial fascia** because it is superficial to the tough connective tissue wrapping (fascia) of the skeletal muscles, consists mostly of adipose tissue.

Besides storing fat, the hypodermis anchors the skin to the underlying structures (mostly to muscles), but loosely enough that the skin can slide relatively freely over those structures.

Sliding skin protects us by ensuring that many blows just glance off our bodies. Because of its fatty composition, the hypodermis also acts as a shock absorber and an insulator that reduces heat loss from the body. The hypodermis thickens markedly when a person gains weight. In females, this "extra" subcutaneous fat accumulates first in the thighs and breasts, but in males it first collects in the anterior abdomen (as a "beer belly").

Epidermis

Structurally, the **epidermis** is a keratinized stratified squamous epithelium consisting of four distinct cell types and four or five distinct layers.

Cells of the Epidermis

The cells populating the epidermis include *keratinocytes, melanocytes, epidermal dendritic cells,* and *tactile cells.* Most epidermal cells are keratinocytes, so we will consider them first. The chief role of **keratinocytes** (kĕ-rat′ĭ-no-sītz″; "keratin cells") is to produce **keratin**, the fibrous protein that helps give the epidermis its protective properties (Greek *kera* = horn) (**Figure 5.2b**, orange cells).

Tightly connected to one another by desmosomes, the keratinocytes arise in the deepest part of the epidermis from a cell layer called the stratum basale. These cells undergo almost continuous mitosis in response to prompting by epidermal growth factor, a peptide produced by various cells throughout the body. As these cells are pushed upward by the production of new cells beneath them, they make the keratin that eventually dominates their cell contents. By the time the keratinocytes reach the free surface of the skin, they are dead, scalelike structures that are little more than keratin-filled plasma membranes.

Millions of these dead cells rub off every day, giving us a totally new epidermis every 25 to 45 days. In body areas regularly subjected to friction, such as the hands and feet, both cell production and keratin formation are accelerated. Persistent friction (from a poorly fitting shoe, for example) causes a thickening of the epidermis called a *callus.*

Melanocytes (mel′ah-no-sītz), the spider-shaped epithelial cells that synthesize the pigment **melanin** (mel′ah-nin; *melan* = black), are found in the deepest layer of the epidermis (Figure 5.2b, gray cells). As melanin is made, it is accumulated in membrane-bound granules called *melanosomes* that are moved along actin filaments by motor proteins to the ends of the melanocyte's processes (the "spider arms"). From there they are taken up by nearby keratinocytes. The melanin granules accumulate on the superficial, or "sunny," side of the keratinocyte nucleus, forming a pigment shield that protects the nucleus from the damaging effects of ultraviolet (UV) radiation in sunlight.

The star-shaped **epidermal dendritic cells** arise from bone marrow and migrate to the epidermis. Also called **Langerhans cells** (lahng′er-hanz) after a German anatomist, they ingest foreign substances and are key activators of our immune system, as described later in this chapter. Their slender processes extend among the surrounding keratinocytes, forming a more or less continuous network (Figure 5.2b, purple cell).

Occasional **tactile (Merkel) cells** are present at the epidermal-dermal junction. Shaped like a spiky hemisphere (Figure 5.2b, blue cell), each tactile cell is intimately associated with a disclike sensory nerve ending. The combination, called a *tactile* or *Merkel disc,* functions as a sensory receptor for touch.

Layers of the Epidermis

Variation in epidermal thickness determines if skin is *thick* or *thin.* In **thick skin,** which covers the palms, fingertips, and soles of the feet, the epidermis consists of five layers, or *strata* (stra′tah; "bed sheets"). From deep to superficial, these layers are stratum basale, stratum spinosum, stratum granulosum, stratum lucidum, and stratum corneum. In **thin skin,** which covers the rest of the body, the stratum lucidum appears to be absent and the other strata are thinner (Figure 5.2a, b).

Stratum Basale (Basal Layer) The **stratum basale** (stra′tum bah-sa′le), the deepest epidermal layer, is attached to the underlying dermis along a wavy borderline that reminds one of corrugated cardboard. For the most part, it consists of a single row of stem cells—a continually renewing cell population—representing the youngest keratinocytes. The many mitotic nuclei seen in this layer reflect the rapid division of these cells and account for its alternate name, **stratum germinativum** (jer′mĭ-nă″tiv-um; "germinating layer"). Each time one of these basal cells divides, one daughter cell is pushed into the cell layer just above to begin its specialization into a mature keratinocyte. The other daughter cell remains in the basal layer to continue the process of producing new keratinocytes.

Some 10–25% of the cells in the stratum basale are melanocytes, and their branching processes extend among the surrounding cells, reaching well into the more superficial stratum spinosum layer. Occasional tactile cells are also seen in this stratum.

Stratum Spinosum (Prickly Layer) The **stratum spinosum** (spi′no-sum; "prickly") is several cell layers thick. These cells contain a weblike system of intermediate filaments, mainly tension-resisting bundles of pre-keratin filaments, which span their cytosol to attach to desmosomes. Looking like tiny versions of the spiked iron balls used in medieval warfare, the keratinocytes in this layer appear to have spines, causing them to be called *prickle cells.* The spines do not exist in the living cells; they are artifacts that arise during tissue preparation when these cells shrink but their numerous desmosomes hold tight. Scattered among the keratinocytes are melanin granules and epidermal dendritic cells, which are most abundant in this epidermal layer.

Stratum Granulosum (Granular Layer) The thin **stratum granulosum** (gran″u-lo′sum) consists of three to five cell layers in which keratinocyte appearance changes drastically, and the process of **keratinization** (in which the cells fill with the protein keratin) begins. These cells flatten, their nuclei and organelles begin to disintegrate, and they accumulate two types of granules. The *keratohyaline granules* (ker″ah-to-hi′ah-lin) help to form keratin in the upper layers, as we will see. The *lamellated*

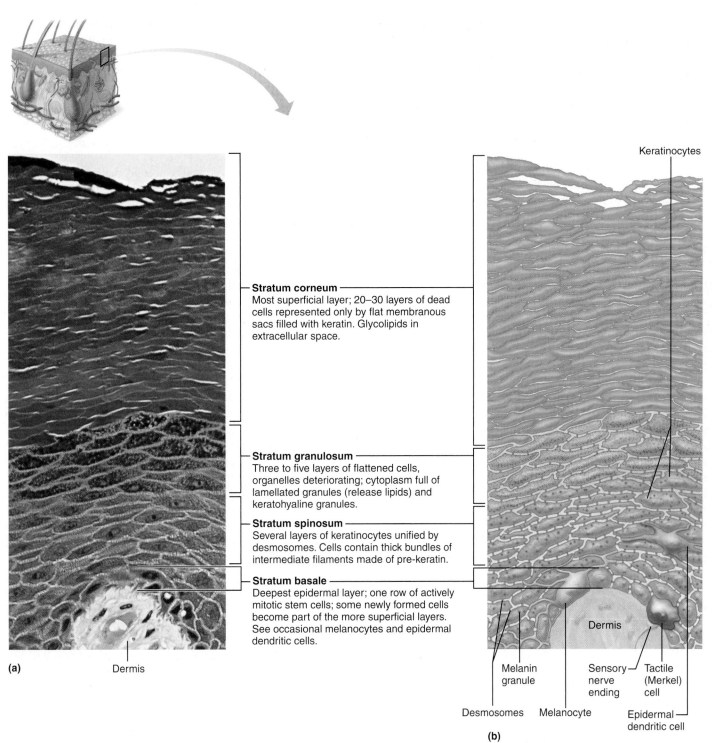

Stratum corneum
Most superficial layer; 20–30 layers of dead cells represented only by flat membranous sacs filled with keratin. Glycolipids in extracellular space.

Stratum granulosum
Three to five layers of flattened cells, organelles deteriorating; cytoplasm full of lamellated granules (release lipids) and keratohyaline granules.

Stratum spinosum
Several layers of keratinocytes unified by desmosomes. Cells contain thick bundles of intermediate filaments made of pre-keratin.

Stratum basale
Deepest epidermal layer; one row of actively mitotic stem cells; some newly formed cells become part of the more superficial layers. See occasional melanocytes and epidermal dendritic cells.

(a)   Dermis

Keratinocytes

Dermis

Melanin granule

Sensory nerve ending

Tactile (Merkel) cell

Desmosomes   Melanocyte

Epidermal dendritic cell

(b)

Figure 5.2 The main structural features of the skin epidermis. (a) Photomicrograph of the four major epidermal layers (200×). **(b)** Diagram showing these four layers and the distribution of different cell types. The four cell types are keratinocytes (orange), melanocytes (gray), epidermal dendritic cells (purple), and tactile cells (blue). A sensory nerve ending (yellow), extending from the dermis (pink), is shown associated with the tactile cell forming a tactile disc (touch receptor). Notice that the keratinocytes are joined by numerous desmosomes. The stratum lucidum, present in thick skin, is not illustrated here.

granules (lam′ĭ-la-ted; "plated") contain a water-resistant gly-colipid that is spewed into the extracellular space and is a major factor in slowing water loss across the epidermis. The plasma membranes of these cells thicken as cytosol proteins bind to the inner membrane face and lipids released by the lamellated granules coat their external surfaces. This makes them more resistant to destruction, so you might say that the keratinocytes are "toughening up" to make the outer strata the strongest skin region.

Like all epithelia, the epidermis relies on capillaries in the underlying connective tissue (the dermis in this case) for its nutrients. Above the stratum granulosum, the epidermal cells are too far from the dermal capillaries and are cut off from nutrients by the glycolipids that coat their external surfaces, so they die. This is a completely normal sequence of events.

Stratum Lucidum (Clear Layer)   Through the light microscope, the **stratum lucidum** (loo′sid-um; "light") appears as a thin translucent band just above the stratum granulosum. It consists of two or three rows of clear, flat, dead keratinocytes with indistinct boundaries. Here, or in the stratum corneum above, the gummy substance of the keratohyaline granules clings to the keratin filaments in the cells, causing them to aggregate in large, cable-like, parallel arrays. As mentioned before, the stratum lucidum is visible only in thick skin.

Stratum Corneum (Horny Layer)   The outermost **stratum corneum** (kor′ne-um) is a broad zone 20 to 30 cell layers thick that accounts for up to three-quarters of the epidermal thickness. Keratin and the thickened plasma membranes of cells in this stratum protect the skin against abrasion and penetration, and the glycolipid between its cells nearly waterproofs this layer. For these reasons, the stratum corneum provides a durable "overcoat" for the body, protecting deeper cells from the hostile external environment (air) and from water loss, and rendering the body relatively insensitive to biological, chemical, and physical assaults. It is amazing that a layer of dead cells can still play so many roles.

The shingle-like cell remnants of the stratum corneum are referred to as *cornified*, or *horny, cells* (*cornu* = horn). They are familiar to everyone as the dandruff shed from the scalp and dander, the loose flakes that slough off dry skin. The average person sheds 18 kg (40 lb) of these skin flakes in a lifetime, providing a lot of fodder for the dust mites that inhabit our homes and bed linens. The common saying "Beauty is only skin deep" is especially interesting in light of the fact that nearly everything we see when we look at someone is dead!

CHECK YOUR UNDERSTANDING

1. While walking barefoot in the barn, Jeremy stepped on a rusty nail that penetrated the depth of the epidermis on the sole of his foot. Name the layers the nail pierced from the superficial skin surface to the junction with the dermis.
2. The stratum basale is also called the stratum germinativum, a name that refers to the major function of this cell layer. What is that function?
3. Why are the desmosomes connecting the keratinocytes so important?
4. Given that epithelia are avascular, what layer would be expected to have the best-nourished cells?

For answers, see Appendix G.

Dermis

The **dermis** (*derm* = skin), the second major skin region, is strong, flexible connective tissue. Its cells are typical of those found in any connective tissue proper: fibroblasts, macrophages, and occasional mast cells and white blood cells. Its semifluid matrix, embedded with fibers, binds the entire body together like a body stocking. It is your "hide" and corresponds exactly to animal hides used to make leather products.

The dermis is richly supplied with nerve fibers, blood vessels, and lymphatic vessels. The major portions of hair follicles, as well as oil and sweat glands, are derived from epidermal tissue but reside in the dermis.

The dermis has two layers, the papillary and reticular, which abut one another along an indistinct boundary **(Figure 5.3)**. The thin superficial **papillary layer** (pap′il-er-e) is areolar connective tissue in which fine interlacing collagen and elastic fibers form a loosely woven mat that is heavily invested with small blood vessels. The looseness of this connective tissue allows phagocytes and other defensive cells to wander freely as they patrol the area for bacteria that may have breached the skin. Its superior surface is thrown into peglike projections called **dermal papillae** (pah-pil′e; *papill* = nipple) that indent the overlying epidermis (see Figure 5.1). Many dermal papillae contain capillary loops (of the *subpapillary plexus*). Others house free nerve endings (pain receptors) and touch receptors called *Meissner's corpuscles* (mīs′nerz kor′pus-lz). On the palms of the hands and soles of the feet, these papillae lie atop larger mounds called *dermal ridges*, which in turn cause the overlying epidermis to form *epidermal ridges* **(Figure 5.4)**. Collectively, these skin ridges, referred to as **friction ridges**, increase friction and enhance the gripping ability of the fingers and feet. Friction ridge patterns are genetically determined and unique to each of us. Because sweat pores open along their crests, our fingertips leave identifying films of sweat called *fingerprints* on almost anything they touch.

The deeper **reticular layer**, accounting for about 80% of the thickness of the dermis, is coarse, irregularly arranged, dense fibrous connective tissue (Figure 5.3c). The network of blood vessels that nourishes this layer, the *cutaneous plexus*, lies between this layer and the hypodermis. Its extracellular matrix contains pockets of adipose cells here and there, and thick bundles of interlacing collagen fibers. The collagen fibers run in various planes, but most run parallel to the skin surface. Separations, or less dense regions, between these bundles form **cleavage**, or **tension, lines** in the skin. These externally invisible lines tend to run longitudinally in the skin of the head and limbs and in circular patterns around the neck and trunk (Figure 5.4b).

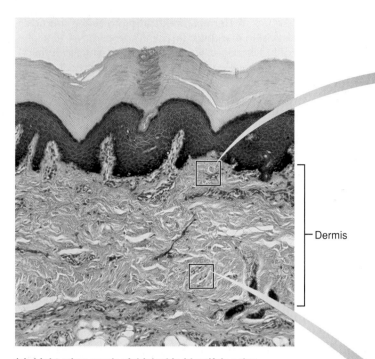

(a) **Light micrograph of thick skin identifying the extent of the dermis, (50×)**

Dermis

Figure 5.3 **The two regions of the dermis.** The superficial papillary layer consists of areolar connective tissue, and the deeper reticular layer is dense irregular fibrous connective tissue.
SOURCE: Kessel and Kardon/Visuals Unlimited.

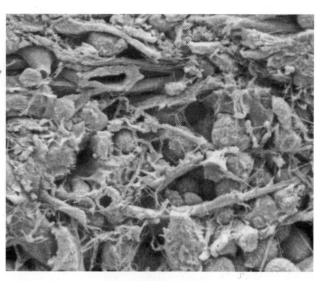

(b) Papillary layer of dermis, SEM (22,700×)

(c) Reticular layer of dermis, SEM (38,500×)

Cleavage lines are important to both surgeons and their patients. When an incision is made *parallel* to these lines, the skin gapes less and heals more readily than when the incision is made *across* cleavage lines.

The collagen fibers of the dermis give skin strength and resiliency that prevent most jabs and scrapes from penetrating the dermis. In addition, collagen binds water, helping to keep skin hydrated. Elastic fibers provide the stretch-recoil properties of skin.

In addition to the epidermal ridges and cleavage lines, a third type of skin marking, flexure lines, reflects dermal modifications. **Flexure lines** are dermal folds that occur at or near joints, where the dermis is tightly secured to deeper structures (notice the deep creases on your palms). Since the skin cannot slide easily to accommodate joint movement in such regions, the dermis folds and deep skin creases form. Flexure lines are also visible on the wrists, fingers, soles, and toes.

HOMEOSTATIC IMBALANCE

Extreme stretching of the skin, such as occurs during pregnancy, can tear the dermis. Dermal tearing is indicated by silvery white scars called *striae* (stri′e; "streaks"), commonly called "stretch marks." Short-term but acute trauma (as from a burn or wielding a hoe) can cause a *blister*, the separation of the epidermal and dermal layers by a fluid-filled pocket. ■

CHECK YOUR UNDERSTANDING

5. What layer of the dermis is responsible for producing fingerprint patterns?
6. What cell component of the hypodermis makes it a good shock absorber?
7. You have just gotten a paper cut. It is very painful, but it doesn't bleed. Has the cut penetrated into the dermis or just the epidermis?

For answers, see Appendix G.

Friction ridges

Openings of
sweat gland ducts

(a)

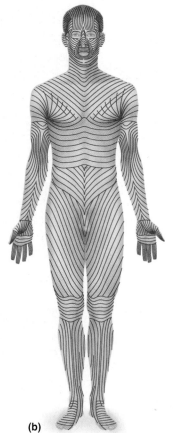

(b)

Figure 5.4 Dermal modifications result in characteristic skin markings. (a) Scanning electron micrograph of friction ridges (epidermal ridges topping the deeper dermal papillary ridges; 200×). Notice the sweat duct openings along the crests of the ridges, which are responsible for fingerprints. **(b)** Cleavage (tension) lines represent separations between underlying collagen fiber bundles in the reticular region of the dermis. They tend to run circularly around the trunk and longitudinally in the limbs.
SOURCE: (a) Kessel and Kardon/Visuals Unlimited.

Skin Color

Three pigments contribute to skin color: melanin, carotene, and hemoglobin. Of these, only melanin is made in the skin. **Melanin** is a polymer made of tyrosine amino acids. Its two forms range in color from yellow to tan to reddish-brown to black. Its synthesis depends on an enzyme in melanocytes called tyrosinase (ti-ro′sĭ-nās) and, as noted earlier, it passes from melanocytes to the basal keratinocytes. Eventually, the melanosomes are broken down by lysosomes, so melanin pigment is found only in the deeper layers of the epidermis.

Human skin comes in different colors. However, distribution of those colors is not random—populations of darker-skinned people tend to be found nearer the equator (where greater protection from the sun is needed), and those with the lightest skin are found closer to the poles. Since all humans have the same relative number of melanocytes, individual and racial differences in skin coloring reflect the relative kind and amount of melanin made and retained. Melanocytes of black- and brown-skinned people produce many more and darker melanosomes than those of fair-skinned individuals, and their keratinocytes retain it longer. *Freckles* and *pigmented nevi* (*moles*) are local accumulations of melanin.

Melanocytes are stimulated to greater activity by chemicals secreted by the surrounding keratinocytes when we expose our skin to sunlight. Prolonged sun exposure causes a substantial melanin buildup, which helps protect the DNA of viable skin cells from UV radiation by absorbing the rays and dissipating the energy as heat. Indeed, the initial signal for speeding up

melanin synthesis seems to be a faster rate of repair of photo-damaged DNA. In all but the darkest people, this response causes visible darkening of the skin (a tan).

HOMEOSTATIC IMBALANCE

Despite melanin's protective effects, excessive sun exposure eventually damages the skin. It causes clumping of elastic fibers, which results in leathery skin; temporarily depresses the immune system; and can alter the DNA of skin cells and in this way lead to skin cancer. The fact that dark-skinned people get skin cancer less often than fair-skinned people and get it in areas with less pigment—the soles of the feet and nail beds—attests to melanin's effectiveness as a natural sunscreen.

Ultraviolet radiation has other consequences as well. It destroys the body's folic acid stores necessary for DNA synthesis, which can have serious consequences, particularly in pregnant women because the deficit may impair the development of the embryo's nervous system. Many chemicals induce photosensitivity; that is, they heighten the skin's sensitivity to UV radiation, setting sun worshippers up for an unsightly skin rash. Such substances include some antibiotic and antihistamine drugs, and many chemicals in perfumes and detergents. Small, itchy, blisterlike lesions erupt all over the body; then the peeling begins, in sheets! ■

Carotene (kar′o-tēn) is a yellow to orange pigment found in certain plant products such as carrots. It tends to accumulate in the stratum corneum and in fatty tissue of the hypodermis. Its color is most obvious in the palms and soles, where the stratum corneum is thickest (for example the skin of the heels), and most intense when large amounts of carotene-rich foods are eaten. However, the yellowish tinge of the skin of some Asian peoples is due to variations in melanin, as well as to carotene. In the body, carotene can be converted to vitamin A, a vitamin that is essential for normal vision, as well as for epidermal health.

The pinkish hue of fair skin reflects the crimson color of the oxygenated pigment **hemoglobin** (he′mo-glo″bin) in the red blood cells circulating through the dermal capillaries. Because Caucasian skin contains only small amounts of melanin, the epidermis is nearly transparent and allows hemoglobin's color to show through.

HOMEOSTATIC IMBALANCE

When hemoglobin is poorly oxygenated, both the blood and the skin of Caucasians appear blue, a condition called *cyanosis* (si″ah-no′sis; *cyan* = dark blue). Skin often becomes cyanotic during heart failure and severe respiratory disorders. In dark-skinned individuals, the skin does not appear cyanotic because of the masking effects of melanin, but cyanosis is apparent in their mucous membranes and nail beds (the same sites where the red cast of normally oxygenated blood is visible).

Many alterations in skin color signal certain disease states, and in many people emotional states:

- *Redness*, or *erythema* (er″ĭ-the′mah): Reddened skin may indicate embarrassment (blushing), fever, hypertension, inflammation, or allergy.
- *Pallor*, or *blanching*: During fear, anger, and certain other types of emotional stress, some people become pale. Pale skin may also signify anemia or low blood pressure.
- *Jaundice* (jawn′dis), or *yellow cast*: An abnormal yellow skin tone usually signifies a liver disorder, in which yellow bile pigments accumulate in the blood and are deposited in body tissues. [Normally, the liver cells secrete the bile pigments (bilirubin) as a component of bile.]
- *Bronzing*: A bronze, almost metallic appearance of the skin is a sign of Addison's disease, in which the adrenal cortex is producing inadequate amounts of its steroid hormones; or a sign of the presence of pituitary gland tumors that inappropriately secrete melanocyte-stimulating hormone (MSH).
- *Black-and-blue marks*, or *bruises*: Black-and-blue marks reveal where blood escaped from the circulation and clotted beneath the skin. Such clotted blood masses are called *hematomas* (he″mah-to′mah; "blood swelling"). ■

CHECK YOUR UNDERSTANDING

8. Melanin and carotene are two pigments that contribute to skin color. What is the third and where is it found?

9. What is cyanosis and what does it indicate?

10. What alteration in skin color may indicate a liver disorder?

For answers, see Appendix G.

Appendages of the Skin

▶ Compare the structure and locations of sweat and oil glands. Also compare the composition and functions of their secretions.

▶ Compare and contrast eccrine and apocrine glands.

▶ List the parts of a hair follicle and explain the function of each part. Also describe the functional relationship of arrector pili muscles to the hair follicles.

▶ Name the regions of a hair and explain the basis of hair color. Describe the distribution, growth, replacement, and changing nature of hair during the life span.

▶ Describe the structure of nails.

Along with the skin itself, the integumentary system includes several derivatives of the epidermis. These **skin appendages** include the nails, sweat glands, sebaceous (oil) glands, and hair follicles and hair. Each of these plays a unique role in maintaining body homeostasis.

A key step in beginning to form any of the skin's appendages is formation of an epithelial bud. This process is stimulated by a reduced production of cell adhesion factor (cadherin). Once the cell-to-cell attractions are broken, the cells can move about and rearrange themselves, allowing an epithelial bud to form.

Sweat (Sudoriferous) Glands

Sweat glands, also called **sudoriferous glands** (su″do-rif′er-us; *sudor* = sweat), are distributed over the entire skin surface except the nipples and parts of the external genitalia. Their number is staggering—up to 3 million of them per person. We have two types of sweat glands: eccrine and apocrine. Regardless of type, the secretory cells are associated with myoepithelial cells, specialized cells that contract when stimulated by the nervous system. Their contraction forces the sweat into and through the gland's duct system to the skin surface.

Eccrine sweat glands (ek′rin; "secreting"), also called **merocrine sweat glands**, are far more numerous and are particularly abundant on the palms, soles of the feet, and forehead. Each is a simple, coiled, tubular gland. The secretory part lies coiled in the dermis, and the duct extends to open in a funnel-shaped *pore* (*por* = channel) at the skin surface (Figure 5.5b). (These sweat pores are different from the so-called pores of a person's complexion, which are actually the external outlets of hair follicles.)

Eccrine gland secretion, commonly called sweat, is a hypotonic filtrate of the blood that passes through the secretory cells of the sweat glands and is released by exocytosis. It is 99% water, with some salts (mostly sodium chloride), vitamin C, antibodies, a microbe-killing peptide dubbed *dermcidin*, and traces of metabolic wastes (urea, uric acid, and ammonia). The exact composition depends on heredity and diet. Small amounts of ingested drugs may also be excreted by this route. Normally, sweat is acidic with a pH between 4 and 6.

Sweating is regulated by the sympathetic division of the autonomic nervous system, over which we have little control. Its

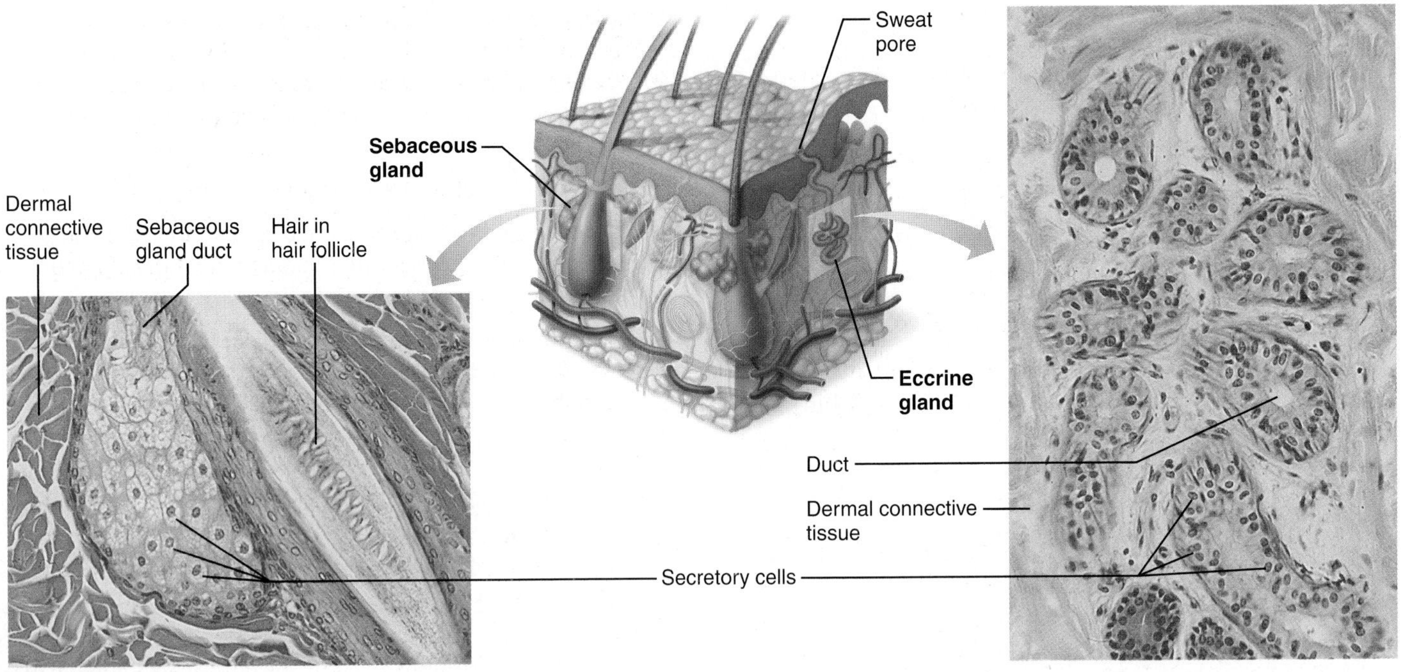

(a) Photomicrograph of a sectioned sebaceous gland (220×)

(b) Photomicrograph of a sectioned eccrine gland (220×)

Figure 5.5 **Cutaneous glands.**

major role is to prevent overheating of the body. Heat-induced sweating begins on the forehead and then spreads inferiorly over the remainder of the body. Emotionally induced sweating—the so-called "cold sweat" brought on by fright, embarrassment, or nervousness—begins on the palms, soles, and axillae (armpits) and then spreads to other body areas.

Apocrine sweat glands (ap'o-krin), approximately 2000 of them, are largely confined to the axillary and anogenital areas. In spite of their name, they are merocrine glands, which release their product by exocytosis like the eccrine sweat glands. They are larger than eccrine glands, tend to lie deeper in the dermis or even in the hypodermis, and their ducts empty into hair follicles. Apocrine secretion contains the same basic components as true sweat, plus fatty substances and proteins. Consequently, it is quite viscous and sometimes has a milky or yellowish color. The secretion is odorless, but when its organic molecules are decomposed by bacteria on the skin, it takes on a musky and generally unpleasant odor, the basis of body odor.

Apocrine glands begin functioning at puberty under the influence of androgens and have little role to play in thermoregulation. Their precise function is not yet known, but they are activated by sympathetic nerve fibers during pain and stress. Because their activity is increased by sexual foreplay, and they enlarge and recede with the phases of a woman's menstrual cycle, they may be the human equivalent of the sexual scent glands of other animals.

Ceruminous glands (sĕ-roo'mĭ-nus; *cera* = wax) are modified apocrine glands found in the lining of the external ear canal. Their secretion mixes with sebum produced by nearby sebaceous glands to form a sticky, bitter substance called *cerumen*, or earwax, that is thought to deter insects and block entry of foreign material.

Mammary glands, another variety of specialized sweat glands, secrete milk. Although they are properly part of the integumentary system, we consider the mammary glands in Chapter 27, along with female reproductive organs.

Sebaceous (Oil) Glands

The **sebaceous glands** (se-ba'shus; "greasy"), or **oil glands** (Figure 5.5a), are simple branched alveolar glands that are found all over the body except in the thick skin of the palms and soles. They are small on the body trunk and limbs, but quite large on the face, neck, and upper chest. These glands secrete an oily substance called **sebum** (se'bum). The central cells of the alveoli accumulate oily lipids until they become so engorged that they burst, so functionally these glands are *holocrine glands* (see p. 122). The accumulated lipids and cell fragments constitute sebum.

Most, but not all, sebaceous glands develop from hair follicles and sebum is secreted into a hair follicle, or occasionally to a pore on the skin surface. Sebum softens and lubricates the hair and skin, prevents hair from becoming brittle, and slows water loss from the skin when the external humidity is low. Perhaps even more important is its *bactericidal* (bacterium-killing) action.

The secretion of sebum is stimulated by hormones, especially androgens. Sebaceous glands are relatively inactive during childhood but are activated in both sexes during puberty, when androgen production begins to rise.

Additionally, and more important to humans physiologically, is the fact that arrector pili contractions force sebum out of the hair follicles to the skin surface.

HOMEOSTATIC IMBALANCE

If a sebaceous gland duct is blocked by accumulated sebum, a *whitehead* appears on the skin surface. If the material oxidizes and dries, it darkens to form a *blackhead*. *Acne* is an active inflammation of the sebaceous glands accompanied by "pimples" (pustules or cysts) on the skin. It is usually caused by bacterial infection, particularly by staphylococcus, and can be mild or extremely severe, leading to permanent scarring.

Seborrhea (seb″o-re′ah; "fast-flowing sebum"), known as "cradle cap" in infants, is caused by overactive sebaceous glands. It begins on the scalp as pink, raised lesions that gradually become yellow to brown and begin to slough off oily scales. ■

CHECK YOUR UNDERSTANDING

11. Which cutaneous glands are associated with hair follicles?

12. When Anthony returned home from a run in 85°F weather, his face was dripping with sweat. Why?

13. What is the difference between heat-induced sweating and a "cold sweat," and which variety of sweat glands is involved?

14. Sebaceous glands are not found in thick skin. Why is their absence in those body regions desirable?

For answers, see Appendix G.

Hairs and Hair Follicles

Hair is an important part of our body image—consider, for example, the spiky hair style of punk rockers and the flowing, glossy manes of some high-fashion models. Millions of hairs are distributed over our entire skin surface except our palms, soles, lips, nipples, and parts of the external genitalia (the head of the penis, for instance). Although hair helps to keep other mammals warm, our sparse body hair is far less luxuriant and useful. Its main function in humans is to sense insects on the skin before they bite or sting us. Hair on the scalp guards the head against physical trauma, heat loss, and sunlight. (Pity the bald man.) Eyelashes shield the eyes, and nose hairs filter large particles like lint and insects from the air we inhale.

Structure of a Hair

Hairs, or **pili** (pi′li), are flexible strands produced by hair follicles and consist largely of dead, keratinized cells. The *hard keratin* that dominates hairs and nails has two advantages over the *soft keratin* found in typical epidermal cells: (1) It is tougher and more durable, and (2) its individual cells do not flake off.

The chief regions of a hair are the *shaft*, the portion in which keratinization is complete, and the *root*, where keratinization is still ongoing. The shaft, which projects from the skin, extends about halfway down the portion of the hair embedded in the skin (Figure 5.6). The root is the remainder of the hair deep within the follicle. If the shaft is flat and ribbonlike in cross section, the hair is kinky; if it is oval, the hair is silky and wavy; if it is perfectly round, the hair is straight and tends to be coarse.

A hair has three concentric layers of keratinized cells (Figure 5.6a, b). Its central core, the *medulla* (mĕ-dul′ah;

"middle"), consists of large cells and air spaces. The medulla, which is the only part of the hair that contains soft keratin, is absent in fine hairs. The *cortex*, a bulky layer surrounding the medulla, consists of several layers of flattened cells. The outermost **cuticle** is formed from a single layer of cells that overlap one another from below like shingles on a roof. This arrangement helps to keep neighboring hairs apart so that the hair does not mat. (Hair conditioners smooth out the rough surface of the cuticle and make our hair look shiny.) The most heavily keratinized part of the hair, the cuticle provides strength and helps keep the inner layers tightly compacted. Because it is subjected to the most abrasion, the cuticle tends to wear away at the tip of the hair shaft, allowing the keratin fibrils in the cortex and medulla to frizz out, creating "split ends."

Hair pigment is made by melanocytes at the base of the hair follicle and transferred to the cortical cells. Various proportions of melanins of different colors (yellow, rust, brown, and black) combine to produce hair color from blond to pitch black. Additionally, red hair is colored by the iron-containing pigment *trichosiderin*. Gray or white hair results from decreased melanin production (mediated by delayed-action genes) and from the replacement of melanin by air bubbles in the hair shaft.

Structure of a Hair Follicle

Hair follicles (*folli* = bag) fold down from the epidermal surface into the dermis. In the scalp, they may even extend into the hypodermis. The deep end of the follicle, located about 4 mm (1/6 in.) below the skin surface, is expanded, forming a **hair bulb** (Figure 5.6c, d). A knot of sensory nerve endings called a **hair follicle receptor**, or **root hair plexus**, wraps around each hair bulb (see Figure 5.1). Bending the hair stimulates these endings. Consequently, our hairs act as sensitive touch receptors.

■ Feel the tickle as you run your hand over the hairs on your forearm.

A *hair papilla*, a nipple-like bit of dermal tissue, protrudes into the hair bulb. This papilla contains a knot of capillaries that supplies nutrients to the growing hair and signals it to grow. Except for its specific location, this papilla is similar to the dermal papillae underlying other epidermal regions.

The wall of a hair follicle is composed of an outer **connective tissue root sheath**, derived from the dermis; a thickened basement membrane called the *glassy membrane*; and an inner **epithelial root sheath**, derived mainly from an invagination of the epidermis (Figure 5.6). The epithelial root sheath, which has external and internal parts, thins as it approaches the hair bulb, so that only a single layer of epithelial cells covers the papilla. However, the cells that compose the **hair matrix**, or actively dividing area of the hair bulb that produces the hair, originate in a region called the *hair bulge* located a fraction of a millimeter above the hair bulb. When chemical signals diffusing from the papilla reach the hair bulge, some of its cells migrate toward the papilla, where they divide to produce the hair cells. As new hair cells are produced by the matrix, the older part of the hair is pushed upward, and its fused cells become increasingly keratinized and die.

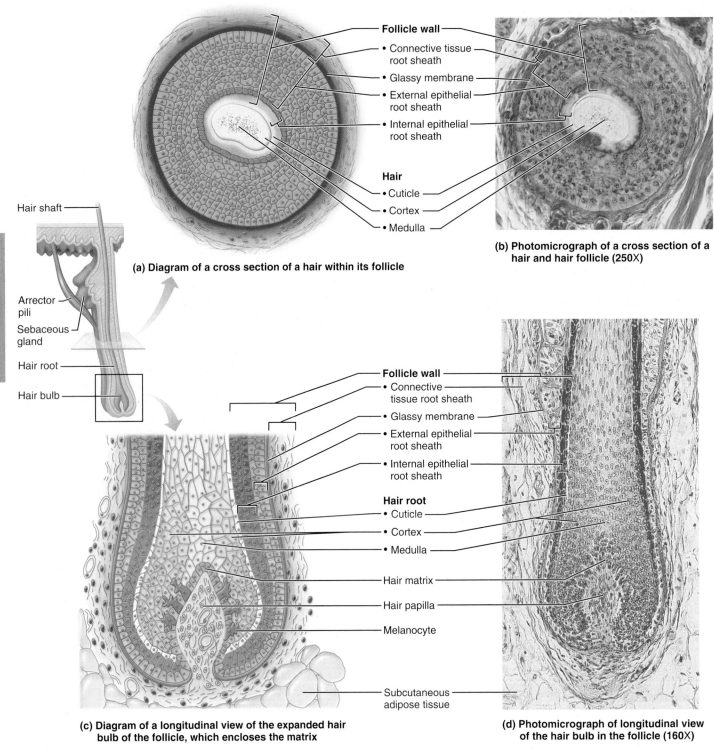

(a) Diagram of a cross section of a hair within its follicle

(b) Photomicrograph of a cross section of a hair and hair follicle (250X)

(c) Diagram of a longitudinal view of the expanded hair bulb of the follicle, which encloses the matrix

(d) Photomicrograph of longitudinal view of the hair bulb in the follicle (160X)

Figure 5.6 **Structure of a hair and hair follicle.**

Associated with each hair follicle is a bundle of smooth muscle cells called an **arrector pili** (ah-rek′tor pi′li; "raiser of hair") muscle. As you can see in Figure 5.1, most hair follicles approach the skin surface at a slight angle. The arrector pili muscle is attached in such a way that its contraction pulls the hair follicle into an upright position and dimples the skin surface to produce goose bumps in response to cold external tem-peratures or fear. This "hair-raising" response is not very useful to humans, with our short sparse hairs, but it is an important way for other animals to retain heat and protect themselves. Furry animals can stay warmer by trapping a layer of insulating air in their fur; and a scared animal with its hair on end looks larger and more formidable to its enemy.

Types and Growth of Hair

Hairs come in various sizes and shapes, but as a rule, they can be classified as vellus or terminal. The body hair of children and adult females is of the pale, fine **vellus hair** (vel′us; *vell* = wool, fleece) variety. The coarser, longer hair of the eyebrows and scalp is **terminal hair**, which may also be darker. At puberty, terminal hairs appear in the axillary and pubic regions of both sexes and on the face and chest (and typically the arms and legs) of males. These terminal hairs grow in response to the stimulating effects of male sex hormones called *androgens* (of which *testosterone* is the most important), and when male hormones are present in large amounts, terminal hair growth is luxuriant.

Hair growth and density are influenced by many factors, but most importantly by nutrition and hormones. Poor nutrition means poor hair growth, whereas conditions that increase local dermal blood flow (such as chronic physical irritation or inflammation) may enhance local hair growth. Many old-time bricklayers who carried their hod on one shoulder all the time developed one hairy shoulder. Undesirable hair growth (such as on a woman's upper lip) may be arrested by *electrolysis* or laser treatments, which use electricity or light energy, respectively, to destroy the hair roots.

HOMEOSTATIC IMBALANCE

In women, small amounts of androgens are normally produced by both the ovaries and the adrenal glands. Excessive hairiness, or **hirsutism** (her′soot-izm; *hirsut* = hairy), as well as other signs of masculinization, may result from an adrenal gland or ovarian tumor that secretes abnormally large amounts of androgens. Since few women want a beard or hairy chest, such tumors are surgically removed as soon as possible. ■

The rate of hair growth varies from one body region to another and with sex and age, but it averages 2.5 mm per week. Each follicle goes through *growth cycles*. In each cycle, an active growth phase, ranging from weeks to years, is followed by a regressive phase. During the regressive phase, the hair matrix cells die and the follicle base and hair bulb shrivel somewhat, dragging the hair papilla upward to abut the region of the follicle that does not regress. The follicle then enters a resting phase for one to three months. After the resting phase, the cycling part of the follicle regenerates and activated bulge cells migrate toward the papilla. As a result, the matrix proliferates again and forms a new hair to replace the old one that has fallen out or will be pushed out by the new hair.

The life span of hairs varies and appears to be under the control of a slew of proteins. The follicles of the scalp remain active for six to ten years before becoming inactive for a few months. Because only a small percentage of the hair is shed at any one time, we lose an average of 90 scalp hairs daily. The follicles of the eyebrow hairs remain active for only three to four months, which explains why your eyebrows are never as long as the hairs on your head.

Hair Thinning and Baldness

A follicle has only a limited number of cycles in it. Given ideal conditions, hair grows fastest from the teen years to the 40s, and then its growth slows. The fact that hairs are not replaced as fast as they are shed leads to hair thinning and some degree of baldness, or **alopecia** (al″o-pe′she-ah), in both sexes. Much less dramatic in women, the process usually begins at the anterior hairline and progresses posteriorly. Coarse terminal hairs are replaced by vellus hairs, and the hair becomes increasingly wispy.

True, or *frank, baldness* is a different story entirely. The most common type, **male pattern baldness**, is a genetically determined, sex-influenced condition. It is thought to be caused by a delayed-action gene that "switches on" in adulthood and changes the response of the hair follicles to DHT (dihydrotestosterone), a metabolite of testosterone. As a result, the follicular growth cycles become so short that many hairs never even emerge from their follicles before shedding, and those that do are fine vellus hairs that look like peach fuzz in the "bald" area.

Until recently, the only cure for male pattern baldness was drugs that inhibit testosterone production, but they also cause loss of sex drive—a trade-off few men would choose. Quite by accident, it was discovered that minoxidil, a drug used to reduce high blood pressure, has the interesting side effect in some bald men of stimulating hair regrowth. Although its results are variable, minoxidil is available over the counter in dropper bottles or spray form for application to the scalp. Finasteride, according to some the most promising cure ever developed for male pattern baldness, hit pharmacy shelves in early 1998 and has had moderate success. Available only by prescription in once-a-day pill form, it must be taken for the rest of a person's life. Once the patient stops taking it, all of the new growth falls out.

HOMEOSTATIC IMBALANCE

Hair thinning can be induced by a number of factors that upset the normal balance between hair loss and replacement. Outstanding examples are acutely high fever, surgery, severe emotional trauma, and certain drugs (excessive vitamin A, some antidepressants and blood thinners, anabolic steroids, and most chemotherapy drugs). Protein-deficient diets and lactation lead to hair thinning because new hair growth stops when protein needed for keratin synthesis is not available or is being used for milk production. In all of these cases, hair regrows if the cause of thinning is removed or corrected. In the rare condition called *alopecia areata*, the immune system attacks the follicles and the hair falls out in patches. But again, the follicles survive. Hair loss due to severe burns, excessive radiation, or other factors that eliminate the follicles is permanent. ■

CHECK YOUR UNDERSTANDING

15. What are the concentric regions of a hair shaft, from the outside in?

16. Why is having your hair cut painless?

17. What is the role of an arrector pili muscle?

18. What is the function of the hair papilla?

For answers, see Appendix G.

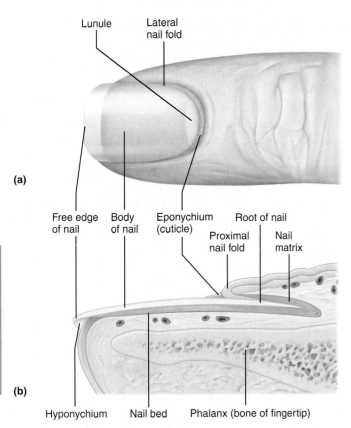

Figure 5.7 **Structure of a nail. (a)** Surface view of the distal part of a finger. **(b)** Sagittal section of the fingertip. The nail matrix that forms the nail lies beneath the lunule.

Nails

A **nail** is a scalelike modification of the epidermis that forms a clear protective covering on the dorsal surface of the distal part of a finger or toe **(Figure 5.7)**. Nails, which correspond to the hooves or claws of other animals, are particularly useful as "tools" to help pick up small objects and to scratch an itch. In contrast to *soft keratin* of the epidermis, nails contain *hard keratin*. Each nail has a *free edge*, a *body* (visible attached portion), and a proximal *root* (embedded in the skin). The deeper layers of the epidermis extend beneath the nail as the *nail bed*, and the nail itself corresponds to the superficial keratinized layers. The thickened proximal portion of the nail bed, called the **nail matrix**, is responsible for nail growth. As the nail cells produced by the matrix become heavily keratinized, the nail body slides distally over the nail bed.

Nails normally appear pink because of the rich bed of capillaries in the underlying dermis. However, the region that lies over the thick nail matrix appears as a white crescent called the *lunule* (lu'nool; "little moon"). The proximal and lateral borders of the nail are overlapped by skin folds, called **nail folds**. The proximal nail fold projects onto the nail body as the **cuticle** or **eponychium** (ep"o-nik'e-um; "on the nail"). The region beneath the free edge of the nail where dirt and debris tend to accumulate is the **hyponychium** ("below nail"), informally called the quick.

Changes in nail appearance may help diagnose certain conditions. For example, yellow-tinged nails may indicate a respira-

tory or thyroid gland disorder, and if combined with thickening of the nail, a fungus infection. An outward concavity of the nail (spoon nail) may signal an iron deficiency, and horizontal lines (Beau's lines) across the nails may hint of malnutrition.

CHECK YOUR UNDERSTANDING

19. Why is the lunule of a nail white instead of pink like the rest of the nail?

20. Why are nails so hard?

For answers, see Appendix G.

Functions of the Integumentary System

▶ Describe how the skin accomplishes at least five different functions.

The skin and its derivatives perform a variety of functions that affect body metabolism and prevent external factors from upsetting body homeostasis. Given its superficial location it is our most vulnerable organ system, exposed to bacteria, abrasion, temperature extremes, and harmful chemicals.

Protection

The skin constitutes at least three types of barriers: chemical, physical, and biological.

Chemical Barriers

The chemical barriers include skin secretions and melanin. Although the skin's surface teems with bacteria, the low pH of skin secretions—the so-called **acid mantle**—retards their multiplication. In addition, many bacteria are killed outright by dermcidin in sweat and bactericidal substances in sebum. Skin cells also secrete natural antibiotics called *defensins* that literally punch holes in bacteria, making them look like sieves. Wounded skin releases large quantities of protective peptides called *cathelicidins* that are particularly effective in preventing infection by group A streptococcus bacteria. As discussed earlier, melanin provides a chemical pigment shield to prevent UV damage to the viable skin cells.

Physical/Mechanical Barriers

Physical, or mechanical, barriers are provided by the continuity of skin and the hardness of its keratinized cells. As a physical barrier, the skin is a remarkable compromise. A thicker epidermis would be more impenetrable, but we would pay the price in loss of suppleness and agility. Epidermal continuity works hand in hand with the acid mantle and certain chemicals in skin secretions to ward off bacterial invasion. The water-resistant glycolipids of the epidermis block most diffusion of water and water-soluble substances between cells, preventing both their loss from and entry into the body through the skin. However, there is a continual small loss of water through the epidermis, and if immersed in water (other than salt water), the skin will take in some water and swell slightly.

Other substances that *do* penetrate the skin in limited amounts include (1) *lipid-soluble substances*, such as oxygen, carbon dioxide, fat-soluble vitamins (A, D, E, and K), and steroids (estrogens); (2) *oleoresins* (o″le-o-rez′inz) of certain plants, such as poison ivy and poison oak; (3) *organic solvents*, such as acetone, dry-cleaning fluid, and paint thinner, which dissolve the cell lipids; (4) *salts of heavy metals*, such as lead and mercury; (5) selected drugs (nitroglycerine, nicotine), and (6) drug agents called *penetration enhancers* that help ferry other drugs into the body. Skin permeability is dramatically enhanced by alcoholic drinks for at least 24 hours after their ingestion.

HOMEOSTATIC IMBALANCE

Organic solvents and heavy metals are devastating to the body and can be lethal. Passage of organic solvents through the skin into the blood can cause the kidneys to shut down and can also cause brain damage. Absorption of lead results in anemia and neurological defects. These substances should never be handled with bare hands. ■

Biological Barriers

Biological barriers include the dendritic cells of the epidermis, macrophages in the dermis, and DNA itself. Epidermal dendritic cells are active elements of the immune system. For the immune response to be activated, the foreign substances, or *antigens*, must be presented to specialized white blood cells called lymphocytes. In the epidermis, the dendritic cells play this role. Dermal macrophages constitute a second line of defense to dispose of viruses and bacteria that have managed to penetrate the epidermis. They, too, act as antigen "presenters."

Although melanin provides a fairly good chemical sunscreen, DNA itself is a remarkably effective biologically based sunscreen. Electrons in DNA molecules absorb UV radiation and transfer it to the atomic nuclei, which heat up and vibrate vigorously. However, since the heat dissipates to surrounding water molecules instantaneously, the DNA converts potentially destructive radiation into harmless heat.

Body Temperature Regulation

The body works best when its temperature remains within homeostatic limits. Like car engines, we need to get rid of the heat generated by our internal reactions. As long as the external temperature is lower than body temperature, the skin surface loses heat to the air and to cooler objects in its environment, just as a car radiator loses heat to the air and other nearby engine parts.

Under normal resting conditions, and as long as the environmental temperature is below 31–32°C (88–90°F), sweat glands secrete about 500 ml (0.5 L) of sweat per day. This routine and unnoticeable sweating is called *insensible perspiration*. When body temperature rises, the nervous system stimulates the dermal blood vessels to dilate and the sweat glands into vigorous secretory activity. Indeed, on a hot day, sweat becomes noticeable and can account for the loss of up to 12 L (about 3 gallons) of body water in one day. This visible output of sweat is referred to as *sensible perspiration*. Evaporation of sweat from the skin surface dissipates body heat and efficiently cools the body, preventing overheating.

When the external environment is cold, dermal blood vessels constrict. Their constriction causes the warm blood to bypass the skin temporarily and allows skin temperature to drop to that of the external environment. Once this has happened, passive heat loss from the body is slowed, conserving body heat. Body temperature regulation is discussed in Chapter 24.

Cutaneous Sensation

The skin is richly supplied with **cutaneous sensory receptors**, which are actually part of the nervous system. The cutaneous receptors are classified as *exteroceptors* (ek″ster-o-sep′torz) because they respond to stimuli arising outside the body. For example, Meissner's corpuscles (in the dermal papillae) and tactile discs allow us to become aware of a caress or the feel of our clothing against our skin, whereas pacinian corpuscles (in the deeper dermis or hypodermis) alert us to bumps or contacts involving deep pressure. Hair follicle receptors report on wind blowing through our hair and a playful tug on a pigtail. Free nerve endings that meander throughout the skin sense painful stimuli (irritating chemicals, extreme heat or cold, and others). We defer detailed discussion of these cutaneous receptors to Chapter 13. Except for Meissner's corpuscles, which are found only in skin that lacks hairs, the cutaneous receptors mentioned above are illustrated in Figure 5.1. One, a tactile disc, is shown in Figure 5.2b.

Metabolic Functions

The skin is a chemical factory, fueled in part by the sun's rays. When sunlight bombards the skin, modified cholesterol molecules circulating through dermal blood vessels are converted to a vitamin D precursor, and transported via the blood to other body areas to be ultimately converted to vitamin D, which plays various roles in calcium metabolism. For example, calcium cannot be absorbed from the digestive tract without vitamin D.

Besides synthesizing the vitamin D precursor, the epidermis has a host of other metabolic functions. It makes chemical conversions that supplement those of the liver. For example, keratinocyte enzymes can (1) "disarm" many cancer-causing chemicals that penetrate the epidermis; (2) convert some harmless chemicals into carcinogens; and (3) activate some steroid hormones—for instance, they can transform cortisone applied to irritated skin into hydrocortisone, a potent anti-inflammatory drug. Skin cells also make several biologically important proteins, including collagenase, an enzyme that aids the natural turnover of collagen (and deters wrinkles).

Blood Reservoir

The dermal vascular supply is extensive and can hold large volumes of blood (about 5% of the body's entire blood volume).

Figure 5.8 **Photographs of skin cancers.**

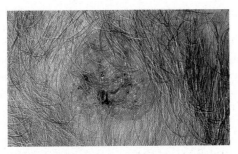

(b) Squamous cell carcinoma

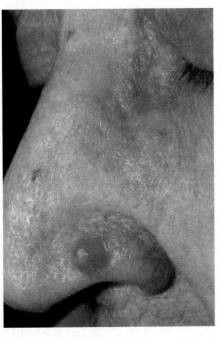

(a) Basal cell carcinoma

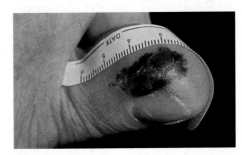

(c) Melanoma

When other body organs, such as vigorously working muscles, need a greater blood supply, the nervous system constricts the dermal blood vessels. This constriction shunts more blood into the general circulation, making it available to the muscles and other body organs.

Excretion

Limited amounts of nitrogen-containing wastes (ammonia, urea, and uric acid) are eliminated from the body in sweat, although most such wastes are excreted in urine. Profuse sweating is an important avenue for water and salt (sodium chloride) loss.

CHECK YOUR UNDERSTANDING

21. What chemicals produced in the skin help provide barriers to bacteria? List at least three and explain how the chemicals are protective.
22. What epidermal cells play a role in body immunity?
23. How is sunlight important to bone health?
24. How does the skin contribute to body metabolism?

For answers, see Appendix G.

Homeostatic Imbalances of Skin

▶ Summarize the characteristics of the three major types of skin cancers.

▶ Explain why serious burns are life threatening. Describe how to determine the extent of a burn and differentiate first-, second-, and third-degree burns.

When skin rebels, it is quite a visible rebellion. Loss of homeostasis in body cells and organs reveals itself on the skin, some-times in startling ways. The skin can develop more than 1000 different conditions and ailments. The most common skin disorders are bacterial, viral, or yeast infections. A number of these are summarized in Related Clinical Terms on p. 168. Less common, but far more damaging to body well-being, are skin cancer and burns, considered next.

Skin Cancer

One in five Americans develops skin cancer at some point. Most tumors that arise in the skin are benign and do not spread (metastasize) to other body areas. (A wart, a neoplasm caused by a virus, is one example.) However, some skin tumors are malignant, or cancerous, and invade other body areas.

A crucial risk factor for skin cancer is overexposure to the UV radiation in sunlight, which damages DNA bases. Adjacent pyrimidine bases often respond by fusing, forming lesions called *dimers*. UV radiation also appears to disable a tumor suppressor gene [*p53* or the patched (*ptc*) gene]. In limited numbers of cases, however, frequent irritation of the skin by infections, chemicals, or physical trauma seems to be a predisposing factor.

Interestingly, sunburned skin accelerates its production of Fas, a protein that causes genetically damaged skin cells to commit suicide, reducing the risk of mutations that will cause sun-linked skin cancer. It is the death of these gene-damaged cells that causes the skin to peel after a sunburn.

There is no such thing as a "healthy tan," but the good news for sun worshippers is the newly developed skin lotions that can fix damaged DNA before the involved cells can develop into cancer cells. These lotions contain tiny oily vesicles (liposomes) filled with enzymes that initiate repair of the DNA mutations most commonly caused by sunlight. The liposomes penetrate the epidermis and enter the keratinocytes, ultimately making their way into the nuclei to bind to specific sites where two DNA bases have fused. There, by selective cutting of the DNA strands, they begin a DNA repair process that is completed by cellular enzymes.

Basal Cell Carcinoma

Basal cell carcinoma (kar″sĭ-no′mah) is the least malignant and most common skin cancer. It accounts for nearly 80% of skin cancers. Stratum basale cells proliferate, invading the dermis and hypodermis. The cancer lesions occur most often on sun-exposed areas of the face and appear as shiny, dome-shaped nodules that later develop a central ulcer with a pearly, beaded edge (Figure 5.8a). Basal cell carcinoma is relatively slow-growing, and metastasis seldom occurs before it is noticed. Full cure by surgical excision is the rule in 99% of cases.

Squamous Cell Carcinoma

Squamous cell carcinoma, the second most common skin cancer, arises from the keratinocytes of the stratum spinosum. The lesion appears as a scaly reddened papule (small, rounded elevation) that arises most often on the head (scalp, ears, and lower lip), and hands (Figure 5.8b). It tends to grow rapidly and metastasize if not removed. If it is caught early and removed surgically or by radiation therapy, the chance of complete cure is good.

Melanoma

Melanoma (mel″ah-no′mah), cancer of melanocytes, is the most dangerous skin cancer because it is highly metastatic and resistant to chemotherapy. It accounts for only 2–3% of skin cancers, but its incidence is increasing rapidly (by 3–8% per year in the United States). Melanoma can begin wherever there is pigment. Most such cancers appear spontaneously, and about one-third develop from preexisting moles. It usually appears as a spreading brown to black patch (Figure 5.8c) that metastasizes rapidly to surrounding lymph and blood vessels.

The key to surviving melanoma is early detection. The chance of survival is poor if the lesion is over 4 mm thick. The usual therapy for melanoma is wide surgical excision accompanied by immunotherapy (immunizing the body against its cancer cells).

The American Cancer Society suggests that sun worshippers regularly examine their skin for new moles or pigmented spots and apply the **ABCD rule** for recognizing melanoma. **A. Asymmetry**: The two sides of the pigmented spot or mole do not match. **B. Border irregularity**: The borders of the lesion exhibit indentations. **C. Color**: The pigmented spot contains several colors (blacks, browns, tans, and sometimes blues and reds). **D. Diameter**: The spot is larger than 6 mm in diameter (the size of a pencil eraser). Some experts have found that adding an E, for elevation above the skin surface, improves diagnosis, so they use the ABCD(E) rule.

Burns

Burns are a devastating threat to the body primarily because of their effects on the skin. A **burn** is tissue damage inflicted by intense heat, electricity, radiation, or certain chemicals, all of which denature cell proteins and cause cell death in the affected areas.

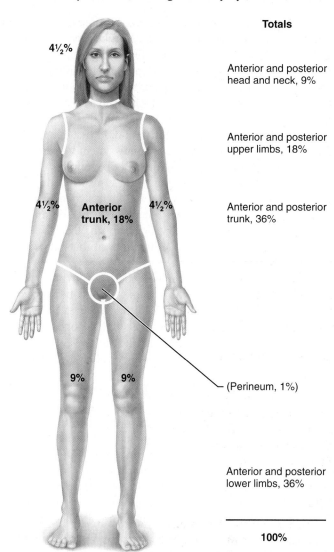

Totals

Anterior and posterior head and neck, 9%

Anterior and posterior upper limbs, 18%

Anterior and posterior trunk, 36%

Anterior and posterior lower limbs, 36%

100%

Figure 5.9 Estimating the extent and severity of burns using the rule of nines. Surface area values for the anterior body surface are indicated on the human figure. Total surface area (anterior and posterior body surfaces) for each body region is indicated to the right of the figure.

The immediate threat to life resulting from severe burns is a catastrophic loss of body fluids containing proteins and electrolytes, resulting in dehydration and electrolyte imbalance. These conditions, in turn, lead to renal shutdown and circulatory shock (inadequate blood circulation due to reduced blood volume). To save the patient, the lost fluids must be replaced immediately via the intravenous (IV) route.

In adults, the volume of fluid lost can be estimated by computing the percentage of body surface burned (extent of the burns) using the **rule of nines**. This method divides the body into 11 areas, each accounting for 9% of total body area, plus an additional area surrounding the genitals accounting for 1% of body surface area (Figure 5.9). This method is only approximate, so special tables are used when greater accuracy is desired.

Burn patients also need thousands of extra food calories daily to replace lost proteins and allow tissue repair. No one can eat enough food to provide these calories, so burn patients are given supplementary nutrients through gastric tubes and IV lines. After the initial crisis has passed, infection becomes the main threat and *sepsis* (widespread bacterial infection) is the leading cause of death in burn victims. Burned skin is sterile for about 24 hours. Thereafter, bacteria, fungi, and other pathogens easily invade areas where the skin barrier is destroyed, and they multiply rapidly in the nutrient-rich environment of dead tissues. Adding to this problem is the fact that the immune system becomes deficient within one to two days after severe burn injury.

Burns are classified according to their severity (depth) as first-, second-, or third-degree burns. In **first-degree burns**, only the epidermis is damaged. Symptoms include localized redness, swelling, and pain. First-degree burns tend to heal in two to three days without special attention. Sunburn is usually a first-degree burn.

Second-degree burns injure the epidermis and the upper region of the dermis. Symptoms mimic those of first-degree burns, but blisters also appear. The burned area is red and painful, but skin regeneration occurs with little or no scarring within three to four weeks if care is taken to prevent infection. First- and second-degree burns are referred to as *partial-thickness burns* (Figure 5.10a).

Third-degree burns are *full-thickness burns*, involving the entire thickness of the skin (Figure 5.10b). The burned area appears gray-white, cherry red, or blackened, and initially there is little or no edema. Since the nerve endings in the area have been destroyed, the burned area is not painful. Although skin regeneration might eventually occur by proliferation of epithelial cells at the edges of the burn or from stem cells in hair follicles, it is usually impossible to wait that long because of fluid loss and infection. For this reason, skin grafting is usually necessary.

To prepare the burned area for grafting, the *eschar* (es′kar), or burned skin, must first be debrided (removed). To prevent infection and fluid loss, the area is then flooded with antibiotics and covered temporarily with a synthetic membrane, animal (pig) skin, cadaver skin, or "living bandage" made from the thin amniotic sac membrane that surrounds a fetus. Then healthy skin is transplanted to the burned site. Unless the graft is taken from the patient (an autograft), however, there is a good chance that it will be rejected by the patient's immune system (see p. 792 in Chapter 21). Even if the graft "takes," extensive scar tissue often forms in the burned areas.

An exciting technique is eliminating many of the traditional problems of skin grafting and rejection. Synthetic skin made of a silicone "epidermis" bound to a spongy "dermal" layer composed of collagen and ground cartilage is applied to the debrided area. In time, the patient's own dermal tissue absorbs and replaces the artificial one. Then the silicone sheet is peeled off and replaced with a network of epidermal cells cultured from the patient's own skin. The artificial skin is not rejected by the body, saves lives, and results in minimal scarring. However, it is more likely to become infected than is an autograft.

In general, burns are considered critical if any of the following conditions exists: (1) over 25% of the body has second-degree burns, (2) over 10% of the body has third-degree burns, or (3) there are third-degree burns of the face, hands, or feet. Facial burns introduce the possibility of burned respiratory pas-

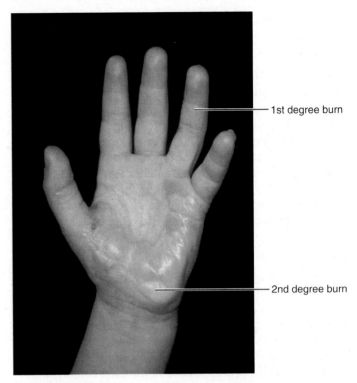

(a) Skin bearing partial thickness burn (1st and 2nd degree burns)

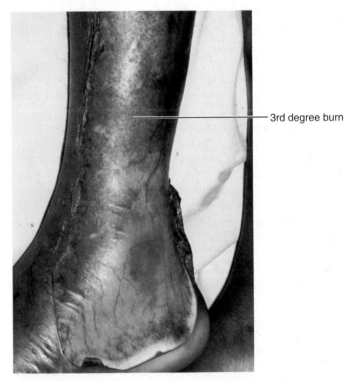

(b) Skin bearing full thickness burn (3rd degree burn)

Figure 5.10 Partial thickness and full thickness burns.

sageways, which can swell and cause suffocation. Burns at joints are also troublesome because scar tissue formation can severely limit joint mobility.

CHECK YOUR UNDERSTANDING

25. Which type of skin cancer develops from the youngest epidermal cells?

26. What name is given to the rule for recognizing the signs of melanoma?

27. The healing of burns and epidermal regeneration is usually uneventful unless the burn is a third-degree burn. What accounts for this difference?

28. Although the anterior head and face represent only a small percentage of the body surface, burns to this area are often much more serious than those to the body trunk. Why?

For answers, see Appendix G.

Developmental Aspects of the Integumentary System

▶ Describe and attempt to explain the causes of changes that occur in the skin from birth to old age.

The epidermis develops from the embryonic ectoderm, and the dermis and hypodermis develop from mesoderm. By the end of the fourth month of development, the skin is fairly well formed. The epidermis has all its strata, dermal papillae are obvious, and rudimentary epidermal derivatives formed by downward projections of cells from the basal layer are present. During the fifth and sixth months, the fetus is covered with a downy coat of delicate colorless hairs called the *lanugo coat* (lah-nu′go; "wool"). This hairy cloak is shed by the seventh month, and vellus hairs make their appearance.

When a baby is born, its skin is covered with *vernix caseosa* (ver′niks kă-se-o′sah; "varnish of cheese"), a white, cheesy-looking substance produced by the sebaceous glands that protects the fetus's skin within the water-filled amnion. The newborn's skin is very thin and often has accumulations in the sebaceous glands on the forehead and nose that appear as small white spots called *milia* (mil′e-ah). These normally disappear by the third week after birth.

During infancy and childhood, the skin thickens, and more subcutaneous fat is deposited. Although we all have approximately the same number of sweat glands, the number that begin to function increases in the first two years after birth and is determined by climate. For this reason, people who grow up in hot climates have more active sweat glands than those raised in cooler areas of the world.

During adolescence, the skin and hair become oilier as sebaceous glands are activated, and acne may appear. Acne generally subsides in early adulthood, and skin reaches its optimal appearance when we reach our 20s and 30s. Thereafter, the skin starts to show the effects of cumulative environmental assaults (abrasion, wind, sun, chemicals). Scaling and various kinds of skin inflammation, or **dermatitis** (der″mah-ti′tis), become more common.

As old age approaches, the rate of epidermal cell replacement slows, the skin thins, and its susceptibility to bruises and other types of injury increases. All of the lubricating substances produced by the skin glands that make young skin so soft start to become deficient. As a result, the skin becomes dry and itchy. However, people with naturally oily skin seem to postpone this dryness until later in life. Elastic fibers clump, and collagen fibers become fewer and stiffer. The subcutaneous fat layer diminishes, leading to the intolerance to cold so common in elderly people. Additionally, declining levels of sex hormones result in similar fat distribution in elderly men and women. The decreasing elasticity of the skin, along with the loss of subcutaneous tissue, inevitably leads to wrinkling. Decreasing numbers of melanocytes and dendritic cells enhance the risk and incidence of skin cancer in this age group. As a rule, redheads and fair-skinned individuals, who have less melanin to begin with, show age-related changes more rapidly than do those with darker skin and hair.

By the age of 50 years, the number of active hair follicles has declined by two-thirds and continues to fall, resulting in hair thinning. Hair loses its luster in old age, and the delayed-action genes responsible for graying and male pattern baldness become active.

Although there is no known way to avoid the aging of the skin, one of the best ways to slow the process is to shield your skin from the sun with protective clothing, and sunscreens or sunblocks with a sun protection factor (SPF) of 15 or higher. Remember, the same sunlight that produces that fashionable tan also causes the sagging, blotchy, wrinkled skin of old age complete with pigmented "liver spots." (It is instructive to note that aged skin that has been protected from the sun has lost some elasticity and is thinned, but it remains unwrinkled and unmarked.) Much of this havoc is due to UVA activation of enzymes called matrix metalloproteinases, which degrade collagen and other dermal components. A drug called tretinoin, related to vitamin A, inhibits these enzymes and is now being used in some skin creams to slow photo-aging. Good nutrition, plenty of fluids, and cleanliness may also delay the process.

CHECK YOUR UNDERSTANDING

29. What is the source of vernix caseosa that covers the skin of the newborn baby?

30. What change in the skin leads to cold intolerance in the elderly?

31. How does UV radiation contribute to wrinkling of the skin?

For answers, see Appendix G.

The skin is only about as thick as a paper towel—not too impressive as organ systems go. Yet, when it is severely damaged, nearly every body system reacts. Metabolism accelerates or may be impaired, immune system changes occur, bones may soften, the cardiovascular system may fail—the list goes on and on. On the other hand, when the skin is intact and performing its functions, the body as a whole benefits. Homeostatic interrelationships between the integumentary system and other organ systems are summarized in *Making Connections* on pp. 166–167.

System Connections

Homeostatic Interrelationships Between the Integumentary System and Other Body Systems

Skeletal System

- Skin protects bones; skin synthesizes a vitamin D precursor needed for normal calcium absorption and deposit of bone (calcium) salts, which make bones hard
- Skeletal system provides support for skin

Muscular System

- Skin protects muscles
- Active muscles generate large amounts of heat, which increases blood flow to the skin and may promote activation of sweat glands of skin

Nervous System

- Skin protects nervous system organs; cutaneous sensory receptors for touch, pressure, pain, and temperature located in skin (see Figure 5.1)
- Nervous system regulates diameter of blood vessels in skin; activates sweat glands, contributing to thermoregulation; interprets cutaneous sensation; activates arrector pili muscles

Endocrine System

- Skin protects endocrine organs; converts some hormones to their active forms; synthesizes a vitamin D precursor
- Androgens produced by the endocrine system activate sebaceous glands and are involved in regulation of hair growth

Cardiovascular System

- Skin protects cardiovascular organs; prevents fluid loss from body; serves as blood reservoir
- Cardiovascular system transports oxygen and nutrients to skin and removes wastes from skin; provides substances needed by skin glands to make their secretions

Lymphatic System/Immunity

- Skin protects lymphatic organs; prevents pathogen invasion; dendritic cells and macrophages help activate the immune system
- Lymphatic system prevents edema by picking up excessive leaked fluid; immune system protects skin cells

Respiratory System

- Skin protects respiratory organs; hairs in nose help filter out dust from inhaled air
- Respiratory system furnishes oxygen to skin cells and removes carbon dioxide via gas exchange with blood

Digestive System

- Skin protects digestive organs; provides vitamin D needed for calcium absorption; performs some of the same chemical conversions as liver cells
- Digestive system provides needed nutrients to the skin

Urinary System

- Skin protects urinary organs; excretes salts and some nitrogenous wastes in sweat
- Urinary system activates vitamin D precursor made by keratinocytes; disposes of nitrogenous wastes of skin metabolism

Reproductive System

- Skin protects reproductive organs; cutaneous receptors respond to erotic stimuli; highly modified sweat glands (mammary glands) produce milk. During pregnancy, skin stretches to accommodate growing fetus; changes in skin pigmentation may occur

5

The Integumentary System and Interrelationships with the Nervous, Cardiovascular, and Lymphatic/Immune Systems

First and foremost, our skin is a barrier. Like the skin of a grape, it keeps its contents juicy and whole. The skin is also a master at self (wound) repair, and interacts intimately with other body systems by making vitamin D (necessary for hard bones) and other potent molecules, all the while protecting deeper tissues from damaging external agents. Perhaps the most crucial roles of the skin in terms of overall body homeostasis are those it plays with the nervous, cardiovascular, and lymphatic systems. These interactions are detailed next.

Nervous System
The whole body benefits from the skin's interaction with the nervous system. The skin houses the tiny sensory receptors that provide a great deal of information about our external environment—its temperature, the pressure exerted by objects, and the presence of dangerous substances. What if we stepped on broken glass or hot pavement but did not have neural monitors in our skin? If we did not actually see, hear, taste, or smell such a damaging event, no reports would be sent to the nervous system. Consequently, the nervous system would be left "in the dark," unable to evaluate the need for a response and to order the steps needed to protect us from further damage or to get first aid.

Nervous and Cardiovascular System
Skin provides the site both for sensing external temperature and for responding to temperature changes. Dermal blood vessels (cardiovascular system organs) and sweat glands (controlled by the nervous system) play crucial roles in thermoregulation. So too do blood and the hot and cold receptors in the skin. When we are chilled, our blood loses heat to internal organs and cools. This loss alerts the nervous system to retain heat by constricting dermal blood vessels. When body and blood temperature rises, dermal vessels dilate and sweating begins.

Thermoregulation is vital: When the body overheats, life-threatening changes occur. Chemical reactions speed up, and as the temperature continues to rise vital proteins are destroyed and cells die. Cold has the opposite effect; cellular activity slows and ultimately stops.

Lymphatic System/Immunity
The role of the skin in immunity is complex. Keratinocytes in the skin manufacture interferons (proteins that block viral infection) and other proteins important to the immune response. Epidermal dendritic cells in the skin interact with antigens (foreign substances) that have penetrated the stratum corneum. The dendritic cells then migrate to lymphatic organs, where they present bits of the antigens to cells that will mount the immune response against them. This "messenger" function alerts the immune system early on to the presence of pathogens in the body.

Even a mild sunburn disrupts the normal immune response because UV radiation disables the skin's presenter cells. This effect may explain why many people infected by the cold sore virus tend to have a cold sore eruption after sun exposure.

Integumentary System

A terrible collision between a trailer truck and a bus has occurred on Route 91. Several of the passengers are rushed to area hospitals for treatment. We will follow a few of these people in clinical case studies that will continue through the book from one organ system to the next.

Case study: Examination of Mrs. DeStephano, a 45-year-old woman, reveals several impairments of homeostasis. Relative to her integumentary system, the following comments are noted on her chart:

- Epidermal abrasions of the right arm and shoulder
- Severe lacerations of the right cheek and temple
- Cyanosis apparent

The lacerated areas are cleaned, sutured, and bandaged by the emergency room (ER) personnel, and Mrs. DeStephano is admitted for further tests.

Relative to her signs:

1. What protective mechanisms are impaired or deficient in the abraded areas?

2. Assuming that bacteria are penetrating the dermis in these areas, what remaining skin defenses might act to prevent further bacterial invasion?

3. What benefit is conferred by suturing the lacerations? (Hint: See Chapter 4, p. 144, Related Clinical Terms, healing by first intention).

4. Mrs. DeStephano's cyanotic skin may hint at what additional problem (and impairment of what body systems or functions)?

(Answers in Appendix G)

RELATED CLINICAL TERMS

Albinism (al′bĭ-nizm; *alb* = white) Inherited condition in which melanocytes do not synthesize melanin owing to a lack of tyrosinase. An albino's skin is pink, the hair pale or white, and the irises of the eyes unpigmented or poorly so.

Boils and carbuncles (kar′bung-klz; "little glowing embers") Inflammation of hair follicles and sebaceous glands in which an infection has spread to the underlying hypodermis; common on the dorsal neck. Carbuncles are composite boils. A common cause is bacterial infection.

Cold sores (fever blisters) Small fluid-filled blisters that itch and smart; usually occur around the lips and in the mucosa of the mouth; caused by a herpes simplex infection. The virus localizes in a cutaneous nerve, where it remains dormant until activated by emotional upset, fever, or UV radiation.

Contact dermatitis Itching, redness, and swelling, progressing to blister formation; caused by exposure of the skin to chemicals (e.g., poison ivy oleoresin) that provoke an allergic response in sensitive individuals.

Decubitus ulcer (de-ku′bĭ-tus) Localized breakdown and ulceration of skin due to interference with its blood supply. Usually occurs over a bony prominence, such as the hip or heel, that is subjected to continuous pressure; also called a bedsore.

Dermatology The branch of medicine that studies and treats disorders of the skin.

Eczema (ek′ze-mah) A skin rash characterized by itching, blistering, oozing, and scaling of the skin. A common allergic reaction in children, but also occurs (typically in a more severe form) in adults. Frequent causes include allergic reactions to certain foods (fish, eggs, and others) or to inhaled dust or pollen. Treated by methods used for other allergic disorders.

Epidermolysis bullosa (EB) A group of hereditary disorders characterized by inadequate or faulty synthesis of keratin, collagen, and/or basement membrane "cement" that results in lack of cohesion between layers of the skin and mucosa; a simple touch causes layers to separate and blister. For this reason, EB victims are called "touch-me-nots." In severe cases fatal blistering occurs in major vital organs. Because the blisters rupture easily, victims suffer frequent infections; treatments are aimed at relieving the symptoms and preventing infection.

Impetigo (im″pĕ-ti′go; *impet* = an attack) Pink, fluid-filled, raised lesions (common around the mouth and nose) that develop a yellow crust and eventually rupture. Caused by staphylococcus infection, it is contagious, and common in school-age children.

Porphyria (por-fer′e-ah; "purple") An inherited condition in which certain enzymes needed to form the heme of hemoglobin of blood are lacking. Without these enzymes, metabolic intermediates of the heme pathway called porphyrins build up, spill into the circulation, and eventually cause lesions throughout the body, especially when exposed to sunlight. The skin becomes lesioned and scarred; fingers, toes, and nose are disfigured; gums degenerate and teeth become prominent; for this reason it's believed to be the basis of folklore about vampires.

Psoriasis (so-ri′ah-sis) A chronic autoimmune condition characterized by raised, reddened epidermal patches covered with silvery scales that itch or burn, crack, and sometimes bleed or become infected. When severe, it may be disfiguring and debilitating. The autoimmune attacks are often triggered by trauma, infection, hormonal changes, and stress. Cortisone-containing topicals may control mild cases. For more severe cases, self-injected drugs called biologicals and/or phototherapy with UV light in conjunction with chemotherapeutic drugs provides some relief.

Rosacea (ro-za′she-ah) A chronic skin eruption produced by dilation of small blood vessels of the face, particularly the nose and cheeks. Papules and acne-like pustules may or may not occur. More common in women, but tends to be more severe when it occurs in men. Cause is unknown, but stress, some endocrine disorders, and anything that produces flushing (hot beverages, alcohol, sunlight, etc.) can aggravate this condition.

Vitiligo (vit″ĭ-li′go; *viti* = a vine, winding) The most prevalent skin pigmentation disorder, characterized by a loss of melanocytes and uneven dispersal of melanin, so that unpigmented skin regions (light spots) are surrounded by normally pigmented areas. An autoimmune disorder.

CHAPTER SUMMARY

The Skin (pp. 149–155)

1. The skin, or integument, is composed of two discrete tissue layers, an outer epidermis and a deeper dermis, resting on subcutaneous tissue, the hypodermis.

Epidermis (pp. 150–152)

2. The epidermis is an avascular, keratinized sheet of stratified squamous epithelium. Most epidermal cells are keratinocytes. Scattered among the keratinocytes in the deepest epidermal layers are melanocytes, epidermal dendritic cells, and tactile cells.

3. From deep to superficial, the strata, or layers of the epidermis, are the basale, spinosum, granulosum, lucidum, and corneum. The stratum lucidum is absent in thin skin. The mitotically active stratum basale is the source of new cells for epidermal growth. The most superficial layers are increasingly keratinized and less viable.

Dermis (pp. 152–153)

4. The dermis, composed mainly of dense, irregular connective tissue, is well supplied with blood vessels, lymphatic vessels, and nerves. Cutaneous receptors, glands, and hair follicles reside within the dermis.

5. The more superficial papillary layer exhibits dermal papillae that protrude into the epidermis above, as well as dermal ridges. Dermal ridges and epidermal ridges together form the friction ridges that produce fingerprints.

6. In the deeper, thicker reticular layer, the connective tissue fibers are much more densely interwoven. Less dense regions between the collagen bundles produce cleavage, or tension, lines in the skin. Points of tight dermal attachment to the hypodermis produce dermal folds, or flexure lines.

Skin Color   (pp. 154–155)

7. Skin color reflects the amount of pigments (melanin and carotene) in the skin and the oxygenation level of hemoglobin in blood.

8. Melanin production is stimulated by exposure to ultraviolet radiation in sunlight. Melanin, produced by melanocytes and transferred to keratinocytes, protects the keratinocyte nuclei from the damaging effects of UV radiation.

9. Skin color is affected by emotional state. Alterations in normal skin color (jaundice, bronzing, erythema, and others) may indicate certain disease states.

Appendages of the Skin   (pp. 155–160)

1. Skin appendages, which derive from the epidermis, include glands (sweat and sebaceous), hairs and hair follicles, and nails.

Sweat (Sudoriferous) Glands   (pp. 155–156)

2. Eccrine (merocrine) sweat glands, with a few exceptions, are distributed over the entire body surface. Their primary function is thermoregulation. They are simple coiled tubular glands that secrete a salt solution containing small amounts of other solutes. Their ducts usually empty to the skin surface via pores.

3. Apocrine sweat glands, which may function as scent glands, are found primarily in the axillary and anogenital areas. Their secretion is similar to eccrine secretion, but it also contains proteins and fatty substances on which bacteria thrive.

Sebaceous (Oil) Glands   (pp. 156–157)

4. Sebaceous glands occur all over the body surface except for the palms and soles. They are simple alveolar glands; their oily holocrine secretion is called sebum. Sebaceous gland ducts usually empty into hair follicles.

5. Sebum lubricates the skin and hair, prevents water loss from the skin, and acts as a bactericidal agent. Sebaceous glands are activated (at puberty) and controlled by androgens.

Hairs and Hair Follicles   (pp. 157–159)

6. A hair, produced by a hair follicle, consists of heavily keratinized cells. A typical hair has a central medulla, a cortex, and an outer cuticle and root and shaft portions. Hair color reflects the amount and kind of melanin present.

7. A hair follicle consists of an inner epithelial root sheath and an outer connective tissue root sheath derived from the dermis. The base of the hair follicle is a hair bulb with a matrix that produces the hair. A hair follicle is richly vascularized and well supplied with nerve fibers. Arrector pili muscles pull the follicles into an upright position and produce goose bumps.

8. Except for hairs of the scalp and around the eyes, hairs formed initially are fine vellus hairs; at puberty, under the influence of androgens, coarser, darker terminal hairs appear in the axillae and the genital region.

9. The rate of hair growth varies in different body regions and with sex and age. Differences in life span of hairs account for differences in length on different body regions. Hair thinning reflects factors that lengthen follicular resting periods, age-related atrophy of hair follicles, and a delayed-action gene.

Nails   (p. 160)

10. A nail is a scalelike modification of the epidermis that covers the dorsum of a finger (or toe) tip. The actively growing region is the nail matrix.

Functions of the Integumentary System   (pp. 160–162)

1. Protection. The skin protects by chemical barriers (the antibacterial nature of sebum, defensins, cathelicidins, the acid mantle, and the UV shield of melanin), physical barriers (the hardened keratinized and lipid-rich surface), and biological barriers (dendritic cells, macrophages, and DNA).

2. Body temperature regulation. The skin vasculature and sweat glands, regulated by the nervous system, play an important role in maintaining body temperature homeostasis.

3. Cutaneous sensation. Cutaneous sensory receptors respond to temperature, touch, pressure, and pain stimuli.

4. Metabolic functions. A vitamin D precursor is synthesized from cholesterol by epidermal cells. Skin cells also play a role in some chemical conversions.

5. Blood reservoir. The extensive vascular supply of the dermis allows the skin to act as a blood reservoir.

6. Excretion. Sweat contains small amounts of nitrogenous wastes and plays a minor role in excretion.

Homeostatic Imbalances of Skin   (pp. 162–165)

1. The most common skin disorders result from infections.

Skin Cancer   (pp. 162–163)

2. The most common cause of skin cancer is exposure to ultraviolet radiation.

3. Basal cell carcinoma and squamous cell carcinoma are cured if they are removed before metastasis. Melanoma, a cancer of melanocytes, is less common but more dangerous.

Burns   (pp. 163–165)

4. In severe burns, the initial threat is loss of protein- and electrolyte-rich body fluids, which may lead to circulatory collapse. The second threat is overwhelming bacterial infection.

5. The extent of a burn may be evaluated by using the rule of nines. The severity of burns is indicated by the terms first degree, second degree, and third degree. Third-degree burns are full-thickness burns that require grafting for successful recovery.

Developmental Aspects of the Integumentary System   (p. 165)

1. The epidermis develops from embryonic ectoderm; the dermis (and hypodermis) develops from mesoderm.

2. The fetus exhibits a downy lanugo coat. Fetal sebaceous glands produce vernix caseosa, which helps protect the fetus's skin from its watery environment.

3. A newborn's skin is thin. During childhood the skin thickens and more subcutaneous fat is deposited. At puberty, sebaceous glands are activated and terminal hairs appear in greater numbers.

4. In old age, the rate of epidermal cell replacement declines and the skin and hair thin. Skin glands become less active. Loss of collagen and elastic fibers and subcutaneous fat leads to wrinkling; delayed-action genes cause graying and balding. Photodamage is a major cause of skin aging.

REVIEW QUESTIONS

Multiple Choice/Matching

(Some questions have more than one correct answer. Select the best answer or answers from the choices given.)

1. Which epidermal cell type is most numerous? (**a**) keratinocyte, (**b**) melanocyte, (**c**) epidermal dendritic cell, (**d**) tactile cell.
2. Which cell functions as part of the immune system? (**a**) a keratinocyte, (**b**) a melanocyte, (**c**) an epidermal dendritic cell, (**d**) a tactile cell.
3. The epidermis provides a physical barrier due largely to the presence of (**a**) melanin, (**b**) carotene, (**c**) collagen, (**d**) keratin.
4. Skin color is determined by (**a**) the amount of blood, (**b**) pigments, (**c**) oxygenation level of the blood, (**d**) all of these.
5. The sensations of touch and pressure are picked up by receptors located in (**a**) the stratum spinosum, (**b**) the dermis, (**c**) the hypodermis, (**d**) the stratum corneum.
6. Which is not a true statement about the papillary layer of the dermis? (**a**) It is largely areolar connective tissue, (**b**) it is most responsible for the toughness of the skin, (**c**) it contains nerve endings that respond to stimuli, (**d**) it is highly vascular.
7. Skin surface markings that reflect points of tight dermal attachment to underlying tissues are called (**a**) tension lines, (**b**) papillary ridges, (**c**) flexure lines, (**d**) dermal papillae.
8. Which of the following is not an epidermal derivative? (**a**) hair, (**b**) sweat gland, (**c**) sensory receptor, (**d**) sebaceous gland.
9. An arrector pili muscle (**a**) is associated with each sweat gland, (**b**) can cause a hair to stand up straight, (**c**) enables each hair to be stretched when wet, (**d**) provides new cells for continued growth of its associated hair.
10. The product of this type of sweat gland includes protein and lipid substances that become odoriferous as a result of bacterial action: (**a**) apocrine gland, (**b**) eccrine gland, (**c**) sebaceous gland, (**d**) pancreatic gland.
11. Sebum (**a**) lubricates the surface of the skin and hair, (**b**) consists of cell fragments and fatty substances, (**c**) in excess may cause seborrhea, (**d**) all of these.
12. The rule of nines is helpful clinically in (**a**) diagnosing skin cancer, (**b**) estimating the extent of a burn, (**c**) estimating how serious a cancer is, (**d**) preventing acne.

Short Answer Essay Questions

13. Which epidermal cells are also called prickle cells? Which contain keratohyaline and lamellated granules?
14. Is a bald man really hairless? Explain.
15. You go to the beach to swim on an extremely hot, sunny summer afternoon. Describe two ways in which your integumentary system acts to preserve homeostasis during your outing.
16. Distinguish clearly between first-, second-, and third-degree burns.
17. Describe the process of hair formation, and list several factors that may influence (**a**) growth cycles and (**b**) hair texture.
18. What is cyanosis and what does it reflect?
19. Why does skin wrinkle and what factors accelerate the wrinkling process?

20. Explain each of these familiar phenomena in terms of what you learned in this chapter: (**a**) pimples, (**b**) dandruff, (**c**) greasy hair and "shiny nose," (**d**) stretch marks from gaining weight, (**e**) freckles.
21. Count Dracula, the most famous vampire, rumored to have killed at least 200,000 people, was based on a real person who lived in eastern Europe about 600 years ago. He was indeed a "monster," although he was not a real vampire. The historical Count Dracula may have suffered from which of the following? (**a**) porphyria, (**b**) EB, (**c**) halitosis, (**d**) vitiligo. Explain your answer.
22. Why are there no skin cancers that originate from stratum corneum cells?
23. A man got his finger caught in a machine at the factory. The damage was less serious than expected, but the entire nail was torn off his right index finger. The parts lost were the body, root, bed, matrix, and eponychium of the nail. First, define each of these parts. Then, tell if this nail is likely to grow back.
24. On an outline diagram of the human body, mark off various regions according to the rule of nines. What percentage of the total body surface is affected if the skin over the following body parts is burned? (**a**) the entire posterior trunk and buttocks, (**b**) an entire lower limb, (**c**) the entire front of the left upper limb.
25. A common belief is that having your hair cut makes it become thicker. Explain why this belief is not true.

 Critical Thinking and Clinical Application Questions

1. Dean, a 40-year-old aging beach boy, is complaining to you that although his suntan made him popular when he was young, now his face is all wrinkled, and he has several darkly pigmented moles that are growing rapidly and are as big as large coins. He shows you the moles, and immediately you think "ABCD." What does that mean and why should he be concerned?
2. Victims of third-degree burns demonstrate the loss of vital functions performed by the skin. What are the two most important problems encountered clinically with such patients? Explain each in terms of the absence of skin.
3. Thelma, a 30-year-old resident of a mental hospital, has an abnormal growth of hair on the dorsum of her right index finger. The orderly comments that she gnaws on that finger continuously. What do you think is the relationship between Thelma's gnawing activity and her hairy finger?
4. A model is concerned about a new scar on her abdomen. She tells her surgeon that there is practically no scar from the appendix operation done when she was 16, but this new gallbladder scar is "gross." Her appendectomy scar is small and obliquely located on the inferior abdominal surface—it is very indistinct. By contrast, the gallbladder scar is large and lumpy and runs at right angles to the central axis of the body trunk. Can you explain why the scars are so different?

5. Osteomalacia, a condition of soft bones, is prevalent in Muslim countries that decree that their women wear the burka, a garment that covers all but their eyes. What is the cause and effect here?

6. Mrs. Gaucher received second-degree burns on her abdomen when she dropped a kettle of boiling water. She asked her doctor (worriedly) if she would need to have a skin graft. What do you think he told her?

Access everything you need to practice, review, and self-assess for both your A&P lecture and lab courses at **myA&P** (www.myaandp.com). There, you'll find powerful online resources, including chapter quizzes and tests, games, A&P Flix animations with quizzes, *Interactive Physiology*® with quizzes, MP3 Tutor Sessions, Practice Anatomy Lab™, and more to help you get a better grade in your course.

6

Skeletal Cartilages (p. 173)

Basic Structure, Types, and Locations (p. 173)

Growth of Cartilage (p. 173)

Classification of Bones (pp. 173–175)

Functions of Bones (pp. 175–176)

Bone Structure (pp. 176–182)

Gross Anatomy (pp. 177–179)

Microscopic Anatomy of Bone (pp. 179–180)

Chemical Composition of Bone (pp. 180–182)

Bone Development (pp. 182–185)

Formation of the Bony Skeleton (pp. 182–184)

Postnatal Bone Growth (pp. 184–185)

Bone Homeostasis: Remodeling and Repair (pp. 185–189)

Bone Remodeling (pp. 185–188)

Bone Repair (pp. 188–189)

Homeostatic Imbalances of Bone (pp. 189–191, 194)

Osteomalacia and Rickets (p. 189)

Osteoporosis (pp. 189–191)

Paget's Disease (pp. 191, 194)

Developmental Aspects of Bones: Timing of Events (p. 194)

Bones and Skeletal Tissues

All of us have heard the expressions "bone tired" and "bag of bones"—rather unflattering and inaccurate images of one of our most phenomenal tissues and our main skeletal elements. Our brains, not our bones, convey feelings of fatigue. As for "bag of bones," they are indeed more prominent in some of us, but without bones to form our internal skeleton we would all creep along the ground like slugs, lacking any definite shape or form. Along with its bones, the skeleton contains resilient cartilages, which we briefly discuss in this chapter. However, our major focus is the structure and function of bone tissue and the dynamics of its formation and remodeling throughout life.

Skeletal Cartilages

▶ Describe the functional properties of the three types of cartilage tissue.

▶ Locate the major cartilages of the adult skeleton.

▶ Explain how cartilage grows.

The human skeleton is initially made up of cartilages and fibrous membranes, but most of these early supports are soon replaced by bone. The few cartilages that remain in adults are found mainly in regions where flexible skeletal tissue is needed.

Basic Structure, Types, and Locations

A **skeletal cartilage** is made of some variety of *cartilage tissue*, which consists primarily of water. The high water content of cartilage accounts for its resilience, that is, its ability to spring back to its original shape after being compressed.

The cartilage, which contains no nerves or blood vessels, is surrounded by a layer of dense irregular connective tissue, the *perichondrium* (per″ĭ-kon′dre-um; "around the cartilage"). The perichondrium acts like a girdle to resist outward expansion when the cartilage is compressed. Additionally, the perichondrium contains the blood vessels from which nutrients diffuse through the matrix to reach the cartilage cells. This mode of nutrient delivery limits cartilage thickness.

As we described in Chapter 4, there are three types of cartilage tissue in the body: hyaline, elastic, and fibrocartilage. All three types have the same basic components—cells called *chondrocytes*, encased in small cavities (lacunae) within an *extracellular matrix* containing a jellylike ground substance and fibers. The skeletal cartilages contain representatives from all three types.

Hyaline cartilages, which look like frosted glass when freshly exposed, provide support with flexibility and resilience. They are the most abundant skeletal cartilages. When viewed under the microscope, their chondrocytes appear spherical (see Figure 4.8g). The only fiber type in their matrix is fine collagen fibers (which, however, are not detectable microscopically). Colored blue in **Figure 6.1**, skeletal hyaline cartilages include (1) *articular cartilages*, which cover the ends of most bones at movable joints; (2) *costal cartilages*, which connect the ribs to the sternum (breastbone); (3) *respiratory cartilages*, which form the skeleton of the *larynx* (*voicebox*) and reinforce other respiratory passageways; and (4) *nasal cartilages*, which support the external nose.

Elastic cartilages look very much like hyaline cartilages (see Figure 4.8h), but they contain more stretchy elastic fibers and so are better able to stand up to repeated bending. They are found in only two skeletal locations, shown in green in Figure 6.1—the external ear and the epiglottis (the flap that bends to cover the opening of the larynx each time we swallow).

Fibrocartilages are highly compressible and have great tensile strength. The perfect intermediate between hyaline and elastic cartilages, fibrocartilages consist of roughly parallel rows of chondrocytes alternating with thick collagen fibers (see Figure 4.8i). Fibrocartilages occur in sites that are subjected to both heavy pressure and stretch, such as the padlike cartilages (menisci) of the knee and the discs between vertebrae, colored red in Figure 6.1.

Growth of Cartilage

Unlike bone, which has a hard matrix, cartilage has a flexible matrix which can accommodate mitosis. It is the ideal tissue to use to lay down the embryonic skeleton and to provide for new skeletal growth. Cartilage grows in two ways. In **appositional growth** (ap″o-zish′un-al; "growth from outside"), cartilage-forming cells in the surrounding perichondrium secrete new matrix against the external face of the existing cartilage tissue. In **interstitial growth** (in″ter-stish′al; "growth from inside"), the lacunae-bound chondrocytes divide and secrete new matrix, expanding the cartilage from within. Typically, cartilage growth ends during adolescence when the skeleton stops growing.

Under certain conditions—during normal bone growth in youth and during old age—calcium salts may be deposited in the matrix and cause it to harden, a process called calcification. Note, however, that calcified cartilage is not bone; cartilage and bone are always distinct tissues.

CHECK YOUR UNDERSTANDING

1. Which type of cartilage is most plentiful in the adult body?

2. What two body structures contain flexible elastic cartilage?

3. Cartilage grows by interstitial growth. What does this mean?

For answers, see Appendix G.

Classification of Bones

▶ Name the major regions of the skeleton and describe their relative functions.

▶ Compare and contrast the structure of the four bone classes and provide examples of each class.

The 206 named bones of the human skeleton are divided into two groups: axial and appendicular. The **axial skeleton** forms the long axis of the body and includes the bones of the skull, vertebral column, and rib cage, shown in orange in Figure 6.1. Generally speaking these bones are most involved in protecting, supporting, or carrying other body parts.

The **appendicular skeleton** (ap″en-dik′u-lar) consists of the bones of the upper and lower limbs and the girdles (shoulder bones and hip bones) that attach the limbs to the axial skeleton. These bones are colored gold in Figure 6.1. Bones of the limbs help us to get from place to place (locomotion) and to manipulate our environment.

Bones come in many sizes and shapes. For example, the pisiform bone of the wrist is the size and shape of a pea, whereas the femur (thigh bone) is nearly 2 feet long in some people and has a large, ball-shaped head. The unique shape of each bone fulfills a particular need. The femur, for example, withstands great weight and pressure, and its hollow-cylinder design provides maximum strength with minimum weight.

6

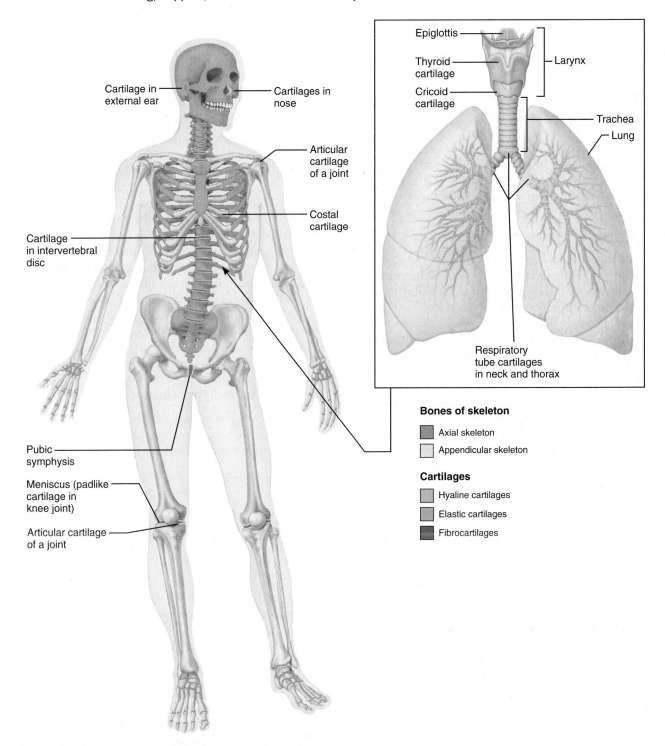

Figure 6.1 The bones and cartilages of the human skeleton. The cartilages that support the respiratory tubes and larynx are drawn separately at the right.

For the most part, bones are classified by their shape as long, short, flat, and irregular (Figure 6.2).

1. **Long bones**, as their name suggests, are considerably longer than they are wide (Figure 6.2a). A long bone has a shaft plus two ends. All limb bones except the patella (kneecap) and the wrist and ankle bones are long bones. Notice that these bones are named for their elongated

shape, *not* their overall size. The three bones in each of your fingers are long bones, even though they are very small.

2. **Short bones** are roughly cube shaped. The bones of the wrist and ankle are examples (Figure 6.2d).

   Sesamoid bones (ses′ah-moid; "shaped like a sesame seed") are a special type of short bone that form in a tendon (for example, the patella). They vary in size and number in different individuals. Some sesamoid bones clearly act to

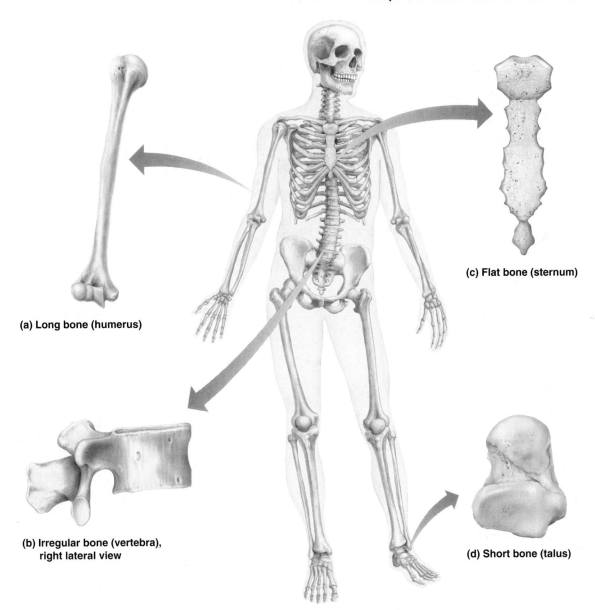

(a) Long bone (humerus)

(b) Irregular bone (vertebra), right lateral view

(c) Flat bone (sternum)

(d) Short bone (talus)

6

Figure 6.2 Classification of bones on the basis of shape.

alter the direction of pull of a tendon. The function of others is not known.

3. **Flat bones** are thin, flattened, and usually a bit curved. The sternum (breastbone), scapulae (shoulder blades), ribs, and most skull bones are flat bones (Figure 6.2c).

4. **Irregular bones** have complicated shapes that fit none of the preceding classes. Examples include the vertebrae and the hip bones (Figure 6.2b).

CHECK YOUR UNDERSTANDING

4. What are the components of the axial skeleton?
5. Contrast the general function of the axial skeleton to that of the appendicular skeleton.
6. What bone class do the ribs and skull bones fall into?

For answers, see Appendix G.

Functions of Bones

▶ List and describe five important functions of bones.

Besides contributing to body shape and form, our bones perform several other important functions:

1. **Support.** Bones provide a framework that supports the body and cradles its soft organs. For example, bones of lower limbs act as pillars to support the body trunk when we stand, and the rib cage supports the thoracic wall.

2. **Protection.** The fused bones of the skull protect the brain. The vertebrae surround the spinal cord, and the rib cage helps protect the vital organs of the thorax.

3. **Movement.** Skeletal muscles, which attach to bones by tendons, use bones as levers to move the body and its parts. As a result, we can walk, grasp objects, and breathe. The design of joints determines the types of movement possible.

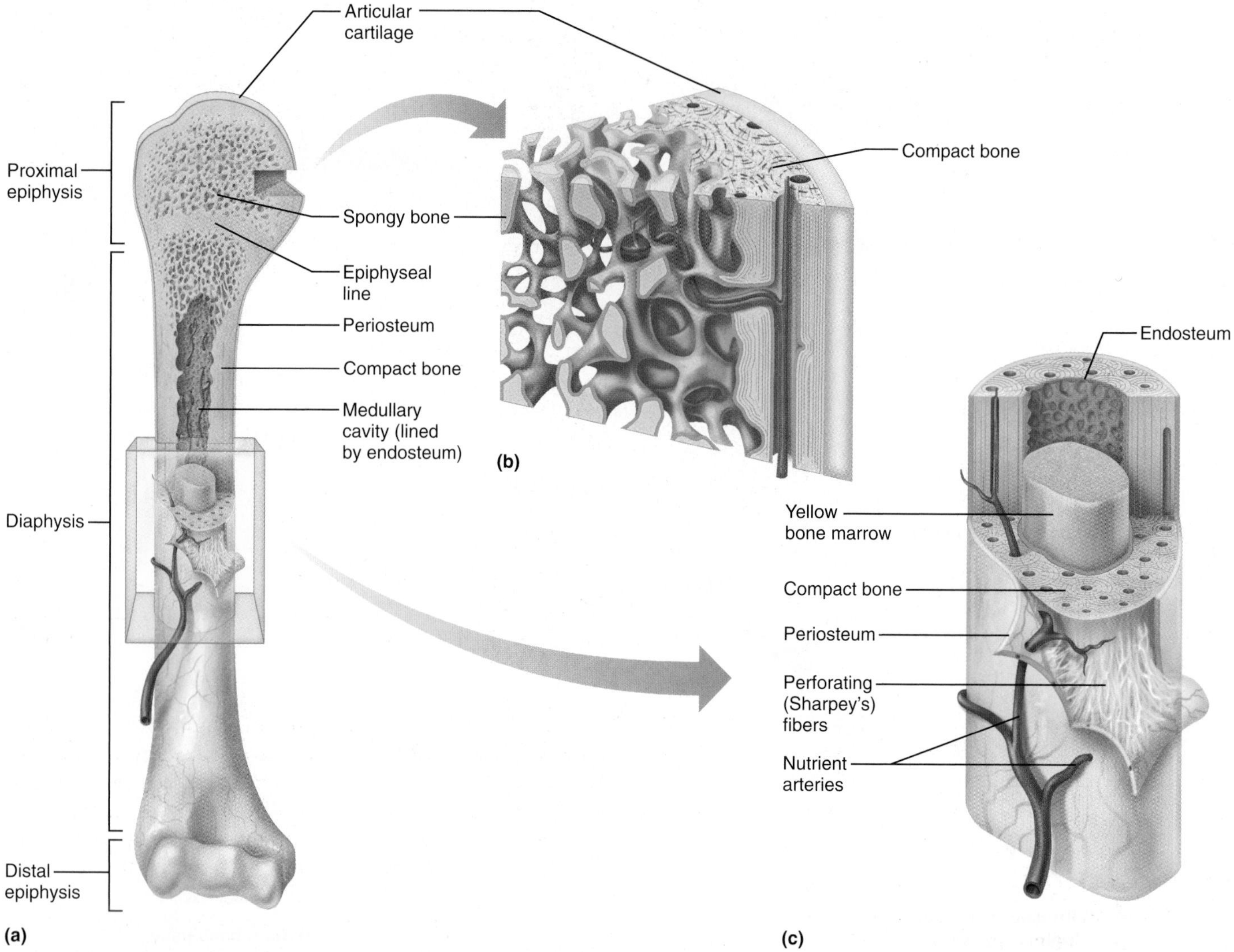

Figure 6.3 **The structure of a long bone (humerus of arm). (a)** Anterior view with bone sectioned frontally to show the interior at the proximal end. **(b)** Enlarged view of spongy bone and compact bone of the epiphysis of (a). (See *A Brief Atlas of the Human Body*, Plates 20 and 21.) **(c)** Enlarged cross-sectional view of the shaft (diaphysis) of (a). Note that the external surface of the diaphysis is covered by periosteum, but the articular surface of the epiphysis is covered with hyaline cartilage.

4. **Mineral and growth factor storage.** Bone is a reservoir for minerals, most importantly calcium and phosphate. The stored minerals are released into the bloodstream as needed for distribution to all parts of the body. Indeed, "deposits" and "withdrawals" of minerals to and from the bones go on almost continuously. Additionally, mineralized bone matrix stores important growth factors such as insulin-like growth factors, transforming growth factor, bone morphogenic proteins, and others.

5. **Blood cell formation.** Most blood cell formation, or **hematopoiesis** (hem"ah-to-poi-e'sis), occurs in the marrow cavities of certain bones.

6. **Triglyceride (fat) storage.** Fat is stored in bone cavities and represents a source of stored energy for the body.

CHECK YOUR UNDERSTANDING

7. What is the functional relationship between skeletal muscles and bones?

8. What two types of substances are stored in bone matrix?
9. What are two functions of a bone's marrow cavities?

For answers, see Appendix G.

Bone Structure

▶ Indicate the functional importance of bone markings.

▶ Describe the gross anatomy of a typical long bone and a flat bone. Indicate the locations and functions of red and yellow marrow, articular cartilage, periosteum, and endosteum.

▶ Describe the histology of compact and spongy bone.

▶ Discuss the chemical composition of bone and the advantages conferred by the organic and inorganic components.

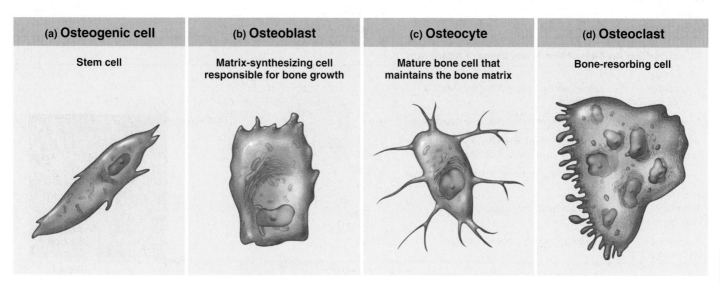

(a) **Osteogenic cell**	(b) **Osteoblast**	(c) **Osteocyte**	(d) **Osteoclast**
Stem cell	Matrix-synthesizing cell responsible for bone growth	Mature bone cell that maintains the bone matrix	Bone-resorbing cell

Figure 6.4 Comparison of different types of bone cells.

Because they contain various types of tissue, bones are *organs*. (Recall that an organ contains several different tissues.) Although bone (osseous) tissue dominates bones, they also contain nervous tissue in their nerves, cartilage in their articular cartilages, fibrous connective tissue lining their cavities, and muscle and epithelial tissues in their blood vessels. We will consider bone structure at three levels: gross, microscopic, and chemical.

Gross Anatomy

Bone Markings

The external surfaces of bones are rarely smooth and featureless. Instead, they display projections, depressions, and openings that serve as sites of muscle, ligament, and tendon attachment, as joint surfaces, or as conduits for blood vessels and nerves. These **bone markings** are named in different ways.

Projections (bulges) that grow outward from the bone surface include heads, trochanters, spines, and others. Each has distinguishing features and functions. In most cases, bone projections are indications of the stresses created by muscles attached to and pulling on them or are modified surfaces where bones meet and form joints.

Depressions and openings include fossae, sinuses, foramina, and grooves. They usually serve to allow passage of nerves and blood vessels. The most important types of bone markings are described in **Table 6.1**. You should familiarize yourself with these terms because you will meet them again as identifying marks of the individual bones studied in the lab.

Bone Textures: Compact and Spongy Bone

Every bone has a dense outer layer that looks smooth and solid to the naked eye. This external layer is **compact bone** (Figures 6.3 and 6.5). Internal to this is **spongy bone** (also called *cancellous bone*), a honeycomb of small needle-like or flat pieces called **trabeculae** (trah-bek′u-le; "little beams"). In living bones the open spaces between trabeculae are filled with red or yellow bone marrow.

Structure of a Typical Long Bone

With few exceptions, all long bones have the same general structure, which includes a shaft, bone ends, and membranes (Figure 6.3).

Diaphysis   A tubular **diaphysis** (di-af′ĭ-sis; *dia* = through, *physis* = growth), or shaft, forms the long axis of the bone. It is constructed of a relatively thick *collar* of compact bone that surrounds a central **medullary cavity** (med′u-lar-e; "middle"), or *marrow cavity*. In adults, the medullary cavity contains fat (yellow marrow) and is called the **yellow marrow cavity**.

Epiphyses   The **epiphyses** (e-pif′ĭ-sēz; singular: epiphysis) are the bone ends (*epi* = upon). In many cases, they are more expanded than the diaphysis. Compact bone forms the exterior of epiphyses, and their interior contains spongy bone. The joint surface of each epiphysis is covered with a thin layer of articular (hyaline) cartilage, which cushions the opposing bone ends during joint movement and absorbs stress. Between the diaphysis and each epiphysis of an adult long bone is an **epiphyseal line**, a remnant of the **epiphyseal plate**, a disc of hyaline cartilage that grows during childhood to lengthen the bone. The region where the diaphysis and epiphysis meet, whether it is the epiphyseal plate or line, is sometimes called the *metaphysis*.

Membranes   A third structural feature of long bones is membranes. The external surface of the entire bone except the joint surfaces is covered by a glistening white, double-layered membrane called the **periosteum** (per″e-os′te-um; *peri* = around, *osteo* = bone). The outer *fibrous layer* is dense irregular connective tissue. The inner *osteogenic layer*, abutting the bone surface, consists primarily of bone-forming cells, called **osteoblasts** (os′te-o-blasts; "bone germinators"), which secrete bone matrix elements, and bone-destroying cells, called **osteoclasts** ("bone breakers"). In addition, there are primitive stem cells, **osteogenic cells**, that give rise to the osteoblasts (Figure 6.4).

TABLE 6.1 Bone Markings

NAME OF BONE MARKING	DESCRIPTION	ILLUSTRATIONS
Projections That Are Sites of Muscle and Ligament Attachment		
Tuberosity (too″bĕ-ros′ĭ-te)	Large rounded projection; may be roughened	
Crest	Narrow ridge of bone; usually prominent	
Trochanter (tro-kan′ter)	Very large, blunt, irregularly shaped process (the only examples are on the femur)	
Line	Narrow ridge of bone; less prominent than a crest	
Tubercle (too′ber-kl)	Small rounded projection or process	
Epicondyle (ep″ĭ-kon′dīl)	Raised area on or above a condyle	
Spine	Sharp, slender, often pointed projection	
Process	Any bony prominence	

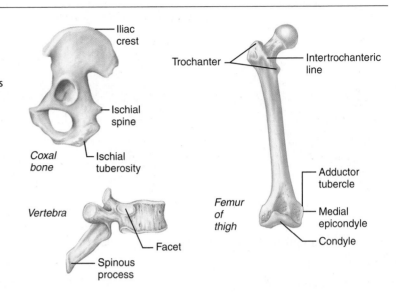

Projections That Help to Form Joints		
Head	Bony expansion carried on a narrow neck	
Facet	Smooth, nearly flat articular surface	
Condyle (kon′dīl)	Rounded articular projection	
Ramus (ra′mus)	Armlike bar of bone	

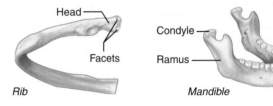

Depressions and Openings		
For Passage of Blood Vessels and Nerves		
Groove	Furrow	
Fissure	Narrow, slitlike opening	
Foramen (fo-ra′men)	Round or oval opening through a bone	
Notch	Indentation at the edge of a structure	
Others		
Meatus (me-a′tus)	Canal-like passageway	
Sinus	Cavity within a bone, filled with air and lined with mucous membrane	
Fossa (fos′ah)	Shallow, basinlike depression in a bone, often serving as an articular surface	

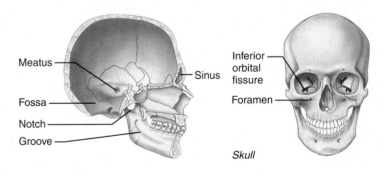

The periosteum is richly supplied with nerve fibers, lymphatic vessels, and blood vessels, which enter the diaphysis via **nutrient foramina** (fo-ra″me-nah; "openings").

The periosteum is secured to the underlying bone by *perforating (Sharpey's) fibers* (Figure 6.3), tufts of collagen fibers that extend from its fibrous layer into the bone matrix. The periosteum also provides anchoring points for tendons and ligaments. At these points the perforating fibers are exceptionally dense.

Internal bone surfaces are covered with a delicate connective tissue membrane called the **endosteum** (en-dos′te-um; "within the bone") (Figure 6.3). The endosteum covers the trabeculae of spongy bone and lines the canals that pass through the compact bone. Like the periosteum, the endosteum contains both bone-forming and bone-destroying cells.

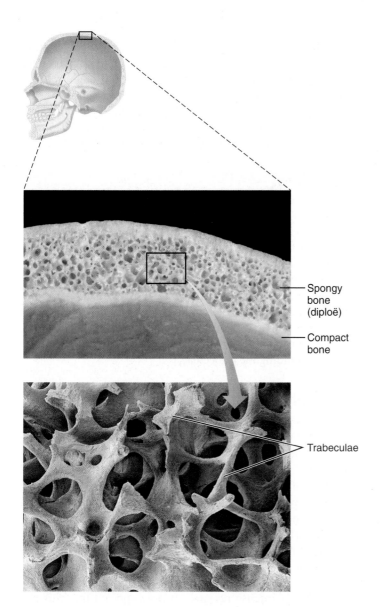

referred to as **red marrow cavities**. In newborn infants, the medullary cavity of the diaphysis and all areas of spongy bone contain red bone marrow. In most adult long bones, the fat-containing medullary cavity extends well into the epiphysis, and little red marrow is present in the spongy bone cavities. For this reason, blood cell production in adult long bones routinely occurs only in the heads of the femur and humerus (the long bone of the arm).

The red marrow found in the diploë of flat bones (such as the sternum) and in some irregular bones (such as the hip bone) is much more active in hematopoiesis, and these sites are routinely used for obtaining red marrow samples when problems with the blood-forming tissue are suspected. However, yellow marrow in the medullary cavity can revert to red marrow if a person becomes very anemic and needs enhanced red blood cell production.

Microscopic Anatomy of Bone

Essentially, four major cell types populate bone tissue: osteogenic cells, osteoblasts, osteocytes, and osteoclasts. These, like other connective tissue cells, are surrounded by an extracellular matrix of their making. The *osteogenic cells,* also called *osteoprogenitor cells*, are mitotically active stem cells found in the membranous periosteum and endosteum. Some of their progeny differentiate into **osteoblasts** (bone-forming cells) while others persist as bone stem cells to provide osteoblasts in the future. We describe the structure and function of the remaining two types of bone cells below.

Compact Bone

Although compact bone looks dense and solid, a microscope reveals that it is riddled with passageways that serve as conduits for nerves, blood vessels, and lymphatic vessels (see Figure 6.7). The structural unit of compact bone is called either the **osteon** (os′te-on) or the **Haversian system** (ha-ver′zhen). Each osteon is an elongated cylinder oriented parallel to the long axis of the bone. Functionally, osteons are tiny weight-bearing pillars.

As shown in the "exploded" view in **Figure 6.6**, an osteon is a group of hollow tubes of bone matrix, one placed outside the next like the growth rings of a tree trunk. Each matrix tube is a **lamella** (lah-mel′ah; "little plate"), and for this reason compact bone is often called **lamellar bone**. Although all of the collagen fibers in a particular lamella run in a single direction, the collagen fibers in adjacent lamellae always run in different directions. This alternating pattern is beautifully designed to withstand torsion stresses—the adjacent lamellae reinforce one another to resist twisting. You can think of the osteon's design as a "twister resister." Collagen fibers are not the only part of bone lamellae that are beautifully ordered. The tiny crystals of bone salts align with the collagen fibers and thus also alternate their direction in adjacent lamellae.

Running through the core of each osteon is the **central canal**, or **Haversian canal**, containing small blood vessels and nerve fibers that serve the needs of the osteon's cells. Canals of a sec-

Figure 6.5 Flat bones consist of a layer of spongy bone sandwiched between two thin layers of compact bone. (Photomicrograph at bottom, 25×.)

Structure of Short, Irregular, and Flat Bones

Short, irregular, and flat bones share a simple design: They all consist of thin plates of periosteum-covered compact bone on the outside and endosteum-covered spongy bone within. However, these bones are not cylindrical and so they have no shaft or epiphyses. They contain bone marrow (between their trabeculae), but no significant marrow cavity is present.

Figure 6.5 shows a typical flat bone of the skull. In flat bones, the spongy bone is called the **diploë** (dip′lo-e; "folded") and the whole arrangement resembles a stiffened sandwich.

Location of Hematopoietic Tissue in Bones

Hematopoietic tissue, **red marrow**, is typically found within the trabecular cavities of spongy bone of long bones and in the diploë of flat bones. For this reason, both these cavities are often

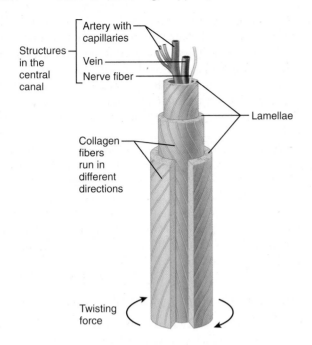

Figure 6.6 A single osteon. The osteon is drawn as if pulled out like a telescope to illustrate the individual lamellae.

ond type called **perforating canals,** or **Volkmann's canals** (folk'mahnz), lie at right angles to the long axis of the bone and connect the blood and nerve supply of the periosteum to those in the central canals and the medullary cavity **(Figure 6.7a)**. Like all other internal bone cavities, these canals are lined with endosteum.

Spider-shaped **osteocytes** (Figures 6.4c and 6.7b) occupy **lacunae** (*lac* = hollow; *una* = little) at the junctions of the lamellae. Hairlike canals called **canaliculi** (kan"ah-lik'u-li) connect the lacunae to each other and to the central canal. The manner in which canaliculi are formed is interesting. When bone is being formed, the osteoblasts secreting bone matrix surround blood vessels and maintain contact with one another by tentacle-like projections containing gap junctions. Then, as the newly secreted matrix hardens and the maturing cells become trapped within it, a system of tiny canals—the canaliculi, filled with tissue fluid and containing the osteocyte extensions—is formed. The canaliculi tie all the osteocytes in an osteon together, permitting nutrients and wastes to be relayed from one osteocyte to the next throughout the osteon. Although bone matrix is hard and impermeable to nutrients, its canaliculi and cell-to-cell relays (via gap junctions) allow bone cells to be well nourished.

One function of osteocytes is to maintain the bone matrix. If they die, the surrounding matrix is resorbed. The osteocytes also act as stress or strain "sensors" in cases of bone deformation or other damaging stimuli. They communicate this information to the cells responsible for bone remodeling (osteoblasts and osteoclasts) so that countermeasures can be taken or repairs made. We discuss the bone-destroying *osteoclast* on p. 186 in conjunction with the topic of bone remodeling.

Not all the lamellae in compact bone are part of osteons. Lying between intact osteons are incomplete lamellae called

interstitial lamellae (in"ter-stish'al) (Figure 6.7c, right photomicrograph). They either fill the gaps between forming osteons or are remnants of osteons that have been cut through by bone remodeling (discussed later). **Circumferential lamellae,** located just deep to the periosteum and just superficial to the endosteum, extend around the entire circumference of the diaphysis (Figure 6.7a) and effectively resist twisting of the long bone.

Spongy Bone

In contrast to compact bone, spongy bone looks like a poorly organized, even haphazard, tissue (see Figure 6.5 and Figure 6.3b). However, the trabeculae in spongy bone align precisely along lines of stress and help the bone resist stress as much as possible. These tiny bone struts are as carefully positioned as the flying buttresses that help to support a Gothic cathedral.

Only a few cells thick, trabeculae contain irregularly arranged lamellae and osteocytes interconnected by canaliculi. No osteons are present. Nutrients reach the osteocytes of spongy bone by diffusing through the canaliculi from capillaries in the endosteum surrounding the trabeculae.

Chemical Composition of Bone

Bone has both organic and inorganic components. Its *organic components* include the cells (osteogenic cells, osteoblasts, osteocytes, and osteoclasts) and **osteoid** (os'te-oid), the organic part of the matrix. Osteoid, which makes up approximately one-third of the matrix, includes ground substance (composed of proteoglycans and glycoproteins) and collagen fibers, both of which are made and secreted by osteoblasts. These organic substances, particularly collagen, contribute not only to a bone's structure but also to the flexibility and great tensile strength that allow the bone to resist stretch and twisting.

Bone's exceptional toughness and tensile strength has been the subject of intense research. It now appears that this resilience comes from the presence of *sacrificial bonds* in or between collagen molecules. These bonds break easily on impact, dissipating energy to prevent the force from rising to a fracture value. In the absence of continued or additional trauma, most of the sacrificial bonds re-form.

The balance of bone tissue (65% by mass) consists of inorganic *hydroxyapatites* (hi-drok"se-ap'ah-tītz), or *mineral salts*, largely calcium phosphates present in the form of tiny, tightly packed, needle-like crystals in and around the collagen fibers in the extracellular matrix. The crystals account for the most notable characteristic of bone—its exceptional hardness, which allows it to resist compression.

The proper combination of organic and inorganic matrix elements allows bones to be exceedingly durable and strong without being brittle. Healthy bone is half as strong as steel in resisting compression and fully as strong as steel in resisting tension.

Because of the salts they contain, bones last long after death and provide an enduring "monument." In fact, skeletal remains many centuries old have revealed the shapes and sizes of ancient peoples, the kinds of work they did, and many of the ailments they suffered, such as arthritis.

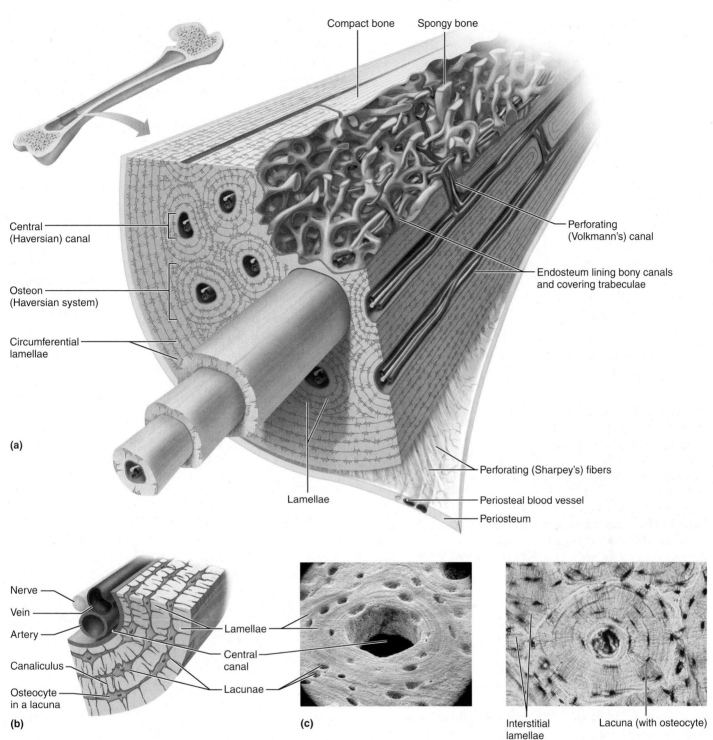

Compact bone

Spongy bone

Central (Haversian) canal

Osteon (Haversian system)

Circumferential lamellae

Perforating (Volkmann's) canal

Endosteum lining bony canals and covering trabeculae

Lamellae

Perforating (Sharpey's) fibers

Periosteal blood vessel

Periosteum

(a)

Nerve

Vein

Artery

Canaliculus

Osteocyte in a lacuna

Lamellae

Central canal

Lacunae

(b)

(c)

Interstitial lamellae

Lacuna (with osteocyte)

Figure 6.7 Microscopic anatomy of compact bone. (a) Diagrammatic view of a pie-shaped segment of compact bone. **(b)** Close-up of a portion of one osteon. Note the position of osteocytes in the lacunae. **(c)** SEM (left) of cross-sectional view of an osteon (180×). Light photomicrographs (right) of a cross-sectional view of an osteon (160×).

SOURCE: (c, left) Kessel and Kardon/Visuals Unlimited.

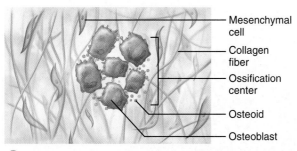

① **Ossification centers appear in the fibrous connective tissue membrane.**
• Selected centrally located mesenchymal cells cluster and differentiate into osteoblasts, forming an ossification center.

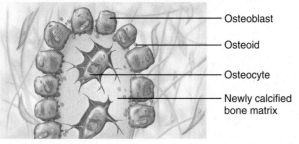

② **Bone matrix (osteoid) is secreted within the fibrous membrane and calcifies.**
• Osteoblasts begin to secrete osteoid, which is calcified within a few days.
• Trapped osteoblasts become osteocytes.

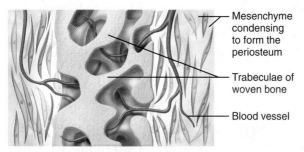

③ **Woven bone and periosteum form.**
• Accumulating osteoid is laid down between embryonic blood vessels in a random manner. The result is a network (instead of lamellae) of trabeculae called woven bone.
• Vascularized mesenchyme condenses on the external face of the woven bone and becomes the periosteum.

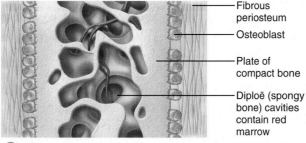

④ **Lamellar bone replaces woven bone, just deep to the periosteum. Red marrow appears.**
• Trabeculae just deep to the periosteum thicken, and are later replaced with mature lamellar bone, forming compact bone plates.
• Spongy bone (diploë), consisting of distinct trabeculae, persists internally and its vascular tissue becomes red marrow.

CHECK YOUR UNDERSTANDING

10. Are crests, tubercles, and spines bony projections or concavities?
11. How does the structure of compact bone differ from that of spongy bone when viewed with the naked eye?
12. What membrane lines the internal canals and covers the trabeculae of a bone?
13. Which component of bone—organic or inorganic—makes it hard?
14. What name is given to a cell that has a ruffled border and acts to break down bone matrix?

For answers, see Appendix G.

Bone Development

▶ Compare and contrast intramembranous ossification and endochondral ossification.

▶ Describe the process of long bone growth that occurs at the epiphyseal plates.

Ossification and **osteogenesis** (os″te-o-jen′ĕ-sis) are synonyms meaning the process of bone formation (*os* = bone, *genesis* = beginning). In embryos this process leads to the *formation of the bony skeleton*. Later another form of ossification known as *bone growth* goes on until early adulthood as the body continues to increase in size. Bones are capable of growing in thickness throughout life. However, ossification in adults serves mainly for bone *remodeling* and repair.

Formation of the Bony Skeleton

Before week 8, the skeleton of a human embryo is constructed entirely from fibrous membranes and hyaline cartilage. Bone tissue begins to develop at about this time and eventually replaces most of the existing fibrous or cartilage structures. When a bone develops from a fibrous membrane, the process is *intramembranous ossification*, and the bone is called a **membrane bone**. Bone development by replacing hyaline cartilage is called *endochondral ossification* (*endo* = within, *chondro* = cartilage), and the resulting bone is called a **cartilage**, or **endochondral**, **bone**. The beauty of using structures (membranes and cartilages) that are flexible and resilient to fashion the embryonic skeleton is that they can accommodate mitosis. Were the early skeleton composed of bone tissue from the outset, growth would be much more difficult.

Intramembranous Ossification

Intramembranous ossification results in the formation of cranial bones of the skull (frontal, parietal, occipital, and temporal bones) and the clavicles. Most bones formed by this process are flat bones. At about week 8 of development, ossification begins on fibrous connective tissue membranes formed by *mesenchymal*

Figure 6.8 Intramembranous ossification. Diagrams ③ and ④ represent much lower magnification than diagrams ① and ②.

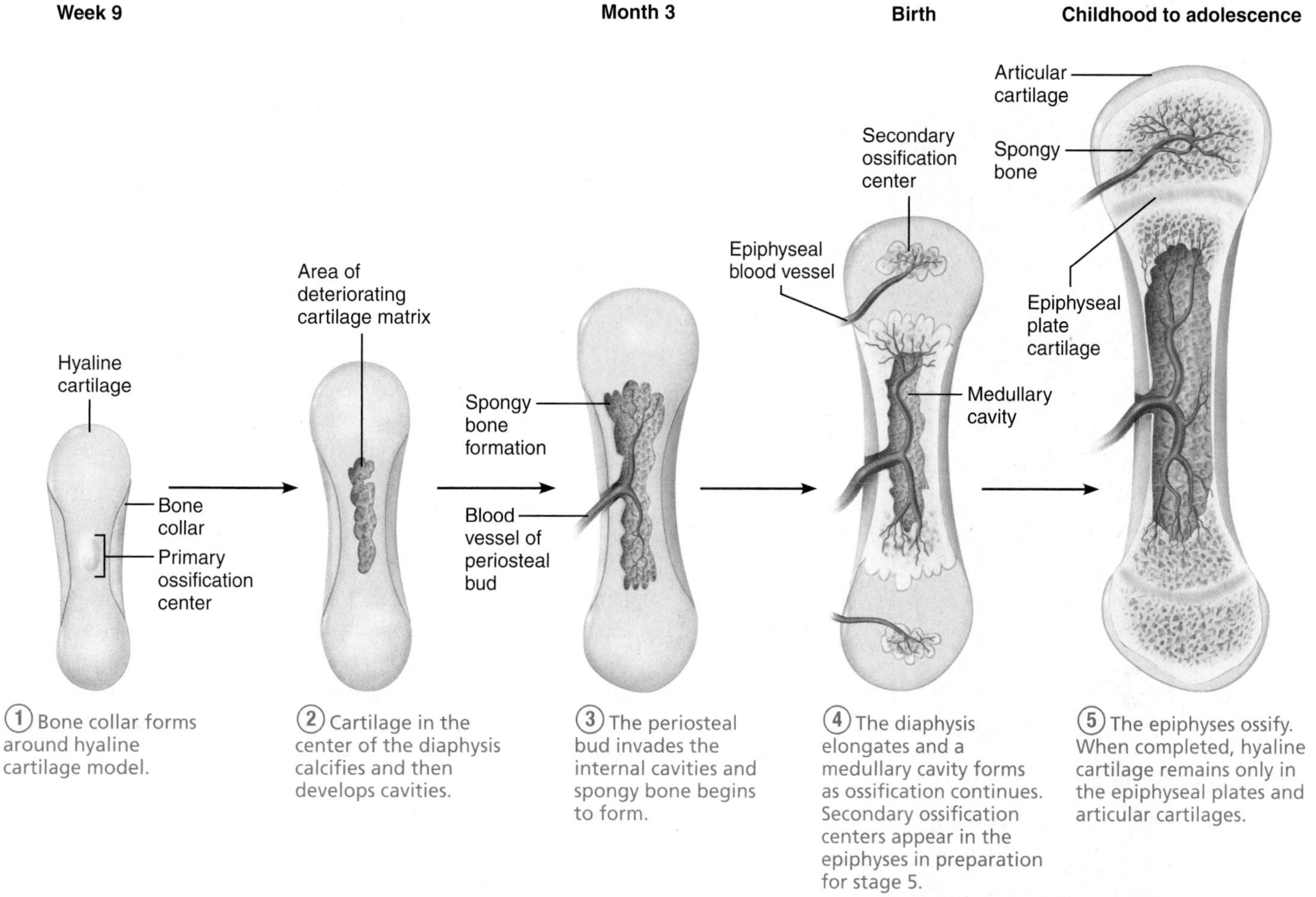

Week 9   **Month 3**   **Birth**   **Childhood to adolescence**

Figure 6.9 Endochondral ossification in a long bone.

cells. Essentially, the process involves the four major steps depicted in **Figure 6.8**.

Endochondral Ossification

Except for the clavicles, essentially all bones of the skeleton below the base of the skull form by **endochondral ossification** (en″do-kon′dral). Beginning in the second month of development, this process uses hyaline cartilage "bones" formed earlier as models, or patterns, for bone construction. It is more complex than intramembranous ossification because the hyaline cartilage must be broken down as ossification proceeds. We will use a forming long bone as our example.

The formation of a long bone typically begins in the center of the hyaline cartilage shaft at a region called the **primary ossification center**. First, the perichondrium covering the hyaline cartilage "bone" is infiltrated with blood vessels, converting it to a vascularized periosteum. As a result of this change in nutrition, the underlying mesenchymal cells specialize into osteoblasts. The stage is now set for ossification to begin, as illustrated in **Figure 6.9**:

① **A bone collar is laid down around the diaphysis of the hyaline cartilage model.** Osteoblasts of the newly converted periosteum secrete osteoid against the hyaline cartilage diaphysis, encasing it in bone. This freshly formed layer of bone is called the *periosteal bone collar.*

② **Cartilage in the center of the diaphysis calcifies and then develops cavities.** As the bone collar forms, chondrocytes within the shaft hypertrophy (enlarge) and signal the surrounding cartilage matrix to calcify. Then, because calcified cartilage matrix is impermeable to diffusing nutrients, the chondrocytes die and the matrix begins to deteriorate. This deterioration opens up cavities, but the hyaline cartilage model is stabilized by the bone collar. Elsewhere, the cartilage remains healthy and continues to grow briskly, causing the cartilage model to elongate.

③ **The periosteal bud invades the internal cavities and spongy bone forms.** In month 3, the forming cavities are invaded by a collection of elements called the **periosteal bud**, which contains a nutrient artery and vein, lymphatic vessels, nerve fibers, red marrow elements, osteoblasts, and osteoclasts. The entering osteoclasts partially erode the calcified cartilage matrix, and the osteoblasts secrete osteoid around the remaining fragments of hyaline cartilage, forming bone-covered cartilage trabeculae. In this way, the earliest version of spongy bone in a developing long bone forms.

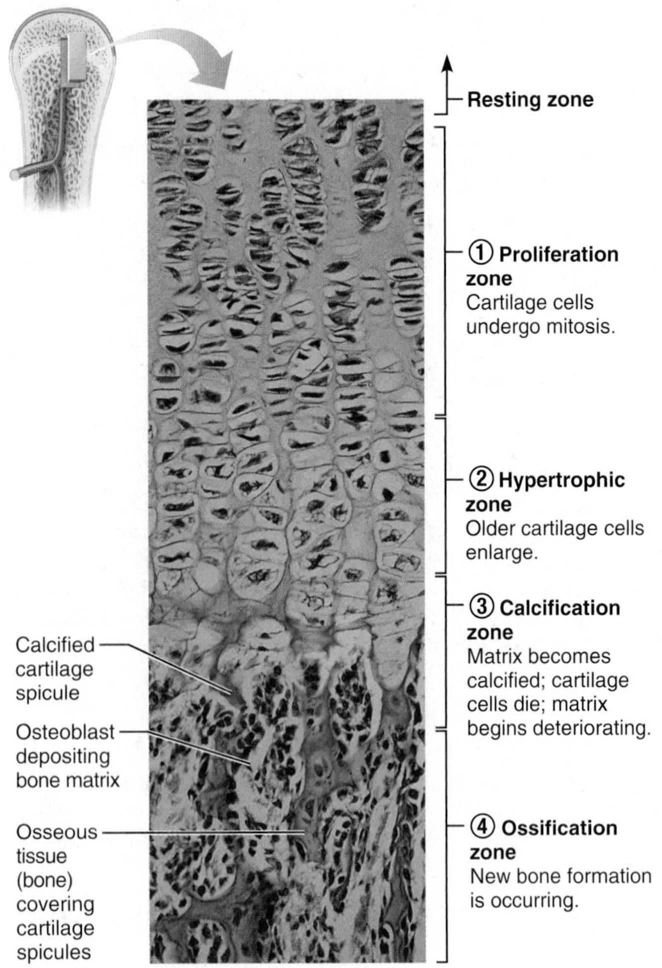

6

Resting zone

① **Proliferation zone**
Cartilage cells undergo mitosis.

② **Hypertrophic zone**
Older cartilage cells enlarge.

③ **Calcification zone**
Matrix becomes calcified; cartilage cells die; matrix begins deteriorating.

④ **Ossification zone**
New bone formation is occurring.

Calcified cartilage spicule

Osteoblast depositing bone matrix

Osseous tissue (bone) covering cartilage spicules

Figure 6.10 Growth in length of a long bone occurs at the epiphyseal plate. The side of the epiphyseal plate facing the epiphysis (distal face) contains resting cartilage cells. The cells of the epiphyseal plate proximal to the resting cartilage area are arranged in four zones—proliferation, hypertrophic, calcification, and ossification—from the region of the earliest stage of growth ① to the region where bone is replacing the cartilage ④ (150×).

④ **The diaphysis elongates and a medullary cavity forms.** As the primary ossification center enlarges, osteoclasts break down the newly formed spongy bone and open up a medullary cavity in the center of the diaphysis. Throughout the fetal period (week 9 until birth), the rapidly growing epiphyses consist only of cartilage, and the hyaline cartilage models continue to elongate by division of viable cartilage cells at the epiphyses. Ossification "chases" cartilage formation along the length of the shaft as cartilage calcifies, is eroded, and then is replaced by bony spicules on the epiphyseal surfaces facing the medullary cavity.

⑤ **The epiphyses ossify.** At birth, most of our long bones have a bony diaphysis surrounding remnants of spongy bone, a widening medullary cavity, and two cartilaginous epiphyses. Shortly before or after birth, **secondary ossification centers** appear in one or both epiphyses, and the epiphyses gain bony tissue. (Typically, the large long bones form sec-

ondary centers in both epiphyses, whereas the small long bones form only one secondary ossification center.) The cartilage in the center of the epiphysis calcifies and deteriorates, opening up cavities that allow a periosteal bud to enter. Then bone trabeculae appear, just as they did earlier in the primary ossification center. (In short bones, only the primary ossification center is formed. Most irregular bones develop from several distinct ossification centers.)

Secondary ossification reproduces almost exactly the events of primary ossification, except that the spongy bone in the interior is retained and no medullary cavity forms in the epiphyses. When secondary ossification is complete, hyaline cartilage remains only at two places: (1) on the epiphyseal surfaces, as the *articular cartilages*, and (2) at the junction of the diaphysis and epiphysis, where it forms the *epiphyseal plates*.

Postnatal Bone Growth

During infancy and youth, long bones lengthen entirely by interstitial growth of the epiphyseal plate cartilage and its replacement by bone, and all bones grow in thickness by appositional growth. Most bones stop growing during adolescence. However, some facial bones, such as those of the nose and lower jaw, continue to grow almost imperceptibly throughout life.

Growth in Length of Long Bones

Longitudinal bone growth mimics many of the events of endochondral ossification. The cartilage is relatively inactive on the side of the epiphyseal plate facing the epiphysis, a region called the *resting* or *quiescent zone*. But the epiphyseal plate cartilage abutting the diaphysis organizes into a pattern that allows fast, efficient growth. The cartilage cells here form tall columns, like coins in a stack. The cells at the "top" (epiphysis-facing side) of the stack abutting the resting zone comprise the *proliferation* or *growth zone* (Figure 6.10). These cells divide quickly, pushing the epiphysis away from the diaphysis, causing the entire long bone to lengthen.

Meanwhile, the older chondrocytes in the stack, which are closer to the diaphysis (*hypertrophic zone* in Figure 6.10), hypertrophy, and their lacunae erode and enlarge, leaving large interconnecting spaces. Subsequently, the surrounding cartilage matrix calcifies and these chondrocytes die and deteriorate, producing the *calcification zone*. This leaves long slender spicules of calcified cartilage at the epiphysis-diaphysis junction, which look like stalactites hanging from the roof of a cave. These calcified spicules ultimately become part of the *ossification* or *osteogenic zone*, and are invaded by marrow elements from the medullary cavity. The cartilage spicules are partly eroded by osteoclasts, then quickly covered with new bone—called woven bone—by osteoblasts, and ultimately replaced by spongy bone. The spicule tips are eventually digested by osteoclasts, and in this way, the medullary cavity also grows longer as the long bone lengthens. During growth, the epiphyseal plate maintains a constant thickness because the rate of cartilage growth on its epiphysis-facing side is balanced by its replacement with bony tissue on its diaphysis-facing side.

Longitudinal growth is accompanied by almost continuous remodeling of the epiphyseal ends to maintain the proper proportions between the diaphysis and epiphyses (Figure 6.11). Bone remodeling involves both new bone formation and bone resorption (destruction). It is described in more detail later in conjunction with the changes that occur in adult bones.

As adolescence ends, the chondroblasts of the epiphyseal plates divide less often and the plates become thinner and thinner until they are entirely replaced by bone tissue. Longitudinal bone growth ends when the bone of the epiphysis and diaphysis fuses. This process, called *epiphyseal plate closure*, happens at about 18 years of age in females and 21 years of age in males. However, as noted earlier, an adult bone can still increase in diameter or thickness by appositional growth if stressed by excessive muscle activity or body weight.

Growth in Width (Thickness)

Growing bones widen as they lengthen. As with cartilages, bones increase in thickness or, in the case of long bones, diameter, by appositional growth. Osteoblasts beneath the periosteum secrete bone matrix on the external bone surface as osteoclasts on the endosteal surface of the diaphysis remove bone (Figure 6.11). However, there is normally slightly less breaking down than building up. This unequal process produces a thicker, stronger bone but prevents it from becoming too heavy.

CHECK YOUR UNDERSTANDING

15. Bones don't begin as bones. What do they begin as?

16. When describing endochondral ossification, some say "bone chases cartilage." What does that mean?

17. Where is the primary ossification center located in a long bone? Where is (are) the secondary ossification center(s) located?

18. As a long bone grows in length, what is happening in the hypertrophic zone of the epiphyseal plate?

For answers, see Appendix G.

Hormonal Regulation of Bone Growth

The growth of bones that occurs until young adulthood is exquisitely controlled by a symphony of hormones. During infancy and childhood, the single most important stimulus of epiphyseal plate activity is *growth hormone* released by the anterior pituitary gland. Thyroid hormones modulate the activity of growth hormone, ensuring that the skeleton has proper proportions as it grows. At puberty, male and female sex hormones (testosterone and estrogens, respectively) are released in increasing amounts. Initially these sex hormones promote the growth spurt typical of adolescence, as well as the masculinization or feminization of specific parts of the skeleton. Later the hormones induce epiphyseal plate closure, ending longitudinal bone growth.

Excesses or deficits of any of these hormones can result in obviously abnormal skeletal growth. For example, hypersecretion of growth hormone in children results in excessive height (gigantism), and deficits of growth hormone or thyroid hormone produce characteristic types of dwarfism.

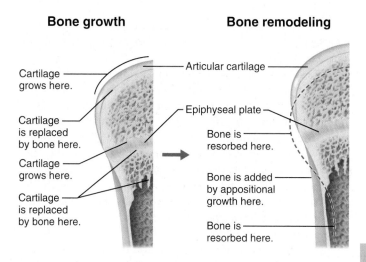

Bone growth   **Bone remodeling**

Cartilage grows here.

Articular cartilage

Cartilage is replaced by bone here.

Epiphyseal plate

Bone is resorbed here.

Cartilage grows here.

Bone is added by appositional growth here.

Cartilage is replaced by bone here.

Bone is resorbed here.

Figure 6.11 Long bone growth and remodeling during youth. The events at the left depict endochondral ossification that occurs at the articular cartilages and epiphyseal plates as the bone grows in length. Events at the right show bone remodeling during long bone growth to maintain proper bone proportions.

Bone Homeostasis: Remodeling and Repair

▶ Compare the locations and remodeling functions of the osteoblasts, osteocytes, and osteoclasts.

▶ Explain how hormones and physical stress regulate bone remodeling.

▶ Describe the steps of fracture repair.

Bones appear to be the most lifeless of body organs, and may even summon images of a graveyard. But as you have just learned, this appearance is deceiving. Bone is a dynamic and active tissue, and small-scale changes in bone architecture occur continually. Every week we recycle 5–7% of our bone mass, and as much as half a gram of calcium may enter or leave the adult skeleton each day! Spongy bone is replaced every three to four years; compact bone, every ten years or so. This is fortunate because when bone remains in place for long periods more of the calcium salts crystallize (see description below) and the bone becomes more brittle—ripe conditions for fracture. And when we break bones—the most common disorder of bone homeostasis—they undergo a remarkable process of self-repair.

Bone Remodeling

In the adult skeleton, bone deposit and bone resorption (removal) occur both at the surface of the periosteum and the surface of the endosteum. Together, the two processes constitute **bone remodeling**, and they are coupled and coordinated by "packets" of adjacent osteoblasts and osteoclasts called *remodeling units* (with help from the stress-sensing osteocytes). In healthy young adults, total bone mass remains constant, an indication that the rates of bone deposit and resorption are essentially equal. Remodeling does not occur uniformly, however. For example, the distal part of the femur, or thigh bone, is fully replaced every five to six months, whereas its shaft is altered much more slowly.

Bone deposit occurs wherever bone is injured or added bone strength is required. For optimal bone deposit, a healthy diet rich in proteins, vitamin C, vitamin D, vitamin A, and several minerals (calcium, phosphorus, magnesium, and manganese, to name a few) is essential.

New matrix deposits by osteocytes are marked by the presence of an *osteoid seam*, an unmineralized band of gauzy-looking bone matrix 10–12 micrometers (μm) wide. Between the osteoid seam and the older mineralized bone, there is an abrupt transition called the *calcification front*. Because the osteoid seam is always of constant width and the change from unmineralized to mineralized matrix is sudden, it seems that the osteoid must mature for about a week before it can calcify.

The precise trigger for calcification is still controversial. However, one critical factor is the product of the local concentrations of calcium and phosphate (P_i) ions (the $Ca^{2+} \cdot P_i$ product). Initially the bone salts are laid down in a noncrystalline form, but when the $Ca^{2+} \cdot P_i$ product reaches a certain level, tiny crystals of hydroxyapatite form spontaneously and then catalyze further crystallization of calcium salts in the area. Other factors involved are matrix proteins that bind and concentrate calcium, and the enzyme *alkaline phosphatase* (shed by the osteoblasts), which is essential for mineralization. Once proper conditions are present, calcium salts are deposited all at once and with great precision throughout the "matured" matrix. Normally, a small percentage of the calcified salts remain in the noncrystallized form to provide a readily available source of calcium ions when blood calcium levels decline toward nonhomeostatic values.

Bone resorption is accomplished by **osteoclasts**, giant multinucleate cells that arise from the same hematopoietic stem cells that differentiate into macrophages. Osteoclasts move along a bone surface, digging grooves as they break down the bone matrix. The part of the osteoclast that touches the bone is highly folded to form a ruffled membrane (see Figure 6.4d) that clings tightly to the bone, sealing off the area of bone destruction. The ruffled border secretes (1) *lysosomal enzymes* that digest the organic matrix and (2) *hydrochloric acid* that converts the calcium salts into soluble forms that pass easily into solution. Osteoclasts may also phagocytize the demineralized matrix and dead osteocytes. The digested matrix end products, growth factors, and dissolved minerals are then endocytosed, transported across the osteoclast (by transcytosis), and released at the opposite side where they enter first the interstitial fluid and then the blood. There is much to learn about osteoclast activation, but proteins secreted by T cells of the immune system appear to be important.

Control of Remodeling

The remodeling that goes on continuously in the skeleton is regulated by two control loops that serve different "masters." One is a negative feedback hormonal loop that maintains Ca^{2+} homeostasis in the blood. The other involves responses to mechanical and gravitational forces acting on the skeleton.

The hormonal feedback becomes much more meaningful when you understand calcium's importance in the body. Ionic calcium is necessary for an amazing number of physiological processes, including transmission of nerve impulses, muscle contraction, blood coagulation, secretion by glands and nerve cells, and cell division. The human body contains 1200–1400 g of calcium, more than 99% present as bone minerals. Most of the remainder is in body cells. Less than 1.5 g is present in blood, and the hormonal control loop normally maintains blood Ca^{2+} within the very narrow range of 9–11 mg per dl (100 ml) of blood. Calcium is absorbed from the intestine under the control of vitamin D metabolites. The daily calcium requirement is 400–800 mg from birth until the age of 10, and 1200–1500 mg from ages 11 to 24.

Hormonal Controls The hormonal controls primarily involve **parathyroid hormone (PTH)**, produced by the parathyroid glands. To a much lesser extent **calcitonin** (kal″sĭ-to′nin), produced by parafollicular cells (C cells) of the thyroid gland, may be involved. As Figure 6.12 illustrates, PTH is released when blood levels of ionic calcium decline. The increased PTH level stimulates osteoclasts to resorb bone, releasing calcium to the blood. Osteoclasts are no respecters of matrix age. When activated, they break down both old and new matrix. Only osteoid, which lacks calcium salts, escapes digestion. As blood concentrations of calcium rise, the stimulus for PTH release ends. The decline of PTH reverses its effects and causes blood Ca^{2+} levels to fall.

In humans, calcitonin appears to be a hormone in search of a function because its effects on calcium homeostasis are negligible. When administered at pharmacological (abnormally high) doses, it does lower blood calcium levels temporarily.

These hormonal controls act not to preserve the skeleton's strength or well-being but rather to maintain blood calcium homeostasis. In fact, if blood calcium levels are low for an extended time, the bones become so demineralized that they develop large, punched-out-looking holes. Thus, the bones serve as a storehouse from which ionic calcium is drawn as needed.

⚖ HOMEOSTATIC IMBALANCE

Minute changes from the homeostatic range for blood calcium can lead to severe neuromuscular problems ranging from hyperexcitability (when blood Ca^{2+} levels are too low) to nonresponsiveness and inability to function (with high blood Ca^{2+} levels). In addition, sustained high blood levels of Ca^{2+}, a condition known as *hypercalcemia* (hi″per-kal-se′me-ah), can lead to undesirable deposits of calcium salts in the blood vessels, kidneys, and other soft organs, which may hamper the functioning of these organs. ■

In addition to the hormones that regulate bone remodeling in response to blood calcium levels, it is now established that *leptin*, a hormone released by adipose tissue, plays a role in regulating bone density. Best known for its effects on weight and energy balance (see pp. 946–947), in animal studies leptin appears to inhibit osteoblasts through an additional pathway mediated by the hypothalamus which activates sympathetic nerves serving

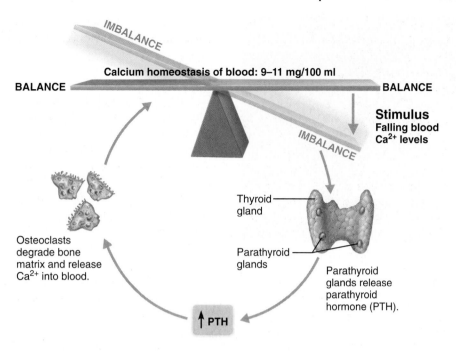

Figure 6.12 Parathyroid hormone (PTH) control of blood calcium levels.

bones. However, the full scope of leptin's bone-modifying activity in humans is still being worked out.

Response to Mechanical Stress The second set of controls regulating bone remodeling, bone's response to mechanical stress (muscle pull) and gravity, serves the needs of the skeleton by keeping the bones strong where stressors are acting. *Wolff's law* holds that a bone grows or remodels in response to the demands placed on it. The first thing to understand is that a bone's anatomy reflects the common stresses it encounters. For example, a bone is loaded (stressed) whenever weight bears down on it or muscles pull on it. This loading is usually off center, however, and tends to *bend* the bone. Bending compresses the bone on one side and subjects it to tension (stretching) on the other (Figure 6.13). As a result of these mechanical stressors, long bones are thickest midway along the diaphysis, exactly where bending stresses are greatest (bend a stick and it will split near the middle). Both compression and tension are minimal toward the center of the bone (they cancel each other out), so a bone can "hollow out" for lightness (using spongy bone instead of compact bone) without jeopardy.

Other observations explained by Wolff's law include these: (1) Handedness (being right or left handed) results in the bones of one upper limb being thicker than those of the less-used limb, and vigorous exercise of the most-used limb leads to large increases in bone strength (Figure 6.14). (2) Curved bones are thickest where they are most likely to buckle. (3) The trabeculae of spongy bone form trusses, or struts, along lines of compression. (4) Large, bony projections occur where heavy, active muscles attach. (The bones of weight lifters have enormous thickenings at the attachment sites of the most-used muscles.) Wolff's law also explains the featureless bones of the fetus and the atrophied bones of bedridden people—situations in which bones are not stressed.

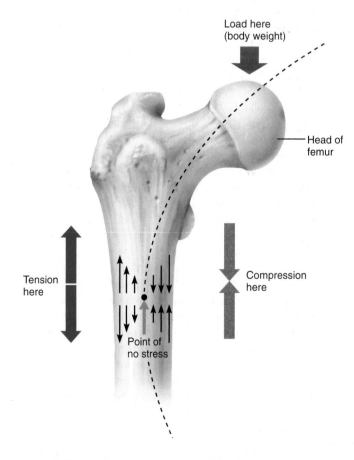

Figure 6.13 Bone anatomy and bending stress. Body weight transmitted to the head of the femur (thigh bone) threatens to bend the bone along the indicated arc, compressing it on one side (converging arrows on right) and stretching it on the other side (diverging arrows on left). Because these two forces cancel each other internally, much less bone material is needed internally than superficially.

(a)

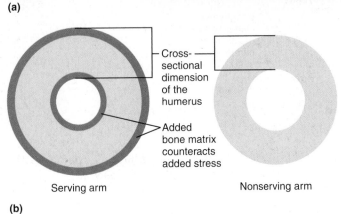

(b)

Figure 6.14 Vigorous exercise can lead to large increases in bone strength. The diagrams show the average difference in the cross-sectional dimensions of the humerus of the arm in the serving and nonserving arms of professional tennis players. The data revealed average increases in bone rigidity and strength of 62% and 45%, respectively, in the serving arms. The structural changes were more pronounced in players who began training at an early age. *SOURCE*: C. B. Ruff, "Gracilization of the Modern Human Skeleton," *American Scientist 94*(6): p. 513, Nov–Dec 2006.

How do mechanical forces communicate with the cells responsible for remodeling? Although the mechanisms by which bone responds to mechanical stimuli are still uncertain, we do know that deforming a bone produces an electrical current. Because compressed and stretched regions are oppositely charged, it has been suggested that electrical signals direct remodeling. This principle underlies some of the devices currently used to speed bone repair and the healing of fractures.

The skeleton is continuously subjected to both hormonal influences and mechanical forces. At the risk of constructing too large a building on too small a foundation, we can speculate that the hormonal loop determines *whether* and *when* remodeling occurs in response to changing blood calcium levels, and mechanical stress determines *where* it occurs. For example, when bone must be broken down to increase blood calcium levels, PTH is released and targets the osteoclasts. However, mechanical forces determine *which* osteoclasts are most sensitive to PTH

stimulation, so that bone in the *least* stressed areas (which is temporarily dispensable) is broken down.

Bone Repair

Despite their remarkable strength, bones are susceptible to **fractures**, or breaks. During youth, most fractures result from exceptional trauma that twists or smashes the bones (sports injuries, automobile accidents, and falls, for example). Excessive intake of vitamin A appears to increase fracture risk in some people. Elevated blood levels of the amino acid derivative homocysteine were also believed to increase fracture risk, but recent studies indicate that it is actually a marker of low bone density and bone frailty. In old age, most fractures occur as bones thin and weaken.

Fractures may be classified by

1. Position of the bone ends after fracture. In *nondisplaced fractures* the bone ends retain their normal position; in *displaced fractures* the bone ends are out of normal alignment.
2. Completeness of the break. If the bone is broken through, the fracture is a *complete fracture*; if not, it is an *incomplete fracture*.
3. Orientation of the break relative to the long axis of the bone. If the break parallels the long axis, the fracture is *linear*; if the break is perpendicular to the bone's long axis, it is *transverse*.
4. Whether the bone ends penetrate the skin. If so, the fracture is an *open (compound) fracture*; if not, it is a *closed (simple) fracture*.

In addition to these four either-or classifications, all fractures can be described in terms of the location of the fracture, the external appearance of the fracture, and/or the nature of the break. **Table 6.2** summarizes the various descriptions.

A fracture is treated by *reduction*, the realignment of the broken bone ends. In *closed (external) reduction*, the bone ends are coaxed into position by the physician's hands. In *open (internal) reduction*, the bone ends are secured together surgically with pins or wires. After the broken bone is reduced, it is immobilized either by a cast or traction to allow the healing process to begin. For a simple fracture the healing time is six to eight weeks for small or medium-sized bones in young adults, but it is much longer for large, weight-bearing bones and for bones of elderly people (because of their poorer circulation).

Repair in a simple fracture involves four major stages (**Figure 6.15**):

① **A hematoma forms.** When a bone breaks, blood vessels in the bone and periosteum, and perhaps in surrounding tissues, are torn and hemorrhage. As a result, a **hematoma** (he″mah-to′mah), a mass of clotted blood, forms at the fracture site. Soon, bone cells deprived of nutrition die, and the tissue at the site becomes swollen, painful, and inflamed.

② **Fibrocartilaginous callus forms.** Within a few days, several events lead to the formation of soft *granulation tissue*, also called the *soft callus* (kal′us; "hard skin"). Capillaries grow into the hematoma and phagocytic cells invade the area and

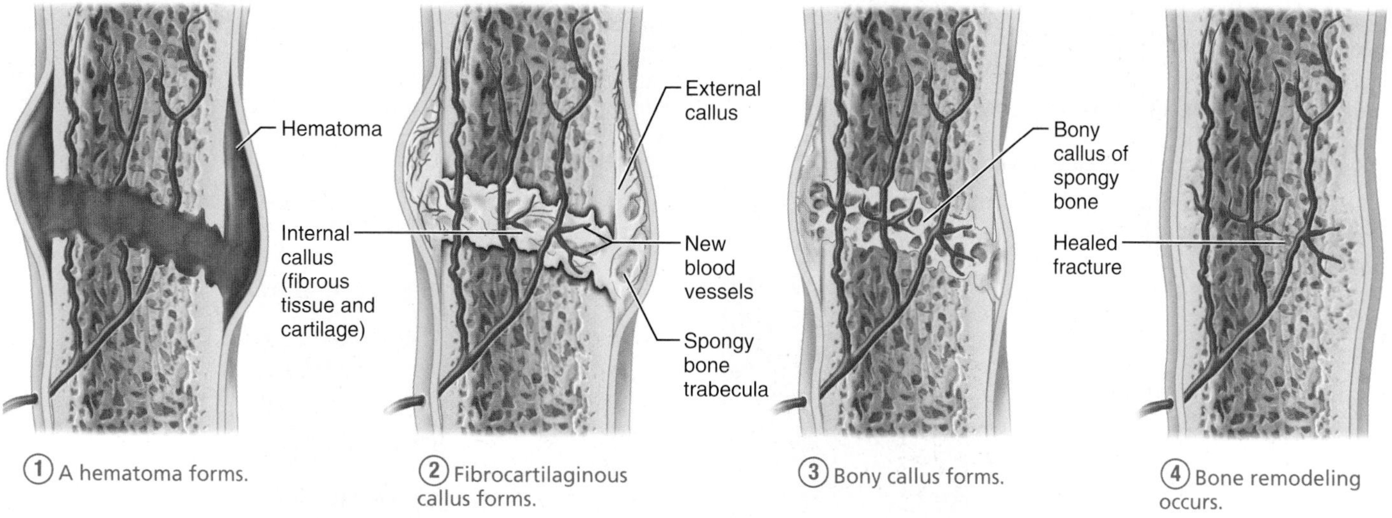

① A hematoma forms.

Hematoma

② Fibrocartilaginous callus forms.

External callus

Internal callus (fibrous tissue and cartilage)

New blood vessels

Spongy bone trabecula

③ Bony callus forms.

Bony callus of spongy bone

Healed fracture

④ Bone remodeling occurs.

Figure 6.15 **Stages in the healing of a bone fracture.**

6

begin cleaning up the debris. Meanwhile, fibroblasts and osteoblasts invade the fracture site from the nearby periosteum and endosteum and begin reconstructing the bone. The fibroblasts produce collagen fibers that span the break and connect the broken bone ends, and some differentiate into chondroblasts that secrete cartilage matrix. Within this mass of repair tissue, osteoblasts begin forming spongy bone, but those farthest from the capillary supply secrete an externally bulging cartilaginous matrix that later calcifies. This entire mass of repair tissue, now called the **fibrocartilaginous callus**, splints the broken bone.

③ **Bony callus forms.** Within a week, new bone trabeculae begin to appear in the fibrocartilaginous callus and gradually convert it to a **bony (hard) callus** of spongy bone. Bony callus formation continues until a firm union is formed about two months later.

④ **Bone remodeling occurs.** Beginning during bony callus formation and continuing for several months after, the bony callus is remodeled. The excess material on the diaphysis exterior and within the medullary cavity is removed, and compact bone is laid down to reconstruct the shaft walls. The final structure of the remodeled area resembles that of the original unbroken bony region because it responds to the same set of mechanical stressors.

CHECK YOUR UNDERSTANDING

19. If osteoclasts in a long bone are more active than osteoblasts, what change in bone mass is likely?

20. Which stimulus—PTH (a hormone) or mechanical forces acting on the skeleton—is more important in maintaining homeostatic blood calcium levels?

21. How does an open fracture differ from a closed fracture?

22. How do bone growth and bone remodeling differ?

For answers, see Appendix G.

Homeostatic Imbalances of Bone

▶ Contrast the disorders of bone remodeling seen in osteoporosis, osteomalacia, and Paget's disease.

Imbalances between bone deposit and bone resorption underlie nearly every disease that affects the adult skeleton.

Osteomalacia and Rickets

Osteomalacia (os″te-o-mah-la′she-ah; "soft bones") includes a number of disorders in which the bones are inadequately mineralized. Osteoid is produced, but calcium salts are not deposited, so bones soften and weaken. The main symptom is pain when weight is put on the affected bones.

Rickets is the analogous disease in children. Because young bones are still growing rapidly, rickets is much more severe than adult osteomalacia. Bowed legs and deformities of the pelvis, skull, and rib cage are common. Because the epiphyseal plates cannot be calcified, they continue to widen, and the ends of long bones become visibly enlarged and abnormally long.

Osteomalacia and rickets are caused by insufficient calcium in the diet or by a vitamin D deficiency. For this reason, drinking vitamin D–fortified milk and exposing the skin to sunlight (which spurs the body to form vitamin D) usually cure these disorders. Although the seeming elimination of rickets in the United States has been heralded as a public health success, rickets still rears its head in isolated situations. For example, if a mother who breast-feeds her infant becomes vitamin D deficient because of dreary winter weather, the infant too will be vitamin D deficient and will develop rickets.

Osteoporosis

For most of us, the phrase "bone problems of the elderly" brings to mind the stereotype of a victim of osteoporosis—a hunched-over old woman shuffling behind her walker.

TABLE 6.2	Common Types of Fractures		
FRACTURE TYPE	**DESCRIPTION AND COMMENTS**	**FRACTURE TYPE**	**DESCRIPTION AND COMMENTS**
Comminuted	Bone fragments into three or more pieces. Particularly common in the aged, whose bones are more brittle	Compression	Bone is crushed. Common in porous bones (i.e., osteoporotic bones) subjected to extreme trauma, as in a fall
Spiral	Ragged break occurs when excessive twisting forces are applied to a bone. Common sports fracture	Epiphyseal	Epiphysis separates from the diaphysis along the epiphyseal plate. Tends to occur where cartilage cells are dying and calcification of the matrix is occurring
Depressed	Broken bone portion is pressed inward. Typical of skull fracture	Greenstick	Bone breaks incompletely, much in the way a green twig breaks. Only one side of the shaft breaks; the other side bends. Common in children, whose bones have relatively more organic matrix and are more flexible than those of adults

Crushed vertebra

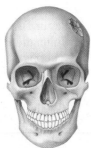
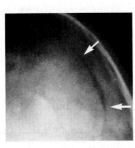

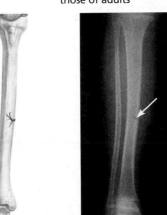

6

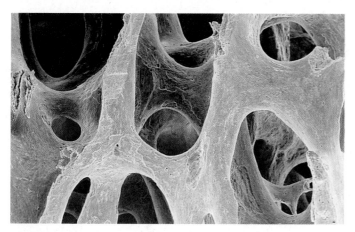

(a) Normal bone

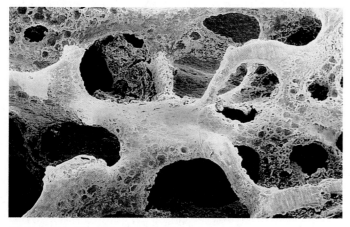

(b) Osteoporotic bone

Figure 6.16 The contrasting architecture of normal versus osteoporotic bone. Scanning electron micrographs, 300×.

Osteoporosis (os″te-o-po-ro′sis) refers to a group of diseases in which bone resorption outpaces bone deposit. The bones become so fragile that something as simple as a hearty sneeze or stepping off a curb can cause them to break. The composition of the matrix remains normal but bone mass is reduced, and the bones become porous and light (Figure 6.16). Even though osteoporosis affects the entire skeleton, the spongy bone of the spine is most vulnerable, and compression fractures of the vertebrae are common. The femur, particularly its neck, is also very susceptible to fracture (called a *broken hip*) in people with osteoporosis.

Osteoporosis occurs most often in the aged, particularly in postmenopausal women. Although men develop it to a lesser degree, 30% of American women between the ages of 60 and 70 have osteoporosis, and 70% have it by age 80. Moreover, 30% of all Caucasian women (the most susceptible group) will experience a bone fracture due to osteoporosis. Sex hormones, particularly estrogen, help to maintain the health and normal density of the skeleton by restraining osteoclast activity and by promoting deposit of new bone. After menopause, however, estrogen secretion wanes, and estrogen deficiency is strongly implicated in osteoporosis in older women. Other factors that contribute to

osteoporosis include a petite body form, insufficient exercise to stress the bones, immobility, a diet poor in calcium and protein, abnormal vitamin D receptors, smoking (which reduces estrogen levels), and hormone-related conditions such as hyperthyroidism, low blood levels of thyroid-stimulating hormone (better known for its role in stimulating the secretion of thyroid hormones), and diabetes mellitus. In addition, recent research indicates that a particular gene, dubbed *LRP5*, may play a role in osteoporosis. It inhibits release of serotonin by cells of the gut. Because serotonin inhibits osteoblast growth, reducing its synthesis increases bone density.

Osteoporosis has traditionally been treated with calcium and vitamin D supplements, weight-bearing exercise, and *hormone (estrogen) replacement therapy* (*HRT*). Frustratingly, HRT only slows the loss of bone but does not reverse it. Additionally, because of the increased risk of heart attack, stroke, and breast cancer associated with estrogen replacement therapy, it is a controversial treatment these days.

Newer drugs are available. These include alendronate (Fosamax), a drug that decreases osteoclast activity and number, and shows promise in reversing osteoporosis in the spine; and selective estrogen receptor modulators (SERMs), such as raloxifene, dubbed "estrogen light" because it mimics estrogen's beneficial bone-sparing properties without targeting the uterus or breast. Additionally, *statins*, drugs used by tens of thousands of people to lower cholesterol levels, have been shown to have an unexpected side effect of increasing bone mineral density up to 8% over four years. Although not a substitute for HRT, estrogenic compounds in soy protein (principally the isoflavones daidzein and genistein) offer a good addition or adjunct for some patients.

How can osteoporosis be prevented (or at least delayed)? The first requirement is to get enough calcium while your bones are still increasing in density (bones reach their peak density during early adulthood). Second, drinking fluoridated water hardens bones (as well as teeth). Conversely, excessive intake of carbonated beverages leaches minerals from bone and decreases bone density. Finally, getting plenty of weight-bearing exercise (walking, jogging, tennis, etc.) throughout life will increase bone mass above normal values and provide a greater buffer against age-related bone loss.

Paget's Disease

Often discovered by accident when X rays are taken for some other reason, **Paget's disease** (paj′ets) is characterized by excessive and haphazard bone deposit and resorption. The newly formed bone, called *Pagetic bone*, is hastily made and has an abnormally high ratio of spongy bone to compact bone. This, along with reduced mineralization, causes a spotty weakening of the bones. Late in the disease, osteoclast activity wanes, but osteoblasts continue to work, often forming irregular bone thickenings or filling the marrow cavity with Pagetic bone.

Paget's disease may affect any part of the skeleton, but it is usually a localized condition. The spine, pelvis, femur, and skull are most often involved and become increasingly deformed and painful. It rarely occurs before the age of 40, and it affects about 3% of North American elderly people. Its cause is unknown, but

System Connections

Homeostatic Interrelationships Between the Skeletal System and Other Body Systems

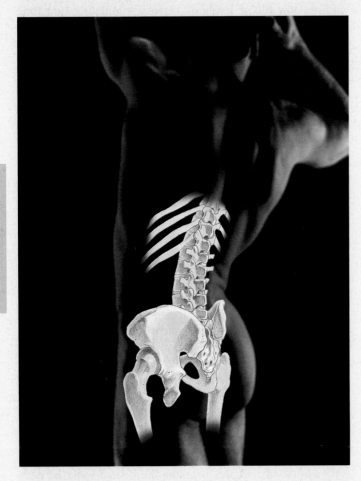

Endocrine System

- Skeletal system provides some bony protection; stores calcium needed for second-messenger signaling mechanisms
- Hormones regulate uptake and release of calcium from bone; promote long bone growth and maturation

Cardiovascular System

- Bone marrow cavities provide site for blood cell formation; matrix stores calcium needed for cardiac muscle activity
- Cardiovascular system delivers nutrients and oxygen to bones; carries away wastes

Lymphatic System/Immunity

- Skeletal system provides some protection to lymphatic organs; bone marrow is site of origin for lymphocytes involved in immune response
- Lymphatic system drains leaked tissue fluids; immune cells protect against pathogens

Respiratory System

- Skeletal system protects lungs by enclosure (rib cage)
- Respiratory system provides oxygen; disposes of carbon dioxide

Digestive System

- Skeletal system provides some bony protection to intestines, pelvic organs, and liver
- Digestive system provides nutrients needed for bone health and growth

Urinary System

- Skeletal system protects pelvic organs (urinary bladder, etc.)
- Urinary system activates vitamin D; disposes of nitrogenous wastes

Reproductive System

- Skeletal system protects some reproductive organs by enclosure
- Gonads produce hormones that influence the form of the skeleton and epiphyseal closure

Integumentary System

- Skeletal system provides support for body organs including the skin
- Skin provides vitamin D needed for proper calcium absorption and use

Muscular System

- Skeletal system provides levers plus ionic calcium for muscle activity
- Muscle pull on bones increases bone strength and viability; helps determine bone shape

Nervous System

- Skeletal system protects brain and spinal cord; provides depot for calcium ions needed for neural function
- Nerves innervate bone and joint capsules, providing for pain and joint sense

Closer Connections

The Skeletal System and Interrelationships with the Muscular, Endocrine, and Integumentary Systems

Our skeleton supports us, protects our "innards" (the protection our brain gets from the skull is indispensable), gives us stature (for some reason, tall people get more respect), contributes to our shape (women are shaped differently than men), and allows us to move. Obviously, the skeletal system has important interactions with many other body systems, not the least of which are the endocrine and integumentary systems. However, its most intimate and mutually beneficial relationship is with the muscular system, so we will consider that first.

Muscular System

The codependence of the skeletal and muscular systems is striking—as one system goes, so goes the other. If we participate in weight-bearing exercise (run, play tennis, do aerobics) regularly, our muscles become more efficient and exert more force on our bones. As a result, our bones stay healthy and strong and increase their mass to assume the added stress.

Since both spongy and compact bone reach peak density during midlife, weight-bearing exercise during youth is important, especially in females who have less bone mass than males and lose it faster.

Regular exercise also stretches the connective tissues binding bones to muscles and to other bones, and reinforcing joints. Since this increases overall flexibility, we have fewer injuries, allowing us to stay active well into old age. (Pain makes couch potatoes.)

Endocrine System

Although mechanical factors are undeniably important in shaping the skeleton and helping to keep it strong, hormones acting individually and in concert direct skeletal growth during youth, and enhance (or impair) skeletal strength in adults. Growth hormone is essential for normal skeletal growth and maintenance throughout life, whereas thyroid and sex hormones ensure that normal skeletal proportions are established during childhood and adolescence. Conversely, PTH serves not the skeleton but a different master—homeostasis of blood calcium levels. Any interference with normal hormonal functioning is soon apparent as a skeletal abnormality or malproportion.

Integumentary System

The skeletal system is absolutely dependent on the integumentary system (the skin) for the calcium that keeps the bones hard and strong. The relationship is indirect: In the presence of sunlight, a vitamin D precursor is produced in the dermal capillary blood. It is activated elsewhere, and (among its other roles) it regulates the carrier system that absorbs calcium from ingested foods into the blood. Because calcium is required for so many body functions, and bones provide the "calcium bank," the bones become increasingly soft and weak in the absence of vitamin D because no daily rations of calcium are allowed to enter the blood from the digestive tract.

Clinical Connections

Skeletal System

Case study: Remember Mrs. DeStephano? When we last heard about her she was being admitted for further studies. Relative to her skeletal system, the following notes have been added to her chart.

- Fracture of superior right tibia (shinbone of leg); skin lacerated; area cleaned and protruding bone fragments subjected to internal (open) reduction and casted
- Nutrient artery of tibia damaged
- Medial meniscus (fibrocartilage disc) of right knee joint crushed; knee joint inflamed and painful

Relative to these notes:

1. What type of fracture does Mrs. DeStephano have?

2. What problems can be predicted with such fractures and how are they treated?

3. What is internal reduction? Why was a cast applied?

4. Given an uncomplicated recovery, approximately how long should it take before Mrs. DeStephano has a good solid bony callus?

5. What complications might be predicted by the fact that the nutrient artery is damaged?

6. What new techniques might be used to enhance fracture repair if healing is delayed or impaired?

7. How likely is it that Mrs. DeStephano's knee cartilage will regenerate? Why?

(Answers in Appendix G)

6

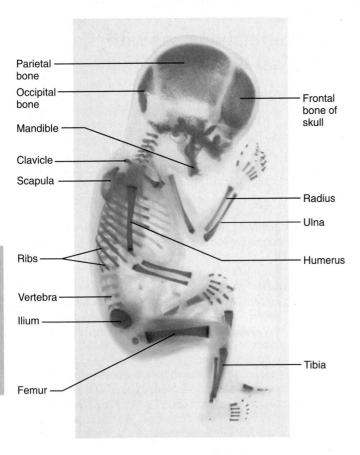

Parietal bone
Occipital bone
Mandible
Clavicle
Scapula
Ribs
Vertebra
Ilium
Femur

Frontal bone of skull
Radius
Ulna
Humerus
Tibia

Figure 6.17 Fetal primary ossification centers at 12 weeks. The darker areas indicate primary ossification centers in the skeleton of a 12-week-old fetus.

it may be initiated by a virus. Drug therapies include calcitonin (now administered by a nasal inhaler), and the newer bisphosphonates (etidronate, alendronate, and others) which have shown success in preventing bone breakdown.

CHECK YOUR UNDERSTANDING

23. Which bone disorder is characterized by excessive deposit of weak, poorly mineralized bone?
24. What are three measures that may help to maintain healthy bone density?
25. What name is given to "adult rickets"?

For answers, see Appendix G.

Developmental Aspects of Bones: Timing of Events

▶ Describe the timing and cause of changes in bone architecture and bone mass throughout life.

Bones are on a precise schedule from the time they form until death. The mesoderm germ layer gives rise to embryonic mesenchymal cells, which in turn produce the membranes and cartilages that form the embryonic skeleton. These structures then ossify according to an amazingly predictable timetable that allows fetal age to be determined easily from either X rays or sonograms. Although each bone has its own developmental schedule, most long bones begin ossifying by 8 weeks after conception and have well-developed primary ossification centers by 12 weeks **(Figure 6.17)**.

At birth, most long bones of the skeleton are well ossified except for their epiphyses. After birth, secondary ossification centers develop in a predictable sequence. The epiphyseal plates persist and provide for long bone growth all through childhood and the sex hormone–mediated growth spurt at adolescence. By the age of 25 years, nearly all bones are completely ossified and skeletal growth ceases.

In children and adolescents, bone formation exceeds bone resorption. In young adults, these processes are in balance, and in old age, resorption predominates. Despite the environmental factors (discussed earlier) that influence bone density, genetics still plays the major role in determining how much a person's bone density will change over a lifetime. A single gene that codes for vitamin D's cellular docking site helps determine both the tendency to accumulate bone mass during early life and a person's risk of osteoporosis later in life.

Beginning in the fourth decade of life, bone mass decreases with age. The only exception appears to be in bones of the skull. Among young adults, skeletal mass is generally greater in males than in females, and greater in blacks than in whites. Age-related bone loss is faster in whites than in blacks (who have greater bone density to begin with) and faster in females than in males. Qualitative changes also occur: More osteons remain incompletely formed, mineralization is less complete, and the amount of nonviable bone increases, reflecting a diminished blood supply to the bones in old age. These age-related changes are also bad news because fractures heal more slowly in old people. Daily ultrasound treatments are helpful in hastening repair of fractures, and electrical stimulation of fracture sites dramatically increases the speed of healing. (Presumably electrical fields inhibit PTH stimulation of osteoclasts and induce formation of growth factors that stimulate osteoblasts at the fracture site.)

CHECK YOUR UNDERSTANDING

26. What is the status of bone structure at birth?
27. The decrease in bone mass that begins in the fourth decade of life affects nearly all bones. What are the exceptions?

For answers, see Appendix G.

Skeletal cartilages and bones—their architecture, composition, and dynamic nature—have been examined in this chapter. We have also discussed the role of bones in maintaining overall body homeostasis, as summarized in *Making Connections*. Now we are ready to look at the individual bones of the skeleton and how they contribute to its functions, both collectively and individually.

RELATED CLINICAL TERMS

Achondroplasia (a-kon″dro-pla′ze-ah; *a* = without; *chondro* = cartilage; *plasi* = mold, shape) A congenital condition involving defective cartilage and endochondral bone growth so that the limbs are too short but the membrane bones are of normal size; a type of dwarfism.

Bony spur Abnormal projection from a bone due to bony overgrowth; common in aging bones.

Ostealgia (os″te-al′je-ah; *algia* = pain) Pain in a bone.

Osteitis (os″te-i′tis; *itis* = inflammation) Inflammation of bony tissue.

Osteogenesis imperfecta Also called brittle bone disease, a disorder in which the bone matrix contains inadequate amounts of collagen, putting it at risk for shattering.

Osteomyelitis (os″te-o-mi″ĕ-l-li′tis) Inflammation of bone and bone marrow caused by pus-forming bacteria that enter the body via a wound (e.g., compound bone fracture), or spread from an infection near the bone. Commonly affects the long bones, causing acute pain and fever. May result in joint stiffness, bone destruction, and shortening of a limb. Treatment involves antibiotic therapy, draining of any abscesses (local collections of pus) formed, and removal of dead bone fragments (which prevent healing).

Osteosarcoma (os″te-o-sar-ko′mah) A form of bone cancer typically arising in a long bone of a limb and most often in those 10–25 years of age. Grows aggressively, painfully eroding the bone; tends to metastasize to the lungs and cause secondary lung tumors. Usual treatment is amputation of the affected bone or limb, followed by chemotherapy and surgical removal of any metastases. Survival rate is about 50% if detected early.

Pathologic fracture Fracture in a diseased bone involving slight (coughing or a quick turn) or no physical trauma. For example, a hip bone weakened by osteoporosis may break and cause the person to fall, rather than breaking because of the fall.

Traction ("pulling") Placing sustained tension on a body region to keep the parts of a fractured bone in proper alignment; also prevents spasms of skeletal muscles, which would separate the fractured bone ends or crush the spinal cord in the case of vertebral column fractures.

CHAPTER SUMMARY

Skeletal Cartilages   (p. 173)

Basic Structure, Types, and Locations   (p. 173)

1. A skeletal cartilage exhibits chondrocytes housed in lacunae (cavities) within the extracellular matrix (ground substance and fibers). It contains large amounts of water (which accounts for its resilience), lacks nerve fibers, is avascular, and is surrounded by a fibrous perichondrium that resists expansion.

2. Hyaline cartilages appear glassy; the fibers are collagenic. They provide support with flexibility and resilience and are the most abundant skeletal cartilages, accounting for the articular, costal, respiratory, and nasal cartilages.

3. Elastic cartilages contain abundant elastic fibers, in addition to collagen fibers, and are more flexible than hyaline cartilages. They support the outer ear and epiglottis.

4. Fibrocartilages, which contain thick collagen fibers, are the most compressible cartilages and are resistant to stretch. They form intervertebral discs and knee joint cartilages.

Growth of Cartilage   (p. 173)

5. Cartilages grow from within (interstitial growth) and by addition of new cartilage tissue at the periphery (appositional growth).

Classification of Bones   (pp. 173–175)

1. Bones are classified as long, short, flat, or irregular on the basis of their shape and their proportion of compact or spongy bone.

Functions of Bones   (pp. 175–176)

1. Bones give the body shape; protect and support body organs; provide levers for muscles to pull on; store calcium and other minerals; and are the site of blood cell production.

Bone Structure   (pp. 176–182)

Gross Anatomy   (pp. 177–179)

1. Bone markings are important anatomical landmarks that reveal sites of muscle attachment, points of articulation, and sites of blood vessel and nerve passage.

2. A long bone is composed of a diaphysis (shaft) and epiphyses (ends). The medullary cavity of the diaphysis contains yellow marrow; the epiphyses contain spongy bone. The epiphyseal line is the remnant of the epiphyseal plate. Periosteum covers the diaphysis; endosteum lines inner bone cavities. Hyaline cartilage covers joint surfaces.

3. Flat bones consist of two thin plates of compact bone enclosing a diploë (spongy bone layer). Short and irregular bones resemble flat bones structurally.

4. In adults, hematopoietic tissue (red marrow) is found within the diploë of flat bones and occasionally within the epiphyses of long bones. In infants, red marrow is also found in the medullary cavity.

Microscopic Anatomy of Bone   (pp. 179–180)

5. The structural unit of compact bone, the osteon, consists of a central canal surrounded by concentric lamellae of bone matrix. Osteocytes, embedded in lacunae, are connected to each other and the central canal by canaliculi.

6. Spongy bone has slender trabeculae containing irregular lamellae, which enclose red marrow–filled cavities.

Chemical Composition of Bone   (pp. 180–182)

7. Bone is composed of living cells (osteogenic cells, osteoblasts, osteocytes, and osteoclasts) and matrix. The matrix includes osteoid, organic substances that are secreted by osteoblasts and give the bone tensile strength. Its inorganic components, the hydroxyapatites (calcium salts), make bone hard.

Bone Development   (pp. 182–185)

Formation of the Bony Skeleton   (pp. 182–184)

1. Intramembranous ossification forms the clavicles and most skull bones. The ground substance of the bone matrix is deposited between collagen fibers within the fibrous membrane to form woven bone. Eventually, compact bone plates enclose the diploë.

2. Most bones are formed by endochondral ossification of a hyaline cartilage model. Osteoblasts beneath the periosteum secrete bone matrix on the cartilage model, forming the bone collar. Deterioration of the cartilage model internally opens up cavities, allowing periosteal bud entry. Bone matrix is deposited around the cartilage remnants but is later broken down.

Postnatal Bone Growth   (pp. 184–185)

3. Long bones increase in length by interstitial growth of the epiphyseal plate cartilage and its replacement by bone.

4. Appositional growth increases bone diameter/thickness.

Bone Homeostasis: Remodeling and Repair   (pp. 185–189)

Bone Remodeling   (pp. 185–188)

1. Bone is continually deposited and resorbed in response to hormonal and mechanical stimuli. Together these processes constitute bone remodeling.

2. An osteoid seam appears at areas of new bone deposit; calcium salts are deposited a few days later.

3. Osteoclasts release lysosomal enzymes and acids on bone surfaces to be resorbed. The dissolved products are transcytosed to the opposite face of the osteoclast for release to the extracellular fluid.

4. The hormonal controls of bone remodeling serve blood calcium homeostasis. When blood calcium levels decline, PTH is released and stimulates osteoclasts to digest bone matrix, releasing ionic calcium. As blood calcium levels rise, PTH secretion declines.

5. Mechanical stress and gravity acting on the skeleton help maintain skeletal strength. Bones thicken, develop heavier prominences, or rearrange their trabeculae in sites where stressed.

Bone Repair   (pp. 188–189)

6. Fractures are treated by open or closed reduction. The healing process involves formation of a hematoma, a fibrocartilaginous callus, a bony callus, and bone remodeling, in succession.

Homeostatic Imbalances of Bone   (pp. 189–191, 194)

1. Imbalances between bone formation and resorption underlie all skeletal disorders.

2. Osteomalacia and rickets occur when bones are inadequately mineralized. The bones become soft and deformed. The most frequent cause is inadequate vitamin D.

3. Osteoporosis is any condition in which bone breakdown outpaces bone formation, causing bones to become weak and porous. Postmenopausal women are particularly susceptible.

4. Paget's disease is characterized by excessive and abnormal bone remodeling.

Developmental Aspects of Bones: Timing of Events   (p. 194)

1. Osteogenesis is predictable and precisely timed.

2. Longitudinal long bone growth continues until the end of adolescence. Skeletal mass increases dramatically during puberty and adolescence, when formation exceeds resorption.

3. Bone mass is fairly constant in young adulthood, but beginning in the 40s, bone resorption exceeds formation.

REVIEW QUESTIONS

Multiple Choice/Matching

(Some questions have more than one correct answer. Select the best answer or answers from the choices given.)

1. Which is a function of the skeletal system? (a) support, (b) hematopoietic site, (c) storage, (d) providing levers for muscle activity, (e) all of these.

2. A bone with approximately the same width, length, and height is most likely (a) a long bone, (b) a short bone, (c) a flat bone, (d) an irregular bone.

3. The shaft of a long bone is properly called the (a) epiphysis, (b) periosteum, (c) diaphysis, (d) compact bone.

4. Sites of hematopoiesis include all but (a) red marrow cavities of spongy bone, (b) the diploë of flat bones, (c) medullary cavities in bones of infants, (d) medullary cavities in bones of a healthy adult.

5. An osteon has (a) a central canal carrying blood vessels, (b) concentric lamellae, (c) osteocytes in lacunae, (d) canaliculi that connect lacunae to the central canal, (e) all of these.

6. The organic portion of matrix is important in providing all but (a) tensile strength, (b) hardness, (c) ability to resist stretch, (d) flexibility.

7. The flat bones of the skull develop from (a) areolar tissue, (b) hyaline cartilage, (c) fibrous connective tissue, (d) compact bone.

8. The remodeling of bone is a function of which cells? (a) chondrocytes and osteocytes, (b) osteoblasts and osteoclasts, (c) chondroblasts and osteoclasts, (d) osteoblasts and osteocytes.

9. Bone remodeling in adults is regulated and directed mainly by (a) growth hormone, (b) thyroid hormones, (c) sex hormones, (d) mechanical stress, (e) PTH.

10. Where within the epiphyseal plate are the dividing cartilage cells located? (a) nearest the shaft, (b) in the marrow cavity, (c) farthest from the shaft, (d) in the primary ossification center.

11. Wolff's law is concerned with (a) calcium homeostasis of the blood, (b) the thickness and shape of a bone being determined by mechanical and gravitational stresses placed on it, (c) the electrical charge on bone surfaces.

12. Formation of the bony callus in fracture repair is followed by (a) hematoma formation, (b) fibrocartilaginous callus formation, (c) bone remodeling to convert woven bone to compact bone, (d) formation of granulation tissue.

13. The fracture type in which the bone ends are incompletely separated is (a) greenstick, (b) compound, (c) simple, (d) comminuted, (e) compression.

14. The disorder in which bones are porous and thin but bone composition is normal is (a) osteomalacia, (b) osteoporosis, (c) Paget's disease.

Short Answer Essay Questions

15. Compare bone to cartilage tissue relative to its resilience, speed of regeneration, and access to nutrients.

16. Describe in proper order the events of endochondral ossification.

17. Osteocytes residing in lacunae of osteons of healthy compact bone are located quite a distance from the blood vessels in the central canals, yet they are well nourished. How can this be explained?

18. As we grow, our long bones increase in diameter, but the thickness of the compact bone of the shaft remains relatively constant. Explain this phenomenon.

19. Describe the process of new bone formation in an adult bone. Use the terms osteoid seam and calcification front in your discussion.

20. Compare and contrast controls of bone remodeling exerted by hormones and by mechanical and gravitational forces, including the actual purpose of each control system and changes in bone architecture that might occur.

21. (a) During what period of life does skeletal mass increase dramatically? Begin to decline? (b) Why are fractures most common in elderly individuals? (c) Why are greenstick fractures most common in children?

22. Yolanda is asked to review a bone slide that her professor has set up under the microscope. She sees concentric layers surrounding a central cavity. Is this bone section taken from the diaphysis or the epiphyseal plate of the specimen?

Critical Thinking and Clinical Application Questions

1. Following a motorcycle accident, a 22-year-old man was rushed to the emergency room. X rays revealed a spiral fracture of his right tibia (main bone of the leg). Two months later, X rays revealed good bony callus formation. What is bony callus?

2. Mrs. Abbruzzo brought her 4-year-old daughter to the doctor, complaining that she didn't "look right." The child's forehead was enlarged, her rib cage was knobby, and her lower limbs were bent and deformed. X rays revealed very thick epiphyseal plates. Mrs. Abbruzzo was advised to increase dietary amounts of vitamin D and milk and to "shoo" the girl outside to play in the sun. Considering the child's signs and symptoms, what disease do you think she has? Explain the doctor's instructions.

3. You overhear some anatomy students imagining out loud what their bones would look like if they had compact bone on the inside and spongy bone on the outside, instead of the other way around. You tell them that such imaginary bones would be poorly designed mechanically and would break easily. Explain your reason for saying this.

4. What would a long bone look like at the end of adolescence if bone remodeling did not occur?

5. Why do you think wheelchair-bound people with paralyzed lower limbs have thin, weak, leg and thigh bones?

6. Jay Beckenstein went to weight-lifting camp in the summer between seventh and eighth grade. He noticed that the camp trainer put tremendous pressure on him and his friends to improve their strength. After an especially vigorous workout, Jay's arm felt extremely sore and weak around the elbow. He went to the camp doctor, who took X rays and then told him that the injury was serious, for the "end of his upper arm bone was starting to twist off." What had happened? Could the same thing happen to Jay's 23-year-old sister, Trixie, who was also starting a program of weight lifting? Why or why not?

7. Old Norse stories tell of a famous Viking named Egil, who lived around 900 AD. His skull was greatly enlarged and misshapen, and the cranial bones were thickened (6 cm, more than 2 inches, thick). After he died, his skull was dug up and it withstood the blow of an ax without damage. In life, he had headaches from the pressure exerted by enlarged vertebrae on his spinal cord. So much blood was diverted to his bones to support their extensive remodeling that his fingers and toes always felt cold and his heart was damaged through overexertion. What bone disorder did Egil probably have?

6

7

The Skeleton

PART 1

THE AXIAL SKELETON

The Skull (pp. 200–216)

The Vertebral Column (pp. 216–223)

The Thoracic Cage (pp. 223–225)

PART 2

THE APPENDICULAR SKELETON

The Pectoral (Shoulder) Girdle (pp. 225–228)

The Upper Limb (pp. 228–233)

The Pelvic (Hip) Girdle (pp. 233–237)

The Lower Limb (pp. 237–242)

Developmental Aspects of the Skeleton (pp. 242–244)

The word *skeleton* comes from the Greek word meaning "dried-up body" or "mummy," a rather unflattering description. Nonetheless, the human skeleton is a triumph of design and engineering that puts most skyscrapers to shame. It is strong, yet light, and almost perfectly adapted for the protective, locomotor, and manipulative functions it performs.

The **skeleton**, or **skeletal system**, composed of bones, cartilages, joints, and ligaments, accounts for about 20% of body mass (about 30 pounds in a 160-pound person). Bones make up most of the skeleton. Cartilages occur only in isolated areas, such as the nose, parts of the ribs, and the joints. Ligaments connect bones and reinforce joints, allowing required movements while restricting motions in other directions. Joints, the junctions between bones, provide for the remarkable mobility of the skeleton. We discuss joints and ligaments separately in Chapter 8.

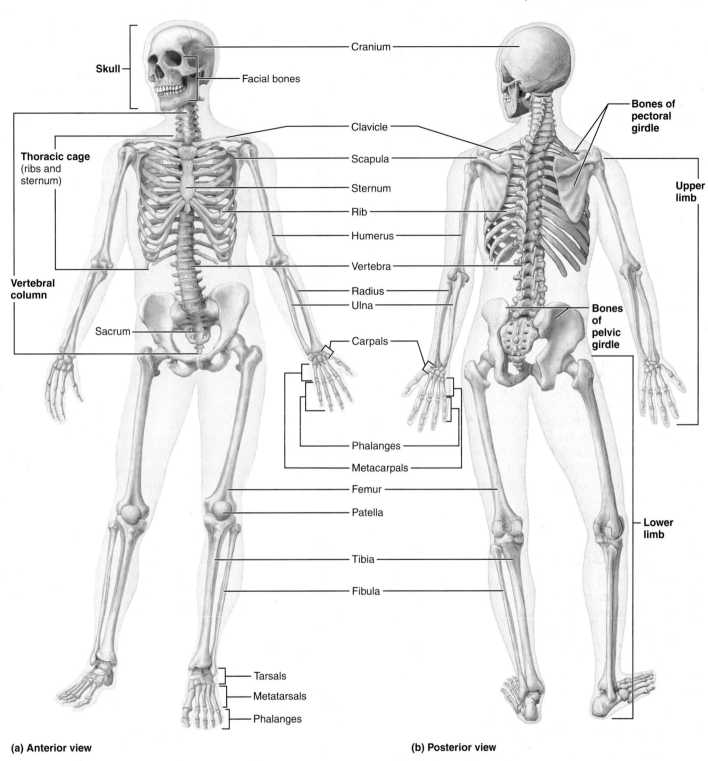

Figure 7.1 The human skeleton. Bones of the axial skeleton are colored green. Bones of the appendicular skeleton are gold.

PART **1**

THE AXIAL SKELETON

▶ Name the major parts of the axial and appendicular skeletons and describe their relative functions.

As described in Chapter 6, the skeleton is divided into *axial* and *appendicular* portions (see Figures 6.1 and 7.1). The **axial skeleton** is structured from 80 bones segregated into three major regions: the *skull*, *vertebral column*, and *thoracic cage* (Figure 7.1). This part of the skeleton (1) forms the longitudinal axis of the body, (2) supports the head, neck, and trunk, and (3) protects the brain, spinal cord, and the organs in the thorax. As we will see later in this chapter, the bones of the appendicular skeleton, which allow us to interact with and manipulate our environment, are appended to the axial skeleton.

CHECK YOUR UNDERSTANDING

1. What are the three main parts of the axial skeleton?
2. Which part of the skeleton—axial or appendicular—is important in protecting internal organs?

For answers, see Appendix G.

The Skull

▶ Name, describe, and identify the skull bones. Identify their important markings.

▶ Compare and contrast the major functions of the cranium and the facial skeleton.

The **skull** is the body's most complex bony structure. It is formed by *cranial* and *facial bones*, 22 in all. The cranial bones, or **cranium** (kra′ne-um), enclose and protect the fragile brain and furnish attachment sites for head and neck muscles. The facial bones (1) form the framework of the face, (2) contain cavities for the special sense organs of sight, taste, and smell, (3) provide openings for air and food passage, (4) secure the teeth, and (5) anchor the facial muscles of expression, which we use to show our feelings. As you will see, the individual skull bones are well suited to their assignments.

Most skull bones are flat bones. Except for the mandible, which is connected to the rest of the skull by freely movable joints, all bones of the adult skull are firmly united by interlocking joints called **sutures** (soo′cherz). The suture lines have a saw-toothed or serrated appearance.

The major skull sutures, the *coronal, sagittal, squamous,* and *lambdoid sutures*, connect cranial bones (Figures 7.2a, 7.4b, and 7.5a). Most other skull sutures connect facial bones and are named according to the specific bones they connect.

Overview of Skull Geography

It is worth surveying basic skull "geography" before describing the individual bones. With the lower jaw removed, the skull resembles a lopsided, hollow, bony sphere. The facial bones form its anterior aspect, and the cranium forms the rest of the skull (**Figure 7.2a**).

The cranium can be divided into a vault and a base. The *cranial vault*, also called the *calvaria* (kal-va′re-ah; "bald part of skull"), forms the superior, lateral, and posterior aspects of the skull, as well as the forehead. The *cranial base*, or *floor*, forms the skull's inferior aspect. Internally, prominent bony ridges divide the base into three distinct "steps" or fossae—the *anterior, middle,* and *posterior cranial fossae* (Figure 7.2b and c). The brain

sits snugly in these cranial fossae, completely enclosed by the cranial vault. Overall, the brain is said to occupy the *cranial cavity*.

In addition to the large cranial cavity, the skull has many smaller cavities. These include the middle and internal ear cavities (carved into the lateral side of its base) and, anteriorly, the nasal cavity and the orbits **(Figure 7.3)**. The *orbits* house the eyeballs. Several bones of the skull contain air-filled sinuses, which lighten the skull.

The skull also has about 85 named openings (foramina, canals, fissures, etc.). The most important of these provide passageways for the spinal cord, the major blood vessels serving the brain, and the 12 pairs of cranial nerves (numbered I through XII), which transmit impulses to and from the brain.

As you read about the bones of the skull, locate each bone on the different skull views in **Figures 7.4**, **7.5**, and **7.6**. The skull bones and their important markings are also summarized in **Table 7.1** (pp. 214–215). The color-coded boxes before a bone's name in the text and in Table 7.1 correspond to the color of that bone in the figures. For example, note the color of the frontal bone in Table 7.1 and see how you can easily find it in Figures 7.4 and 7.5.

Cranium

The eight cranial bones are the paired parietal and temporal bones and the unpaired frontal, occipital, sphenoid, and ethmoid bones. Together, these construct the brain's protective bony "helmet." Because its superior aspect is curved, the cranium is self-bracing. This allows the bones to be thin, and, like an eggshell, the cranium is remarkably strong for its weight.

Frontal Bone

The shell-shaped **frontal bone** (Figures 7.4a, 7.5, and 7.7) forms the anterior cranium. It articulates posteriorly with the paired parietal bones via the prominent *coronal suture.*

The most anterior part of the frontal bone is the vertical *squamous part*, commonly called the *forehead*. The frontal squamous region ends inferiorly at the **supraorbital margins**, the thickened superior margins of the orbits that lie under the eyebrows. From here, the frontal bone extends posteriorly, forming the superior wall of the *orbits* and most of the **anterior cranial fossa** **(Figure 7.7a and b)**. This fossa supports the frontal lobes of the brain. Each supraorbital margin is pierced by a **supraorbital foramen (notch)**, which allows the supraorbital artery and nerve to pass to the forehead (Figure 7.4a).

The smooth portion of the frontal bone between the orbits is the **glabella** (glah-bel′ah). Just inferior to this the frontal bone meets the nasal bones at the *frontonasal suture* (Figure 7.4a). The areas lateral to the glabella are riddled internally with sinuses, called the **frontal sinuses** (Figures 7.5b and 7.3).

Parietal Bones and the Major Sutures

The two large **parietal bones** are curved, rectangular bones that form most of the superior and lateral aspects of the skull; hence they form the bulk of the cranial vault. The four largest sutures occur where the parietal bones articulate (form a joint) with other cranial bones:

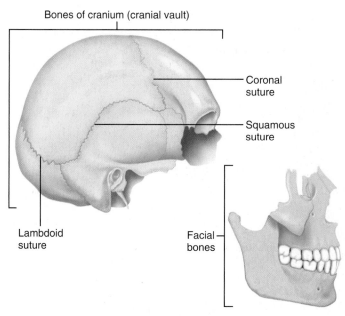

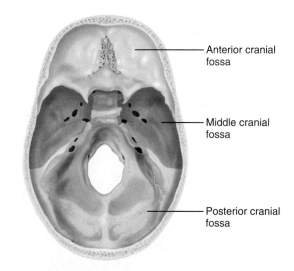

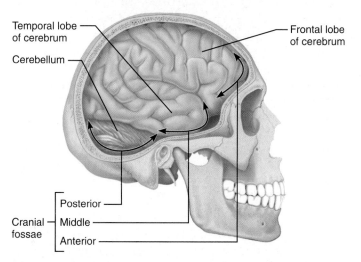

(a) Cranial and facial divisions of the skull

(b) Superior view of the cranial fossae

(c) Lateral view of cranial fossae showing the contained brain regions

Figure 7.2 **The skull: Cranial and facial divisions and fossae.**

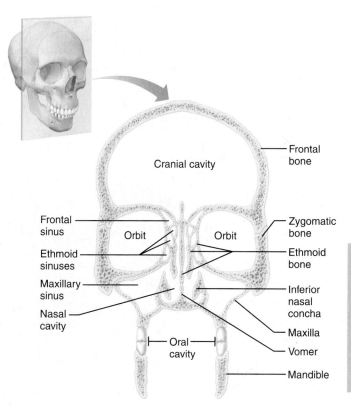

Figure 7.3 **Major cavities of the skull, frontal section.**

1. The **coronal suture** (kŏ-ro′nul), where the parietal bones meet the frontal bone anteriorly (Figures 7.2a and 7.5)
2. The **sagittal suture**, where the parietal bones meet superiorly at the cranial midline (Figure 7.4b)
3. The **lambdoid suture** (lam′doid), where the parietal bones meet the occipital bone posteriorly (Figures 7.2a, 7.4b, and 7.5)
4. The **squamous** (or **squamosal**) **suture** (one on each side), where a parietal and temporal bone meet on the lateral aspect of the skull (Figures 7.2a and 7.5)

Occipital Bone

The **occipital bone** (ok-sip′ĭ-tal) forms most of the skull's posterior wall and base. It articulates anteriorly with the paired parietal and temporal bones via the *lambdoid* and *occipitomastoid sutures*, respectively (Figure 7.5). It also joins with the sphenoid bone in the cranial floor via its basilar region, which bears a midline projection called the *pharyngeal tubercle* (fah-rin′je-ul) (Figure 7.6a).

Internally, the occipital bone forms the walls of the **posterior cranial fossa** (Figures 7.7 and 7.2c), which supports the cerebellum of the brain. In the base of the occipital bone is the **foramen magnum** ("large hole") through which the inferior part of the brain connects with the spinal cord. The foramen magnum is flanked laterally by two occipital condyles (Figure 7.6). The rockerlike **occipital condyles** articulate with the first vertebra of the spinal column in a way that permits a nodding ("yes") motion

7

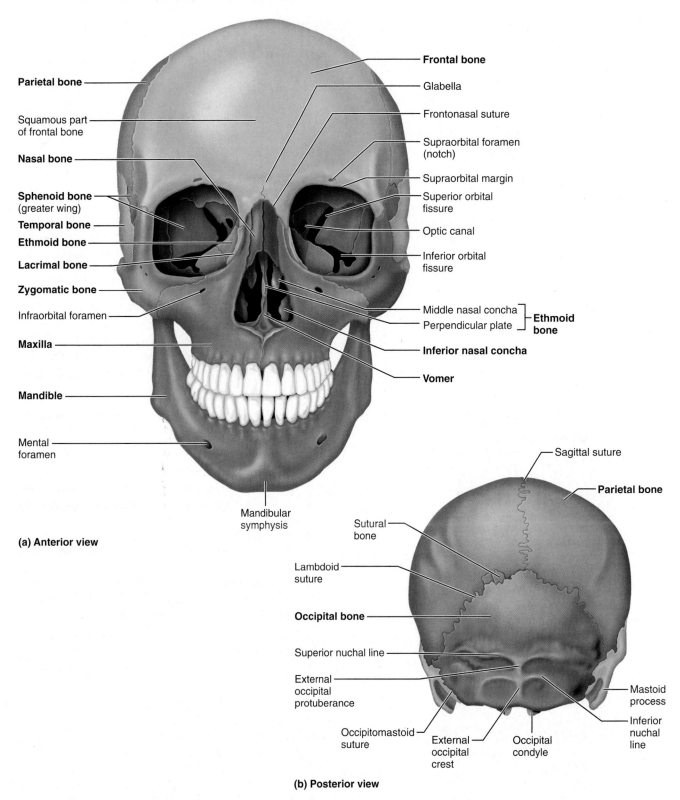

Parietal bone

Squamous part
of frontal bone

Nasal bone

Sphenoid bone
(greater wing)

Temporal bone

Ethmoid bone

Lacrimal bone

Zygomatic bone

Infraorbital foramen

Maxilla

Mandible

Mental
foramen

Frontal bone

Glabella

Frontonasal suture

Supraorbital foramen
(notch)

Supraorbital margin

Superior orbital
fissure

Optic canal

Inferior orbital
fissure

Middle nasal concha ⎤
                     ⎥ Ethmoid
Perpendicular plate ⎦ bone

Inferior nasal concha

Vomer

Mandibular
symphysis

(a) Anterior view

Sagittal suture

Parietal bone

Sutural
bone

Lambdoid
suture

Occipital bone

Superior nuchal line

External
occipital
protuberance

Occipitomastoid
suture

External
occipital
crest

Occipital
condyle

Mastoid
process

Inferior
nuchal
line

(b) Posterior view

Figure 7.4 **Anatomy of the anterior and posterior aspects of the skull.** (See *A Brief Atlas of the Human Body*, Figures 1 and 7.)

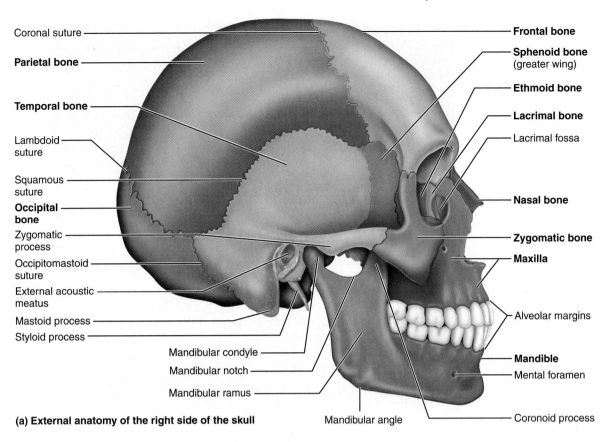

Coronal suture

Parietal bone

Temporal bone

Lambdoid suture

Squamous suture

Occipital bone

Zygomatic process

Occipitomastoid suture

External acoustic meatus

Mastoid process

Styloid process

Mandibular condyle

Mandibular notch

Mandibular ramus

Frontal bone

Sphenoid bone (greater wing)

Ethmoid bone

Lacrimal bone

Lacrimal fossa

Nasal bone

Zygomatic bone

Maxilla

Alveolar margins

Mandible

Mental foramen

Mandibular angle

Coronoid process

(a) External anatomy of the right side of the skull

7

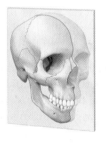

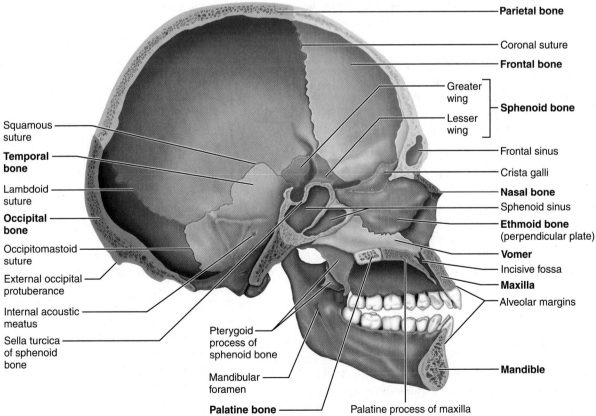

Parietal bone

Coronal suture

Frontal bone

Greater wing

Lesser wing

Sphenoid bone

Frontal sinus

Crista galli

Nasal bone

Sphenoid sinus

Ethmoid bone (perpendicular plate)

Vomer

Incisive fossa

Maxilla

Alveolar margins

Mandible

Squamous suture

Temporal bone

Lambdoid suture

Occipital bone

Occipitomastoid suture

External occipital protuberance

Internal acoustic meatus

Sella turcica of sphenoid bone

Pterygoid process of sphenoid bone

Mandibular foramen

Palatine bone

Palatine process of maxilla

(b) Midsagittal section showing the internal anatomy of the left half of skull

Figure 7.5 Bones of the lateral aspect of the skull, external and internal views. (See *A Brief Atlas of the Human Body*, Figures 2 and 3.)

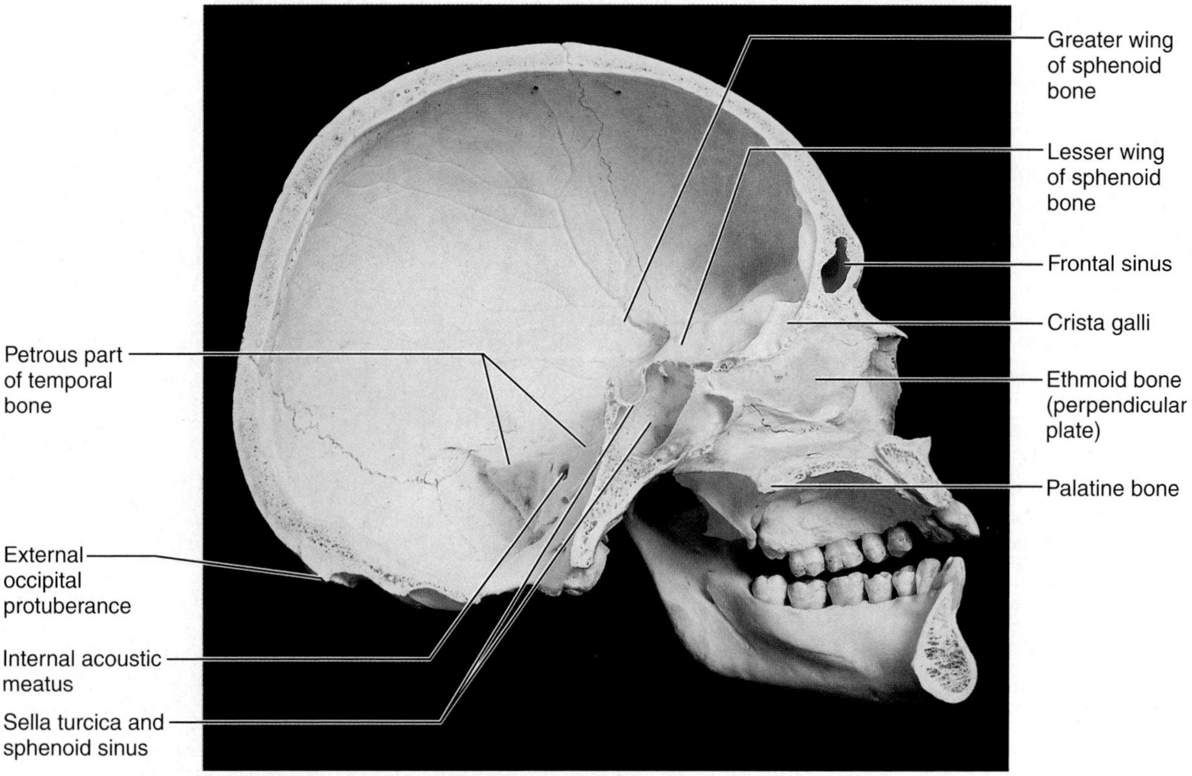

Greater wing
of sphenoid
bone

Lesser wing
of sphenoid
bone

Frontal sinus

Crista galli

Ethmoid bone
(perpendicular
plate)

Palatine bone

Petrous part
of temporal
bone

External
occipital
protuberance

Internal acoustic
meatus

Sella turcica and
sphenoid sinus

(c) Photo of skull cut through the midline, same view as in (b)

Figure 7.5 *(continued)* **Bones of the lateral aspect of the skull, external and internal views.** (See *A Brief Atlas of the Human Body,* Figures 2 and 3.)

of the head. Hidden medially and superiorly to each occipital condyle is a **hypoglossal canal** (Figure 7.7), through which a cranial nerve (XII) of the same name passes.

Just superior to the foramen magnum is a median protrusion called the **external occipital protuberance** (Figures 7.4, 7.5, and 7.6). You can feel this knoblike projection just below the most bulging part of your posterior skull. A number of inconspicuous ridges, the *external occipital crest* and the *superior* and *inferior nuchal lines* (nu′kal), mark the occipital bone near the foramen magnum. The external occipital crest secures the *ligamentum nuchae* (lig″ah-men′tum noo′ke; *nucha* = back of the neck), a sheetlike elastic ligament that connects the vertebrae of the neck to the skull. The nuchal lines, and the bony regions between them, anchor many neck and back muscles. The superior nuchal line marks the upper limit of the neck.

Temporal Bones

The two **temporal bones** are best viewed on the lateral skull surface (Figure 7.5). They lie inferior to the parietal bones and meet them at the squamous sutures. The temporal bones form the inferolateral aspects of the skull and parts of the cranial floor. The use of the terms *temple* and *temporal,* from the Latin word *temporum,* meaning "time," came about because gray hairs, a sign of time's passing, usually appear first at the temples.

Each temporal bone has a complicated shape **(Figure 7.8)** and is described in terms of its four major areas, the *squamous,*

tympanic, mastoid, and *petrous regions.* The flaring **squamous region** abuts the squamous suture. It has a barlike **zygomatic process** that meets the zygomatic bone of the face anteriorly. Together, these two bony structures form the **zygomatic arch,** which you can feel as the projection of your cheek (*zygoma* = cheekbone). The small, oval **mandibular fossa** (man-dib′u-lar) on the inferior surface of the zygomatic process receives the condyle of the mandible (lower jawbone), forming the freely movable *temporomandibular joint.*

The **tympanic region** (tim-pan′ik; "eardrum") (Figure 7.8) of the temporal bone surrounds the **external acoustic meatus,** or external ear canal, through which sound enters the ear. The external acoustic meatus and the eardrum at its deep end are part of the *external ear.* In a dried skull, the eardrum has been removed and part of the middle ear cavity deep to the external meatus can also be seen. Below the external acoustic meatus is the needle-like **styloid process** (sti′loid; "stakelike"), an attachment point for several tongue and neck muscles and for a ligament that secures the hyoid bone of the neck to the skull (see Figure 7.12).

The **mastoid region** (mas′toid; "breast") of the temporal bone exhibits the conspicuous **mastoid process,** an anchoring site for some neck muscles (Figures 7.5, 7.6, and 7.8). This process can be felt as a lump just posterior to the ear. The **stylomastoid foramen,** between the styloid and mastoid processes, allows cranial nerve VII (the facial nerve) to leave the skull (Figure 7.6).

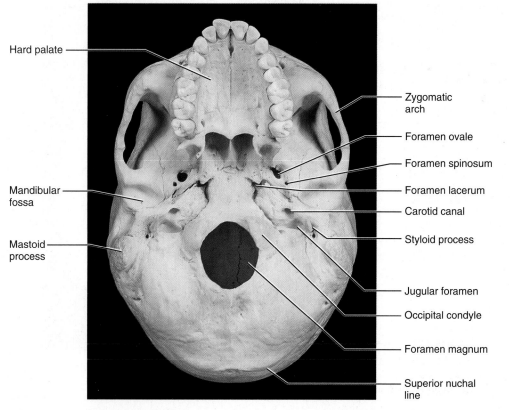

Maxilla (palatine process)
Hard palate
Palatine bone (horizontal plate)

Zygomatic bone

Temporal bone (zygomatic process)

Vomer

Mandibular fossa

Styloid process

Mastoid process

Temporal bone (petrous part)

Pharyngeal tubercle of basilar region of the occipital bone

Parietal bone

External occipital crest

External occipital protuberance

Incisive fossa
Intermaxillary suture
Median palatine suture
Infraorbital foramen
Maxilla

Sphenoid bone (greater wing)

Foramen ovale
Foramen spinosum
Foramen lacerum
Carotid canal
External acoustic meatus
Stylomastoid foramen
Jugular foramen

Occipital condyle

Inferior nuchal line
Superior nuchal line

Foramen magnum

(a) Inferior view of the skull (mandible removed)

7

Hard palate

Mandibular fossa

Mastoid process

Zygomatic arch

Foramen ovale
Foramen spinosum
Foramen lacerum
Carotid canal
Styloid process

Jugular foramen

Occipital condyle

Foramen magnum

Superior nuchal line

(b) Photo of inferior view of the skull

Figure 7.6 Inferior aspect of the skull, mandible removed. (See *A Brief Atlas of the Human Body*, Figures 4 and 5.)

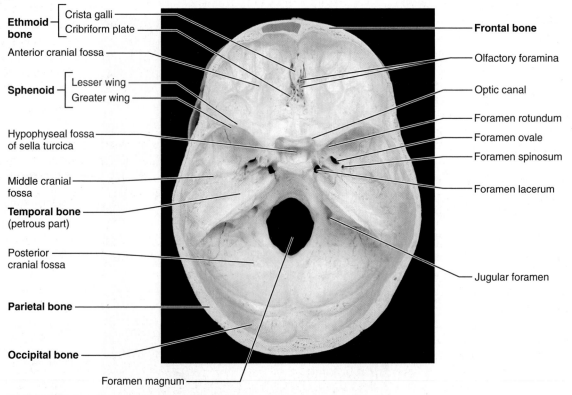

View

Ethmoid bone
— Cribriform plate
— Crista galli

Anterior cranial fossa

Sphenoid
— Lesser wing
— Greater wing

Hypophyseal fossa of sella turcica

Middle cranial fossa

Temporal bone (petrous part)

Posterior cranial fossa

Parietal bone

Occipital bone

Foramen magnum

Frontal bone

Olfactory foramina

Optic canal

Foramen rotundum

Foramen ovale

Foramen spinosum

Foramen lacerum

Internal acoustic meatus

Jugular foramen

Hypoglossal canal

(a) Superior view of the skull, calvaria removed

Ethmoid bone
— Crista galli
— Cribriform plate

Anterior cranial fossa

Sphenoid
— Lesser wing
— Greater wing

Hypophyseal fossa of sella turcica

Middle cranial fossa

Temporal bone (petrous part)

Posterior cranial fossa

Parietal bone

Occipital bone

Foramen magnum

Frontal bone

Olfactory foramina

Optic canal

Foramen rotundum

Foramen ovale

Foramen spinosum

Foramen lacerum

Jugular foramen

(b) Superior view of the skull, calvaria removed

Figure 7.7 **The floor of the cranial cavity.** The fossae are named according to relative location as anterior, middle, and posterior fossae. (See *A Brief Atlas of the Human Body*, Figures 4 and 5.)

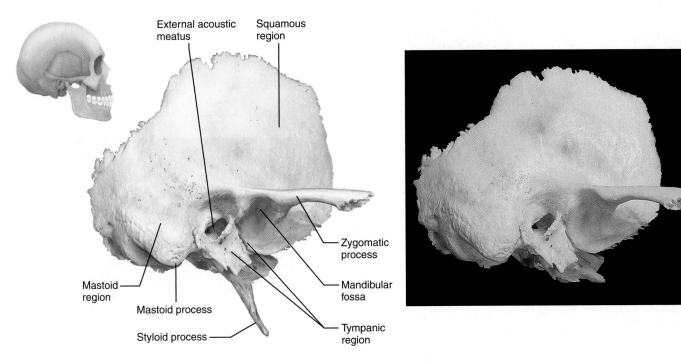

Figure 7.8 The temporal bone. Right lateral view. (See *A Brief Atlas of the Human Body*, Figures 2 and 8.)

HOMEOSTATIC IMBALANCE

The mastoid process is full of air cavities, the **mastoid sinuses**, or **mastoid air cells**. Its position adjacent to the middle ear cavity (a high-risk area for infections spreading from the throat) puts it at risk for infection itself. A mastoid sinus infection, or *mastoiditis*, is notoriously difficult to treat. Because the mastoid air cells are separated from the brain by only a very thin bony plate, mastoid infections may spread to the brain as well. Surgical removal of the mastoid process was once the best way to prevent life-threatening brain inflammations in people susceptible to repeated bouts of mastoiditis. Today, antibiotic therapy is the treatment of choice. ∎

The deep **petrous** (pet'rus) part of the temporal bone contributes to the cranial base (Figures 7.6 and 7.7). It looks like a miniature mountain ridge (*petrous* = rocky) between the occipital bone posteriorly and the sphenoid bone anteriorly. The posterior slope of this ridge lies in the posterior cranial fossa; the anterior slope is in the middle cranial fossa. Together, the sphenoid bone and the petrous portions of the temporal bones construct the **middle cranial fossa** (Figures 7.7 and 7.2b), which supports the temporal lobes of the brain. Housed inside the petrous region are the *middle* and *internal ear cavities*, which contain sensory receptors for hearing and balance.

Several foramina penetrate the bone of the petrous region (Figure 7.6). The large **jugular foramen** at the junction of the occipital and petrous temporal bones allows passage of the internal jugular vein and three cranial nerves (IX, X, and XI). The **carotid canal** (kar-rot'id), just anterior to the jugular foramen, transmits the internal carotid artery into the cranial cavity. The two internal carotid arteries supply blood to over 80% of the cerebral hemispheres of the brain; their closeness to the internal ear cavities explains why, during excitement or exertion, we

sometimes hear our rapid pulse as a thundering sound in the head. The **foramen lacerum** (la'ser-um) is a jagged opening (*lacerum* = torn or lacerated) between the petrous temporal bone and the sphenoid bone. It is almost completely closed by cartilage in a living person, but it is conspicuous in a dried skull, and students usually ask its name. The **internal acoustic meatus**, positioned superolateral to the jugular foramen (Figures 7.5b and c, and 7.7), transmits cranial nerves VII and VIII.

Sphenoid Bone

The bat-shaped **sphenoid bone** (sfe'noid; *sphen* = wedge) spans the width of the middle cranial fossa (Figure 7.7). The sphenoid is considered the keystone of the cranium because it forms a central wedge that articulates with all other cranial bones. It is a challenging bone to study because of its complex shape. As shown in **Figure 7.9**, it consists of a central body and three pairs of processes: the greater wings, lesser wings, and pterygoid processes (ter'ĭ-goid). Within the **body** of the sphenoid are the paired **sphenoid sinuses** (see Figures 7.5b and c, and 7.14).

The superior surface of the body bears a saddle-shaped prominence, the **sella turcica** (sel'ah ter'sĭ-kah), meaning "Turk's saddle." The seat of this saddle, called the **hypophyseal fossa**, forms a snug enclosure for the pituitary gland (hypophysis).

The **greater wings** project laterally from the sphenoid body, forming parts of (1) the middle cranial fossa (Figures 7.7 and 7.2b), (2) the dorsal walls of the orbits (Figure 7.4a), and (3) the external wall of the skull, where they are seen as flag-shaped, bony areas medial to the zygomatic arch (Figure 7.5). The horn-like **lesser wings** form part of the floor of the anterior cranial fossa (Figure 7.7) and part of the medial walls of the orbits. The trough-shaped **pterygoid processes** project inferiorly from the

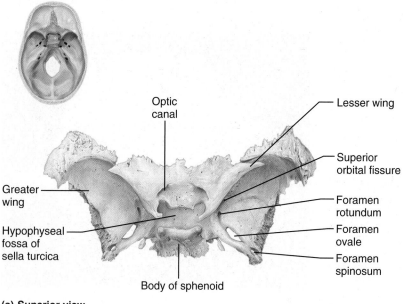

(a) Superior view

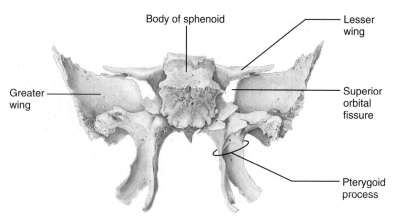

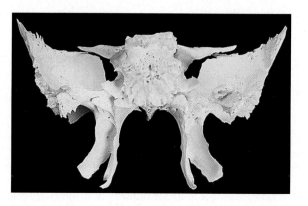

(b) Posterior view

Figure 7.9 **The sphenoid bone.** (See *A Brief Atlas of the Human Body*, Figures 5 and 9).

junction of the body and greater wings (Figure 7.9b). They anchor the pterygoid muscles, which are important in chewing.

A number of openings in the sphenoid bone are visible in Figures 7.7 and 7.9. The **optic canals** lie anterior to the sella turcica; they allow the optic nerves (cranial nerves II) to pass to the eyes. On each side of the sphenoid body is a crescent-shaped row of four openings. The anteriormost of these, the **superior orbital fissure**, is a long slit between the greater and lesser wings. It allows cranial nerves that control eye movements (III, IV, VI) to enter the orbit. This fissure is most obvious in an anterior view of the skull (Figure 7.4. See also Figure 7.9b.). The **foramen rotundum** and **foramen ovale** (o-va′le) provide passageways for branches of cranial nerve V (the maxillary and mandibular nerves, respectively) to reach the face (Figure 7.7). The foramen rotundum is in the medial part of the greater wing and is usually oval, despite its name meaning "round opening." The foramen ovale, a large, oval foramen posterior to the foramen rotundum, is also visible in an inferior view of the skull (Figure 7.6). Posterolateral to the foramen ovale is the small **foramen**

spinosum (Figure 7.7); it transmits the *middle meningeal artery*, which serves the internal faces of some cranial bones.

Ethmoid Bone

Like the temporal and sphenoid bones, the delicate **ethmoid bone** has a complex shape (**Figure 7.10**). Lying between the sphenoid and the nasal bones of the face, it is the most deeply situated bone of the skull. It forms most of the bony area between the nasal cavity and the orbits.

The superior surface of the ethmoid is formed by the paired horizontal **cribriform plates** (krib′rĭ-form) (see also Figure 7.7), which help form the roof of the nasal cavities and the floor of the anterior cranial fossa. The cribriform plates are punctured by tiny holes (*cribr* = sieve) called *olfactory foramina* that allow the filaments of the olfactory nerves to pass from the smell receptors in the nasal cavities to the brain. Projecting superiorly between the cribriform plates is a triangular process called the **crista galli** (kris′tah gah′le; "rooster's comb"). The outermost

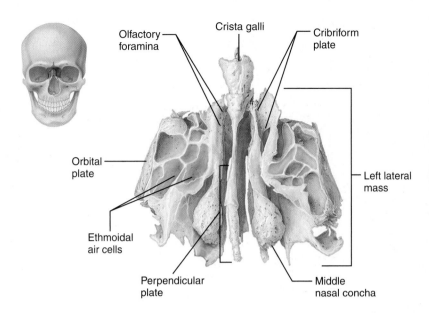

Olfactory foramina · Crista galli · Cribriform plate · Orbital plate · Left lateral mass · Ethmoidal air cells · Perpendicular plate · Middle nasal concha

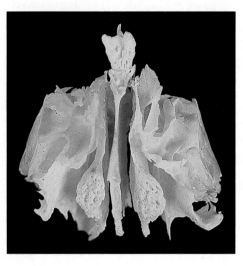

Figure 7.10 The ethmoid bone. Anterior view. (See *A Brief Atlas of the Human Body,* Figures 3 and 10.)

covering of the brain (the dura mater) attaches to the crista galli and helps secure the brain in the cranial cavity.

The **perpendicular plate** of the ethmoid bone projects inferiorly in the median plane and forms the superior part of the nasal septum, which divides the nasal cavity into right and left halves (Figure 7.5b and c). Flanking the perpendicular plate on each side is a **lateral mass** riddled with the **ethmoid sinuses**, also called the **ethmoidal air cells** (Figures 7.10 and 7.15), for which the bone itself is named (*ethmos* = sieve). Extending medially from the lateral masses, the delicately coiled **superior** and **middle nasal conchae** (kong′ke; *concha* = shell), named after the conch shells found on warm ocean beaches, protrude into the nasal cavity (Figures 7.10 and 7.14a). The lateral surfaces of the ethmoid's lateral masses are called **orbital plates** because they contribute to the medial walls of the orbits.

Sutural Bones

Sutural bones are tiny irregularly shaped bones or bone clusters that occur within sutures, most often in the lambdoid suture (Figure 7.4b). Structurally unimportant, their number varies, and not all skulls exhibit them. The significance of these tiny bones is unknown.

CHECK YOUR UNDERSTANDING

3. Look at Figure 7.4. Which of the skull bones illustrated in view (a) are cranial bones?
4. Which bone forms the crista galli?
5. Which skull bones house the external ear canals?
6. What bones abut one another at the sagittal suture? At the lambdoid suture?

For answers, see Appendix G.

Facial Bones

The facial skeleton is made up of 14 bones (see Figures 7.4a and 7.5a), of which only the mandible and the vomer are unpaired. The maxillae, zygomatics, nasals, lacrimals, palatines, and inferior nasal conchae are paired bones. As a rule, the facial skeleton of men is more elongated than that of women. Women's faces tend to be rounder and less angular.

Mandible

The U-shaped **mandible** (man′dĭ-bl), or lower jawbone (Figures 7.4a and 7.5, and **Figure 7.11a**), is the largest, strongest bone of the face. It has a body, which forms the chin, and two upright *rami* (*rami* = branches). Each ramus meets the body posteriorly at a **mandibular angle**. At the superior margin of each ramus are two processes separated by the **mandibular notch**. The anterior **coronoid process** (kor′o-noid; "crown-shaped") is an insertion point for the large temporalis muscle that elevates the lower jaw during chewing. The posterior **mandibular condyle** articulates with the mandibular fossa of the temporal bone, forming the *temporomandibular joint* on the same side.

The mandibular **body** anchors the lower teeth. Its superior border, called the **alveolar margin** (al-ve′o-lar), contains the sockets (*alveoli*) in which the teeth are embedded. In the midline of the mandibular body is a slight depression, the **mandibular symphysis** (sim′fih-sis), indicating where the two mandibular bones fused during infancy (Figure 7.4a).

Large **mandibular foramina**, one on the medial surface of each ramus, permit the nerves responsible for tooth sensation to pass to the teeth in the lower jaw. Dentists inject lidocaine into these foramina to prevent pain while working on the lower teeth. The **mental foramina**, openings on the lateral aspects of the mandibular body, allow blood vessels and nerves to pass to the skin of the chin (*ment* = chin) and lower lip.

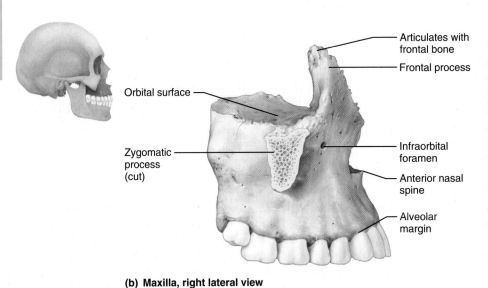

(a) **Mandible, right lateral view**

(b) **Maxilla, right lateral view**

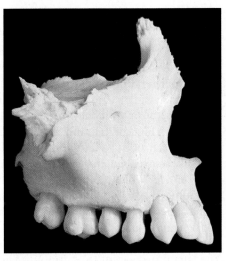

(c) **Maxilla, photo of right lateral view**

Figure 7.11 Detailed anatomy of the mandible and the maxilla. (See *A Brief Atlas of the Human Body*, Figures 11 and 12.)

Maxillary Bones

The **maxillary bones**, or **maxillae** (mak-sil′le; "jaws") (Figures 7.4 to 7.6 and 7.11b and c), are fused medially. They form the upper jaw and the central portion of the facial skeleton. All facial bones except the mandible articulate with the maxillae. Hence, the maxillae are considered the keystone bones of the facial skeleton.

The maxillae carry the upper teeth in their **alveolar margins**. Just inferior to the nose the maxillae meet medially, forming the pointed **anterior nasal spine** at their junction. The **palatine processes** (pă′lah-tīn) of the maxillae project posteriorly from the alveolar margins and fuse medially at the *intermaxillary suture*, forming the anterior two-thirds of the hard palate, or bony roof of the mouth (Figures 7.5b and c and 7.6). Just posterior to

the teeth is a midline foramen, called the **incisive fossa**, which serves as a passageway for blood vessels and nerves.

The **frontal processes** extend superiorly to the frontal bone, forming part of the lateral aspects of the bridge of the nose (Figures 7.4a and 7.11b). The regions that flank the nasal cavity laterally contain the **maxillary sinuses** (see Figure 7.15), the largest of the paranasal sinuses. They extend from the orbits to the roots of the upper teeth. Laterally, the maxillae articulate with the zygomatic bones via their **zygomatic processes**.

The **inferior orbital fissure** is located deep within the orbit (Figure 7.4a) at the junction of the maxilla with the greater wing of the sphenoid. It permits the zygomatic nerve, the maxillary nerve (a branch of cranial nerve V), and blood vessels to pass to the face. Just below the eye socket on each side is an **infraorbital foramen** that allows the infraorbital nerve (a continuation of the maxillary nerve) and artery to reach the face.

Zygomatic Bones

The irregularly shaped **zygomatic bones** (Figures 7.4a, 7.5a, and 7.6) are commonly called the cheekbones (*zygoma* = cheekbone). They articulate with the zygomatic processes of the temporal bones posteriorly, the zygomatic process of the frontal bone superiorly, and with the zygomatic processes of the maxillae anteriorly. The zygomatic bones form the prominences of the cheeks and part of the inferolateral margins of the orbits.

Nasal Bones

The thin, basically rectangular **nasal bones** (na′zal) are fused medially, forming the bridge of the nose (Figures 7.4a and 7.5a). They articulate with the frontal bone superiorly, the maxillary bones laterally, and the perpendicular plate of the ethmoid bone posteriorly. Inferiorly they attach to the cartilages that form most of the skeleton of the external nose.

Lacrimal Bones

The delicate fingernail-shaped **lacrimal bones** (lak′rĭ-mal) contribute to the medial walls of each orbit (Figures 7.4a and 7.5a). They articulate with the frontal bone superiorly, the ethmoid bone posteriorly, and the maxillae anteriorly. Each lacrimal bone contains a deep groove that helps form a **lacrimal fossa**. The lacrimal fossa houses the *lacrimal sac*, part of the passageway that allows tears to drain from the eye surface into the nasal cavity (*lacrima* = tears).

Palatine Bones

Each L-shaped **palatine bone** is fashioned from two bony plates, the *horizontal* and *perpendicular* (see Figures 7.14a and 7.6a), and has three important articular processes, the *pyramidal*, *sphenoidal*, and *orbital*. The **horizontal plates**, joined at the median palatine suture, complete the posterior portion of the hard palate. The superiorly projecting **perpendicular (vertical) plates** form part of the posterolateral walls of the nasal cavity and a small part of the orbits.

Vomer

The slender, plow-shaped **vomer** (vo′mer; "plow") lies in the nasal cavity, where it forms part of the nasal septum (see Figures 7.4a and 7.14b). It is described below in connection with the nasal cavity.

Inferior Nasal Conchae

The paired **inferior nasal conchae** are thin, curved bones in the nasal cavity. They project medially from the lateral walls of the nasal cavity, just inferior to the middle nasal conchae of the ethmoid bone (see Figures 7.4a and 7.14a). They are the largest of the three pairs of conchae and, like the others, they form part of the lateral walls of the nasal cavity.

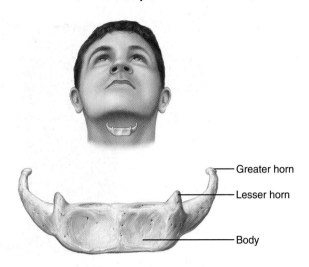

Greater horn
Lesser horn
Body

Figure 7.12 The hyoid bone, anterior view.

CHECK YOUR UNDERSTANDING

7. Women with prominent (high) cheekbones are often considered beautiful by the modeling industry. What bones are the "cheekbones"?
8. Johnny was vigorously exercising the only joints in the skull that are freely movable. What would you guess he was doing?
9. What bones are the keystone bones of the facial skeleton?

For answers, see Appendix G.

The Hyoid Bone

Though not really part of the skull, the **hyoid bone** (hi′oid; "U-shaped") lies just inferior to the mandible in the anterior neck, and looks like a miniature version of it (Figure 7.12). The hyoid bone is unique in that it is the only bone of the body that does not articulate directly with any other bone. Instead, it is anchored by the narrow *stylohyoid ligaments* to the styloid processes of the temporal bones. Horseshoe-shaped, with a body and two pairs of *horns*, or *cornua*, the hyoid bone acts as a movable base for the tongue. Its body and greater horns are attachment points for neck muscles that raise and lower the larynx during swallowing and speech.

Special Characteristics of the Orbits and Nasal Cavity

▶ Define the bony boundaries of the orbits, nasal cavity, and paranasal sinuses.

Two restricted skull regions, the orbits and the nasal cavity, are formed from an amazing number of bones. Even though we have already described the individual bones forming these structures, we give a brief summary here to pull the parts together.

The Orbits

The cone-shaped **orbits** are bony cavities in which the eyes are firmly encased and cushioned by fatty tissue. The muscles that

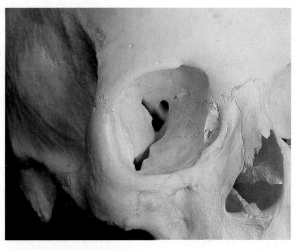

(a) Photograph, right orbit

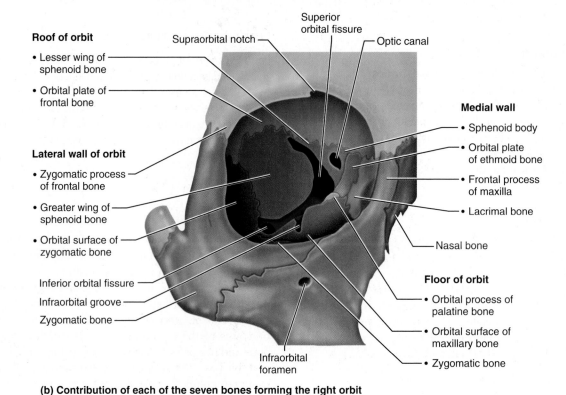

Roof of orbit
- Lesser wing of sphenoid bone
- Orbital plate of frontal bone

Supraorbital notch

Superior orbital fissure

Optic canal

Medial wall
- Sphenoid body
- Orbital plate of ethmoid bone
- Frontal process of maxilla
- Lacrimal bone

Nasal bone

Lateral wall of orbit
- Zygomatic process of frontal bone
- Greater wing of sphenoid bone
- Orbital surface of zygomatic bone

Inferior orbital fissure

Infraorbital groove

Zygomatic bone

Infraorbital foramen

Floor of orbit
- Orbital process of palatine bone
- Orbital surface of maxillary bone
- Zygomatic bone

(b) Contribution of each of the seven bones forming the right orbit

Figure 7.13 Bones that form the orbits. (See *A Brief Atlas of the Human Body*, Figure 14.)

move the eyes and the tear-producing lacrimal glands are also housed in the orbits. The walls of each orbit are formed by parts of seven bones—the frontal, sphenoid, zygomatic, maxilla, palatine, lacrimal, and ethmoid bones. Their relationships are shown in **Figure 7.13**. Also seen in the orbits are the superior and inferior orbital fissures and the optic canals, described earlier.

The Nasal Cavity

The **nasal cavity** is constructed of bone and hyaline cartilage **(Figure 7.14)**. The *roof* of the nasal cavity is formed by the cribriform plates of the ethmoid. The *lateral walls* are largely shaped by the superior and middle conchae of the ethmoid bone, the

perpendicular plates of the palatine bones, and the inferior nasal conchae. The depressions under cover of the conchae on the lateral walls are called *meatuses* (*meatus* = passage), so there are superior, middle, and inferior meatuses. The *floor* of the nasal cavity is formed by the palatine processes of the maxillae and the palatine bones. The nasal cavity is divided into right and left parts by the *nasal septum*. The bony portion of the septum is formed by the vomer inferiorly and the perpendicular plate of the ethmoid bone superiorly (Figure 7.14b). A sheet of cartilage called the *septal cartilage* completes the septum anteriorly.

The nasal septum and conchae are covered with a mucussecreting mucosa that moistens and warms the entering air and helps cleanse it of debris. The scroll-shaped conchae increase

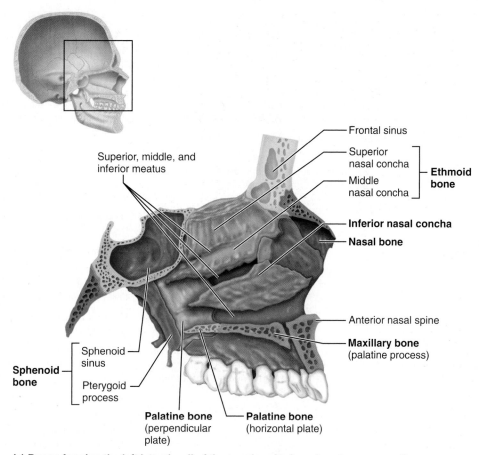

(a) Bones forming the left lateral wall of the nasal cavity (nasal septum removed)

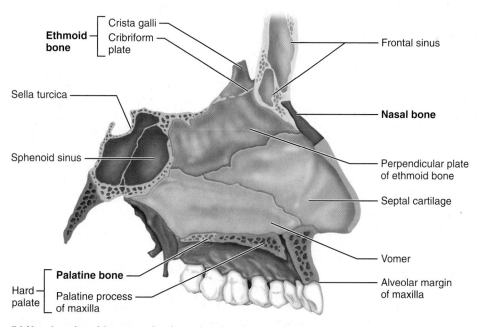

(b) Nasal cavity with septum in place showing the contributions of the ethmoid bone, the vomer, and septal cartilage

Figure 7.14 Bones of the nasal cavity. (See *A Brief Atlas of the Human Body*, Figure 15.)

TABLE 7.1	Bones of the Skull		
BONE COLOR CODE*		**COMMENTS**	**IMPORTANT MARKINGS**
Cranial Bones			
▢	**Frontal (1)** (Figures 7.4a, 7.5, and 7.7)	Forms forehead, superior part of orbits, and most of the anterior cranial fossa; contains sinuses	**Supraorbital foramina (notches):** allow the supraorbital arteries and nerves to pass
▢	**Parietal (2)** (Figures 7.4 and 7.5)	Form most of the superior and lateral aspects of the skull	
▢	**Occipital (1)** (Figures 7.4b, 7.5, 7.6, and 7.7)	Forms posterior aspect and most of the base of the skull	**Foramen magnum:** allows passage of the spinal cord from the brain stem to the vertebral canal
			Hypoglossal canals: allow passage of the hypoglossal nerves (cranial nerve XII)
			Occipital condyles: articulate with the atlas (first vertebra)
			External occipital protuberance and **nuchal lines:** sites of muscle attachment
			External occipital crest: attachment site of ligamentum nuchae
▢	**Temporal (2)** (Figures 7.5, 7.6, 7.7, and 7.8)	Form inferolateral aspects of the skull and contributes to the middle cranial fossa; has squamous, mastoid, tympanic, and petrous regions	**Zygomatic process:** helps to form the zygomatic arch, which forms the prominence of the cheek
			Mandibular fossa: articular point of the mandibular condyle
			External acoustic meatus: canal leading from the external ear to the eardrum
			Styloid process: attachment site for several neck muscles and for a ligament to the hyoid bone
			Mastoid process: attachment site for several neck and tongue muscles
			Stylomastoid foramen: allows cranial nerve VII (facial nerve) to pass
			Jugular foramen: allows passage of the internal jugular vein and cranial nerves IX, X, and XI
			Internal acoustic meatus: allows passage of cranial nerves VII and VIII
			Carotid canal: allows passage of the internal carotid artery
▢	**Sphenoid (1)** (Figures 7.4a, 7.5, 7.6, 7.7, and 7.9)	Keystone of the cranium; contributes to the middle cranial fossa and orbits; main parts are the body, greater wings, lesser wings, and pterygoid processes	**Sella turcica:** hypophyseal fossa portion is the seat of the pituitary gland
			Optic canals: allow passage of optic nerves (cranial nerves II) and the ophthalmic arteries
			Superior orbital fissures: allow passage of cranial nerves III, IV, VI, part of V (ophthalmic division), and ophthalmic vein
			Foramen rotundum (2): allows passage of the maxillary division of cranial nerve V
			Foramen ovale (2): allows passage of the mandibular division of cranial nerve V
			Foramen spinosum (2): allows passage of the middle meningeal artery

TABLE 7.1   (continued)

BONE COLOR CODE*	COMMENTS	IMPORTANT MARKINGS
Ethmoid (1) (Figures 7.4a, 7.5, 7.7, 7.10, and 7.14)	Helps to form the anterior cranial fossa; forms part of the nasal septum and the lateral walls and roof of the nasal cavity; contributes to the medial wall of the orbit	**Crista galli:** attachment point for the falx cerebri, a dural membrane fold **Cribriform plates:** allow passage of filaments of the olfactory nerves (cranial nerve I) **Superior** and **middle nasal conchae:** form part of lateral walls of nasal cavity; increase turbulence of air flow
Auditory ossicles (malleus, incus, and stapes) (2 each)	Found in middle ear cavity; involved in sound transmission; see Figure 15.25b, p. 575	

Facial Bones

BONE COLOR CODE*	COMMENTS	IMPORTANT MARKINGS
Mandible (1) (Figures 7.4a, 7.5, and 7.11a)	The lower jaw	**Coronoid processes:** insertion points for the temporalis muscles **Mandibular condyles:** articulate with the temporal bones in the temporomandibular joints of the jaw **Mandibular symphysis:** medial fusion point of the mandibular bones **Alveoli:** sockets for the teeth **Mandibular foramina:** permit the inferior alveolar nerves to pass **Mental foramina:** allow blood vessels and nerves to pass to the chin and lower lip
Maxilla (2) (Figure 7.4a, 7.5, 7.6, and 7.11b)	Keystone bones of the face; form the upper jaw and parts of the hard palate, orbits, and nasal cavity walls	**Alveoli:** sockets for teeth **Zygomatic processes:** help form the zygomatic arches **Palatine process:** forms the anterior hard palate; meet medially in intermaxillary suture **Frontal process:** forms part of lateral aspect of bridge of nose **Incisive fossa:** permits blood vessels and nerves to pass through anterior hard palate (fused palatine processes) **Inferior orbital fissure:** permits maxillary branch of cranial nerve V, the zygomatic nerve, and blood vessels to pass **Infraorbital foramen:** allows passage of infraorbital nerve to skin of face
Zygomatic (2) (Figures 7.4a, 7.5a, and 7.6a)	Form the cheeks and part of the orbits	
Nasal (2) (Figures 7.4a and 7.5)	Form the bridge of the nose	
Lacrimal (2) (Figures 7.4a and 7.5a)	Form part of the medial orbit walls	**Lacrimal fossa:** houses the lacrimal sac, which helps to drain tears into the nasal cavity
Palatine (2) (Figures 7.5b, 7.6a, and 7.14)	Form posterior part of the hard palate and a small part of nasal cavity and orbit walls	**Median palatine suture:** medial fusion point of the horizontal plates of the palatine bones, which form the posterior part of the hard palate
Vomer (1) (Figures 7.4a and 7.14b)	Inferior part of the nasal septum	
Inferior nasal concha (2) (Figures 7.4a and 7.14a)	Form part of the lateral walls of the nasal cavity	

7

*The color code beside each bone name corresponds to the bone's color in Figures 7.4 to 7.13. The number in parentheses ( ) following the bone name indicates the total number of such bones in the body.

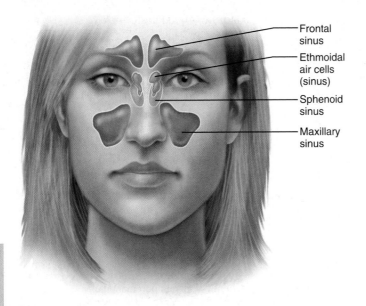

(a) Anterior aspect

Frontal sinus
Ethmoidal air cells (sinus)
Sphenoid sinus
Maxillary sinus

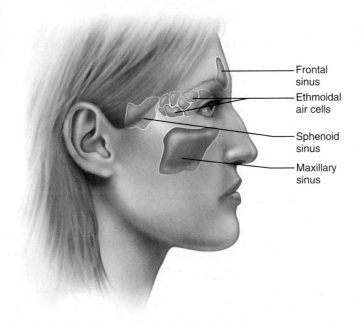

(b) Medial aspect

Frontal sinus
Ethmoidal air cells
Sphenoid sinus
Maxillary sinus

Figure 7.15 Paranasal sinuses.

the turbulence of air flowing through the nasal cavity. This swirling forces more of the inhaled air into contact with the warm, damp mucosa and encourages trapping of airborne particles (dust, pollen, bacteria) in the sticky mucus.

Paranasal Sinuses

Five skull bones—the frontal, sphenoid, ethmoid, and paired maxillary bones—contain mucosa-lined, air-filled sinuses that give them a rather moth-eaten appearance in an X-ray image. These particular sinuses are called **paranasal sinuses** because they cluster around the nasal cavity **(Figure 7.15)**.

Small openings connect the sinuses to the nasal cavity and act as "two-way streets": Air enters the sinuses from the nasal cavity, and mucus formed by the sinus mucosae drains into the nasal cavity. The mucosa of the sinuses also helps to warm and humidify inspired air. The paranasal sinuses lighten the skull and enhance the resonance of the voice.

CHECK YOUR UNDERSTANDING

10. What bones contain the paranasal sinuses?

11. The perpendicular plates of the palatine bones and the superior and middle conchae of the ethmoid bone form a substantial part of the nasal cavity walls. Which bone forms the roof of that cavity?

12. What bone forms the bulk of the orbit floor and what sense organ is found in the orbit of a living person?

For answers, see Appendix G.

The Vertebral Column

General Characteristics

▶ Describe the structure of the vertebral column, list its components, and describe its curvatures.

▶ Indicate a common function of the spinal curvatures and the intervertebral discs.

Some people think of the **vertebral column** as a rigid supporting rod, but this is inaccurate. Also called the **spine** or **spinal column**, the vertebral column consists of 26 irregular bones connected in such a way that a flexible, curved structure results **(Figure 7.16)**.

Serving as the axial support of the trunk, the spine extends from the skull to the pelvis, where it transmits the weight of the trunk to the lower limbs. It also surrounds and protects the delicate spinal cord and provides attachment points for the ribs and for the muscles of the back and neck.

In the fetus and infant, the vertebral column consists of 33 separate bones, or **vertebrae** (ver′tĕ-bre). Inferiorly, nine of these eventually fuse to form two composite bones, the sacrum and the tiny coccyx. The remaining 24 bones persist as individual vertebrae separated by intervertebral discs.

Regions and Curvatures

The vertebral column is about 70 cm (28 inches) long in an average adult and has five major regions (Figure 7.16). The seven vertebrae of the neck are the **cervical vertebrae** (ser′vi-kal), the next 12 are the **thoracic vertebrae** (tho-ras′ik), and the five supporting the lower back are the **lumbar vertebrae** (lum′bar). Remembering common meal times—7 AM, 12 noon, and 5 PM—will help you recall the number of bones in these three regions of the spine. The vertebrae become progressively larger from the cervical to the lumbar region, as they must support greater and greater weight.

Inferior to the lumbar vertebrae is the **sacrum** (sa′krum), which articulates with the hip bones of the pelvis. The terminus of the vertebral column is the tiny **coccyx** (kok′siks).

All of us have the same number of cervical vertebrae. Variations in numbers of vertebrae in other regions occur in about 5% of people.

When you view the vertebral column from the side, you can see the four curvatures that give it its S, or sinusoid, shape. The **cervical** and **lumbar curvatures** are concave posteriorly; the **thoracic** and **sacral curvatures** are convex posteriorly. These curvatures increase the resilience and flexibility of the spine, allowing it to function like a spring rather than a rigid rod.

HOMEOSTATIC IMBALANCE

There are several types of abnormal spinal curvatures. Some are congenital (present at birth); others result from disease, poor posture, or unequal muscle pull on the spine. *Scoliosis* (sko″le-o′sis), literally, "twisted disease," is an abnormal *lateral* curvature that occurs most often in the thoracic region. It is quite common during late childhood, particularly in girls, for some unknown reason. Other, more severe cases result from abnormal vertebral structure, lower limbs of unequal length, or muscle paralysis. If muscles on one side of the body are nonfunctional, those of the opposite side exert an unopposed pull on the spine and force it out of alignment. Scoliosis is treated (with body braces or surgically) before growth ends to prevent permanent deformity and breathing difficulties due to a compressed lung.

Kyphosis (ki-fo′sis), or hunchback, is a *dorsally* exaggerated *thoracic* curvature. It is particularly common in elderly people because of osteoporosis, but may also reflect tuberculosis of the spine, rickets, or osteomalacia.

Lordosis, or swayback, is an accentuated *lumbar* curvature. It, too, can result from spinal tuberculosis or osteomalacia. Temporary lordosis is common in those carrying a large load up front, such as men with "potbellies" and pregnant women. In an attempt to preserve their center of gravity, these individuals automatically throw back their shoulders, accentuating their lumbar curvature. ■

Ligaments

Like a tall, tremulous TV transmitting tower or cell-phone tower, the vertebral column cannot possibly stand upright by itself. It must be held in place by an elaborate system of cable-like supports. In the case of the vertebral column, straplike ligaments and the trunk muscles assume this role.

The major supporting ligaments are the **anterior** and **posterior longitudinal ligaments** (Figure 7.17). These run as continuous bands down the front and back surfaces of the vertebrae from the neck to the sacrum. The broad anterior ligament is strongly attached to both the bony vertebrae and the discs. Along with its supporting role, it prevents hyperextension of the spine (bending too far backward). The posterior ligament, which resists hyperflexion of the spine (bending too sharply forward), is narrow and relatively weak. It attaches only to the discs. However, the **ligamentum flavum**, which connects adjacent vertebrae, contains elastic connective tissue and is

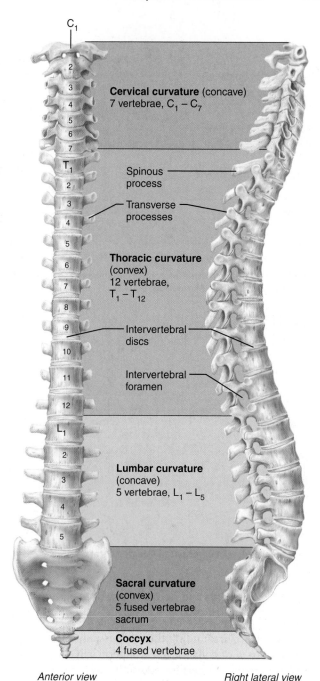

Anterior view   Right lateral view

Figure 7.16 The vertebral column. Notice the curvatures in the lateral view. (The terms *convex* and *concave* refer to the curvature of the posterior aspect of the vertebral column.) (See *A Brief Atlas of the Human Body*, Figure 17.)

especially strong. It stretches as we bend forward and then recoils when we resume an erect posture. Short ligaments connect each vertebra to those immediately above and below.

Intervertebral Discs

Each **intervertebral disc** is a cushionlike pad composed of two parts. The inner gelatinous **nucleus pulposus** (pul-po′sus; "pulp") acts like a rubber ball, giving the disc its elasticity and

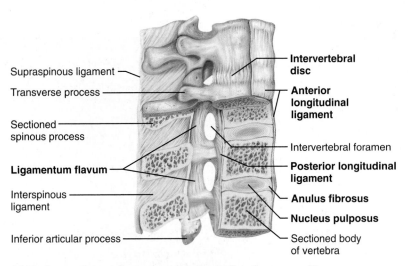

Supraspinous ligament

Transverse process

Sectioned spinous process

Ligamentum flavum

Interspinous ligament

Inferior articular process

Intervertebral disc

Anterior longitudinal ligament

Intervertebral foramen

Posterior longitudinal ligament

Anulus fibrosus

Nucleus pulposus

Sectioned body of vertebra

(a) Median section of three vertebrae, illustrating the composition of the discs and the ligaments

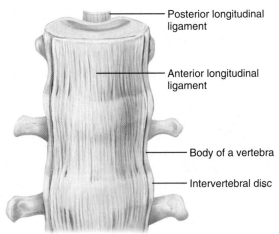

Posterior longitudinal ligament

Anterior longitudinal ligament

Body of a vertebra

Intervertebral disc

(b) Anterior view of part of the spinal column, showing the anterior longitudinal ligament

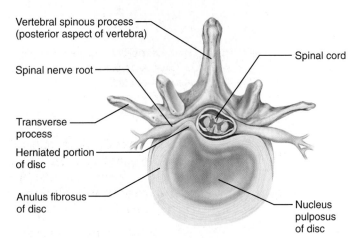

Vertebral spinous process (posterior aspect of vertebra)

Spinal nerve root

Transverse process

Herniated portion of disc

Anulus fibrosus of disc

Spinal cord

Nucleus pulposus of disc

(c) Superior view of a herniated intervertebral disc

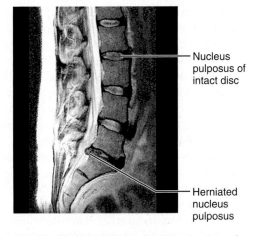

Nucleus pulposus of intact disc

Herniated nucleus pulposus

(d) MRI of lumbar region of vertebral column in sagittal section showing herniated disc

Figure 7.17 Ligaments and fibrocartilage discs uniting the vertebrae.

compressibility. Surrounding the nucleus pulposus is a strong collar composed of collagen fibers superficially and fibrocartilage internally, the **anulus fibrosus** (an′u-lus fi-bro′sus; "ring of fibers") (Figure 7.17a, c). The anulus fibrosus limits the expansion of the nucleus pulposus when the spine is compressed. It also acts like a woven strap to bind successive vertebrae together, withstands twisting forces, and resists tension in the spine.

Sandwiched between the bodies of neighboring vertebrae, the intervertebral discs act as shock absorbers during walking, jumping, and running. They allow the spine to flex and extend, and to a lesser extent to bend laterally. At points of compression, the discs flatten and bulge out a bit between the vertebrae. The discs are thickest in the lumbar and cervical regions, which enhances the flexibility of these regions.

Collectively the discs account for about 25% of the height of the vertebral column. They flatten somewhat during the course of the day, so we are always a few millimeters shorter at night than when we awake in the morning.

HOMEOSTATIC IMBALANCE

Severe or sudden physical trauma to the spine—for example, from bending forward while lifting a heavy object—may result in herniation of one or more discs. A **herniated (prolapsed) disc** (commonly called a *slipped disc*) usually involves rupture of the anulus fibrosus followed by protrusion of the spongy nucleus pulposus through the anulus (Figure 7.17c, d). If the protrusion presses on the spinal cord or on spinal nerves exiting from the cord, numbness or excruciating pain may result.

Herniated discs are generally treated with moderate exercise, massage, heat therapy, and painkillers. If this fails, the protruding disc may have to be removed surgically and a bone graft done to fuse the adjoining vertebrae. For those preferring to avoid general anesthesia, the disc can be partially vaporized with a laser in an outpatient procedure called percutaneous laser disc decompression that takes only 30 to 40 minutes. If necessary, tears in the anulus can be sealed by electrothermal means at the same time. The patient leaves with only an adhesive bandage to mark the spot. ■

13. What are the five major regions of the vertebral column?

14. In which two of these regions is the vertebral column concave posteriorly?

15. Besides the spinal curvatures, which skeletal elements help to make the vertebral column flexible?

For answers, see Appendix G.

General Structure of Vertebrae

▶ Discuss the structure of a typical vertebra and describe regional features of cervical, thoracic, and lumbar vertebrae.

All vertebrae have a common structural pattern **(Figure 7.18)**. Each vertebra consists of a **body**, or **centrum**, anteriorly and a **vertebral arch** posteriorly. The disc-shaped body is the weight-bearing region. Together, the body and vertebral arch enclose an opening called the **vertebral foramen**. Successive vertebral foramina of the articulated vertebrae form the long **vertebral canal**, through which the spinal cord passes.

The vertebral arch is a composite structure formed by two pedicles and two laminae. The **pedicles** (ped′ĭ-kelz; "little feet"), short bony pillars projecting posteriorly from the vertebral body, form the sides of the arch. The **laminae** (lam′ĭ-ne), flattened plates that fuse in the median plane, complete the arch posteriorly. The pedicles have notches on their superior and inferior borders, providing lateral openings between adjacent vertebrae called **intervertebral foramina** (see Figure 7.16). The spinal nerves issuing from the spinal cord pass through these foramina.

Seven processes project from the vertebral arch. The **spinous process** is a median posterior projection arising at the junction of the two laminae. A **transverse process** extends laterally from each side of the vertebral arch. The spinous and transverse processes are attachment sites for muscles that move the vertebral column and for ligaments that stabilize it. The paired **superior** and **inferior articular processes** protrude superiorly and inferiorly, respectively, from the pedicle-lamina junctions. The smooth joint surfaces of the articular processes, called *facets* ("little faces"), are covered with hyaline cartilage. The inferior articular processes of each vertebra form movable joints with the superior articular processes of the vertebra immediately below. Thus, successive vertebrae join both at their bodies and at their articular processes.

Regional Vertebral Characteristics

Beyond their common structural features, vertebrae exhibit variations that allow different regions of the spine to perform slightly different functions and movements. In general, movements that can occur between vertebrae are (1) flexion and extension (anterior bending and posterior straightening of the spine), (2) lateral flexion (bending the *upper body* to the right or left), and (3) rotation (in which vertebrae rotate on one another in the longitudinal axis of the spine). The regional vertebral characteristics described in this section are illustrated and summarized in Table 7.2 on p. 222.

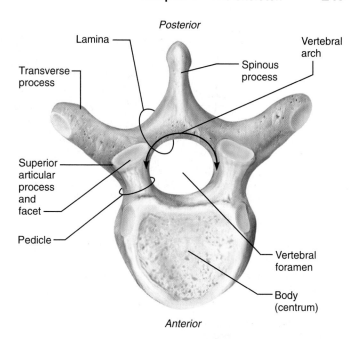

Figure 7.18 Structure of a typical vertebra. Superior view. Only bone features are illustrated in this and subsequent bone figures in this chapter. Articular cartilage is not depicted.

Cervical Vertebrae

The seven cervical vertebrae, identified as C_1–C_7, are the smallest, lightest vertebrae (see Figure 7.16). The first two (C_1 and C_2) are unusual and we will skip them for the moment. The "typical" cervical vertebrae (C_3–C_7) have the following distinguishing features (see Figure 7.20 and Table 7.2):

1. The body is oval—wider from side to side than in the anteroposterior dimension.
2. Except in C_7, the spinous process is short, projects directly back, and is *bifid* (bi′fĭd), or split at its tip.
3. The vertebral foramen is large and generally triangular.
4. Each transverse process contains a **transverse foramen** through which the vertebral arteries pass to service the brain.

The spinous process of C_7 is not bifid and is much larger than those of the other cervical vertebrae (see Figure 7.20a). Because its spinous process is palpable through the skin, C_7 can be used as a landmark for counting the vertebrae and is called the **vertebra prominens** ("prominent vertebra").

The first two cervical vertebrae, the atlas and the axis, are somewhat more robust than the typical cervical vertebra. They have no intervertebral disc between them, and they are highly modified, reflecting their special functions. The **atlas** (C_1) has no body and no spinous process **(Figure 7.19a and b)**. Essentially, it is a ring of bone consisting of *anterior* and *posterior arches* and a *lateral mass* on each side. Each lateral mass has articular facets on both its superior and inferior surfaces. The superior articular facets receive the occipital condyles of the skull—they "carry" the skull, just as Atlas supported the heavens in Greek mythology. These joints allow you to nod "yes." The inferior articular facets form joints with the axis (C_2) below.

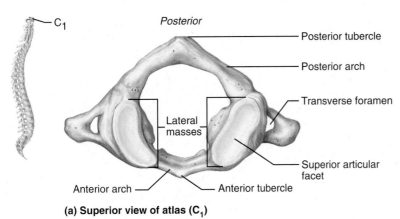

(a) Superior view of atlas (C₁)

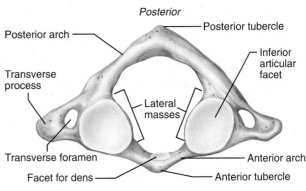

(b) Inferior view of atlas (C₁)

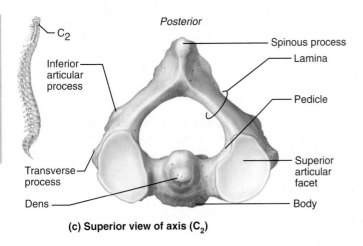

(c) Superior view of axis (C₂)

Figure 7.19 The first and second cervical vertebrae. (See *A Brief Atlas of the Human Body*, Figure 18.)

The **axis**, which has a body and the other typical vertebral processes, is not as specialized as the atlas. In fact, its only unusual feature is the knoblike **dens** (denz; "tooth") projecting superiorly from its body. The dens is actually the "missing" body of the atlas, which fuses with the axis during embryonic development. Cradled in the anterior arch of the atlas by the transverse ligaments **(Figure 7.20a)**, the dens acts as a pivot for the rotation of the atlas. Hence, this joint allows you to rotate your head from side to side to indicate "no."

Thoracic Vertebrae

The 12 thoracic vertebrae (T_1–T_{12}) all articulate with the ribs (see Table 7.2, Figure 7.16, and Figure 7.20b). The first looks much like C_7, and the last four show a progression toward lumbar vertebral structure. The thoracic vertebrae increase in size from the first to the last. Unique characteristics of these vertebrae include the following:

1. The body is roughly heart shaped. It typically bears two small *facets*, commonly called *demifacets* (half-facets), on each side, one at the superior edge (the *superior costal facet*) and the other at the inferior edge (the *inferior costal facet*). The demifacets receive the heads of the ribs. (The bodies of T_{10}–T_{12} vary from this pattern by having only a single facet to receive their respective ribs.)

2. The vertebral foramen is circular.
3. The spinous process is long and points sharply downward.
4. With the exception of T_{11} and T_{12}, the transverse processes have facets, the *transverse costal facets*, that articulate with the tubercles of the ribs.
5. The superior and inferior articular facets lie mainly in the frontal plane, a situation that prevents flexion and extension, but which allows this region of the spine to rotate. Lateral flexion, though possible, is restricted by the ribs.

Lumbar Vertebrae

The lumbar region of the vertebral column, commonly referred to as the small of the back, receives the most stress. The enhanced weight-bearing function of the five lumbar vertebrae (L_1–L_5) is reflected in their sturdier structure. Their bodies are massive and kidney shaped in a superior view (see Table 7.2, Figure 7.16, and Figure 7.20). Other characteristics typical of these vertebrae:

1. The pedicles and laminae are shorter and thicker than those of other vertebrae.
2. The spinous processes are short, flat, and hatchet shaped and are easily seen when a person bends forward. These processes are robust and project directly backward, adaptations for the attachment of the large back muscles.
3. The vertebral foramen is triangular.
4. The orientation of the facets of the articular processes of the lumbar vertebrae differs substantially from that of the other vertebra types (see Table 7.2). These modifications lock the lumbar vertebrae together and provide stability by preventing rotation of the lumbar spine. Flexion and extension are possible (as when you do sit-ups), as is lateral flexion.

Sacrum

The triangular sacrum, which shapes the posterior wall of the pelvis, is formed by five fused vertebrae (S_1–S_5) in adults **(Figure 7.21**, and see Figure 7.16). It articulates superiorly (via its **superior articular processes**) with L_5 and inferiorly with the coccyx. Laterally, the sacrum articulates, via its **auricular surfaces**, with the two hip bones to form the **sacroiliac joints** (sa″kro-il′e-ak) of the pelvis.

The **sacral promontory** (prom′on-tor″e; "high point of land projecting into the sea"), the anterosuperior margin of the first

7

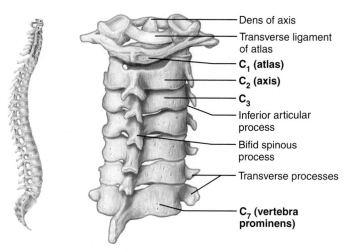

Dens of axis

Transverse ligament of atlas

C₁ (atlas)

C₂ (axis)

C₃

Inferior articular process

Bifid spinous process

Transverse processes

C₇ (vertebra prominens)

(a) Cervical vertebrae

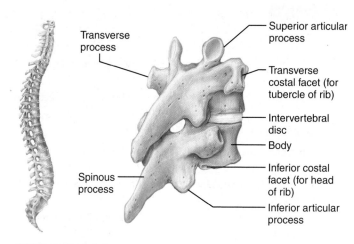

Transverse process

Superior articular process

Transverse costal facet (for tubercle of rib)

Intervertebral disc

Body

Inferior costal facet (for head of rib)

Inferior articular process

Spinous process

(b) Thoracic vertebrae

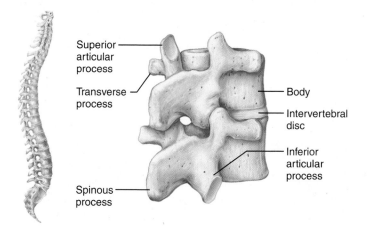

Superior articular process

Transverse process

Body

Intervertebral disc

Inferior articular process

Spinous process

(c) Lumbar vertebrae

Figure 7.20 Posterolateral views of articulated vertebrae.
Notice the bulbous tip on the spinous process of C₇, the vertebra prominens. (See *A Brief Atlas of the Human Body*, Figures 19, 20, and 21.)

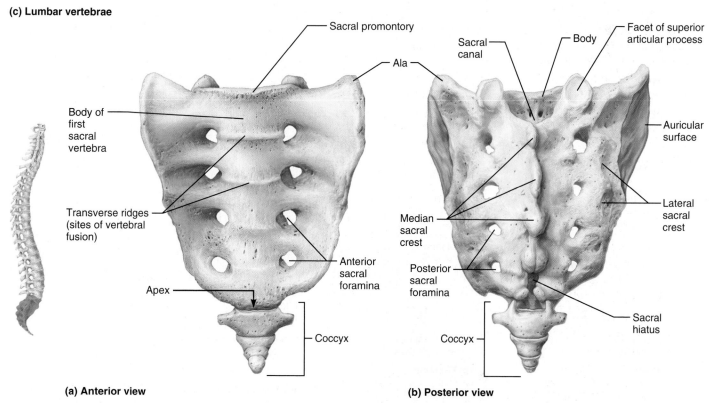

Sacral promontory

Ala

Body of first sacral vertebra

Transverse ridges (sites of vertebral fusion)

Apex

Anterior sacral foramina

Coccyx

(a) Anterior view

Sacral canal

Body

Facet of superior articular process

Auricular surface

Median sacral crest

Posterior sacral foramina

Lateral sacral crest

Coccyx

Sacral hiatus

(b) Posterior view

Figure 7.21 The sacrum and coccyx. (See *A Brief Atlas of the Human Body*, Figure 22.)

TABLE 7.2	Regional Characteristics of Cervical, Thoracic, and Lumbar Vertebrae		
CHARACTERISTIC	CERVICAL (3–7)	THORACIC	LUMBAR
Body	Small, wide side to side	Larger than cervical; heart shaped; bears two costal facets	Massive; kidney shaped
Spinous process	Short; bifid; projects directly posteriorly	Long; sharp; projects inferiorly	Short; blunt; rectangular; projects directly posteriorly
Vertebral foramen	Triangular	Circular	Triangular
Transverse processes	Contain foramina	Bear facets for ribs (except T_{11} and T_{12})	Thin and tapered
Superior and inferior articulating processes	Superior facets directed superoposteriorly	Superior facets directed posteriorly	Superior facets directed posteromedially (or medially)
	Inferior facets directed inferoanteriorly	Inferior facets directed anteriorly	Inferior facets directed anterolaterally (or laterally)
Movements allowed	Flexion and extension; lateral flexion; rotation; the spine region with the greatest range of movement	Rotation; lateral flexion possible but restricted by ribs; flexion and extension limited	Flexion and extension; some lateral flexion; rotation prevented

Superior View

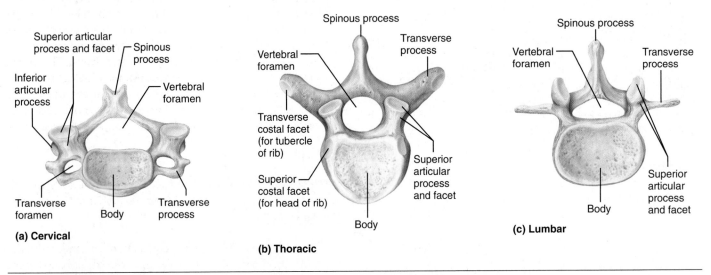

(a) Cervical

(b) Thoracic

(c) Lumbar

Right Lateral View

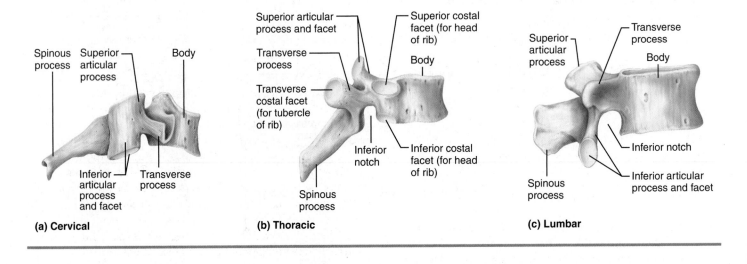

(a) Cervical

(b) Thoracic

(c) Lumbar

sacral vertebra, bulges anteriorly into the pelvic cavity. The body's center of gravity lies about 1 cm posterior to this landmark. Four ridges, the **transverse ridges**, cross its concave anterior aspect, marking the lines of fusion of the sacral vertebrae. The **anterior sacral foramina** lie at the lateral ends of these ridges and transmit blood vessels and anterior rami of the sacral spinal nerves. The regions lateral to these foramina expand superiorly as the winglike **alae**.

In its posterior midline the sacral surface is roughened by the **median sacral crest** (the fused spinous processes of the sacral vertebrae). This is flanked laterally by the **posterior sacral foramina**, which transmit the posterior rami of the sacral spinal nerves, and then the **lateral sacral crests** (remnants of the transverse processes of S_1–S_5).

The vertebral canal continues inside the sacrum as the **sacral canal**. Since the laminae of the fifth (and sometimes the fourth) sacral vertebrae fail to fuse medially, an enlarged external opening called the **sacral hiatus** (hi-a′tus; "gap") is obvious at the inferior end of the sacral canal.

Coccyx

The coccyx, our tailbone, is a small triangular bone (Figure 7.21, and see Figure 7.16). It consists of four (or in some cases three or five) vertebrae fused together. The coccyx articulates superiorly with the sacrum. (The name *coccyx* is from the Greek word meaning "cuckoo" and was so named because of its fancied resemblance to a bird's beak.) Except for the slight support the coccyx affords the pelvic organs, it is a nearly useless bone. Occasionally, a baby is born with an unusually long coccyx, which may need to be removed surgically.

■ ■ ■

The characteristics of the regional vertebrae are summarized in **Table 7.2.**

CHECK YOUR UNDERSTANDING

16. What is the normal number of cervical vertebrae? Of thoracic vertebrae?
17. How would a complete fracture of the dens affect the mobility of the vertebral column?
18. How can you distinguish a lumbar vertebra from a thoracic vertebra?

For answers, see Appendix G.

The Thoracic Cage

▶ Name and describe the bones of the thoracic cage (bony thorax).
▶ Differentiate true from false ribs.

Anatomically, the thorax is the chest, and its bony underpinnings are called the **thoracic cage** or **bony thorax**. Elements of the thoracic cage include the thoracic vertebrae dorsally, the ribs

laterally, and the sternum and costal cartilages anteriorly. The costal cartilages secure the ribs to the sternum **(Figure 7.22a)**.

Roughly cone shaped with its broad dimension positioned inferiorly, the bony thorax forms a protective cage around the vital organs of the thoracic cavity (heart, lungs, and great blood vessels), supports the shoulder girdles and upper limbs, and provides attachment points for many muscles of the neck, back, chest, and shoulders. The *intercostal spaces* between the ribs are occupied by the intercostal muscles, which lift and depress the thorax during breathing.

Sternum

The **sternum** (breastbone) lies in the anterior midline of the thorax. Vaguely resembling a dagger, it is a flat bone approximately 15 cm (6 inches) long, resulting from the fusion of three bones: the manubrium, the body, and the xiphoid process. The *manubrium* (mah-nu′bre-um; "knife handle"), is the superior portion which is shaped like the knot in a necktie. The manubrium articulates via its **clavicular notches** (klah-vik′ular) with the clavicles (collarbones) laterally, and just below this, it also articulates with the first two pairs of ribs. The *body*, or midportion, forms the bulk of the sternum. The sides of the body are notched where it articulates with the costal cartilages of the second to seventh ribs. The *xiphoid process* (zif′oid; "swordlike") forms the inferior end of the sternum. This small, variably shaped process is a plate of hyaline cartilage in youth, but it is usually ossified in adults over the age of 40. The xiphoid process articulates only with the sternal body and serves as an attachment point for some abdominal muscles.

HOMEOSTATIC IMBALANCE

In some people, the xiphoid process projects posteriorly. In such cases, blows to the chest can push the xiphoid into the underlying heart or liver, causing massive hemorrhage. ■

The sternum has three important anatomical landmarks: the jugular notch, the sternal angle, and the xiphisternal joint (Figure 7.22). The easily palpated **jugular** (*suprasternal*) **notch** is the central indentation in the superior border of the manubrium. If you slide your finger down the anterior surface of your neck, it will land in the jugular notch. The jugular notch is generally in line with the disc between the second and third thoracic vertebrae and the point where the left common carotid artery issues from the aorta (Figure 7.22b).

The **sternal angle** is felt as a horizontal ridge across the front of the sternum, where the manubrium joins the sternal body. This cartilaginous joint acts like a hinge, allowing the sternal body to swing anteriorly when we inhale. The sternal angle is in line with the disc between the fourth and fifth thoracic vertebrae and at the level of the second pair of ribs. It is a handy reference point for finding the second rib and thus for counting the ribs during a physical examination and for listening to sounds made by specific heart valves.

The **xiphisternal joint** (zif″ĭ-ster′nul) is the point where the sternal body and xiphoid process fuse. It lies at the level of the

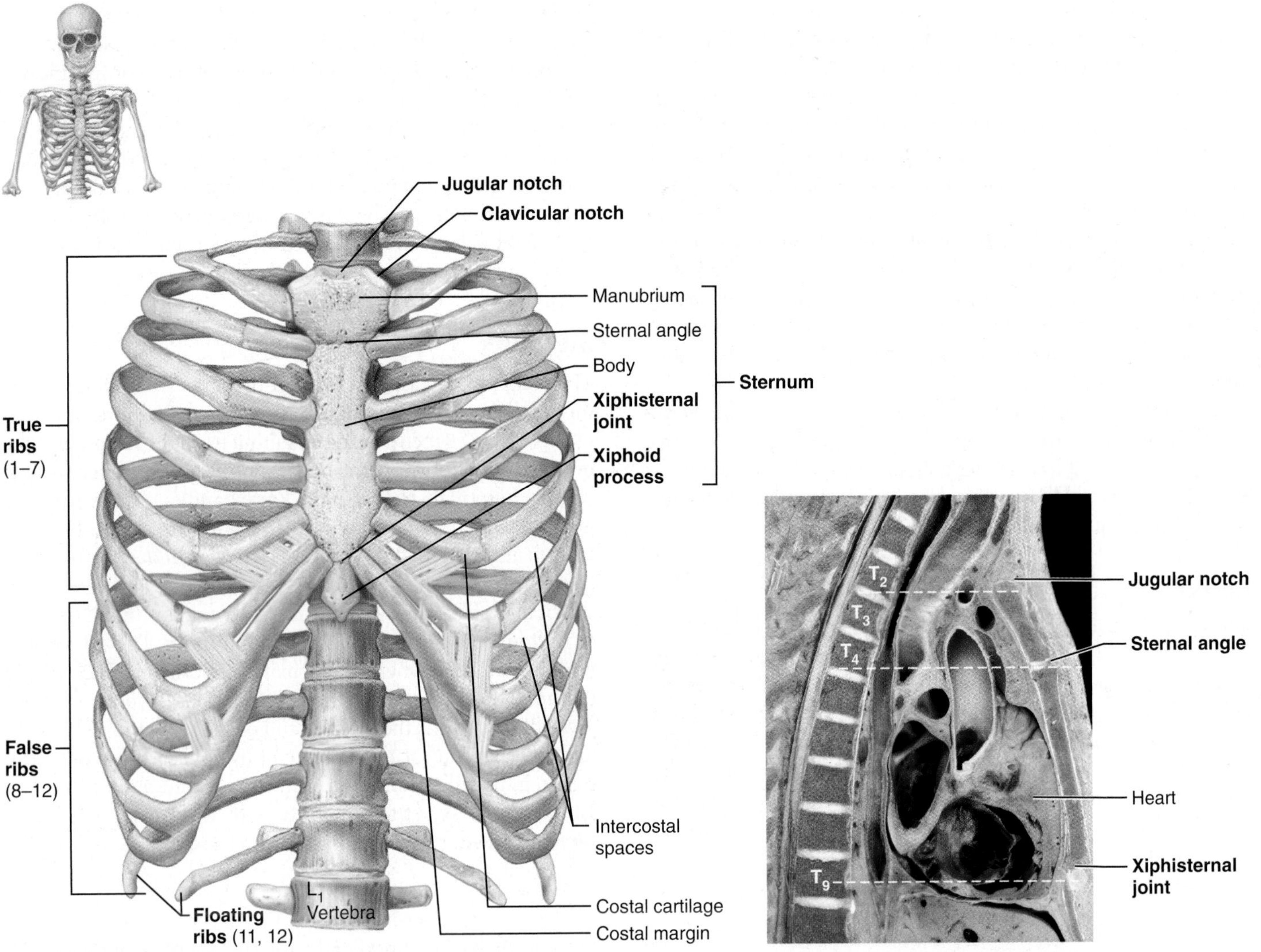

7

(a) Skeleton of the thoracic cage, anterior view

(b) Midsagittal section through the thorax, showing the relationship of surface anatomical landmarks of the thorax to the vertebral column

Figure 7.22 **The thoracic cage.** (See *A Brief Atlas of the Human Body,* Figure 23a–d.)

ninth thoracic vertebra. The heart lies on the diaphragm just deep to this joint.

Ribs

Twelve pairs of **ribs** form the flaring sides of the thoracic cage (Figure 7.22a). All ribs attach posteriorly to the thoracic vertebrae (bodies and transverse processes) and curve inferiorly toward the anterior body surface. The superior seven rib pairs attach directly to the sternum by individual costal cartilages (bars of hyaline cartilage). These are **true** or **vertebrosternal ribs** (ver″tĕ-bro-ster′nal). (Notice that the anatomical name indicates the two attachment points of a rib—the posterior attachment given first.)

The remaining five pairs of ribs are called **false ribs** because they either attach indirectly to the sternum or entirely lack a sternal attachment. Rib pairs 8–10 attach to the sternum indirectly, each joining the costal cartilage immediately above it.

These ribs are also called **vertebrochondral ribs** (ver″tĕ-bro-kon′dral). The inferior margin of the rib cage, or **costal margin**, is formed by the costal cartilages of ribs 7–10. Rib pairs 11 and 12 are called **vertebral ribs** or **floating ribs** because they have no anterior attachments. Instead, their costal cartilages lie embedded in the muscles of the lateral body wall.

The ribs increase in length from pair 1 to pair 7, then decrease in length from pair 8 to pair 12. Except for the first rib, which lies deep to the clavicle, the ribs are easily felt in people of normal weight.

A typical rib is a bowed flat bone (Figure 7.23). The bulk of a rib is simply called the *shaft.* Its superior border is smooth, but its inferior border is sharp and thin and has a *costal groove* on its inner face that lodges the intercostal nerves and blood vessels.

In addition to the shaft, each rib has a head, neck, and tubercle. The wedge-shaped *head,* the posterior end, articulates with the vertebral bodies by two facets: One joins the body of the same-numbered thoracic vertebra, the other articulates with the body of the vertebra immediately superior. The *neck* is the

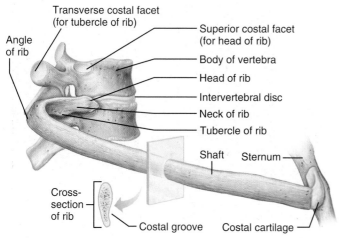

(a) Vertebral and sternal articulations of a typical true rib

Transverse costal facet (for tubercle of rib)
Angle of rib
Superior costal facet (for head of rib)
Body of vertebra
Head of rib
Intervertebral disc
Neck of rib
Tubercle of rib
Shaft
Sternum
Cross-section of rib
Costal groove
Costal cartilage

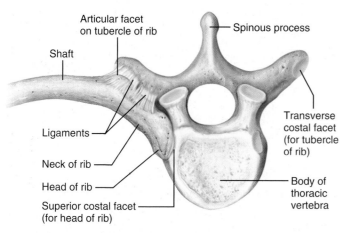

(b) Superior view of the articulation between a rib and a thoracic vertebra

Articular facet on tubercle of rib
Spinous process
Shaft
Ligaments
Neck of rib
Head of rib
Superior costal facet (for head of rib)
Transverse costal facet (for tubercle of rib)
Body of thoracic vertebra

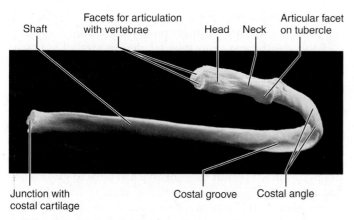

(c) A typical rib (rib 6, right), posterior view

Shaft
Facets for articulation with vertebrae
Head   Neck
Articular facet on tubercle
Junction with costal cartilage
Costal groove
Costal angle

Figure 7.23 Ribs. All ribs illustrated in this figure are right ribs. (See *A Brief Atlas of the Human Body*, Figure 23e and f.)

constricted portion of the rib just beyond the head. Lateral to this, the knoblike *tubercle* articulates with the costal facet of the transverse process of the same-numbered thoracic vertebra. Beyond the tubercle, the shaft angles sharply forward (at the angle of the rib) and then extends to attach to its costal cartilage ante-

riorly. The costal cartilages provide secure but flexible rib attachments to the sternum.

The first pair of ribs is quite atypical. They are flattened superiorly to inferiorly and are quite broad, forming a horizontal table that supports the subclavian blood vessels that serve the upper limbs. There are also other exceptions to the typical rib pattern. Rib 1 and ribs 10–12 articulate with only one vertebral body, and ribs 11 and 12 do not articulate with a vertebral transverse process.

CHECK YOUR UNDERSTANDING

19. How does a true rib differ from a false rib?

20. What is the sternal angle and what is its clinical importance?

21. Besides the ribs and sternum, there is a third group of bones making up the thoracic cage. What is it?

For answers, see Appendix G.

PART 2

THE APPENDICULAR SKELETON

Bones of the limbs and their girdles are collectively called the **appendicular skeleton** because they are *appended* to the axial skeleton that forms the longitudinal axis of the body (see Figure 7.1). The yokelike *pectoral girdles* (pek′tor-al; "chest") attach the upper limbs to the body trunk. The more sturdy *pelvic girdle* secures the lower limbs. Although the bones of the upper and lower limbs differ in their functions and mobility, they have the same fundamental plan: Each limb is composed of three major segments connected by movable joints.

The appendicular skeleton enables us to carry out the movements typical of our freewheeling and manipulative lifestyle. Each time we take a step, throw a ball, or pop a caramel into our mouth, we are making good use of our appendicular skeleton.

The Pectoral (Shoulder) Girdle

▶ Identify bones forming the pectoral girdle and relate their structure and arrangement to the function of this girdle.

▶ Identify important bone markings on the pectoral girdle.

The **pectoral**, or **shoulder**, **girdle** consists of the *clavicle* (klav′ĭ-kl) anteriorly and the *scapula* (skap′u-lah) posteriorly (**Figure 7.24** and Table 7.3 on p. 232). The paired pectoral girdles and their associated muscles form your shoulders. Although the term *girdle* usually signifies a beltlike structure encircling the body, a single pectoral girdle, or even the pair, does not quite satisfy this description. Anteriorly, the medial end of each clavicle joins the sternum; the distal ends of the clavicles meet the scapulae laterally. However, the scapulae fail to complete the ring posteriorly, because their medial borders do not join each other or the axial skeleton. Instead, the scapulae are attached to the thorax and vertebral column only by the muscles that clothe their surfaces.

The pectoral girdles attach the upper limbs to the axial skeleton and provide attachment points for many of the muscles that

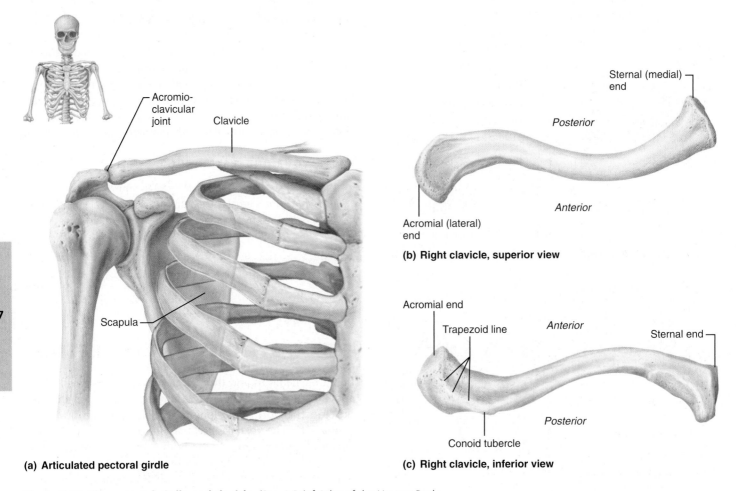

(a) Articulated pectoral girdle

(b) Right clavicle, superior view

(c) Right clavicle, inferior view

Figure 7.24 The pectoral girdle and clavicle. (See *A Brief Atlas of the Human Body,* Figure 24.)

move the upper limbs. These girdles are very light and allow the upper limbs a degree of mobility not seen anywhere else in the body. This mobility is due to the following factors:

1. Because only the clavicle attaches to the axial skeleton, the scapula can move quite freely across the thorax, allowing the arm to move with it.
2. The socket of the shoulder joint (the scapula's glenoid cavity) is shallow and poorly reinforced, so it does not restrict the movement of the humerus (arm bone). Although this arrangement is good for flexibility, it is bad for stability: Shoulder dislocations are fairly common.

Clavicles

The **clavicles** ("little keys"), or collarbones, are slender, doubly curved bones that can be felt along their entire course as they extend horizontally across the superior thorax (Figure 7.24). Each clavicle is cone shaped at its medial **sternal end**, which attaches to the sternal manubrium, and flattened at its lateral **acromial end** (ah-kro′me-al), which articulates with the scapula. The medial two-thirds of the clavicle is convex anteriorly; its lateral third is concave anteriorly. Its superior surface is fairly smooth, but the inferior surface is ridged and grooved by ligaments and by the action of the muscles that attach to it. The

trapezoid line and the *conoid tubercle*, for example, are anchoring points for a ligament which runs to attach to the scapula.

Besides anchoring many muscles, the clavicles act as braces: They hold the scapulae and arms out laterally, away from the narrower superior part of the thorax. This bracing function becomes obvious when a clavicle is fractured: The entire shoulder region collapses medially. The clavicles also transmit compression forces from the upper limbs to the axial skeleton, for example, when someone pushes a car to a gas station.

The clavicles are not very strong and are likely to fracture, for example, when a person uses outstretched arms to break a fall. The curves in the clavicle ensure that it usually fractures anteriorly (outward). If it were to collapse posteriorly (inward), bone splinters would damage the subclavian artery, which passes just deep to the clavicle to serve the upper limb. The clavicles are exceptionally sensitive to muscle pull and become noticeably larger and stronger in those who perform manual labor or athletics involving the shoulder and arm muscles.

Scapulae

The **scapulae**, or *shoulder blades*, are thin, triangular flat bones (Figure 7.24a and Figure 7.25). Interestingly, their name derives from a word meaning "spade" or "shovel," for ancient cultures

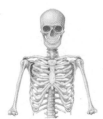

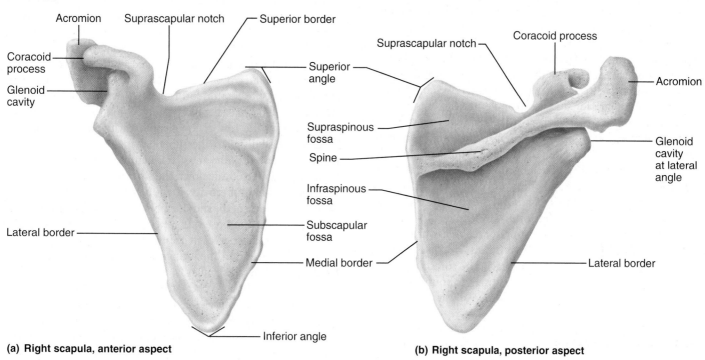

(a) Right scapula, anterior aspect

(b) Right scapula, posterior aspect

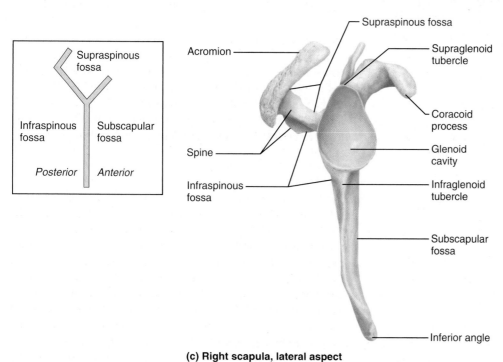

(c) Right scapula, lateral aspect

Figure 7.25 **The scapula.** View (c) is accompanied by a schematic representation of its orientation. (See *A Brief Atlas of the Human Body*, Figure 24.)

7

made spades from the shoulder blades of animals. The scapulae lie on the dorsal surface of the rib cage, between ribs 2 and 7.

Each scapula has three borders. The *superior border* is the shortest, sharpest border. The *medial*, or *vertebral*, *border* parallels the vertebral column. The thick *lateral*, or *axillary*, *border* abuts the armpit and ends superiorly in a small, shallow fossa, the **glenoid cavity** (gle'noid; "pit-shaped"). This cavity articulates with the humerus of the arm, forming the shoulder joint.

Like all triangles, the scapula has three corners or *angles*. The superior scapular border meets the medial border at the *superior angle* and the lateral border at the *lateral angle*. The medial and lateral borders join at the *inferior angle*. The inferior angle moves extensively as the arm is raised and lowered, and is an important landmark for studying scapular movements.

The anterior, or costal, surface of the scapula is concave and relatively featureless. Its posterior surface bears a prominent **spine** that is easily felt through the skin. The spine ends laterally in an enlarged, roughened triangular projection called the **acromion** (ah-kro'me-on; "point of the shoulder"). The acromion articulates with the acromial end of the clavicle, forming the **acromioclavicular joint.**

Projecting anteriorly from the superior scapular border is the **coracoid process** (kor'ah-coid); *corac* means "beaklike," but this process looks more like a bent little finger. The coracoid process helps anchor the biceps muscle of the arm. It is bounded by the **suprascapular notch** (a nerve passage) medially and by the glenoid cavity laterally.

Several large fossae appear on both sides of the scapula and are named according to location. The *infraspinous* and *supraspinous fossae* are inferior and superior, respectively, to the spine. The *subscapular fossa* is the shallow concavity formed by the entire anterior scapular surface. Lying within these fossae are muscles with similar names.

CHECK YOUR UNDERSTANDING

22. What two bones construct each pectoral girdle?
23. Where is the single point of attachment of the pectoral girdle to the axial skeleton?
24. What is the major shortcoming of the flexibility allowed by the shoulder joint?

For answers, see Appendix G.

The Upper Limb

▶ Identify or name the bones of the upper limb and their important markings.

Thirty separate bones form the bony framework of each upper limb (see Figures 7.26 to 7.28, and **Table 7.3** on p. 232). Each of these bones may be described regionally as a bone of the arm, forearm, or hand. (Keep in mind that anatomically the "arm" is only that part of the upper limb between the shoulder and elbow.)

Arm

The **humerus** (hu'mer-us), the sole bone of the arm, is a typical long bone **(Figure 7.26)**. The largest, longest bone of the upper limb, it articulates with the scapula at the shoulder and with the radius and ulna (forearm bones) at the elbow.

At the proximal end of the humerus is its smooth, hemispherical **head**, which fits into the glenoid cavity of the scapula in a manner that allows the arm to hang freely at one's side. Immediately inferior to the head is a slight constriction, the **anatomical neck.** Just inferior to this are the lateral **greater tubercle** and the more medial **lesser tubercle**, separated by the **intertubercular sulcus**, or *bicipital groove* (bi-sip'ĭ-tal). These tubercles are sites of attachment of the rotator cuff muscles. The intertubercular sulcus guides a tendon of the biceps muscle of the arm to its attachment point at the rim of the glenoid cavity (the supraglenoid tubercle). Just distal to the tubercles is the **surgical neck**, so named because it is the most frequently fractured part of the humerus. About midway down the shaft on its lateral side is the V-shaped **deltoid tuberosity**, the roughened attachment site for the deltoid muscle of the shoulder. Nearby, the **radial groove** runs obliquely down the posterior aspect of the shaft, marking the course of the radial nerve, an important nerve of the upper limb.

At the distal end of the humerus are two condyles: a medial **trochlea** (trok'le-ah; "pulley"), which looks like an hourglass tipped on its side, and the lateral ball-like **capitulum** (kah-pit'u-lum). These condyles articulate with the ulna and the radius, respectively (Figure 7.26c and d). The condyle pair is flanked by the **medial** and **lateral epicondyles** (muscle attachment sites). Directly above these epicondyles are the **medial** and **lateral supracondylar ridges**. The ulnar nerve, which runs behind the medial epicondyle, is responsible for the painful, tingling sensation you experience when you hit your "funny bone."

Superior to the trochlea on the anterior surface is the **coronoid fossa**; on the posterior surface is the deeper **olecranon fossa** (o-lek'rah-non). These two depressions allow the corresponding processes of the ulna to move freely when the elbow is flexed and extended. A small **radial fossa**, lateral to the coronoid fossa, receives the head of the radius when the elbow is flexed.

Forearm

Two parallel long bones, the radius and the ulna, form the skeleton of the forearm, or *antebrachium* (an"te-bra'ke-um) **(Figure 7.27)**. Unless a person's forearm muscles are very bulky, these bones are easily palpated along their entire length. Their proximal ends articulate with the humerus; their distal ends form joints with bones of the wrist. The radius and ulna articulate with each other both proximally and distally at small **radioulnar joints** (ra"de-o-ul'nar), and they are connected along their entire length by a flat, flexible ligament, the **interosseous membrane** (in"ter-os'e-us; "between the bones").

In the anatomical position, the radius lies laterally (on the thumb side) and the ulna medially. However, when you rotate your forearm so that the palm faces posteriorly (a movement called pronation), the distal end of the radius crosses over the ulna and the two bones form an X (see Figure 8.6a, p. 258).

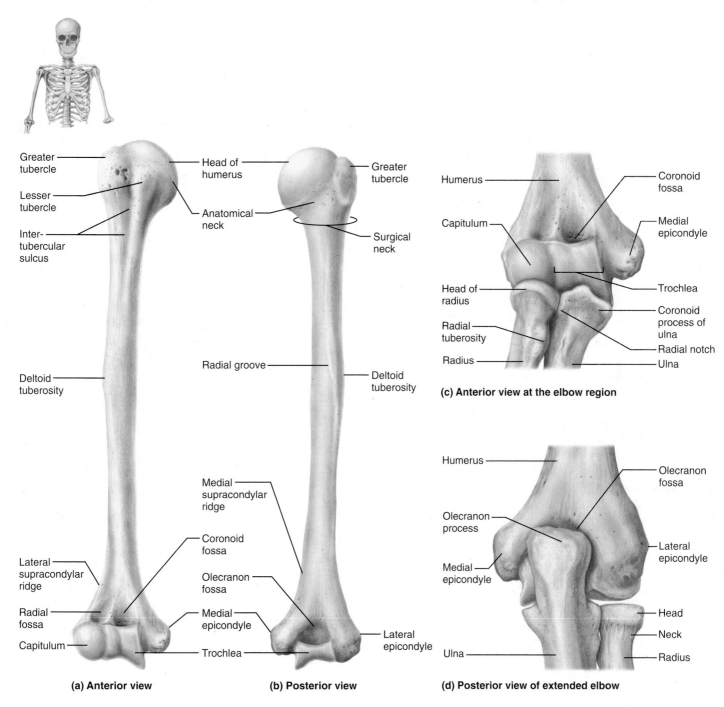

Figure 7.26 The humerus of the right arm and detailed views of articulation at the elbow. (See *A Brief Atlas of the Human Body*, Figure 25.)

Ulna

The **ulna** (ul'nah; "elbow") is slightly longer than the radius. It has the main responsibility for forming the elbow joint with the humerus. Its proximal end looks like the adjustable end of a monkey wrench: it bears two prominent processes, the **olecranon** (elbow) and **coronoid processes,** separated by a deep concavity, the **trochlear notch** (Figure 7.27c). Together, these two processes grip the trochlea of the humerus, forming a hinge joint that allows the forearm to be bent upon the arm (flexed), then straightened again (extended). When the forearm

is fully extended, the olecranon process "locks" into the olecranon fossa (Figure 7.26d), keeping the forearm from hyperextending (moving posteriorly beyond the elbow joint). The posterior olecranon process forms the angle of the elbow when the forearm is flexed and is the bony part that rests on the table when you lean on your elbows. On the lateral side of the coronoid process is a small depression, the **radial notch**, where the ulna articulates with the head of the radius.

Distally the ulnar shaft narrows and ends in a knoblike **head** (Figure 7.27d). Medial to the head is a **styloid process**, from which a ligament runs to the wrist. The ulnar head is separated

7

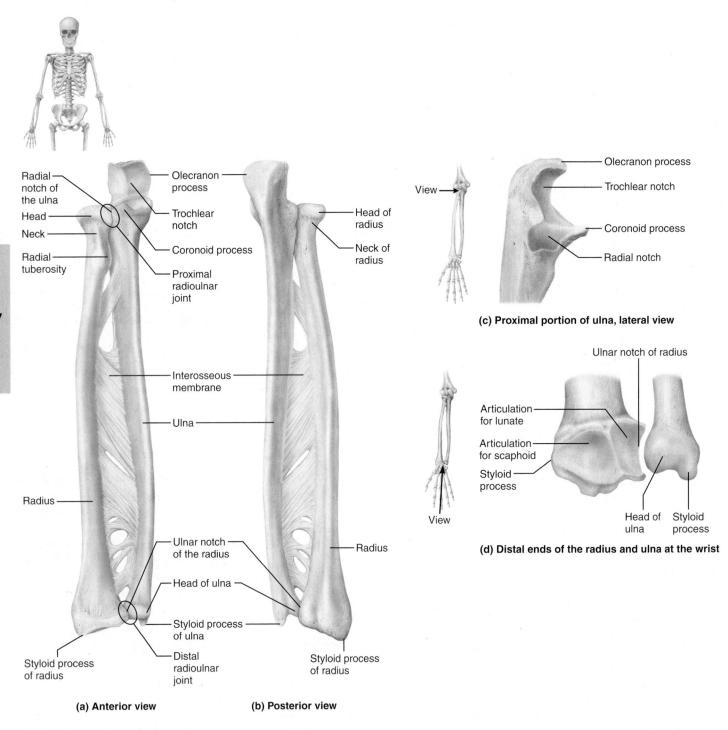

(a) Anterior view

(b) Posterior view

(c) Proximal portion of ulna, lateral view

(d) Distal ends of the radius and ulna at the wrist

Figure 7.27 Radius and ulna of the right forearm. Note the structural details of the ulnar head and distal portion of radius and ulna. (See *A Brief Atlas of the Human Body*, Figure 26.)

from the bones of the wrist by a disc of fibrocartilage and plays little or no role in hand movements.

Radius

The **radius** ("rod") is thin at its proximal end and wide distally—the opposite of the ulna. The **head** of the radius is shaped somewhat like the head of a nail (Figure 7.27). The superior surface of this head is concave, and it articulates with the capitulum

of the humerus. Medially, the head articulates with the radial notch of the ulna (Figure 7.26c). Just inferior to the head is the rough **radial tuberosity**, which anchors the biceps muscle of the arm. Distally, where the radius is expanded, it has a medial **ulnar notch** (Figure 7.27d), which articulates with the ulna, and a lateral **styloid process** (an anchoring site for ligaments that run to the wrist). Between these two markings, the radius is concave where it articulates with carpal bones of the wrist.

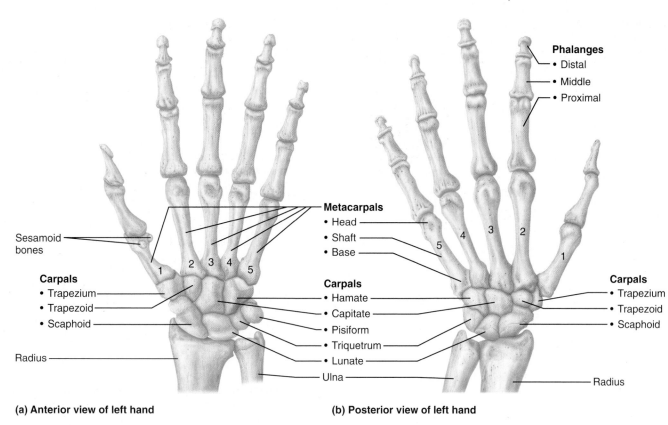

Sesamoid bones

Carpals
• Trapezium
• Trapezoid
• Scaphoid

Radius

1 2 3 4 5

Metacarpals
• Head
• Shaft
• Base

Carpals
• Hamate
• Capitate
• Pisiform
• Triquetrum
• Lunate

Ulna

(a) Anterior view of left hand

Phalanges
• Distal
• Middle
• Proximal

5 4 3 2

1

Carpals
• Trapezium
• Trapezoid
• Scaphoid

Radius

(b) Posterior view of left hand

Figure 7.28 Bones of the left hand. (See *A Brief Atlas of the Human Body*, Figure 27.)

The ulna contributes more heavily to the elbow joint, and the radius is the major forearm bone contributing to the wrist joint. When the radius moves, the hand moves with it.

HOMEOSTATIC IMBALANCE

Colle's fracture is a break in the distal end of the radius. It is a common fracture when a falling person attempts to break his or her fall with outstretched hands. ■

Hand

The skeleton of the hand **(Figure 7.28)** includes the bones of the *carpus* (wrist); the bones of the *metacarpus* (palm); and the *phalanges* (bones of the fingers).

Carpus (Wrist)

A "wrist" watch is actually worn on the distal forearm (over the lower ends of the radius and ulna), not on the wrist at all. The true wrist, or carpus, is the proximal part of the structure we generally call our "hand." The carpus consists of eight marble-size short bones, or **carpals** (kar′palz), closely united by ligaments. Because gliding movements occur between these bones, the carpus as a whole is quite flexible.

The carpals are arranged in two irregular rows of four bones each (Figure 7.28). In the proximal row (lateral to medial) are the **scaphoid** (skaf′oid; "boat-shaped"), **lunate** (lu′nāt; "moon-like"), **triquetrum** (tri-kwet′rum; "triangular"), and **pisiform** (pi′sĭ-form; "pea-shaped"). Only the scaphoid and lunate artic-

ulate with the radius to form the wrist joint. The carpals of the distal row (lateral to medial) are the **trapezium** (trah-pe′ze-um; "little table"), **trapezoid** (tra′peh-zoid; "four-sided"), **capitate** ("head-shaped"), and **hamate** (ham′āt; "hooked").

There are numerous memory-jogging phrases to help you recall the carpals in the order given above. If you don't have one, try: Sally left the party to take Cindy home. As with all such memory jogs, the first letter of each word is the first letter of the term you need to remember.

HOMEOSTATIC IMBALANCE

The arrangement of its bones is such that the carpus is concave anteriorly and a ligament roofs over this concavity, forming the notorious *carpal tunnel*. Besides the median nerve (which supplies the lateral side of the hand), several long muscle tendons crowd into this tunnel. Overuse and inflammation of the tendons cause them to swell, compressing the median nerve, which causes tingling and numbness of the areas served, and movements of the thumb weaken. Pain is greatest at night. Those who repeatedly flex their wrists and fingers, such as those who work at computer keyboards all day, are particularly susceptible to this nerve impairment, called *carpal tunnel syndrome*. This condition is treated by splinting the wrist during sleep or by surgery. ■

Metacarpus (Palm)

Five **metacarpals** radiate from the wrist like spokes to form the **metacarpus** or palm of the hand (*meta* = beyond). These small long bones are not named, but instead are numbered 1 to 5

TABLE 7.3	Bones of the Appendicular Skeleton, Part 1: Pectoral Girdle and Upper Limb			
BODY REGION	**BONES***	**ILLUSTRATION**	**LOCATION**	**MARKINGS**
Pectoral girdle (Figures 7.24, 7.25)	Clavicle (2)		Clavicle is in superoanterior thorax; articulates medially with sternum and laterally with scapula	Acromial end; sternal end
	Scapula (2)		Scapula is in posterior thorax; forms part of the shoulder; articulates with humerus and clavicle	Glenoid cavity; spine; acromion; coracoid process; infraspinous, supraspinous, and subscapular fossae
Upper limb Arm (Figure 7.26)	Humerus (2)		Humerus is sole bone of arm; between scapula and elbow	Head; greater and lesser tubercles; intertubercular sulcus; radial groove; deltoid tuberosity; trochlea; capitulum; coronoid and olecranon fossae; epicondyles; radial fossa
Forearm (Figure 7.27)	Ulna (2)		Ulna is the medial bone of forearm between elbow and wrist; with the humerus forms elbow joint	Coronoid process; olecranon process; radial notch; trochlear notch; styloid process; head
Hand (Figure 7.28)	Radius (2)		Radius is the lateral bone of forearm; articulates with carpals to form part of the wrist joint	Head; radial tuberosity; styloid process; ulnar notch
	8 Carpals (16) scaphoid lunate triquetrum pisiform trapezium trapezoid capitate hamate		Carpals form a bony crescent at the wrist; arranged in two rows of four bones each	
	5 Metacarpals (10)		Metacarpals form the palm; one in line with each digit	
	14 Phalanges (28) distal middle proximal		Phalanges form the fingers; three in digits 2–5; two in digit 1 (the thumb)	

Anterior view of pectoral girdle and upper limb

*The number in parentheses ( ) following the bone name denotes the total number of such bones in the body.

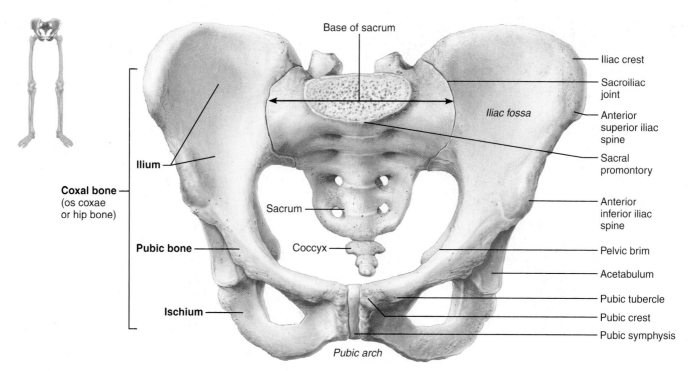

Figure 7.29 Articulated pelvis showing the two hip (coxal) bones (which together form the pelvic girdle), the sacrum, and the coccyx.

from thumb to little finger. The **bases** of the metacarpals articulate with the carpals proximally and each other medially and laterally (Figure 7.28). Their bulbous **heads** articulate with the proximal phalanges of the fingers. When you clench your fist, the heads of the metacarpals become prominent as your *knuckles.*

Metacarpal 1, associated with the thumb, is the shortest and most mobile. It occupies a more anterior position than the other metacarpals. Consequently, the joint between metacarpal 1 and the trapezium is a unique saddle joint that allows *opposition,* the action of touching your thumb to the tips of your other fingers.

Phalanges (Fingers)

The **fingers**, or **digits** of the upper limb, are numbered 1 to 5 beginning with the thumb, or **pollex** (pol′eks). In most people, the third finger is the longest. Each hand contains 14 miniature long bones called **phalanges** (fah-lan′jêz). Except for the thumb, each finger has three phalanges: *distal, middle,* and *proximal.* The thumb has no middle phalanx. [Phalanx (fa′langks; "a closely knit row of soldiers") is the singular term for phalanges.]

CHECK YOUR UNDERSTANDING

25. Which bones play the major role in forming the elbow joint?

26. Which bones of the upper limb have a styloid process?

27. Where are carpals found and what type of bone (short, irregular, long, or flat) are they?

For answers, see Appendix G.

The Pelvic (Hip) Girdle

▶ Name the bones contributing to the os coxae, and relate the pelvic girdle's strength to its function.

▶ Describe differences in the male and female pelves and relate these to functional differences.

The **pelvic girdle**, or **hip girdle**, attaches the lower limbs to the axial skeleton, transmits the full weight of the upper body to the lower limbs, and supports the visceral organs of the pelvis (Figures 7.29 and 7.30 and Table 7.4, p. 236). Unlike the pectoral girdle, which is sparingly attached to the thoracic cage, the pelvic girdle is secured to the axial skeleton by some of the strongest ligaments in the body. And unlike the shallow glenoid cavity of the scapula, the corresponding sockets of the pelvic girdle are deep and cuplike and firmly secure the head of the femur in place. Thus, even though both the shoulder and hip joints are ball-and-socket joints, very few of us can wheel or swing our legs about with the same degree of freedom as our arms. The pelvic girdle lacks the mobility of the pectoral girdle but is far more stable.

The pelvic girdle is formed by a pair of **hip bones**, each also called an **os coxae** (ahs kok′se), or **coxal bone** (*coxa* = hip). Each hip bone unites with its partner anteriorly and with the sacrum posteriorly **(Figure 7.29)**. The deep, basinlike structure formed by the hip bones, together with the sacrum and coccyx, is called the **bony pelvis**.

Each large, irregularly shaped hip bone consists of three separate bones during childhood: the ilium, ischium, and pubis **(Figure 7.30)**. In adults, these bones are firmly fused and their

7

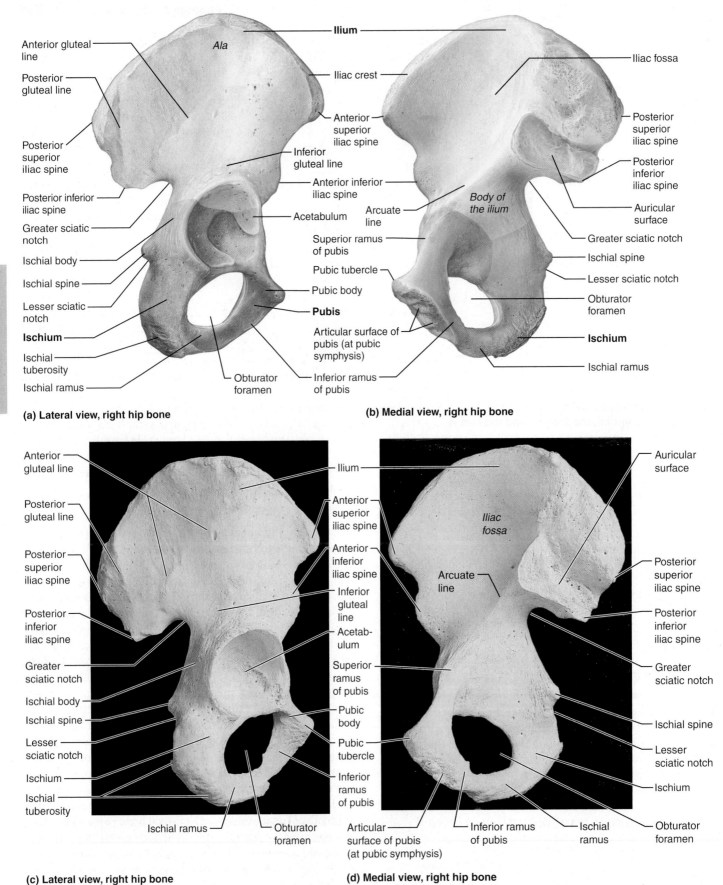

(a) Lateral view, right hip bone

Anterior gluteal line
Posterior gluteal line
Posterior superior iliac spine
Posterior inferior iliac spine
Greater sciatic notch
Ischial body
Ischial spine
Lesser sciatic notch
Ischium
Ischial tuberosity
Ischial ramus

Ilium
Ala
Iliac crest
Anterior superior iliac spine
Inferior gluteal line
Anterior inferior iliac spine
Acetabulum
Pubic body
Obturator foramen

(b) Medial view, right hip bone

Iliac fossa
Posterior superior iliac spine
Posterior inferior iliac spine
Auricular surface
Greater sciatic notch
Ischial spine
Lesser sciatic notch
Obturator foramen
Ischium
Ischial ramus

Body of the ilium
Arcuate line
Superior ramus of pubis
Pubic tubercle
Pubis
Articular surface of pubis (at pubic symphysis)
Inferior ramus of pubis

(c) Lateral view, right hip bone

Anterior gluteal line
Posterior gluteal line
Posterior superior iliac spine
Posterior inferior iliac spine
Greater sciatic notch
Ischial body
Ischial spine
Lesser sciatic notch
Ischium
Ischial tuberosity
Ischial ramus
Obturator foramen

Ilium
Anterior superior iliac spine
Anterior inferior iliac spine
Inferior gluteal line
Acetabulum
Superior ramus of pubis
Pubic body
Pubic tubercle
Inferior ramus of pubis

(d) Medial view, right hip bone

Auricular surface
Iliac fossa
Arcuate line
Posterior superior iliac spine
Posterior inferior iliac spine
Greater sciatic notch
Ischial spine
Lesser sciatic notch
Ischium
Obturator foramen
Ischial ramus
Inferior ramus of pubis
Articular surface of pubis (at pubic symphysis)

Figure 7.30 Bones of the pelvic girdle. Lateral and medial views of the right hip bone. The point of fusion of the ilium (gold), ischium (violet), and pubic (red) bones at the acetabulum is indicated in the diagrams **(a, b)**. (See *A Brief Atlas of the Human Body*, Figure 28.)

boundaries are indistinguishable. Their names are retained, however, to refer to different regions of the composite hip bone.

At the point of fusion of the ilium, ischium, and pubis is a deep hemispherical socket called the **acetabulum** (as″ĕ-tab′u-lum; "vinegar cup") on the lateral surface of the pelvis (see Figure 7.30). The acetabulum receives the head of the femur, or thigh bone, at this *hip joint*.

Ilium

The **ilium** (il′e-um; "flank") is a large flaring bone that forms the superior region of a coxal bone. It consists of a **body** and a superior winglike portion called the **ala** (a′lah). When you rest your hands on your hips, you are resting them on the thickened superior margins of the alae, the **iliac crests**, to which many muscles attach. Each iliac crest ends anteriorly in the blunt **anterior superior iliac spine** and posteriorly in the sharp **posterior superior iliac spine**.

Located below these are the less prominent *anterior* and *posterior inferior iliac spines*. All of these spines are attachment points for the muscles of the trunk, hip, and thigh. The anterior superior iliac spine is an especially important anatomical landmark. It is easily felt through the skin and is visible in thin people. The posterior superior iliac spine is difficult to palpate, but its position is revealed by a skin dimple in the sacral region.

Just inferior to the posterior inferior iliac spine, the ilium indents deeply to form the **greater sciatic notch** (si-at′ik), through which the thick cordlike sciatic nerve passes to enter the thigh. The broad posterolateral surface of the ilium, the **gluteal surface** (gloo′te-al), is crossed by three ridges, the **posterior**, **anterior**, and **inferior gluteal lines**, to which the gluteal (buttock) muscles attach.

The medial surface of the iliac ala exhibits a concavity called the **iliac fossa**. Posterior to this, the roughened **auricular surface** (aw-rik′u-lar; "ear-shaped") articulates with the same-named surface of the sacrum, forming the *sacroiliac joint* (Figure 7.29). The weight of the body is transmitted from the spine to the pelvis through the sacroiliac joints. Running inferiorly and anteriorly from the auricular surface is a robust ridge called the **arcuate line** (ar′ku-at; "bowed"). The arcuate line helps define the **pelvic brim**, the superior margin of the *true pelvis*, which we will discuss shortly. Anteriorly, the body of the ilium joins the pubis; inferiorly it joins the ischium.

Ischium

The **ischium** (is′ke-um; "hip") forms the posteroinferior part of the hip bone (Figures 7.29 and 7.30). Roughly L- or arc-shaped, it has a thicker, superior **body** adjoining the ilium and a thinner, inferior **ramus** (*ramus* = branch). The ramus joins the pubis anteriorly. The ischium has three important markings. Its **ischial spine** projects medially into the pelvic cavity and serves as a point of attachment of the *sacrospinous ligament* running from the sacrum. Just inferior to the ischial spine is the **lesser sciatic notch**. A number of nerves and blood vessels pass through this notch to supply the anogenital area. The inferior surface of the ischial body is rough and grossly thickened as the **ischial**

tuberosity. When we sit, our weight is borne entirely by the ischial tuberosities, which are the strongest parts of the hip bones.

A massive ligament runs from the sacrum to each ischial tuberosity. This *sacrotuberous ligament* (not illustrated) helps hold the pelvis together. The ischial tuberosity is also a site of attachment of the large hamstring muscles of the posterior thigh.

Pubis

The **pubis** (pu′bis; "sexually mature"), or **pubic bone**, forms the anterior portion of the hip bone (Figures 7.29 and 7.30). In the anatomical position, it lies nearly horizontally and the urinary bladder rests upon it. Essentially, the pubis is V shaped with **superior** and **inferior rami** issuing from its flattened medial **body**. The anterior border of the pubis is thickened to form the **pubic crest**. At the lateral end of the pubic crest is the **pubic tubercle**, one of the attachments for the *inguinal ligament*. As the two rami of the pubic bone run laterally to join with the body and ramus of the ischium, they define a large opening in the hip bone, the **obturator foramen** (ob″tu-ra′tor), through which a few blood vessels and nerves pass. Although the obturator foramen is large, it is nearly closed by a fibrous membrane in life (*obturator* = closed up).

The bodies of the two pubic bones are joined by a fibrocartilage disc, forming the midline **pubic symphysis** joint. Inferior to this joint, the inferior pubic rami angle laterally, forming an inverted V-shaped arch called the **pubic arch** or **subpubic angle**. The acuteness of this arch helps to differentiate the male and female pelves.

Pelvic Structure and Childbearing

The differences between the male and female pelves are striking. The female pelvis is modified for childbearing: It tends to be wider, shallower, lighter, and rounder than that of a male. The female pelvis not only accommodates a growing fetus, but it must be large enough to allow the infant's relatively large head to exit at birth. The major differences between the typical male and female pelves are summarized and illustrated in **Table 7.4**.

The pelvis is said to consist of a false (greater) pelvis and a true (lesser) pelvis separated by the **pelvic brim**, a continuous oval ridge that runs from the pubic crest through the arcuate line and sacral promontory (Figure 7.29). The **false pelvis**, that portion superior to the pelvic brim, is bounded by the alae of the ilia laterally and the lumbar vertebrae posteriorly. The false pelvis is really part of the abdomen and helps support the abdominal viscera. It does not restrict childbirth in any way.

The **true pelvis** is the region inferior to the pelvic brim that is almost entirely surrounded by bone. It forms a deep bowl containing the pelvic organs. Its dimensions, particularly those of its *inlet* and *outlet*, are critical to the uncomplicated delivery of a baby, and they are carefully measured by an obstetrician.

The **pelvic inlet** *is* the pelvic brim, and its widest dimension is from right to left along the frontal plane. As labor begins, an infant's head typically enters the inlet with its forehead facing one ilium and its occiput facing the other. A sacral promontory

7

TABLE 7.4 Comparison of the Male and Female Pelves

CHARACTERISTIC	FEMALE	MALE
General structure and functional modifications	Tilted forward; adapted for childbearing; true pelvis defines the birth canal; cavity of the true pelvis is broad, shallow, and has a greater capacity	Tilted less far forward; adapted for support of a male's heavier build and stronger muscles; cavity of the true pelvis is narrow and deep
Bone thickness	Less; bones lighter, thinner, and smoother	Greater; bones heavier and thicker, and markings are more prominent
Acetabula	Smaller; farther apart	Larger; closer
Pubic angle/arch	Broader (80° to 90°); more rounded	Angle is more acute (50° to 60°)
Anterior view	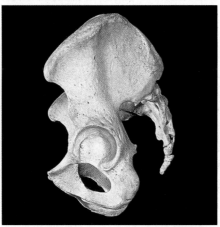 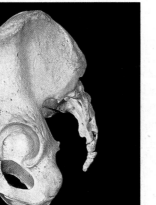	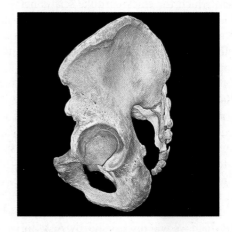

Pelvic brim

Pubic arch

Sacrum	Wider; shorter; sacral curvature is accentuated	Narrow; longer; sacral promontory more ventral
Coccyx	More movable; straighter	Less movable; curves ventrally
Greater sciatic notch	Wide and shallow	Narrow and deep
Left lateral view		
Pelvic inlet (brim)	Wider; oval from side to side	Narrow; basically heart shaped
Pelvic outlet	Wider; ischial tuberosities shorter, farther apart and everted	Narrower; ischial tuberosities longer, sharper, and point more medially
Posteroinferior view	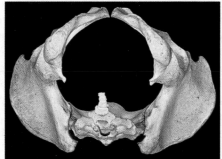	

that is particularly large can impair the infant's entry into the true pelvis.

The **pelvic outlet**, illustrated in the photos at the bottom of Table 7.4, is the inferior margin of the true pelvis. It is bounded anteriorly by the pubic arch, laterally by the ischia, and posteriorly by the sacrum and coccyx. Both the coccyx and the ischial spines protrude into the outlet opening, so a sharply angled coccyx or unusually large spines can interfere with delivery. The largest dimension of the outlet is the anteroposterior diameter.

Generally, after the baby's head passes through the inlet, it rotates so that the forehead faces posteriorly and the occiput anteriorly, and this is the usual position of the baby's head as it leaves the mother's body (see Figure 28.18c). Thus, during birth, the infant's head makes a quarter turn to follow the widest dimensions of the true pelvis.

CHECK YOUR UNDERSTANDING

28. The ilium and pubis help to form the os coxae. What other bone is involved in forming the os coxae?

29. The pelvic girdle is a heavy, strong girdle. How does its structure reflect its function?

30. Which of the following terms or phrases refer to the female pelvis? Wider, shorter sacrum; cavity narrow and deep; narrow heart-shaped inlet; more movable coccyx; long ischial spines.

For answers, see Appendix G.

The Lower Limb

▶ Identify the lower limb bones and their important markings.

The lower limbs carry the entire weight of the erect body and are subjected to exceptional forces when we jump or run. Thus, it is not surprising that the bones of the lower limbs are thicker and stronger than comparable bones of the upper limbs. The three segments of each lower limb are the thigh, the leg, and the foot (see Table 7.5 on p. 242).

Thigh

The **femur** (fe′mur; "thigh"), the single bone of the thigh (Figure 7.31), is the largest, longest, strongest bone in the body. Its durable structure reflects the fact that the stress on the femur during vigorous jumping can reach 280 kg/cm^2 (about 2 tons per square inch)! The femur is clothed by bulky muscles that prevent us from palpating its course down the length of the thigh. Its length is roughly one-quarter of a person's height.

Proximally, the femur articulates with the hip bone and then courses medially as it descends toward the knee. This arrangement allows the knee joints to be closer to the body's center of gravity and provides for better balance. The medial course of the two femurs is more pronounced in women because of their wider pelvis, a situation that may contribute to the greater incidence of knee problems in female athletes.

The ball-like **head** of the femur has a small central pit called the **fovea capitis** (fo′ve-ah kă′pĭ-tis; "pit of the head"). The short *ligament of the head of the femur* runs from this pit to the acetabulum, where it helps secure the femur. The head is carried on a *neck* that angles *laterally* to join the shaft. This arrangement reflects the fact that the femur articulates with the lateral aspect (rather than the inferior region) of the pelvis. The neck is the weakest part of the femur and is often fractured, an injury commonly called a broken hip.

At the junction of the shaft and neck are the lateral **greater trochanter** (tro-kan′ter) and posteromedial **lesser trochanter**. These projections serve as sites of attachment for thigh and buttock muscles. The two trochanters are connected by the **intertrochanteric line** anteriorly and by the prominent **intertrochanteric crest** posteriorly.

Inferior to the intertrochanteric crest on the posterior shaft is the **gluteal tuberosity**, which blends into a long vertical ridge, the **linea aspera** (lin′e-ah as′per-ah; "rough line"), inferiorly. Distally, the linea aspera diverges, forming the **medial** and **lateral supracondylar lines**. All of these markings are sites of muscle attachment. Except for the linea aspera, the femur shaft is smooth and rounded.

Distally, the femur broadens and ends in the wheel-like **lateral** and **medial condyles**, which articulate with the tibia of the leg. The **medial** and **lateral epicondyles** (sites of muscle attachment) flank the condyles superiorly. On the superior part of the medial epicondyle is a bump, the **adductor tubercle**. The smooth **patellar surface**, between the condyles on the anterior femoral surface, articulates with the *patella* (pah-tel′ah), or kneecap (see Figure 7.31 and Table 7.5).

Between the condyles on the posterior aspect of the femur is the deep, U-shaped **intercondylar fossa**, and superior to that on the shaft is the smooth popliteal surface.

The **patella** ("small pan") is a triangular sesamoid bone enclosed in the (quadriceps) tendon that secures the anterior thigh muscles to the tibia. It protects the knee joint anteriorly and improves the leverage of the thigh muscles acting across the knee.

Leg

Two parallel bones, the tibia and fibula, form the skeleton of the leg, the region of the lower limb between the knee and the ankle (Figure 7.32). These two bones are connected by an *interosseous membrane* and articulate with each other both proximally and distally. Unlike the joints between the radius and ulna of the forearm, the *tibiofibular joints* (tib″e-o-fib′u-lar) of the leg allow essentially no movement. The bones of the leg thus form a less flexible but stronger and more stable limb than those of the forearm. The medial tibia articulates proximally with the femur to form the modified hinge joint of the knee and distally with the talus bone of the foot at the ankle. The fibula, by contrast, does not contribute to the knee joint and merely helps stabilize the ankle joint.

Tibia

The **tibia** (tib′e-ah; "shinbone") receives the weight of the body from the femur and transmits it to the foot. It is second only to the femur in size and strength. At its broad proximal end are the

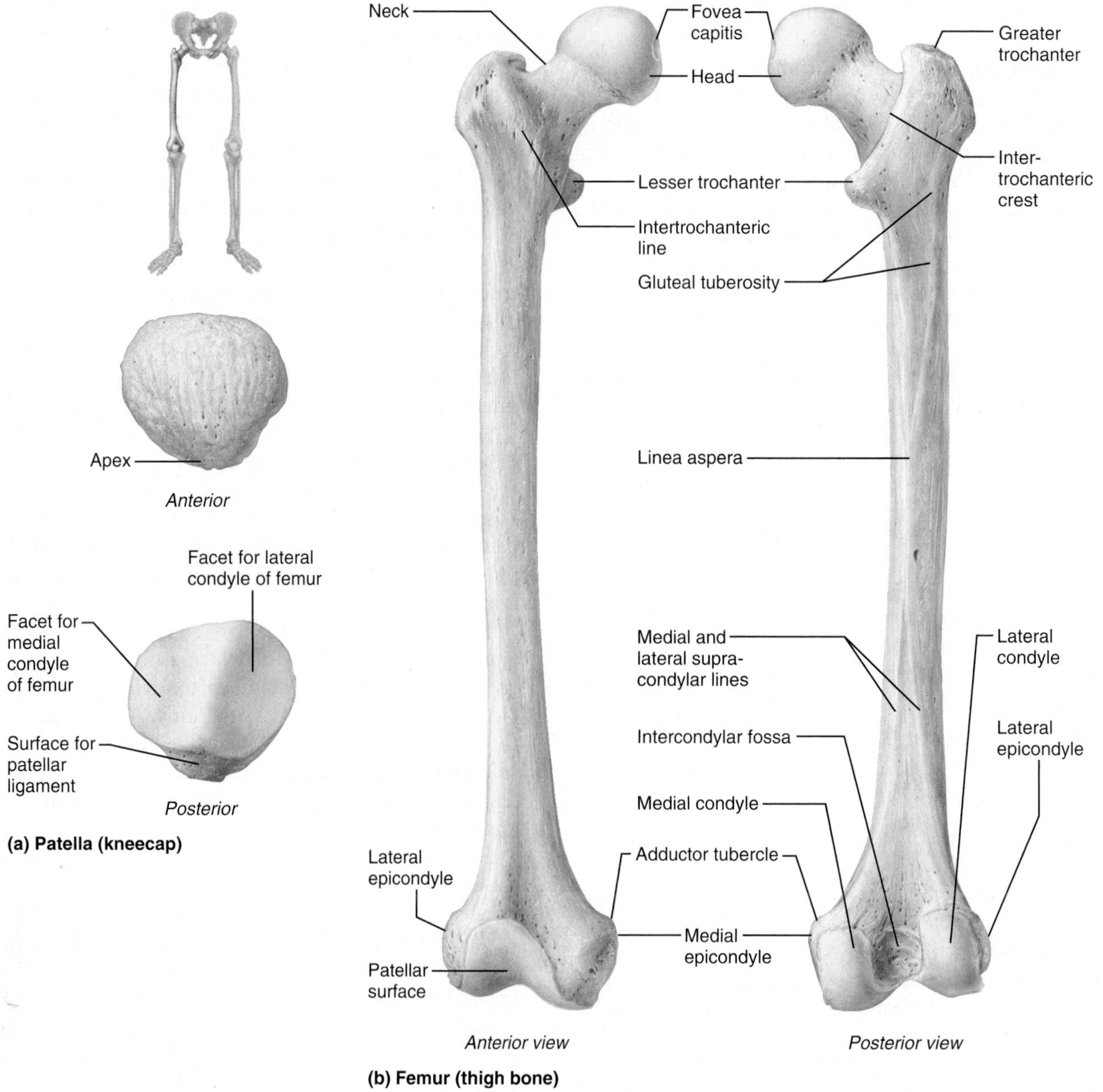

Figure 7.31 **Bones of the right knee and thigh.** (See *A Brief Atlas of the Human Body*, Figure 29.)

concave **medial** and **lateral condyles**, which look like two huge checkers lying side by side. These are separated by an irregular projection, the **intercondylar eminence**. The tibial condyles articulate with the corresponding condyles of the femur. The inferior region of the lateral tibial condyle bears a facet that indicates the site of the *proximal tibiofibular joint*. Just inferior to the condyles, the tibia's anterior surface displays the rough **tibial tuberosity**, to which the patellar ligament attaches.

The tibial shaft is triangular in cross section. Neither the tibia's sharp **anterior border** nor its medial surface is covered by muscles, so they can be felt just deep to the skin along their entire length. The anguish of a "bumped" shin is an experience familiar to nearly everyone. Distally the tibia is flat where it

articulates with the talus bone of the foot. Medial to that joint surface is an inferior projection, the **medial malleolus** (mah-le′o-lus; "little hammer"), which forms the medial bulge of the ankle. The **fibular notch**, on the lateral surface of the tibia, participates in the *distal tibiofibular joint*.

Fibula

The **fibula** (fib′u-lah; "pin") is a sticklike bone with slightly expanded ends. It articulates proximally and distally with the lateral aspects of the tibia. Its proximal end is its **head**; its distal end is the **lateral malleolus**. The lateral malleolus forms the conspicuous lateral ankle bulge and articulates with the talus. The fibular shaft is heavily ridged and appears to have been twisted a

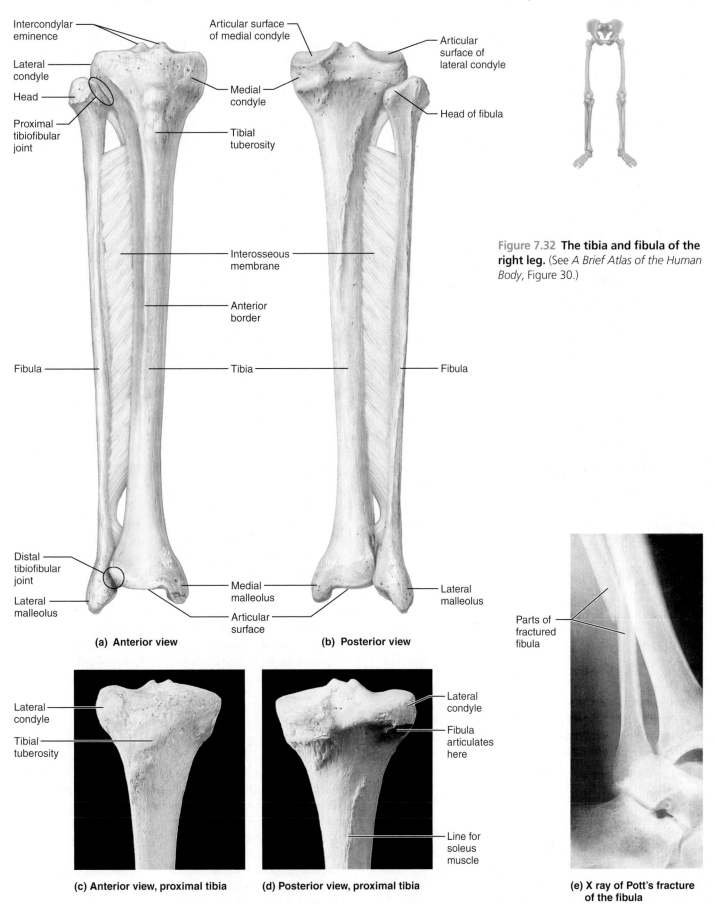

Intercondylar eminence

Lateral condyle

Head

Proximal tibiofibular joint

Articular surface of medial condyle

Medial condyle

Tibial tuberosity

Interosseous membrane

Anterior border

Fibula

Tibia

Distal tibiofibular joint

Lateral malleolus

Medial malleolus

Articular surface

(a) Anterior view

Articular surface of lateral condyle

Head of fibula

Fibula

Medial malleolus

Lateral malleolus

(b) Posterior view

Figure 7.32 The tibia and fibula of the right leg. (See *A Brief Atlas of the Human Body*, Figure 30.)

7

Lateral condyle

Tibial tuberosity

(c) Anterior view, proximal tibia

Lateral condyle

Fibula articulates here

Line for soleus muscle

(d) Posterior view, proximal tibia

Parts of fractured fibula

(e) X ray of Pott's fracture of the fibula

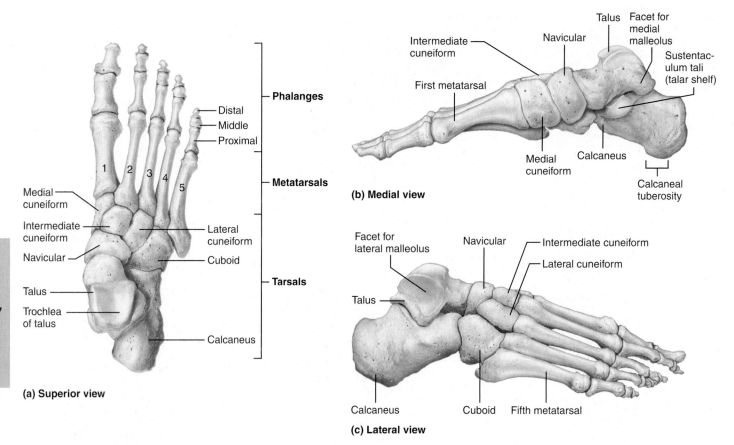

Figure 7.33 Bones of the right foot. (See *A Brief Atlas of the Human Body*, Figure 31a, c, and d.)

quarter turn. The fibula does not bear weight, but several muscles originate from it.

HOMEOSTATIC IMBALANCE

A *Pott's fracture* occurs at the distal end of the fibula, the tibia, or both. It is a common sports injury. (See Figure 7.32e.) ■

CHECK YOUR UNDERSTANDING

31. What lower limb bone is the second largest bone in the body?
32. Where is the medial malleolus located?
33. Which of the following sites is not a site of muscle attachment? Greater trochanter, lesser trochanter, gluteal tuberosity, lateral condyle.

For answers, see Appendix G.

Foot

▶ Name the arches of the foot and explain their importance.

The skeleton of the foot includes the bones of the *tarsus*, the bones of the *metatarsus*, and the *phalanges*, or toe bones (**Figure 7.33**). The foot has two important functions: It supports our

body weight, and it acts as a lever to propel the body forward when we walk and run. A single bone could serve both purposes, but it would adapt poorly to uneven ground. Segmentation makes the foot pliable, avoiding this problem.

Tarsus

The **tarsus** is made up of seven bones called **tarsals** (tar′salz) that form the posterior half of the foot. It corresponds to the carpus of the hand. Body weight is carried primarily by the two largest, most posterior tarsals: the **talus** (ta′lus; "ankle"), which articulates with the tibia and fibula superiorly, and the strong **calcaneus** (kal-ka′ne-us; "heel bone"), which forms the heel of the foot and carries the talus on its superior surface. The thick *calcaneal*, or *Achilles*, *tendon* of the calf muscles attaches to the posterior surface of the calcaneus. The part of the calcaneus that touches the ground is the **calcaneal tuberosity**, and its shelflike projection that supports part of the talus is the **sustentaculum tali** (sus″ten-tak′u-lum ta′le; "supporter of the talus") or **talar shelf**. The tibia articulates with the talus at the *trochlea* of the talus. The remaining tarsals are the lateral **cuboid**, the medial **navicular** (nah-vik′u-lar), and the anterior **medial, intermediate**, and **lateral cuneiform bones** (ku-ne′i-form; "wedge-shaped"). The cuboid and cuneiform bones articulate with the metatarsal bones anteriorly.

Metatarsus

The **metatarsus** consists of five small, long bones called **metatarsals**. These are numbered 1 to 5 beginning on the medial (great toe) side of the foot. The first metatarsal, which plays an important role in supporting body weight, is short and thick. The arrangement of the metatarsals is more parallel than that of the metacarpals of the hands. Distally, where the metatarsals articulate with the proximal phalanges of the toes, the enlarged head of the first metatarsal forms the "ball" of the foot.

Phalanges (Toes)

The 14 phalanges of the toes are a good deal smaller than those of the fingers and so are less nimble. But their general structure and arrangement are the same. There are three phalanges in each digit except for the great toe, the **hallux**. The hallux has only two, proximal and distal.

Arches of the Foot

A segmented structure can hold up weight only if it is arched. The foot has three arches: two *longitudinal arches* (*medial* and *lateral*) and one *transverse arch* (Figure 7.34), which account for its awesome strength. These arches are maintained by the interlocking shapes of the foot bones, by strong ligaments, and by the pull of some tendons during muscle activity. The ligaments and muscle tendons provide a certain amount of springiness. In general, the arches "give," or stretch slightly, when weight is applied to the foot and spring back when the weight is removed, which makes walking and running more economical in terms of energy use than would otherwise be the case.

If you examine your wet footprints, you will see that the medial margin from the heel to the head of the first metatarsal leaves no print. This is because the **medial longitudinal arch** curves well above the ground. The talus is the keystone of this arch, which originates at the calcaneus, rises toward the talus, and then descends to the three medial metatarsals.

The **lateral longitudinal arch** is very low. It elevates the lateral part of the foot just enough to redistribute some of the weight to the calcaneus and the head of the fifth metatarsal (to the ends of the arch). The cuboid is the keystone bone of this arch.

The two longitudinal arches serve as pillars for the **transverse arch**, which runs obliquely from one side of the foot to the other, following the line of the joints between the tarsals and metatarsals. Together, the arches of the foot form a half-dome that distributes about half of a person's standing and walking weight to the heel bones and half to the heads of the metatarsals.

⚖ HOMEOSTATIC IMBALANCE

Standing immobile for extended periods places excessive strain on the tendons and ligaments of the feet (because the muscles are inactive) and can result in fallen arches, or "flat feet," particularly if a person is overweight. Running on hard surfaces can also cause arches to fall unless the runner wears shoes that give proper arch support. ■

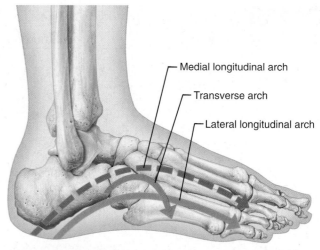

(a) Lateral aspect of right foot

- Medial longitudinal arch
- Transverse arch
- Lateral longitudinal arch

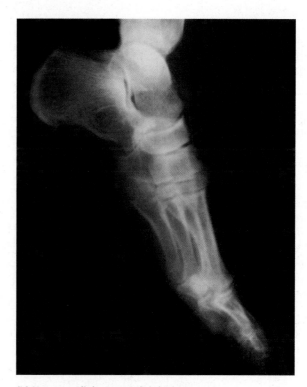

(b) X ray, medial aspect of right foot

Figure 7.34 **Arches of the foot.**

The bones of the thigh, leg, and foot are summarized in **Table 7.5.**

CHECK YOUR UNDERSTANDING

34. Besides supporting our weight, what is a major function of the arches of the foot?

35. What are the two largest tarsal bones in each foot, and which one forms the heel of the foot?

For answers, see Appendix G.

TABLE 7.5	Bones of the Appendicular Skeleton, Part 2: Pelvic Girdle and Lower Limb			
BODY REGION	**BONES***	**ILLUSTRATION**	**LOCATION**	**MARKINGS**
Pelvic girdle (Figures 7.29, 7.30)	Coxal (2) (hip)		Each coxal (hip) bone is formed by the fusion of an ilium, ischium, and pubic bone; the coxal bones articulate anteriorly at the pubic symphysis and form sacroiliac joints with the sacrum posteriorly; girdle consisting of both coxal bones is basinlike	Iliac crest; anterior and posterior iliac spines; auricular surface; greater and lesser sciatic notches; obturator foramen; ischial tuberosity and spine; acetabulum; pubic arch; pubic crest; pubic tubercle
Lower limb Thigh (Figure 7.31)	Femur (2)		Femur is the sole bone of thigh; between hip joint and knee; largest bone of the body	Head; greater and lesser trochanters; neck; lateral and medial condyles and epicondyles; gluteal tuberosity; linea aspera
Kneecap (Figure 7.31)	Patella (2)		Patella is a sesamoid bone formed within the tendon of the quadriceps (anterior thigh) muscles	
Leg (Figure 7.32)	Tibia (2)		Tibia is the larger and more medial bone of leg; between knee and foot	Medial and lateral condyles; tibial tuberosity; anterior border; medial malleolus
	Fibula (2)		Fibula is the lateral bone of leg; sticklike	Head; lateral malleolus
Foot (Figure 7.33)	7 Tarsals (14) talus calcaneus navicular cuboid lateral cuneiform intermediate cuneiform medial cuneiform		Tarsals are seven bones forming the proximal part of the foot; the talus articulates with the leg bones at the ankle joint; the calcaneus, the largest tarsal, forms the heel	
	5 Metatarsals (10)		Metatarsals are five bones numbered 1–5	
	14 Phalanges (28) distal middle proximal		Phalanges form the toes; three in digits 2–5, two in digit 1 (the great toe)	

Anterior view of pelvic girdle and left lower limb

*The number in parentheses ( ) following the bone name denotes the total number of such bones in the body.

Developmental Aspects of the Skeleton

▶ Define fontanelles and indicate their significance.

▶ Describe how skeletal proportions change through life.

▶ Discuss how age-related skeletal changes may affect health.

The membrane bones of the skull start to ossify late in the second month of development. The rapid deposit of bone matrix at the ossification centers produces cone-shaped protrusions in the developing bones. At birth, the skull bones are still incomplete and are connected by as yet unossified remnants of fibrous membranes called **fontanelles** (fon″tah-nelz′) (Figure 7.35). The fontanelles allow the infant's head to be compressed slightly during birth, and they accommodate brain growth in the fetus and infant. A baby's pulse can be felt surging in these "soft spots"; hence their name (*fontanelle* = little fountain). The large, diamond-shaped *anterior fontanelle* is palpable for 1-½ to 2 years after birth. The others are replaced by bone by the end of the first year.

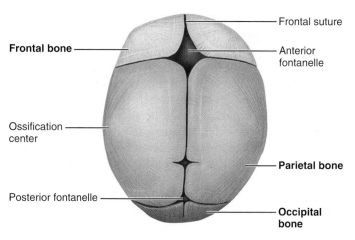

- Frontal suture
- **Frontal bone**
- Anterior fontanelle
- Ossification center
- **Parietal bone**
- Posterior fontanelle
- **Occipital bone**

(a) Superior view

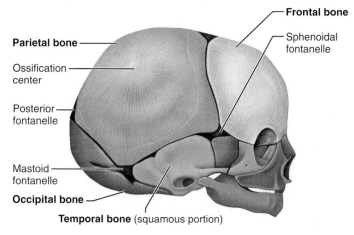

- **Frontal bone**
- **Parietal bone**
- Sphenoidal fontanelle
- Ossification center
- Posterior fontanelle
- Mastoid fontanelle
- **Occipital bone**
- **Temporal bone** (squamous portion)

(b) Lateral view

Figure 7.35 Skull of a newborn. Notice that the infant's skull has more bones than that of an adult. (See *A Brief Atlas of the Human Body,* Figure 16.)

⚖ HOMEOSTATIC IMBALANCE

Several congenital abnormalities may distort the skull. Most common is *cleft palate*, a condition in which the right and left halves of the palate fail to fuse medially **(Figure 7.36)**. The persistent opening between the oral and nasal cavities interferes with sucking and can lead to aspiration (inhalation) of food into the lungs and *aspiration pneumonia.* ∎

The skeleton changes throughout life, but the changes in childhood are most dramatic. At birth, the baby's cranium is huge relative to its face, and several bones are still unfused (e.g., the mandible and frontal bones). The maxillae and mandible are foreshortened, and the contours of the face are flat (Figure 7.38). By 9 months after birth, the cranium is already half of its adult size (volume) because of the rapid growth of the brain. By 8 to 9 years, the cranium has almost reached adult proportions.

Between the ages of 6 and 13, the head appears to enlarge substantially as the face literally grows out from the skull. The jaws, cheekbones, and nose become more prominent. These facial changes are correlated with the expansion of the nose and

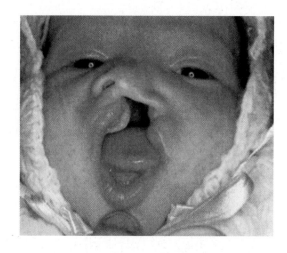

Figure 7.36 A baby born with a cleft lip and palate.

paranasal sinuses, and development of the permanent teeth. Figure 7.38 tracks how differential bone growth alters body proportions throughout life.

Only the thoracic and sacral curvatures are well developed at birth. These so-called **primary curvatures** are convex posteriorly, and an infant's spine arches, like that of a four-legged animal **(Figure 7.37)**.

The **secondary curvatures**—cervical and lumbar—are convex anteriorly and are associated with a child's development. They result from reshaping of the intervertebral discs rather than from modifications of the vertebrae. The cervical curvature is present before birth but is not pronounced until the baby starts to lift its head (at about 3 months). The lumbar curvature develops when the baby begins to walk (at about 12 months). The lumbar curvature positions the weight of the trunk over the body's center of gravity, providing optimal balance when standing.

Vertebral problems (scoliosis or lordosis) may appear during the early school years, when rapid growth of the limb bones stretches many muscles. During the preschool years, lordosis is often present, but this is usually rectified as the abdominal

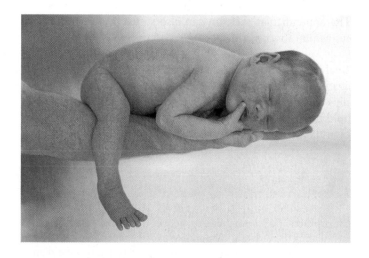

Figure 7.37 The C-shaped spine of a newborn infant.

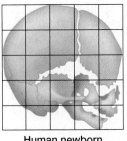
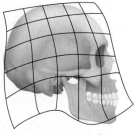

Human newborn   Human adult

(a)

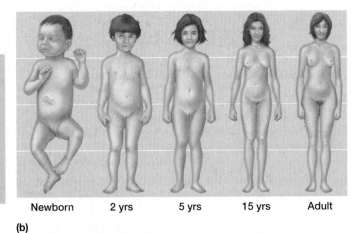

Newborn   2 yrs   5 yrs   15 yrs   Adult

(b)

Figure 7.38 Different growth rates of body parts determine body proportions. (a) Differential growth transforms the rounded, foreshortened skull of a newborn to the sloping skull of an adult. **(b)** During growth of a human, the arms and legs grow faster than the head and trunk, as seen in this conceptualization of different-aged individuals all drawn at the same height.

muscles become stronger and the pelvis tilts forward. The thorax grows wider, but a true "military posture" (head erect, shoulders back, abdomen in, and chest out) does not develop until adolescence.

HOMEOSTATIC IMBALANCE

The appendicular skeleton can also suffer from a number of congenital abnormalities. One that occurs in just over 1% of infants and is quite severe is *dysplasia of the hip* (dis-pla′ze-ah; "bad formation"). The acetabulum forms incompletely or the ligaments of the hip joint are loose, so the head of the femur slips out of its socket. Early treatment (a splint or harness to hold the femur in place or surgery to tighten hip ligaments) is essential to prevent permanent crippling. ■

During youth, growth of the skeleton not only increases overall body height but also changes body proportions (Figure 7.38). At birth, the head and trunk are approximately 1½ times as long as the lower limbs. The lower limbs grow more rapidly than the trunk from this time on, and by the age of 10, the head and trunk are approximately the same height as the lower limbs, a condition that persists thereafter. During puberty, the female pelvis broadens in preparation for childbearing, and the entire male skeleton becomes more robust. Once adult height is reached, a healthy skeleton changes very little until late middle age.

Old age affects many parts of the skeleton, especially the spine. As the discs become thinner, less hydrated, and less elastic, the risk of disc herniation increases. By 55 years, a loss of several centimeters in stature is common. Further shortening can be produced by osteoporosis of the spine or by kyphosis (called "dowager's hump" in the elderly). What was done during youth may be undone in old age as the vertebral column gradually resumes its initial arc shape.

The thorax becomes more rigid with age, largely because the costal cartilages ossify. This loss of rib cage elasticity causes shallow breathing, which leads to less efficient gas exchange.

All bones, you will recall, lose mass with age. Cranial bones lose less mass than most, but changes in facial contours with age are common. As the bony tissue of the jaws declines, the jaws look small and childlike once again. If the elderly person loses his or her teeth, this loss of bone from the jaws is accelerated, because the alveolar region bone is resorbed. As bones become more porous, they are more likely to fracture, especially the vertebrae and the neck of the femur.

CHECK YOUR UNDERSTANDING

36. What developmental events result in a dramatic enlargement of the facial skeleton between the ages of 6 and 13?

37. Under what conditions does the lumbar curvature of the spine develop?

For answers, see Appendix G.

Our skeleton is a marvelous substructure, to be sure, but it is much more than that. It is a protector and supporter of other body systems, and without it (and the joints considered in Chapter 8), our muscles would be almost useless. The homeostatic relationships between the skeletal system and other body systems are illustrated in *Making Connections* in Chapter 6 (pp. 192–193).

RELATED CLINICAL TERMS

Chiropractic (ki″ro-prak′tik) A system of treating disease by manipulating the vertebral column based on the theory that most diseases are due to pressure on nerves caused by faulty bone alignment; a specialist in this field is a chiropractor.

Clubfoot A relatively common congenital defect (1 in 700 births) in which the soles of the feet face medially and the toes point inferiorly; may be genetically induced or reflect an abnormal position of the foot during fetal development.

Laminectomy Surgical removal of a vertebral lamina; most often done to relieve the symptoms of a ruptured disc.

Orthopedist (or″tho-pe′dist) or **orthopedic surgeon** A physician who specializes in restoring lost skeletal system function or repairing damage to bones and joints.

Pelvimetry Measurement of the dimensions of the inlet and outlet of the pelvis, usually to determine whether the pelvis is of adequate size to allow normal delivery of a baby.

Spina bifida (spi′nah bĭ′fĭ-dah; "cleft spine") Congenital defect of the vertebral column in which one or more of the vertebral arches are incomplete; ranges in severity from inconsequential to severe conditions that impair neural functioning and encourage nervous system infections.

Spinal fusion Surgical procedure involving insertion of bone chips (or crushed bone) to immobilize and stabilize a specific region of the vertebral column, particularly in cases of vertebral fracture and herniated discs.

CHAPTER SUMMARY

1. The axial skeleton forms the longitudinal axis of the body. Its principal subdivisions are the skull, vertebral column, and thoracic cage. It provides support and protection (by enclosure).
2. The appendicular skeleton consists of the bones of the pectoral and pelvic girdles and the limbs. It allows mobility for manipulation and locomotion.

PART 1: THE AXIAL SKELETON

The Skull   (pp. 200–216)

1. The skull is formed by 22 bones. The cranium forms the vault and base of the skull, which protect the brain. The facial skeleton provides openings for the respiratory and digestive passages and attachment points for facial muscles.
2. Except for the temporomandibular joints, all bones of the adult skull are joined by immovable sutures.
3. **Cranium.** The eight bones of the cranium include the paired parietal and temporal bones and the single frontal, occipital, ethmoid, and sphenoid bones (see Table 7.1, pp. 214–215).
4. **Facial bones.** The 14 bones of the face include the paired maxillae, zygomatics, nasals, lacrimals, palatines, and inferior nasal conchae and the single mandible and vomer bones (Table 7.1).
5. **Orbits and nasal cavity.** Both the orbits and the nasal cavities are complicated bony regions formed of several bones.
6. **Paranasal sinuses.** Paranasal sinuses occur in the frontal, ethmoid, sphenoid, and maxillary bones.
7. **Hyoid bone.** The hyoid bone, supported in the neck by ligaments, serves as an attachment point for tongue and neck muscles.

The Vertebral Column   (pp. 216–223)

1. **General characteristics.** The vertebral column includes 24 movable vertebrae (7 cervical, 12 thoracic, and 5 lumbar) and the sacrum and coccyx.
2. The fibrocartilage intervertebral discs act as shock absorbers and provide flexibility to the vertebral column.
3. The primary curvatures of the vertebral column are the thoracic and sacral; the secondary curvatures are the cervical and lumbar. Curvatures increase spine flexibility.
4. **General structure of vertebrae.** With the exception of C_1 and C_2, all vertebrae have a body, two transverse processes, two superior and two inferior articular processes, a spinous process, and a vertebral arch.
5. **Regional vertebral characteristics.** Special features distinguish the regional vertebrae (see Table 7.2, p. 222).

The Thoracic Cage   (pp. 223–225)

1. The bones of the thoracic cage include the 12 rib pairs, the sternum, and the thoracic vertebrae. The thoracic cage protects the organs of the thoracic cavity.
2. **Sternum.** The sternum consists of the fused manubrium, body, and xiphoid process.
3. **Ribs.** The first seven rib pairs are called true ribs; the rest are called false ribs. Ribs 11 and 12 are floating ribs.

PART 2: THE APPENDICULAR SKELETON

The Pectoral (Shoulder) Girdle*   (pp. 225–228)

1. Each pectoral girdle consists of one clavicle and one scapula. The pectoral girdles attach the upper limbs to the axial skeleton.
2. **Clavicles.** The clavicles hold the scapulae laterally away from the thorax. The sternoclavicular joints are the only attachment points of the pectoral girdle to the axial skeleton.
3. **Scapulae.** The scapulae articulate with the clavicles and with the humerus bones of the arms.

The Upper Limb*   (pp. 228–233)

1. Each upper limb consists of 30 bones and is specialized for mobility.
2. **Arm/forearm/hand.** The skeleton of the arm is composed solely of the humerus; the skeleton of the forearm is composed of the radius and ulna; and the skeleton of the hand consists of the carpals, metacarpals, and phalanges.

The Pelvic (Hip) Girdle*   (pp. 233–237)

1. The pelvic girdle, a heavy structure specialized for weight bearing, is composed of two hip bones that secure the lower limbs to the axial skeleton. Together with the sacrum and coccyx, the hip bones form the basinlike bony pelvis.
2. Each hip bone consists of three fused bones: ilium, ischium, and pubis. The acetabulum occurs at the point of fusion.
3. **Ilium/ischium/pubis.** The ilium is the superior flaring portion of the hip bone. Each ilium forms a secure joint with the sacrum posteriorly. The ischium is a curved bar of bone; we sit on the ischial tuberosities. The V-shaped pubic bones articulate anteriorly at the pubic symphysis.
4. **Pelvic structure and childbearing.** The male pelvis is deep and narrow with larger, heavier bones than those of the female. The female pelvis, which forms the birth canal, is shallow and wide.

*For associated bone markings, see the pages indicated in the section heads.

The Lower Limb*   (pp. 237–242)

1. Each lower limb consists of the thigh, leg, and foot and is specialized for weight bearing and locomotion.
2. **Thigh.** The femur is the only bone of the thigh. Its ball-shaped head articulates with the acetabulum.
3. **Leg.** The bones of the leg are the tibia, which participates in forming both the knee and ankle joints, and the fibula.
4. **Foot.** The bones of the foot include the tarsals, metatarsals, and phalanges. The most important tarsals are the calcaneus (heel bone) and the talus, which articulates with the tibia superiorly.
5. The foot is supported by three arches (lateral, medial, and transverse) that distribute body weight to the heel and ball of the foot.

Developmental Aspects of the Skeleton   (pp. 242–244)

1. Fontanelles, which allow brain growth and ease birth passage, are present in the skull at birth. Growth of the cranium after birth is related to brain growth. Increase in size of the facial skeleton follows tooth development and enlargement of nose and sinus cavities.
2. The vertebral column is C shaped at birth (thoracic and sacral curvatures are present); the secondary curvatures form when the baby begins to lift its head and walk.
3. Long bones continue to grow in length until late adolescence. The head and torso, initially 1½ times the length of the lower limbs, equal their length by the age of 10.
4. Changes in the female pelvis (preparatory for childbirth) occur during puberty.
5. Once at adult height, the skeleton changes little until late middle age. With old age, the intervertebral discs thin; this, along with osteoporosis, leads to a gradual loss in height and increased risk of disc herniation. Loss of bone mass increases the risk of fractures, and thoracic cage rigidity promotes breathing difficulties.

*For associated bone markings, see the pages indicated in the section heads.

REVIEW QUESTIONS

Multiple Choice/Matching

(Some questions have more than one correct answer. Select the best answer or answers from the choices given.)

1. Match the bones in column B with their description in column A. (Note that some descriptions require more than a single choice.)

Column A	Column B
_____ (1) connected by the coronal suture	(a) ethmoid
_____ (2) keystone bone of cranium	(b) frontal
_____ (3) keystone bone of the face	(c) mandible
_____ (4) form the hard palate	(d) maxillary
_____ (5) allows the spinal cord to pass	(e) occipital
_____ (6) forms the chin	(f) palatine
_____ (7) contain paranasal sinuses	(g) parietal
_____ (8) contains mastoid sinuses	(h) sphenoid
	(i) temporal

2. Match the key terms with the bone descriptions that follow.
   Key: (a) clavicle   (b) ilium   (c) ischium
         (d) pubis   (e) sacrum   (f) scapula
         (g) sternum

   _____ (1) bone of the axial skeleton to which the pectoral girdle attaches
   _____ (2) markings include glenoid cavity and acromion
   _____ (3) features include the ala, crest, and greater sciatic notch
   _____ (4) doubly curved; acts as a shoulder strut
   _____ (5) pelvic girdle bone that articulates with the axial skeleton
   _____ (6) the "sit-down" bone
   _____ (7) anteriormost bone of the pelvic girdle
   _____ (8) part of the vertebral column

3. Use key choices to identify the bone descriptions that follow.
   Key: (a) carpals   (b) femur   (c) fibula
         (d) humerus   (e) radius   (f) tarsals
         (g) tibia   (h) ulna

   _____ (1) articulates with the acetabulum and the tibia
   _____ (2) forms the lateral aspect of the ankle
   _____ (3) bone that "carries" the hand
   _____ (4) the wrist bones
   _____ (5) end shaped like a monkey wrench
   _____ (6) articulates with the capitulum of the humerus
   _____ (7) largest bone of this "group" is the calcaneus

Short Answer Essay Questions

4. Name the cranial and facial bones and compare and contrast the functions of the cranial and facial skeletons.
5. How do the relative proportions of the cranium and face of a fetus compare with those of an adult skull?
6. Name and diagram the normal vertebral curvatures. Which are primary and which are secondary curvatures?
7. List at least two specific anatomical characteristics each for typical cervical, thoracic, and lumbar vertebrae that would allow anyone to identify each type correctly.
8. What is the function of the intervertebral discs?
9. Distinguish between the anulus fibrosus and nucleus pulposus regions of a disc. Which provides durability and strength? Which provides resilience? Which part is involved in a "slipped" disc?
10. What is a true rib? A false rib?
11. The major function of the shoulder girdle is flexibility. What is the major function of the pelvic girdle? Relate these functional differences to anatomical differences seen in these girdles.
12. List three important differences between the male and female pelves.
13. Briefly describe the anatomical characteristics and impairment of function seen in cleft palate and hip dysplasia.
14. Compare a young adult skeleton to that of an extremely aged person relative to bone mass in general and the bony structure of the skull, thorax, and vertebral column in particular.
15. Peter Howell, a teaching assistant in the anatomy class, picked up a hip bone and pretended it was a telephone. He held the big hole in this bone right up to his ear and said, "Hello, obturator, obturator (operator, operator)." Name the structure he was helping the students to learn.

Critical Thinking and Clinical Application Questions

1. Justiniano worked in a poultry-packing plant where his job was cutting open chickens and stripping out their visceral organs. After work, he typed for long hours on his computer keyboard, writing a book about his work in the plant. Soon, his wrist and hand began to hurt whenever he flexed it, and he began to awaken at night with pain and tingling on the thumb-half of his hand. What condition did he probably have?

2. Ralph had polio as a boy and was partially paralyzed in one lower limb for over a year. Although no longer paralyzed, he now has a severe lateral curvature of the lumbar spine. Explain what has happened and identify his condition.

3. Mary's grandmother slipped on a scatter rug and fell heavily to the floor. Her left lower limb was laterally rotated and noticeably shorter than the right, and when she attempted to get up, she winced with pain. Mary surmised that her grandmother might have "fractured her hip," which later proved to be true. What bone was probably fractured and at what site? Why is a "fractured hip" a common type of fracture in the elderly?

4. Mrs. Shea came up with what she considered to be a clever idea to bypass the long lines at Disney World. She had her husband rent a wheelchair and he wheeled her around from one exhibit to another for the better part of three days. As they sat on the plane, waiting to take off for Chicago, she complained to him that she had two sore spots on her buttocks. Why? What do you suppose would happen (to her buttocks) if she was wheeled around for a few more days?

8

Classification of Joints (pp. 248–249)

Fibrous Joints (pp. 249–250)

    Sutures (p. 249)

    Syndesmoses (pp. 249–250)

    Gomphoses (p. 250)

Cartilaginous Joints (pp. 250–251)

    Synchondroses (pp. 250–251)

    Symphyses (p. 251)

Synovial Joints (pp. 251–269)

    General Structure (pp. 251–252)

    Bursae and Tendon Sheaths (p. 252)

    Factors Influencing the Stability of Synovial Joints (pp. 252–253)

    Movements Allowed by Synovial Joints (pp. 253–259)

    Types of Synovial Joints (p. 259)

    Selected Synovial Joints (pp. 259–269)

Homeostatic Imbalances of Joints (pp. 269–271)

    Common Joint Injuries (pp. 269–270)

    Inflammatory and Degenerative Conditions (pp. 270–271)

Developmental Aspects of Joints (p. 272)

Joints

The graceful movements of ballet dancers and the rough-and-tumble grapplings of football players demonstrate the great variety of motion allowed by **joints**, or **articulations**—the sites where two or more bones meet. Our joints have two fundamental functions: They give our skeleton mobility, and they hold it together, sometimes playing a protective role in the process.

Joints are the weakest parts of the skeleton. Nonetheless, their structure resists various forces, such as crushing or tearing, that threaten to force them out of alignment.

Classification of Joints

▶ Define joint or articulation.

▶ Classify joints structurally and functionally.

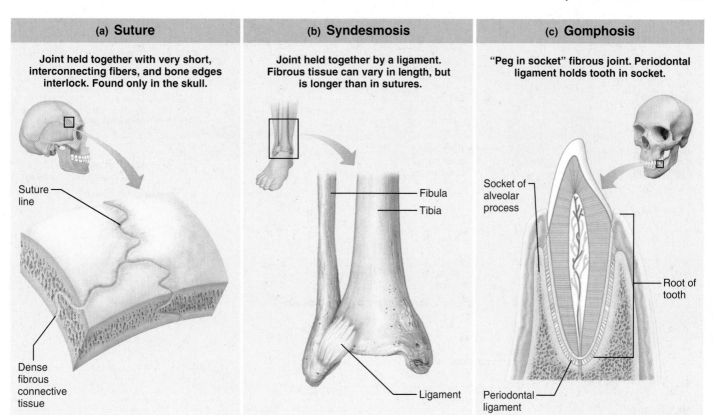

(a) **Suture**	(b) **Syndesmosis**	(c) **Gomphosis**
Joint held together with very short, interconnecting fibers, and bone edges interlock. Found only in the skull.	Joint held together by a ligament. Fibrous tissue can vary in length, but is longer than in sutures.	"Peg in socket" fibrous joint. Periodontal ligament holds tooth in socket.

Figure 8.1 Fibrous joints.

Joints are classified by structure and by function. The *structural classification* focuses on the material binding the bones together and whether or not a joint cavity is present. Structurally, there are *fibrous, cartilaginous,* and *synovial joints* (**Table 8.1** on p. 252).

The *functional classification* is based on the amount of movement allowed at the joint. On this basis, there are **synarthroses** (sin″ar-thro′sēz; *syn* = together, *arthro* = joint), which are immovable joints; **amphiarthroses** (am″fe-ar-thro′seēz; *amphi* = on both sides), slightly movable joints; and **diarthroses** (di″ar-thro′sēz; *dia* = through, apart), or freely movable joints. Freely movable joints predominate in the limbs. Immovable and slightly movable joints are largely restricted to the axial skeleton. This localization of functional joint types is understandable because the less movable the joint, the more stable it is likely to be.

In general, fibrous joints are immovable, and synovial joints are freely movable. However, cartilaginous joints have both rigid and slightly movable examples. Since the structural categories are more clear-cut, we will use the structural classification in this discussion, indicating functional properties where appropriate.

Fibrous Joints

▶ Describe the general structure of fibrous joints. Name and give an example of each of the three common types of fibrous joints.

In **fibrous joints**, the bones are joined by fibrous tissue, namely dense fibrous connective tissue, and no joint cavity is present. The amount of movement allowed depends on the length of the connective tissue fibers uniting the bones. Although a few are slightly movable, most fibrous joints are immovable. The three types of fibrous joints are *sutures, syndesmoses,* and *gomphoses.*

Sutures

Sutures, literally "seams," occur only between bones of the skull (**Figure 8.1a**). The wavy articulating bone edges interlock, and the junction is completely filled by a minimal amount of very short connective tissue fibers that are continuous with the periosteum. The result is nearly rigid splices that knit the bones together, yet allow the skull to expand as the brain grows during youth. During middle age, the fibrous tissue ossifies and the skull bones fuse into a single unit. At this stage, the closed sutures are more precisely called **synostoses** (sin″os-to′sēz), literally, "bony junctions." Because movement of the cranial bones would damage the brain, the immovable nature of sutures is a protective adaptation.

Syndesmoses

In **syndesmoses** (sin″des-mo′sēz), the bones are connected exclusively by *ligaments* (*syndesmos* = ligament), cords or bands of fibrous tissue. Although the connecting fibers are always longer than those in sutures, they vary quite a bit in length.

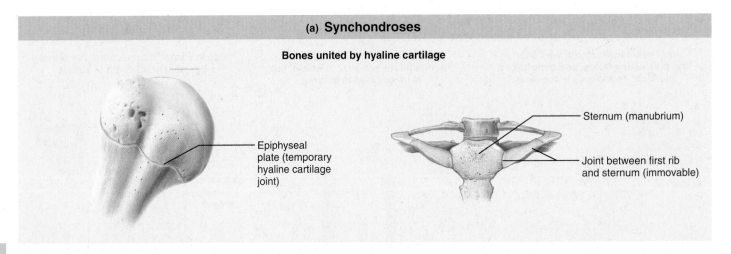

(a) Synchondroses

Bones united by hyaline cartilage

Epiphyseal plate (temporary hyaline cartilage joint)

Sternum (manubrium)

Joint between first rib and sternum (immovable)

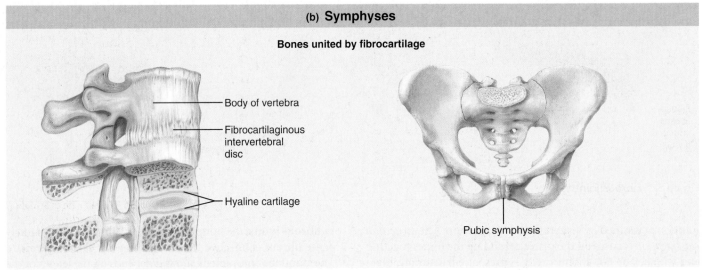

(b) Symphyses

Bones united by fibrocartilage

Body of vertebra

Fibrocartilaginous intervertebral disc

Hyaline cartilage

Pubic symphysis

Figure 8.2 Cartilaginous joints.

The amount of movement allowed depends on the length of the connecting fibers, and slight to considerable movement is possible. For example, the ligament connecting the distal ends of the tibia and fibula is short (Figure 8.1b), and this joint allows only slightly more movement than a suture, a characteristic best described as "give." True movement is still prevented, so the joint is classed functionally as an immovable joint, or synarthrosis. (Note, however, that some authorities classify this joint as an amphiarthrosis.) On the other hand, the fibers of the ligament-like interosseous membrane connecting the radius and ulna along their length (Figure 7.27, p. 230) are long enough to permit rotation of the radius around the ulna and the joint is diarthrotic.

Gomphoses

A **gomphosis** (gom-fo′sis) is a peg-in-socket fibrous joint (Figure 8.1c). The only example is the articulation of a tooth with its bony alveolar socket. The term *gomphosis* comes from the Greek *gompho*, meaning "nail" or "bolt," and refers to the way teeth are embedded in their sockets (as if hammered in).

The fibrous connection in this case is the short **periodontal ligament** (Figure 23.11, p. 863).

Cartilaginous Joints

▶ Describe the general structure of cartilaginous joints. Name and give an example of each of the two common types of cartilaginous joints.

In **cartilaginous joints** (kar″ti-laj′ĭ-nus), the articulating bones are united by cartilage. Like fibrous joints, they lack a joint cavity and are not highly movable. The two types of cartilaginous joints are *synchondroses* and *symphyses*.

Synchondroses

A bar or plate of *hyaline cartilage* unites the bones at a **synchondrosis** (sin″kon-dro′sis; "junction of cartilage"). Virtually all synchondroses are synarthrotic.

The most common examples of synchondroses are the epiphyseal plates in long bones of children (Figure 8.2a). Epiphyseal plates are temporary joints and eventually become synostoses. Another example of a synchondrosis is the immovable joint between the costal cartilage of the first rib and the manubrium of the sternum (Figure 8.2a).

Symphyses

In **symphyses** (sim′fih-sēz; "growing together") the articular surfaces of the bones are covered with articular (hyaline) cartilage, which in turn is fused to an intervening pad, or plate, of *fibrocartilage*, which is the main connecting material. Since fibrocartilage is compressible and resilient, it acts as a shock absorber and permits a limited amount of movement at the joint. Symphyses are amphiarthrotic joints designed for strength with flexibility. Examples include the intervertebral joints and the pubic symphysis of the pelvis (Figure 8.2b, and see **Table 8.2** on p. 254).

CHECK YOUR UNDERSTANDING

1. What term is a synonym for "joint"?
2. What functional joint class contains the least mobile joints?
3. Of sutures, symphyses, and synchondroses, which are cartilaginous joints?
4. How are joint mobility and stability related?

For answers, see Appendix G.

Synovial Joints

▶ Describe the structural characteristics of synovial joints.

▶ Compare the structures and functions of bursae and tendon sheaths.

▶ List three natural factors that stabilize synovial joints.

Synovial joints (si-no′ve-al; "joint eggs") are those in which the articulating bones are separated by a fluid-containing joint cavity. This arrangement permits substantial freedom of movement, and all synovial joints are freely movable diarthroses. Nearly all joints of the limbs—indeed, most joints of the body—fall into this class.

General Structure

Synovial joints have six distinguishing features **(Figure 8.3)**:

1. **Articular cartilage.** Glassy-smooth hyaline cartilage covers the opposing bone surfaces as **articular cartilage**. These thin (1 mm or less) but spongy cushions absorb compression placed on the joint and thereby keep the bone ends from being crushed.
2. **Joint (synovial) cavity.** A feature unique to synovial joints, the **joint cavity** is really just a potential space that contains a small amount of synovial fluid.
3. **Articular capsule.** The joint cavity is enclosed by a two-layered **articular capsule**, or *joint capsule*. The external layer is a tough **fibrous capsule**, composed of dense irregular connective tissue, that is continuous with the periostea of the articulating bones. It strengthens the joint

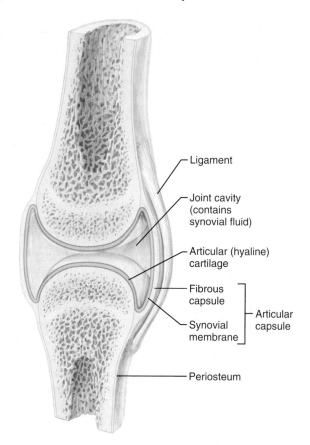

Figure 8.3 General structure of a synovial joint. The articulating bone ends are covered with articular cartilage and enclosed within an articular capsule which is typically reinforced by ligaments externally. Internally, the fibrous capsule is lined with a smooth synovial membrane that secretes synovial fluid.

so that the bones are not pulled apart. The inner layer of the joint capsule is a **synovial membrane** composed of loose connective tissue. Besides lining the fibrous capsule internally, it covers all internal joint surfaces that are not hyaline cartilage.

4. **Synovial fluid.** A small amount of slippery **synovial fluid** occupies all free spaces within the joint capsule. This fluid is derived largely by filtration from blood flowing through the capillaries in the synovial membrane. Synovial fluid has a viscous, egg-white consistency (*ovum* = egg) due to hyaluronic acid secreted by cells in the synovial membrane, but it thins and becomes less viscous, as it warms during joint activity.

Synovial fluid, which is also found *within* the articular cartilages, provides a slippery weight-bearing film that reduces friction between the cartilages. Without this lubricant, rubbing would wear away joint surfaces and excessive friction could overheat and destroy the joint tissues, essentially "cooking" them. The synovial fluid is forced from the cartilages when a joint is compressed; then as pressure on the joint is relieved, synovial fluid seeps back into the articular cartilages like water into a sponge, ready to be squeezed out again the next time the joint is loaded (put under pressure). This process, called *weeping lubrication,*

TABLE 8.1	Summary of Joint Classes		
STRUCTURAL CLASS	**STRUCTURAL CHARACTERISTICS**	**TYPES**	**MOBILITY**
Fibrous	Bone ends/parts united by collagen fibers	Suture (short fibers)	Immobile (synarthrosis)
		Syndesmosis (longer fibers)	Slightly mobile (amphiarthrosis) and immobile
		Gomphosis (periodontal ligament)	Immobile
Cartilaginous	Bone ends/parts united by cartilage	Synchondrosis (hyaline cartilage)	Immobile
		Symphysis (fibrocartilage)	Slightly movable
Synovial	Bone ends/parts covered with articular cartilage and enclosed within an articular capsule lined with synovial membrane	(1) Plane (4) Condyloid (2) Hinge (5) Saddle (3) Pivot (6) Ball and socket	Freely movable (diarthrosis; movements depend on design of joint)

lubricates the free surfaces of the cartilages and nourishes their cells. (Remember, cartilage is avascular.) Synovial fluid also contains phagocytic cells that rid the joint cavity of microbes and cellular debris.

5. **Reinforcing ligaments.** Synovial joints are reinforced and strengthened by a number of bandlike **ligaments**. Most often, these are **capsular**, or **intrinsic**, **ligaments**, which are thickened parts of the fibrous capsule. In other cases, they remain distinct and are found outside the capsule (as **extracapsular ligaments**) or deep to it (as **intracapsular ligaments**). Since intracapsular ligaments are covered with synovial membrane, they do not actually lie *within* the joint cavity.

People said to be double-jointed amaze the rest of us by placing both heels behind their neck. However, they have the normal number of joints. It's just that their joint capsules and ligaments are more stretchy and loose than average.

6. **Nerves and blood vessels.** Synovial joints are richly supplied with sensory nerve fibers that innervate the capsule. Some of these fibers detect pain, as anyone who has suffered joint injury is aware, but most monitor joint position and stretch, thus helping to maintain muscle tone. Stretching these structures sends nerve impulses to the central nervous system, resulting in reflexive contraction of muscles surrounding the joint. Synovial joints are also richly supplied with blood vessels, most of which supply the synovial membrane. There, extensive capillary beds produce the blood filtrate that is the basis of synovial fluid.

Besides the basic components described above, certain synovial joints have other structural features. Some, such as the hip and knee joints, have cushioning **fatty pads** between the fibrous capsule and the synovial membrane or bone. Others have discs or wedges of fibrocartilage separating the articular surfaces. Where present, these so-called **articular discs**, or **menisci** (mě-nis′ki; "crescents"), extend inward from the articular capsule and partially or completely divide the synovial cavity in two (see the menisci of the knee in Figure 8.8a, b, e, and f). Articular discs improve the fit between articulating bone ends, making the joint more stable and minimizing wear

and tear on the joint surfaces. Besides the knees, articular discs occur in the jaw, and a few other joints (see notations in the Structural Type column in Table 8.2).

Bursae and Tendon Sheaths

Bursae and tendon sheaths are not strictly part of synovial joints, but they are often found closely associated with them (Figure 8.4). Essentially bags of lubricant, they act as "ball bearings" to reduce friction between adjacent structures during joint activity. **Bursae** (ber′se; "purse") are flattened fibrous sacs lined with synovial membrane and containing a thin film of synovial fluid. They occur where ligaments, muscles, skin, tendons, or bones rub together.

A **tendon sheath** is essentially an elongated bursa that wraps completely around a tendon subjected to friction, like a bun around a hot dog. They are common where several tendons are crowded together within narrow canals (in the wrist region, for example).

Factors Influencing the Stability of Synovial Joints

Because joints are constantly stretched and compressed, they must be stabilized so that they do not dislocate (come out of alignment). The stability of a synovial joint depends chiefly on three factors: the shapes of the articular surfaces; the number and positioning of ligaments; and muscle tone.

Articular Surfaces

The shapes of articular surfaces determine what movements are possible at a joint, but surprisingly, articular surfaces play only a minor role in joint stability. Many joints have shallow sockets or noncomplementary articulating surfaces ("misfits") that actually hinder joint stability. But when articular surfaces are large and fit snugly together, or when the socket is deep, stability is vastly improved. The ball and deep socket of the hip joint provide the best example of a joint made extremely stable by the shape of its articular surfaces.

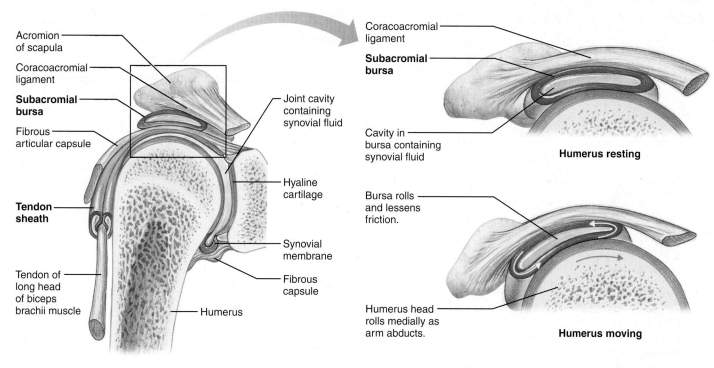

(a) Frontal section through the right shoulder joint

Acromion of scapula
Coracoacromial ligament
Subacromial bursa
Fibrous articular capsule
Tendon sheath
Tendon of long head of biceps brachii muscle

Joint cavity containing synovial fluid
Hyaline cartilage
Synovial membrane
Fibrous capsule
Humerus

Coracoacromial ligament
Subacromial bursa
Cavity in bursa containing synovial fluid

Humerus resting

Bursa rolls and lessens friction.
Humerus head rolls medially as arm abducts.

Humerus moving

(b) Enlargement of (a), showing how a bursa eliminates friction where a ligament (or other structure) would rub against a bone

Figure 8.4 Bursae and tendon sheaths.

Ligaments

The capsules and ligaments of synovial joints unite the bones and prevent excessive or undesirable motion. As a rule, the more ligaments a joint has, the stronger it is. However, when other stabilizing factors are inadequate, undue tension is placed on the ligaments and they stretch. Stretched ligaments stay stretched, like taffy, and a ligament can stretch only about 6% of its length before it snaps. Thus, when ligaments are the major means of bracing a joint, the joint is not very stable.

Muscle Tone

For most joints, the muscle tendons that cross the joint are the most important stabilizing factor. These tendons are kept taut at all times by the tone of their muscles. (*Muscle tone is* defined as low levels of contractile activity in relaxed muscles that keep the muscles healthy and ready to react to stimulation.) Muscle tone is extremely important in reinforcing the shoulder and knee joints and the arches of the foot.

CHECK YOUR UNDERSTANDING

5. What are the two layers of the articular capsule?
6. How do bursae and tendon sheaths improve joint function?
7. Generally speaking, what factor is most important in stabilizing synovial joints?
8. What is the importance of weeping lubrication?

For answers, see Appendix G.

Movements Allowed by Synovial Joints

▶ Name and describe (or perform) the common body movements.

▶ Name and provide examples of the six types of synovial joints based on the movement(s) allowed.

Every skeletal muscle of the body is attached to bone or other connective tissue structures at no fewer than two points. The muscle's **origin** is attached to the immovable (or less movable) bone. Its other end, the **insertion**, is attached to the movable bone. Body movement occurs when muscles contract across joints and their insertion moves toward their origin. The movements can be described in directional terms relative to the lines, or *axes*, around which the body part moves and the planes of space along which the movement occurs, that is, along the transverse, frontal, or sagittal plane. (See Chapter 1 to review these planes.)

Range of motion allowed by synovial joints varies from **nonaxial movement** (slipping movements only, since there is no axis around which movement can occur) to **uniaxial movement** (movement in one plane) to **biaxial movement** (movement in two planes) to **multiaxial movement** (movement in or around all three planes of space and axes). Range of motion varies greatly in different people. In some, such as trained gymnasts or acrobats, range of joint movement may be extraordinary. The ranges of motion at the major joints are given in the far right column of Table 8.2.

There are three general types of movements: *gliding, angular movements,* and *rotation.* The most common body movements

TABLE 8.2   Structural and Functional Characteristics of Body Joints

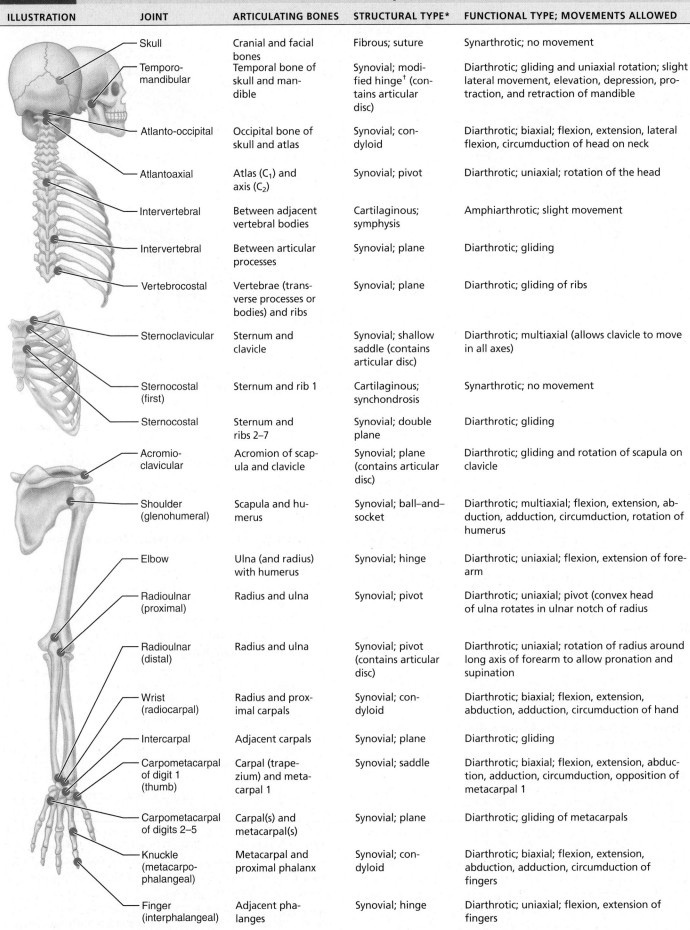

ILLUSTRATION	JOINT	ARTICULATING BONES	STRUCTURAL TYPE*	FUNCTIONAL TYPE; MOVEMENTS ALLOWED
	Skull	Cranial and facial bones	Fibrous; suture	Synarthrotic; no movement
	Temporo-mandibular	Temporal bone of skull and mandible	Synovial; modified hinge† (contains articular disc)	Diarthrotic; gliding and uniaxial rotation; slight lateral movement, elevation, depression, protraction, and retraction of mandible
	Atlanto-occipital	Occipital bone of skull and atlas	Synovial; condyloid	Diarthrotic; biaxial; flexion, extension, lateral flexion, circumduction of head on neck
	Atlantoaxial	Atlas (C$_1$) and axis (C$_2$)	Synovial; pivot	Diarthrotic; uniaxial; rotation of the head
	Intervertebral	Between adjacent vertebral bodies	Cartilaginous; symphysis	Amphiarthrotic; slight movement
	Intervertebral	Between articular processes	Synovial; plane	Diarthrotic; gliding
	Vertebrocostal	Vertebrae (transverse processes or bodies) and ribs	Synovial; plane	Diarthrotic; gliding of ribs
	Sternoclavicular	Sternum and clavicle	Synovial; shallow saddle (contains articular disc)	Diarthrotic; multiaxial (allows clavicle to move in all axes)
	Sternocostal (first)	Sternum and rib 1	Cartilaginous; synchondrosis	Synarthrotic; no movement
	Sternocostal	Sternum and ribs 2–7	Synovial; double plane	Diarthrotic; gliding
	Acromio-clavicular	Acromion of scapula and clavicle	Synovial; plane (contains articular disc)	Diarthrotic; gliding and rotation of scapula on clavicle
	Shoulder (glenohumeral)	Scapula and humerus	Synovial; ball-and-socket	Diarthrotic; multiaxial; flexion, extension, abduction, adduction, circumduction, rotation of humerus
	Elbow	Ulna (and radius) with humerus	Synovial; hinge	Diarthrotic; uniaxial; flexion, extension of forearm
	Radioulnar (proximal)	Radius and ulna	Synovial; pivot	Diarthrotic; uniaxial; pivot (convex head of ulna rotates in ulnar notch of radius
	Radioulnar (distal)	Radius and ulna	Synovial; pivot (contains articular disc)	Diarthrotic; uniaxial; rotation of radius around long axis of forearm to allow pronation and supination
	Wrist (radiocarpal)	Radius and proximal carpals	Synovial; condyloid	Diarthrotic; biaxial; flexion, extension, abduction, adduction, circumduction of hand
	Intercarpal	Adjacent carpals	Synovial; plane	Diarthrotic; gliding
	Carpometacarpal of digit 1 (thumb)	Carpal (trapezium) and metacarpal 1	Synovial; saddle	Diarthrotic; biaxial; flexion, extension, abduction, adduction, circumduction, opposition of metacarpal 1
	Carpometacarpal of digits 2–5	Carpal(s) and metacarpal(s)	Synovial; plane	Diarthrotic; gliding of metacarpals
	Knuckle (metacarpo-phalangeal)	Metacarpal and proximal phalanx	Synovial; condyloid	Diarthrotic; biaxial; flexion, extension, abduction, adduction, circumduction of fingers
	Finger (interphalangeal)	Adjacent phalanges	Synovial; hinge	Diarthrotic; uniaxial; flexion, extension of fingers

TABLE 8.2	(continued)			
ILLUSTRATION	**JOINT**	**ARTICULATING BONES**	**STRUCTURAL TYPE***	**FUNCTIONAL TYPE; MOVEMENTS ALLOWED**

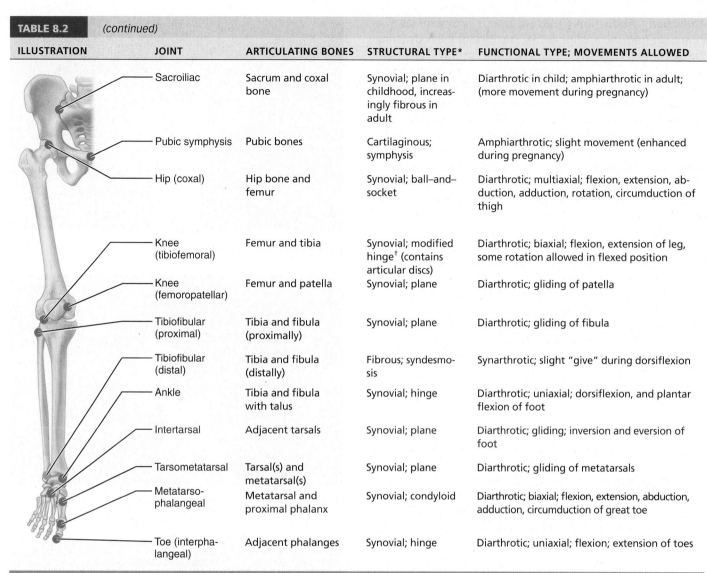

	Sacroiliac	Sacrum and coxal bone	Synovial; plane in childhood, increasingly fibrous in adult	Diarthrotic in child; amphiarthrotic in adult; (more movement during pregnancy)
	Pubic symphysis	Pubic bones	Cartilaginous; symphysis	Amphiarthrotic; slight movement (enhanced during pregnancy)
	Hip (coxal)	Hip bone and femur	Synovial; ball–and–socket	Diarthrotic; multiaxial; flexion, extension, abduction, adduction, rotation, circumduction of thigh
	Knee (tibiofemoral)	Femur and tibia	Synovial; modified hinge† (contains articular discs)	Diarthrotic; biaxial; flexion, extension of leg, some rotation allowed in flexed position
	Knee (femoropatellar)	Femur and patella	Synovial; plane	Diarthrotic; gliding of patella
	Tibiofibular (proximal)	Tibia and fibula (proximally)	Synovial; plane	Diarthrotic; gliding of fibula
	Tibiofibular (distal)	Tibia and fibula (distally)	Fibrous; syndesmosis	Synarthrotic; slight "give" during dorsiflexion
	Ankle	Tibia and fibula with talus	Synovial; hinge	Diarthrotic; uniaxial; dorsiflexion, and plantar flexion of foot
	Intertarsal	Adjacent tarsals	Synovial; plane	Diarthrotic; gliding; inversion and eversion of foot
	Tarsometatarsal	Tarsal(s) and metatarsal(s)	Synovial; plane	Diarthrotic; gliding of metatarsals
	Metatarso-phalangeal	Metatarsal and proximal phalanx	Synovial; condyloid	Diarthrotic; biaxial; flexion, extension, abduction, adduction, circumduction of great toe
	Toe (interphalangeal)	Adjacent phalanges	Synovial; hinge	Diarthrotic; uniaxial; flexion; extension of toes

* **Fibrous joints** indicated by orange circles; **cartilaginous joints** by blue circles; **synovial joints** by purple circles.
† These modified hinge joints are structurally bicondylar.

allowed by synovial joints are described next and illustrated in **Figure 8.5**.

Gliding Movements

Gliding movements (Figure 8.5a) are the simplest joint movements. Gliding occurs when one flat, or nearly flat, bone surface glides or slips over another (back-and-forth and side-to-side) without appreciable angulation or rotation. Gliding movements occur at the intercarpal and intertarsal joints, and between the flat articular processes of the vertebrae (Table 8.2).

Angular Movements

Angular movements (Figure 8.5b–e) increase or decrease the angle between two bones. These movements may occur in any plane of the body and include flexion, extension, hyperextension, abduction, adduction, and circumduction.

Flexion Flexion (flek′shun) is a bending movement, usually along the sagittal plane, that *decreases the angle* of the joint and brings the articulating bones closer together. Examples include bending the head forward on the chest (Figure 8.5b) and bending the body trunk or the knee from a straight to an angled position (Figure 8.5c and d). As a less obvious example, the arm is flexed at the shoulder when the arm is lifted in an anterior direction (Figure 8.5d).

Extension Extension is the reverse of flexion and occurs at the same joints. It involves movement along the sagittal plane that *increases the angle* between the articulating bones and typically straightens a flexed limb or body part. Examples include straightening a flexed neck, body trunk, elbow, or knee (Figure 8.5b–d). Excessive extension such as extending the head or hip joint beyond anatomical position (Figure 8.5b, c) is called **hyperextension** (literally, "superextension").

8

Abduction Abduction ("moving away") is movement of a limb *away* from the midline or median plane of the body, along the frontal plane. Raising the arm or thigh laterally is an example of abduction (Figure 8.5e). For the fingers or toes, abduction means spreading them apart. In this case "midline" is the longest digit: the third finger or second toe. Notice, however, that lateral bending of the trunk away from the body midline in the frontal plane is called *lateral flexion*, not abduction.

Adduction Adduction ("moving toward") is the opposite of abduction, so it is the movement of a limb *toward* the body midline or, in the case of the digits, toward the midline of the hand or foot (Figure 8.5e).

Circumduction Circumduction (Figure 8.5e) is moving a limb so that it describes a cone in space (*circum* = around; *duco* = to draw). The distal end of the limb moves in a circle, while the point of the cone (the shoulder or hip joint) is more or less stationary. A pitcher winding up to throw a ball is actually circumducting his or her pitching arm. Because circumduction consists of flexion, abduction, extension, and adduction performed in succession, it is the quickest way to exercise the many muscles that move the hip and shoulder ball-and-socket joints.

Rotation

Rotation is the turning of a bone around its own long axis. It is the only movement allowed between the first two cervical vertebrae and is common at the hip (Figure 8.5f) and shoulder joints. Rotation may be directed toward the midline or away from it. For example, in *medial rotation* of the thigh, the femur's anterior surface moves toward the median plane of the body; *lateral rotation* is the opposite movement.

Special Movements

Certain movements do not fit into any of the above categories and occur at only a few joints. Some of these special movements are illustrated in **Figure 8.6**.

Supination and Pronation The terms **supination** (soo″pĭ-na′shun; "turning backward") and **pronation** (pro-na′shun; "turning forward") refer to the movements of the radius around the ulna (Figure 8.6a). Rotating the forearm laterally so that the palm faces anteriorly or superiorly is supination. In the anatomical position, the hand is supinated and the radius and ulna are parallel.

In pronation, the forearm rotates medially and the palm faces posteriorly or inferiorly. Pronation moves the distal end of the radius across the ulna so that the two bones form an X. This is the forearm's position when we are standing in a relaxed manner. Pronation is a much weaker movement than supination.

A trick to help you keep these terms straight: A *pro* basketball player pronates his or her forearm to dribble the ball.

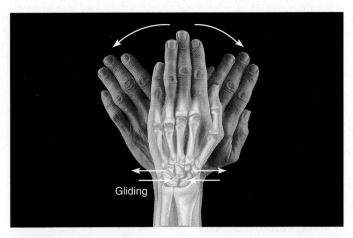

Gliding

(a) Gliding movements at the wrist

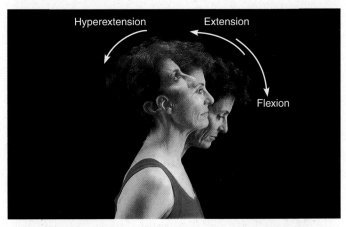

Hyperextension Extension Flexion

(b) Angular movements: flexion, extension, and hyperextension of the neck

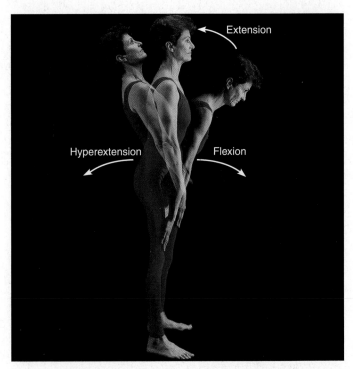

Extension Hyperextension Flexion

(c) Angular movements: flexion, extension, and hyperextension of the vertebral column

Figure 8.5 Movements allowed by synovial joints.

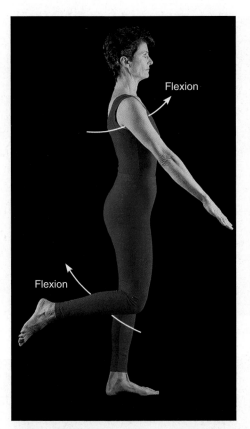

(d) Angular movements: flexion and extension at the shoulder and knee

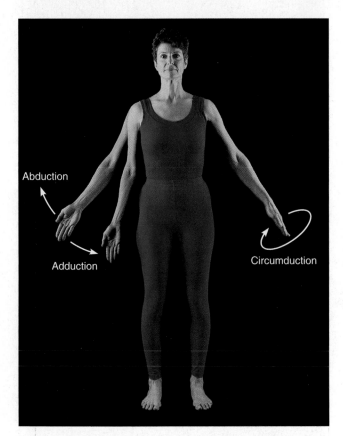

(e) Angular movements: abduction, adduction, and circumduction of the upper limb at the shoulder

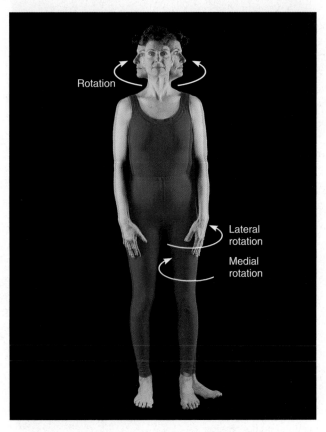

(f) Rotation of the head, neck, and lower limb

Figure 8.5 *(continued)*

8

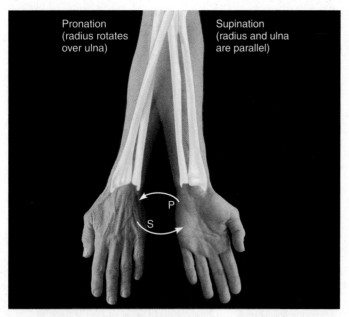

(a) Pronation (P) and supination (S)

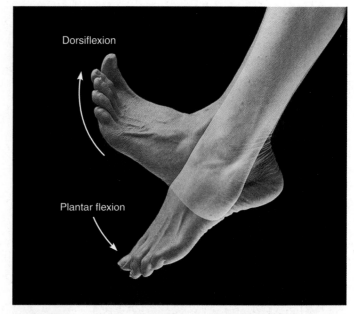

(b) Dorsiflexion and plantar flexion

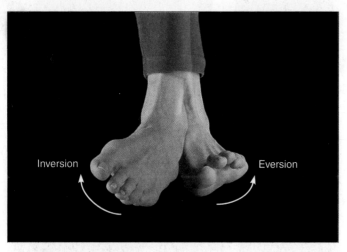

(c) Inversion and eversion

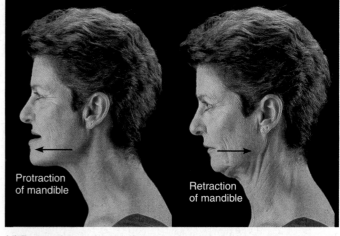

(d) Protraction and retraction

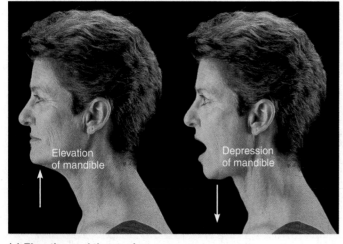

(e) Elevation and depression

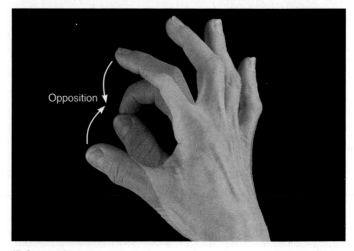

(f) Opposition

Figure 8.6 **Special body movements.**

Dorsiflexion and Plantar Flexion of the Foot The up-and-down movements of the foot at the ankle are given more specific names (Figure 8.6b). Lifting the foot so that its superior surface approaches the shin is **dorsiflexion** (corresponds to wrist extension), whereas depressing the foot (pointing the toes) is **plantar flexion** (corresponds to wrist flexion).

Inversion and Eversion **Inversion** and **eversion** are special movements of the foot (Figure 8.6c). In inversion, the sole of the foot turns medially. In eversion, the sole faces laterally.

Protraction and Retraction Nonangular anterior and posterior movements in a transverse plane are called **protraction** and **retraction**, respectively (Figure 8.6d). The mandible is protracted when you jut out your jaw and retracted when you bring it back.

Elevation and Depression **Elevation** means lifting a body part superiorly (Figure 8.6e). For example, the scapulae are elevated when you shrug your shoulders. Moving the elevated part inferiorly is **depression**. During chewing, the mandible is alternately elevated and depressed.

Opposition The saddle joint between metacarpal 1 and the trapezium allows a movement called **opposition** of the thumb (Figure 8.6f). This movement is the action taken when you touch your thumb to the tips of the other fingers on the same hand. It is opposition that makes the human hand such a fine tool for grasping and manipulating objects.

Types of Synovial Joints

Although all synovial joints have structural features in common, they do not have a common structural plan. Based on the shape of their articular surfaces, which in turn determine the movements allowed, synovial joints can be classified further into six major categories—plane, hinge, pivot, condyloid, saddle, and ball-and-socket joints.

Plane Joints

In **plane joints** (Figure 8.7a) the articular surfaces are essentially flat, and they allow only short nonaxial gliding movements. Examples are the gliding joints introduced earlier—the intercarpal and intertarsal joints, and the joints between vertebral articular processes. Gliding does not involve rotation around any axis, and gliding joints are the only examples of nonaxial plane joints.

Hinge Joints

In **hinge joints** (Figure 8.7b), the cylindrical end of one bone conforms to a trough-shaped surface on another. Motion is along a single plane and resembles that of a mechanical hinge. Uniaxial hinge joints permit flexion and extension only, typified by bending and straightening the elbow and interphalangeal joints.

Pivot Joints

In a **pivot joint** (Figure 8.7c), the rounded end of one bone conforms to a "sleeve" or ring composed of bone (and possibly ligaments) of another. The only movement allowed is uniaxial rotation of one bone around its own long axis. An example is the joint between the atlas and dens of the axis, which allows you to move your head from side to side to indicate "no." Another is the proximal radioulnar joint, where the head of the radius rotates within a ringlike ligament secured to the ulna.

Condyloid Joints

In **condyloid joints** (kon′dĭ-loid; "knuckle-like"), or **ellipsoidal joints**, the oval articular surface of one bone fits into a complementary depression in another (Figure 8.7d). The important characteristic is that both articulating surfaces are oval. The biaxial condyloid joints permit all *angular* motions, that is, flexion and extension, abduction and adduction, and circumduction. The radiocarpal (wrist) joints and the metacarpophalangeal (knuckle) joints are typical condyloid joints.

Saddle Joints

Saddle joints (Figure 8.7e) resemble condyloid joints, but they allow greater freedom of movement. Each articular surface has *both* concave and convex areas; that is, it is shaped like a saddle. The articular surfaces then fit together, concave to convex surfaces. The most clear-cut examples of saddle joints in the body are the carpometacarpal joints of the thumbs, and the movements allowed by these joints are clearly demonstrated by twiddling your thumbs.

Ball-and-Socket Joints

In **ball-and-socket joints** (Figure 8.7f), the spherical or hemispherical head of one bone articulates with the cuplike socket of another. These joints are multiaxial and the most freely moving synovial joints. Universal movement is allowed (that is, in all axes and planes, including rotation). The shoulder and hip joints are the only examples.

CHECK YOUR UNDERSTANDING

9. John bent over to pick up a dime. What movement was occurring at his hip joint, at his knees, and between his index finger and thumb?
10. On the basis of movement allowed, which of the following joints are uniaxial? Hinge, condyloid, saddle, pivot.

For answers, see Appendix G.

Selected Synovial Joints

▶ Describe the elbow, knee, hip, jaw, and shoulder joints in terms of articulating bones, anatomical characteristics of the joint, movements allowed, and joint stability.

(Text continues on p. 262.)

8

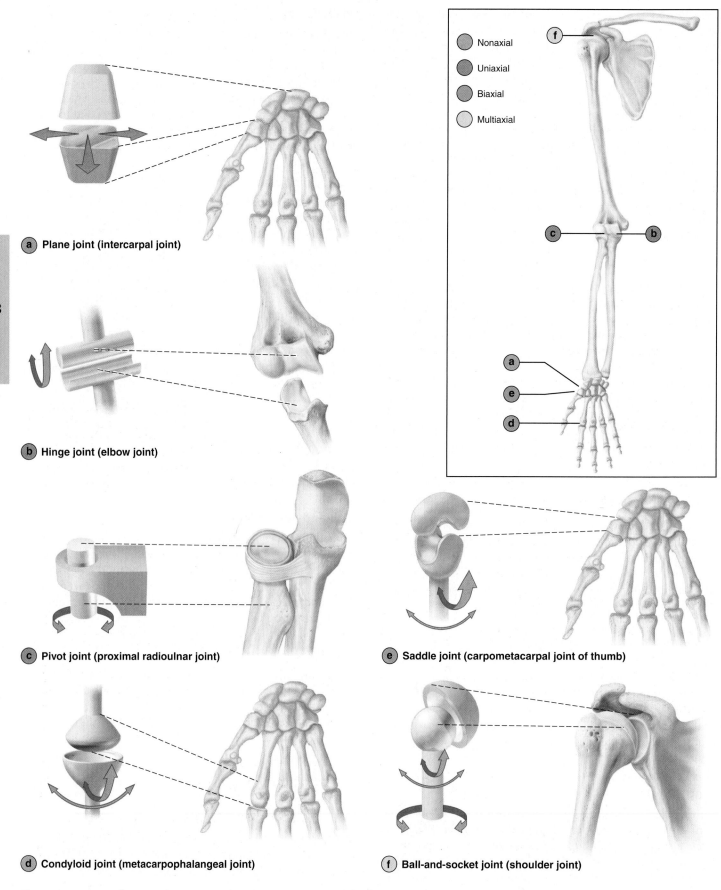

(a) **Plane joint (intercarpal joint)**

(b) **Hinge joint (elbow joint)**

(c) **Pivot joint (proximal radioulnar joint)**

(d) **Condyloid joint (metacarpophalangeal joint)**

(e) **Saddle joint (carpometacarpal joint of thumb)**

(f) **Ball-and-socket joint (shoulder joint)**

Nonaxial

Uniaxial

Biaxial

Multiaxial

Figure 8.7 Types of synovial joints. Dashed lines indicate the articulating bones in each example.

A CLOSER LOOK
Joints: From Knights in Shining Armor to Bionic Humans

The technology for fashioning joints in medieval suits of armor developed over centuries. The technology for creating the prostheses (artificial joints) used in medicine today developed, in relative terms, in a flash—less than 60 years. Unlike the joints in medieval armor, which was worn outside the body, today's artificial joints must function inside the body. The history of joint prostheses dates to the 1940s and 1950s, when World War II and the Korean War left large numbers of wounded who needed artificial limbs. It was predicted that by the year 2003, over a third of a million Americans would receive total joint replacements each year, mostly because of the destructive effects of osteoarthritis or rheumatoid arthritis. However, the actual number of people needing joint prostheses has burgeoned far beyond this as injured military people return from service abroad.

To produce durable, mobile joints requires a substance that is strong, nontoxic, and resistant to the corrosive effects of organic acids in blood. In 1963, Sir John Charnley, an English orthopedic surgeon, performed the first total hip replacement and revolutionized the therapy of arthritic hips. His device consisted of a metal ball on a stem and a cup-shaped polyethylene plastic socket anchored to the pelvis by methyl methacrylate cement. This cement proved to be exceptionally strong and relatively problem free. Hip prostheses were followed by knee prostheses, but not until ten years later did smoothly operating total knee joint replacements become a reality. Today, the metal parts of the prostheses are strong cobalt and titanium alloys, and the number of knee replacements equals the number of hip replacements.

Replacements are now available for many other joints, including fingers, elbows, and shoulders. Total hip and knee replacements last about 10 to 15 years in elderly patients who do not excessively stress the joint. Most such operations are done to reduce pain and restore about 80% of original joint function.

Replacement joints are not yet strong or durable enough for young, active people, but making them so is a major goal.

The problem is that the prostheses work loose over time, so researchers are seeking to enhance the fit between implant and bone. One solution is to strengthen the cement that binds them (simply eliminating air bubbles from the cement increases its durability). Another solution currently being tested is a robotic surgeon, ROBODOC, to drill a better-fitting hole for the femoral prosthesis in hip surgery. In cementless prostheses, researchers are exploring better ways to get the bone to grow so that it binds more strongly to the implant. A supersmooth titanium coating seems to encourage direct bone on-growth.

Dramatic changes are also occurring in the way artificial joints are made. CAD/CAM (computer-aided design and computer-aided manufacturing) techniques have significantly reduced the time and cost of creating individualized joints. Fed the patient's X rays and medical information, the computer draws from a database of hundreds of normal joints and generates possible designs and modifications for a prosthesis. Once the best design is selected, the computer produces a program to direct the machines that shape it.

Joint replacement therapy is coming of age, but equally exciting are techniques that call on the ability of the patient's own tissues to regenerate.

- Osteochondral grafting: Healthy bone and cartilage are removed from one part of the body and transplanted to the injured joint.
- Autologous chondrocyte implantation: Healthy chondrocytes are removed from the body, cultivated in the lab, and implanted at the damaged joint.
- Mesenchymal stem cell regeneration: Undifferentiated mesenchymal cells are removed from bone marrow and placed in a gel, which is packed into an area of eroded cartilage.

These techniques offer hope for younger patients, since they could stave off the need for a joint prosthesis for several years.

And so, through the centuries, the focus has shifted from jointed armor to artificial joints that can be put inside the body to restore lost function. Modern technology has accomplished what the armor designers of the Middle Ages never dreamed of.

A hip prosthesis.

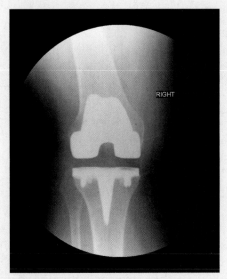

X ray of right knee showing total knee replacement prosthesis (co-designed by Kenneth Gustke, M.D., of Florida Orthopedic Institute).

8

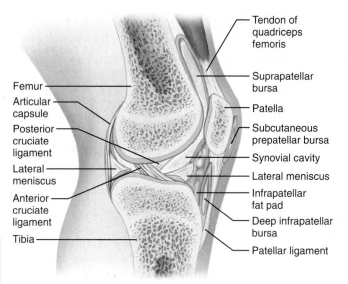

(a) Sagittal section through the right knee joint

Anterior

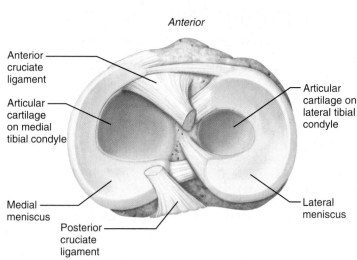

(b) Superior view of the right tibia in the knee joint, showing the menisci and cruciate ligaments

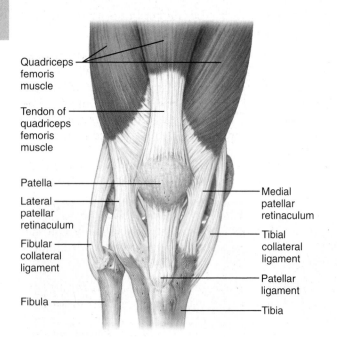

(c) Anterior view of right knee

(d) Posterior view of the joint capsule, including ligaments

Figure 8.8 The knee joint.

In this section, we examine five joints in detail: knee, elbow, shoulder, hip, and temporomandibular (jaw) joint. All have the six distinguishing characteristics of synovial joints, and we will not discuss these common features again. Instead, we will emphasize the unique structural features, functional abilities, and, in certain cases, functional weaknesses of each of these joints.

Knee Joint

The knee joint is the largest and most complex joint in the body (Figure 8.8). Despite its single joint cavity, the knee consists of

three joints in one: an intermediate one between the patella and the lower end of the femur (the **femoropatellar joint**), and lateral and medial joints (collectively known as the **tibiofemoral joint**) between the femoral condyles above and the C-shaped **menisci**, or *semilunar cartilages*, of the tibia below (Figure 8.8b and e). Besides deepening the shallow tibial articular surfaces, the menisci help prevent side-to-side rocking of the femur on the tibia and absorb shock transmitted to the knee joint. However, the menisci are attached only at their outer margins and are frequently torn free.

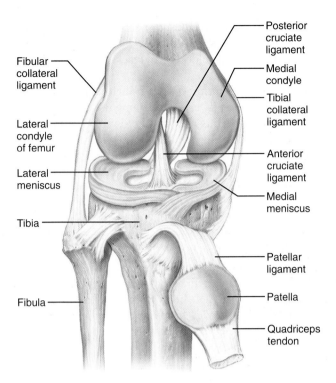

(e) Anterior view of flexed knee, showing the cruciate ligaments (articular capsule removed, and quadriceps tendon cut and reflected distally)

Figure 8.8 *(continued)*

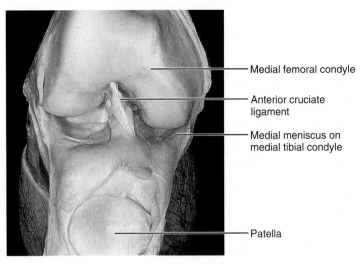

(f) Photograph of an opened knee joint; view similar to (e)

The tibiofemoral joint acts primarily as a hinge, permitting flexion and extension. However, structurally it is a bicondylar joint. Some rotation is possible when the knee is partly flexed, and when the knee is extending. But, when the knee is fully extended, side-to-side movements and rotation are strongly resisted by ligaments and the menisci. The femoropatellar joint is a plane joint, and the patella glides across the distal end of the femur during knee flexion.

The knee joint is unique in that its joint cavity is only partially enclosed by a capsule. The relatively thin articular capsule is present only on the sides and posterior aspects of the knee, where it covers the bulk of the femoral and tibial condyles. Anteriorly, where the capsule is absent, three broad ligaments run from the patella to the tibia below. These are the **patellar ligament** flanked by the **medial** and **lateral patellar retinacula** (ret″ĭ-nak′u-lah; "retainers"), which merge imperceptibly into the articular capsule on each side (Figure 8.8c). The patellar ligament and retinacula are actually continuations of the tendon of the bulky quadriceps muscle of the anterior thigh. Physicians tap the patellar ligament to test the knee-jerk reflex.

The synovial cavity of the knee joint has a complicated shape, with several extensions that lead into "blind alleys." At least a dozen bursae are associated with this joint, some of which are shown in Figure 8.8a. For example, notice the *subcutaneous prepatellar bursa*, which is often injured when the knee is bumped anteriorly.

All three types of joint ligaments stabilize and strengthen the capsule of the knee joint. The ligaments of two of the types, capsular and extracapsular, all act to prevent hyperextension of the knee and are stretched taut when the knee is extended. These include the following:

1. The extracapsular **fibular** and **tibial collateral ligaments** are also critical in preventing lateral or medial rotation when the knee is extended. The broad, flat tibial collateral ligament runs from the medial epicondyle of the femur to the medial condyle of the tibial shaft below and is fused to the medial meniscus (Figure 8.8c–e).
2. The **oblique popliteal ligament** (pop″lĭ-te′al) is actually part of the tendon of the semimembranosus muscle that fuses with the joint capsule and helps stabilize the posterior aspect of the knee joint (Figure 8.8d).
3. The **arcuate popliteal ligament** arcs superiorly from the head of the fibula over the popliteus muscle and reinforces the joint capsule posteriorly (Figure 8.8d).

The knee's *intracapsular ligaments* are called *cruciate ligaments* (kroo′she-āt) because they cross each other, forming an X (*cruci* = cross) in the notch between the femoral condyles. They act as restraining straps to help prevent anterior-posterior displacement of the articular surfaces and to secure the articulating bones when we stand (Figure 8.8a, b, e). Although these ligaments are in the joint capsule, they are *outside* the synovial cavity, and synovial membrane nearly covers their surfaces. Note that the two cruciate ligaments both run superiorly to the femur and are named for their *tibial* attachment site.

The **anterior cruciate ligament** attaches to the *anterior* intercondylar area of the tibia (Figure 8.8b). From there it passes posteriorly, laterally, and upward to attach to the femur on the medial side of its lateral condyle. This ligament prevents forward sliding of the tibia on the femur and checks hyperextension of the knee. It is somewhat lax when the knee is flexed, and taut when the knee is extended.

8

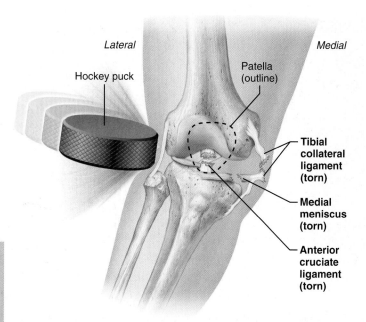

Figure 8.9 **A common knee injury.** Anterior view of a knee being hit by a hockey puck. Such blows to the lateral side tear both the tibial collateral ligament and the medial meniscus because the two are attached. The anterior cruciate ligament also tears.

The stronger **posterior cruciate ligament** is attached to the *posterior* intercondylar area of the tibia and passes anteriorly, medially, and superiorly to attach to the femur on the lateral side of the medial condyle (Figure 8.8a, b). This ligament prevents backward displacement of the tibia or forward sliding of the femur.

The knee capsule is heavily reinforced by muscle tendons. Most important are the strong tendons of the quadriceps muscles of the anterior thigh and the tendon of the semimembranosus muscle posteriorly (Figure 8.8c and d). The greater the strength and tone of these muscles, the less the chance of knee injury.

The knees have a built-in locking device that provides steady support for the body in the standing position. As we begin to stand up, the wheel-shaped femoral condyles roll like ball bearings across the tibial condyles and the flexed leg begins to extend at the knee. Because the lateral femoral condyle stops rolling before the medial condyle stops, the femur *spins* (rotates) medially on the tibia, until the cruciate and collateral ligaments of the knee are twisted and taut and the menisci are compressed. The tension in the ligaments effectively locks the joint into a rigid structure that cannot be flexed again until it is unlocked. This unlocking is accomplished by the popliteus muscle (see Figure 8.8d and Table 10.15, p. 370). It rotates the femur laterally on the tibia, causing the ligaments to become untwisted and slack.

⚖ HOMEOSTATIC IMBALANCE

Of all body joints, the knees are most susceptible to sports injuries because of their high reliance on nonarticular factors for stability and the fact that they carry the body's weight. The knee can absorb a vertical force equal to nearly seven times body weight. However, it is very vulnerable to *horizontal* blows, such as those that occur during blocking and tackling in football and in ice hockey.

When thinking of common knee injuries, remember the 3 Cs: collateral ligaments, cruciate ligaments, and cartilages (menisci). Most dangerous are *lateral* blows to the extended knee. These forces tear the tibial collateral ligament and the medial meniscus attached to it, as well as the anterior cruciate ligament (Figure 8.9). It is estimated that 50% of all professional football players have serious knee injuries during their careers.

Although less devastating than the injury just described, injuries that affect only the anterior cruciate ligament (ACL) are becoming more common, particularly as women's sports become more vigorous and competitive. Most ACL injuries occur when a runner changes direction quickly, twisting a hyperextended knee. A torn ACL heals poorly, so repair usually requires a ligament graft taken from one of the larger ligaments (for example, patellar, Achilles, or semitendinosus). ∎

Shoulder (Glenohumeral) Joint

In the shoulder joint, stability has been sacrificed to provide the most freely moving joint of the body. The shoulder joint is a ball-and-socket joint. The large hemispherical head of the humerus fits in the small, shallow glenoid cavity of the scapula (Figure 8.10), like a golf ball sitting on a tee. Although the glenoid cavity is slightly deepened by a rim of fibrocartilage, the **glenoid labrum** (*labrum* = lip), it is only about one-third the size of the humeral head and contributes little to joint stability (Figure 8.10d).

The articular capsule enclosing the joint cavity (from the margin of the glenoid cavity to the anatomical neck of the humerus) is remarkably thin and loose, qualities that contribute to this joint's freedom of movement. The few ligaments reinforcing the shoulder joint are located primarily on its anterior aspect. The superiorly located **coracohumeral ligament** (kor′ah-ko-hu′mer-ul) provides the only strong thickening of the capsule and helps support the weight of the upper limb (Figure 8.10c). Three **glenohumeral ligaments** (glĕ″no-hu′mer-ul) strengthen the front of the capsule somewhat but are weak and may even be absent (Figure 8.10c, d).

Muscle tendons that cross the shoulder joint contribute most to this joint's stability. The "superstabilizer" is the tendon of the long head of the biceps brachii muscle of the arm (Figure 8.10c). This tendon attaches to the superior margin of the glenoid labrum, travels through the joint cavity, and then runs within the intertubercular sulcus of the humerus. It secures the head of the humerus against the glenoid cavity.

Four other tendons (and the associated muscles) make up the **rotator cuff**. This cuff encircles the shoulder joint and blends with the articular capsule. The muscles include the subscapularis, supraspinatus, infraspinatus, and teres minor. (The rotator cuff muscles are illustrated in Figure 10.14, p. 352.) The rotator cuff can be severely stretched when the arm is vigorously circumducted; this is a common injury of baseball pitchers. As

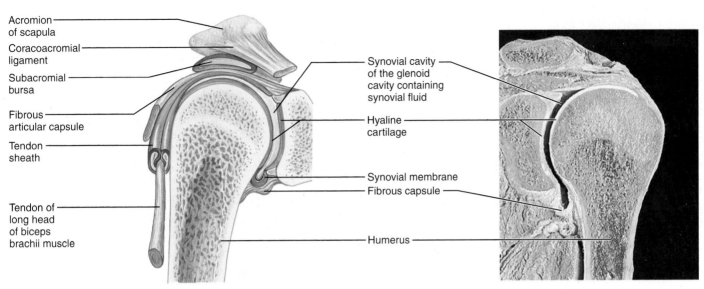

Acromion of scapula
Coracoacromial ligament
Subacromial bursa
Fibrous articular capsule
Tendon sheath
Tendon of long head of biceps brachii muscle

Synovial cavity of the glenoid cavity containing synovial fluid
Hyaline cartilage
Synovial membrane
Fibrous capsule
Humerus

(a) Frontal section through right shoulder joint

(b) Cadaver photo corresponding to (a)

8

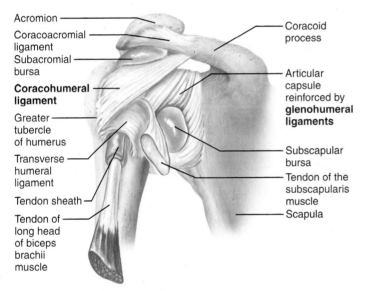

Acromion
Coracoacromial ligament
Subacromial bursa
Coracohumeral ligament
Greater tubercle of humerus
Transverse humeral ligament
Tendon sheath
Tendon of long head of biceps brachii muscle

Coracoid process
Articular capsule reinforced by **glenohumeral ligaments**
Subscapular bursa
Tendon of the subscapularis muscle
Scapula

(c) Anterior view of right shoulder joint capsule

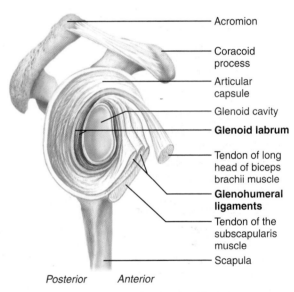

Acromion
Coracoid process
Articular capsule
Glenoid cavity
Glenoid labrum
Tendon of long head of biceps brachii muscle
Glenohumeral ligaments
Tendon of the subscapularis muscle
Scapula

Posterior   *Anterior*

(d) Lateral view of socket of right shoulder joint, humerus removed

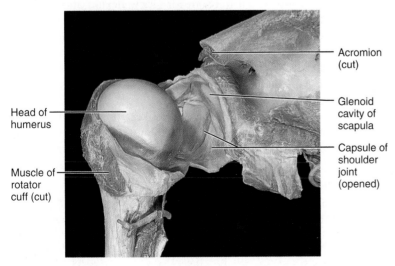

Head of humerus
Muscle of rotator cuff (cut)

Acromion (cut)
Glenoid cavity of scapula
Capsule of shoulder joint (opened)

(e) Anterior view of an opened shoulder joint

Figure 8.10 **The shoulder joint.**

8

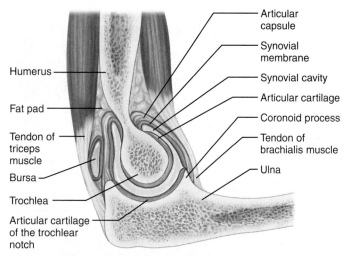

(a) Median sagittal section through right elbow (lateral view)

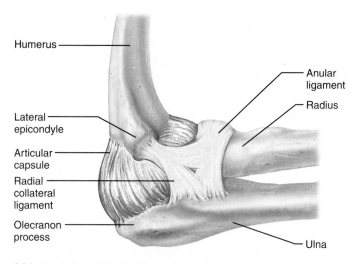

(b) Lateral view of right elbow joint

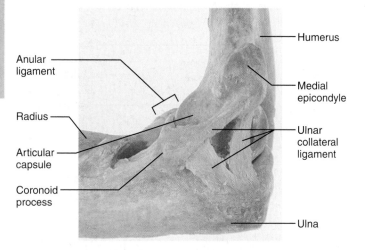

(c) Cadaver photo of medial view of right elbow

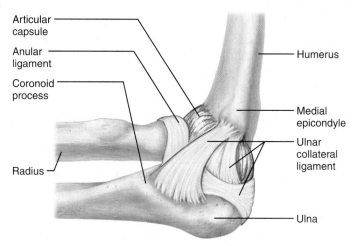

(d) Medial view of right elbow

Figure 8.11 **The elbow joint.**

noted in Chapter 7, shoulder dislocations are fairly common. Because the shoulder's reinforcements are weakest anteriorly and inferiorly, the humerus tends to dislocate in the forward and downward direction.

Elbow Joint

Our upper limbs are flexible extensions that permit us to reach out and manipulate things in our environment. Besides the shoulder joint, the most prominent of the upper limb joints is the elbow. The elbow joint provides a stable and smoothly operating hinge that allows flexion and extension only (Figure 8.11). Within the joint, both the radius and ulna articulate with the condyles of the humerus, but it is the close gripping of the trochlea by the ulna's trochlear notch that forms the "hinge" and stabilizes this joint (Figure 8.11a). A relatively lax articular capsule extends inferiorly from the humerus to the ulna and radius, and to the **anular ligament** (an'u-lar) surrounding the head of the radius (Figure 8.11b, c).

Anteriorly and posteriorly, the articular capsule is thin and allows substantial freedom for elbow flexion and extension. However, side-to-side movements are restricted by two strong capsular ligaments: the **ulnar collateral ligament** medially, and the **radial collateral ligament**, a triangular ligament on the lateral side (Figure 8.11b, c, and d). Additionally, tendons of several arm muscles, such as the biceps and triceps, cross the elbow joint and provide security.

The radius is a passive "onlooker" in the angular elbow movements. However, its head rotates within the anular ligament during supination and pronation of the forearm.

Hip (Coxal) Joint

The hip joint, like the shoulder joint, is a ball-and-socket joint. It has a good range of motion, but not nearly as wide as the shoulder's range. Movements occur in all possible planes but are limited by the joint's strong ligaments and its deep socket.

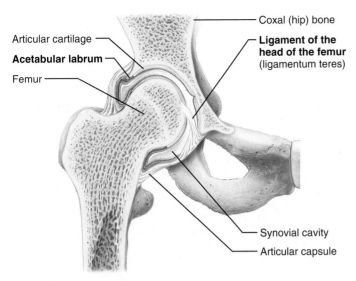

(a) **Frontal section through the right hip joint**

Coxal (hip) bone
Ligament of the head of the femur (ligamentum teres)
Articular cartilage
Acetabular labrum
Femur
Synovial cavity
Articular capsule

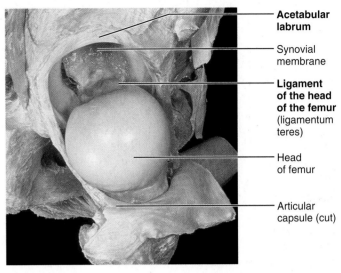

(b) **Photo of the interior of the hip joint, lateral view**

Acetabular labrum
Synovial membrane
Ligament of the head of the femur (ligamentum teres)
Head of femur
Articular capsule (cut)

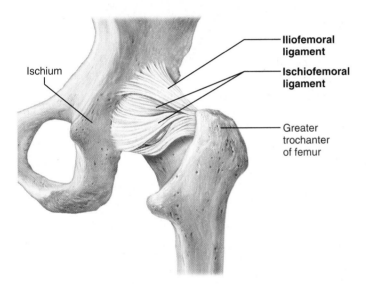

(c) **Posterior view of right hip joint, capsule in place**

Ischium
Iliofemoral ligament
Ischiofemoral ligament
Greater trochanter of femur

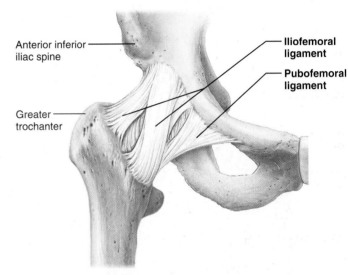

(d) **Anterior view of right hip joint, capsule in place**

Anterior inferior iliac spine
Greater trochanter
Iliofemoral ligament
Pubofemoral ligament

Figure 8.12 **The hip joint.**

The hip joint is formed by the articulation of the spherical head of the femur with the deeply cupped acetabulum of the hip bone **(Figure 8.12)**. The depth of the acetabulum is enhanced by a circular rim of fibrocartilage called the **acetabular labrum** (as″ĕ-tab′u-lar) (Figure 8.12a, b). The labrum's diameter is less than that of the head of the femur, and these articular surfaces fit snugly together, so hip joint dislocations are rare.

The thick articular capsule extends from the rim of the acetabulum to the neck of the femur and completely encloses the joint. Several strong ligaments reinforce the capsule of the hip joint. These include the **iliofemoral ligament** (il″e-o-fem′o-ral), a strong V-shaped ligament anteriorly; the **pubofemoral ligament** (pu″bo-fem′o-ral), a triangular thickening of the inferior part of the capsule; and the **ischiofemoral ligament** (iske″o-fem′o-ral), a spiraling posterior ligament (Figure 8.12c, d).

These ligaments are arranged in such a way that they "screw" the femur head into the acetabulum when a person stands up straight, thereby providing more stability.

The **ligament of the head of the femur**, also called the **ligamentum teres**, is a flat intracapsular band that runs from the femur head to the lower lip of the acetabulum (Figure 8.12a, b). This ligament is slack during most hip movements, so it is not important in stabilizing the joint. In fact, its mechanical function (if any) is unclear, but it does contain an artery that helps supply the head of the femur. Damage to this artery may lead to severe arthritis of the hip joint.

Muscle tendons that cross the joint and the bulky hip and thigh muscles that surround it contribute to its stability and strength. In this joint, however, stability comes chiefly from the deep socket that securely encloses the femoral head and the strong capsular ligaments.

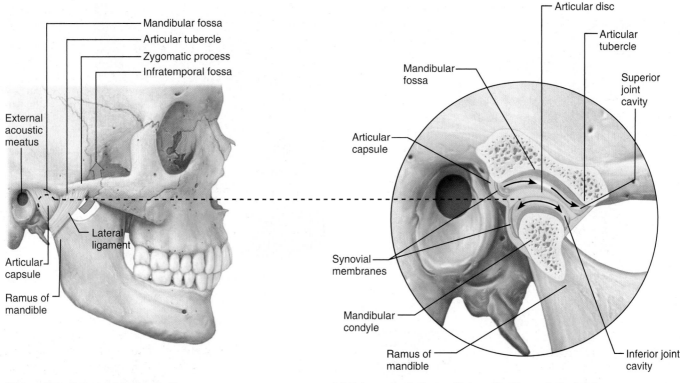

(a) Location of the joint in the skull

(b) Enlargement of a sagittal section through the joint

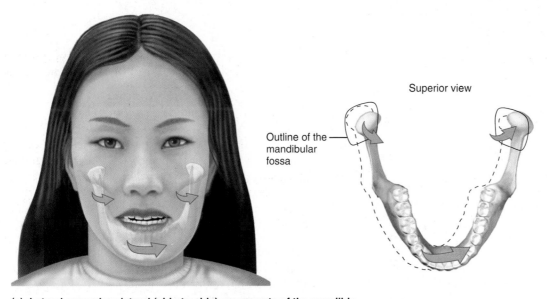

(c) Lateral excursion: lateral (side-to-side) movements of the mandible

Figure 8.13 The temporomandibular (jaw) joint. In **(b)**, note that the two parts of the joint cavity allow different movements, indicated by arrows. The inferior compartment of the joint cavity allows the mandibular condyle to rotate in opening and closing the mouth. The superior compartment lets the mandibular condyle move forward to brace against the articular tubercle when the mouth opens wide, and also allows lateral excursion of this joint **(c)**.

Temporomandibular Joint

The **temporomandibular joint (TMJ)**, or jaw joint, lies just anterior to the ear. At this joint, the mandibular condyle articulates with the inferior surface of the squamous temporal bone (Figure 8.13). The mandibular condyle is egg shaped, whereas the articular surface of the temporal bone has a more complex shape. Posteriorly, it forms the concave **mandibular fossa**; anteriorly it forms a dense knob called the **articular tubercle**. The lateral aspect of the loose articular capsule that encloses the joint is thickened into a **lateral ligament**. Within the capsule, an articular disc divides the synovial cavity into superior and inferior compartments (Figure 8.13a, b).

Two distinct kinds of movement occur at the TMJ. First, the concave inferior disc surface receives the mandibular condyle and allows the familiar hingelike movement of depressing and elevating the mandible while opening and closing the mouth. Second, the superior disc surface glides anteriorly along with the mandibular condyle when the mouth is opened wide. This anterior movement braces the condyle against the articular tubercle, so that the mandible is not forced through the thin roof of the mandibular fossa when one bites hard foods such as nuts or hard candies. The superior compartment also allows this joint to glide from side to side. As the posterior teeth are drawn into occlusion during grinding, the mandible moves with a side-to-side movement called *lateral excursion* (Figure 8.13c). This lateral jaw movement is unique to mammals and it is readily apparent in horses and cows as they chew.

⚡ HOMEOSTATIC IMBALANCE

Because of its shallow socket, the TMJ is the most easily dislocated joint in the body. Even a deep yawn can dislocate it. This joint almost always dislocates anteriorly, the mandibular condyle ending up in a skull region called the *infratemporal fossa* (Figure 8.13a). In such cases, the mouth remains wide open. To realign a dislocated TMJ, the physician places his or her thumbs in the patient's mouth between the lower molars and the cheeks, and then pushes the mandible inferiorly and posteriorly.

At least 5% of Americans suffer from painful temporomandibular disorders, the most common symptoms of which are pain in the ear and face, tenderness of the jaw muscles, popping sounds when the mouth opens, and joint stiffness. Usually caused by painful spasms of the chewing muscles, TMJ disorders often afflict people who grind their teeth; however, it can also result from jaw trauma or from poor occlusion of the teeth. Treatment usually focuses on getting the jaw muscles to relax by using massage, applying moist heat or ice, muscle-relaxant drugs, and adopting stress reduction techniques. For tooth grinders, use of a bite plate during sleep is generally recommended. ∎

CHECK YOUR UNDERSTANDING

11. Of the five joints studied in more detail—hip, shoulder, elbow, knee, and temporomandibular—which two have menisci? Which act mainly as a uniaxial hinge? Which depend mainly on muscles and their tendons for stability?

For answers, see Appendix G.

Homeostatic Imbalances of Joints

▶ Name the most common joint injuries and discuss the symptoms and problems associated with each.

▶ Compare and contrast the common types of arthritis.

▶ Describe the cause and consequences of Lyme disease.

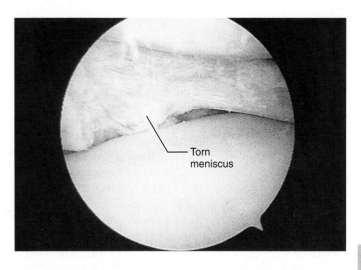

Figure 8.14 Arthroscopic photograph of a torn medial meniscus. (Courtesy of the author's tennis game.)

Few of us pay attention to our joints unless something goes wrong with them. Although remarkably strong, joints are definitely more at risk for injury from the same forces that act on the bony skeleton. Besides traumatic injuries, joint pain and malfunction can be caused by a number of factors, but most result from inflammatory or degenerative conditions.

Common Joint Injuries

For most of us, sprains and dislocations are the most common trauma-induced joint injuries, but cartilage injuries are equally threatening to athletes.

Cartilage Tears

Many aerobics devotees, encouraged to "feel the burn" during their workout, may feel the snap and pop of their overstressed cartilage instead. Although most cartilage injuries involve tearing of the knee menisci, tears and overuse damage to the articular cartilages of other joints is becoming increasingly common in competitive young athletes.

Cartilage tears typically occur when a meniscus is subjected to compression and shear stress at the same time. Cartilage is avascular and it rarely can obtain sufficient nourishment to repair itself, so it usually stays torn. Cartilage fragments (called loose bodies) can interfere with joint function by causing the joint to lock or bind, so most sports physicians recommend that the damaged cartilage be removed. Today, this can be done by **arthroscopic surgery** (ar-thro-skop′ik; "looking into joints"), a procedure that enables patients to be out of the hospital the same day. The arthroscope, a small instrument bearing a tiny lens and fiber-optic light source, enables the surgeon to view the joint interior, as in **Figure 8.14**. The surgeon can then repair a ligament, or remove cartilage fragments through one or more tiny slits, minimizing tissue damage and scarring. Removal of part of a meniscus does not severely impair knee joint mobility, but the joint is definitely less stable. Removal of the entire meniscus is an invitation to early onset of osteoarthritis in the joint.

Sprains

In a **sprain**, the ligaments reinforcing a joint are stretched or torn. The lumbar region of the spine, the ankle, and the knee are common sprain sites. Partially torn ligaments will repair themselves, but they heal slowly because ligaments are so poorly vascularized. Sprains tend to be painful and immobilizing.

Completely ruptured ligaments require prompt surgical repair because inflammation in the joint will break down the neighboring tissues and turn the injured ligament to "mush." Surgical repair can be difficult: A ligament consists of hundreds of fibrous strands, and sewing one back together has been compared to trying to sew two hairbrushes together.

When important ligaments are too severely damaged to be repaired, they must be removed and replaced with grafts or substitute ligaments. For example, a piece of tendon from a muscle, or woven collagen bands, can be stapled to the articulating bones.

Dislocations

A **dislocation (luxation)** occurs when bones are forced out of alignment. It is usually accompanied by sprains, inflammation, and difficulty in moving the joint. Dislocations may result from serious falls and are common contact sports injuries. Joints of the jaw, shoulders, fingers, and thumbs are most commonly dislocated. Like fractures, dislocations must be *reduced*; that is, the bone ends must be returned to their proper positions by a physician. *Subluxation* is a partial dislocation of a joint.

Repeat dislocations of the same joint are common because the initial dislocation stretches the joint capsule and ligaments. The resulting loose capsule provides poor reinforcement for the joint.

Inflammatory and Degenerative Conditions

Inflammatory conditions that affect joints include bursitis and tendonitis, various forms of arthritis, and Lyme disease.

Bursitis and Tendonitis

Bursitis is inflammation of a bursa and is usually caused by a blow or friction. Falling on one's knee may result in a painful bursitis of the prepatellar bursa, known as *housemaid's knee* or *water on the knee*. Prolonged leaning on one's elbows may damage the bursa close to the olecranon process, producing *student's elbow*, or *olecranon bursitis*. Severe cases are treated by injecting anti-inflammatory drugs into the bursa. If excessive fluid accumulates, removing some fluid by needle aspiration may relieve the pressure.

Tendonitis is inflammation of tendon sheaths, typically caused by overuse. Its symptoms (pain and swelling) and treatment (rest, ice, and anti-inflammatory drugs) mirror those of bursitis.

Arthritis

The term **arthritis** describes over 100 different types of inflammatory or degenerative diseases that damage the joints. In all its forms, arthritis is the most widespread crippling disease in the United States. One out of seven Americans suffers its ravages. To a greater or lesser degree, all forms of arthritis have the same initial symptoms: pain, stiffness, and swelling of the joint.

Acute forms of arthritis usually result from bacterial invasion and are treated with antibiotics. The synovial membrane thickens and fluid production decreases, causing increased friction and pain. Chronic forms of arthritis include osteoarthritis, rheumatoid arthritis, and gouty arthritis.

Osteoarthritis (Degenerative Joint Disease) Osteoarthritis **(OA)** is the most common chronic arthritis. A chronic (long-term) degenerative condition, OA is often called "wear-and-tear arthritis." OA is most prevalent in the aged and is probably related to the normal aging process (although it is seen occasionally in younger people and some forms have a genetic basis). More women than men are affected, but 85% of all Americans develop this condition.

Current theory holds that normal joint use prompts the release of (metalloproteinase) enzymes that break down articular cartilage, especially its collagen fibrils. In healthy individuals, this damaged cartilage is eventually replaced, but in people with OA, more cartilage is destroyed than replaced. Although its specific cause is unknown, OA may reflect the cumulative effects of years of compression and abrasion acting at joint surfaces, causing excessive amounts of the cartilage-destroying enzymes to be released. The result is softened, roughened, pitted, and eroded articular cartilages. Because this process occurs most where an uneven orientation of forces cause extensive microdamage, badly aligned or overworked joints are likely to develop OA.

As the disease progresses, the exposed bone tissue thickens and forms bony spurs (osteophytes) that enlarge the bone ends and may restrict joint movement. Patients complain of stiffness on arising that lessens somewhat with activity. The affected joints may make a crunching noise, called *crepitus* (krep′ĭ-tus), as they move and the roughened articular surfaces rub together. The joints most often affected are those of the cervical and lumbar spine and the fingers, knuckles, knees, and hips.

The course of osteoarthritis is usually slow and irreversible. In many cases, its symptoms are controllable with a mild pain reliever like aspirin or acetaminophen, along with moderate activity to keep the joints mobile. Rubbing a hot-pepper-like substance called capsaicin on the skin over the painful joints helps lessen the pain of OA. Glucosamine and chondroitin sulfate, nutritional supplements consisting of macromolecules normally present in cartilage, appear to decrease pain and inflammation in some people and may help to preserve the articular cartilage. Osteoarthritis is rarely crippling, but it can be, particularly when the hip or knee joints are involved.

Rheumatoid Arthritis Rheumatoid arthritis **(RA)** (roo′mah-toid) is a chronic inflammatory disorder with an insidious onset. Though it usually arises between the ages of 30 and 50, it may occur at any age. It affects three times as many women as men. While not as common as osteoarthritis, rheumatoid arthritis causes disability in millions. It occurs in more than 1% of Americans.

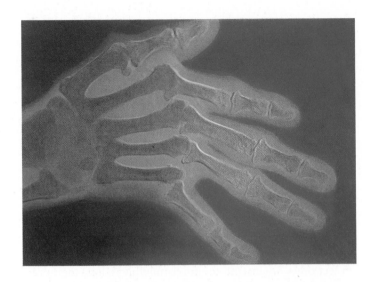

Figure 8.15 X ray of a hand deformed by rheumatoid arthritis.

In the early stages of RA, joint tenderness and stiffness are common. Many joints, particularly the small joints of the fingers, wrists, ankles, and feet, are afflicted at the same time and bilaterally. For example, if the right elbow is affected, most likely the left elbow is also affected. The course of RA is variable and marked by flare-ups (exacerbations) and remissions (*rheumat* = susceptible to change). Along with pain and swelling, its manifestations may include anemia, osteoporosis, muscle weakness, and cardiovascular problems.

RA is an *autoimmune disease*—a disorder in which the body's immune system attacks its own tissues. The initial trigger for this reaction is unknown, but the streptococcus bacterium and viruses have been suspect. Perhaps these microorganisms bear molecules similar to some naturally present in the joints (possibly glucosaminoglycans, complex carbohydrates found in cartilage, joint fluid, and other connective tissues), and the immune system, once activated, attempts to destroy both.

RA begins with inflammation of the synovial membrane (*synovitis*) of the affected joints. Inflammatory cells (lymphocytes, neutrophils, and others) migrate into the joint cavity from the blood and unleash a deluge of inflammatory chemicals that destroy body tissues when released inappropriately in large amounts as in RA. Synovial fluid accumulates, causing joint swelling, and in time, the inflamed synovial membrane thickens into a **pannus** ("rag"), an abnormal tissue that clings to the articular cartilages. The pannus erodes the cartilage (and sometimes the underlying bone) and eventually scar tissue forms and connects the bone ends. Later this scar tissue ossifies and the bone ends fuse together, immobilizing the joint. This end condition, called *ankylosis* (ang″kǐ-lo′sis; "stiff condition"), often produces bent, deformed fingers (Figure 8.15). Not all cases of RA progress to the severely crippling ankylosis stage, but all cases do involve restriction of joint movement and extreme pain.

A wonder drug for RA sufferers is still undiscovered. Currently the pendulum is swinging from conservative RA therapy utilizing aspirin, long-term antibiotic therapy, and physical therapy to a more progressive treatment course using immunosuppressants such as methotrexate, or anti-inflammatory drugs.

Particularly promising are etanercept (Enbrel) and infliximab (Remicade), the first in a class of drugs called *biologic response modifiers* that neutralize some of the harmful properties of the inflammatory chemicals. Unexpected success has been achieved in clinical studies using a tandem drug therapy approach (methotrexate in combination with etanercept). The arthritis of 35% of those treated went into remission and the arthritic joints of some patients actually improved after a year of therapy. Joint prostheses (artificial joints), if available, are the last resort for severely crippled RA patients (see *A Closer Look*, p. 261). Indeed, some RA sufferers have over a dozen artificial joints.

Gouty Arthritis Uric acid, a normal waste product of nucleic acid metabolism, is ordinarily excreted in urine without any problems. However, when blood levels of uric acid rise excessively (due to its excessive production or slow excretion), it may be deposited as needle-shaped urate crystals in the soft tissues of joints. An inflammatory response follows, leading into an agonizingly painful attack of **gouty arthritis** (gow′te), or **gout**. The initial attack typically affects one joint, often at the base of the great toe.

Gout is far more common in men than in women because men naturally have higher blood levels of uric acid (perhaps because estrogens increase the rate of its excretion). Because gout seems to run in families, genetic factors are definitely implicated.

Untreated gout can be very destructive; the articulating bone ends fuse and immobilize the joint. Fortunately, several drugs (colchicine, nonsteroidal anti-inflammatory drugs, glucocorticoids, and others) that terminate or prevent gout attacks are available. Patients are advised to drink plenty of water and to avoid alcohol excess (which promotes uric acid overproduction), and foods high in purine-containing nucleic acids, such as liver, kidneys, and sardines.

Lyme Disease

Lyme disease is an inflammatory disease caused by spirochete bacteria transmitted by the bites of ticks that live on mice and deer. It often results in joint pain and arthritis, especially in the knees, and is characterized by a skin rash, flu-like symptoms, and foggy thinking. If untreated, neurological disorders and irregular heartbeat may ensue.

Because symptoms vary from person to person, the disease is hard to diagnose. Antibiotic therapy is the usual treatment, but it takes a long time to kill the infecting bacteria. Currently, first-generation vaccines have been approved by the U.S. Food and Drug Administration and it is hoped that these will prevent the rapid spread of new cases.

CHECK YOUR UNDERSTANDING

12. What does the term "arthritis" mean?

13. How would you determine by looking at someone suffering from arthritis if he or she has OA or RA?

14. What is the cause of Lyme disease?

For answers, see Appendix G.

Developmental Aspects of Joints

▶ Discuss factors that promote or disturb joint homeostasis.

As bones form from mesenchyme in the embryo, the joints develop in parallel. By week 8, the synovial joints resemble adult joints in form and arrangement, and synovial fluid is being secreted. During childhood, a joint's size, shape, and flexibility are modified by use. Active joints have thicker capsules and ligaments, and larger bony supports.

Injuries aside, relatively few interferences with joint function occur until late middle age. Eventually advancing years take their toll and ligaments and tendons shorten and weaken. The intervertebral discs become more likely to herniate, and osteoarthritis rears its ugly head. Virtually everyone has osteoarthritis to some degree by the time they are in their 70s. The middle years also see an increased incidence of rheumatoid arthritis.

Exercise that coaxes joints through their full range of motion, such as regular stretching and aerobics, is the key to postponing the immobilizing effects of aging on ligaments and tendons, to keeping cartilages well nourished, and to strengthening the mus- cles that stabilize the joints. The key word for exercising is "prudently," because excessive or abusive use of the joints guarantees early onset of osteoarthritis. The buoyancy of water relieves much of the stress on weight-bearing joints, and people who swim or exercise in a pool often retain good joint function as long as they live. As with so many medical problems, it is easier to prevent joint problems than to cure or correct them.

CHECK YOUR UNDERSTANDING

15. What is the effect of regular exercise on joint health and structure?

For answers, see Appendix G.

The importance of joints is obvious: The skeleton's ability to protect other organs and to move smoothly reflects their presence. Now that we are familiar with joint structure and with the movements that joints allow, we are ready to consider how the muscles attached to the skeleton cause body movements by acting across its joints.

RELATED CLINICAL TERMS

Ankylosing spondylitis (ang'kĭ-lōz"ing spon"dĭ-li'tis; *ankyl* = crooked, bent; *spondyl* = vertebra) A variant of rheumatoid arthritis that chiefly affects males; it usually begins in the sacroiliac joints and progresses superiorly along the spine. The vertebrae become interconnected by fibrous tissue, causing the spine to become rigid ("poker back").

Arthrology (ar-throl'o-je; *logos* = study) The study of joints.

Arthroplasty ("joint reforming") Replacing a diseased joint with an artificial joint.

Chondromalacia patellae (kon-dro-mal-a'sĭ-ah; "softening of cartilage by the patella") Damage and softening of the articular cartilages on the posterior patellar surface and the anterior surface of the distal femur; most often seen in adolescent athletes. Produces a sharp pain in the knee when the leg is extended (in climbing stairs, for example). May result when the quadriceps femoris, the main group of muscles on the anterior thigh, pulls unevenly on the patella, persistently rubbing it against the femur in the knee joint; often corrected by exercises that strengthen weakened parts of the quadriceps muscles.

Rheumatism A term used by laypeople to indicate disease involving muscle or joint pain; consequently may be used to apply to arthritis, bursitis, etc.

Synovitis (sin"o-vi'tis) Inflammation of the synovial membrane of a joint. In healthy joints, only small amounts of synovial fluid are present, but synovitis causes copious amounts to be produced, leading to swelling and limitation of joint movement.

CHAPTER SUMMARY

1. Joints, or articulations, are sites where bones meet. Their functions are to hold bones together and to allow various degrees of skeletal movement.

Classification of Joints   (pp. 248–249)

1. Joints are classified structurally as fibrous, cartilaginous, or synovial. They are classed functionally as synarthrotic, amphiarthrotic, or diarthrotic.

Fibrous Joints   (pp. 249–250)

1. Fibrous joints occur where bones are connected by fibrous tissue; no joint cavity is present. Nearly all fibrous joints are synarthrotic.
2. **Sutures/syndesmoses/gomphoses.** The major types of fibrous joints are sutures, syndesmoses, and gomphoses.

Cartilaginous Joints   (pp. 250–251)

1. In cartilaginous joints, the bones are united by cartilage; no joint cavity is present.
2. **Synchondroses/symphyses.** Cartilaginous joints include synchondroses and symphyses. Synchondroses are synarthrotic; all symphyses are amphiarthrotic.

Synovial Joints   (pp. 251–269)

1. Most body joints are synovial joints, all of which are diarthrotic.

General Structure   (pp. 251–252)

2. All synovial joints have a joint cavity enclosed by a fibrous capsule lined with synovial membrane and reinforced by ligaments; articulating bone ends covered with articular cartilage; and synovial fluid in the joint cavity. Some (e.g., the knee) contain fibrocartilage discs that absorb shock.

Bursae and Tendon Sheaths (p. 252)

3. Bursae are fibrous sacs lined with synovial membrane and containing synovial fluid. Tendon sheaths are similar to bursae but are cylindrical structures that surround muscle tendons. Both allow adjacent structures to move smoothly over one another.

Factors Influencing the Stability of Synovial Joints (pp. 252–253)

4. Articular surfaces providing the most stability have large surfaces and deep sockets and fit snugly together.
5. Ligaments prevent undesirable movements and reinforce the joint.
6. The tone of muscles whose tendons cross the joint is the most important stabilizing factor in many joints.

Movements Allowed by Synovial Joints (pp. 253–259)

7. When a skeletal muscle contracts, the insertion (movable attachment) moves toward the origin (immovable attachment).
8. Synovial joints differ in their range of motion. Motion may be nonaxial (gliding), uniaxial (in one plane), biaxial (in two planes), or multiaxial (in all three planes).
9. Three common types of movements can occur when muscles contract across joints: (a) gliding movements, (b) angular movements (which include flexion, extension, abduction, adduction, and circumduction), and (c) rotation.
10. Special movements include supination and pronation, inversion and eversion, protraction and retraction, elevation and depression, and opposition.

Types of Synovial Joints (p. 259)

11. The six major categories of synovial joints are plane joints (nonaxial movement), hinge joints (uniaxial), pivot joints (uniaxial, rotation permitted), condyloid joints (biaxial with angular movements in two planes), saddle joints (biaxial, like condyloid joints, but with freer movement), and ball-and-socket joints (multiaxial and rotational movement).

Selected Synovial Joints (pp. 259–269)

12. The knee joint is the largest joint in the body. It is a hinge joint formed by the articulation of the tibial and femoral condyles (and anteriorly by the patella and patellar surface of the femur). Extension, flexion, and (some) rotation are allowed. Its articular surfaces are shallow and condyloid. C-shaped menisci deepen the articular surfaces. The joint cavity is enclosed by a capsule only on the sides and posterior aspect. Several ligaments help prevent displacement of the joint surfaces. Muscle tone of the quadriceps and semimembranosus muscles is important in knee stability.
13. The shoulder joint is a ball-and-socket joint formed by the glenoid cavity of the scapula and the humeral head. The most freely movable joint of the body, it allows all angular and rotational movements. Its articular surfaces are shallow. Its capsule is lax and poorly reinforced by ligaments. The tendons of the biceps brachii and rotator cuff muscles help to stabilize it.

14. The elbow is a hinge joint in which the ulna (and radius) articulates with the humerus, allowing flexion and extension. Its articular surfaces are highly complementary and are the most important factor contributing to joint stability.
15. The hip joint is a ball-and-socket joint formed by the acetabulum of the coxal bone and the femoral head. It is highly adapted for weight bearing. Its articular surfaces are deep and secure. Its capsule is heavy and strongly reinforced by ligaments.
16. The temporomandibular joint is formed by (1) the mandibular condyle and (2) the mandibular fossa and articular tubercle of the temporal bone. This joint allows both a hingelike opening and closing of the mouth and an anterior gliding of the mandible. It often dislocates anteriorly and exhibits a number of TMJ disorders.

Homeostatic Imbalances of Joints (pp. 269–271)

Common Joint Injuries (p. 269–270)

1. Cartilage injuries, particularly of the knee, are common in contact sports and may result from excessive compression and shear stress. The avascular cartilage is unable to repair itself.
2. Sprains involve stretching or tearing of joint ligaments. Because ligaments are poorly vascularized, healing is slow.
3. Dislocations involve displacement of the articular surfaces of bones. They must be reduced.

Inflammatory and Degenerative Conditions (pp. 270–271)

4. Bursitis and tendonitis are inflammations of a bursa and a tendon sheath, respectively.
5. Arthritis is joint inflammation or degeneration accompanied by stiffness, pain, and swelling. Acute forms generally result from bacterial infection. Chronic forms include osteoarthritis, rheumatoid arthritis, and gouty arthritis.
6. Osteoarthritis is a degenerative condition most common in the aged. Weight-bearing joints are most affected.
7. Rheumatoid arthritis, the most crippling arthritis, is an autoimmune disease involving severe inflammation of the joints.
8. Gouty arthritis, or gout, is joint inflammation caused by the deposit of urate salts in soft joint tissues.
9. Lyme disease is an infectious disease caused by the bite of a tick infected with spirochete bacteria.

Developmental Aspects of Joints (p. 272)

1. Joints form from mesenchyme and in tandem with bone development in the embryo.
2. Excluding traumatic injury, joints usually function well until late middle age, at which time symptoms of connective tissue stiffening and osteoarthritis begin to appear. Prudent exercise delays these effects, whereas excessive exercise promotes the early onset of arthritis.

8

REVIEW QUESTIONS

Multiple Choice/Matching

(Some questions have more than one correct answer. Select the best answer or answers from the choices given.)

1. Match the key terms to the appropriate descriptions.
   Key: (a) fibrous joints   (b) cartilaginous joints
          (c) synovial joints

   _____ (1) exhibit a joint cavity
   _____ (2) types are sutures and syndesmoses
   _____ (3) bones connected by collagen fibers
   _____ (4) types include synchondroses and symphyses
   _____ (5) all are diarthrotic
   _____ (6) many are amphiarthrotic
   _____ (7) bones connected by a disc of hyaline cartilage or fibrocartilage
   _____ (8) nearly all are synarthrotic
   _____ (9) shoulder, hip, jaw, and elbow joints

2. Freely movable joints are (a) synarthroses, (b) diarthroses, (c) amphiarthroses.

3. Anatomical characteristics of a synovial joint include (a) articular cartilage, (b) a joint cavity, (c) an articular capsule, (d) all of these.

4. Factors that influence the stability of a synovial joint include (a) shape of articular surfaces, (b) presence of strong reinforcing ligaments, (c) tone of surrounding muscles, (d) all of these.

5. The description "Articular surfaces deep and secure; capsule heavily reinforced by ligaments and muscle tendons; extremely stable joint" best describes (a) the elbow joint, (b) the hip joint, (c) the knee joint, (d) the shoulder joint.

6. Ankylosis means (a) twisting of the ankle, (b) tearing of ligaments, (c) displacement of a bone, (d) immobility of a joint due to fusion of its articular surfaces.

7. An autoimmune disorder in which joints are affected bilaterally and which involves pannus formation and gradual joint immobilization is (a) bursitis, (b) gout, (c) osteoarthritis, (d) rheumatoid arthritis.

Short Answer Essay Questions

8. Define joint.

9. Discuss the relative value (to body homeostasis) of immovable, slightly movable, and freely movable joints.

10. Compare the structure, function, and common body locations of bursae and tendon sheaths.

11. Joint movements may be nonaxial, uniaxial, biaxial, or multiaxial. Define what each of these terms means.

12. Compare and contrast the paired movements of flexion and extension with adduction and abduction.

13. How does rotation differ from circumduction?

14. Name two types of uniaxial, biaxial, and multiaxial joints.

15. What is the specific role of the menisci of the knee? of the anterior and posterior cruciate ligaments?

16. The knee has been called "a beauty and a beast." Provide several reasons that might explain the negative (beast) part of this description.

17. Why are sprains and cartilage injuries a particular problem?

18. List the functions of the following elements of a synovial joint: fibrous part of the capsule, synovial fluid, articular cartilage.

 Critical Thinking and Clinical Application Questions

1. Sophie worked cleaning homes for 30 years so she could send her two children to college. Several times, she had been forced to call her employers to tell them she could not come in to work because one of her kneecaps was swollen and painful. What is Sophie's condition, and what probably caused it?

2. As Harry was jogging down the road, he tripped and his left ankle twisted violently to the side. When he picked himself up, he was unable to put any weight on that ankle. The diagnosis was severe dislocation and sprains of the left ankle. The orthopedic surgeon stated that she would perform a closed reduction of the dislocation and attempt ligament repair by using arthroscopy. (a) Is the ankle joint normally a stable joint? (b) What does its stability depend on? (c) What is a closed reduction? (d) Why is ligament repair necessary? (e) What does arthroscopy entail? (f) How will the use of this procedure minimize Harry's recuperation time (and suffering)?

3. Mrs. Bell, a 45-year-old woman, appeared at her physician's office complaining of unbearable pain in the distal interphalangeal joint of her right great toe. The joint was red and swollen. When asked about previous episodes, she recalled a similar attack two years earlier that disappeared as suddenly as it had come. Her diagnosis was arthritis. (a) What type? (b) What is the precipitating cause of this particular type of arthritis?

4. Grace heard on the evening TV news that the deer population in her state had been increasing rapidly in the past few years and it was common knowledge that deer walked the streets at night. After the program, she suddenly exclaimed, "So that's why those three boys in my son's class got Lyme disease last year." Explain what she meant by that comment.

5. Tony Bowers, an exhausted biology student, was attending a lecture. After 30 minutes or so, he lost interest and began to doze. As the lecture ended, the hubbub aroused him and he let go with a tremendous yawn. To his great distress, he couldn't close his mouth—his lower jaw was "stuck" open. What do you think had happened?

 Access everything you need to practice, review, and self-assess for both your A&P lecture and lab courses at **myA&P** (www.myaandp.com). There, you'll find powerful online resources, including chapter quizzes and tests, games, A&P Flix animations with quizzes, *Interactive Physiology*® with quizzes, MP3 Tutor Sessions, Practice Anatomy Lab™, and more to help you get a better grade in your course.

9

Muscles and Muscle Tissue

Overview of Muscle Tissues (pp. 276–277)

Types of Muscle Tissue (p. 276)

Special Characteristics of Muscle Tissue (p. 276)

Muscle Functions (pp. 276–277)

Skeletal Muscle (pp. 277–305)

Gross Anatomy of a Skeletal Muscle (pp. 277–278)

Microscopic Anatomy of a Skeletal Muscle Fiber (pp. 278–284)

Sliding Filament Model of Contraction (p. 284)

Physiology of Skeletal Muscle Fibers (pp. 284–289)

Contraction of a Skeletal Muscle (pp. 289–296)

Muscle Metabolism (pp. 296–300)

Force of Muscle Contraction (pp. 300–302)

Velocity and Duration of Contraction (pp. 302–303)

Effect of Exercise on Muscles (pp. 304–305)

Smooth Muscle (pp. 305–311)

Microscopic Structure of Smooth Muscle Fibers (pp. 305–307)

Contraction of Smooth Muscle (pp. 307–311)

Types of Smooth Muscle (p. 311)

Developmental Aspects of Muscles (pp. 311–312, 316)

B ecause flexing muscles look like mice scurrying beneath the skin, some scientist long ago dubbed them *muscles*, from the Latin *mus* meaning "little mouse." Indeed, we tend to think of the rippling muscles of professional boxers or weight lifters when we hear the word *muscle*. But muscle is also the dominant tissue in the heart and in the walls of other hollow organs. In all its forms, muscle tissue makes up nearly half the body's mass. Muscles are distinguished by their ability to transform chemical energy (ATP) into directed mechanical energy. In so doing, they become capable of exerting force.

Overview of Muscle Tissues

▶ Compare and contrast the basic types of muscle tissue.

▶ List four important functions of muscle tissue.

Types of Muscle Tissue

The three types of muscle tissue—*skeletal, cardiac,* and *smooth*—were introduced in Chapter 4. Now we are ready to describe the three types of muscle tissue in detail, but before we do, let's introduce some terminology. First, skeletal and smooth muscle cells (but not cardiac muscle cells) are elongated, and for this reason, are called **muscle fibers**. Second, whenever you see the prefixes **myo** or **mys** (both are word roots meaning "muscle") or **sarco** (flesh), the reference is to muscle. For example, the plasma membrane of muscle cells is called the *sarcolemma* (sar″ko-lem′ah), literally, "muscle" (sarco) "husk" (lemma), and muscle cell cytoplasm is called *sarcoplasm*. Okay, let's get to it.

Skeletal muscle tissue is packaged into the *skeletal muscles,* organs that attach to and cover the bony skeleton. Skeletal muscle fibers are the longest muscle cells and have obvious stripes called *striations* (see Figure 4.10a, p. 136). Although it is often activated by reflexes, skeletal muscle is called **voluntary muscle** because it is the only type subject to conscious control. When you think of skeletal muscle tissue, the key words to keep in mind are *skeletal, striated,* and *voluntary.*

Skeletal muscle is responsible for overall body mobility. It can contract rapidly, but it tires easily and must rest after short periods of activity. Nevertheless, it can exert tremendous power, a fact revealed by reports of people lifting cars to save their loved ones. Skeletal muscle is also remarkably adaptable. For example, your hand muscles can exert a force of a fraction of an ounce to pick up a paper clip, and the same muscles can exert a force of about 70 pounds to pick up this book!

Cardiac muscle tissue occurs only in the heart (the body's blood pump), where it constitutes the bulk of the heart walls. Like skeletal muscle cells, cardiac muscle cells are striated (see Figure 4.10b, p. 137), but cardiac muscle is not voluntary. Indeed, it can and does contract without being stimulated by the nervous system. Most of us have no conscious control over how fast our heart beats. Key words to remember for cardiac muscle are *cardiac, striated,* and *involuntary.*

Cardiac muscle usually contracts at a fairly steady rate set by the heart's pacemaker, but neural controls allow the heart to speed up for brief periods, as when you race across the tennis court to make that overhead smash.

Smooth muscle tissue is found in the walls of hollow visceral organs, such as the stomach, urinary bladder, and respiratory passages. Its role is to force fluids and other substances through internal body channels. Smooth muscle cells like skeletal muscle cells are elongated "fibers," but smooth muscle has no striations (see Figure 4.10c, p. 137). Like cardiac muscle, it is not subject to voluntary control. Contractions of smooth muscle fibers are slow and sustained. We can describe smooth muscle tissue as *visceral, nonstriated,* and *involuntary.*

Special Characteristics of Muscle Tissue

What enables muscle tissue to perform its duties? Four special characteristics or abilities are key.

Excitability, also termed **responsiveness** or **irritability**, is the ability to receive and respond to a stimulus, that is, any change in the environment either inside or outside the body. In the case of muscle, the stimulus is usually a chemical—for example, a neurotransmitter released by a nerve cell, or a local change in pH. The response (sometimes separated out as an additional characteristic called *conductivity*), is generation of an electrical impulse that passes along the plasma membrane of the muscle cell and causes the cell to contract.

Contractility is the ability to shorten forcibly when adequately stimulated. This ability sets muscle apart from all other tissue types.

Extensibility is the ability to be stretched or extended. Muscle cells shorten when contracting, but they can be stretched, even beyond their resting length, when relaxed.

Elasticity is the ability of a muscle cell to recoil and resume its resting length after being stretched.

Muscle Functions

Muscle performs at least four important functions for the body. It produces movement, maintains posture, stabilizes joints, generates heat, and more.

Producing Movement

Just about all movements of the human body and its parts result from muscle contraction. Skeletal muscles are responsible for all locomotion and manipulation. They enable you to respond quickly to changes in the external environment—for example, to jump out of the way of a car, to direct your eyeballs, and to smile or frown.

Blood courses through your body because of the rhythmically beating cardiac muscle of your heart and the smooth muscle in the walls of your blood vessels, which helps maintain blood pressure. Smooth muscle in organs of the digestive, urinary, and reproductive tracts propels, or squeezes, substances (foodstuffs, urine, a baby) through the organs and along the tract.

Maintaining Posture and Body Position

We are rarely aware of the workings of the skeletal muscles that maintain body posture. Yet these muscles function almost continuously, making one tiny adjustment after another to counteract the never-ending downward pull of gravity.

Stabilizing Joints

Even as muscles pull on bones to cause movements, they stabilize and strengthen the joints of the skeleton (Chapter 8).

Generating Heat

Muscles generate heat as they contract. This heat is vitally important in maintaining normal body temperature. Because skeletal muscle accounts for at least 40% of body mass, it is the muscle type most responsible for generating heat.

Additional Functions

What else do muscles do? Skeletal muscles protect the more fragile internal organs (the viscera) by enclosing them. Smooth muscle also forms valves to regulate the passage of substances through internal body openings, dilates and constricts the pupils of your eyes, and forms the arrector pili muscles attached to hair follicles.

■ ■ ■

In much of this chapter, we examine the structure and function of skeletal muscle. Then we consider smooth muscle more briefly, largely by comparing it with skeletal muscle. We describe cardiac muscle in detail in Chapter 18, but for easy comparison, the characteristics of all three muscle types are included in the summary in Table 9.3 on p. 309.

CHECK YOUR UNDERSTANDING

1. When describing muscle, what does "striated" mean?
2. Harry was pondering an exam question that said, "What muscle type has elongated cells and is found in the walls of the urinary bladder?" What should he have responded?

For answers, see Appendix G.

Skeletal Muscle

▶ Describe the gross structure of a skeletal muscle.

▶ Describe the microscopic structure and functional roles of the myofibrils, sarcoplasmic reticulum, and T tubules of skeletal muscle fibers.

▶ Describe the sliding filament model of muscle contraction.

For easy reference, **Table 9.1** summarizes the levels of skeletal muscle organization, gross to microscopic, that we describe in the following sections.

Gross Anatomy of a Skeletal Muscle

Each **skeletal muscle** is a discrete organ, made up of several kinds of tissues. Skeletal muscle fibers predominate, but blood vessels, nerve fibers, and substantial amounts of connective tissue are also present. A skeletal muscle's shape and its attachments in the body can be examined easily without the help of a microscope.

Nerve and Blood Supply

In general, each muscle is served by one nerve, an artery, and by one or more veins. These structures all enter or exit near the central part of the muscle and branch profusely through its connective tissue sheaths (described below). Unlike cells of cardiac

and smooth muscle tissues, which can contract in the absence of nerve stimulation, each skeletal muscle fiber is supplied with a nerve ending that controls its activity.

Skeletal muscle has a rich blood supply. This is understandable because contracting muscle fibers use huge amounts of energy and require more or less continuous delivery of oxygen and nutrients via the arteries. Muscle cells also give off large amounts of metabolic wastes that must be removed through veins if contraction is to remain efficient. Muscle capillaries, the smallest of the body's blood vessels, are long and winding and have numerous cross-links, features that accommodate changes in muscle length. They straighten when the muscle is stretched and contort when the muscle contracts.

Connective Tissue Sheaths

In an intact muscle, the individual muscle fibers are wrapped and held together by several different connective tissue sheaths. Together these connective tissue sheaths support each cell and reinforce the muscle as a whole, preventing the bulging muscles from bursting during exceptionally strong contractions. We will consider these from external to internal (see Figure 9.1 and the top three rows of Table 9.1).

1. **Epimysium.** The **epimysium** (ep″ĭ-mis′e-um; meaning "outside the muscle") is an "overcoat" of dense irregular connective tissue that surrounds the whole muscle. Sometimes it blends with the deep fascia that lies between neighboring muscles or the superficial fascia deep to the skin.

2. **Perimysium and fascicles.** Within each skeletal muscle, the muscle fibers are grouped into **fascicles** (fas′ĭ-klz; "bundles") that resemble bundles of sticks. Surrounding each fascicle is a layer of fibrous connective tissue called **perimysium** (per″ĭ-mis′e-um; meaning "around the muscle [fascicles]").

3. **Endomysium.** The **endomysium** (en″do-mis′e-um; meaning "within the muscle") is a whispy sheath of connective tissue that surrounds each individual muscle fiber. It consists of fine areolar connective tissue.

As shown in Figure 9.1, all of these connective tissue sheaths are continuous with one another as well as with the tendons that join muscles to bones. When muscle fibers contract, they pull on these sheaths, which in turn transmit the pulling force to the bone to be moved. The sheaths contribute somewhat to the natural elasticity of muscle tissue, and also provide entry and exit routes for the blood vessels and nerve fibers that serve the muscle.

Attachments

Recall from Chapter 8 that most skeletal muscles span joints and are attached to bones (or other structures) in at least two places, and that when a muscle contracts, the movable bone, the muscle's **insertion**, moves toward the immovable or less movable bone, the muscle's **origin**. In the muscles of the limbs, the origin typically lies proximal to the insertion.

Muscle attachments, whether origin or insertion, may be direct or indirect. In **direct**, or **fleshy**, **attachments**, the epimysium of the muscle is fused to the periosteum of a bone or

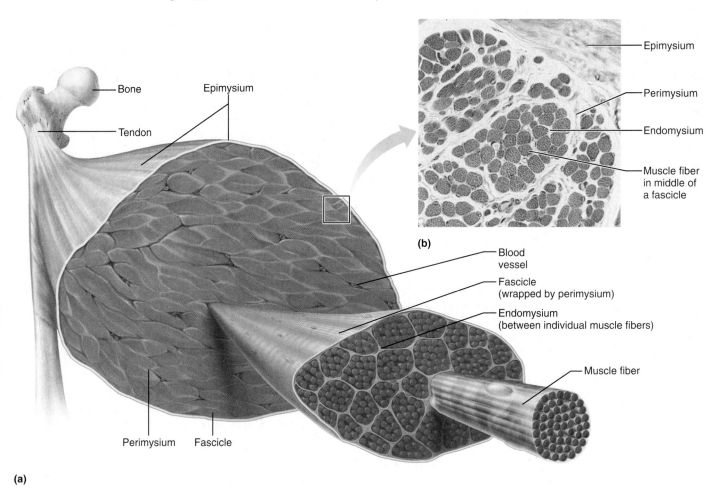

(a)

Figure 9.1 Connective tissue sheaths of skeletal muscle: epimysium, perimysium, and endomysium. (b) Photomicrograph of a cross section of part of a skeletal muscle (150×). (See *A Brief Atlas of the Human Body*, Plate 29.)

perichondrium of a cartilage. In **indirect attachments**, the muscle's connective tissue wrappings extend beyond the muscle either as a ropelike **tendon** (Figure 9.1a) or as a sheetlike **aponeurosis** (ap″o-nu-ro′sis). The tendon or aponeurosis anchors the muscle to the connective tissue covering of a skeletal element (bone or cartilage) or to the fascia of other muscles.

Of the two, indirect attachments are much more common because of their durability and small size. Tendons are mostly tough collagen fibers which can withstand the abrasion of rough bony projections that would tear apart the more delicate muscle tissues. Because of their relatively small size, more tendons than fleshy muscles can pass over a joint—so tendons also conserve space.

Before moving on to microscopic anatomy, you may want to review the top three rows of Table 9.1.

Microscopic Anatomy of a Skeletal Muscle Fiber

Each skeletal muscle fiber is a long cylindrical cell with multiple oval nuclei just beneath its **sarcolemma** or plasma membrane **(Figure 9.2b)**. Skeletal muscle fibers are huge cells. Their diameter typically ranges from 10 to 100 μm—up to ten times that of an average body cell—and their length is phenomenal, some up to 30 cm long. Their large size and multiple nuclei are not surprising once you learn that hundreds of embryonic cells fuse to produce each fiber.

Sarcoplasm, the cytoplasm of a muscle cell, is similar to the cytoplasm of other cells, but it contains unusually large amounts of **glycosomes** (granules of stored glycogen that provide glucose during periods of muscle cell activity) and **myoglobin**, a red pigment that stores oxygen. Myoglobin is similar to hemoglobin, the pigment that transports oxygen in blood. The usual organelles are present, along with some that are highly modified in muscle fibers: myofibrils, the sarcoplasmic reticulum, and T tubules (unique modifications of the sarcolemma). Let's look at these three special structures more closely because they play important roles in muscle contraction.

Myofibrils

Each muscle fiber contains many rodlike **myofibrils** that run parallel to its length (Figure 9.2b). The myofibrils, each 1–2 μm in diameter, are so densely packed in the fiber that mitochondria and other organelles appear to be squeezed between them. Hundreds to thousands of myofibrils are in a single muscle

TABLE 9.1	Structure and Organizational Levels of Skeletal Muscle		
STRUCTURE AND ORGANIZATIONAL LEVEL		**DESCRIPTION**	**CONNECTIVE TISSUE WRAPPINGS**
Muscle (organ) 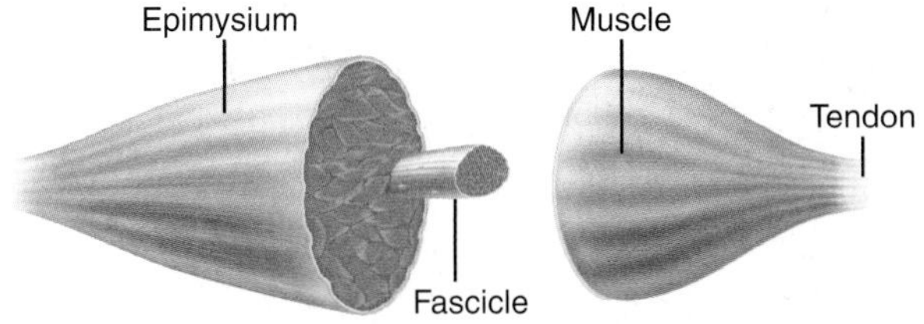 Epimysium, Muscle, Tendon, Fascicle		A muscle consists of hundreds to thousands of muscle cells, plus connective tissue wrappings, blood vessels, and nerve fibers.	Covered externally by the epimysium
Fascicle (a portion of the muscle) 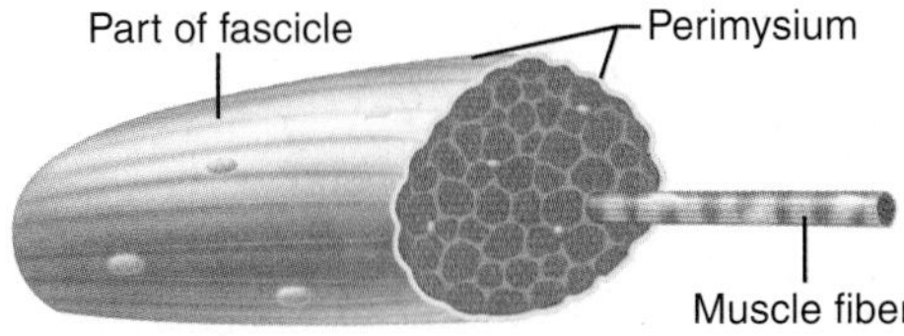 Part of fascicle, Perimysium, Muscle fiber		A fascicle is a discrete bundle of muscle cells, segregated from the rest of the muscle by a connective tissue sheath.	Surrounded by a perimysium
Muscle Fiber (cell) 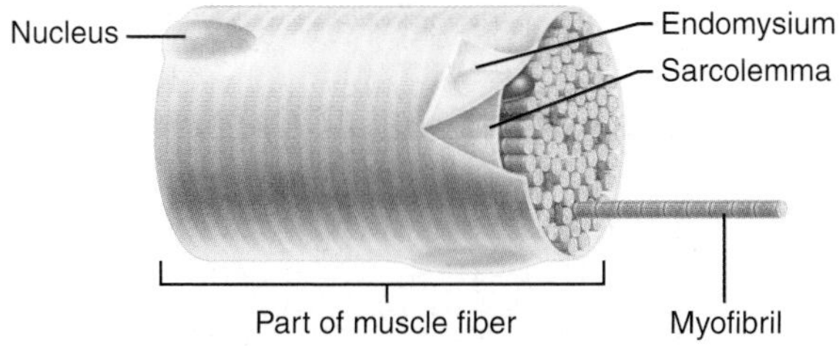 Nucleus, Endomysium, Sarcolemma, Part of muscle fiber, Myofibril		A muscle fiber is an elongated multinucleate cell; it has a banded (striated) appearance.	Surrounded by endomysium
Myofibril or Fibril (complex organelle composed of bundles of myofilaments) 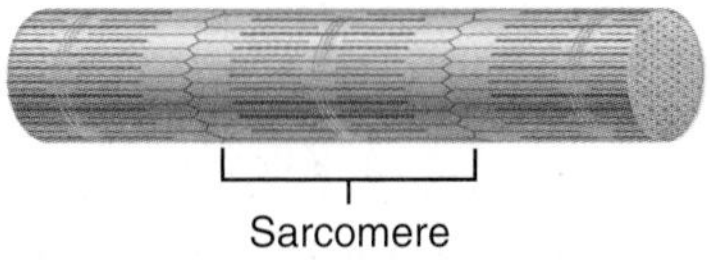 Sarcomere		Myofibrils are rodlike contractile elements that occupy most of the muscle cell volume. Composed of sarcomeres arranged end to end, they appear banded, and bands of adjacent myofibrils are aligned.	
Sarcomere (a segment of a myofibril) 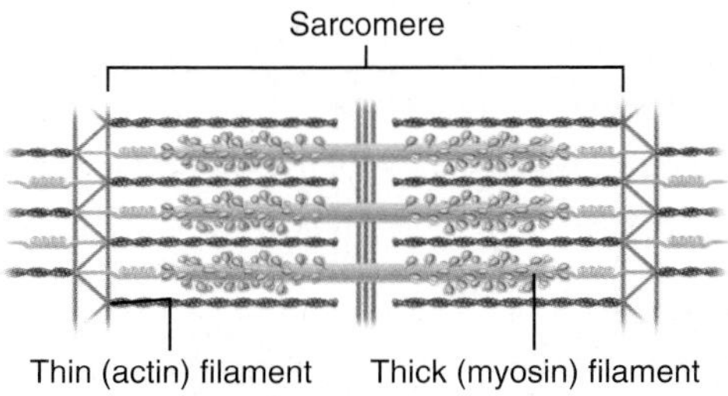 Sarcomere, Thin (actin) filament, Thick (myosin) filament		A sarcomere is the contractile unit, composed of myofilaments made up of contractile proteins.	
Myofilament or Filament (extended macromolecular structure) 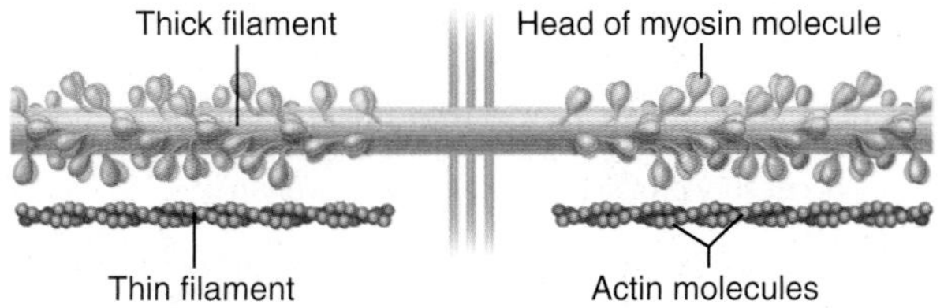 Thick filament, Head of myosin molecule, Thin filament, Actin molecules		Contractile myofilaments are of two types—thick and thin. The thick filaments contain bundled myosin molecules; the thin filaments contain actin molecules (plus other proteins). The sliding of the thin filaments past the thick filaments produces muscle shortening. Elastic filaments (not shown here) maintain the organization of the A band and provide for elastic recoil when muscle contraction ends.	

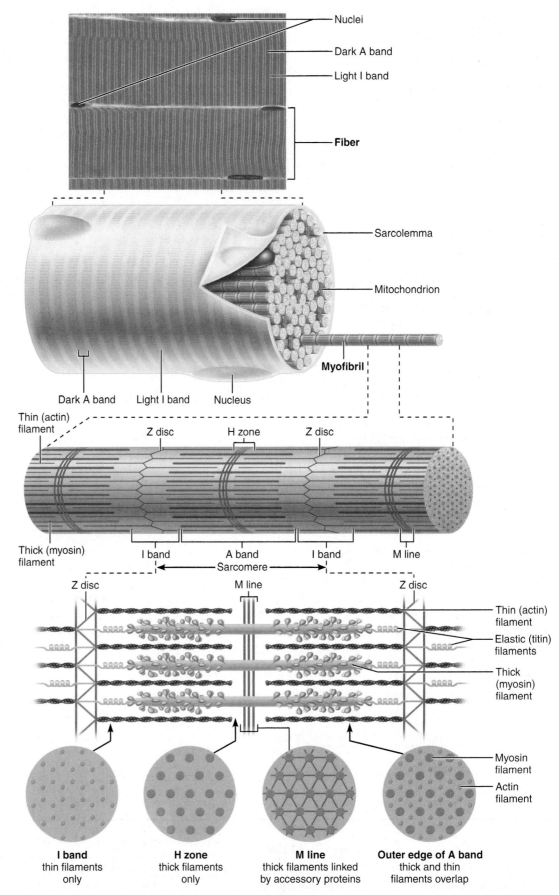

(a) Photomicrograph of **portions of two isolated muscle fibers** (700×). Notice the obvious striations (alternating dark and light bands).

Nuclei

Dark A band

Light I band

Fiber

(b) Diagram of **part of a muscle fiber** showing the myofibrils. One **myofibril** is extended from the cut end of the fiber.

Sarcolemma

Mitochondrion

Myofibril

Dark A band   Light I band   Nucleus

(c) Small part of one **myofibril** enlarged to **show the myofilaments** responsible for the banding pattern. Each **sarcomere** extends from one Z disc to the next.

Thin (actin) filament

Z disc   H zone   Z disc

Thick (myosin) filament

I band   A band   I band   M line

Sarcomere

(d) **Enlargement of one sarcomere** (sectioned lengthwise). Notice the myosin heads on the thick filaments.

Z disc   M line   Z disc

Thin (actin) filament

Elastic (titin) filaments

Thick (myosin) filament

(e) Cross-sectional view of a sarcomere cut through in different locations.

Myosin filament

Actin filament

I band
thin filaments only

H zone
thick filaments only

M line
thick filaments linked by accessory proteins

Outer edge of A band
thick and thin filaments overlap

Figure 9.2 Microscopic anatomy of a skeletal muscle fiber. (See *A Brief Atlas of the Human Body*, Plate 28.)

fiber, depending on its size, and they account for about 80% of cellular volume. These myofibrils contain the contractile elements of skeletal muscle cells, the sarcomeres, which contain even smaller rodlike structures called *myofilaments*. Table 9.1 (bottom three rows) summarizes these structures, which we discuss next.

Striations, Sarcomeres, and Myofilaments **Striations**, a repeating series of dark and light bands, are evident along the length of each myofibril. In an intact muscle fiber, the dark **A bands** and light **I bands** are nearly perfectly aligned with one another, giving the cell as a whole its striated appearance.

As illustrated in Figure 9.2c, each dark A band has a lighter region in its midsection called the **H zone** (*H* for *helle*; "bright"). Each H zone is bisected vertically by a dark line called the **M line** (*M* for middle) formed by molecules of the protein myomesin. The light I bands also have a midline interruption, a darker area called the **Z disc** (or Z line).

A **sarcomere** (sar′ko-měr; literally, "muscle segment") is the smallest contractile unit of a muscle fiber—the *functional unit* of skeletal muscle. Averaging 2 μm long, a sarcomere is the region of a myofibril between two successive Z discs. In other words, it contains an A band flanked by half an I band at each end (Figure 9.2c). Within each myofibril, the sarcomeres are aligned end-to-end like boxcars in a train.

If we examine the banding pattern of a myofibril at the molecular level, we see that it arises from an orderly arrangement of two types of even smaller structures within the sarcomeres. These smaller structures, the **myofilaments** or **filaments**, are the muscle equivalents of the actin- or myosin-containing microfilaments described in Chapter 3. As you will recall, the proteins actin and myosin play a role in motility and shape changes in virtually every cell in the body. This property reaches its highest development in the contractile muscle fibers.

As you can see in Figure 9.2c and d, the central **thick filaments** containing myosin (red) extend the entire length of the A band. The more lateral **thin filaments** containing actin (blue) extend across the I band and partway into the A band. The Z disc, a coin-shaped sheet composed largely of the protein alpha-actinin, anchors the thin filaments. The third type of myofilament illustrated in Figure 9.2d, the *elastic filament*, is described in the next section. Intermediate (desmin) filaments (not illustrated) extending from the Z disc connect each myofibril to the next throughout the width of the muscle cell.

Looking at the banding pattern more closely, we see that the H zone of the A band appears less dense because the thin filaments do not extend into this region. The M line in the center of the H zone is slightly darker because of the presence there of fine protein strands that hold adjacent thick filaments together. The myofilaments are connected to the sarcolemma and held in register at the Z discs and the M lines.

A longitudinal view of the myofilaments such as that in Figure 9.2d is a bit misleading because it looks as if each thick (red) filament interdigitates with only four thin (blue) filaments. The cross section of a sarcomere on the far right in Figure 9.2e shows an area where thick and thin filaments overlap. Notice that each thick filament is actually surrounded by a hexagonal arrangement of six thin filaments, and each thin filament is enclosed by three thick filaments.

Ultrastructure and Molecular Composition of the Myofilaments
Muscle contraction depends on the myosin- and actin-containing myofilaments. As noted earlier, thick filaments (about 16 nm in diameter) are composed primarily of the protein myosin. Each myosin molecule consists of two heavy and four light polypeptide chains, and has a rodlike *tail* attached by a flexible hinge to two globular *heads* (Figure 9.3). The tail consists of two intertwined helical polypeptide heavy chains. The globular heads, each associated with two light chains, are the "business end" of myosin. During contraction, they link the thick and thin filaments together, forming **cross bridges** (Figure 9.4), and swivel around their point of attachment. As we will explain shortly, these cross bridges act as motors to generate the tension developed by a contracting muscle cell.

Each thick filament contains about 300 myosin molecules bundled together with their tails forming the central part of the thick filament and their heads facing outward and at each end (Figure 9.3). As a result, the central portion of a thick filament (in the H zone) is smooth, but its ends are studded with a staggered array of myosin heads. The heads bear actin and ATP-binding sites and also contain ATPase enzymes that split ATP to generate energy for muscle contraction.

The thin filaments (7–8 nm thick) are composed chiefly of the protein **actin** (blue in Figure 9.3). Actin has kidney-shaped polypeptide subunits, called *globular actin* or *G actin*, which bear the active sites to which the myosin heads attach during contraction. In the thin filaments, G actin subunits are polymerized into long actin filaments called *fibrous*, or *F, actin*. The backbone of each thin filament appears to be formed by two intertwined actin filaments that look like a twisted double strand of pearls (Figure 9.3).

Several regulatory proteins are also present in thin filaments. Polypeptide strands of **tropomyosin** (tro″po-mi′o-sin), a rod-shaped protein, spiral about the actin core and help stiffen and stabilize it. Successive tropomyosin molecules are arranged end-to-end along the actin filaments, and in a relaxed muscle fiber, they block myosin-binding sites on actin so that the myosin heads on the thick filaments cannot bind to the thin filaments. The other major protein in thin filaments is **troponin** (tro′po-nin), a globular three-polypeptide complex (Figure 9.3). One of its polypeptides (TnI) is an inhibitory subunit that binds to actin. Another (TnT) binds to tropomyosin and helps position it on actin. The third (TnC) binds calcium ions. Both troponin and tropomyosin help control the myosin-actin interactions involved in contraction.

The **elastic filament** we referred to earlier is composed of the giant protein **titin** (Figure 9.2d). This protein extends from the Z disc to the thick filament, and then runs within the thick filament (forming its core) to attach to the M line. It holds the thick filaments in place, thus maintaining the organization of the A band, and helps the muscle cell to spring back into shape after being stretched. (The part of the titin that spans the I bands is extensible, unfolding when the muscle is stretched and recoiling

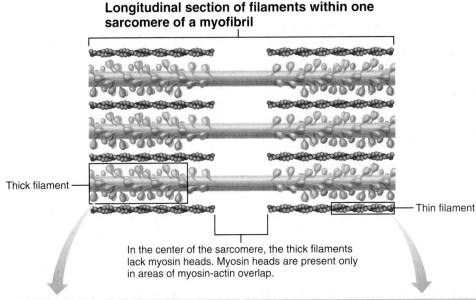

Longitudinal section of filaments within one sarcomere of a myofibril

Thick filament

Thin filament

In the center of the sarcomere, the thick filaments lack myosin heads. Myosin heads are present only in areas of myosin-actin overlap.

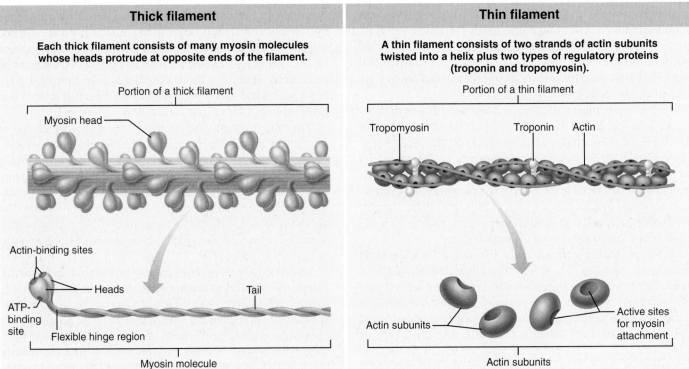

Thick filament	**Thin filament**

Each thick filament consists of many myosin molecules whose heads protrude at opposite ends of the filament.

Portion of a thick filament

Myosin head

Actin-binding sites

Heads

Tail

ATP-binding site

Flexible hinge region

Myosin molecule

A thin filament consists of two strands of actin subunits twisted into a helix plus two types of regulatory proteins (troponin and tropomyosin).

Portion of a thin filament

Tropomyosin   Troponin   Actin

Actin subunits

Active sites for myosin attachment

Actin subunits

Figure 9.3 Composition of thick and thin filaments.

when the tension is released.) Titin does not resist stretching in the ordinary range of extension, but it stiffens as it uncoils, helping the muscle to resist excessive stretching, which might pull the sarcomeres apart.

Another important structural protein is **dystrophin**, which links the thin filaments to the integral proteins of the sarcolemma (which in turn are anchored to the extracellular matrix). Other proteins that act to bind filaments or sarcomeres together and maintain their alignment include *nebulin, myomesin,* and *C proteins.*

Sarcoplasmic Reticulum and T Tubules

Skeletal muscle fibers contain two sets of intracellular tubules that participate in regulation of muscle contraction: (1) the sarcoplasmic reticulum and (2) T tubules.

Sarcoplasmic Reticulum   Shown in blue in **Figure 9.5**, the **sarcoplasmic reticulum (SR)** is an elaborate smooth endoplasmic reticulum (see p. 84–85). Its interconnecting tubules surround each myofibril the way the sleeve of a loosely crocheted sweater surrounds your arm. Most of these tubules run

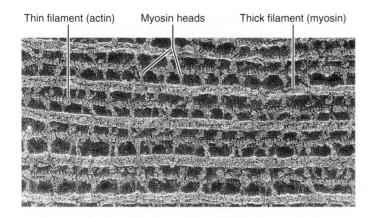

Thin filament (actin)   Myosin heads   Thick filament (myosin)

Figure 9.4 Transmission electron micrograph of part of a sarcomere clearly showing the myosin heads forming cross bridges that generate the contractile force. (277,000×)

longitudinally along the myofibril communicating at the H zone. Others called **terminal cisternae** ("end sacs") form larger, perpendicular cross channels at the A band–I band junctions and they always occur in pairs. Closely associated with the SR are large numbers of mitochondria and glycogen granules, both involved in producing the energy used during contraction.

The major role of the SR is to regulate intracellular levels of ionic calcium. It stores calcium and releases it on demand when the muscle fiber is stimulated to contract. As you will see, calcium provides the final "go" signal for contraction.

T Tubules At each A band–I band junction, the sarcolemma of the muscle cell protrudes deep into the cell interior, forming an elongated tube called the **T tubule** (T for "transverse"). The T tubules, shown in gray in Figure 9.5, tremendously increase the muscle fiber's surface area. Possibly the result of fusing tube-like caveolae (inpocketings of the sarcolemma), the lumen of the T tubule is continuous with the extracellular space. Along its length, each T tubule runs between the paired terminal cisternae of the SR, forming **triads**, successive groupings of the three membranous structures (terminal cisterna, T tubule, and terminal cisterna). As they pass from one myofibril to the next, the T tubules also encircle each sarcomere.

Muscle contraction is ultimately controlled by nerve-initiated electrical impulses that travel along the sarcolemma. Because T tubules are continuations of the sarcolemma, they conduct impulses to the deepest regions of the muscle cell and to every sarcomere. These impulses signal for the release of calcium from the adjacent terminal cisternae. You can think of the T tubules as

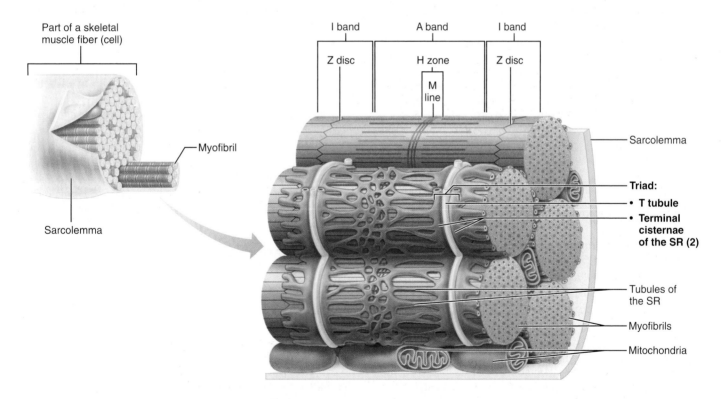

Figure 9.5 Relationship of the sarcoplasmic reticulum and T tubules to myofibrils of skeletal muscle. The tubules of the SR (blue) encircle each myofibril like a "holey" sleeve. These tubules fuse to form a net of communicating channels at the level of the H zone and saclike elements called terminal cisternae abutting the A-I junctions. The T tubules (gray) are inward invaginations of the sarcolemma that run deep into the cell between the terminal cisternae. Sites of close contact of these three elements (terminal cisterna, T tubule, and terminal cisterna) are called triads.

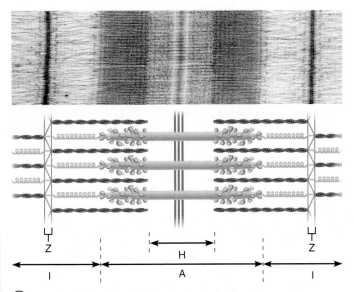

(1) Fully relaxed sarcomere of a muscle fiber

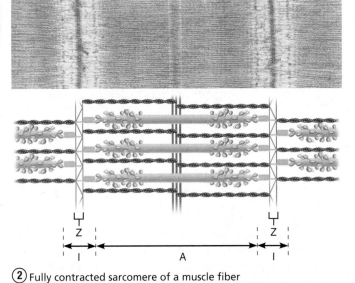

(2) Fully contracted sarcomere of a muscle fiber

Figure 9.6 Sliding filament model of contraction. The numbers indicate events in a (1) relaxed and a (2) fully contracted sarcomere. At full contraction, the Z discs abut the thick filaments and the thin filaments overlap each other. The photomicrographs (top view in each case) show enlargements of 29,200×.

a rapid telegraph system that ensures that every myofibril in the muscle fiber contracts at virtually the same time.

Triad Relationships   The roles of the T tubules and SR in providing signals for contraction are tightly linked. At the triads, where these organelles come into closest contact, something that resembles a *double zipper* of integral proteins protrudes into the intermembrane spaces. The protruding integral proteins of the T tubule act as voltage sensors. Those of the SR, called *foot proteins*, form gated channels through which Ca^{2+} can be released from the SR cisternae. We will return to consider their interaction shortly.

Sliding Filament Model of Contraction

We almost always think "shortening" when we hear the word **contraction**, but to physiologists the term refers only to the activation of myosin's cross bridges, which are the force-generating sites. Shortening occurs if and when the tension generated by the cross bridges on the thin filaments exceeds the forces opposing shortening and pulls the thin filaments toward the M line. Contraction ends when the cross bridges become inactive and the tension declines, inducing *relaxation* of the muscle fiber.

The **sliding filament model of contraction** states that during contraction the thin filaments slide past the thick ones so that the actin and myosin filaments overlap to a greater degree. In a relaxed muscle fiber, the thick and thin filaments overlap only at the ends of the A band (Figure 9.6, (1)).

When muscle fibers are stimulated by the nervous system, the myosin heads on the thick filaments latch onto myosin-binding sites on actin in the thin filaments, and the sliding begins. These cross bridge attachments are formed and broken several times during a contraction, acting like tiny ratchets to generate tension and propel the thin filaments toward the center of the sarcomere. As this event occurs simultaneously in sarcomeres throughout the cell, the muscle cell shortens. Notice that as the thin filaments slide centrally, the Z discs to which they are attached are pulled *toward* the M line (Figure 9.6, (2)). Overall, as a muscle cell shortens, the I bands shorten, the distance between successive Z discs is reduced, the H zones disappear, and the contiguous A bands move closer together but do not change in length.

CHECK YOUR UNDERSTANDING

3. How does the term *epimysium* relate to the role and position of this connective tissue sheath?

4. Which myofilaments have binding sites for calcium? What specific molecule binds calcium?

5. Which structure—T tubule, mitochondrion, or SR—contains the highest concentration of calcium ions in a resting muscle fiber? Which structure provides the ATP needed for muscle activity?

For answers, see Appendix G.

Physiology of Skeletal Muscle Fibers

▶ Explain how muscle fibers are stimulated to contract by describing events that occur at the neuromuscular junction.

▶ Describe how an action potential is generated.

▶ Follow the events of excitation-contraction coupling that lead to cross bridge activity.

The sliding filament model tells us how a muscle fiber contracts, but what induces it to contract in the first place? For a skeletal muscle fiber to contract

1. It must be activated, that is, stimulated by a nerve ending so that a change in membrane potential occurs.

2. Next, it must generate and propagate an electrical current, called an **action potential**, along its sarcolemma.
3. Then, a short-lived rise in intracellular calcium ion levels that is the final trigger for contraction must occur.

Step 1, the activation step, occurs at the neuromuscular junction and sets the stage for the events that follow. Together steps 2 and 3, which link the electrical signal to contraction, are called *excitation-contraction coupling*. This series of events is summarized in Figure 9.7, and considered in more detail below.

The Nerve Stimulus and Events at the Neuromuscular Junction

The nerve cells that activate skeletal muscle fibers are called *somatic motor neurons,* or *motor neurons of the somatic (voluntary) nervous system.* These motor neurons "reside" in the brain or spinal cord, but their long threadlike extensions called *axons* travel, bundled within nerves, to the muscle cells they serve. The axon of each motor neuron divides profusely as it enters the muscle, and each axon ending gives off several short, curling branches that collectively form an elliptical **neuromuscular junction** with a single muscle fiber (Figure 9.8).

As a rule, each muscle fiber has only one neuromuscular junction, located approximately midway along its length. The axon terminal and the muscle fiber are exceedingly close (1–2 nm apart), but they remain separated by a space, the **synaptic cleft** (Figure 9.8), which is filled with a gel-like extracellular substance rich in glycoproteins and collagen fibers. Within the moundlike axon terminal are **synaptic vesicles**, small membranous sacs containing the neurotransmitter **acetylcholine** (as″ĕ-til-ko′lēn), or **ACh**. The trough-like part of the muscle fiber's sarcolemma that helps form the neuromuscular junction is highly folded. These **junctional folds** provide a large surface area for the millions of **ACh receptors** located there (Figure 9.8). Hence, the neuromuscular junction includes the axonal endings, the synaptic cleft, and the junctional folds of the sarcolemma.

How does a motor neuron stimulate a skeletal muscle fiber? The simplest explanation is that when a nerve impulse reaches the end of an axon, the axon terminal releases ACh into the synaptic cleft. ACh diffuses across the cleft and attaches to ACh receptors on the sarcolemma of the muscle fiber, which triggers electrical events that ultimately cause action potential generation. This process is covered in step-by-step detail in: *Focus on Events at the Neuromuscular Junction* (Figure 9.8) on p. 286. Study this figure before continuing.

After ACh binds to the ACh receptors, its effects are quickly terminated by its enzymatic breakdown to its building blocks, acetic acid and choline, by **acetylcholinesterase** (as″ĕ-til-ko″lin-es′ter-ās), an enzyme located in the synaptic cleft. This removal of ACh prevents continued (and most likely undesirable) muscle fiber contraction in the absence of additional nervous system stimulation.

⚖ HOMEOSTATIC IMBALANCE

Many toxins, drugs, and diseases interfere with events at the neuromuscular junction. For example, *myasthenia gravis*

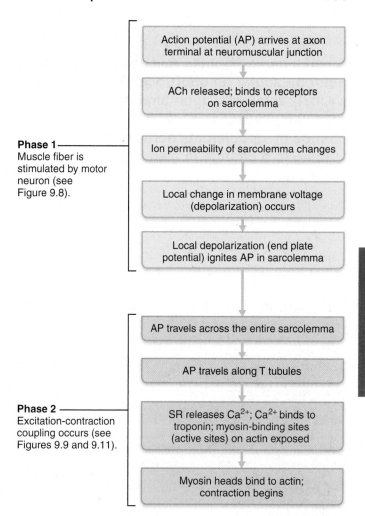

Phase 1 — Muscle fiber is stimulated by motor neuron (see Figure 9.8).

Action potential (AP) arrives at axon terminal at neuromuscular junction

ACh released; binds to receptors on sarcolemma

Ion permeability of sarcolemma changes

Local change in membrane voltage (depolarization) occurs

Local depolarization (end plate potential) ignites AP in sarcolemma

Phase 2 — Excitation-contraction coupling occurs (see Figures 9.9 and 9.11).

AP travels across the entire sarcolemma

AP travels along T tubules

SR releases Ca²⁺; Ca²⁺ binds to troponin; myosin-binding sites (active sites) on actin exposed

Myosin heads bind to actin; contraction begins

Figure 9.7 The phases leading to muscle fiber contraction.

(*asthen* = weakness; *gravi* = heavy), a disease characterized by drooping upper eyelids, difficulty swallowing and talking, and generalized muscle weakness, involves a shortage of ACh receptors. Serum analysis reveals antibodies to ACh receptors, suggesting that myasthenia gravis is an autoimmune disease. Although normal numbers of receptors are initially present, they appear to be destroyed as the disease progresses. ∎

Generation of an Action Potential Across the Sarcolemma

Like the plasma membranes of all cells, a resting sarcolemma is *polarized.* That is, a voltmeter would show there is a potential difference (voltage) across the membrane and the inside is negative relative to the outer membrane face. (The resting membrane potential is described in Chapter 3.)

The action potential (AP) is the result of a predictable sequence of electrical changes that once initiated occurs along the entire surface of the sarcolemma. Essentially three steps are involved, as shown in Figure 9.9 and summarized below.

① **Local depolarization and generation of an end plate potential.** Binding of ACh molecules to ACh receptors at the

Figure 9.8

FOCUS Events at the Neuromuscular Junction

When a nerve impulse reaches a neuromuscular junction, acetylcholine (ACh) is released. Upon binding to sarcolemma receptors, ACh causes a change in sarcolemma permeability leading to a change in membrane potential.

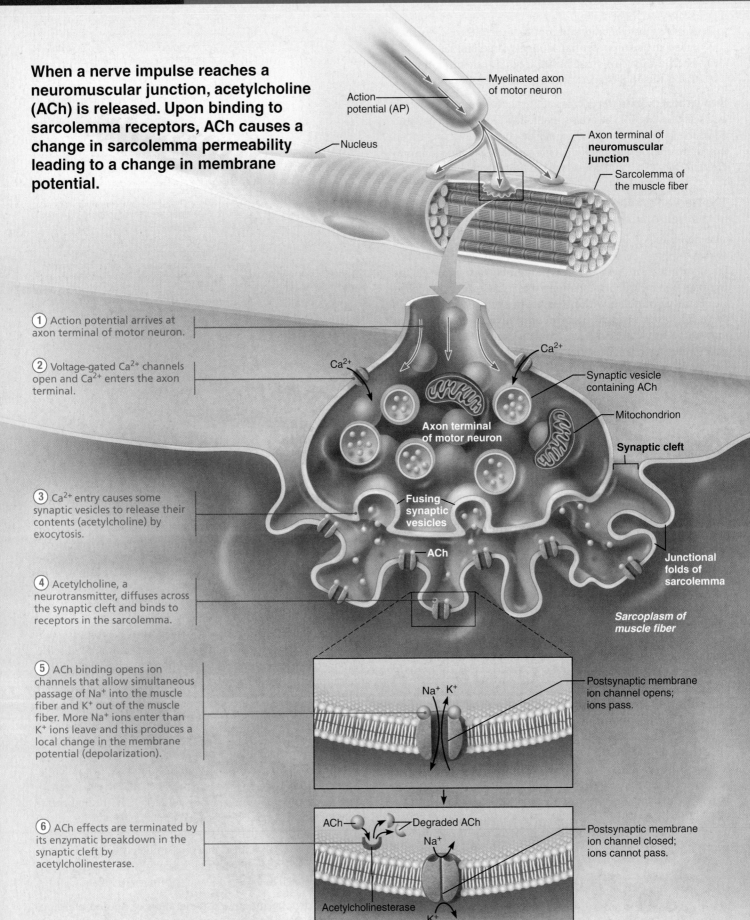

Action potential (AP)

Myelinated axon of motor neuron

Axon terminal of **neuromuscular junction**

Nucleus

Sarcolemma of the muscle fiber

① Action potential arrives at axon terminal of motor neuron.

② Voltage-gated Ca^{2+} channels open and Ca^{2+} enters the axon terminal.

Ca^{2+}

Ca^{2+}

Synaptic vesicle containing ACh

Axon terminal of motor neuron

Mitochondrion

Synaptic cleft

③ Ca^{2+} entry causes some synaptic vesicles to release their contents (acetylcholine) by exocytosis.

Fusing synaptic vesicles

ACh

Junctional folds of sarcolemma

Sarcoplasm of muscle fiber

④ Acetylcholine, a neurotransmitter, diffuses across the synaptic cleft and binds to receptors in the sarcolemma.

⑤ ACh binding opens ion channels that allow simultaneous passage of Na^+ into the muscle fiber and K^+ out of the muscle fiber. More Na^+ ions enter than K^+ ions leave and this produces a local change in the membrane potential (depolarization).

Na^+ K^+

Postsynaptic membrane ion channel opens; ions pass.

⑥ ACh effects are terminated by its enzymatic breakdown in the synaptic cleft by acetylcholinesterase.

ACh

Degraded ACh

Na^+

Postsynaptic membrane ion channel closed; ions cannot pass.

Acetylcholinesterase

K^+

A&P Flix *View this animation at myA&P*

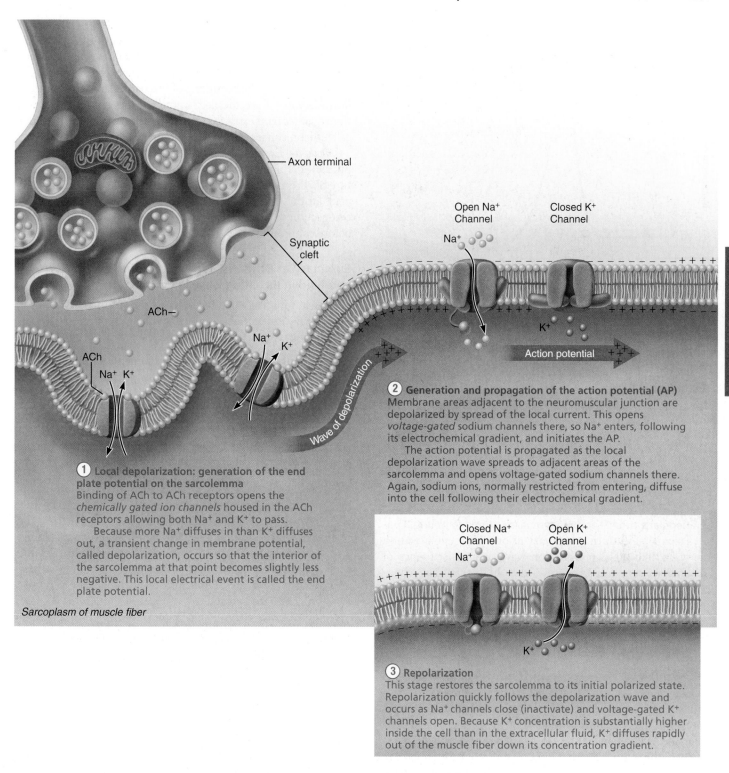

--- Axon terminal

Synaptic cleft

Open Na+ Channel

Closed K+ Channel

Na+

ACh—

Na+ K+

ACh

Na+ K+

① Local depolarization: generation of the end plate potential on the sarcolemma
Binding of ACh to ACh receptors opens the *chemically gated ion channels* housed in the ACh receptors allowing both Na+ and K+ to pass.
    Because more Na+ diffuses in than K+ diffuses out, a transient change in membrane potential, called depolarization, occurs so that the interior of the sarcolemma at that point becomes slightly less negative. This local electrical event is called the end plate potential.

Sarcoplasm of muscle fiber

Action potential

K+

Wave of depolarization

② Generation and propagation of the action potential (AP)
Membrane areas adjacent to the neuromuscular junction are depolarized by spread of the local current. This opens *voltage-gated* sodium channels there, so Na+ enters, following its electrochemical gradient, and initiates the AP.
    The action potential is propagated as the local depolarization wave spreads to adjacent areas of the sarcolemma and opens voltage-gated sodium channels there. Again, sodium ions, normally restricted from entering, diffuse into the cell following their electrochemical gradient.

Closed Na+ Channel

Open K+ Channel

Na+

K+

③ Repolarization
This stage restores the sarcolemma to its initial polarized state. Repolarization quickly follows the depolarization wave and occurs as Na+ channels close (inactivate) and voltage-gated K+ channels open. Because K+ concentration is substantially higher inside the cell than in the extracellular fluid, K+ diffuses rapidly out of the muscle fiber down its concentration gradient.

Figure 9.9 Summary of events in the generation and propagation of an action potential in a skeletal muscle fiber. The axon terminal plasma membrane and the sarcolemma are shown at different scales.

neuromuscular junction opens *chemically (ligand) gated ion channels* that allow Na+ and K+ to pass (also see Figure 9.8). Because more Na+ diffuses in than K+ diffuses out, a transient change in membrane potential occurs as the interior of the sarcolemma becomes slightly less negative, an event called **depolarization**.

② **Generation and propagation of the action potential.** Initially, depolarization is a local electrical event called an **end plate potential**, but it ignites the action potential that spreads in all directions from the neuromuscular junction across the sarcolemma, just as ripples move away from pebbles dropped into a stream. This local depolarization (end plate potential) then spreads to adjacent membrane areas

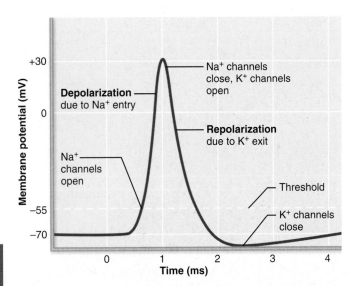

Figure 9.10 **Action potential scan showing changes in Na⁺ and K⁺ ion channels.**

and opens *voltage-gated* (p. 81) sodium channels there. Na^+ enters, following its electrochemical gradient, and once a certain membrane voltage, referred to as *threshold*, is reached, an action potential is generated (initiated).

The action potential is *propagated* (moves along the length of the sarcolemma) as the local depolarization wave spreads to adjacent areas of the sarcolemma and opens voltage-gated sodium channels there. Again, Na^+, normally restricted from entering, diffuses into the cell following its electrochemical gradient.

③ **Repolarization.** The sarcolemma is restored to its initial polarized state during **repolarization**. The repolarization wave, like the depolarization wave, is a consequence of changes in membrane permeability. In this case, Na^+ channels close and voltage-gated K^+ channels open. Since the potassium ion concentration is substantially higher inside the cell than in the extracellular fluid, K^+ diffuses rapidly out of the muscle fiber, restoring negatively charged conditions inside (also see **Figure 9.10**).

During repolarization, a muscle fiber is said to be in a **refractory period**, because the cell cannot be stimulated again until repolarization is complete. Note that repolarization restores only the *electrical conditions* of the resting (polarized) state. The ATP-dependent Na^+-K^+ pump restores the *ionic conditions* of the resting state, but hundreds of action potentials can occur before ionic imbalances interfere with contractile activity.

Once initiated, the action potential is unstoppable. It ultimately results in contraction of the muscle fiber. Although the action potential itself is very brief, only 1–2 milliseconds (ms), the contraction phase of a muscle fiber may persist for 100 ms or more and far outlasts the electrical event that triggers it.

Excitation-Contraction Coupling

Excitation-contraction (E-C) coupling is the sequence of events by which transmission of an action potential along the

sarcolemma leads to the sliding of myofilaments. The action potential is brief and ends well before any signs of contraction are obvious. The events of excitation-contraction coupling occur during the *latent period* (*laten* = hidden), between action potential initiation and the beginning of mechanical activity (contraction). As you will see, the electrical signal does not act directly on the myofilaments. Instead, it causes the rise in intracellular calcium ion concentration that allows the filaments to slide.

Focus on Excitation-Contraction Coupling (**Figure 9.11**) on pp. 290–291 illustrates the steps in this process. This Focus feature also reveals how the integral proteins of the "double zippers" in the triads interact to provide the Ca^{2+} necessary for contraction to occur. Make sure you understand this material before continuing on.

Summary of Different Types of Channels Involved in Initiating Muscle Contraction

So let's summarize what has to happen from the nerve ending on to finally excite muscle cells. Essentially this process involves activation of four sets of ion channels:

1. The process is initiated when the nerve impulse reaches the neuron terminal and opens voltage-gated calcium channels in the axonal membrane. Calcium entry triggers release of ACh into the synaptic cleft.
2. Released ACh binds to ACh receptors in the sarcolemma, opening chemically gated Na^+-K^+ channels. Greater influx of Na^+ causes a local voltage change (the end plate potential).
3. Local depolarization opens voltage-gated sodium channels in the neighboring region of the sarcolemma. This allows more sodium to enter, which further depolarizes the sarcolemma, resulting in AP generation and propagation.
4. Transmission of an AP along the T tubules changes the shape of voltage-sensitive proteins in the T tubules, which in turn stimulate SR calcium release channels to release Ca^{2+} into the cytosol.

Muscle Fiber Contraction: Cross Bridge Activity

As we have noted, cross bridge formation (attachment of myosin heads to actin) requires Ca^{2+}. Let's look more closely at how calcium ions promote muscle cell contraction. When intracellular calcium levels are low, the muscle cell is relaxed, and the active (myosin-binding) sites on actin are physically blocked by tropomyosin molecules. As Ca^{2+} levels rise, the ions bind to regulatory sites on troponin. To activate its group of seven actins, a troponin must bind two calcium ions, change shape, and then roll tropomyosin into the groove of the actin helix, away from the myosin-binding sites. In short, the tropomyosin "blockade" is removed when sufficient calcium is present. Once binding sites on actin are exposed, the events of the cross bridge cycle occur in rapid succession, as depicted in *Focus on the Cross Bridge Cycle* (**Figure 9.12**) on p. 292.

Sliding of thin filaments continues as long as the calcium signal and adequate ATP are present. When nerve impulses are delivered rapidly, intracellular Ca^{2+} levels increase greatly due to successive "puffs" or rounds of Ca^{2+} released from the SR. In such cases, the muscle cells do not completely relax between successive stimuli and contraction is stronger and more sustained (within limits) until nervous stimulation ceases. As the Ca^{2+} pumps of the SR reclaim calcium ions from the cytosol and troponin again changes shape, actin's myosin-binding sites are again covered by tropomyosin. The contraction ends, and the muscle fiber relaxes.

When the cycle is back where it started, the myosin head is in its upright high-energy configuration (see step ① in Focus Figure 9.12), ready to take another "step" and attach to an actin site farther along the thin filament. This "walking" of the myosin heads along the adjacent thin filaments during muscle shortening is much like a centipede's gait. The thin filaments cannot slide backward as the cycle repeats again and again because some myosin heads ("legs") are always in contact with actin (the "ground"). Contracting muscles routinely shorten by 30–35% of their total resting length, so each myosin cross bridge attaches and detaches many times during a single contraction. It is likely that only half of the myosin heads of a thick filament are pulling at the same instant. The others are randomly seeking their next binding site.

Except for the brief period following muscle cell excitation, calcium ion concentrations in the cytosol are kept almost undetectably low. There is a reason for this: ATP is the cell's energy source, and its hydrolysis yields inorganic phosphate (P_i). P_i would combine with calcium ions to form hydroxyapatite crystals, the stony-hard salts found in bone matrix, if calcium ion concentrations were always high. Such calcified muscle cells would die.

HOMEOSTATIC IMBALANCE

Rigor mortis (death rigor) illustrates the fact that cross bridge detachment is ATP driven. Most muscles begin to stiffen 3 to 4 hours after death. Peak rigidity occurs at 12 hours and then gradually dissipates over the next 48 to 60 hours. Dying cells are unable to exclude calcium (which is in higher concentration in the extracellular fluid), and the calcium influx into muscle cells promotes formation of myosin cross bridges. Shortly after breathing stops, ATP synthesis ceases, but ATP continues to be consumed and cross bridge detachment is impossible. Actin and myosin become irreversibly cross-linked, producing the stiffness of rigor mortis, which gradually disappears as muscle proteins break down after death. ■

CHECK YOUR UNDERSTANDING

6. What are the three structural components of a neuromuscular junction?
7. What is the final trigger for contraction? What is the initial trigger?
8. What prevents the filaments from sliding back to their original position each time a myosin cross bridge detaches from actin?
9. What would happen if a muscle fiber suddenly ran out of ATP when sarcomeres had only partially contracted?

For answers, see Appendix G.

Contraction of a Skeletal Muscle

▶ Define motor unit and muscle twitch, and describe the events occurring during the three phases of a muscle twitch.

▶ Explain how smooth, graded contractions of a skeletal muscle are produced.

▶ Differentiate between isometric and isotonic contractions.

In its relaxed state, a muscle is soft and unimpressive, not what you would expect of a prime mover of the body. However, within a few milliseconds, it can contract to become a hard elastic structure with dynamic characteristics that intrigue not only biologists but engineers and physicists as well.

Before we consider muscle contraction on the organ level, let's note a few principles of muscle mechanics.

1. The principles governing contraction of a single muscle fiber and of a skeletal muscle consisting of a large number of fibers are pretty much the same.
2. The force exerted by a contracting muscle on an object is called **muscle tension**, and the opposing force exerted on the muscle by the weight of the object to be moved is called the **load**.
3. A contracting muscle does not always shorten and move the load. If muscle tension develops but the load is not moved, the contraction is called *isometric* ("same measure"), as when you try to lift a 2000-lb car. If the muscle tension developed overcomes the load and muscle shortening occurs, the contraction is *isotonic* ("same tension"), as when you lift a 5-lb sack of sugar. We will describe these major types of contraction in detail, but for now the important thing to remember when reading the accompanying graphs is that *increasing muscle tension* is measured for isometric contractions, whereas the *amount of muscle shortening* (distance in millimeters) is measured for isotonic contractions.
4. A skeletal muscle contracts with varying force and for different periods of time in response to stimuli of varying frequencies and intensities. To understand how this occurs, we must look at the nerve-muscle functional unit called a *motor unit*. This is our next topic.

The Motor Unit

Each muscle is served by at least one *motor nerve*, and each motor nerve contains axons (fibrous extensions) of up to hundreds of motor neurons. As an axon enters a muscle, it branches into a number of terminals, each of which forms a neuromuscular junction with a single muscle fiber. A **motor unit** consists of a motor neuron and all the muscle fibers it supplies (Figure 9.13). When a motor neuron fires (transmits an action potential), all the muscle fibers it innervates contract.

The number of muscle fibers per motor unit may be as high as several hundred or as few as four. Muscles that exert fine control (such as those controlling the fingers and eyes) have small motor units. By contrast, large, weight-bearing muscles, whose movements are less precise (such as the hip muscles), have large motor units. The muscle fibers in a single motor unit are not

Excitation-contraction (E-C) coupling is the sequence of events by which transmission of an action potential along the sarcolemma leads to the sliding of myofilaments.

Setting the stage
The events at the neuromuscular junction set the stage for E-C coupling by providing excitation. Released acetylcholine (ACh) binds to receptor proteins on the sarcolemma and triggers an action potential in a muscle fiber.

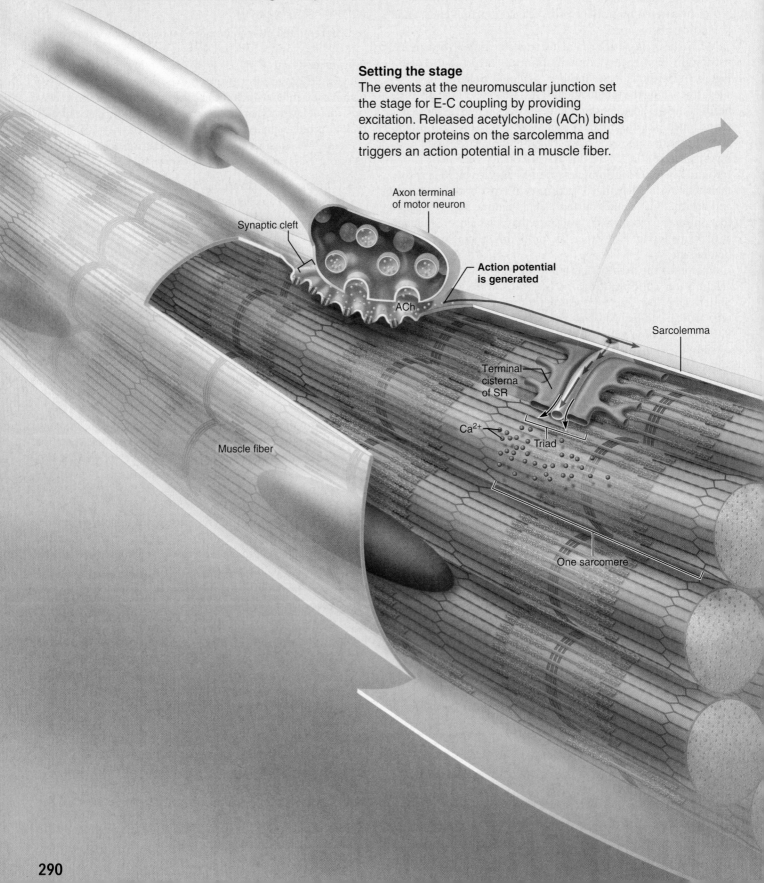

Axon terminal of motor neuron

Synaptic cleft

Action potential is generated

ACh

Sarcolemma

Terminal cisterna of SR

Ca^{2+}

Triad

Muscle fiber

One sarcomere

Steps in E-C Coupling:

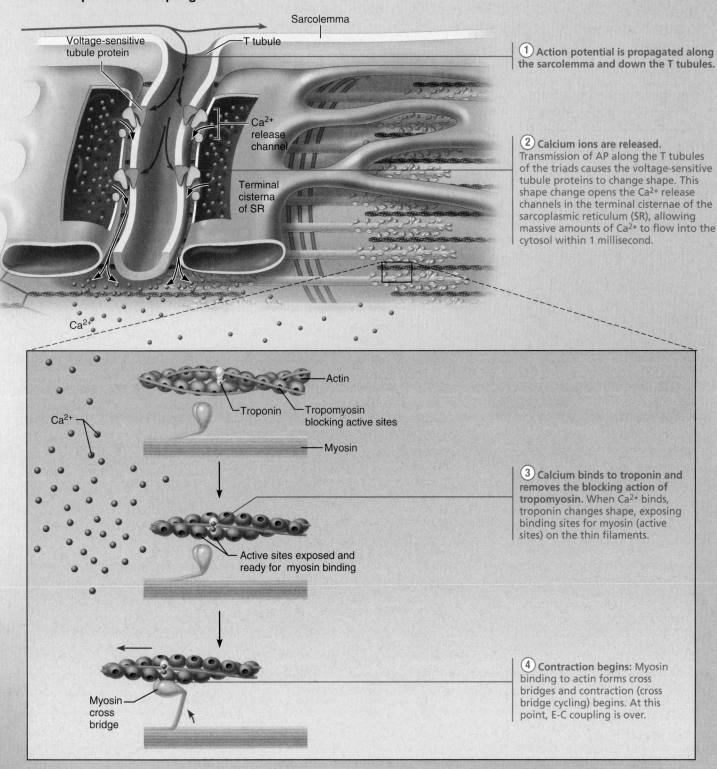

Sarcolemma

Voltage-sensitive tubule protein

T tubule

Ca²⁺ release channel

Terminal cisterna of SR

Ca²⁺

Actin

Troponin

Tropomyosin blocking active sites

Myosin

Ca²⁺

Active sites exposed and ready for myosin binding

Myosin cross bridge

① Action potential is propagated along the sarcolemma and down the T tubules.

② Calcium ions are released. Transmission of AP along the T tubules of the triads causes the voltage-sensitive tubule proteins to change shape. This shape change opens the Ca²⁺ release channels in the terminal cisternae of the sarcoplasmic reticulum (SR), allowing massive amounts of Ca²⁺ to flow into the cytosol within 1 millisecond.

③ Calcium binds to troponin and removes the blocking action of tropomyosin. When Ca²⁺ binds, troponin changes shape, exposing binding sites for myosin (active sites) on the thin filaments.

④ Contraction begins: Myosin binding to actin forms cross bridges and contraction (cross bridge cycling) begins. At this point, E-C coupling is over.

The aftermath

The short-lived Ca²⁺ signal ends, and Ca²⁺ levels fall as Ca²⁺ is continuously pumped back into the SR by active transport. The blocking action of tropomyosin is restored, inhibiting myosin-actin interaction and relaxation occurs. The sequence of E-C coupling events followed by a drop in Ca²⁺ levels is repeated each time a nerve impulse arrives at the neuromuscular junction.

Figure 9.12 **FOCUS** Cross Bridge Cycle

The cross bridge cycle is the series of events during which myosin heads pull thin filaments toward the center of the sarcomere.

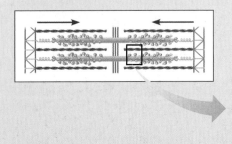

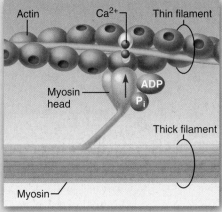

Actin — Ca²⁺ — Thin filament

Myosin head

ADP

Pᵢ

Thick filament

Myosin —

① **Cross bridge formation.** Energized myosin head attaches to actin myofilament, forming a cross bridge.

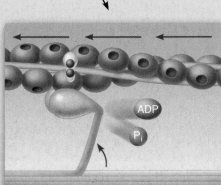

ADP

Pᵢ

ATP

② **The power (working) stroke.** ADP and Pᵢ are released and the myosin head pivots and bends, changing to its bent low-energy shape. As a result it pulls on the actin filament, sliding it toward the M line.

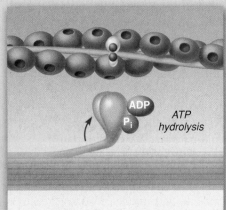

ADP

Pᵢ

ATP hydrolysis

④ **Cocking of myosin head.** As ATP is hydrolyzed to ADP and Pᵢ, the myosin head returns to its prestroke high-energy, or "cocked," position.

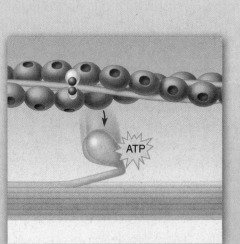

ATP

③ **Cross bridge detachment.** After ATP attaches to myosin, the link between myosin and actin weakens, and the myosin head detaches (the cross bridge "breaks").

A&PFlix *View this animation at myA&P*

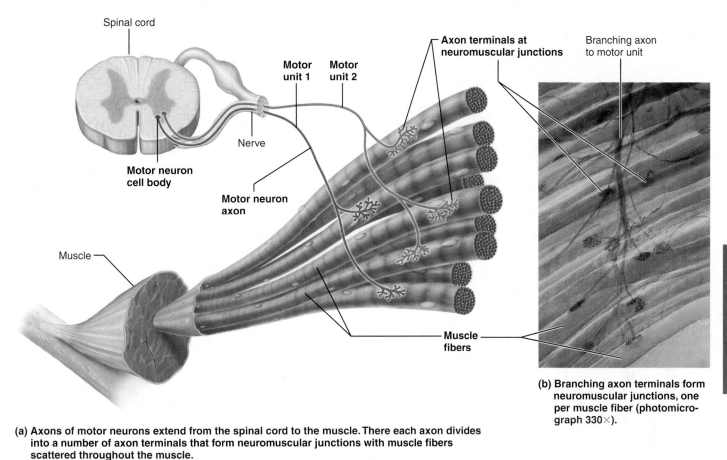

(a) Axons of motor neurons extend from the spinal cord to the muscle. There each axon divides into a number of axon terminals that form neuromuscular junctions with muscle fibers scattered throughout the muscle.

(b) **Branching axon terminals form neuromuscular junctions, one per muscle fiber (photomicrograph 330×).**

Figure 9.13 A motor unit consists of a motor neuron and all the muscle fibers it innervates. (See *A Brief Atlas of the Human Body*, Plate 30.)

clustered together but are spread throughout the muscle. As a result, stimulation of a single motor unit causes a weak contraction of the *entire* muscle.

The Muscle Twitch

Muscle contraction is easily investigated in the laboratory using an isolated muscle. The muscle is attached to an apparatus that produces a **myogram**, a graphic recording of contractile activity. The line recording the activity is called a *tracing*.

The response of a motor unit to a single action potential of its motor neuron is called a **muscle twitch**. The muscle fibers contract quickly and then relax. Every twitch myogram has three distinct phases **(Figure 9.14a)**.

1. **Latent period.** The **latent period** is the first few milliseconds following stimulation when excitation-contraction coupling is occurring. During this period, muscle tension is beginning to increase but no response is seen on the myogram.
2. **Period of contraction.** The period of contraction is when cross bridges are active, from the onset to the peak of tension development, and the myogram tracing rises to a peak. This period lasts 10–100 ms. If the tension (pull) becomes great enough to overcome the resistance of a load, the muscle shortens.

3. **Period of relaxation.** The period of contraction is followed by the period of relaxation. This final phase, lasting 10–100 ms, is initiated by reentry of Ca^{2+} into the SR. Because contractile force is declining, muscle tension decreases to zero and the tracing returns to the baseline. If the muscle shortened during contraction, it now returns to its initial length. Notice that a muscle contracts faster than it relaxes, as revealed by the asymmetric nature of the myogram tracing.

As you can see in Figure 9.14b, twitch contractions of some muscles are rapid and brief, as with the muscles controlling eye movements. In contrast, the fibers of fleshy calf muscles (gastrocnemius and soleus) contract more slowly and remain contracted for much longer periods. These differences between muscles reflect metabolic properties of the myofibrils and enzyme variations.

Graded Muscle Responses

Muscle twitches—like those single, jerky contractions provoked in a laboratory—may result from certain neuromuscular problems, but this is *not* the way our muscles normally operate. Instead, healthy muscle contractions are relatively smooth and vary in strength as different demands are placed on them. These variations, needed for proper control of skeletal movement, are

9

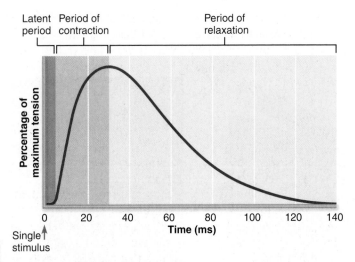

(a) Myogram showing the three phases of an isometric twitch

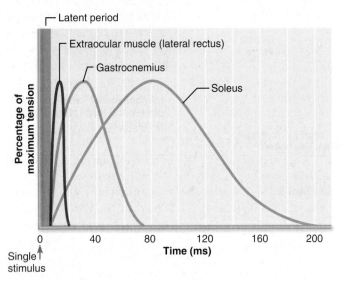

(b) Comparison of the relative duration of twitch responses of three muscles

Figure 9.14 **The muscle twitch.**

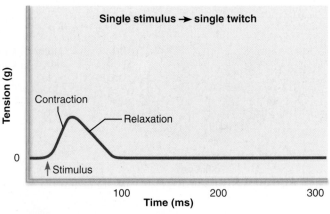

(a) **A single stimulus is delivered. The muscle contracts and relaxes.**

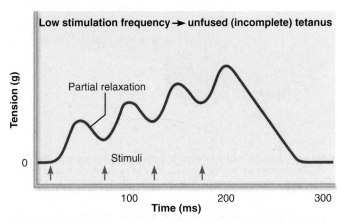

(b) **If another stimulus is applied before the muscle relaxes completely, then more tension results. This is temporal (or wave) summation and results in unfused (or incomplete) tetanus.**

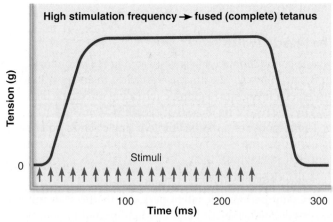

(c) **At higher stimulus frequencies, there is no relaxation at all between stimuli. This is fused (complete) tetanus.**

Figure 9.15 **Muscle response to changes in stimulation frequency.**

referred to as **graded muscle responses**. In general, muscle contraction can be graded in two ways: (1) by changing the frequency of stimulation and (2) by changing the strength of stimulation.

Muscle Response to Changes in Stimulus Frequency The nervous system achieves greater muscular force by increasing the firing rate of motor neurons. For example, if two identical stimuli (electrical shocks or nerve impulses) are delivered to a muscle in rapid succession, the second twitch will be stronger than the first. On a myogram the second twitch will appear to ride on the shoulders of the first (Figure 9.15b). This phenomenon, called **temporal** or **wave summation**, occurs because the second contraction occurs before the muscle has completely relaxed. Because the muscle is already partially contracted when the next stimulus arrives and more calcium is being squirted into the cytosol to replace that being reclaimed by the SR,

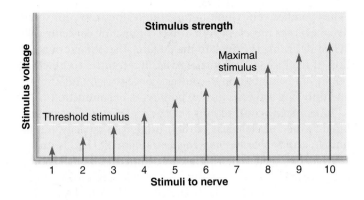

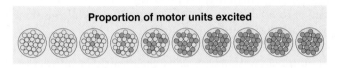

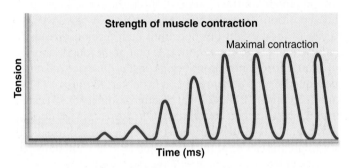

Figure 9.16 Relationship between stimulus intensity (graph at top) and muscle tension (tracing below). Below threshold voltage, no muscle response is seen on the tracing (stimuli 1 and 2). Once threshold (3) is reached, increases in voltage excite (recruit) more and more motor units until the maximal stimulus is reached (7). Further increases in stimulus voltage produce no further increase in contractile strength.

muscle tension produced during the second contraction causes more shortening than the first. In other words, the contractions are summed. (However, the refractory period is *always* honored. Thus, if a second stimulus is delivered before repolarization is complete, no wave summation occurs.)

If the stimulus strength is held constant and the muscle is stimulated at an increasingly faster rate, the relaxation time between the twitches becomes shorter and shorter, the concentration of Ca^{2+} in the cytosol higher and higher, and the degree of wave summation greater and greater, progressing to a sustained but quivering contraction referred to as **unfused** or **incomplete tetanus** (Figure 9.15b).

Finally, as the stimulation frequency continues to increase, muscle tension increases until a maximal tension is reached. At this point all evidence of muscle relaxation disappears and the contractions fuse into a smooth, sustained contraction plateau called **fused** or **complete tetanus** (tet′ah-nus; *tetan* = rigid, tense) (Figure 9.15c). (Note that this term is often confused with the bacterial disease called tetanus that causes severe involuntary contractions.) In the real world, fused tetanus happens

infrequently, for example, when someone shows superhuman strength by lifting a fallen tree limb off a companion.

Vigorous muscle activity cannot continue indefinitely. Prolonged tetanus inevitably leads to *muscle fatigue*, a situation in which the muscle is unable to contract and its tension drops to zero.

Muscle Response to Changes in Stimulus Strength Wave summation contributes to contractile force, but its primary function is to produce smooth, continuous muscle contractions by rapidly stimulating a specific number of muscle cells. The force of contraction is controlled more precisely by **recruitment**, also called **multiple motor unit summation**.

In the laboratory, recruitment is achieved by delivering shocks of increasing voltage to the muscle, calling more and more muscle fibers into play. Stimuli that produce no observable contractions are called **subthreshold stimuli**. The stimulus at which the first observable contraction occurs is called the **threshold stimulus** (Figure 9.16). Beyond this point, the muscle contracts more and more vigorously as the stimulus strength is increased. The **maximal stimulus** is the strongest stimulus that produces increased contractile force. It represents the point at which all the muscle's motor units are recruited. Increasing the stimulus intensity beyond the maximal stimulus does not produce a stronger contraction. In the body, the same phenomenon is caused by neural activation of an increasingly large number of motor units serving the muscle.

The recruitment process is not random. Instead it is dictated by the *size principle*. In any muscle, motor units with the smallest muscle fibers are controlled by small, highly excitable motor neurons, and these motor units tend to be activated first. As motor units with larger and larger muscle fibers begin to be excited, contractile strength increases. The largest motor units, containing large, coarse muscle fibers, have as much as 50 times the contractile force of the smallest ones. They are controlled by the largest, least excitable (highest-threshold) neurons and are activated only when the most powerful contraction is necessary (Figure 9.17).

The size principle is important because it allows the increases in force during weak contractions (for example, those that maintain posture or slow movements) to occur in small steps, whereas gradations in muscle force are progressively greater when large amounts of force are needed for vigorous activities such as jumping or running. This principle explains how the same hand that pats your cheek can deliver a stinging slap.

Although *all* the motor units of a muscle may be recruited simultaneously to produce an exceptionally strong contraction, motor units are more commonly activated asynchronously in the body. At a given instant, some are in tetanus (usually unfused tetanus) while others are resting and recovering. This technique helps prolong a strong contraction by preventing or delaying fatigue. It also explains how weak contractions promoted by infrequent stimuli can remain smooth.

Muscle Tone

Skeletal muscles are described as voluntary, but even relaxed muscles are almost always slightly contracted, a phenomenon

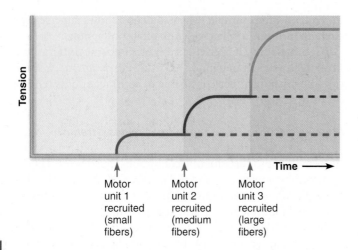

Figure 9.17 The size principle of recruitment. Recruitment of motor neurons controlling skeletal muscle fibers is orderly—small, highly excitable motor neurons are generally recruited more readily than large, less excitable ones. This phenomenon is referred to as the *size principle*. In weaker contractions, small motor units containing small-diameter muscle fibers are recruited. As contractile strength increases, larger and larger motor units containing larger numbers of increasingly larger-diameter muscle fibers are activated. Consequently, the contractions get stronger and stronger in a predictable way.

called **muscle tone**. Muscle tone is due to spinal reflexes that activate first one group of motor units and then another in response to activation of stretch receptors in the muscles. Muscle tone does not produce active movements, but it keeps the muscles firm, healthy, and ready to respond to stimulation. Skeletal muscle tone also helps stabilize joints and maintain posture.

Isotonic and Isometric Contractions

As noted earlier, there are two main categories of contractions—*isotonic* and *isometric*. In **isotonic contractions** (*iso* = same; *ton* = tension), muscle length changes and moves the load. Once sufficient tension has developed to move the load, the tension remains relatively constant through the rest of the contractile period (**Figure 9.18a**).

Isotonic contractions come in two "flavors"—*concentric* and *eccentric*. **Concentric contractions** are those in which the muscle *shortens* and does work, such as picking up a book or kicking a ball. These contractions are probably more familiar. However, **eccentric contractions**, in which the muscle generates force as it *lengthens*, are equally important for coordination and purposeful movements. Eccentric contractions occur in your calf muscle, for example, as you walk up a steep hill. Eccentric contractions are about 50% more forceful than concentric ones at the same load and more often cause delayed-onset muscle soreness. (Consider how your calf muscles *feel* the day after hiking up that hill.) Just why this is so is unclear, but it may be that the muscle stretching that occurs during such contractions causes microtears in the muscles.

Biceps curls provide a simple example of how concentric and eccentric contractions work together in our everyday activities.

When you flex your elbow to raise this textbook to your shoulder, the biceps muscle in your arm is contracting concentrically. When returning the book to the desktop, the isotonic contraction of the biceps is eccentric. Basically, eccentric contractions put the body in position to contract concentrically. All jumping and throwing activities involve both types of contraction.

In **isometric contractions** (*metric* = measure), tension may build to the muscle's peak tension-producing capacity, but the muscle *neither shortens nor lengthens* (Figure 9.18b). Isometric contractions occur when a muscle attempts to move a load that is greater than the force (tension) the muscle is able to develop—think of trying to lift a piano singlehandedly. Muscles contract isometrically when they act primarily to maintain upright posture or to hold joints in stationary positions while movements occur at other joints.

Let's consider knee bends as an example. When the squat position is held for a few seconds, the quadriceps muscles of the anterior thigh contract isometrically to hold the knee in the flexed position. They also contract isometrically when we begin to rise to the upright position until their tension exceeds the load (weight of the upper body). At that point muscle shortening (concentric contraction) begins. So the quadriceps contractile sequence for a deep knee bend from start to finish is (1) flex knee (eccentric), (2) hold squat position (isometric), (3) extend knee (isometric, then concentric). Of course, this list does not even begin to consider the isometric contractions of the posterior thigh muscles or of the trunk muscles that maintain a relatively erect trunk posture during the movement.

Electrochemical and mechanical events occurring within a muscle are identical in both isotonic and isometric contractions. However, the result is different. In isotonic contractions, the thin filaments are sliding. In isometric contractions, the cross bridges are generating force but are *not* moving the thin filaments, so there is no change in the banding pattern from that of the resting state. (You could say that they are "spinning their wheels" on the same actin binding sites.)

CHECK YOUR UNDERSTANDING

10. What is a motor unit?
11. What is happening in the muscle during the latent period of a twitch contraction?
12. Jay is competing in a chin-up competition. What type of muscle contractions are occurring in his biceps muscles immediately after he grabs the bar? As his body begins to move upward toward the bar? When his body begins to approach the mat?

For answers, see Appendix G.

Muscle Metabolism

▶ Describe three ways in which ATP is regenerated during skeletal muscle contraction.

▶ Define oxygen deficit and muscle fatigue. List possible causes of muscle fatigue.

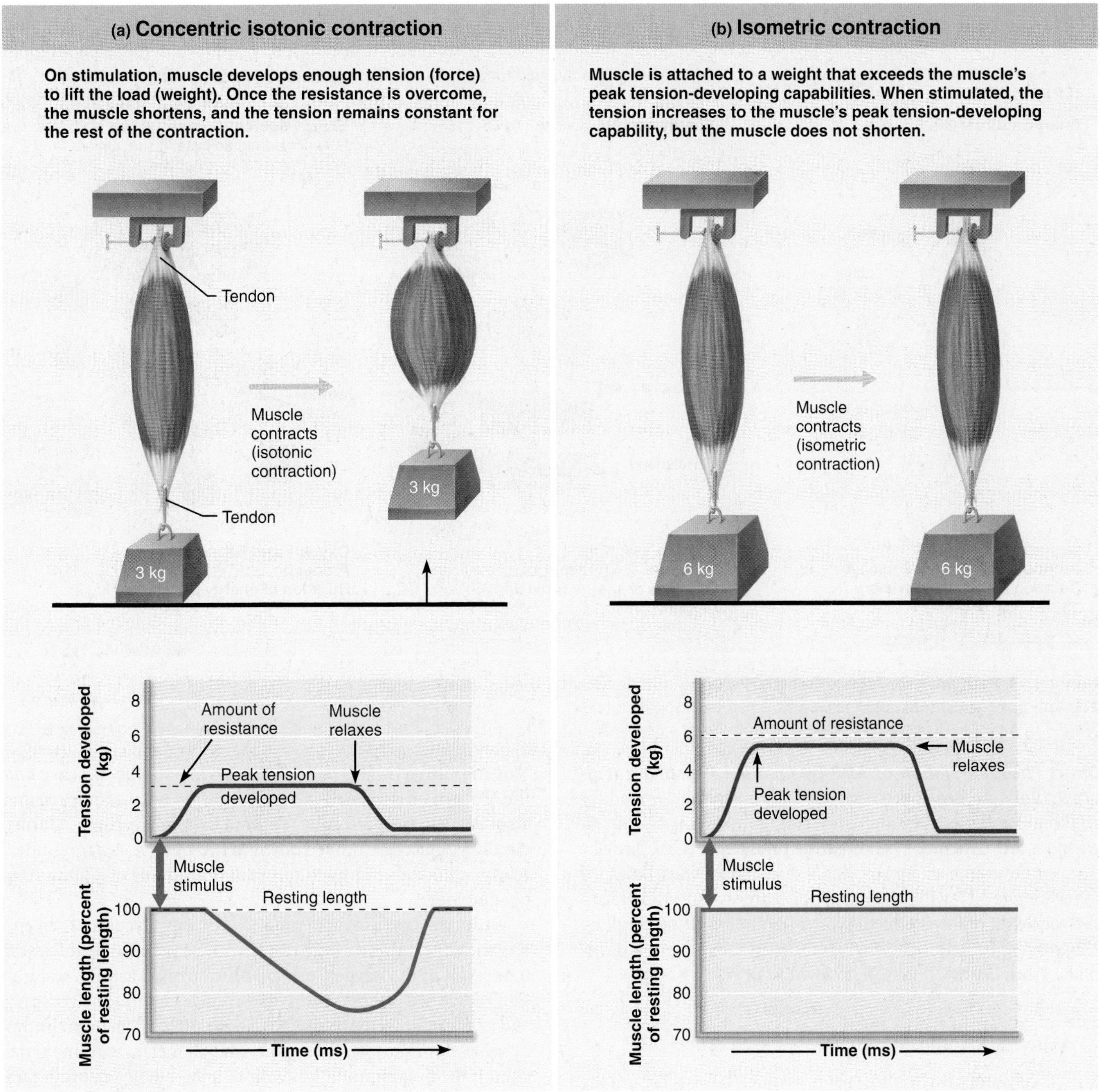
(a) Concentric isotonic contraction
On stimulation, muscle develops enough tension (force) to lift the load (weight). Once the resistance is overcome, the muscle shortens, and the tension remains constant for the rest of the contraction.
Tendon
Muscle contracts (isotonic contraction)
3 kg
Tendon
3 kg
Tension developed (kg)
8
6
4
2
0
Amount of resistance
Muscle relaxes
Peak tension developed
Muscle stimulus
Resting length
Muscle length (percent of resting length)
100
90
80
70
Time (ms)
(b) Isometric contraction
Muscle is attached to a weight that exceeds the muscle's peak tension-developing capabilities. When stimulated, the tension increases to the muscle's peak tension-developing capability, but the muscle does not shorten.
Muscle contracts (isometric contraction)
6 kg
6 kg
Tension developed (kg)
8
6
4
2
0
Amount of resistance
Muscle relaxes
Peak tension developed
Muscle stimulus
Resting length
Muscle length (percent of resting length)
100
90
80
70
Time (ms)

Figure 9.18 **Isotonic (concentric) and isometric contractions.**

9

Providing Energy for Contraction

How does the body provide the energy needed for contraction? As a muscle contracts, ATP supplies the energy for cross bridge movement and detachment and for operation of the calcium pump in the SR. Surprisingly, muscles store very limited reserves of ATP—4 to 6 seconds' worth at most, just enough to get you going. Because ATP is the *only* energy source used directly for contractile activities, it must be regenerated as fast as it is broken down if contraction is to continue.

Fortunately, after ATP is hydrolyzed to ADP and inorganic phosphate in muscle fibers, it is regenerated within a fraction of a second by one or more of the three pathways summarized in Figure 9.19: (1) direct phosphorylation of ADP by creatine phosphate, (2) the anaerobic pathway called glycolysis, which converts glucose to lactic acid, and (3) aerobic respiration. All body cells use glycolysis and aerobic respiration to produce ATP, so we touch on these metabolic pathways here but describe them in detail later, in Chapter 24.

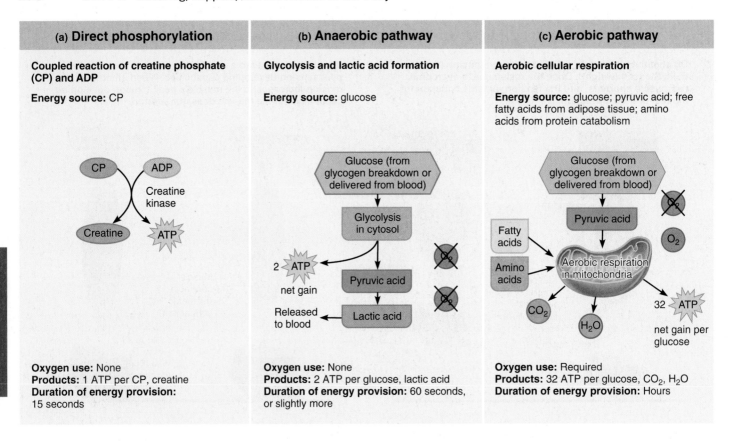

Figure 9.19 Pathways for regenerating ATP during muscle activity. The fastest pathway is direct phosphorylation **(a)**, and the slowest is aerobic respiration **(c)**.

Direct Phosphorylation of ADP by Creatine Phosphate (Figure 9.19a) As we begin to exercise vigorously, the demand for ATP soars and the ATP stored in working muscles is consumed within a few twitches. Then **creatine phosphate (CP)** (kre′ah-tin), a unique high-energy molecule stored in muscles, is tapped to regenerate ATP while the metabolic pathways are adjusting to the suddenly higher demands for ATP. The result of coupling CP with ADP is almost instant transfer of energy and a phosphate group from CP to ADP to form ATP:

$$\text{Creatine phosphate} + \text{ADP} \xrightarrow{\text{creatine kinase}} \text{creatine} + \text{ATP}$$

Muscle cells store two to three times as much CP as ATP, and the CP-ADP reaction, catalyzed by the enzyme **creatine kinase**, is so efficient that the amount of ATP in muscle cells changes very little during the initial period of contraction.

Together, stored ATP and CP provide for maximum muscle power for 14–16 seconds—long enough to energize a 100-meter dash (slightly longer if the activity is less vigorous). The coupled reaction is readily reversible, and to keep CP "on tap," CP reserves are replenished during periods of rest or inactivity.

Anaerobic Pathway: Glycolysis and Lactic Acid Formation (Figure 9.19b) As stored ATP and CP are exhausted, more ATP is generated by breakdown (catabolism) of glucose obtained from the blood or of glycogen stored in the muscle. The initial phase of glucose breakdown is **glycolysis** (gli-kol′ĭ-sis;

"sugar splitting"). This pathway occurs in both the presence *and* the absence of oxygen, but because it does not *use* oxygen, it is an *anaerobic* (an-a′er-ōb-ik; "without oxygen") pathway. During glycolysis, glucose is broken down to two *pyruvic acid* molecules, releasing enough energy to form small amounts of ATP (2 ATP per glucose).

Ordinarily, pyruvic acid produced during glycolysis then enters the mitochondria and reacts with oxygen to produce still more ATP in the oxygen-using pathway called aerobic respiration, described shortly. But when muscles contract vigorously and contractile activity reaches about 70% of the maximum possible (for example, when you run 600 meters with maximal effort), the bulging muscles compress the blood vessels within them, impairing blood flow and oxygen delivery. Under these anaerobic conditions, most of the pyruvic acid produced during glycolysis is converted into **lactic acid**, and the overall process is referred to as **anaerobic glycolysis**. Thus, during oxygen deficit, lactic acid is the end product of cellular metabolism of glucose.

Most of the lactic acid diffuses out of the muscles into the bloodstream and is gone from the muscle tissue within 30 minutes after exercise stops. Subsequently, the lactic acid is picked up by liver, heart, or kidney cells, which can use it as an energy source. Additionally, liver cells can reconvert it to pyruvic acid or glucose and release it back into the bloodstream for muscle use, or convert it to glycogen for storage.

The anaerobic pathway harvests only about 5% as much ATP from each glucose molecule as the aerobic pathway, but it pro-

Short-duration exercise				Prolonged-duration exercise

6 seconds	10 seconds	30–40 seconds	End of exercise	Hours
ATP stored in muscles is used first.	ATP is formed from creatine phosphate and ADP.	Glycogen stored in muscles is broken down to glucose, which is oxidized to generate ATP.		ATP is generated by breakdown of several nutrient energy fuels by aerobic pathway. This pathway uses oxygen released from myoglobin or delivered in the blood by hemoglobin. When it ends, the oxygen deficit is paid back.

Figure 9.20 Comparison of energy sources used during short-duration exercise and prolonged-duration exercise.

duces ATP about 2½ times faster. For this reason, when large amounts of ATP are needed for moderate periods (30–40 seconds) of strenuous muscle activity, glycolysis can provide most of the ATP needed as long as the required fuels and enzymes are available. Together, stored ATP and CP and the glycolysis–lactic acid pathway can support strenuous muscle activity for nearly a minute.

Although anaerobic glycolysis readily fuels spurts of vigorous exercise, it has shortcomings. Huge amounts of glucose are used to produce relatively small harvests of ATP, and the accumulating lactic acid is partially responsible for muscle soreness during intense exercise.

Aerobic Respiration (Figure 9.19c)
During rest and light to moderate exercise, even if prolonged, 95% of the ATP used for muscle activity comes from aerobic respiration. **Aerobic respiration** occurs in the mitochondria, requires oxygen, and involves a sequence of chemical reactions in which the bonds of fuel molecules are broken and the energy released is used to make ATP.

During aerobic respiration, which includes glycolysis and the reactions that take place in the mitochondria, glucose is broken down entirely, yielding water, carbon dioxide, and large amounts of ATP as the final products.

$$\text{Glucose} + \text{oxygen} \rightarrow \text{carbon dioxide} + \text{water} + \text{ATP}$$

The carbon dioxide released diffuses out of the muscle tissue into the blood and is removed from the body by the lungs.

As exercise begins, muscle glycogen provides most of the fuel. Shortly thereafter, bloodborne glucose, pyruvic acid from glycolysis, and free fatty acids are the major sources of fuels. After about 30 minutes, fatty acids become the major energy fuels. Aerobic respiration provides a high yield of ATP (about 32 ATP per glucose), but it is slow because of its many steps and it requires continuous delivery of oxygen and nutrient fuels to keep it going.

Energy Systems Used During Sports Activities
Which pathways predominate during exercise? As long as it has enough oxygen, a muscle cell will form ATP by the aerobic pathway. When ATP demands are within the capacity of the aerobic pathway, light to moderate muscular activity can continue for several hours in well-conditioned individuals (Figure 9.20). However, when exercise demands begin to exceed the ability of the muscle cells to carry out the necessary reactions quickly enough, glycolysis begins to contribute more and more of the total ATP generated. The length of time a muscle can continue to contract using aerobic pathways is called **aerobic endurance**, and the point at which muscle metabolism converts to anaerobic glycolysis is called **anaerobic threshold**.

Exercise physiologists have been able to estimate the relative importance of each energy-producing system to athletic performance. Activities that require a surge of power but last only a few seconds, such as weight lifting, diving, and sprinting, rely entirely on ATP and CP stores. The more on-and-off or burstlike activities of tennis, soccer, and a 100-meter swim appear to be fueled almost entirely by anaerobic glycolysis (Figure 9.20).

Prolonged activities such as marathon runs and jogging, where endurance rather than power is the goal, depend mainly on aerobic respiration. Levels of CP and ATP don't change much during prolonged exercise because ATP is generated at the same rate as it is used—a "pay as you go" system. Compared to anaerobic energy production, aerobic generation of ATP is relatively slow, but the ATP harvest is enormous.

Muscle Fatigue

Muscle fatigue is a state of *physiological inability to contract* even though the muscle still may be receiving stimuli. Although many factors appear to contribute to fatigue, its specific causes are not fully understood. Most experimental evidence indicates that fatigue is due to a problem in excitation-contraction coupling or, in rare cases, problems at the neuromuscular junction. Availability of ATP declines during contraction, but normally it is unusual for a muscle to totally run out of ATP. So, ATP is not a fatigue-producing factor in moderate exercise. A total lack of ATP results in **contractures**, states of continuous contraction because the cross bridges are unable to detach (not unlike what happens in rigor mortis). Writer's cramp is a familiar example of temporary contractures.

Several ionic imbalances contribute to muscle fatigue. As action potentials are transmitted, potassium is lost from the muscle cells, and the Na^+-K^+ pumps are inadequate to reverse the ionic imbalances quickly, so K^+ accumulates in the fluids of the T tubules. This ionic change disturbs the membrane potential of the muscle cells and halts Ca^{2+} release from the SR. Theoretically, in short-duration exercise, an accumulation of inorganic phosphate (P_i) from CP and ATP breakdown may interfere with calcium release from the SR or alternatively with the release of P_i from myosin and thus hamper myosin's power strokes. Lactic acid has long been assumed to be a major cause of fatigue, but it seems to be more important in provoking central (psychological) fatigue (in which the muscles are still willing to "go" but we feel too tired to continue the activity) than physiological fatigue. Excessive intracellular accumulation of lactic acid (which causes the muscles to ache) raises the concentration of H^+ and alters contractile proteins; however, pH is normally regulated within normal limits in all but the greatest degree of exertion. Additionally, lactic acid has recently been shown to counteract high K^+ levels which do lead to muscle fatigue (as noted above).

In general, intense exercise of short duration produces fatigue rapidly via ionic disturbances that alter E-C coupling, but recovery is also rapid. In contrast to short-duration exercise, the slow-developing fatigue of prolonged low-intensity exercise may require several hours for complete recovery. It appears that this type of exercise damages the SR, interfering with Ca^{2+} regulation and release, and therefore with muscle activation.

Oxygen Deficit

Whether or not fatigue occurs, vigorous exercise causes a muscle's chemistry to change dramatically. For a muscle to return to its resting state, its oxygen reserves must be replenished, the accumulated lactic acid must be reconverted to pyruvic acid, glycogen stores must be replaced, and ATP and creatine phosphate reserves must be resynthesized. Additionally, the liver must convert any lactic acid persisting in blood to glucose or glycogen. During anaerobic muscle contraction, all of these oxygen-requiring activities occur more slowly and are (at least partially) deferred until oxygen is again available. For this reason, we say an *oxygen deficit* is incurred, which must be repaid. **Oxygen deficit** is defined as the extra amount of oxygen that the body must take in for these restorative processes. It represents the difference between the amount of oxygen needed for totally aerobic muscle activity and the amount actually used. All anaerobic sources of ATP used during muscle activity contribute to this deficit.

Heat Production During Muscle Activity

Only about 40% of the energy released during muscle contraction is converted to useful work (still, this percentage is significantly higher than that of many mechanical devices). The rest is given off as heat, which has to be dealt with if body homeostasis is to be maintained. When you exercise vigorously, you start to feel hot as your blood is warmed by the liberated heat. Like a car's cooling system that dissipates heat, heat buildup in the body is prevented from reaching dangerous levels by several homeostatic processes, including sweating and radiation of heat from the skin surface. Shivering represents the opposite side of homeostatic balance, in which muscle contractions are used to produce more heat.

CHECK YOUR UNDERSTANDING

13. When Eric returned from jogging, he was breathing heavily, sweating profusely, and complained that his legs ached and felt weak. He wife poured him a sports drink and urged him to take it easy until he could "catch his breath." On the basis of what you have learned about muscle energy metabolism, respond to the following questions: Why is Eric breathing heavily? What ATP-generating pathway have his working muscles been using that leads to such breathlessness? What metabolic products might account for his sore muscles and his feeling of muscle weakness?

For answers, see Appendix G.

Force of Muscle Contraction

▶ Describe factors that influence the force, velocity, and duration of skeletal muscle contraction.

▶ Describe three types of skeletal muscle fibers and explain the relative value of each type.

The force of muscle contraction is affected by (1) the number of muscle fibers stimulated, (2) the relative size of the fibers, (3) the frequency of stimulation, and (4) the degree of muscle stretch (Figure 9.21). Let's briefly examine the role of each of these factors.

Number of Muscle Fibers Stimulated

As already discussed, the more motor units that are recruited, the greater the muscle force.

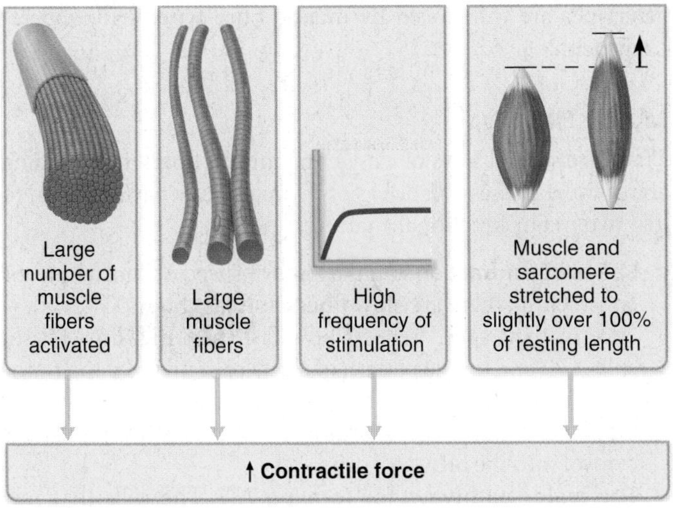

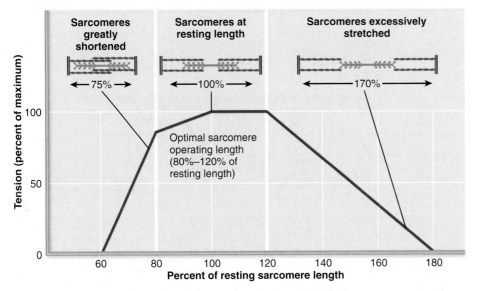

Large number of muscle fibers activated

Large muscle fibers

High frequency of stimulation

Muscle and sarcomere stretched to slightly over 100% of resting length

↑ **Contractile force**

Figure 9.21 Factors influencing force of skeletal muscle contraction.

Size of the Muscle Fibers

The bulkier the muscle (the greater its cross-sectional area), the more tension it can develop and the greater its strength, but there is more to it than this. As noted earlier, the large fibers of large motor units are very effective in producing the most powerful movements. Regular resistance exercise increases muscle force by causing muscle cells to *hypertrophy* (hi-per′tro-fe), or increase in size.

Frequency of Stimulation

As a muscle begins to contract, the force generated by the cross bridges—the **internal tension**—stretches the connective tissue sheaths (noncontractile components). These in turn become taut and transfer their tension, called the **external tension**, to the load (muscle insertion) and when the contraction ends, re-

coil of the noncontractile components helps to return the muscle to its resting length.

Time is required to take up slack and stretch the noncontractile components, and while this is happening, the internal tension is already declining. So, in brief twitch contractions, the external tension is always less than the internal tension. However, when a muscle is stimulated rapidly, contractions are summed, becoming stronger and more vigorous and ultimately producing tetanus (see Figure 9.15). During tetanic contractions more time is available to stretch the noncontractile components, and external tension approaches the internal tension. So, the more rapidly a muscle is stimulated, the greater force it exerts.

Degree of Muscle Stretch

The optimal operating length for muscle fibers is the length at which they can generate maximum force (Figure 9.21 and Figure 9.22). Within a sarcomere, the ideal **length-tension relationship** occurs when a muscle is slightly stretched and the thin and thick filaments overlap optimally, because this relationship permits sliding along nearly the entire length of the thin filaments. If a muscle fiber is stretched so much that the filaments do not overlap, the myosin heads have nothing to attach to and cannot generate tension. Alternatively, if the sarcomeres are so compressed and cramped that the Z discs abut the thick myofilaments, and the thin filaments touch and interfere with one another, little or no further shortening can occur.

Identical relationships exist in a whole muscle. If you stretch a muscle to various extents and then stimulate it tetanically, the active tension the muscle can generate varies with length as shown in Figure 9.22. A severely stretched muscle (say one over 180% of its optimal length) cannot develop tension. Likewise, at 75% of a muscle's resting length, force generation (or shortening) is limited because the actin myofilaments in its sarcomeres overlap and the thick filaments run into the Z discs, restricting further shortening.

Figure 9.22 Length-tension relationships of sarcomeres in skeletal muscles. Maximum force is generated when the muscle is between 80 and 120% of its optimal resting length. Increases and decreases beyond this optimal range result in decreased force and inability to generate tension.

Sarcomeres greatly shortened

←75%→

Sarcomeres at resting length

←100%→

Sarcomeres excessively stretched

←170%→

Optimal sarcomere operating length (80%–120% of resting length)

Tension (percent of maximum)

100

50

0

60   80   100   120   140   160   180

Percent of resting sarcomere length

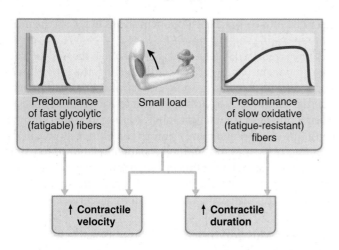

Figure 9.23 Factors influencing velocity and duration of skeletal muscle contraction.

In the body, skeletal muscles are maintained near their optimal operating length by the way they are attached to bones. The joints normally prevent bone movements that would stretch attached muscles beyond their optimal range.

Velocity and Duration of Contraction

Muscles vary in how fast they can contract and in how long they can continue to contract before they fatigue. These characteristics are influenced by muscle fiber type, load, and recruitment.

Muscle Fiber Type

There are several ways of classifying muscle fibers, but learning about these classes will be easier if you initially pay attention to just two major functional characteristics:

- **Speed of contraction.** On the basis of speed of shortening, or contraction, there are **slow fibers** and **fast fibers**. The difference in their speed reflects how fast their myosin ATPases split ATP, and on the pattern of electrical activity of their motor neurons. Duration of contraction also varies with fiber type and depends on how quickly Ca^{2+} is moved from the cytosol into the SR.
- **The major pathways for forming ATP.** The cells that rely mostly on the oxygen-using aerobic pathways for ATP generation are **oxidative fibers**, and those that rely more on anaerobic glycolysis are **glycolytic fibers**.

Using these two criteria, we can classify skeletal muscle cells as being **slow oxidative (SO) fibers**, **fast oxidative (FO) fibers**, or **fast glycolytic (FG) fibers**. Details about each group are given in **Table 9.2**, but a word to the wise: Do not approach this information by rote memorization—you'll just get frustrated. Instead, start with what you know for any category and see how the characteristics listed support that. For example, think about a *slow oxidative fiber* (Table 9.2, first column, and **Figure 9.23**,

TABLE 9.2	Structural and Functional Characteristics of the Three Types of Skeletal Muscle Fibers		
	SLOW OXIDATIVE FIBERS	**FAST OXIDATIVE FIBERS**	**FAST GLYCOLYTIC FIBERS**
Metabolic Characteristics			
Speed of contraction	Slow	Fast	Fast
Myosin ATPase activity	Slow	Fast	Fast
Primary pathway for ATP synthesis	Aerobic	Aerobic (some anaerobic glycolysis)	Anaerobic glycolysis
Myoglobin content	High	High	Low
Glycogen stores	Low	Intermediate	High
Recruitment order	First	Second	Third
Rate of fatigue	Slow (fatigue-resistant)	Intermediate (moderately fatigue-resistant)	Fast (fatigable)
Activities Best Suited For			
	Endurance-type activities—e.g., running a marathon; maintaining posture (antigravity muscles)	Sprinting, walking	Short-term intense or powerful movements, e.g., hitting a baseball
Structural Characteristics			
Color	Red	Red to pink	White (pale)
Fiber diameter	Small	Intermediate	Large
Mitochondria	Many	Many	Few
Capillaries	Many	Many	Few

right side). We can see that it

- Contracts relatively *slowly* because its myosin ATPases are slow (a criterion)
- Depends on *oxygen* delivery and aerobic pathways (*high oxidative capacity*—a criterion)
- Is fatigue resistant and has high endurance (typical of fibers that depend on aerobic metabolism)
- Is thin (a large amount of cytoplasm impedes diffusion of O_2 and nutrients from the blood)
- Has relatively little power (a thin cell can contain only a limited number of myofibrils)
- Has many mitochondria (actual sites of oxygen use)
- Has a rich capillary supply (the better to deliver blood-borne O_2)
- Is red (its color stems from an abundant supply of myoglobin, muscle's oxygen-binding pigment that stores O_2 reserves in the cell and aids diffusion of O_2 through the cell)

Add these features together and you have muscle fibers best suited to endurance-type activities. Now think about a *fast glycolytic fiber* (Table 9.2, third column, and Figure 9.23, left side). In contrast, it

- Contracts *rapidly* due to the activity of fast myosin ATPases
- Does not use oxygen
- Depends on plentiful *glycogen* reserves for fuel rather than on blood-delivered nutrients
- Tires quickly because glycogen reserves are short-lived and lactic acid accumulates quickly, making it a fatigable fiber
- Has a large diameter, indicating the plentiful contractile myofilaments that allow it to contract powerfully before it "poops out"
- Has few mitochondria, little myoglobin and low capillary density (and so is white), and is a much thicker cell (because it doesn't depend on continuous oxygen and nutrient diffusion from the blood)

For these reasons, the fast glycolytic fibers are best suited for short-term, rapid, intense movements (moving furniture across the room, for example).

Finally, consider the less common intermediate muscle fiber types, called *fast oxidative fibers* (Table 9.2, middle column). They have many characteristics (fiber diameter and power for example) intermediate between the other two types. Like fast glycolytic fibers, they contract quickly, but like slow oxidative fibers, they are oxygen dependent and have a rich supply of myoglobin and capillaries.

Some muscles have a predominance of one fiber type, but most contain a mixture of fiber types, which gives them a range of contractile speeds and fatigue resistance (Figure 9.24). For example, a calf muscle can propel us in a sprint (using its white fast glycolytic fibers) or a long-distance race (making good use of its slow and fast oxidative fibers). But, as might be expected, all muscle fibers in a particular *motor unit* are of the same type.

Although everyone's muscles contain mixtures of the three fiber types, some people have relatively more of one kind. These differences are genetically initiated, but are modified by

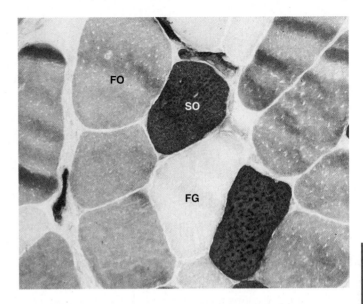

Figure 9.24 Cross section of the three types of fibers in skeletal muscle. From generally smallest to largest, they are slow oxidative fibers (SO), fast oxidative fibers (FO), and fast glycolytic fibers (FG). The staining technique used differentiates the fibers by the abundance of their mitochondria, which contain mitochondrial enzymes (600×).

exercise and no doubt determine athletic capabilities, such as endurance versus strength, to a large extent. For example, muscles of marathon runners have a high percentage of slow oxidative fibers (about 80%), while those of sprinters contain a higher percentage (about 60%) of fast oxidative and glycolytic fibers. Interconversion between the "fast" fiber types occurs as a result of specific exercise regimes, as we'll describe below.

Load Because muscles are attached to bones, they are always pitted against some resistance, or load, when they contract. As you might expect, they contract fastest when there is no added load on them. A greater load results in a longer latent period, a slower contraction, and a shorter duration of contraction (Figure 9.25). If the load exceeds the muscle's maximum tension, the speed of shortening is zero and the contraction is isometric (see Figure 9.18b).

Recruitment Just as many hands on a project can get a job done more quickly and also can keep working longer, the more motor units that are contracting, the faster and more prolonged the contraction.

CHECK YOUR UNDERSTANDING

14. List two factors that influence contractile force and two that influence velocity of contraction.

15. Jim called several friends to help him move. Would he prefer to have those with more slow oxidative muscle fibers or those with more fast glycolytic fibers as his helpers? Why?

For answers, see Appendix G.

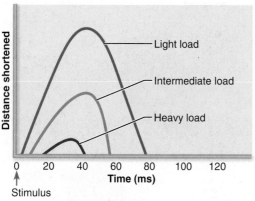

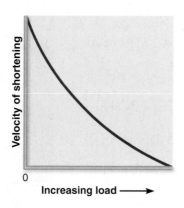

Figure 9.25 **Influence of load on contraction duration and velocity.**

(a) The greater the load, the less the muscle shortens and the shorter the duration of contraction

(b) The greater the load, the slower the contraction

Effect of Exercise on Muscles

▶ Compare and contrast the effects of aerobic and resistance exercise on skeletal muscles and on other body systems.

The amount of work a muscle does is reflected in changes in the muscle itself. When used actively or strenuously, muscles may increase in size or strength or become more efficient and fatigue resistant. Muscle inactivity, on the other hand, *always* leads to muscle weakness and wasting.

Adaptations to Exercise

Aerobic, or **endurance**, **exercise** such as swimming, jogging, fast walking, and biking results in several recognizable changes in skeletal muscles. There is an increase in the number of capillaries surrounding the muscle fibers, and in the number of mitochondria within them, and the fibers synthesize more myoglobin. These changes occur in all fiber types, but are most dramatic in slow oxidative fibers, which depend primarily on aerobic pathways. The changes result in more efficient muscle metabolism and in greater endurance, strength, and resistance to fatigue. Additionally, regular endurance exercise may convert fast glycolytic fibers into fast oxidative fibers.

The moderately weak but sustained muscle activity required for endurance exercise does not promote significant skeletal muscle hypertrophy, even though the exercise may go on for hours. Muscle hypertrophy, illustrated by the bulging biceps and chest muscles of a professional weight lifter, results mainly from high-intensity **resistance exercise** (typically under anaerobic conditions) such as weight lifting or isometric exercise, in which the muscles are pitted against high-resistance or immovable forces. Here strength, not stamina, is important, and a few minutes every other day is sufficient to allow a proverbial weakling to put on 50% more muscle within a year.

The increased muscle bulk largely reflects increases in the size of individual muscle fibers (particularly the fast glycolytic variety) rather than an increased number of muscle fibers. [However, some of the increased muscle size may result either from longitudinal splitting or tearing of the fibers and subsequent growth of these "split" cells, or from the proliferation and fusion of satellite cells (see p. 312). The controversy is still raging.] Vigorously stressed muscle fibers contain more mitochondria, form more myofilaments and myofibrils, and store more glycogen. The amount of connective tissue between the cells also increases. Collectively these changes promote significant increases in muscle strength and size. Fast oxidative fibers can be shifted to fast glycolytic fibers in response to resistance activities. However, if the specific exercise routine is discontinued, the fibers previously converted revert to their original metabolic properties.

Resistance training can produce magnificently bulging muscles, but if done unwisely, some muscles may develop more than others. Because muscles work in antagonistic pairs or groups, opposing muscles must be equally strong to work together smoothly. When muscle training is not balanced, individuals can become *muscle-bound*, which means they lack flexibility, have a generally awkward stance, and are unable to make full use of their muscles.

Whatever the activity, exercise gains adhere to the *overload principle*. Forcing a muscle to work hard promotes increased muscle strength and endurance, and as muscles adapt to the increased demands, they must be overloaded even more to produce further gains. However, a heavy-workout day should be followed by one of rest or an easy workout to allow the muscles to recover and repair themselves. Doing too much too soon, or ignoring the warning signs of muscle or joint pain, increases the risk of **overuse injuries** that may prevent future sports activities, or even lead to lifetime disability.

Endurance and resistance exercises produce different patterns of muscular response, so it is important to know what your exercise goals are. Lifting weights will not improve your endurance for a triathlon. By the same token, jogging will do little to improve your muscle definition or to enhance your strength for moving furniture. A program that alternates aerobic activities with anaerobic ones provides the best program for optimal health.

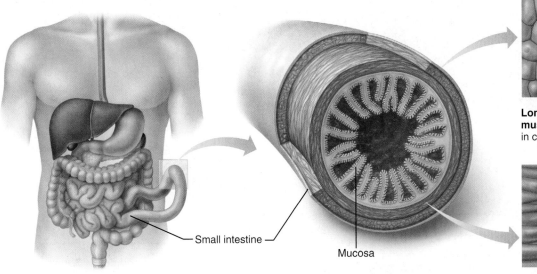

Longitudinal layer of smooth muscle (shows smooth muscle fibers in cross section)

Circular layer of smooth muscle (shows longitudinal views of smooth muscle fibers)

(a)

(b) **Cross section of the intestine showing the smooth muscle layers (one circular and the other longitudinal) running at right angles to each other.**

— Small intestine —

Mucosa

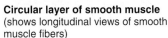

Figure 9.26 Arrangement of smooth muscle in the walls of hollow organs.

HOMEOSTATIC IMBALANCE

To remain healthy, muscles must be active. Complete immobilization due to enforced bed rest or loss of neural stimulation results in *disuse atrophy* (degeneration and loss of mass), which begins almost as soon as the muscles are immobilized. Under such conditions, muscle strength can decrease at the rate of 5% per day!

As noted earlier, even at rest, muscles receive weak intermittent stimuli from the nervous system. When totally deprived of neural stimulation, a paralyzed muscle may atrophy to one-quarter of its initial size. Lost muscle tissue is replaced by fibrous connective tissue, making muscle rehabilitation impossible. ■

CHECK YOUR UNDERSTANDING

16. Relative to their effect on muscle size and function, how do aerobic and anaerobic exercise differ?

For answers, see Appendix G.

Smooth Muscle

▶ Compare the gross and microscopic anatomy of smooth muscle cells to that of skeletal muscle cells.

▶ Compare and contrast the contractile mechanisms and the means of activation of skeletal and smooth muscles.

▶ Distinguish between single-unit and multiunit smooth muscle structurally and functionally.

Except for the heart, which is made of cardiac muscle, the muscle in the walls of all the body's hollow organs is almost entirely smooth muscle. The chemical and mechanical events of contraction are essentially the same in all muscle tissues, but smooth muscle is distinctive in several ways that are summarized in **Table 9.3**.

Microscopic Structure of Smooth Muscle Fibers

Smooth muscle fibers are spindle-shaped cells of variable size, each with one centrally located nucleus (**Figure 9.26b**). Typically, they have a diameter of 5–10 μm and are 30–200 μm long. Skeletal muscle fibers are up to 10 times wider and thousands of times longer.

Smooth muscle lacks the coarse connective tissue sheaths seen in skeletal muscle. However, a small amount of fine connective tissue (endomysium), secreted by the smooth muscles themselves and containing blood vessels and nerves, is found between smooth muscle fibers.

Most smooth muscle is organized into sheets of closely apposed fibers. These sheets occur in the walls of all but the smallest blood vessels and in the walls of hollow organs of the respiratory, digestive, urinary, and reproductive tracts. In most cases, two sheets of smooth muscle are present, with their fibers oriented at right angles to each other, as in the intestine (Figure 9.26). In the *longitudinal layer*, the muscle fibers run parallel to the long axis of the organ. Consequently, when the muscle contracts, the organ dilates and shortens. In the *circular layer*, the fibers run around the circumference of the organ. Contraction of this layer constricts the *lumen* (cavity) of the organ and causes the organ to elongate.

The alternating contraction and relaxation of these opposing layers mixes substances in the lumen and squeezes them through the organ's internal pathway. This propulsive action is

9

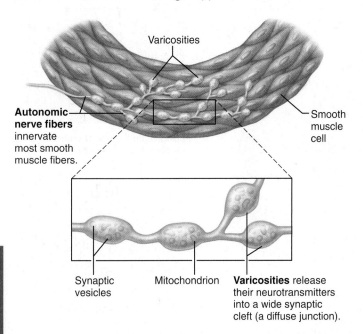

Figure 9.27 **Innervation of smooth muscle.**

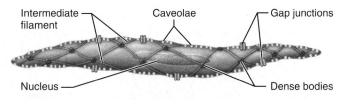

(a) Relaxed smooth muscle fiber (note that adjacent fibers are connected by gap junctions)

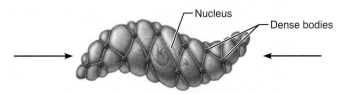

(b) Contracted smooth muscle fiber

Figure 9.28 **Intermediate filaments and dense bodies of smooth muscle fibers harness the pull generated by myosin cross bridges.** Intermediate filaments attach to dense bodies throughout the sarcoplasm.

called **peristalsis** (per″ĭ-stal′sis; "around contraction"). Contraction of smooth muscle in the rectum, urinary bladder, and uterus helps those organs to expel their contents. Smooth muscle contraction also accounts for the constricted breathing of asthma and for stomach cramps.

Smooth muscle lacks the highly structured, specific neuromuscular junctions of skeletal muscle. Instead, the innervating nerve fibers, which are part of the autonomic (involuntary) nervous system, have numerous bulbous swellings, called **varicosities (Figure 9.27)**. The varicosities release neurotransmitter into a wide synaptic cleft in the general area of the smooth muscle cells. Such junctions are called **diffuse junctions**. Comparing the specificity of neural input to skeletal and smooth muscles, you could say that skeletal muscle gets priority mail while smooth muscle gets bulk mailings.

The sarcoplasmic reticulum of smooth muscle fibers is much less developed than that of skeletal muscle and lacks a specific pattern relative to the myofilaments. Some SR tubules of smooth muscle touch the sarcolemma at several sites, forming what resembles half-triads that may couple the action potential to calcium release from the SR. T tubules are notably absent, but the sarcolemma of the smooth muscle fiber has multiple **caveolae**, pouchlike infoldings that sequester bits of extracellular fluid containing a high concentration of Ca^{2+} close to the membrane **(Figure 9.28a)**. Consequently, when calcium channels in the caveolae open, Ca^{2+} influx occurs rapidly. Although the SR *does* release some of the calcium that triggers contraction, most enters through calcium channels directly from the extracellular space. Contraction ends when calcium is actively transported into the SR and out of the cell. This situation is quite different from what we see in skeletal muscle, which does not depend on extracellular Ca^{2+} for excitation-contraction coupling.

There are no striations, as the name *smooth muscle* indicates, and therefore no sarcomeres. Smooth muscle fibers *do* contain interdigitating thick and thin filaments, but they are much longer than those in skeletal muscle, and the type of myosin contained differs in smooth muscle. The proportion and organization of the myofilaments are also different:

1. **Thick filaments are fewer but have myosin heads along their entire length.** The ratio of thick to thin filaments is much lower in smooth muscle than in skeletal muscle (1:13 compared to 1:2). However, thick filaments of smooth muscle contain actin-gripping myosin heads along their *entire length*, a feature that allows smooth muscle to be as powerful as a skeletal muscle of the same size.

2. **No troponin complex in thin filaments.** As opposed to skeletal muscle which has calcium-binding troponin on the thin filaments, no troponin complex is present in smooth muscle. Instead, a protein called *calmodulin* acts as the calcium-binding site.

3. **Thick and thin filaments arranged diagonally.** Bundles of contractile proteins crisscross within the smooth muscle cell so they spiral down the long axis of the cell like the stripes on a barber pole. Because of this diagonal arrangement, the smooth muscle cells contract in a twisting way so that they look like tiny corkscrews (Figure 9.28b).

4. **Intermediate filament–dense body network.** Smooth muscle fibers contain a lattice-like arrangement of noncontractile *intermediate filaments* that resist tension. They attach at regular intervals to cytoplasmic structures called **dense bodies** (Figure 9.28). The dense bodies, which are also tethered to the sarcolemma, act as anchoring points for thin filaments and therefore correspond to Z discs of skeletal muscle. The intermediate filament–dense body network forms a strong, cable-like intracellular cytoskeleton that harnesses the pull generated by the sliding of the thick

and thin filaments. During contraction, areas of the sarcolemma between the dense bodies bulge outward, giving the cell a puffy appearance, as in Figure 9.28b. Dense bodies at the sarcolemma surface also bind the muscle cell to the connective tissue fibers outside the cell (endomysium) and to adjacent cells. This arrangement transmits the pulling force to the surrounding connective tissue and partly accounts for the synchronous contraction of most smooth muscle.

Contraction of Smooth Muscle

Mechanism of Contraction

In most cases, adjacent smooth muscle fibers exhibit slow, synchronized contractions, the whole sheet responding to a stimulus in unison. This synchronization reflects electrical coupling of smooth muscle cells by *gap junctions*, specialized cell connections described in Chapter 3. Skeletal muscle fibers are electrically isolated from one another, each stimulated to contract by its own neuromuscular junction. By contrast, gap junctions allow smooth muscles to transmit action potentials from fiber to fiber.

Some smooth muscle fibers in the stomach and small intestine are *pacemaker cells* and, once excited, they act as "drummers" to set the contractile pace for the entire muscle sheet. Additionally, these pacemakers have fluctuating membrane potentials and are self-excitatory, that is, they depolarize spontaneously in the absence of external stimuli. However, both the rate and the intensity of smooth muscle contraction may be modified by neural and chemical stimuli.

Contraction in smooth muscle is like that in skeletal muscle in the following ways: (1) actin and myosin interact by the sliding filament mechanism; (2) the final trigger for contraction is a rise in the intracellular calcium ion level; and (3) the sliding process is energized by ATP.

During excitation-contraction coupling, Ca^{2+} is released by the tubules of the SR, but, as mentioned above, it also moves into the cell via membrane channels from the extracellular space. By binding to troponin, calcium ions activate myosin in all striated muscle types, but in smooth muscle, they activate myosin by interacting with a regulatory molecule called **calmodulin**, a cytoplasmic calcium-binding protein. Calmodulin, in turn, interacts with a kinase enzyme called **myosin kinase** or **myosin light chain kinase** which phosphorylates the myosin, activating it. This sequence of events is depicted in **Figure 9.29**. (Note that this is just one pathway of smooth muscle activation. There are others. For example, in some smooth muscles, regulatory proteins associated with actin appear to play a role.)

As in skeletal muscle, smooth muscle relaxes when intracellular Ca^{2+} levels drop, but getting muscle to cease its contractile activity is quite a bit more complex in smooth muscle then in skeletal muscle. Events known to be involved include calcium detachment from calmodulin, active transport of Ca^{2+} into the SR and the extracellular fluid, and dephosphorylation of myosin by a phosphorylase enzyme, which reduces the activity of the myosin ATPases.

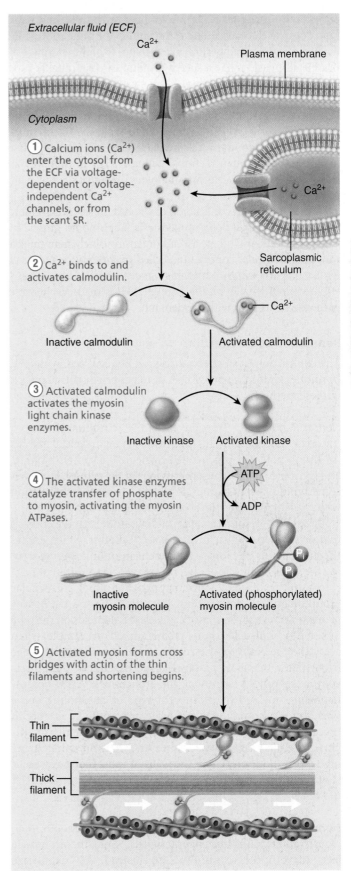

Figure 9.29 Sequence of events in excitation-contraction coupling of smooth muscle.

Smooth muscle takes 30 times longer to contract and relax than does skeletal muscle and can maintain the same contractile tension for prolonged periods at less than 1% of the energy cost. If skeletal muscle is like a speedy windup car that quickly runs down, then smooth muscle is like a steady, heavy-duty engine that lumbers along tirelessly.

Part of the striking energy economy of smooth muscle is the sluggishness of its ATPases compared to those in skeletal muscle. Moreover, smooth muscle myofilaments may latch together during prolonged contractions, saving energy in that way as well. Smooth muscle cells may maintain that *latch state* even after dephosphorylation of myosin.

The ATP-efficient contraction of smooth muscle is extremely important to overall body homeostasis. The smooth muscle in small arterioles and other visceral organs routinely maintains a moderate degree of contraction, called *smooth muscle tone*, day in and day out without fatiguing. Smooth muscle has low energy requirements. Typically, enough ATP is made via aerobic pathways to keep up with the demand.

Regulation of Contraction

The contraction of smooth muscle can be regulated by nerves, hormones, or local chemical changes. Let's briefly consider each of these methods.

Neural Regulation   In some cases, the activation of smooth muscle by a neural stimulus is identical to that in skeletal muscle: An action potential is generated by neurotransmitter binding, and is coupled to a rise in calcium ions in the cytosol. However, some types of smooth muscle respond to neural stimulation with graded potentials (local electrical signals) only.

Recall that all somatic nerve endings, that is, nerve endings that serve skeletal muscle, release acetylcholine, which excites the skeletal muscle. However, different autonomic nerves serving the smooth muscle of visceral organs release different neurotransmitters, each of which may excite or inhibit a particular group of smooth muscle cells. The effect of a specific neurotransmitter on a given smooth muscle cell depends on the type of receptor molecules on its sarcolemma. For example, when acetylcholine binds to ACh receptors on smooth muscle in the bronchioles (small air passageways of the lungs), the muscle contracts strongly, narrowing the bronchioles. When norepinephrine, released by a different type of autonomic nerve fiber, binds to norepinephrine receptors on the *same* smooth muscle cells, the effect is inhibitory, so the muscle relaxes, dilating the air passageways. However, when norepinephrine binds to smooth muscle in the walls of most blood vessels, it stimulates the smooth muscle cells to contract and constrict the vessel.

Hormones and Local Chemical Factors   Not all smooth muscle activation results from neural signals. Some smooth muscle layers have no nerve supply at all. Instead, they depolarize spontaneously or in response to chemical stimuli that bind to G protein–linked receptors. Others respond to both neural and chemical stimuli.

Chemical factors that cause smooth muscle contraction or relaxation without an action potential (by enhancing or inhibiting Ca^{2+} entry into the sarcoplasm) include certain hormones, lack of oxygen, histamine, excess carbon dioxide, and low pH. The direct response to these chemical stimuli alters smooth muscle activity according to local tissue needs and probably is most responsible for smooth muscle tone. For example, the hormone gastrin stimulates contraction of stomach smooth muscle so that it can churn foodstuffs more efficiently. We will consider how the smooth muscle of specific organs is activated as we discuss each organ in subsequent chapters.

Special Features of Smooth Muscle Contraction

Smooth muscle is intimately involved in the functioning of most hollow organs and has a number of unique characteristics. We have already considered some of these—smooth muscle tone; slow, prolonged contractile activity; and low energy requirements. But smooth muscle also responds differently to stretch and can shorten more than other muscle types. Let's take a look.

Response to Stretch   Up to a point, when skeletal muscle is stretched, it responds with more vigorous contractions. Stretching of smooth muscle also provokes contraction, which automatically moves substances along an internal tract. However, the increased tension persists only briefly, and soon the muscle adapts to its new length and relaxes, while still retaining the ability to contract on demand. This **stress-relaxation response** allows a hollow organ to fill or expand slowly (within certain limits) to accommodate a greater volume without promoting strong contractions that would expel its contents. This is an important attribute, because organs such as the stomach and intestines must be able to store their contents temporarily to provide sufficient time for digestion and absorption of the nutrients. Likewise, your urinary bladder must be able to store the continuously made urine until it is convenient to empty your bladder, or you would spend all your time in the bathroom.

Length and Tension Changes   Smooth muscle stretches much more than skeletal muscle and generates more tension than skeletal muscles stretched to a comparable extent. As we saw in Figure 9.22, precise, highly organized sarcomeres limit how far a skeletal muscle can be stretched before it is unable to generate force. In contrast, the lack of sarcomeres and the irregular, overlapping arrangement of smooth muscle filaments allow them to generate considerable force, even when they are substantially stretched. The total length change that skeletal muscles can undergo and still function efficiently is about 60% (from 30% shorter to 30% longer than resting length), but smooth muscle can contract when it is anywhere from twice to half its resting length—a total length change of 150%. This capability allows hollow organs to tolerate tremendous changes in volume without becoming flabby when they empty.

Hyperplasia   Besides being able to hypertrophy (increase in cell size), which is common to all muscle cells, certain smooth

TABLE 9.3	Comparison of Skeletal, Cardiac, and Smooth Muscle		
CHARACTERISTIC	**SKELETAL**	**CARDIAC**	**SMOOTH**
Body location	Attached to bones or (some facial muscles) to skin	Walls of the heart	Single-unit muscle in walls of hollow visceral organs (other than the heart); multiunit muscle in intrinsic eye muscles, airways, large arteries
Cell shape and appearance	Single, very long, cylindrical, multinucleate cells with obvious striations	Branching chains of cells; uni- or binucleate; striations	Single, fusiform, uninucleate; no striations
Connective tissue components	Epimysium, perimysium, and endomysium	Endomysium attached to fibrous skeleton of heart	Endomysium
Presence of myofibrils composed of sarcomeres	Yes	Yes, but myofibrils are of irregular thickness	No, but actin and myosin filaments are present throughout; dense bodies anchor actin filaments
Presence of T tubules and site of invagination	Yes; two in each sarcomere at A-I junctions	Yes; one in each sarcomere at Z disc; larger diameter than those of skeletal muscle	No; only caveolae

TABLE 9.3	Comparison of Skeletal, Cardiac, and Smooth Muscle *(continued)*		
CHARACTERISTIC	**SKELETAL**	**CARDIAC**	**SMOOTH**
Elaborate sarcoplasmic reticulum	Yes	Less than skeletal muscle (1–8% of cell volume); scant terminal cisternae	Equivalent to cardiac muscle (1–8% of cell volume); some SR contacts the sarcolemma
Presence of gap junctions	No	Yes; at intercalated discs	Yes; in single-unit muscle
Cells exhibit individual neuromuscular junctions	Yes	No	Not in single-unit muscle; yes in multiunit muscle
Regulation of contraction	Voluntary via axon terminals of the somatic nervous system	Involuntary; intrinsic system regulation; also autonomic nervous system controls; hormones; stretch	Involuntary; autonomic nerves, hormones, local chemicals; stretch
Source of Ca^{2+} for calcium pulse	Sarcoplasmic reticulum (SR)	SR and from extracellular fluid	SR and from extracellular fluid
Site of calcium regulation	Troponin on actin-containing thin filaments	Troponin on actin-containing thin filaments	Calmodulin in the cytosol
Presence of pacemaker(s)	No	Yes	Yes (in single-unit muscle only)
Effect of nervous system stimulation	Excitation	Excitation or inhibition	Excitation or inhibition
Speed of contraction	Slow to fast	Slow	Very slow
Rhythmic contraction	No	Yes	Yes in single-unit muscle
Response to stretch	Contractile strength increases with degree of stretch (to a point)	Contractile strength increases with degree of stretch	Stress-relaxation response
Respiration	Aerobic and anaerobic	Aerobic	Mainly aerobic

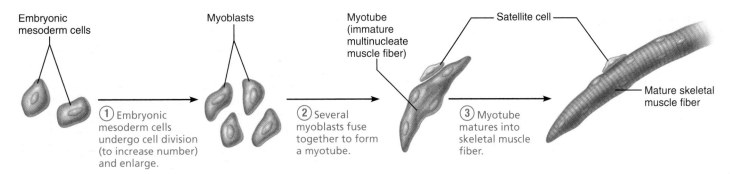

Figure 9.30 Formation of a multinucleate skeletal muscle fiber by fusion of myoblasts.

muscle fibers can divide to increase their numbers, that is, they undergo *hyperplasia*. One example is the response of the uterus to estrogen. At puberty, girls' plasma estrogen levels rise. As estrogen binds to uterine smooth muscle receptors, it stimulates the synthesis of more uterine smooth muscle, causing the uterus to grow to adult size. During pregnancy, high blood levels of estrogen stimulate uterine hyperplasia to accommodate the growing fetus.

Types of Smooth Muscle

The smooth muscle in different body organs varies substantially in its (1) fiber arrangement and organization, (2) innervation, and (3) responsiveness to various stimuli. For simplicity, however, smooth muscle is usually categorized into two major types: *single-unit* and *multiunit*.

Single-Unit Smooth Muscle

Single-unit smooth muscle, commonly called **visceral muscle** because it is in the walls of all hollow organs except the heart, is far more common. All the smooth muscle characteristics described so far pertain to single-unit smooth muscle. For example, the cells of single-unit smooth muscle

1. Are arranged in opposing (longitudinal and circular) sheets
2. Are innervated by ANS varicosities and often exhibit rhythmic spontaneous action potentials
3. Are electrically coupled by gap junctions and so contract as a unit (for this reason recruitment is not an option in smooth muscle)
4. Respond to various chemical stimuli

Multiunit Smooth Muscle

The smooth muscles in the large airways to the lungs and in large arteries, the arrector pili muscles attached to hair follicles, and the internal eye muscles that adjust pupil size and allow the eye to focus visually are all examples of **multiunit smooth muscle**.

In contrast to what we see in single-unit muscle, gap junctions are rare, and spontaneous synchronous depolarizations are infrequent. Like skeletal muscle, multiunit smooth muscle

1. Consists of muscle fibers that are structurally independent of one another
2. Is richly supplied with nerve endings, each of which forms a motor unit with a number of muscle fibers
3. Responds to neural stimulation with graded contractions that involve recruitment

However, while skeletal muscle is served by the somatic (voluntary) division of the nervous system, multiunit smooth muscle (like single-unit smooth muscle) is innervated by the autonomic (involuntary) division and is also responsive to hormonal controls.

CHECK YOUR UNDERSTANDING

17. Compare the structure of skeletal muscle fibers to that of smooth muscle fibers.
18. Calcium is the trigger for contraction of all muscle types. How does its binding site differ in skeletal and smooth muscle fibers?
19. How does the stress-relaxation response suit the role of smooth muscle in hollow organs?

For answers, see Appendix G.

Developmental Aspects of Muscles

▶ Describe embryonic development of muscle tissues and the changes that occur in skeletal muscles with age.

With rare exceptions, all three types of muscle tissue develop from embryonic mesoderm cells called **myoblasts**. In forming skeletal muscle tissue several myoblasts fuse to form multinuclear *myotubes* **(Figure 9.30)**. This process is guided by the integrins (cell adhesion proteins) in the myoblast membranes. Soon functional sarcomeres are present, and skeletal muscle fibers are contracting by week 7 when the embryo is only about 2.5 cm (1 inch long).

Initially, ACh receptors "sprout" over the entire surface of the developing myoblasts. As spinal nerves invade the muscle masses, the nerve endings target individual myoblasts and release the growth factor *agrin*. This chemical activates a muscle kinase (MuSK), which stimulates clustering and maintenance of ACh receptors at the newly forming neuromuscular junction in each muscle fiber. Then, the nerve endings provide an independent chemical signal that causes elimination of the receptor sites not innervated and not stabilized by agrin.

Electrical activity in the neurons serving the muscle fibers also plays a critical role in muscle fiber maturation. As the muscle fibers are brought under the control of the somatic nervous system, the number of fast and slow contractile fiber types is determined.

Myoblasts producing cardiac and smooth muscle cells do not fuse. However, both develop gap junctions at a very early embryonic stage. Cardiac muscle is pumping blood just 3 weeks after fertilization.

Specialized skeletal and cardiac muscle cells stop dividing early on but retain the ability to lengthen and thicken in a growing child and to hypertrophy in adults. However, myoblast-like cells associated with skeletal muscle, called *satellite cells* (Figure 9.30), help repair injured fibers and allow *very limited* regeneration of dead skeletal muscle fibers. Cardiac muscle was thought to have no regenerative capability whatsoever, but recent studies suggest that cardiac cells do divide at a modest rate. Nonetheless, injured heart muscle is repaired mostly by scar tissue. Smooth muscles are able to regenerate throughout life.

At birth, a baby's movements are uncoordinated and largely reflexive. Muscular development reflects the level of neuromuscular coordination, which develops in a head-to-toe and proximal-to-distal direction. In other words, a baby can lift its head before it can walk, and gross movements precede fine ones. All through childhood, our control of our skeletal muscles becomes more and more sophisticated. By midadolescence, we reach the peak of our *natural* neural control of muscles, and can either accept that level of development or improve it by athletic or other types of training.

A frequently asked question is whether the difference in strength between women and men has a biological basis. It does. Individuals vary, but on average, women's skeletal muscles make up approximately 36% of body mass, whereas men's account for about 42%. Men's greater muscular development is due primarily to the effects of testosterone on skeletal muscle, not to the effects of exercise. Body strength per unit muscle mass, however, is the same in both sexes. Strenuous muscle exercise causes more muscle enlargement in males than in females, again because of the influence of testosterone. Some athletes take large doses of synthetic male sex hormones ("steroids") to increase their muscle mass. This illegal and physiologically dangerous practice is discussed in *A Closer Look*, opposite.

Because of its rich blood supply, skeletal muscle is amazingly resistant to infection throughout life. Given good nutrition and moderate exercise, relatively few problems afflict skeletal muscles. However, muscular dystrophy, the world's most common genetic disorder, is a serious condition that deserves more than a passing mention.

HOMEOSTATIC IMBALANCE

The term **muscular dystrophy** refers to a group of inherited muscle-destroying diseases that generally appear during childhood. The affected muscles initially enlarge due to fat and connective tissue deposit, but the muscle fibers atrophy and degenerate.

The most common and serious form is **Duchenne muscular dystrophy (DMD)**, which is inherited as a sex-linked recessive disease: Females carry and transmit the abnormal gene, but it is expressed almost exclusively in males (one in every 3500 births). This tragic disease is usually diagnosed when the boy is between 2 and 7 years old. Active, normal-appearing children become clumsy and fall frequently as their skeletal muscles weaken. The disease progresses relentlessly from the extremities upward, finally affecting the head and chest muscles and cardiac muscle of the heart. Victims rarely live beyond their early 20s, dying of respiratory failure.

Recent research has pinned down the cause of DMD: The diseased muscle fibers lack *dystrophin*, a cytoplasmic protein that links the cytoskeleton to the extracellular matrix and, like a girder, helps stabilize the sarcolemma. The fragile sarcolemma of DMD patients tears during contraction, allowing entry of excess Ca^{2+}. The deranged calcium homeostasis damages the contractile fibers which then break down, and inflammatory cells (macrophages and lymphocytes) accumulate in the surrounding connective tissue. As the regenerative capacity of the muscle is lost, and damaged cells undergo apoptosis, muscle mass drops.

There is still no cure for DMD, and thus far the only medication that has improved muscle strength and function is the steroid prednisone. One initially promising technique, *myoblast transfer therapy*, involves injecting diseased muscle with healthy myoblast cells that fuse with the unhealthy ones. The idea is that the normal gene provided would allow the fiber to produce dystrophin and so to grow normally. The therapy has shown some success in mice, but human trials have been disappointing. The large size of the dystrophin gene and of human muscles presents a huge challenge to that therapy. Two newer experimental therapies have each produced striking reversals of disease symptoms in dystrophic animal models. One is injection of adeno-associated viruses carrying pared-down microdystrophin genes. The second is infusion into the bloodstream of dystrophic mesangioblasts (stem cells harvested from blood vessels) corrected by inserting microdystrophin genes. A different approach being tested is coaxing dystrophic muscles to produce more *utrophin*, a similar protein present in low amounts in adults but at much higher levels in fetal muscles. In mice at least, utrophin can compensate for dystrophin deficiency. ∎

As we age, the amount of connective tissue in our skeletal muscles increases, the number of muscle fibers decreases, and the muscles become stringier, or more sinewy. By the age of 30, even in healthy people, a gradual loss of muscle mass, called *sarcopenia* (sar-co-pe′ne-ah), begins to occur as muscle proteins start to degrade more rapidly than they can be replaced. Just why this happens is still a question, but apparently the same regulatory molecules (transcription factors, enzymes, hormones, and others) that promote muscle growth also oversee this type of muscle atrophy. Because skeletal muscles form so much of the body mass, body weight and muscle strength

(Text continues on p. 316.)

A CLOSER LOOK

Athletes Looking Good and Doing Better with Anabolic Steroids?

Society loves a winner and top athletes reap large social and monetary rewards. It is not surprising that some will grasp at anything that might increase their performance—including "juice," or anabolic steroids. These drugs are variants of the male sex hormone testosterone engineered by pharmaceutical companies. They were introduced in the 1950s to treat anemia and certain muscle-wasting diseases and to prevent muscle atrophy in patients immobilized after surgery. Testosterone is responsible for the increase in muscle and bone mass and other physical changes that occur during puberty and converts boys into men.

Convinced that megadoses of steroids could produce enhanced masculinizing effects in grown men, many athletes and bodybuilders were using them by the early 1960s. Investigations of the so-called Balco Scandal have stunned fans of major league baseball players with revelations in 2004 and since of rampant steroid use by Barry Bonds, of the San Francisco Giants, and many other elite athletes. It is still going on. In October of 2007, Marion Jones, one of the most celebrated of women athletes of all time, admitted that she was using performance-enhancing steroids when she won five gold medals in the 2000 Olympics. Furthermore, steroid use today is not confined to athletes. Indeed, it is estimated that nearly one in every 10 young men has tried them, and the practice is also spreading among young women.

It is difficult to determine the extent of anabolic steroid use because most international competitions ban the use of drugs. Users (and prescribing physicians or drug dealers) are naturally reluctant to talk about it, and users stop doping before the event, aware that evidence of drug use is hard to find a week after its use is stopped. Additionally, "underground" suppliers of performance-enhancing drugs keep producing new versions of designer steroids that evade standard antidoping tests. The Olympic Analytical Laboratory in Los Angeles rocked the sports world in November of 2003 when it revealed that a number of elite athletes tested positive for tetrahydrogestrinone (THG), a designer steroid not previously known or tested for. Nonetheless, there is little question that

many professional bodybuilders and athletes competing in events that require muscle strength (e.g., shot put, discus throwing, and weight lifting) are heavy users. Sports figures such as football players have also admitted to using steroids as an adjunct to training, diet, and psychological preparation for games. These athletes claim that anabolic steroids enhance muscle mass and strength, and raise oxygen-carrying capability owing to greater red blood cell volume.

Typically, bodybuilders who use steroids combine high doses (up to 200 mg/day) via injection or transdermal skin patches with heavy resistance training. Intermittent use begins several months before an event, and commonly entails the use of many anabolic steroid supplements (a method called stacking). Doses are increased gradually as the competition nears.

Do the drugs do all that is claimed? Research studies report increased isometric strength and body weight in steroid users. While these are results weight lifters dream about, for runners and others requiring fine muscle coordination and endurance these changes may not translate into improved performance. The "jury is still out" on this question.

Do the alleged advantages of steroids outweigh their risks? Absolutely not. Physicians say they cause bloated faces (Cushingoid sign of steroid excess); acne and hair loss; shriveled testes and infertility; damage to the liver that promotes liver cancer; and changes in blood cholesterol levels that may predispose users to coronary heart disease. In addition, females can develop masculine characteristics

such as smaller breasts, enlarged clitoris, excess body hair, and thinning scalp hair. The psychiatric hazards of anabolic steroid use may be equally threatening: Recent studies indicate that one-third of users suffer serious mental problems. Depression, delusions, and manic behavior—in which users undergo Jekyll-and-Hyde personality swings and become extremely violent (termed 'roid rage)—are all common.

A more recent arrival on the scene, sold over the counter as a "nutritional performance-enhancer," is androstenedione, which is converted to testosterone in the body. Though it is taken orally (and much of it is destroyed by the liver soon after ingestion), the few milligrams that survive temporarily boost testosterone levels. Reports of its use by baseball great Mark McGwire before he retired, and of athletic wanna-bes from the fifth grade up sweeping the supplement off the drugstore shelves, are troubling, particularly since it is not regulated by the U.S. Food and Drug Administration (FDA) and its long-term effects are unpredictable and untested. A study at Massachusetts General Hospital found that males who took androstenedione developed higher levels of the female hormone estrogen as well as testosterone, raising their risk of feminizing effects such as enlarged breasts. Youths with elevated levels of estrogen or testosterone may enter puberty early, stunting bone growth and leading to shorter-than-normal adult height. Some people admit to a willingness to try almost anything to win, short of killing themselves. Are they unwittingly doing this as well?

System Connections

Homeostatic Interrelationships Between the Muscular System and Other Body Systems

Endocrine System

- Growth hormone and androgens influence skeletal muscle strength and mass; other hormones help regulate cardiac and smooth muscle activity

Cardiovascular System

- Skeletal muscle activity increases efficiency of cardiovascular functioning; helps prevent atherosclerosis and causes cardiac hypertrophy
- Cardiovascular system delivers needed oxygen and nutrients to muscles

Lymphatic System/Immunity

- Physical exercise may enhance or depress immunity depending on its intensity
- Lymphatic vessels drain leaked tissue fluids; immune system protects muscles from disease

Respiratory System

- Muscular exercise increases respiratory capacity and efficiency of gas exchange
- Respiratory system provides oxygen and disposes of carbon dioxide

Digestive System

- Physical activity increases gastrointestinal motility and elimination when at rest
- Digestive system provides nutrients needed for muscle health; liver metabolizes lactic acid

Urinary System

- Physical activity promotes normal voiding behavior; skeletal muscle forms the voluntary sphincter of the urethra
- Urinary system disposes of nitrogenous wastes

Reproductive System

- Skeletal muscle helps support pelvic organs (e.g., uterus); assists erection of penis and clitoris
- Testicular androgen promotes increased skeletal muscle

Integumentary System

- Muscular exercise enhances circulation to skin and improves skin health
- Skin protects the muscles by external enclosure; helps dissipate heat generated by the muscles

Skeletal System

- Skeletal muscle activity maintains bone health and strength
- Bones provide levers for muscle activity

Nervous System

- Facial muscle activity allows emotions to be expressed
- Nervous system stimulates and regulates muscle activity

9

THE MUSCULAR SYSTEM and Interrelationships with the Cardiovascular, Endocrine, Lymphatic/Immunity, and Skeletal Systems

Our skeletal muscles are a marvel. In the well conditioned, they ripple with energy. In those of us who are less athletic, they enable us to perform the rather remarkable tasks of moving and getting around. No one would argue that the nervous system is indispensable for activating muscles to contract and for keeping them healthy via tone. Let's look at how skeletal muscle activity affects other body systems from the vantage point of overall health and disease prevention.

Cardiovascular System

The single most important barometer of how "well" we age is the health of our cardiovascular system. More than any other factor, regular exercise helps to maintain that health. Anything that gets you huffing and puffing on a regular basis, be it racquetball or a vigorous walk, helps to keep heart muscle healthy and strong. It also keeps blood vessels clear, delaying atherosclerosis and helping to prevent the most common type of high blood pressure and hypertensive heart disease—ailments that can lead to the deterioration of heart muscle and the kidneys. Uncluttered blood vessels also stave off painful or disabling intermittent claudication in which muscle pain due to ischemia hinders walking. Furthermore, regular exercise boosts blood levels of clot-busting enzymes, helping to ward off heart attacks and strokes, other scourges of old age.

Endocrine System

Muscle has a high rate of metabolism, and even at rest it uses much more energy than does fat. Consequently, exercise that builds moderate muscle mass helps to keep weight down and prevents obesity. Obesity is one of the risk factors for development of age-related diabetes mellitus—the metabolic disorder in which body cells are unresponsive to insulin (secreted by the pancreas) and, hence, unable to utilize glucose normally. Additionally, exercise helps to maintain normal cellular responses to insulin. On the other side of the coin, several hormones, including growth hormone, thyroid hormone, and sex hormones, are essential for normal development and maturation of the skeletal muscles.

Lymphatic System/Immunity

Physical exercise has a marked effect on immunity. Moderate or mild exercise causes a temporary rise in the number of phagocytes, T cells (a particular group of white blood cells), and antibodies, all of which populate lymphatic organs and mount the attack against infectious disease. By contrast, strenuous exercise depresses the immune system. The way in which exercise affects immunity—including these seemingly contradictory observations—is still a mystery, but the so-called stress hormones are definitely involved. Like major stressors such as surgery and serious burns, strenuous exercise increases blood levels of stress hormones such as epinephrine and glucocorticoids. These hormones depress the immune system during severe stress. This is thought to be a protective mechanism—a way of preventing large numbers of slightly damaged cells from being rejected.

Skeletal System

Last but not least, weight-bearing exercise of the skeletal muscles promotes skeletal strength and helps prevent osteoporosis. Since osteoporosis severely detracts from the quality of life by increasing risk of fractures, this is an extremely important interaction. But without their bony attachments, muscles would be ineffective in causing body movement.

9

Clinical Connections

Muscular System

Case study: Let's continue our tale of Mrs. DeStephano's medical problems, this time looking at the notes made detailing observations of her skeletal musculature.

- Severe lacerations of the muscles of the right leg and knee
- Damage to the blood vessels serving the right leg and knee
- Transection of the sciatic nerve (the large nerve serving most of the lower limb), just above the right knee

Her physician orders daily passive range-of-motion (ROM) exercise and electrical stimulation for her right leg and a diet high in protein, carbohydrates, and vitamin C.

1. Describe the step-by-step process of wound healing that will occur in her fleshy (muscle) wounds, and note the consequences of the specific restorative process that occurs.

2. What complications in healing can be anticipated owing to vascular (blood vessel) damage in the right leg?

3. What complications in muscle structure and function result from transection of the sciatic nerve? Why are passive ROM and electrical stimulation of her right leg muscles ordered?

4. Explain the reasoning behind the dietary recommendations.

(Answers in Appendix G)

decline in tandem. Muscle strength has usually decreased by about 50% by the age of 80 years. This "flesh wasting" condition has serious health implications for the elderly, particularly because falling becomes a common event.

But we don't have to slow up during old age. Muscle is responsive to exercise throughout life. Regular exercise helps reverse sarcopenia, and frail elders who begin to "pump iron" (lift leg and hand weights) can rebuild muscle mass and dramatically increase their strength. Performing those lifting exercises rapidly can improve a person's ability to carry out the "explosive" movements needed to rise from a chair or catch one's balance. Even moderate activity, like taking a walk daily, results in improved neuromuscular functioning and enhances independent living.

Muscles can also suffer indirectly. Aging of the cardiovascular system affects nearly every organ in the body, and muscles are no exception. As atherosclerosis takes its toll and begins to block distal arteries, a circulatory condition called *intermittent claudication* (klaw″dĭ-ka′shun; "limping") occurs in some individuals. This condition restricts blood delivery to the legs, leading to excruciating pains in the leg muscles during walking, which forces the person to stop and rest to get relief.

Smooth muscle is remarkably trouble free. The few problems that impair its functioning stem from external irritants. In the gastrointestinal tract, irritation might result from ingestion of excess alcohol, spicy foods, or bacterial infection. Under such conditions, smooth muscle motility increases in an attempt to rid the body of irritating agents, and diarrhea or vomiting occurs.

CHECK YOUR UNDERSTANDING

20. How is the multinucleate condition achieved during development of skeletal muscle fibers?
21. What does it mean when we say "muscles get stringier with age"?
22. How can we defer (or reverse) some of the effects of age on skeletal muscles?

For answers, see Appendix G.

The capacity for movement is a property of all cells but, with the exception of muscle, these movements are largely restricted to intracellular events. Skeletal muscles, the major focus of this chapter, permit us to interact with our external environment in an amazing number of ways, and they also contribute to our internal homeostasis as summarized in *Making Connections* (pp. 314–315). In this chapter we have covered muscle anatomy from the gross level to the molecular level and have considered muscle physiology in some detail. Chapter 10 continues from this point to explain how skeletal muscles interact with bones and with each other, and then describes the individual skeletal muscles that make up the muscular system of the body.

RELATED CLINICAL TERMS

Fibromyositis (*fibro* = fiber; *itis* = inflammation) Also known as **fibromyalgia**; a group of conditions involving chronic inflammation of a muscle, its connective tissue coverings and tendons, and capsules of nearby joints. Symptoms are nonspecific and involve varying degrees of tenderness associated with specific trigger points, as well as fatigue and frequent awakening from sleep.

Hernia Protrusion of an organ through its body cavity wall; may be congenital (owing to failure of muscle fusion during development), but most often is caused by heavy lifting or obesity and subsequent muscle weakening.

Myalgia (mi-al′je-ah; *algia* = pain) Muscle pain resulting from any muscle disorder.

Myofascial pain syndrome Pain caused by a tightened band of muscle fibers, which twitch when the skin over them is touched. Mostly associated with overused or strained postural muscles.

Myopathy (mi-op′ah-the; *path* = disease, suffering) Any disease of muscle.

Myotonic dystrophy A form of muscular dystrophy that is less common than DMD; in the U.S. it affects about 14 of 100,000 people. Symptoms include a gradual reduction in muscle mass and control of the skeletal muscles, abnormal heart rhythm, and diabetes mellitus. May appear at any time; not sex-linked. Underlying genetic defect is multiple repeats of a particular gene on chromosome 19. Because the number of repeats tends to increase from generation to generation, subsequent generations develop more severe symptoms. No effective treatment.

RICE Acronym for *rest, ice, compression,* and *elevation,* the standard treatment for a pulled muscle, or excessively stretched tendons or ligaments.

Spasm A sudden, involuntary twitch in smooth or skeletal muscle ranging in severity from merely irritating to very painful; may be due to chemical imbalances. In spasms of the eyelid or facial muscles, called tics, psychological factors have been implicated. Stretching and massaging the affected area may help to end the spasm. A cramp is a prolonged spasm; usually occurs at night or after exercise.

Strain Commonly called a "pulled muscle," a strain is excessive stretching and possible tearing of a muscle due to muscle overuse or abuse; the injured muscle becomes painfully inflamed (myositis), and adjacent joints are usually immobilized.

Tetanus (1) A state of sustained contraction of a muscle that is a normal aspect of skeletal muscle functioning. (2) An acute infectious disease caused by the anaerobic bacterium *Clostridium tetani* and resulting in persistent painful spasms of some of the skeletal muscles. Progresses to fixed rigidity of the jaws (lockjaw) and spasms of trunk and limb muscles; usually fatal due to respiratory failure.

CHAPTER SUMMARY

Media study tools that could provide you additional help in reviewing specific key topics of Chapter 9 are referenced below.

iP = *Interactive Physiology*

Overview of Muscle Tissues (pp. 276–277)

Types of Muscle Tissue (p. 276)

1. Skeletal muscle is attached to the skeleton, is striated, and can be controlled voluntarily.
2. Cardiac muscle forms the heart, is striated, and is controlled involuntarily.
3. Smooth muscle, located chiefly in the walls of hollow organs, is controlled involuntarily. Its fibers are not striated.

Special Characteristics of Muscle Tissue (p. 276)

4. Special functional characteristics of muscle include excitability, contractility, extensibility, and elasticity.

Muscle Functions (pp. 276–277)

5. Muscles move internal and external body parts, maintain posture, stabilize joints, generate heat, and protect some visceral organs.

Skeletal Muscle (pp. 277–305)

Gross Anatomy of a Skeletal Muscle (pp. 277–278)

1. Skeletal muscle fibers (cells) are protected and strengthened by connective tissue coverings. Superficial to deep, these are epimysium, perimysium, and endomysium.
2. Skeletal muscle attachments (origins/insertions) may be direct or indirect via tendons or aponeuroses. Indirect attachments withstand friction better.

Microscopic Anatomy of a Skeletal Muscle Fiber (pp. 278–284)

3. Skeletal muscle fibers are long, striated, and multinucleate.
4. Myofibrils are contractile elements that occupy most of the cell volume. Their banded appearance results from a regular alternation of dark (A) and light (I) bands. Myofibrils are chains of sarcomeres; each sarcomere contains thick (myosin) and thin (actin) myofilaments arranged in a regular array. The heads of myosin molecules form cross bridges that interact with the thin filaments.
5. The sarcoplasmic reticulum (SR) is a system of membranous tubules surrounding each myofibril. Its function is to release and then sequester calcium ions.
6. T tubules are invaginations of the sarcolemma that run between the terminal cisternae of the SR. They allow an electrical stimulus to be delivered quickly deep into the cell.

Sliding Filament Model of Contraction (p. 284)

7. According to the sliding filament model, the thin filaments are pulled toward the sarcomere centers by cross bridge (myosin head) activity of the thick filaments.

Physiology of Skeletal Muscle Fibers (pp. 284–289)

8. Regulation of skeletal muscle cell contraction involves (a) generation and transmission of an action potential along the sarcolemma and (b) excitation-contraction coupling.
9. An end plate potential is set up when acetylcholine released by a nerve ending binds to ACh receptors on the sarcolemma, causing local changes in membrane permeability which allow ion flows that depolarize the membrane at that site.

10. Current flows from the locally depolarized area spread to the adjacent area of the sarcolemma, opening voltage-gated Na^+ channels which allow Na^+ influx. Then Na^+ channels close and voltage-gated K^+ channels open, repolarizing the membrane. These events generate the action potential. Once initiated, the action potential is self-propagating and unstoppable.
11. In excitation-contraction coupling, the action potential is propagated down the T tubules, causing calcium to be released from the SR into the cytosol.
12. Sliding of the filaments is triggered by a rise in intracellular calcium ion levels. Troponin binding of calcium moves tropomyosin away from myosin-binding sites on actin, allowing cross bridge binding. Myosin ATPases split ATP, which energizes the power strokes. ATP binding to the myosin head is necessary for cross bridge detachment. Cross bridge activity ends when calcium is pumped back into the SR.

iP Muscular System; Topic: Sliding Filament Theory, pp. 18–29.

Contraction of a Skeletal Muscle (pp. 289–296)

13. A motor unit is one motor neuron and all the muscle cells it innervates. The neuron's axon has several branches, each of which forms a neuromuscular junction with one muscle cell.
14. A motor unit's response to a single brief threshold stimulus is a twitch. A twitch has three phases: the latent period (preparatory events occurring), the period of contraction (the muscle tenses and may shorten), and the period of relaxation (muscle tension declines and the muscle resumes its resting length).
15. Graded responses of muscles to rapid stimuli are wave summation and unfused and fused tetanus. A graded response to increasingly strong stimuli is multiple motor unit summation, or recruitment. The type and order of motor unit recruitment follows the size principle.
16. Isotonic contractions occur when the muscle shortens (concentric contraction) or lengthens (eccentric contraction) as the load is moved. Isometric contractions occur when muscle tension produces neither shortening nor lengthening.

iP Muscular System; Topic: Contraction of Motor Units, pp. 1–11.

Muscle Metabolism (pp. 296–300)

17. The energy source for muscle contraction is ATP, obtained from a coupled reaction of creatine phosphate with ADP and from aerobic and anaerobic metabolism of glucose.
18. When ATP is produced by anaerobic pathways, lactic acid accumulates and ionic imbalances disturb the membrane potential, and an oxygen deficit occurs. To return the muscles to their resting state, ATP must be produced aerobically and used to regenerate creatine phosphate, glycogen reserves must be restored, and accumulated lactic acid must be oxidized.
19. Only about 40% of energy released during ATP hydrolysis powers contractile activity. The rest is liberated as heat.

iP Muscular System; Topic: Muscle Metabolism, pp. 1–7.

Force of Muscle Contraction (pp. 300–302)

20. The force of muscle contraction is affected by the number and size of contracting muscle cells (the more and the larger the cells, the greater the force), the frequency of stimulation, and the degree of muscle stretch.

21. In twitch contractions, the external tension exerted on the load is always less than the internal tension. When a muscle is tetanized, the external tension equals the internal tension.

22. When the thick and thin filaments are optimally overlapping, the muscle can generate maximum force. With excessive increase or decrease in muscle length, force declines.

Velocity and Duration of Contraction (pp. 302–303)

23. Factors determining the velocity and duration of muscle contraction include the load (the greater the load, the slower the contraction) and muscle fiber types.

24. The three types of muscle fibers are: (1) fast glycolytic (fatigable) fibers, (2) slow oxidative (fatigue-resistant) fibers, and (3) fast oxidative (fatigue-resistant) fibers. Most muscles contain a mixture of fiber types. The fast muscle fiber types are interconvertible with certain exercise regimens.

Effect of Exercise on Muscles (pp. 304–305)

25. Regular aerobic exercise results in increased efficiency, endurance, strength, and resistance to fatigue of skeletal muscles.

26. Resistance exercises cause skeletal muscle hypertrophy and large gains in skeletal muscle strength.

27. Immobilization of muscles leads to muscle weakness and severe atrophy.

28. Improper training and excessive exercise result in overuse injuries, which may be disabling.

Smooth Muscle (pp. 305–311)

Microscopic Structure of Smooth Muscle Fibers (pp. 305–307)

1. Smooth muscle fibers are spindle shaped and uninucleate. They display no striations.

2. Smooth muscle cells are most often arranged in sheets. They lack elaborate connective tissue coverings.

3. The SR is poorly developed and T tubules are absent. Actin and myosin filaments are present, but sarcomeres are not. Intermediate filaments and dense bodies form an intracellular network that harnesses the pull generated during cross bridge activity and transfers it to the extracellular matrix.

Contraction of Smooth Muscle (pp. 307–311)

4. Smooth muscle fibers may be electrically coupled by gap junctions, and the pace of contraction may be set by pacemaker cells.

5. Smooth muscle contraction is energized by ATP and is activated by a calcium pulse. However, calcium binds to calmodulin rather than to troponin (which is not present in smooth muscle fibers), and myosin must be phosphorylated to become active in contraction.

6. Smooth muscle contracts for extended periods at low energy cost and without fatigue.

7. Neurotransmitters of the autonomic nervous system may inhibit or stimulate smooth muscle fibers. Smooth muscle contraction may also be initiated by pacemaker cells, hormones, or local chemical factors that influence intracellular calcium levels, and by mechanical stretch.

8. Special features of smooth muscle contraction include the stress-relaxation response, the ability to generate large amounts of force when extensively stretched, and hyperplasia under certain conditions.

Types of Smooth Muscle (p. 311)

9. Single-unit smooth muscle has electrically coupled fibers that contract synchronously and often spontaneously.

10. Multiunit smooth muscle has independent, well-innervated fibers that lack gap junctions and pacemaker cells. Stimulation occurs via autonomic nerves (or hormones). Multiunit muscle contractions are rarely synchronous.

Developmental Aspects of Muscles (pp. 311–312, 316)

1. Muscle tissue develops from embryonic mesoderm cells called myoblasts. Skeletal muscle fibers are formed by the fusion of several myoblasts. Smooth and cardiac cells develop from single myoblasts and display gap junctions.

2. For the most part, specialized skeletal and cardiac muscle cells lose their ability to divide but retain the ability to hypertrophy. Smooth muscle regenerates well and undergoes hyperplasia.

3. Skeletal muscle development reflects maturation of the nervous system and occurs in cephalocaudal and proximal-to-distal directions. Natural neuromuscular control reaches its peak in midadolescence.

4. Women's muscles account for about 36% of their total body weight and men's for about 42%, a difference due chiefly to the effects of male hormones on skeletal muscle growth.

5. Skeletal muscle is richly vascularized and quite resistant to infection, but in old age, skeletal muscles become fibrous, decline in strength, and atrophy unless an appropriate exercise regimen is followed.

REVIEW QUESTIONS

Multiple Choice/Matching

(Some questions have more than one correct answer. Select the best answer or answers from the choices given.)

1. The connective tissue covering that encloses the sarcolemma of an individual muscle fiber is called the (a) epimysium, (b) perimysium, (c) endomysium, (d) periosteum.

2. A fascicle is a (a) muscle, (b) bundle of muscle fibers enclosed by a connective tissue sheath, (c) bundle of myofibrils, (d) group of myofilaments.

3. Thick and thin myofilaments have different compositions. For each descriptive phrase, indicate whether the filament is (a) thick or (b) thin.

_____ (1) contains actin
_____ (2) contains ATPases
_____ (3) attaches to the Z disc
_____ (4) contains myosin
_____ (5) contains troponin
_____ (6) does not lie in the I band

4. The function of the T tubules in muscle contraction is to (a) make and store glycogen, (b) release Ca^{2+} into the cell interior and then pick it up again, (c) transmit the action potential deep into the muscle cells, (d) form proteins.

5. The sites where the motor nerve impulse is transmitted from the nerve endings to the skeletal muscle cell membranes are the

(a) neuromuscular junctions, (b) sarcomeres, (c) myofilaments, (d) Z discs.

6. Contraction elicited by a single brief stimulus is called (a) a twitch, (b) wave summation, (c) multiple motor unit summation, (d) fused tetanus.

7. A smooth, sustained contraction resulting from very rapid stimulation of the muscle, in which no evidence of relaxation is seen, is called (a) a twitch, (b) wave summation, (c) multiple motor unit summation, (d) fused tetanus.

8. Characteristics of isometric contractions include all but (a) shortening, (b) increased muscle tension throughout the contraction phase, (c) absence of shortening, (d) use in resistance training.

9. During muscle contraction, ATP is provided by (a) a coupled reaction of creatine phosphate with ADP, (b) aerobic respiration of glucose, and (c) anaerobic glycolysis.

_____ (1) Which provides ATP fastest?
_____ (2) Which does (do) not require that oxygen be available?
_____ (3) Which provides the highest yield of ATP per glucose molecule?
_____ (4) Which results in the formation of lactic acid?
_____ (5) Which has carbon dioxide and water products?
_____ (6) Which is most important in endurance sports?

10. The neurotransmitter released by somatic motor neurons is (a) acetylcholine, (b) acetylcholinesterase, (c) norepinephrine.

11. The ions that enter the skeletal muscle cell during action potential generation are (a) calcium ions, (b) chloride ions, (c) sodium ions, (d) potassium ions.

12. Myoglobin has a special function in muscle tissue. It (a) breaks down glycogen, (b) is a contractile protein, (c) holds a reserve supply of oxygen in the muscle.

13. Aerobic exercise results in all of the following except (a) increased cardiovascular system efficiency, (b) more mitochondria in the muscle cells, (c) increased size and strength of existing muscle cells, (d) increased neuromuscular system coordination.

14. The smooth muscle type found in the walls of digestive and urinary system organs and that exhibits gap junctions and pacemaker cells is (a) multiunit, (b) single-unit.

Short Answer Essay Questions

15. Name and describe the four special functional abilities of muscle that are the basis for muscle response.

16. Distinguish between (a) direct and indirect muscle attachments and (b) a tendon and an aponeurosis.

17. (a) Describe the structure of a sarcomere and indicate the relationship of the sarcomere to myofilaments. (b) Explain the sliding filament theory of contraction using appropriately labeled diagrams of a relaxed and a contracted sarcomere.

18. What is the importance of acetylcholinesterase in muscle cell contraction?

19. Explain how a slight (but smooth) contraction differs from a vigorous contraction of the same muscle; use the concepts of multiple motor unit summation.

20. Explain what is meant by the term excitation-contraction coupling.

21. Define and draw a motor unit.

22. Describe the three distinct types of skeletal muscle fibers.

23. True or false: Most muscles contain a predominance of one skeletal muscle fiber type. Explain the reasoning behind your choice.

24. Describe some cause(s) of muscle fatigue and define this term clearly.

25. Define oxygen deficit.

26. Smooth muscle has some unique properties, such as low energy usage, and the ability to maintain contraction over long periods. Tie these properties to the function of smooth muscle in the body.

Critical Thinking and Clinical Application Questions

1. Jim Fitch decided that his physique left much to be desired, so he joined a local health club and began to "pump iron" three times weekly. After three months of training, during which he was able to lift increasingly heavier weights, he noticed that his arm and chest muscles were substantially larger. Explain the structural and functional basis of these changes.

2. When a suicide victim was found, the coroner was unable to remove the drug vial clutched in his hand. Explain the reasons for this. If the victim had been discovered three days later, would the coroner have had the same difficulty? Explain.

3. Muscle-relaxing drugs are administered to a patient during major surgery. Which of the two chemicals described next would be a good skeletal muscle relaxant and why?
   - Chemical A binds to and blocks ACh receptors of muscle cells.
   - Chemical B floods the muscle cells' cytoplasm with Ca^{2+}.

4. Michael is answering a series of questions dealing with skeletal muscle cell excitation and contraction. In response to "What protein changes shape when Ca^{2+} binds to it?" he writes "tropomyosin." What should he have responded and what is the result of that calcium ion binding?

PEARSON

myA&P™
place

Access everything you need to practice, review, and self-assess for both your A&P lecture and lab courses at **myA&P** (www.myaandp.com). There, you'll find powerful online resources, including chapter quizzes and tests, games, A&P Flix animations with quizzes, **Interactive Physiology**® with quizzes, MP3 Tutor Sessions, Practice Anatomy Lab™, and more to help you get a better grade in your course.

10

The Muscular System

Interactions of Skeletal Muscles in the Body (p. 321)

Naming Skeletal Muscles (pp. 321–322)

Muscle Mechanics: Importance of Fascicle Arrangement and Leverage (pp. 322–324)

Arrangement of Fascicles (pp. 322–323)

Lever Systems: Bone-Muscle Relationships (pp. 323–324)

Major Skeletal Muscles of the Body (pp. 324–382)

The human body enjoys an incredibly wide range of movements. The gentle blinking of your eye, standing on tiptoe, and wielding a sledgehammer are just a small sample of the different activities promoted by your muscular system. Muscle tissue includes all contractile tissues (skeletal, cardiac, and smooth muscle), but when we study the muscular system, **skeletal muscles** take center stage. These muscular "machines" that enable us to perform so many different activities are the focus of this chapter. Before describing the individual muscles in detail, we will describe the manner in which muscles "play" with or against each other to bring about movements, consider the criteria used for naming muscles, and explain the principles of leverage.

Interactions of Skeletal Muscles in the Body

▶ Describe the function of prime movers, antagonists, synergists, and fixators.

The arrangement of body muscles permits them to work either together or in opposition to achieve a wide variety of movements. As you eat, for example, you alternately raise your fork to your lips and lower it to your plate, and both sets of actions are accomplished by your arm and hand muscles. But muscles can only *pull*; they never *push*. Generally as a muscle shortens, its *insertion* (attachment on the movable bone) moves toward its *origin* (its fixed or immovable point of attachment). Whatever one muscle or muscle group can do, another muscle or group of muscles can "undo."

Muscles can be classified into four *functional* groups: prime movers, antagonists, synergists, and fixators. A muscle that has the major responsibility for producing a specific movement is a **prime mover**, or **agonist** (ag′o-nist; "leader"), of that movement. The biceps brachii muscle, which fleshes out the anterior arm (and inserts on the radius), is a prime mover of elbow flexion.

Muscles that oppose, or reverse, a particular movement are called **antagonists** (an-tag′o-nists; "against the leaders"). When a prime mover is active, the antagonist muscles may be stretched or may remain relaxed. Usually however, antagonists help to regulate the action of a prime mover by contracting slightly to provide some resistance, thus helping to prevent overshooting the mark or to slow or stop the movement. As you might expect, a prime mover and its antagonist are located on opposite sides of the joint across which they act. Antagonists can also be prime movers in their own right. For example, flexion of the forearm by the biceps brachii muscle of the arm is antagonized by the triceps brachii, the prime mover for extending the forearm. As noted in Chapter 9, it is important that the two members of any agonist/antagonist pair be challenged and developed equally to prevent undue tension on the less developed muscle and joint inflexibility.

In addition to agonists and antagonists, most movements involve the action of one or more **synergists** (sin′er-jists; *syn* = together, *erg* = work). Synergists help prime movers by (1) adding a little extra force to the same movement or (2) reducing undesirable or unnecessary movements that might occur as the prime mover contracts. This second function deserves more explanation. When a muscle crosses two or more joints, its contraction causes movement at all of the spanned joints unless other muscles act as joint stabilizers. For example, the finger flexor muscles cross both the wrist and the interphalangeal joints, but you can make a fist without bending your wrist because synergistic muscles stabilize the wrist. Additionally, as some flexors act, they may cause several other (undesirable) movements at the same joint. Synergists can prevent this, allowing all of the prime mover's force to be exerted in the desired direction.

When synergists immobilize a bone, or a muscle's origin so that the prime mover has a stable base on which to act, they are more specifically called **fixators** (fik′sa-terz). Recall from Chap-

ter 7 that the scapula is held to the axial skeleton only by muscles and is quite freely movable. The fixator muscles that run from the axial skeleton to the scapula can immobilize the scapula so that only the desired movements occur at the mobile shoulder joint. Additionally, muscles that help to maintain upright posture are fixators.

In summary, although prime movers seem to get all the credit for causing certain movements, antagonistic and synergistic muscles are also important in producing smooth, coordinated, and precise movements. Furthermore, a muscle may act as a prime mover in one movement, an antagonist for another movement, a synergist for a third movement, and so on.

Naming Skeletal Muscles

▶ List the criteria used in naming muscles. Provide an example to illustrate the use of each criterion.

Skeletal muscles are named according to a number of criteria, each of which describes the muscle in some way. Paying attention to these cues can simplify the task of learning muscle names and actions.

1. **Location of the muscle.** Some muscle names indicate the bone or body region with which the muscle is associated. For example, the temporalis (tem″por-ă′lis) muscle overlies the temporal bone, and intercostal (*costal* = rib) muscles run between the ribs.

2. **Shape of the muscle.** Some muscles are named for their distinctive shapes. For example, the deltoid (del′toid) muscle is roughly triangular (*deltoid* = triangle), and together the right and left trapezius (trah-pe′ze-us) muscles form a trapezoid.

3. **Relative size of the muscle.** Terms such as *maximus* (largest), *minimus* (smallest), *longus* (long), and *brevis* (short) are often used in muscle names—as in gluteus maximus and gluteus minimus (the large and small gluteus muscles, respectively).

4. **Direction of muscle fibers.** The names of some muscles reveal the direction in which their fibers (and fascicles) run in reference to some imaginary line, usually the midline of the body or the longitudinal axis of a limb bone. In muscles with the term *rectus* (straight) in their names, the fibers run parallel to that imaginary line (axis). The terms *transversus* and *oblique* indicate that the muscle fibers run respectively at right angles and obliquely to that line. Specific examples include the rectus femoris (straight muscle of the thigh, or femur) and transversus abdominis (transverse muscle of the abdomen).

5. **Number of origins.** When *biceps*, *triceps*, or *quadriceps* forms part of a muscle's name, you can assume that the muscle has two, three, or four origins, respectively. For example, the biceps brachii (bra′ke-i) muscle of the arm has two origins, or *heads*.

6. **Location of the attachments.** Some muscles are named according to their points of origin and insertion. The origin is always named first. For instance, the sternocleidomastoid

(ster″no-kli″do-mas′toid) muscle of the neck has a dual origin on the sternum (*sterno*) and clavicle (*cleido*), and it inserts on the *mastoid* process of the temporal bone.

7. **Action.** When muscles are named for the movement they produce, action words such as *flexor*, *extensor*, or *adductor* appear in the muscle's name. For example, the adductor longus, located on the medial thigh, brings about thigh adduction, and the supinator (soo′pĭ-na″tor) muscle supinates the forearm. (To review the terminology for various actions, see Chapter 8, Figures 8.5, 8.6, pp. 256–258.)

Often, several criteria are combined in the naming of a muscle. For instance, the name *extensor carpi radialis longus* tells us the muscle's action (extensor), what joint it acts on (*carpi* = wrist), and that it lies close to the radius of the forearm (radialis); it also hints at its size (longus) relative to other wrist extensor muscles. Unfortunately, not all muscle names are this descriptive.

CHECK YOUR UNDERSTANDING

1. The term "prime mover" is used in the business world to indicate people that get things done—the movers and shakers. What is its physiological meaning?
2. What criteria are used in naming each of the following muscles: *iliacus, adductor brevis, quadriceps femoris*?

For answers, see Appendix G.

Muscle Mechanics: Importance of Fascicle Arrangement and Leverage

▶ Name the common patterns of muscle fascicle arrangement and relate these to power generation.

▶ Define lever, and explain how a lever operating at a mechanical advantage differs from one operating at a mechanical disadvantage.

▶ Name the three types of lever systems and indicate the arrangement of effort, fulcrum, and load in each. Also note the advantages of each type of lever system.

We discussed most factors contributing to muscle force and speed (load, fiber type, etc.) in Chapter 9 with two important exceptions—the patterns of fascicle arrangement in muscles and lever systems. We attend to these factors next.

Arrangement of Fascicles

All skeletal muscles consist of fascicles (bundles of fibers), but fascicle arrangements vary, resulting in muscles with different shapes and functional capabilities. The most common patterns of fascicle arrangement are circular, convergent, parallel, and pennate **(Figure 10.1).**

The fascicular pattern is **circular** when the fascicles are arranged in concentric rings (Figure 10.1a). Muscles with this arrangement surround external body openings, which they

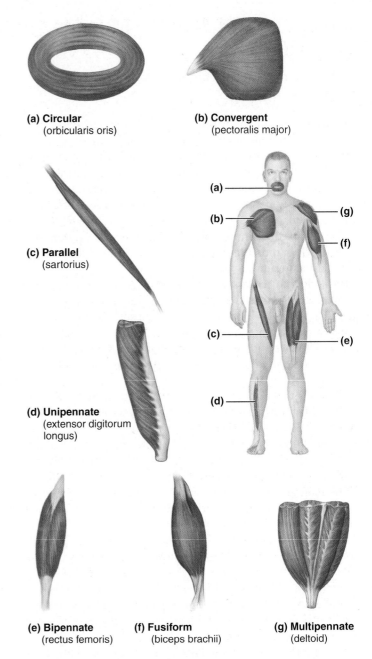

(a) Circular
(orbicularis oris)

(b) Convergent
(pectoralis major)

(c) Parallel
(sartorius)

(d) Unipennate
(extensor digitorum longus)

(e) Bipennate
(rectus femoris)

(f) Fusiform
(biceps brachii)

(g) Multipennate
(deltoid)

Figure 10.1 Patterns of fascicle arrangement in muscles.

close by contracting. A general term for such muscles is *sphincters* ("squeezers"). Examples are the orbicularis muscles surrounding the eyes and the mouth.

A **convergent** muscle has a broad origin, and its fascicles *converge* toward a single tendon of insertion. Such a muscle is triangular or fan shaped like the pectoralis major muscle of the anterior thorax (Figure 10.1b).

In a **parallel** arrangement, the long axes of the fascicles run parallel to the long axis of the muscle. Such muscles are either *straplike* like the sartorius muscle of the thigh (Figure 10.1c), or spindle shaped with an expanded belly (midsection), like the biceps brachii muscle of the arm (Figure 10.1f). However, some authorities classify the spindle-shaped muscles into a separate class as **fusiform muscles.** This is the approach we use here.

Effort x **length of effort arm** = **load** x **length of load arm**
(force x **distance)** = **(resistance** x **distance)**

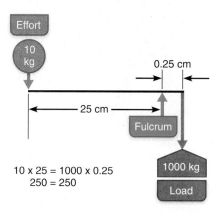

10 x 25 = 1000 x 0.25
250 = 250

(a) Mechanical advantage with a power lever

Figure 10.2 Lever systems operating at a mechanical advantage and a mechanical disadvantage. The equation at the top expresses the relationships among the forces and distances in any lever system. **(a)** Mechanical advantage with a power lever. When using a jack, the load lifted is greater than the applied muscular effort. Only 10 kg of force (the effort) is used to lift a 1000-kg car (the load).
(*Figure continues on p. 324*)

10

In a **pennate** (pen′āt) pattern, the fascicles (and thus the muscle fibers) are short and they attach obliquely (*penna* = feather) to a central tendon that runs the length of the muscle. If, as in the extensor digitorum longus muscle of the leg, the fascicles insert into only one side of the tendon, the muscle is *unipennate* (Figure 10.1d). If the fascicles insert into the tendon from opposite sides, so that the muscle's "grain" resembles a feather, the arrangement is *bipennate* (Figure 10.1e). The rectus femoris of the thigh is bipennate. A *multipennate* arrangement looks like many feathers situated side by side, with all their quills inserted into one large tendon. The deltoid muscle, which forms the roundness of the shoulder, is multipennate (Figure 10.1g).

The arrangement of a muscle's fascicles determines its range of motion (the amount of movement produced when a muscle shortens) and its power. Because skeletal muscle fibers may shorten to about 70% of their resting length when they contract, the longer and the more nearly parallel the muscle fibers are to a muscle's long axis, the more the muscle can shorten. Muscles with parallel fascicle arrangement shorten the most, but they are not usually very powerful. Muscle power depends more on the total number of muscle fibers in the muscle. The greater the number of muscle fibers, the greater the power. The stocky bipennate and multipennate muscles, which "pack in" the most fibers, shorten very little but are very powerful.

CHECK YOUR UNDERSTANDING

   3. Of the muscles illustrated in Figure 10.1, which could shorten most? Which two would likely be most powerful? Why?

For answers, see Appendix G.

Lever Systems: Bone-Muscle Relationships

The operation of most skeletal muscles involves the use of leverage and **lever systems** (partnerships between the muscular and skeletal systems). A **lever** is a rigid bar that moves on a fixed point called the **fulcrum**, when a force is applied to it. The applied force, or **effort**, is used to move a resistance, or **load**. In your body, your joints are the fulcrums, and your bones act as levers. Muscle contraction provides the effort which is applied at the muscle's insertion point on a bone. The load is the bone itself, along with overlying tissues and anything else you are trying to move with that lever.

A lever allows a given effort to move a heavier load, or to move a load farther or faster, than it otherwise could. If, as shown in **Figure 10.2a**, the load is close to the fulcrum and the effort is applied far from the fulcrum, a small effort exerted over a relatively large distance can be used to move a large load over a small distance. Such a lever is said to operate at a **mechanical advantage** and is commonly called a *power lever*. For example, as shown to the right in Figure 10.2a, a person can lift a car with such a lever, in this case, a jack. The car moves up only a small distance with each downward "push" of the jack handle, but relatively little muscle effort is needed.

If, on the other hand, the load is far from the fulcrum and the effort is applied near the fulcrum, the force exerted by the muscle must be greater than the load to be moved or supported, as Figure 10.2b shows. This lever system operates at a **mechanical disadvantage** and is a *speed lever*. These levers are useful because they allow a load to be moved rapidly over a large distance (with a wide range of motion). Wielding a shovel is an example. As you can see, small differences in the site of a muscle's insertion (relative to the fulcrum or joint) can translate into large

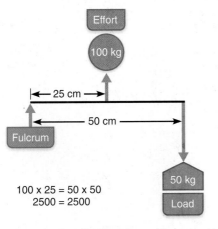

(b) Mechanical disadvantage with a speed lever

Figure 10.2 *(continued)* **Lever systems operating at a mechanical advantage and a mechanical disadvantage. (b)** Mechanical disadvantage with a speed lever. When using a shovel to lift dirt, the muscular force is greater than the load lifted. A muscular force (effort) of 100 kg is used to lift 50 kg of dirt (the load). Levers operating at a mechanical disadvantage are common in the body.

differences in the amount of force a muscle must generate to move a given load or resistance.

Regardless of type, all levers follow the same basic principle:

$$\frac{\text{Effort farther than}}{\text{load from fulcrum}} = \frac{\text{lever operates at a}}{\text{mechanical advantage}}$$

$$\frac{\text{Effort nearer than}}{\text{load to fulcrum}} = \frac{\text{lever operates at a}}{\text{mechanical disadvantage}}$$

Depending on the relative position of the three elements—effort, fulcrum, and load—a lever belongs to one of three classes. In **first-class levers**, the effort is applied at one end of the lever and the load is at the other, with the fulcrum somewhere between. Seesaws and scissors are first-class levers. First-class leverage also occurs when you lift your head off your chest (Figure 10.3a). Some first-class levers in the body operate at a mechanical advantage (for strength), but others, such as the action of the triceps muscle in extending the forearm against resistance, operate at a mechanical disadvantage (for speed and distance).

In a **second-class lever**, the effort is applied at one end of the lever and the fulcrum is located at the other, with the load between them. A wheelbarrow demonstrates this type of lever system. Second-class levers are uncommon in the body, but the best example is the act of standing on your toes (Figure 10.3b). All second-class levers in the body work at a mechanical advantage because the muscle insertion is always farther from the fulcrum than is the load. Second-class levers are levers of strength, but speed and range of motion are sacrificed for that strength.

In **third-class levers**, the effort is applied between the load and the fulcrum. These levers are speedy and *always* operate at a mechanical disadvantage. Tweezers or forceps provide this type of leverage. Most skeletal muscles of the body act in third-class lever systems. An example is the activity of the biceps muscle of the arm, lifting the distal forearm and anything carried in the

hand (Figure 10.3c). Third-class lever systems permit a muscle to be inserted very close to the joint across which movement occurs, which allows rapid, extensive movements (as in throwing) with relatively little shortening of the muscle. Muscles involved in third-class levers tend to be thicker and more powerful.

In conclusion, differences in the positioning of the three elements modify muscle activity with respect to (1) speed of contraction, (2) range of movement, and (3) the weight of the load that can be lifted. In lever systems that operate at a mechanical disadvantage (speed levers), force is lost but speed and range of movement are gained. Systems that operate at a mechanical advantage (power levers) are slower, more stable, and used where strength is a priority.

CHECK YOUR UNDERSTANDING

4. Which of the three lever systems involved in muscle mechanics would be the fastest lever—first-, second-, or third-class?
5. What benefit is provided by a lever that operates at a mechanical advantage?

For answers, see Appendix G.

Major Skeletal Muscles of the Body

▶ Name and identify the muscles described in Tables 10.1 to 10.17. State the origin, insertion, and action of each.

The grand plan of the muscular system is all the more impressive because of the sheer number of skeletal muscles in the body—more than 600 of them (many more than are shown in **Figures 10.4** and **10.5** combined)! Trying to remember all the

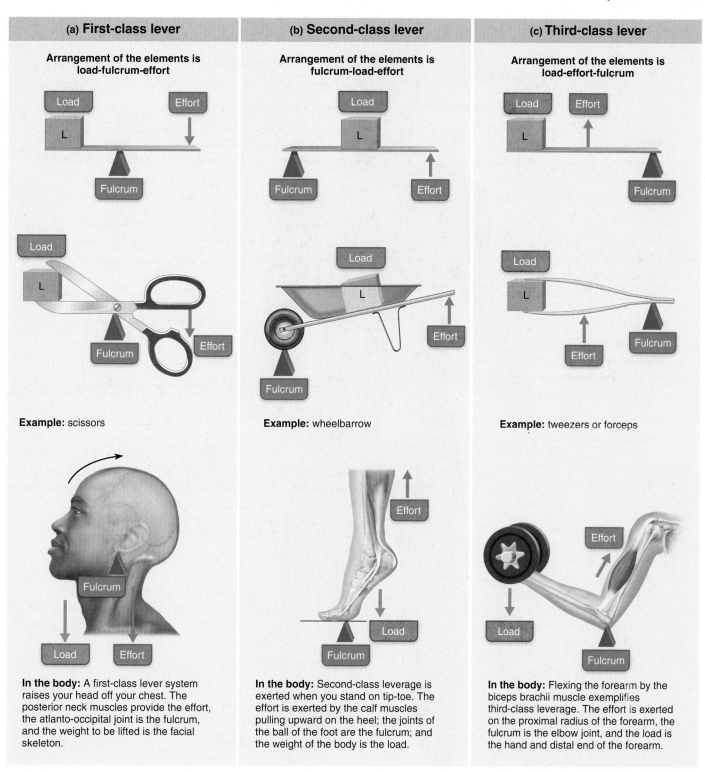

| **(a) First-class lever** | **(b) Second-class lever** | **(c) Third-class lever** |

Arrangement of the elements is **load-fulcrum-effort**

Arrangement of the elements is **fulcrum-load-effort**

Arrangement of the elements is **load-effort-fulcrum**

Example: scissors

Example: wheelbarrow

Example: tweezers or forceps

In the body: A first-class lever system raises your head off your chest. The posterior neck muscles provide the effort, the atlanto-occipital joint is the fulcrum, and the weight to be lifted is the facial skeleton.

In the body: Second-class leverage is exerted when you stand on tip-toe. The effort is exerted by the calf muscles pulling upward on the heel; the joints of the ball of the foot are the fulcrum; and the weight of the body is the load.

In the body: Flexing the forearm by the biceps brachii muscle exemplifies third-class leverage. The effort is exerted on the proximal radius of the forearm, the fulcrum is the elbow joint, and the load is the hand and distal end of the forearm.

Figure 10.3 Lever systems.

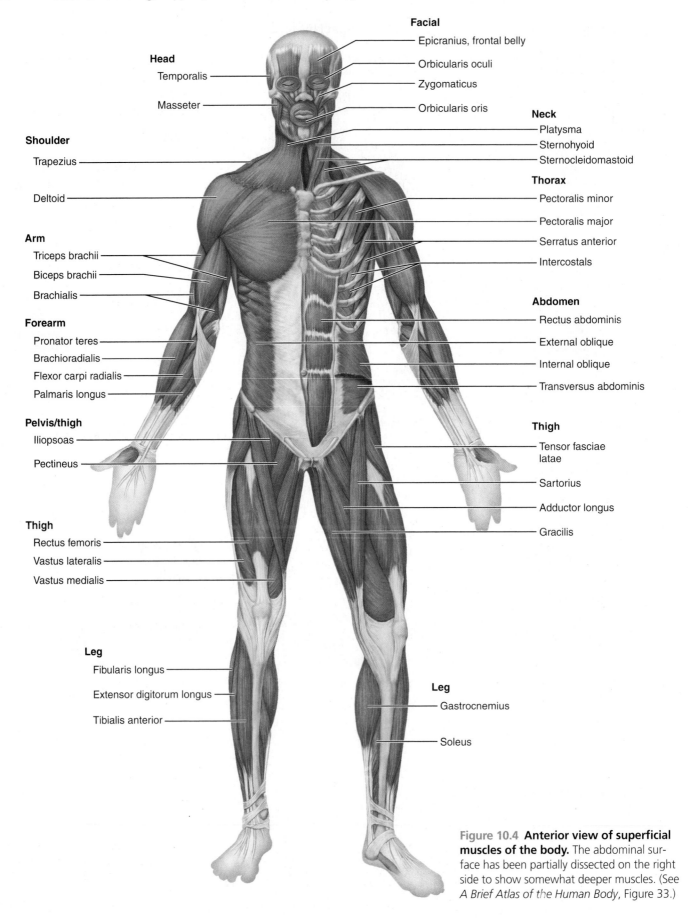

Facial
Epicranius, frontal belly
Orbicularis oculi
Zygomaticus
Orbicularis oris

Head
Temporalis
Masseter

Neck
Platysma
Sternohyoid
Sternocleidomastoid

Shoulder
Trapezius
Deltoid

Thorax
Pectoralis minor
Pectoralis major
Serratus anterior
Intercostals

Arm
Triceps brachii
Biceps brachii
Brachialis

Abdomen
Rectus abdominis
External oblique
Internal oblique
Transversus abdominis

Forearm
Pronator teres
Brachioradialis
Flexor carpi radialis
Palmaris longus

Pelvis/thigh
Iliopsoas
Pectineus

Thigh
Tensor fasciae latae
Sartorius
Adductor longus
Gracilis

Thigh
Rectus femoris
Vastus lateralis
Vastus medialis

Leg
Fibularis longus
Extensor digitorum longus
Tibialis anterior

Leg
Gastrocnemius
Soleus

Figure 10.4 Anterior view of superficial muscles of the body. The abdominal surface has been partially dissected on the right side to show somewhat deeper muscles. (See *A Brief Atlas of the Human Body*, Figure 33.)

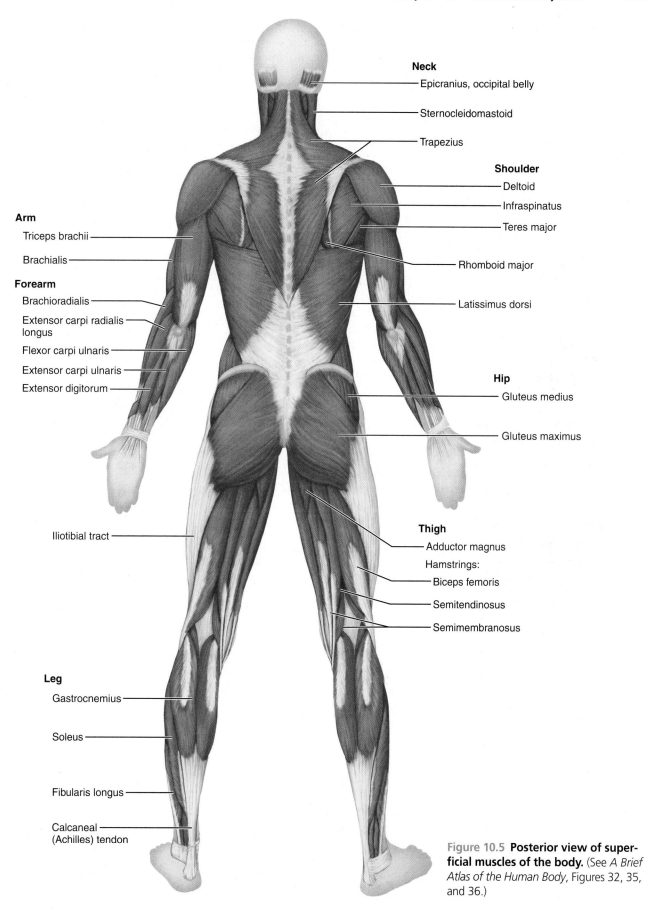

Neck
- Epicranius, occipital belly
- Sternocleidomastoid
- Trapezius

Shoulder
- Deltoid
- Infraspinatus
- Teres major
- Rhomboid major
- Latissimus dorsi

Arm
- Triceps brachii
- Brachialis

Forearm
- Brachioradialis
- Extensor carpi radialis longus
- Flexor carpi ulnaris
- Extensor carpi ulnaris
- Extensor digitorum

Hip
- Gluteus medius
- Gluteus maximus

Thigh
- Adductor magnus
- Hamstrings:
- Biceps femoris
- Semitendinosus
- Semimembranosus

- Iliotibial tract

Leg
- Gastrocnemius
- Soleus
- Fibularis longus
- Calcaneal (Achilles) tendon

10

Figure 10.5 Posterior view of superficial muscles of the body. (See *A Brief Atlas of the Human Body*, Figures 32, 35, and 36.)

names, locations, and actions of these muscles is a monumental task. Take heart; here we consider only the principal muscles (approximately 125 pairs of them). Although this number is far fewer than 600, the job of learning about all these muscles will still require a concerted effort on your part.

Memorization will be easier if you can apply what you have learned in a practical, or clinical, way; that is, with a *functional anatomy focus*. Once you are satisfied that you have learned the name of a muscle and can identify it on a cadaver, model, or diagram, you must then flesh out your learning by asking yourself, "What does it do?" [It might be a good idea to review body movements (pp. 253–259) before you get to this point.]

In the tables that follow, the muscles of the body have been grouped by function and by location, roughly from head to foot. Each table is keyed to a particular figure or group of figures illustrating the muscles it describes. The legend at the beginning of each table provides an overview of the types of movements effected by the muscles listed and gives pointers on the way those muscles interact with one another. The table itself describes each muscle's shape, location relative to other muscles, origin and insertion, primary actions, and innervation. (Because some instructors want students to defer learning the muscle innervations until the nervous system has been studied, you might want to check on what is expected of you in this regard.)

As you consider each muscle, be alert to the information its name provides. After reading its entire description, identify the muscle on the corresponding figure and, in the case of superficial muscles, also on Figure 10.4 or Figure 10.5. Doing so will help you to link the descriptive material in the table to a visual image of the muscle's location in the body. Also try to relate a muscle's attachments and location to its actions. This will focus your attention on functional details that often escape student awareness. For example, both the elbow and knee joints are hinge joints that allow flexion and extension. However, the knee flexes to the dorsum of the body (the calf moves toward the posterior thigh), whereas elbow flexion carries the forearm toward the anterior aspect of the arm. Therefore, leg flexors are located on the posterior thigh, while forearm flexors are found on the anterior aspect of the humerus. Because many muscles have several actions, we have indicated the primary action of each muscle in blue type in the tables.

Finally, keep in mind that the *best* way to learn muscle actions is to act out their movements yourself while feeling for the muscles contracting (bulging) beneath your skin.

The sequence of the tables in this chapter is

- **Table 10.1** Muscles of the Head, Part I: Facial Expression (Figure 10.6); pp. 329–331.
- **Table 10.2** Muscles of the Head, Part II: Mastication and Tongue Movement (Figure 10.7); pp. 332–333.
- **Table 10.3** Muscles of the Anterior Neck and Throat: Swallowing (Figure 10.8); pp. 334–335.
- **Table 10.4** Muscles of the Neck and Vertebral Column: Head Movements and Trunk Extension (Figure 10.9); pp. 336–339.
- **Table 10.5** Muscles of the Thorax: Breathing (Figure 10.10); pp. 340–341.
- **Table 10.6** Muscles of the Abdominal Wall: Trunk Movements and Compression of Abdominal Viscera (Figure 10.11); pp. 342–343.
- **Table 10.7** Muscles of the Pelvic Floor and Perineum: Support of Abdominopelvic Organs (Figure 10.12); pp. 344–345.
- **Table 10.8** Superficial Muscles of the Anterior and Posterior Thorax: Movements of the Scapula (Figure 10.13); pp. 346–349.
- **Table 10.9** Muscles Crossing the Shoulder Joint: Movements of the Arm (Humerus) (Figure 10.14); pp. 350–352.
- **Table 10.10** Muscles Crossing the Elbow Joint: Flexion and Extension of the Forearm (Figure 10.14); p. 353.
- **Table 10.11** Muscles of the Forearm: Movements of the Wrist, Hand, and Fingers (Figures 10.15 and 10.16); pp. 354–357.
- **Table 10.12** Summary of Actions of Muscles Acting on the Arm, Forearm, and Hand (Figure 10.17); pp. 358–359.
- **Table 10.13** Intrinsic Muscles of the Hand: Fine Movements of the Fingers (Figure 10.18); pp. 360–362.
- **Table 10.14** Muscles Crossing the Hip and Knee Joints: Movements of the Thigh and Leg (Figures 10.19 and 10.20); pp. 363–369.
- **Table 10.15** Muscles of the Leg: Movements of the Ankle and Toes (Figures 10.21 to 10.23); pp. 370–375.
- **Table 10.16** Intrinsic Muscles of the Foot: Toe Movement and Arch Support (Figure 10.24); pp. 376–379.
- **Table 10.17** Summary of Major Actions of Muscles Acting on the Thigh, Leg, and Foot (Figure 10.25); pp. 380–381.

MUSCLE GALLERY

TABLE 10.1   **Muscles of the Head, Part I: Facial Expression** (Figure 10.6)

The muscles that promote facial expression lie in the scalp and face just deep to the skin. They are thin and variable in shape and strength, and adjacent muscles tend to be fused. They are unusual muscles in that they insert into skin (or other muscles), not bones. In the scalp, the main muscle is the **epicranius**, which has distinct anterior and posterior parts. The lateral scalp muscles are vestigial in humans. Muscles clothing the facial bones lift the eyebrows, flare the nostrils, open and close the eyes and mouth, and provide one of the best tools for influencing others—the smile. The tremendous importance of facial muscles in nonverbal communication becomes especially clear when they are paralyzed, as in some stroke victims and in the expressionless "mask" of patients with Parkinson's disease. All muscles listed in this table are innervated by *cranial nerve VII*, the *facial nerve* (see Table 13.2). The external muscles of the eyes, which act to direct the eyeballs, and the levator palpebrae superioris muscles that raise the eyelids are described in Chapter 15.

MUSCLE	DESCRIPTION	ORIGIN (O) AND INSERTION (I)	ACTION	NERVE SUPPLY
MUSCLES OF THE SCALP				
Epicranius (occipitofrontalis) (ep"ĭ-kra'ne-us; ok-sip"ĭ-to-fron-ta'lis) (*epi* = over; *cran* = skull)	Bipartite muscle consisting of the frontal and occipital bellies connected by a cranial aponeurosis, the galea aponeurotica; the alternate actions of these two muscles pull scalp forward and backward			
▪ **Frontal belly** (fron'tal) (*front* = forehead)	Covers forehead and dome of skull; no bony attachments	O—galea aponeurotica I—skin of eyebrows and root of nose	With aponeurosis fixed, raises the eyebrows (as in surprise); wrinkles forehead skin horizontally	Facial nerve (cranial VII)
▪ **Occipital belly** (ok-sip"ĭ-tal') (*occipito* = base of skull)	Overlies posterior occiput; by pulling on the galea, fixes origin of frontalis	O—occipital and temporal bones I—galea aponeurotica	Fixes aponeurosis and pulls scalp posteriorly	Facial nerve
MUSCLES OF THE FACE				
Corrugator supercilii (kor'ah-ga-ter soo"per-sĭ'le-i) (*corrugo* = wrinkle; *supercilium* = eyebrow)	Small muscle; activity associated with that of orbicularis oculi	O—arch of frontal bone above nasal bone I—skin of eyebrow	Draws eyebrows together and inferiorly; wrinkles skin of forehead vertically (as in frowning)	Facial nerve

10

MUSCLE GALLERY

| TABLE 10.1 | Muscles of the Head, Part I: Facial Expression (Figure 10.6) *(continued)* |

MUSCLE	DESCRIPTION	ORIGIN (O) AND INSERTION (I)	ACTION	NERVE SUPPLY
Orbicularis oculi (or-bik'u-lar-is ok'u-li) (*orb* = circular; *ocul* = eye)	Thin, tripartite sphincter muscle of eyelid; surrounds rim of the orbit	O—frontal and maxillary bones and ligaments around orbit I—tissue of eyelid	Closes eye; various parts can be activated individually; produces blinking, squinting, and draws eyebrows inferiorly	Facial nerve
Zygomaticus—major and minor (zi-go-mat'ĭ-kus) (*zygomatic* = cheekbone)	Muscle pair extending diagonally from cheekbone to corner of mouth	O—zygomatic bone I—skin and muscle at corner of mouth	Raises lateral corners of mouth upward (smiling muscle)	Facial nerve
Risorius (ri-zor'e-us) (*risor* = laughter)	Slender muscle inferior and lateral to zygomaticus	O—lateral fascia associated with masseter muscle I—skin at angle of mouth	Draws corner of lip laterally; tenses lips; synergist of zygomaticus	Facial nerve
Levator labii superioris (lĕ-va'tor la'be-i soo-per"e-or'is) (*leva* = raise; *labi* = lip; *superior* = above, over)	Thin muscle between orbicularis oris and inferior eye margin	O—zygomatic bone and infraorbital margin of maxilla I—skin and muscle of upper lip	Opens lips; raises and furrows the upper lip	Facial nerve
Depressor labii inferioris (de-pres'or la'be-i in-fer"e-or'is) (*depressor* = depresses; *infer* = below)	Small muscle running from mandible to lower lip	O—body of mandible lateral to its midline I—skin and muscle of lower lip	Draws lower lip inferiorly (as in a pout)	Facial nerve
Depressor anguli oris (ang'gu-li or-is) (*angul* = angle, corner; *or* = mouth)	Small muscle lateral to depressor labii inferioris	O—body of mandible below incisors I—skin and muscle at angle of mouth below insertion of zygomaticus	Draws corners of mouth downward and laterally (as in a "tragedy mask" grimace); zygomaticus antagonist	Facial nerve
Orbicularis oris	Complicated, multilayered muscle of the lips with fibers that run in many different directions; most run circularly	O—arises indirectly from maxilla and mandible; fibers blended with fibers of other facial muscles associated with the lips I—encircles mouth; inserts into muscle and skin at angles of mouth	Closes lips; purses and protrudes lips; kissing and whistling muscle	Facial nerve
Mentalis (men-ta'lis) (*ment* = chin)	One of the muscle pair forming a V-shaped muscle mass on chin	O—mandible below incisors I—skin of chin	Wrinkles chin; protrudes lower lip	Facial nerve
Buccinator (bu'sĭ-na"ter) (*bucc* = cheek or "trumpeter")	Thin, horizontal cheek muscle; principal muscle of cheek; deep to masseter (see also Figure 10.7)	O—molar region of maxilla and mandible I—orbicularis oris	Compresses cheek (as in whistling and sucking); trampoline-like action holds food between teeth during chewing; draws corner of mouth laterally; well developed in nursing infants	Facial nerve
Platysma (plah-tiz'mah) (*platy* = broad, flat)	Unpaired, thin, sheetlike superficial neck muscle; not strictly a head muscle, but plays a role in facial expression	O—fascia of chest (over pectoral muscles and deltoid) I—lower margin of mandible, and skin and muscle at corner of mouth	Tenses skin of neck (e.g., during shaving); helps depress mandible; pulls lower lip back and down, i.e., produces downward sag of mouth	Facial nerve

MUSCLE GALLERY

TABLE 10.1 *(continued)*

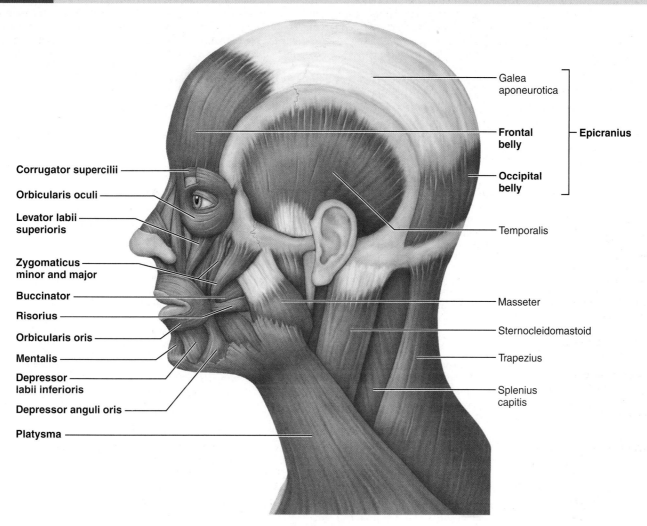

Figure 10.6 Lateral view of muscles of the scalp, face, and neck.

TABLE 10.2 Muscles of the Head, Part II: Mastication and Tongue Movement (Figure 10.7)

Four pairs of muscles are involved in mastication (chewing and biting) activities, and all are innervated by the *mandibular branch* of *cranial nerve V* (the *trigeminal nerve*). The prime movers of jaw closure (and biting) are the powerful **masseter** and **temporalis** muscles, which can be palpated easily when the teeth are clenched (Figure 10.7a). Side-to-side grinding movements are brought about by the **pterygoid** muscles (Figure 10.7b). The **buccinator** muscles (see Table 10.1) also play a role in chewing. Normally, gravity is sufficient to depress the mandible, but if there is resistance to jaw opening, neck muscles such as the digastric and mylohyoid muscles (see Table 10.3) are activated.

The tongue is composed of muscle fibers that curl, squeeze, and fold the tongue during speaking and chewing. These **intrinsic tongue muscles**, arranged in several planes, change the shape of the tongue and contribute to its exceptional nimbleness, but they do not really move the tongue. They are considered in Chapter 23 with the digestive system. In this table, we consider only the **extrinsic tongue muscles**, which anchor and move the tongue (Figure 10.7c). All extrinsic tongue muscles are innervated by *cranial nerve XII*, the *hypoglossal nerve* (see Table 13.2).

MUSCLE	DESCRIPTION	ORIGIN (O) AND INSERTION (I)	ACTION	NERVE SUPPLY
MUSCLES OF MASTICATION				
Masseter (mah-se′ter) (*maseter* = chewer)	Powerful muscle that covers lateral aspect of mandibular ramus	O—zygomatic arch and zygomatic bone I—angle and ramus of mandible	Prime mover of jaw closure; elevates mandible	Trigeminal nerve (cranial V)
Temporalis (tem″por-ă′lis) (*tempora* = time; pertaining to the temporal bone)	Fan-shaped muscle that covers parts of the temporal, frontal, and parietal bones	O—temporal fossa I—coronoid process of mandible via a tendon that passes deep to zygomatic arch	Closes jaw; elevates and retracts mandible; maintains position of the mandible at rest; deep anterior part may help protract mandible	Trigeminal nerve
Medial pterygoid (me′de-ul ter′ĭ-goid) (*medial* = toward median plane; *pterygoid* = winglike)	Deep two-headed muscle that runs along internal surface of mandible and is largely concealed by that bone	O—medial surface of lateral pterygoid plate of sphenoid bone, maxilla, and palatine bone I—medial surface of mandible near its angle	Acts with the lateral pterygoid muscle to protrude (protract) mandible and to promote side-to-side side (grinding) movements; synergist of temporalis and masseter muscles in elevation of the mandible	Trigeminal nerve
Lateral pterygoid (*lateral* = away from median plane)	Deep two-headed muscle; lies superior to medial pterygoid muscle	O—greater wing and lateral pterygoid plate of sphenoid bone I—condyle of mandible and capsule of temporomandibular joint	Provides forward sliding and side-to-side grinding movements of the lower teeth; protrudes mandible (pulls it anteriorly)	Trigeminal nerve
Buccinator	See Table 10.1	See Table 10.1	Compresses the cheek; helps keep food between grinding surfaces of teeth during chewing	Facial nerve (cranial VII)
MUSCLES PROMOTING TONGUE MOVEMENTS (EXTRINSIC MUSCLES)				
Genioglossus (je″ne-o-glah′sus) (*geni* = chin; *glossus* = tongue)	Fan-shaped muscle; forms bulk of inferior part of tongue; its attachment to mandible prevents tongue from falling backward and obstructing respiration	O—internal surface of mandible near symphysis I—inferior aspect of the tongue and body of hyoid bone	Protracts tongue; can depress or act in concert with other extrinsic muscles to retract tongue	Hypoglossal nerve (cranial XII)
Hyoglossus (hi′o-glos″us) (*hyo* = pertaining to hyoid bone)	Flat, quadrilateral muscle	O—body and greater horn of hyoid bone I—inferolateral tongue	Depresses tongue and draws its sides downward	Hypoglossal nerve
Styloglossus (sti-lo-glah′sus) (*stylo* = pertaining to *styloid* process)	Slender muscle running superiorly to and at right angles to hyoglossus	O—styloid process of temporal bone I—inferolateral tongue	Retracts (and elevates) tongue	Hypoglossal nerve

MUSCLE GALLERY

TABLE 10.2 *(continued)*

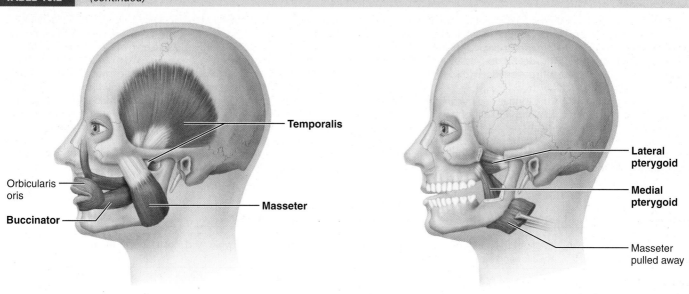

(a)

(b)

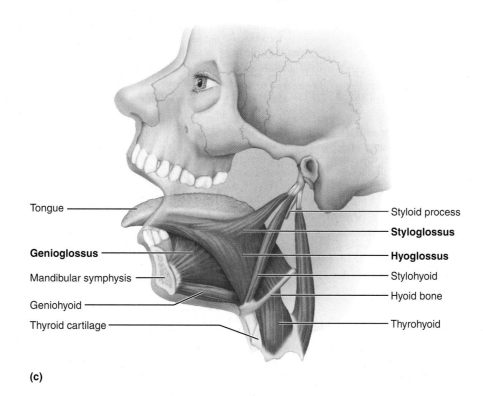

(c)

Figure 10.7 Muscles promoting mastication and tongue movements. (a) Lateral view of the temporalis, masseter, and buccinator muscles. **(b)** Lateral view of the deep chewing muscles, the medial and lateral pterygoid muscles. **(c)** Extrinsic muscles of the tongue. Some suprahyoid muscles of the throat are also illustrated.

MUSCLE GALLERY

TABLE 10.3	**Muscles of the Anterior Neck and Throat: Swallowing** (Figure 10.8)

The neck is divided into two triangles (anterior and posterior) by the sternocleidomastoid muscle (Figure 10.8a). In this table, we consider the muscles of the *anterior* triangle, which are divided into **suprahyoid** and **infrahyoid muscles** (above and below the hyoid bone respectively). Most of these muscles are deep (throat) muscles involved in swallowing.

Swallowing begins when the tongue and buccinator muscles of the cheeks squeeze the food back along the roof of the mouth toward the pharynx. Then a rapid series of muscular movements in the posterior mouth and pharynx complete the process. Events of swallowing include: (1) The *suprahyoid muscles* pull the hyoid bone upward and forward toward the mandible, which widens the pharynx to receive the food. Since the hyoid bone is attached by the thyrohyoid membrane to the larynx (Figure 10.8c), the larynx is also pulled upward and forward under the cover of the flaplike epiglottis, a maneuver that closes off the respiratory passageway (larynx) so that food is not aspirated (inhaled) into the lungs. (2) Small muscles that elevate the soft palate close off the nasal passages to prevent food from entering the superior nasal cavity. (These muscles, the *tensor* and *levator veli palatini*, are not described in the table but are illustrated in Figure 10.8c.) (3) Food is propelled through the pharynx into the esophagus inferiorly by muscles in the wall of the pharynx, the **pharyngeal constrictor muscles**. (4) The *infrahyoid muscles* return the hyoid bone and larynx to their more inferior positions as swallowing ends.

MUSCLE	DESCRIPTION	ORIGIN (O) AND INSERTION (I)	ACTION	NERVE SUPPLY
SUPRAHYOID MUSCLES (soo″prah-hi′oid)	Muscles that help form floor of oral cavity, anchor tongue, elevate hyoid, and move larynx superiorly during swallowing; lie superior to hyoid bone			
Digastric (di-gas′trik) (*di* = two; *gaster* = belly)	Consists of two bellies united by an intermediate tendon, forming a V shape under the chin	O—lower margin of mandible (anterior belly) and mastoid process of the temporal bone (posterior belly) I—by a connective tissue loop to hyoid bone	Open mouth and depress mandible; acting in concert, the digastric muscles elevate hyoid bone and steady it during swallowing and speech	Mandibular branch of trigeminal nerve (cranial V) for anterior belly; facial nerve (cranial VII) for posterior belly
Stylohyoid (sti″lo-hi′oid) (also see Figure 10.7)	Slender muscle below angle of jaw; parallels posterior belly of digastric muscle	O—styloid process of temporal bone I—hyoid bone	Elevates and retracts hyoid, thereby elongating floor of mouth during swallowing	Facial nerve
Mylohyoid (mi″lo-hi′oid) (*myle* = molar)	Flat, triangular muscle just deep to digastric muscle; this muscle pair forms a sling that forms the floor of the anterior mouth	O—medial surface of mandible I—hyoid bone and median raphe (a median strip of connective tissue between the mylohyoid muscles)	Elevates hyoid bone and floor of mouth, enabling tongue to exert backward and upward pressure that forces food bolus into pharynx	Mandibular branch of trigeminal nerve
Geniohyoid (je′ne-o-hy″oid) (also see Figure 10.7) (*geni* = chin)	Narrow muscle in contact with its partner medially; runs from chin to hyoid bone deep to mylohyoid	O—inner surface of mandibular symphysis I—hyoid bone	Pulls hyoid bone superiorly and anteriorly, shortening floor of mouth and widening pharynx for receiving food	First cervical spinal nerve via hypoglossal nerve (cranial XII)
INFRAHYOID MUSCLES	Straplike muscles that depress the hyoid bone and larynx during swallowing and speaking (see also Figure 10.9c)			
Sternohyoid (ster″no-hi′oid) (*sterno* = sternum)	Most medial muscle of the neck: thin; superficial except inferiorly, where covered by sternocleidomastoid	O—manubrium and medial end of clavicle I—lower margin of hyoid bone	Depresses larynx and hyoid bone if mandible is fixed; may also flex skull	Cervical spinal nerves 1–3 (C_1–C_3) through ansa cervicalis (slender nerve root in cervical plexus)
Sternothyroid (ster′no-thi′roid) (*thyro* = thyroid cartilage)	Lateral and deep to sternohyoid	O—posterior surface of manubrium of sternum I—thyroid cartilage	Pulls larynx and hyoid bone inferiorly	As for sternohyoid
Omohyoid (o″mo-hi′oid) (*omo* = shoulder)	Straplike muscle with two bellies united by an intermediate tendon; lateral to sternohyoid	O—superior surface of scapula I—hyoid bone, lower border	Depresses and retracts hyoid bone	As for sternohyoid
Thyrohyoid (thi″ro-hi′oid) (also see Figure 10.7)	Appears as a superior continuation of sternothyroid muscle	O—thyroid cartilage I—hyoid bone	Depresses hyoid bone or elevates larynx if hyoid is fixed	First cervical nerve via hypoglossal nerve

MUSCLE GALLERY

TABLE 10.3	*(continued)*

MUSCLE	DESCRIPTION	ORIGIN (O) AND INSERTION (I)	ACTION	NERVE SUPPLY
Pharyngeal constrictor muscles—superior, middle, and inferior (far-rin'je-al)	Composite of three paired muscles whose fibers run circularly in pharynx wall; superior muscle is innermost and inferior one is outermost; substantial overlap	O—attached anteriorly to mandible and medial pterygoid plate (superior), hyoid bone (middle), and laryngeal cartilages (inferior) I—posterior median raphe of pharynx	Constrict pharynx during swallowing, which propels a food bolus to esophagus (via a massagelike action called peristalsis)	Pharyngeal plexus [branches of vagus nerve (X)]

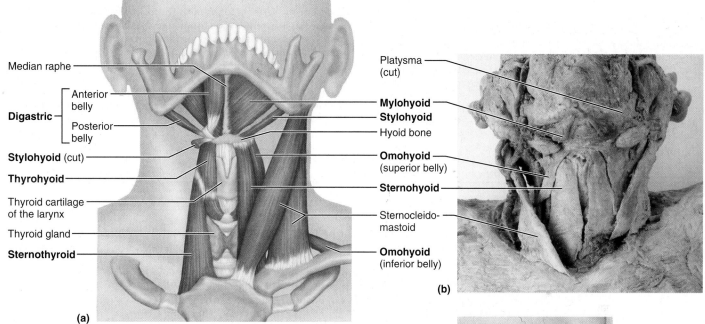

10

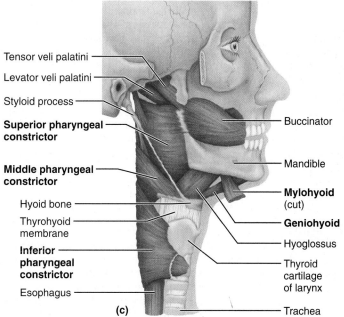

Figure 10.8 Muscles of the anterior neck and throat that promote swallowing. (a) Anterior view of the suprahyoid and infrahyoid muscles. The sternocleidomastoid muscle (not involved in swallowing) is shown on the right side of the illustration to provide an anatomical landmark. Deeper neck muscles are illustrated on the left side. **(b)** Cadaver photo of suprahyoid and infrahyoid muscles. (See *A Brief Atlas of the Human Body,* Figures 44 and 45.) **(c)** Lateral view of the constrictor muscles of the pharynx shown in their proper anatomical relationship to the buccinator (a chewing muscle) and the hyoglossus muscle (which promotes tongue movements).

MUSCLE GALLERY

| TABLE 10.4 | Muscles of the Neck and Vertebral Column: Head Movements and Trunk Extension (Figure 10.9) |

Head movements

The head is moved by muscles originating from the axial skeleton. The major head flexors are the **sternocleidomastoid muscles** (Figure 10.9 a, c), with some help from the suprahyoid and infrahyoid muscles described in Table 10.3. Lateral head movements (rotating or tilting the head) result when the muscles on only one side of the neck contract. These actions are effected by the sternocleidomastoids and a number of deeper neck muscles, considered in this table. Head extension is aided by the trapezius muscles of the back, but the main extensors of the head are the **splenius** muscles deep to the trapezius muscles (Figure 10.9b).

Trunk extension

Trunk extension is effected by the *deep* or *intrinsic back muscles* associated with the bony vertebral column. These deep muscles of the back also maintain the normal curvatures of the spine, acting as postural muscles. As you consider these back muscles, keep in mind that they are deep. The superficial back muscles that cover them are concerned primarily with movements of the shoulder girdle and upper limbs (see Tables 10.8 and 10.9).

The deep muscles of the back form a broad, thick column extending from the sacrum to the skull. Many muscles of varying length contribute to this mass. It helps to regard each of these individual muscles as a string that when pulled causes one or several vertebrae to extend or to rotate on the vertebrae below. The largest of the deep back muscle groups is the **erector spinae** group (Figure 10.9d). Because the origins and insertions of the different muscle groups overlap extensively, and many of these muscles are long, large regions of the vertebral column can be moved simultaneously and smoothly. Acting in concert, the deep back muscles extend (or hyperextend) the spine, but contraction of the muscles on only one side causes lateral bending (flexion) of the spine. Lateral flexion is automatically accompanied by some degree of rotation of the vertebral column. During vertebral movements, the articular facets of the vertebrae glide on each other.

In addition to the long back muscles, a number of short muscles extend from one vertebra to the next. These small muscles act primarily as synergists in extension and rotation of the spine and as spine stabilizers. They are not described in the table but you can deduce their actions by examining their origins and insertions in Figure 10.9e.

As noted, it is the trunk *extensors* that we consider in this table. The more superficial muscles, which have other functions, are considered in subsequent tables. For example, the anterior muscles of the abdominal wall that cause trunk *flexion* are described in Table 10.6.

MUSCLE	DESCRIPTION	ORIGIN (O) AND INSERTION (I)	ACTION	NERVE SUPPLY
ANTEROLATERAL NECK MUSCLES (FIGURE 10.9a AND c)				
Sternocleidomastoid (ster″no-kli″do-mas′toid) (*sterno* = breastbone; *cleido* = clavicle; *mastoid* = mastoid process)	Two-headed muscle located deep to platysma on anterolateral surface of neck; fleshy parts on either side of neck delineate limits of anterior and posterior triangles; key muscular landmark in neck; spasms of one of these muscles may cause torticollis (wryneck)	O—manubrium of sternum and medial portion of clavicle I—mastoid process of temporal bone and superior nuchal line of occipital bone	Flexes and laterally rotates the head; simultaneous contraction of both muscles causes neck flexion, generally against resistance as when one raises head when lying on back; acting alone, each muscle rotates head toward shoulder on opposite side and tilts or laterally flexes head to its own side	Accessory nerve (cranial nerve XI) and branches of cervical spinal nerves C_2 and C_3 (ventral rami)
Scalenes (ska′lēnz)—anterior, middle, and posterior (*scalene* = uneven)	Located more laterally than anteriorly on neck; deep to platysma and sternocleidomastoid	O—transverse processes of cervical vertebrae I—anterolaterally on first two ribs	Elevate first two ribs (aid in inspiration); flex and rotate neck	Cervical spinal nerves
INTRINSIC MUSCLES OF THE BACK (FIGURE 10.9b, d, e)				
Splenius (sple′ne-us)—capitis and cervicis portions (kă′pĭ-tis; ser-vis′us) (*splenion* = bandage; *caput* = head; *cervi* = neck) (Figures 10.9b and 10.6)	Broad bipartite superficial muscle (capitis and cervicis parts) extending from upper thoracic vertebrae to skull; capitis portion known as "bandage muscle" because it covers and holds down deeper neck muscles	O—ligamentum nuchae,* spinous processes of vertebrae C_7–T_6 I—mastoid process of temporal bone and occipital bone (capitis); transverse processes of C_2–C_4 vertebrae (cervicis)	Extend or hyperextend head; when splenius muscles on one side are activated, head is rotated and bent laterally toward same side	Cervical spinal nerves (dorsal rami)

*The ligamentum nuchae (lig″ah-men′tum noo′ke) is a strong, elastic ligament extending from the occipital bone of the skull along the tips of the spinous processes of the cervical vertebrae. It binds the cervical vertebrae together and inhibits excessive head and neck flexion, thus preventing damage to the spinal cord in the vertebral canal.

MUSCLE GALLERY

TABLE 10.4   (continued)

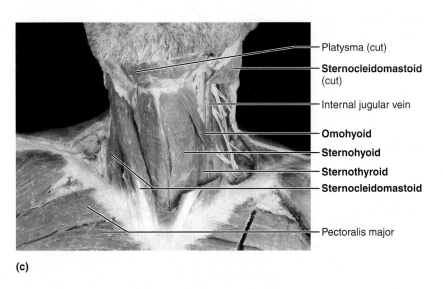

1st cervical vertebra

Sternocleido-mastoid

Base of occipital bone

Mastoid process

Middle scalene

Anterior scalene

Posterior scalene

(a) Anterior

Mastoid process

Splenius capitis

Spinous processes of the vertebrae

Splenius cervicis

(b) Posterior

10

Platysma (cut)

Sternocleidomastoid (cut)

Internal jugular vein

Omohyoid

Sternohyoid

Sternothyroid

Sternocleidomastoid

Pectoralis major

(c)

Figure 10.9 **Muscles of the neck and vertebral column causing movements of the head and trunk.** (See *A Brief Atlas of the Human Body*, Plate 44.) **(a)** Muscles of the anterolateral neck; superficial platysma muscle and the deeper neck muscles removed. **(b)** Deep muscles of the posterior neck; superficial muscles removed. **(c)** Photograph of the anterior and lateral regions of the neck.

MUSCLE GALLERY

TABLE 10.4 **Muscles of the Neck and Vertebral Column: Head Movements and Trunk Extension (Figure 10.9)** *(continued)*

MUSCLE	DESCRIPTION	ORIGIN (O) AND INSERTION (I)	ACTION	NERVE SUPPLY
Erector spinae (e-rek'tor spi'ne) Also called **sacrospinalis** (Figure 10.9d, left side)	Prime mover of back extension. Each side consists of three columns—the iliocostalis, longissimus, and spinalis muscles—forming intermediate layer of intrinsic back muscles. Erector spinae provide resistance that helps control action of bending forward at the waist and act as powerful extensors to promote return to erect position. During full flexion (i.e., when touching fingertips to floor), erector spinae are relaxed and strain is borne entirely by ligaments of back; on reversal of the movement, these muscles are initially inactive, and extension is initiated by hamstring muscles of thighs and gluteus maximus muscles of buttocks. As a result of this peculiarity, lifting a load or moving suddenly from a bent-over position is potentially dangerous (in terms of possible injury) to muscles and ligaments of back and intervertebral discs; erector spinae muscles readily go into painful spasms following injury to back structures.			
▪ **Iliocostalis** (il"e-o-kos-tă'lis)—lumborum, thoracis, and cervicis portions (lum'bor-um; tho-ra'sis) (*ilio* = ilium; *cost* = rib; *thorac* = thorax)	Most lateral muscle group of erector spinae muscles; extend from pelvis to neck	O—iliac crests (lumborum); inferior 6 ribs (thoracis); ribs 3 to 6 (cervicis) I—angles of ribs (lumborum and thoracis); transverse processes of cervical vertebrae C_6–C_4 (cervicis)	Extend and laterally flex the vertebral column; maintain erect posture; acting on one side, bend vertebral column to same side	Spinal nerves (dorsal rami)
▪ **Longissimus** (lon-jis'ĭ-mus)— thoracis, cervicis, and capitis parts (*longissimus* = longest)	Intermediate tripartite muscle group of erector spinae; extend by many muscle slips from lumbar region to skull; mainly pass between transverse processes of the vertebrae	O—transverse processes of lumbar through cervical vertebrae I—transverse processes of thoracic or cervical vertebrae and to ribs superior to origin as indicated by name; capitis inserts into mastoid process of temporal bone	Thoracis and cervicis act together to extend and laterally flex vertebral column; capitis extends head and turns the face toward same side	Spinal nerves (dorsal rami)
▪ **Spinalis** (spi-nă'lis)—thoracis and cervicis parts (*spin* = vertebral column, spine)	Most medial muscle column of erector spinae; cervicis usually rudimentary and poorly defined	O—spinous process of upper lumbar and lower thoracic vertebrae I—spinous process of upper thoracic and cervical vertebrae	Extends vertebral column	Spinal nerves (dorsal rami)
Semispinalis (sem'e-spĭ-nă'lis)—thoracis, cervicis, and capitis regions (*semi* = half) (Figure 10.9d, right side)	Composite muscle forming part of deep layer of intrinsic back muscles; extends from thoracic region to head	O—transverse processes of C_7–T_{12} I—occipital bone (capitis) and spinous processes of cervical (cervicis) and thoracic vertebrae T_1–T_4 (thoracis)	Extends vertebral column and head and rotates them to opposite side; acts synergistically with sternocleidomastoid muscles of opposite side	Spinal nerves (dorsal rami)
Quadratus lumborum (kwod-ra'tus lum-bor'um) (*quad* = four-sided; *lumb* = lumbar region) (See also Figure 10.19a)	Fleshy muscle forming part of posterior abdominal wall	O—iliac crest and lumbar fascia I—transverse processes of lumbar vertebrae L_1–L_4 and lower margin of 12th rib	Flexes vertebral column laterally when acting separately; when pair acts jointly, lumbar spine is extended and 12th rib is fixed; maintains upright posture; assists in forced inspiration	T_{12} and upper lumbar spinal nerves (ventral rami)

MUSCLE GALLERY

TABLE 10.4 *(continued)*

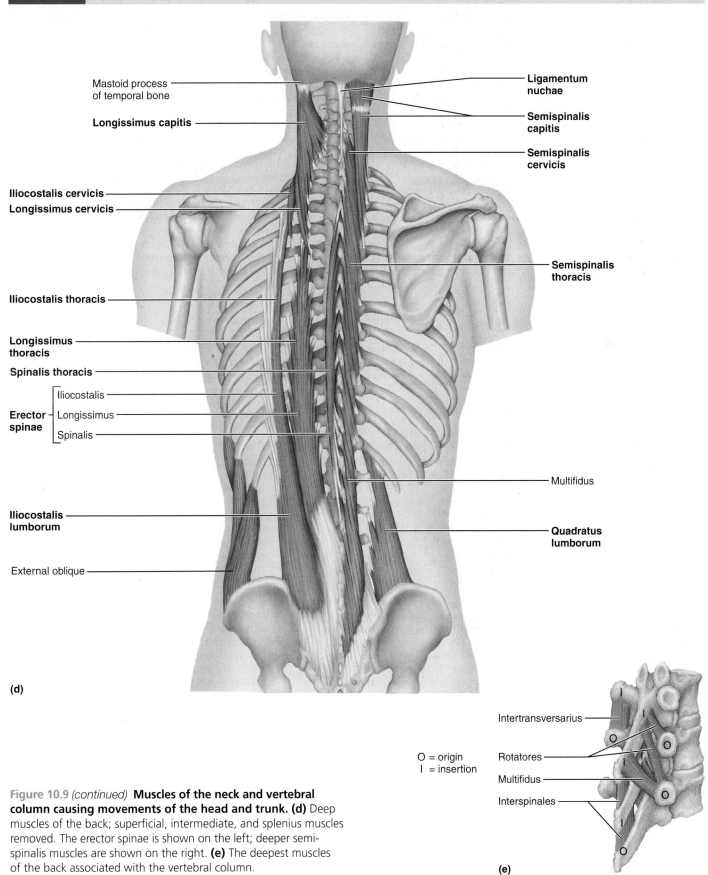

Mastoid process of temporal bone

Longissimus capitis

Iliocostalis cervicis

Longissimus cervicis

Iliocostalis thoracis

Longissimus thoracis

Spinalis thoracis

Erector spinae
- Iliocostalis
- Longissimus
- Spinalis

Iliocostalis lumborum

External oblique

Ligamentum nuchae

Semispinalis capitis

Semispinalis cervicis

Semispinalis thoracis

Multifidus

Quadratus lumborum

(d)

O = origin
I = insertion

Intertransversarius

Rotatores

Multifidus

Interspinales

Figure 10.9 *(continued)* **Muscles of the neck and vertebral column causing movements of the head and trunk. (d)** Deep muscles of the back; superficial, intermediate, and splenius muscles removed. The erector spinae is shown on the left; deeper semispinalis muscles are shown on the right. **(e)** The deepest muscles of the back associated with the vertebral column.

(e)

MUSCLE GALLERY

TABLE 10.5   Muscles of the Thorax: Breathing (Figure 10.10)

The primary function of the deep muscles of the thorax is to promote movements necessary for breathing. Breathing consists of two phases—inspiration, or inhaling, and expiration, or exhaling—caused by cyclic changes in the volume of the thoracic cavity.

Two main layers of muscles help form the anterolateral wall of the thorax.* The thoracic muscles are very short, most extending only from one rib to the next. On contraction, they draw the somewhat flexible ribs closer together. The **external intercostal muscles**, considered inspiratory muscles, form the more superficial layer (Figure 10.10a). They lift the rib cage, an action that increases the anterior to posterior and side-to-side dimensions of the thorax. The **internal intercostal muscles** form the deeper layer and may aid active (forced) expiration by depressing the rib cage. (However, quiet expiration is largely a passive phenomenon, resulting from relaxation of the external intercostals and diaphragm and elastic recoil of the lungs.)

The **diaphragm**, the most important muscle of inspiration, forms a muscular partition between the thoracic and abdominopelvic cavities (Figure 10.10b, c). In the relaxed state, the diaphragm is dome shaped. When it contracts it moves inferiorly and flattens, increasing the volume of the thoracic cavity, which draws air into the respiratory system passageways. The alternating rhythmic contraction and relaxation of the diaphragm also causes pressure changes in the abdominopelvic cavity below that facilitate the return of blood to the heart. In addition you can contract the diaphragm voluntarily to push down on the abdominal viscera and increase the pressure in the abdominopelvic cavity to help evacuate pelvic organ contents (urine, feces, or a baby) or during weight lifting. When you take a deep breath to fix the diaphragm, the abdomen becomes a firm pillar that will not buckle under the weight being lifted. Needless to say, it is important to have good control of the urinary bladder and anal sphincters during such maneuvers.

With the exception of the diaphragm, which is served by the *phrenic nerves*, the muscles listed in this table are served by *the intercostal nerves*, which run between the ribs.

Forced breathing (as during exercise) calls into play a number of other muscles that insert into the ribs. For example, during forced inspiration the scalene and sternocleidomastoid muscles of the neck help lift the ribs. Forced expiration is aided by muscles that pull the ribs inferiorly and those that push the diaphragm superiorly by compressing the abdominal contents (abdominal wall muscles).

MUSCLE	DESCRIPTION	ORIGIN (O) AND INSERTION (I)	ACTION	NERVE SUPPLY
External intercostals (in"ter-kos'talz) (*external* = toward the outside; *inter* = between; *cost* = rib)	11 pairs lie between ribs; fibers run obliquely (down and forward) from each rib to rib below; in lower intercostal spaces, fibers are continuous with external oblique muscle, forming part of abdominal wall	O—inferior border of rib above I—superior border of rib below	With first ribs fixed by scalene muscles, pull ribs toward one another to elevate rib cage; aid in inspiration; synergists of diaphragm	Intercostal nerves
Internal intercostals (*internal* = toward the inside, deep)	11 pairs lie between ribs; fibers run deep to and at right angles to those of external intercostals (i.e., run downward and posteriorly); lower internal intercostal muscles are continuous with fibers of internal oblique muscle of abdominal wall	O—superior border of rib below I—inferior border (costal groove) of rib above	With 12th ribs fixed by quadratus lumborum, muscles of posterior abdominal wall, and oblique muscles of the abdominal wall, they draw ribs together and depress rib cage; aid in forced expiration; antagonistic to external intercostals	Intercostal nerves
Diaphragm (di'ah-fram) (*dia* = across; *phragm* = partition)	Broad muscle pierced by the aorta, inferior vena cava, and esophagus, forms floor of thoracic cavity; in relaxed state is dome shaped; fibers converge from margins of thoracic cage toward a boomerang-shaped central tendon	O—inferior, internal surface of rib cage and sternum, costal cartilages of last six ribs and lumbar vertebrae I—central tendon	Prime mover of inspiration; flattens on contraction, increasing vertical dimensions of thorax; when strongly contracted, dramatically increases intra-abdominal pressure	Phrenic nerves

*Although there is a third (deepest) muscle layer of the thoracic wall, the muscles are small and discontinuous. Additionally, their function is unclear, so they are not included in this table.

MUSCLE GALLERY

TABLE 10.5 *(continued)*

Figure 10.10 Muscles of respiration. (a) Deep muscles of the thorax. The external intercostals (inspiratory muscles) are shown on the left and the internal intercostals (expiratory muscles) are shown on the right. These two muscle layers run obliquely and at right angles to each other. **(b)** Inferior view of the diaphragm, the prime mover of inspiration. Notice that its muscle fibers converge toward a central tendon, an arrangement that causes the diaphragm to flatten and move inferiorly as it contracts. **(c)** Photograph of the diaphragm, superior view. (See *A Brief Atlas of the Human Body*, Figure 63.)

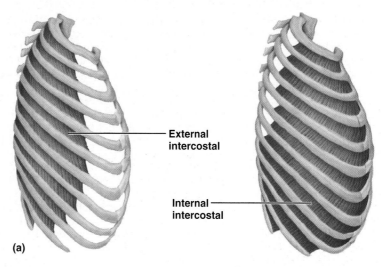

External intercostal

Internal intercostal

(a)

10

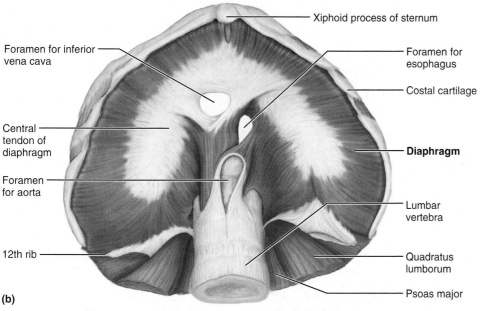

Xiphoid process of sternum

Foramen for inferior vena cava

Foramen for esophagus

Costal cartilage

Central tendon of diaphragm

Diaphragm

Foramen for aorta

Lumbar vertebra

12th rib

Quadratus lumborum

Psoas major

(b)

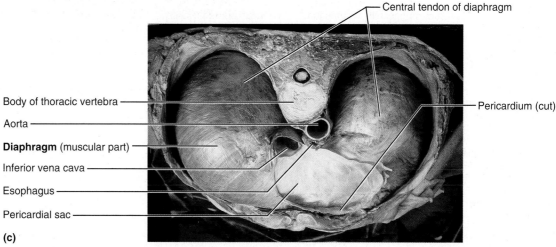

Central tendon of diaphragm

Body of thoracic vertebra

Aorta

Diaphragm (muscular part)

Inferior vena cava

Esophagus

Pericardial sac

Pericardium (cut)

(c)

MUSCLE GALLERY

| TABLE 10.6 | Muscles of the Abdominal Wall: Trunk Movements and Compression of Abdominal Viscera (Figure 10.11) |

Unlike the thorax, the anterior and lateral abdominal wall has no bony reinforcements (ribs). Instead, it is a composite of four paired muscles, their investing fasciae, and aponeuroses. Three broad flat muscle pairs, layered one atop the next, form the lateral abdominal walls: The fibers of the **external oblique muscle** run inferomedially and at right angles to those of the **internal oblique**, which immediately underlies it (Figure 10.11a, b). The fibers of the deep **transversus abdominis muscle** run horizontally across the abdomen at an angle to both. This alternation of fascicle directions is similar to the construction of plywood (which is made of sheets with different grains) and provides great strength. These three muscles blend into broad insertion aponeuroses anteriorly. The aponeuroses, in turn, enclose a fourth muscle pair medially, the straplike **rectus abdominis muscles**, and then fuse, forming the **linea alba** ("white line"), a tendinous raphe (seam) that runs from the sternum to the pubic symphysis (Figure 10.11a, c). The snug enclosure of the rectus abdominis muscles within the aponeuroses prevents them from "bowstringing" (protruding anteriorly) when they contract. The quadratus lumborum muscles of the *posterior* abdominal wall are covered in Table 10.4.

The abdominal muscles protect and support the viscera most effectively when they are well toned. When weak or severely stretched (as during pregnancy), they allow the abdomen to become pendulous (i.e., to form a potbelly). Additional functions include lateral flexion and rotation of the trunk and flexion of the trunk against resistance (as in sit-ups). During inspiration, the abdominal muscles relax, allowing the abdominal viscera to be pushed inferiorly by the descending diaphragm. When these abdominal muscles contract, several different activities may be effected. For example, when they contract simultaneously, the ribs are pulled inferiorly and the abdominal contents are compressed. This pushes the visceral organs upward on the diaphragm, aiding forced expiration. When the abdominal muscles contract with the diaphragm and the glottis is closed (an action called the Valsalva maneuver), the increased intra-abdominal pressure helps to promote urination, defecation, childbirth, vomiting, coughing, screaming, sneezing, burping, and nose blowing. (Next time you perform one of these activities, feel your abdominal muscles contract under your skin.) These muscles also contract during heavy lifting— sometimes so forcefully that hernias result. Contraction of the abdominal muscles as the deep back muscles contract helps prevent hyperextension of the spine and splints the entire body trunk.

MUSCLE	DESCRIPTION	ORIGIN (O) AND INSERTION (I)	ACTION	NERVE SUPPLY
MUSCLES OF THE ANTERIOR AND LATERAL ABDOMINAL WALL	Four paired flat muscles; important in supporting and protecting abdominal viscera and in promoting lateral flexion and flexion of the vertebral column			
Rectus abdominis (rek'tus ab-dom'ĭ-nis) (*rectus* = straight; *abdom* = abdomen)	Medial superficial muscle pair; extend from pubis to rib cage; ensheathed by aponeuroses of lateral muscles; segmented by three tendinous intersections	O—pubic crest and symphysis I—xiphoid process and costal cartilages of ribs 5–7	Flex and rotate lumbar region of vertebral column; fix and depress ribs, stabilize pelvis during walking, increase intra-abdominal pressure; used in sit-ups, curls	Intercostal nerves (T_6 or T_7–T_{12})
External oblique (o-blēk') (*external* = toward outside; *oblique* = running at an angle)	Largest and most superficial of the three lateral muscles; fibers run downward and medially (same direction outstretched fingers take when hands put into pants pockets); aponeurosis turns under inferiorly, forming inguinal ligament	O—by fleshy strips from outer surfaces of lower eight ribs I—most fibers insert into linea alba via a broad aponeurosis; some insert into pubic crest and tubercle and iliac crest	When pair contract simultaneously, flex vertebral column and compress abdominal wall and increase intra-abdominal pressure; acting individually, aid muscles of back in trunk rotation and lateral flexion; used in oblique curls	Intercostal nerves (T_7–T_{12})
Internal oblique (*internal* = toward the inside; deep)	Most fibers run upward and medially; however, the muscle fans so its inferior fibers run downward and medially	O—lumbar fascia, iliac crest, and inguinal ligament I—linea alba, pubic crest, last three or four ribs, and costal margin	As for external oblique	Intercostal nerves (T_7–T_{12}) and L_1
Transversus abdominis (trans-ver'sus) (*transverse* = running straight across)	Deepest (innermost) muscle of abdominal wall; fibers run horizontally	O—inguinal ligament, lumbar fascia, cartilages of last six ribs; iliac crest I—linea alba, pubic crest	Compresses abdominal contents	Intercostal nerves (T_7–T_{12}) and L_1

MUSCLE GALLERY

TABLE 10.6 *(continued)*

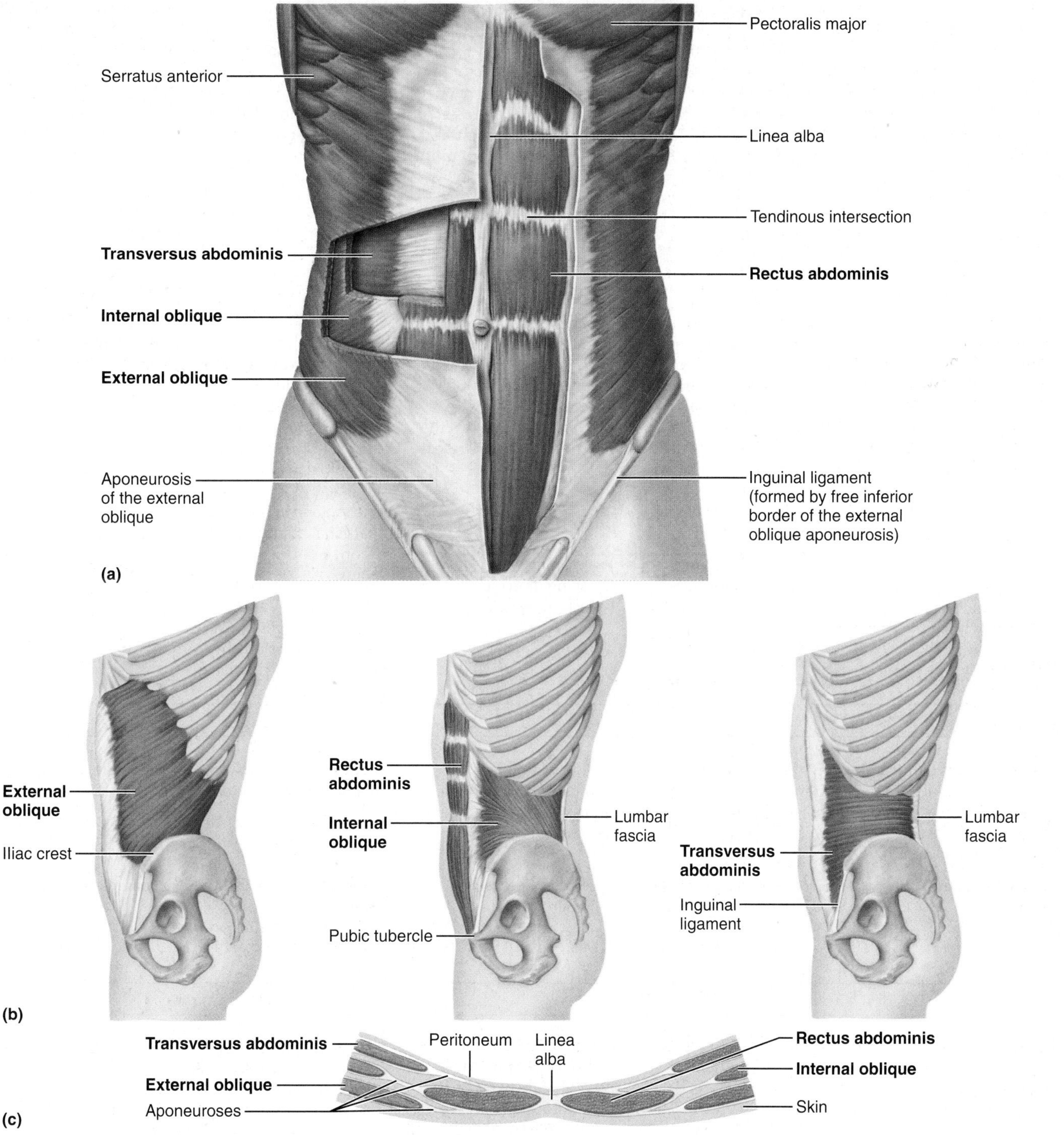

(a)

(b)

(c)

Figure 10.11 Muscles of the abdominal wall. (a) Anterior view of the muscles forming the anterolateral abdominal wall; superficial muscles partially cut away to reveal the deeper muscles. **(b)** Lateral view of the trunk, illustrating the fiber direction and attachments of the abdominal muscles. Although shown in the same view, the rectus abdominis is deep to the fascia of the internal oblique muscle. **(c)** Transverse section through the anterolateral abdominal wall (midregion), showing how the aponeuroses of the lateral abdominal muscles contribute to the rectus abdominis sheath.

MUSCLE GALLERY

TABLE 10.7   Muscles of the Pelvic Floor and Perineum: Support of Abdominopelvic Organs (Figure 10.12)

Two paired muscles, the **levator ani** and **coccygeus**, form the funnel-shaped pelvic floor, or **pelvic diaphragm** (Figure 10.12a). This diaphragm (1) seals the inferior opening of the bony pelvis, (2) supports the pelvic organs, (3) lifts the pelvic floor superiorly to release feces, and (4) resists increased intra-abdominal pressure (which would expel contents of the urinary bladder, rectum, and uterus). The pelvic diaphragm is pierced by the rectum and urethra (urinary tube), and by the vagina in females. The body region inferior to the pelvic diaphragm is the *perineum*. The relationships of the perineum are worth explaining. Inferior to the muscles of the pelvic floor, and stretching between the two sides of the pubic arch in the anterior half of the perineum, is the **urogenital diaphragm** (Figure 10.12b). This thin triangular sheet of muscle contains the **external urethral sphincter**, a sphincter muscle that surrounds the urethra and allows voluntary control of urination. Superficial to the urogenital diaphragm, and covered by the skin of the perineum, is the *superficial perineal space*, which contains muscles (**ischiocavernosus** and **bulbospongiosus**) that help maintain erection of the penis and clitoris (Figure 10.12c). In the posterior half of the perineum encircling the anus is the **external anal sphincter**, which allows voluntary control of defecation. Just anterior to this sphincter is the **central tendon of the perineum**, a strong tendon into which many of the perineal muscles insert.

MUSCLE	DESCRIPTION	ORIGIN (O) AND INSERTION (I)	ACTION	NERVE SUPPLY
MUSCLES OF THE PELVIC DIAPHRAGM (FIGURE 10.12a)				
Levator ani (lĕ-va′tor a′ne) (*levator* = raises; *ani* = anus)	Broad, thin, tripartite muscle (pubococcygeus, puborectalis, and iliococcygeus parts); its fibers extend inferomedially, forming a muscular "sling" around male prostate (or female vagina), urethra, and anorectal junction before meeting in the median plane	O—extensive linear origin inside pelvis from pubis to ischial spine I—inner surface of coccyx, levator ani of opposite side, and (in part) into the structures that penetrate it	Supports and maintains position of pelvic viscera; resists downward thrusts that accompany rises in intrapelvic pressure during coughing, vomiting, and expulsive efforts of abdominal muscles; forms sphincters at anorectal junction and vagina; lifts anal canal during defecation	S_3, S_4, and inferior rectal nerve (branch of pudendal nerve)
Coccygeus (kok-sij′e-us) (*coccy* = coccyx)	Small triangular muscle lying posterior to levator ani; forms posterior part of pelvic diaphragm	O—spine of ischium I—sacrum and coccyx	Supports pelvic viscera; supports coccyx and pulls it forward after it has been reflected posteriorly by defecation and childbirth	S_4 and S_5
MUSCLES OF THE UROGENITAL DIAPHRAGM (FIGURE 10.12b)				
Deep transverse perineal muscle (per″ĭ-ne′al) (*deep* = far from surface; *transverse* = across; *perine* = near anus)	Together the pair spans distance between ischial rami; in females, lies posterior to vagina	O—ischial rami I—midline central tendon of perineum; some fibers into vaginal wall in females	Supports pelvic organs; steadies central tendon	Pudendal nerve
External urethral sphincter (*sphin* = squeeze)	Muscle encircling urethra and vagina (female)	O—ischiopubic rami I—midline raphe	Constricts urethra; allows voluntary inhibition of urination; helps support pelvic organs	Pudendal nerve
MUSCLES OF THE SUPERFICIAL PERINEAL SPACE (FIGURE 10.12c)				
Ischiocavernosus (is′ke-o-kav′ern-o′sus) (*ischi* = hip; *caverna* = hollow chamber)	Runs from pelvis to base of penis or clitoris	O—ischial tuberosities I—crus of corpora cavernosa of male penis or female clitoris	Retards venous drainage and maintains erection of penis or clitoris	Pudendal nerve
Bulbospongiosus (bul″bo-spun″je-o′sus) (*bulbon* = bulb; *spongio* = sponge)	Encloses base of penis (bulb) in males and lies deep to labia in females	O—central tendon of perineum and midline raphe of penis I—anteriorly into corpora cavernosa of penis or clitoris	Empties male urethra; assists in erection of penis and of clitoris	Pudendal nerve
Superficial transverse perineal muscles (*superficial* = closer to surface)	Paired muscle bands posterior to urethral (and in females, vaginal) opening; variable; sometimes absent	O—ischial tuberosity I—central tendon of perineum	Stabilizes and strengthens midline tendon of perineum	Pudendal nerve

MUSCLE GALLERY

TABLE 10.7 *(continued)*

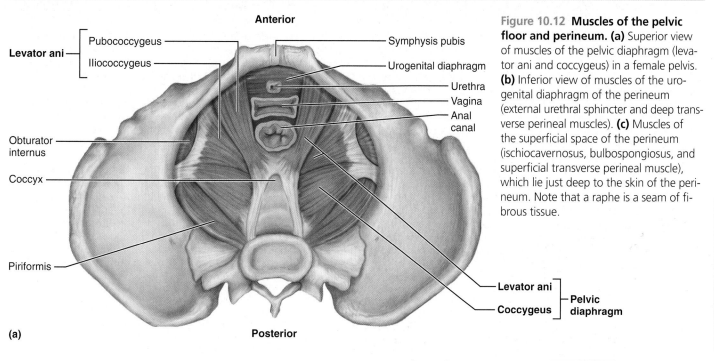

Anterior

Levator ani — Pubococcygeus
Iliococcygeus

Symphysis pubis
Urogenital diaphragm
Urethra
Vagina
Anal canal

Obturator internus

Coccyx

Piriformis

Levator ani
Coccygeus — Pelvic diaphragm

(a)

Posterior

Figure 10.12 **Muscles of the pelvic floor and perineum. (a)** Superior view of muscles of the pelvic diaphragm (levator ani and coccygeus) in a female pelvis. **(b)** Inferior view of muscles of the urogenital diaphragm of the perineum (external urethral sphincter and deep transverse perineal muscles). **(c)** Muscles of the superficial space of the perineum (ischiocavernosus, bulbospongiosus, and superficial transverse perineal muscle), which lie just deep to the skin of the perineum. Note that a raphe is a seam of fibrous tissue.

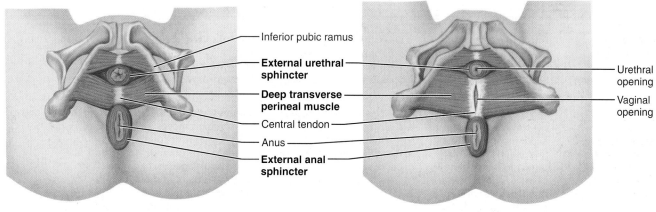

Inferior pubic ramus
External urethral sphincter
Deep transverse perineal muscle
Central tendon
Anus
External anal sphincter

Urethral opening
Vaginal opening

(b) Male — Female

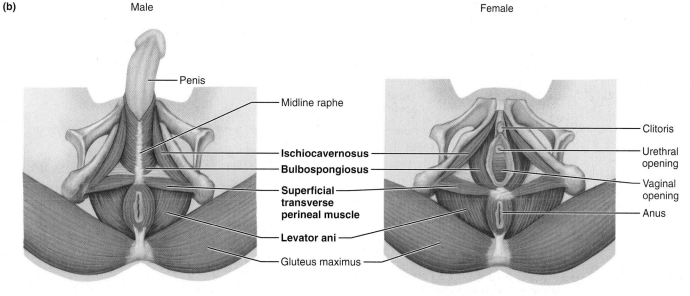

Penis
Midline raphe

Ischiocavernosus
Bulbospongiosus
Superficial transverse perineal muscle
Levator ani
Gluteus maximus

Clitoris
Urethral opening
Vaginal opening
Anus

(c) Male — Female

10

MUSCLE GALLERY

TABLE 10.8 **Superficial Muscles of the Anterior and Posterior Thorax: Movements of the Scapula** (Figure 10.13)

Most superficial thorax muscles are *extrinsic shoulder muscles*, which run from the ribs and vertebral column to the shoulder girdle. They both fix the scapula in place and move it to increase the range of arm movements. The anterior muscles of this group include the **pectoralis major**, **pectoralis minor**, **serratus anterior**, and **subclavius** (Figure 10.13a). Except for the pectoralis major, which inserts into the humerus, all muscles of the anterior group insert into the pectoral girdle. The posterior muscles include the **latissimus dorsi** and **trapezius muscles** superficially and the underlying **levator scapulae** and **rhomboids** (Figure 10.13c). The latissimus dorsi, like the pectoralis major muscles anteriorly, insert into the humerus and are more concerned with movements of the arm than of the scapula, so their consideration is deferred to Table 10.9 (arm-moving muscles).

The important movements of the pectoral girdle involve displacements of the scapula, i.e., its elevation and depression, rotation, lateral (forward) movements, and medial (backward) movements. The clavicles rotate around their own axes to provide both stability and precision to scapular movements.

Except for the serratus anterior, the anterior muscles stabilize and depress the shoulder girdle. Thus, most scapular movements are promoted by the serratus anterior muscles anteriorly and by posterior thoracic muscles. The arrangement of muscle attachments to the scapula is such that one muscle cannot bring about a simple (linear) movement on its own. To effect scapular movements, several muscles must act in combination.

The prime movers of shoulder (scapular) elevation are the superior trapezius fibers and the levator scapulae. When acting together to shrug the shoulder, their opposite rotational effects counterbalance each other. The scapula is depressed largely by gravity (weight of the arm), but when it is depressed against resistance, the inferior part of the trapezius, the pectoralis minor, and the serratus anterior (along with the latissimus dorsi, Table 10.9) are active. Anterolateral movements (abduction) of the scapula on the thorax wall, as in pushing or punching movements, mainly reflect serratus anterior activity. Posteromedial movement (adduction) of the scapula is effected mainly by the trapezius (midpart) and the rhomboids. Although the serratus anterior and trapezius muscles are antagonists in forward/backward movements of the scapulae, they act together to coordinate *rotational* scapular movements.

MUSCLE	DESCRIPTION	ORIGIN (O) AND INSERTION (I)	ACTION	NERVE SUPPLY
MUSCLES OF THE ANTERIOR THORAX (FIGURE 10.13a)				
Pectoralis minor (pek"to-ra'lis mi'nor) (*pectus* = chest, breast; *minor* = lesser)	Flat, thin muscle directly beneath and obscured by pectoralis major	O—anterior surfaces of ribs 3–5 (or 2–4) I—coracoid process of scapula	With ribs fixed, draws scapula forward and downward; with scapula fixed, draws rib cage superiorly	Medial and lateral pectoral nerves (C_6–C_8)
Serratus anterior (ser-a'tus) (*serratus* = saw)	Fan-shaped muscle; lies deep to scapula, deep and inferior to pectoral muscles on lateral rib cage; forms medial wall of axilla; origins have serrated, or sawtooth, appearance; paralysis results in "winging" of vertebral border of scapula away from chest wall, making arm elevation impossible	O—by a series of muscle slips from ribs 1–8 (or 9) I—entire anterior surface of vertebral border of scapula	Rotates scapula so that its inferior angle moves laterally and upward; prime mover to protract and hold scapula against chest wall; raises point of shoulder; important role in abduction and raising of arm and in horizontal arm movements (pushing, punching); called "boxer's muscle"	Long thoracic nerve (C_5–C_7)
Subclavius (sub-kla've-us) (*sub* = under, beneath; *clav* = clavicle)	Small cylindrical muscle extending from rib 1 to clavicle	O—costal cartilage of rib 1 I—groove on inferior surface of clavicle	Helps stabilize and depress pectoral girdle	Nerve to subclavius (C_5 and C_6)

MUSCLE GALLERY

TABLE 10.8 (continued)

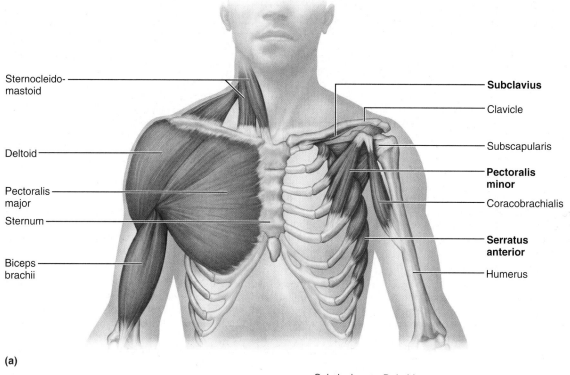

(a)

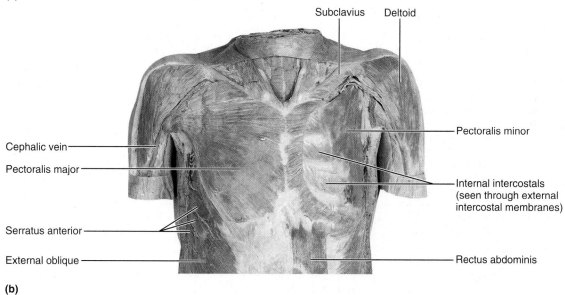

(b)

Figure 10.13 Superficial muscles of the thorax and shoulder acting on the scapula and arm. (a) Anterior view. The superficial muscles, which effect arm movements, are shown on the left side of the illustration. These muscles are removed on the right to show the muscles that stabilize or move the pectoral girdle. **(b)** Photo of superficial muscles of anterior thorax.

TABLE 10.8 **Superficial Muscles of the Anterior and Posterior Thorax: Movements of the Scapula (Figure 10.13)** *(continued)*

MUSCLE	DESCRIPTION	ORIGIN (O) AND INSERTION (I)	ACTION	NERVE SUPPLY
MUSCLES OF THE POSTERIOR THORAX (FIGURE 10.13c–e)				
Trapezius (trah-pe′ze-us) (*trapezion* = irregular four-sided figure)	Most superficial muscle of posterior thorax; flat, and triangular in shape; upper fibers run inferiorly to scapula; middle fibers run horizontally to scapula; lower fibers run superiorly to scapula	O—occipital bone, ligamentum nuchae, and spinous processes of C_7 and all thoracic vertebrae I—a continuous insertion along acromion and spine of scapula and lateral third of clavicle	Stabilizes, raises, retracts, and rotates scapula; middle fibers retract (adduct) scapula; superior fibers elevate scapula (as in shrugging the shoulders) or can help extend head with scapula fixed; inferior fibers depress scapula (and shoulder)	Accessory nerve (cranial nerve XI); C_3 and C_4
Levator scapulae (skap′u-le) (*levator* = raises)	Located at back and side of neck, deep to trapezius; thick, straplike muscle	O—transverse processes of C_1–C_4 I—medial border of the scapula, superior to the spine	Elevates/adducts scapula in concert with superior fibers of trapezius; tilts glenoid cavity downward when scapula is fixed, flexes neck to same side	Cervical spinal nerves and dorsal scapular nerve (C_3–C_5)
Rhomboids (rom′boidz)—major and minor (*rhomboid* = diamond shaped)	Two roughly diamond shaped muscles lying deep to trapezius and inferior to levator scapulae; rhomboid minor is the more superior muscle	O—spinous processes of C_7 and T_1 (minor) and spinous processes of T_2–T_5 (major) I—medial border of scapula	Stabilize scapula; act together (and with middle trapezius fibers) to retract (adduct) scapula, thus "squaring shoulders"; rotate scapula so that glenoid cavity is downward (as when arm is lowered against resistance; e.g., paddling a canoe)	Dorsal scapular nerve (C_4 and C_5)

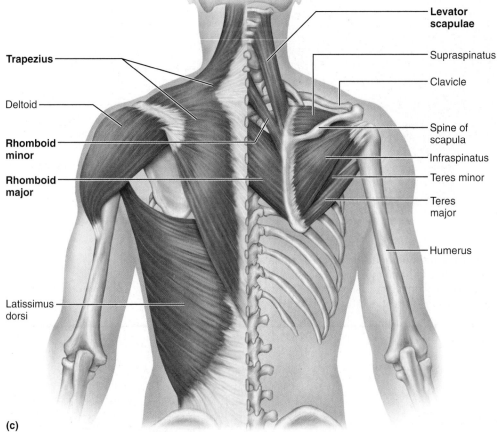

Figure 10.13 *(continued)* **Superficial muscles of the thorax and shoulder acting on the scapula and arm. (c)** Posterior view. The superficial muscles are shown on the left side of the illustration. Superficial muscles are removed on the right side to reveal the deeper muscles acting on the scapula, and the rotator cuff muscles that help stabilize the shoulder joint.

(c)

MUSCLE GALLERY

TABLE 10.8 *(continued)*

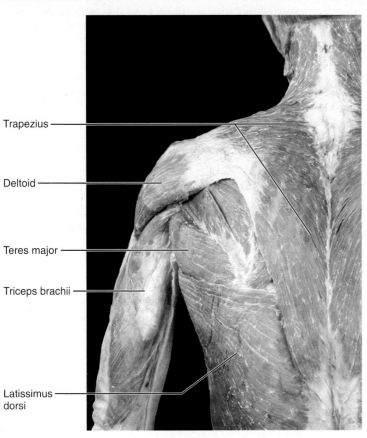

Trapezius

Deltoid

Teres major

Triceps brachii

Latissimus dorsi

(d)

Figure 10.13 *(continued)* **(d)** Dissection showing the superficial muscles of the back, left side. **(e)** Trapezius muscle has been removed in this dissection to expose the deeper muscles of the back, right side.

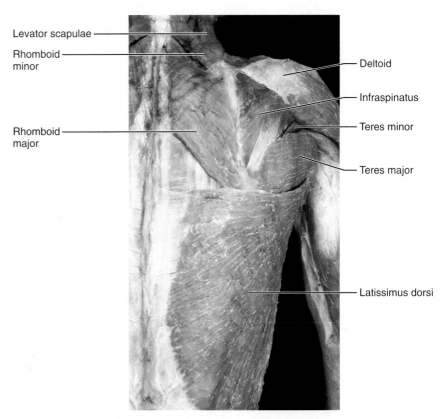

Levator scapulae

Rhomboid minor

Rhomboid major

Deltoid

Infraspinatus

Teres minor

Teres major

Latissimus dorsi

(e)

MUSCLE GALLERY

| **TABLE 10.9** | **Muscles Crossing the Shoulder Joint: Movements of the Arm (Humerus)** (Figure 10.14) |

Recall that the ball-and-socket shoulder joint is the most flexible joint in the body, but pays the price of instability. Several muscles cross each shoulder joint to insert on the humerus. All muscles acting on the humerus originate from the pectoral girdle; however, two of these—the latissimus dorsi and pectoralis major—primarily originate on the axial skeleton.

Of the nine muscles covered here, only the **pectoralis major, latissimus dorsi**, and **deltoid muscles** are prime movers of arm movements (Figure 10.14a, b). The remaining six are synergists and fixators. Four of these, the **supraspinatus, infraspinatus, teres minor**, and **subscapularis**, (marked with an asterisk* in Figure 10.14b, d), are *rotator cuff muscles*. They originate on the scapula, and their tendons blend with the fibrous capsule of the shoulder joint en route to the humerus. Although the rotator cuff muscles act as synergists in the angular and rotational movements of the arm, their main function is to reinforce the capsule of the shoulder joint to prevent dislocation of the humerus. The remaining two muscles, the small **teres major** and **coracobrachialis**, cross the shoulder joint but do not contribute to its reinforcement.

Generally speaking, muscles that originate *anterior* to the shoulder joint (pectoralis major, coracobrachialis, and anterior fibers of the deltoid) *flex* the arm, i.e., lift it anteriorly. The prime mover of arm flexion is the pectoralis major. The biceps brachii of the arm also assists in this action (Figure 10.14a, c; see Table 10.10). Muscles originating *posterior* to the shoulder joint extend the arm. These include the latissimus dorsi and posterior fibers of the deltoid muscles (both prime movers of arm extension) and the teres major. Note that the latissimus dorsi and pectoralis muscles are *antagonists* of one another in the flexion-extension movements of the arm.

The middle region of the fleshy deltoid muscle of the shoulder, which extends over the superolateral side of the humerus, is the prime mover of arm abduction. The main arm adductors are the pectoralis major anteriorly and latissimus dorsi posteriorly. The small muscles acting on the humerus promote lateral and medial rotation of the arm. The interactions among these nine muscles are complex and each contributes to several movements. A summary of their actions is provided in Table 10.12 (Part I).

MUSCLE	DESCRIPTION	ORIGIN (O) AND INSERTION (I)	ACTION	NERVE SUPPLY
Pectoralis major (pek"to-ra'lis ma'jer) (*pectus* = breast, chest; *major* = larger)	Large, fan-shaped muscle covering superior portion of chest; forms anterior axillary fold; divided into clavicular and sternal parts	O—sternal end of clavicle, sternum, cartilage of ribs 1–6 (or 7), and aponeurosis of external oblique muscle I—fibers converge to insert by a short tendon into intertubercular sulcus and greater tubercle of humerus	Prime mover of arm flexion; rotates arm medially; adducts arm against resistance; with scapula (and arm) fixed, pulls rib cage upward, thus can help in climbing, throwing, pushing, and in forced inspiration	Lateral and medial pectoral nerves (C_5–C_8 and T_1)
Deltoid (del'toid) (*delta* = triangular)	Thick, multipennate muscle forming rounded shoulder muscle mass; responsible for roundness of shoulder; a site commonly used for intramuscular injection, particularly in males, where it tends to be quite fleshy	O—embraces insertion of the trapezius; lateral third of clavicle; acromion and spine of scapula I—deltoid tuberosity of humerus	Prime mover of arm abduction when all its fibers contract simultaneously; antagonist of pectoralis major and latissimus dorsi, which adduct the arm; if only anterior fibers are active, can act powerfully in flexion and medial rotation of humerus, therefore synergist of pectoralis major; if only posterior fibers are active, causes extension and lateral rotation of arm; active during rhythmic arm swinging movements during walking	Axillary nerve (C_5 and C_6)

MUSCLE GALLERY

TABLE 10.9 (continued)

MUSCLE	DESCRIPTION	ORIGIN (O) AND INSERTION (I)	ACTION	NERVE SUPPLY
Latissimus dorsi (lah-tis′ĭ-mus dor′si) (*latissimus* = widest; *dorsi* = back)	Broad, flat, triangular muscle of lower back (lumbar region); extensive superficial origins; covered by trapezius superiorly; contributes to the posterior wall of axilla	O—indirect attachment via lumbodorsal fascia into spines of lower six thoracic vertebrae, lumbar vertebrae, lower 3 to 4 ribs, and iliac crest; also from scapula's inferior angle I—spirals around teres major to insert in floor of intertubercular sulcus of humerus	Prime mover of arm extension; powerful arm adductor; medially rotates arm at shoulder; because of its power in these movements, it plays an important role in bringing the arm down in a power stroke, as in striking a blow, hammering, swimming, and rowing; with arms fixed overhead, it pulls the rest of the body upward and forward	Thoracodorsal nerve (C_6–C_8)

10

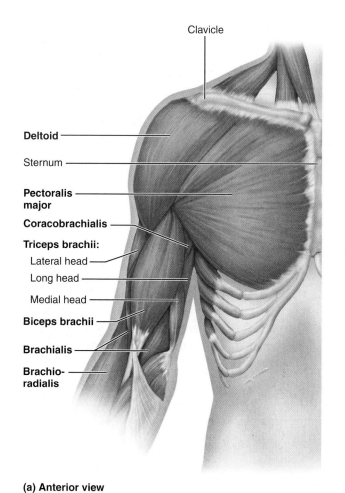

(a) Anterior view

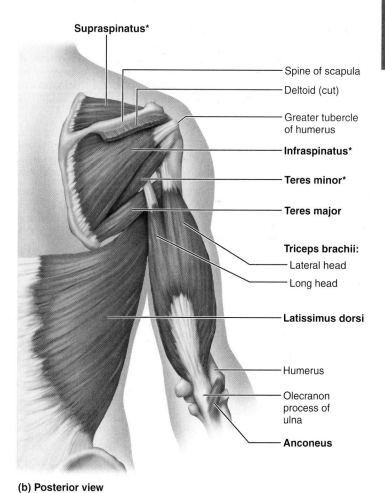

(b) Posterior view

Figure 10.14 Muscles crossing the shoulder and elbow joint, causing movements of the arm and forearm, respectively. (a) Superficial muscles of the anterior thorax, shoulder, and arm, anterior view. (See *A Brief Atlas of the Human Body,* Figures 35 and 36.) **(b)** The triceps brachii muscle of the postorior arm, shown in relation to the deep scapular muscles. The deltoid muscle of the shoulder has been removed.

*Rotator cuff muscles

MUSCLE GALLERY

TABLE 10.9   **Muscles Crossing the Shoulder Joint: Movements of the Arm (Humerus) (Figure 10.14)** *(continued)*

MUSCLE	DESCRIPTION	ORIGIN (O) AND INSERTION (I)	ACTION	NERVE SUPPLY
Subscapularis (sub-scap″u-lar′is) (*sub* = under; *scapular* = scapula)	Forms part of posterior wall of axilla; tendon of insertion passes in front of shoulder joint; a rotator cuff muscle	O—subscapular fossa of scapula I—lesser tubercle of humerus	Chief medial rotator of humerus; assisted by pectoralis major; helps to hold head of humerus in glenoid cavity, thereby stabilizing shoulder joint	Subscapular nerves (C_5–C_7)
Supraspinatus (soo″prah-spi-nah′tus) (*supra* = above, over; *spin* = spine)	Named for its location on posterior aspect of scapula; deep to trapezius; a rotator cuff muscle	O—supraspinous fossa of scapula I—superior part of greater tubercle of humerus	Initiates abduction; stabilizes shoulder joint; helps to prevent downward dislocation of humerus, as when carrying a heavy suitcase	Suprascapular nerve
Infraspinatus (in″frah-spi-nah′tus) (*infra* = below)	Partially covered by deltoid and trapezius; named for its scapular location; a rotator cuff muscle	O—infraspinous fossa of scapula I—greater tubercle of humerus posterior to insertion of supraspinatus	Rotates humerus laterally; helps to hold head of humerus in glenoid cavity, stabilizing the shoulder joint	Suprascapular nerve
Teres minor (te′rēz) (*teres* = round; *minor* = lesser)	Small, elongated muscle; lies inferior to infraspinatus and may be inseparable from that muscle; a rotator cuff muscle	O—lateral border of dorsal scapular surface I—greater tubercle of humerus inferior to infraspinatus insertion	Same action(s) as infraspinatus muscle	Axillary nerve
Teres major	Thick, rounded muscle; located inferior to teres minor; helps to form posterior wall of axilla (along with latissimus dorsi and subscapularis)	O—posterior surface of scapula at inferior angle I—crest of lesser tubercle on anterior humerus; insertion tendon fused with that of latissimus dorsi	Extends, medially rotates, and adducts humerus; synergist of latissimus dorsi	Lower subscapular nerve (C_6 and C_7)
Coracobrachialis (kor″ah-ko-bra″ke-al′is) (*coraco* = coracoid; *brachi* = arm)	Small, cylindrical muscle	O—coracoid process of scapula I — medial surface of humerus shaft	Flexion and adduction of the humerus; synergist of pectoralis major	Musculocutaneous nerve (C_5–C_7)

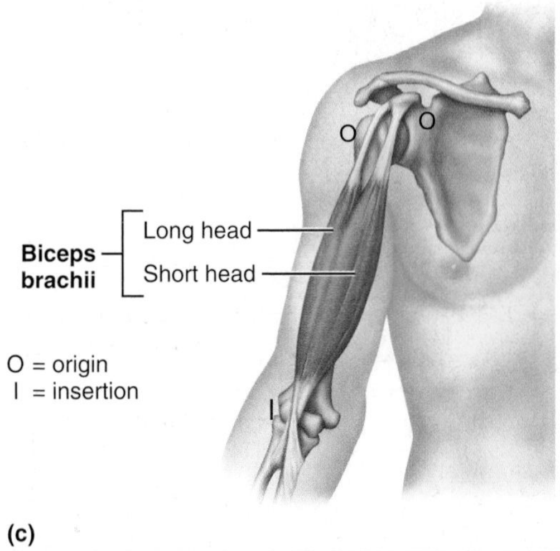

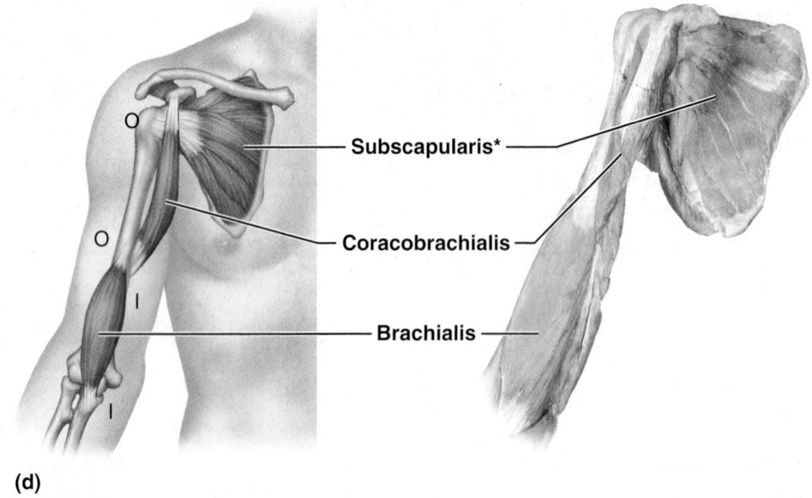

(c)

(d)

Figure 10.14 *(continued)* **Muscles crossing the shoulder and elbow joint, causing movements of the arm and forearm, respectively. (c)** The isolated biceps brachii muscle of the anterior arm. **(d)** The brachialis muscle and the coracobrachialis and subscapularis muscles shown in isolation in the diagram on the left, and in a dissection on the right.

*Rotator cuff muscles

MUSCLE GALLERY

TABLE 10.10   **Muscles Crossing the Elbow Joint: Flexion and Extension of the Forearm (Figure 10.14)**

Muscles fleshing out the arm cross the elbow joint to insert on the forearm bones. Since the elbow is a hinge joint, movements promoted by these arm muscles are limited almost entirely to flexion and extension of the forearm. Walls of fascia divide the arm into two muscle compartments—the *posterior extensors* and *anterior flexors*. The main forearm extensor is the bulky **triceps brachii** muscle, which forms nearly the entire musculature of the posterior compartment (Figure 10.14 a, b).

All anterior arm muscles flex the forearm (elbow). In order of decreasing strength, these are the **brachialis, biceps brachii**, and **brachioradialis** (Figure 10.14a–d). The brachialis and biceps insert (respectively) into the ulna and radius and contract simultaneously during flexion;

they are the chief forearm flexors. The biceps brachii, a muscle that bulges when the forearm is flexed, is familiar to almost everyone. The brachialis, which lies deep to the biceps, is less known, but is equally important in flexing the elbow. Because the brachioradialis arises from the distal humerus and inserts on the distal forearm, it resides mainly in the forearm. Its force is exerted far from the fulcrum, so the brachioradialis is a weak forearm flexor. The biceps muscle also supinates the forearm and is ineffective in flexing the elbow when the forearm *must* stay pronated. (This is why doing chin-ups with palms facing anteriorly is harder than with palms facing posteriorly.)

The actions of the muscles described here are summarized in Table 10.12 (Part II).

MUSCLE	DESCRIPTION	ORIGIN (O) AND INSERTION (I)	ACTION	NERVE SUPPLY
POSTERIOR MUSCLES				
Triceps brachii (tri′seps bra′ke-i) (*triceps* = three heads; *brachi* = arm)	Large fleshy muscle; the only muscle of posterior compartment of arm; three-headed origin; long and lateral heads lie superficial to medial head	O—long head: infraglenoid tubercle of scapula; lateral head: posterior shaft of humerus; medial head: posterior humeral shaft distal to radial groove I—by common tendon into olecranon process of ulna	Powerful forearm extensor (prime mover, particularly medial head); antagonist of forearm flexors; long and lateral heads mainly active in extension against resistance; long head tendon may help stabilize shoulder joint and assist in arm adduction	Radial nerve (C_6–C_8)
Anconeus (an-ko′ne-us) (*ancon* = elbow) (see Figure 10.16)	Short triangular muscle; partially blended with distal end of triceps on posterior humerus	O—lateral epicondyle of humerus I—lateral aspect of olecranon process of ulna	Controls ulnar abduction during forearm pronation; synergist of triceps brachii in elbow extension	Radial nerve
ANTERIOR MUSCLES				
Biceps brachii (bi′seps) (*biceps* = two heads)	Two-headed fusiform muscle; bellies unite as insertion point is approached; tendon of long head helps stabilize shoulder joint	O—short head: coracoid process; long head: supraglenoid tubercle and lip of glenoid cavity; tendon of long head runs within capsule and into intertubercular sulcus of humerus I—by common tendon into radial tuberosity	Flexes elbow joint and supinates forearm; these actions usually occur at same time (e.g., when you open a bottle of wine, it turns the corkscrew and pulls the cork); weak flexor of arm at shoulder	Musculocutaneous nerve (C_5 and C_6)
Brachialis (bra′ke-al-is)	Strong muscle that is immediately deep to biceps brachii on distal humerus	O—front of distal humerus; embraces insertion of deltoid muscle I—coronoid process of ulna and capsule of elbow joint	A major forearm flexor (lifts ulna as biceps lifts the radius)	Musculocutaneous nerve
Brachioradialis (bra″ke-o-ra″de-al′is) (*radi* = radius, ray) (also see Figure 10.15)	Superficial muscle of lateral forearm; forms lateral boundary of cubital fossa; extends from distal humerus to distal forearm	O—lateral supracondylar ridge at distal end of humerus I—base of styloid process of radius	Synergist in forearm flexion; acts to best advantage when forearm is partially flexed and semi-pronated; stabilizes the elbow during rapid flexion *and* extension	Radial nerve (an important exception: the radial nerve typically serves extensor muscles)

10

MUSCLE GALLERY

| TABLE 10.11 | Muscles of the Forearm: Movements of the Wrist, Hand, and Fingers (Figures 10.15 and 10.16) |

The many muscles in the forearm perform several basic functions: some cause wrist movements, some move the fingers and thumb, and a few help pronate and supinate the forearms. In most cases, their fleshy portions contribute to the roundness of the proximal forearm and then they taper to long tendons distally to insert into the hand. At the wrist, these tendons are securely anchored by a bandlike thickening of deep fascia called **flexor** and **extensor reti-nacula** ("retainers") (Figure 10.15a). These "wrist bands" keep the tendons from jumping outward when tensed. Crowded together in the wrist and palm, the muscle tendons are surrounded by slippery tendon sheaths that minimize friction as they slide against one another.

Although many forearm muscles arise from the humerus (and thus cross both the elbow and wrist joints), their actions on the elbow are slight. Flexion and extension are the movements typically effected at both the wrist and finger joints. In addition, the wrist can be abducted and adducted by the forearm muscles.

The forearm muscles are subdivided by fascia into two main compartments (the *anterior flexors* and *posterior extensors*), each with superficial and deep muscle layers. Most flexors in the anterior compartment arise from a common tendon on the humerus and are in-

nervated largely by the median nerve. Two anterior compartment muscles are not flexors but pronators, the **pronator teres** and **prona-tor quadratus** (Figure 10.15a–c). Pronation is one of the most important forearm movements.

Muscles of the posterior compartment extend the wrist and fingers. One exception is the **supinator** muscle, which assists the biceps brachii muscle of the arm in supinating the forearm (Figure 10.15b, c and 10.16b). (Also residing in the posterior compartment is the brachioradialis muscle, the weak elbow flexor considered in Table 10.10.) Most muscles of the posterior compartment arise from a common tendon on the humerus. All posterior forearm muscles are supplied by the radial nerve.

As described above, most muscles that move the hand are located in the forearm and "operate" the fingers via their long tendons, like operating a puppet by strings. This design makes the hand less bulky and enables it to perform finer movements. The hand movements promoted by the forearm muscles are assisted by the small *intrinsic* muscles of the hand, which control the most delicate and precise finger movements (see Table 10.13). The actions of the forearm muscles are summarized in Table 10.12 (Parts II and III).

MUSCLE	DESCRIPTION	ORIGIN (O) AND INSERTION (I)	ACTION	NERVE SUPPLY
PART I: ANTERIOR MUSCLES (FIGURE 10.15)	These eight muscles of the anterior fascial compartment are listed from the lateral to the medial aspect. Most arise from a common flexor tendon attached to the medial epicondyle of the humerus and have additional origins as well. Most of the tendons of insertion of these flexors are held in place at the wrist by a thickening of deep fascia called the *flexor retinaculum*.			
SUPERFICIAL MUSCLES				
Pronator teres (pro-na′tor te′rēz) (*pronation* = turning palm posteriorly, or down; *teres* = round)	Two-headed muscle; seen in superficial view between proximal margins of brachioradialis and flexor carpi radialis; forms medial boundary of cubital fossa	O—medial epicondyle of humerus; coronoid process of ulna I—by common tendon into lateral radius, midshaft	Pronates forearm; weak flexor of elbow	Median nerve
Flexor carpi radialis (flek′sor kar′pe ra″de-al′is) (*flex* = decrease angle between two bones; *carpi* = wrist; *radi* = radius)	Runs diagonally across forearm; midway, its fleshy belly is replaced by a flat tendon that becomes cordlike at wrist	O—medial epicondyle of humerus I—base of second and third metacarpals; insertion tendon easily seen and provides guide to position of radial artery (used for pulse taking) at wrist	Powerful flexor of wrist; abducts hand; weak synergist of elbow flexion	Median nerve
Palmaris longus (pahl-ma′ris lon′gus) (*palma* = palm; *longus* = long)	Small fleshy muscle with a long insertion tendon; often absent; may be used as guide to find median nerve that lies lateral to it at wrist	O—medial epicondyle of humerus I—palmar aponeurosis; (fascia of palm)	Tenses skin and fascia of palm during hand movements; weak wrist flexor; weak synergist for elbow flexion	Median nerve
Flexor carpi ulnaris (ul-na′ris) (*ulnar* = ulna)	Most medial muscle of this group; two-headed; ulnar nerve lies lateral to its tendon	O—medial epicondyle of humerus; olecranon process and posterior surface of ulna I—pisiform and hamate bones and base of fifth metacarpal	Powerful flexor of wrist; also adducts hand in concert with extensor carpi ulnaris (posterior muscle); stabilizes wrist during finger extension	Ulnar nerve (C_7 and C_8)

MUSCLE GALLERY

TABLE 10.11 (continued)

MUSCLE	DESCRIPTION	ORIGIN (O) AND INSERTION (I)	ACTION	NERVE SUPPLY
Flexor digitorum superficialis (di″ji-tor′um soo″per-fish″e-al′is) (*digit* = finger, toe; *superficial* = close to surface)	Two-headed muscle; more deeply placed (therefore, actually forms an intermediate layer); overlain by muscles above but visible at distal end of forearm	O—medial epicondyle of humerus, coronoid process of ulna; shaft of radius I—by four tendons into middle phalanges of fingers 2–5	Flexes wrist and middle phalanges of fingers 2–5; the important finger flexor when speed and flexion against resistance are required	Median nerve (C_7, C_8, and T_1)

DEEP MUSCLES

MUSCLE	DESCRIPTION	ORIGIN (O) AND INSERTION (I)	ACTION	NERVE SUPPLY
Flexor pollicis longus (pah′li-kis) (*pollix* = thumb)	Partly covered by flexor digitorum superficialis; parallels flexor digitorum profundus laterally	O—anterior surface of radius and interosseous membrane I—distal phalanx of thumb	Flexes distal phalanx of thumb	Branch of median nerve (C_8, T_1)
Flexor digitorum profundus (pro-fun′dus) (*profund* = deep)	Extensive origin; overlain entirely by flexor digitorum superficialis	O—coronoid process, anteromedial surface of ulna, and interosseous membrane I—by four tendons into distal phalanges of fingers 2–5	Flexes distal interphalangeal joints; slow-acting flexor of any or all fingers; assists in flexing wrist	Medial half by ulnar nerve; lateral half by median nerve

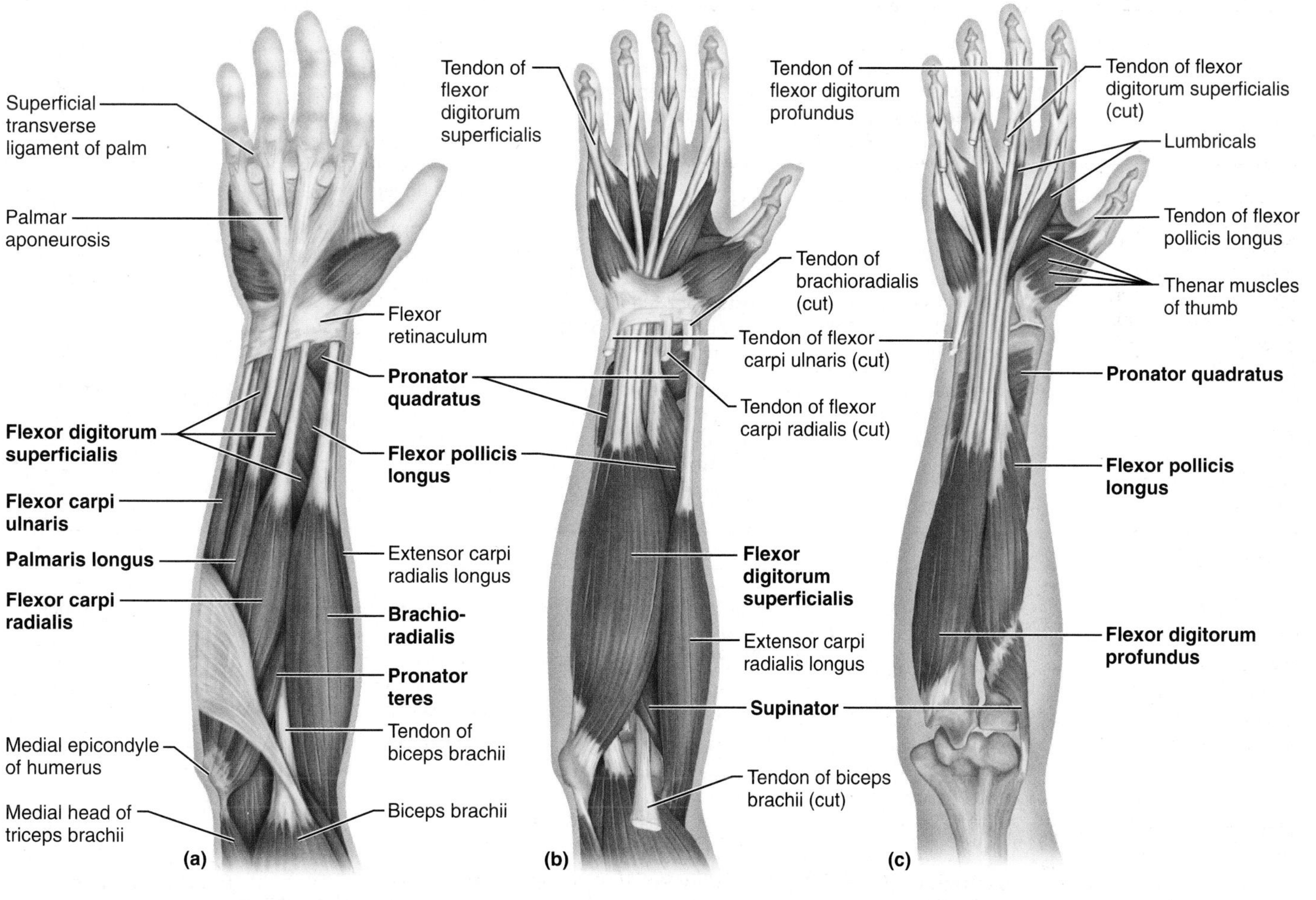

Figure 10.15 **Muscles of the anterior fascial compartment of the forearm acting on the right wrist and fingers. (a)** Superficial view. **(b)** The brachioradialis, flexors carpi radialis and ulnaris, and palmaris longus muscles have been removed to reveal the flexor digitorum superficialis. **(c)** Deep muscles of the anterior compartment. The lumbricals and thenar muscles (intrinsic hand muscles) are also illustrated. (See *A Brief Atlas of the Human Body*, Figure 37.)

TABLE 10.11	**Muscles of the Forearm: Movements of the Wrist, Hand, and Fingers (Figures 10.15 and 10.16)** *(continued)*

MUSCLE	DESCRIPTION	ORIGIN (O) AND INSERTION (I)	ACTION	NERVE SUPPLY
Pronator quadratus (kwod-ra′tus) (*quad* = square, four-sided)	Deepest muscle of distal forearm; passes down-ward and laterally; only muscle that arises solely from ulna and inserts solely into radius	O—distal portion of ante-rior ulnar shaft I—distal surface of ante-rior radius	Prime mover of forearm pronation; acts with pronator teres; also helps hold ulna and radius together	Median nerve (C_8 and T_1)
PART II: POSTERIOR MUSCLES (FIGURE 10.16)	These muscles of the posterior fascial compartment are listed from the lateral to the medial aspect. They are all in-nervated by the radial nerve or its branches. More than half of the posterior compartment muscles arise from a common extensor origin tendon attached to the posterior surface of the lateral epicondyle of the humerus and adjacent fascia. The extensor tendons are held in place at the posterior aspect of the wrist by the *extensor retinaculum,* which prevents "bowstringing" of these tendons when the wrist is hyperextended. The *extensor* muscles of the fingers end in a broad hood over the dorsal side of the digits, the extensor expansion.			

SUPERFICIAL MUSCLES

MUSCLE	DESCRIPTION	ORIGIN (O) AND INSERTION (I)	ACTION	NERVE SUPPLY
Brachioradialis (see Table 10.10)	See Table 10.10	See Table 10.10	See Table 10.10	See Table 10.10
Extensor carpi radialis longus (ek-sten′sor) (*extend* = increase angle between two bones)	Parallels brachioradialis on lateral forearm, and may blend with it	O—lateral supracondylar ridge of humerus I—base of second metacarpal	Extends wrist in conjunc-tion with the extensor carpi ulnaris and abducts wrist in conjunction with the flexor carpi radialis	Radial nerve (C_6 and C_7)
Extensor carpi radialis brevis (brĕ′vis) (*brevis* = short)	Somewhat shorter than extensor carpi radialis longus and lies deep to it	O—lateral epicondyle of humerus I—base of third metacarpal	Extends and abducts wrist; acts synergistically with extensor carpi radi-alis longus to steady wrist during finger flexion	Deep branch of radial nerve
Extensor digitorum	Lies medial to extensor carpi radialis brevis; a detached portion of this muscle, called *extensor digiti minimi,* extends little finger	O—lateral epicondyle of humerus I—by four tendons into extensor expansions and distal phalanges of fingers 2–5	Prime mover of finger ex-tension; extends wrist; can abduct (flare) fingers	Posterior interosseous nerve, a branch of radial nerve (C_5 and C_6)
Extensor carpi ulnaris	Most medial of superficial posterior muscles; long, slender muscle	O—lateral epicondyle of humerus and posterior border of ulna I—base of fifth metacarpal	Extends wrist in conjunc-tion with the extensor carpi radialis and adducts wrist in conjunction with flexor carpi ulnaris	Posterior interosseous nerve

DEEP MUSCLES

MUSCLE	DESCRIPTION	ORIGIN (O) AND INSERTION (I)	ACTION	NERVE SUPPLY
Supinator (soo″pĭ-na′tor) (*supination* = turning palm anteriorly or upward)	Deep muscle at posterior aspect of elbow; largely concealed by superficial muscles	O—lateral epicondyle of humerus; proximal ulna I—proximal end of radius	Assists biceps brachii to forcibly supinate forearm; works alone in slow supi-nation; antagonist of pro-nator muscles	Posterior interosseous nerve
Abductor pollicis longus (ab-duk′tor) (*abduct* = movement away from median plane)	Lateral and parallel to ex-tensor pollicis longus; just distal to supinator	O—posterior surface of radius and ulna; interos-seous membrane I—base of first metacarpal and trapezium	Abducts and extends thumb	Posterior interosseous nerve
Extensor pollicis brevis and longus	Deep muscle pair with a common origin and action; overlain by exten-sor carpi ulnaris	O—dorsal shaft of radius and ulna; interosseous membrane I—base of proximal (bre-vis) and distal (longus) phalanx of thumb	Extends thumb	Posterior interosseous nerve

10

MUSCLE GALLERY

TABLE 10.11 *(continued)*

MUSCLE	DESCRIPTION	ORIGIN (O) AND INSERTION (I)	ACTION	NERVE SUPPLY
Extensor indicis (in'dĭ-kis) (*indicis* = index finger)	Tiny muscle arising close to wrist	O—posterior surface of distal ulna; interosseous membrane I—extensor expansion of index finger; joins tendon of extensor digitorum	Extends index finger and assists in wrist extension	Posterior interosseous nerve

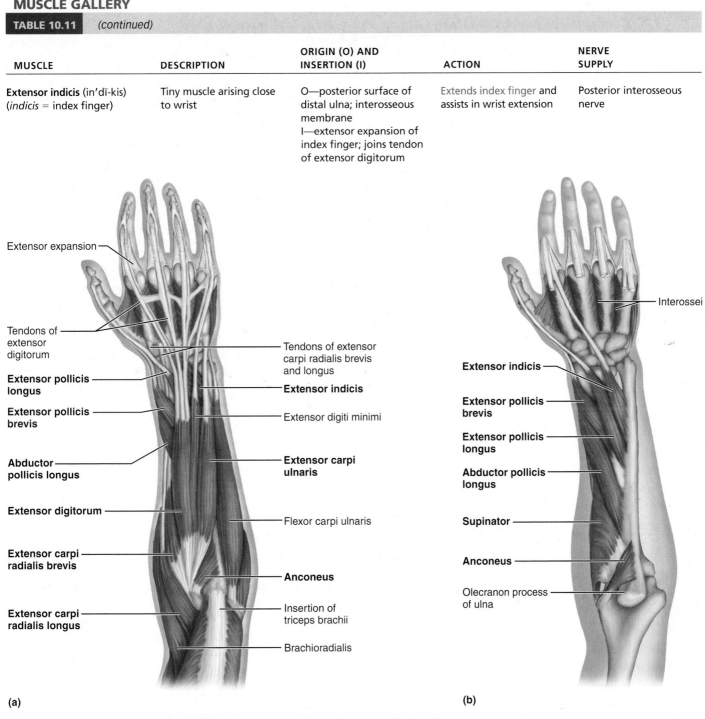

(a)

(b)

Figure 10.16 Muscles of the posterior fascial compartment of the right forearm acting on the wrist and fingers. (a) Superficial muscles, posterior view. (See *A Brief Atlas of the Human Body*, Figure 37b.) **(b)** Deep posterior muscles, superficial muscles removed. The interossei, the deepest layer of intrinsic hand muscles, are also illustrated.

10

MUSCLE GALLERY

TABLE 10.12 Summary of Actions of Muscles Acting on the Arm, Forearm, and Hand (Figure 10.17)

Part I: Muscles Acting on the Arm (Humerus) (PM = prime mover)

	ACTIONS AT THE SHOULDER					
	Flexion	Extension	Abduction	Adduction	Medial Rotation	Lateral Rotation
Pectoralis	× (PM)			× (PM)	×	
Latissimus dorsi		× (PM)		× (PM)	×	
Teres major		×		×	×	
Deltoid	× (PM) (anterior fibers)	× (PM) (posterior fibers)	× (PM)		× (anterior fibers)	× (posterior fibers)
Subscapularis					× (PM)	
Supraspinatus			×			
Infraspinatus						× (PM)
Teres minor				× (weak)		× (PM)
Coracobrachialis	×			×		
Biceps brachii	× (weak)					
Triceps brachii				×		

Part II: Muscles Acting on the Forearm

	ACTIONS ON THE FOREARM			
	Elbow Flexion	Elbow Extension	Pronation	Supination
Biceps brachii	× (PM)			×
Brachialis	× (PM)			
Triceps brachii		× (PM)		
Anconeus		×		
Pronator teres	× (weak)		×	
Pronator quadratus			× (PM)	
Supinator				×
Brachioradialis	×			

Part III: Muscles Acting on the Wrist and Fingers

	ACTIONS ON THE WRIST				ACTIONS ON THE FINGERS	
	Flexion	Extension	Abduction	Adduction	Flexion	Extension
Anterior Compartment						
Flexor carpi radialis	× (PM)		×			
Palmaris longus	× (weak)					
Flexor carpi ulnaris	× (PM)			×		
Flexor digitorum superficialis	× (PM)				×	
Flexor pollicis longus					× (thumb)	
Flexor digitorum profundus	×				×	
Posterior Compartment						
Extensor carpi radialis longus and brevis		×	×			
Extensor digitorum		× (PM)				× (and abducts)
Extensor carpi ulnaris		×		×		
Abductor pollicis longus			×		(abducts thumb)	
Extensor pollicis longus and brevis						× (thumb)
Extensor indicis		× (weak)				× (index finger)

10

MUSCLE GALLERY

TABLE 10.12 *(continued)*

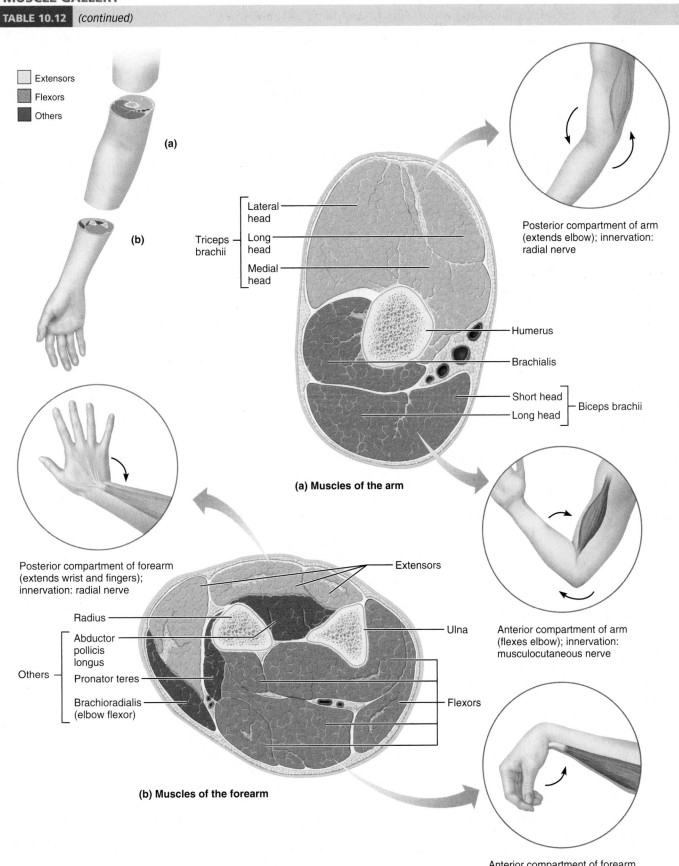

Extensors
Flexors
Others

(a)

(b)

Triceps brachii
Lateral head
Long head
Medial head

Posterior compartment of arm (extends elbow); innervation: radial nerve

Humerus
Brachialis
Short head
Long head — Biceps brachii

(a) Muscles of the arm

Anterior compartment of arm (flexes elbow); innervation: musculocutaneous nerve

Posterior compartment of forearm (extends wrist and fingers); innervation: radial nerve

Extensors

Radius
Abductor pollicis longus
Pronator teres
Brachioradialis (elbow flexor)
Others

Ulna

Flexors

(b) Muscles of the forearm

Anterior compartment of forearm (flexes wrist and fingers); innervation: median or ulnar nerve

10

Figure 10.17 **Summary of actions of muscles of the arm and forearm.**

MUSCLE GALLERY

TABLE 10.13   **Intrinsic Muscles of the Hand: Fine Movements of the Fingers (Figure 10.18)**

In this table we consider the small muscles that lie entirely in the hand. All are in the palm, none on the hand's dorsal side. All move the metacarpals and fingers. Small, weak muscles, they mostly control precise movements (such as threading a needle), leaving the powerful movements of the fingers ("power grip") to the forearm muscles.

The intrinsic muscles include the main abductors and adductors of the fingers, as well as muscles that produce the movement of opposition—moving the thumb toward the little finger—that enables you to grip objects in the palm (the handle of a hammer, for example). Many palm muscles are specialized to move the thumb, and surprisingly many move the little finger. Thumb movements are defined differently from movements of other fingers because the thumb lies at a right angle to the rest of the hand. The thumb flexes by bending medially along the palm, not by bending anteriorly, as do

the other fingers. (To demonstrate this difference, start with your hand in the anatomical position or this will not be clear!) The thumb extends by pointing laterally (as in hitchhiking), not posteriorly, as do the other fingers. To abduct the fingers is to splay them laterally, but to abduct the thumb is to point it anteriorly. Adduction of the thumb brings it back posteriorly.

The intrinsic muscles of the palm are divided into three groups, those in (1) the *thenar eminence* (ball of the thumb); (2) the *hypothenar eminence* (ball of the little finger); and (3) the midpalm. Thenar and hypothenar muscles are almost mirror images of each other, each containing a small flexor, an abductor, and an opponens muscle. The midpalmar muscles, called **lumbricals** and **interossei**, extend our fingers at the interphalangeal joints. The interossei are also the main finger abductors and adductors.

MUSCLE	DESCRIPTION	ORIGIN (O) AND INSERTION (I)	ACTION	NERVE SUPPLY
THENAR MUSCLES IN BALL OF THUMB (the'nar) (*thenar* = palm)				
Abductor pollicis brevis (*pollex* = thumb)	Lateral muscle of thenar group; superficial	O—flexor retinaculum and nearby carpals I—lateral base of thumb's proximal phalanx	Abducts thumb (at carpometacarpal joint)	Median nerve (C_8, T_1)
Flexor pollicis brevis	Medial and deep muscle of thenar group	O—flexor retinaculum and nearby carpals I—lateral side of base of proximal phalanx of thumb	Flexes thumb (at carpometacarpal and metacarpophalangeal joints)	Median (or occasionally ulnar) nerve (C_8, T_1)
Opponens pollicis (o-pŏn'enz) (*opponens* = opposition)	Deep to abductor pollicis brevis, on metacarpal 1	O—flexor retinaculum and trapezium I—whole anterior side of metacarpal 1	Opposition: moves thumb to touch tip of little finger	Median (or occasionally ulnar) nerve
Adductor pollicis	Fan-shaped with horizontal fibers; distal to other thenar muscles; oblique and transverse heads	O—capitate bone and bases of metacarpals 2–4; front of metacarpal 3 I—medial side of base of proximal phalanx of thumb	Adducts and helps to oppose thumb	Ulnar nerve (C_8, T_1)
HYPOTHENAR MUSCLES IN BALL OF LITTLE FINGER				
Abductor digiti minimi (dĭ'jĭ-ti min'ĭ-mi) (*digiti minimi* = little finger)	Medial muscle of hypothenar group; superficial	O—pisiform bone I—medial side of proximal phalanx of little finger	Abducts little finger at metacarpophalangeal joint	Ulnar nerve
Flexor digiti minimi brevis	Lateral deep muscle of hypothenar group	O—hamate bone and flexor retinaculum I—same as abductor digiti minimi	Flexes little finger at metacarpophalangeal joint	Ulnar nerve
Opponens digiti minimi	Deep to abductor digiti minimi	O—same as flexor digiti minimi brevis I—most of length of medial side of metacarpal 5	Helps in opposition: brings metacarpal 5 toward thumb to cup the hand	Ulnar nerve

MUSCLE GALLERY

TABLE 10.13 *(continued)*

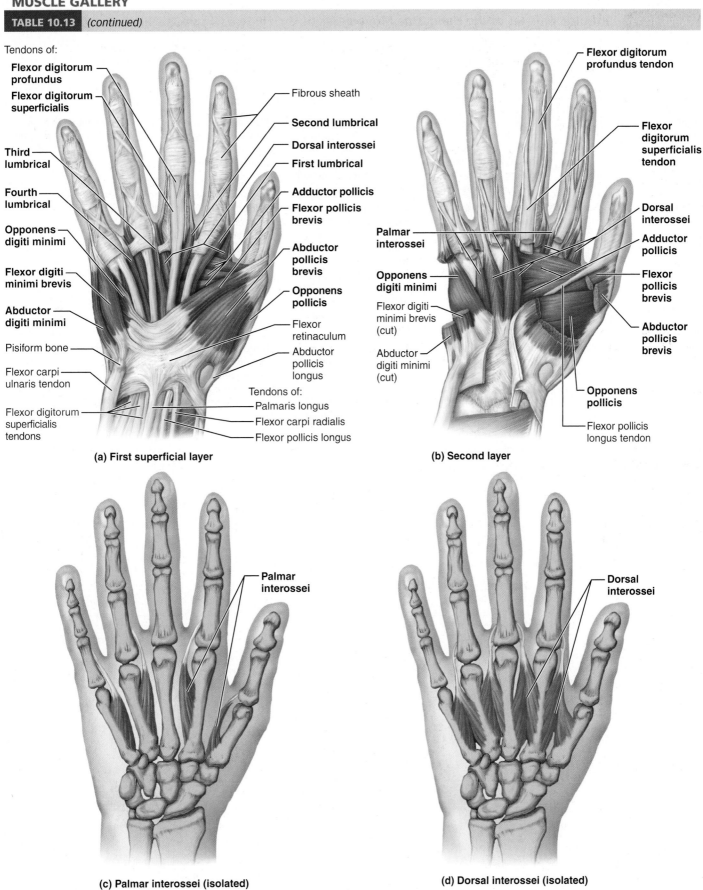

Tendons of:
- Flexor digitorum profundus
- Flexor digitorum superficialis

Third lumbrical

Fourth lumbrical

Opponens digiti minimi

Flexor digiti minimi brevis

Abductor digiti minimi

Pisiform bone

Flexor carpi ulnaris tendon

Flexor digitorum superficialis tendons

Fibrous sheath

Second lumbrical

Dorsal interossei

First lumbrical

Adductor pollicis

Flexor pollicis brevis

Abductor pollicis brevis

Opponens pollicis

Flexor retinaculum

Abductor pollicis longus

Tendons of:
- Palmaris longus
- Flexor carpi radialis
- Flexor pollicis longus

(a) First superficial layer

Flexor digitorum profundus tendon

Flexor digitorum superficialis tendon

Palmar interossei

Opponens digiti minimi

Flexor digiti minimi brevis (cut)

Abductor digiti minimi (cut)

Dorsal interossei

Adductor pollicis

Flexor pollicis brevis

Abductor pollicis brevis

Opponens pollicis

Flexor pollicis longus tendon

(b) Second layer

Palmar interossei

(c) Palmar interossei (isolated)

Dorsal interossei

(d) Dorsal interossei (isolated)

Figure 10.18 Hand muscles, ventral views of right hand.

10

MUSCLE GALLERY

TABLE 10.13	Intrinsic Muscles of the Hand: Fine Movements of the Fingers (Figure 10.18) *(continued)*

MUSCLE	DESCRIPTION	ORIGIN (O) AND INSERTION (I)	ACTION	NERVE SUPPLY
MIDPALMAR MUSCLES				
Lumbricals (lum′brĭ-klz) (*lumbric* = earthworm)	Four worm-shaped muscles in palm, one to each finger (except thumb); unusual because they originate from the tendons of another muscle	O—lateral side of each tendon of flexor digitorum profundus in palm I—lateral edge of extensor expansion on proximal phalanx of fingers 2–5	Flex fingers at metacarpophalangeal joints but extend fingers at interphalangeal joints	Median nerve (lateral two) and ulnar nerve (medial two)
Palmar interossei (in″ter-os′e-i) (*interossei* = between bones)	Four long, cone-shaped muscles in the spaces between the metacarpals; lie ventral to the dorsal interossei	O—the side of each metacarpal that faces the midaxis of the hand (metacarpal 3) but absent from metacarpal 3 I—extensor expansion on first phalanx of each finger (except finger 3), on side facing midaxis of hand	Adductors of fingers: pull fingers in toward third digit; act with lumbricals to extend fingers at interphalangeal joints and flex them at metacarpophalangeal joints	Ulnar nerve
Dorsal interossei	Four bipennate muscles filling spaces between the metacarpals; deepest palm muscles, also visible on dorsal side of hand (Figure 10.16b)	O—sides of metacarpals I—extensor expansion over proximal phalanx of fingers 2–4 on side opposite midaxis of hand (finger 3), but on *both* sides of finger 3	Abduct (diverge) fingers; extend fingers at interphalangeal joints and flex them at metacarpophalangeal joints	Ulnar nerve

MUSCLE GALLERY

TABLE 10.14	Muscles Crossing the Hip and Knee Joints: Movements of the Thigh and Leg (Figures 10.19 and 10.20)

The muscles fleshing out the thigh are difficult to segregate into groups on the basis of action. Some thigh muscles act only at the hip joint, others only at the knee, while still others act at both joints. However, *most anterior* muscles of the hip and thigh flex the femur at the hip and extend the leg at the knee— producing the foreswing phase of walking. The *posterior* muscles of the hip and thigh, by contrast, mostly extend the thigh and flex the leg—the backswing phase of walking. A third group of muscles in this region, the *medial*, or *adductor*, muscles, all adduct the thigh; they have no effect on the leg. In the thigh, the anterior, posterior, and adductor muscles are separated by walls of fascia into *anterior, posterior,* and *medial compartments* (see Figure 10.25a). The deep fascia of the thigh, the *fascia lata*, surrounds and encloses all three groups of muscles like a support stocking.

Movements of the thigh (occurring at the hip joint) are accomplished largely by muscles anchored to the pelvic girdle. Like the shoulder joint, the hip joint is a ball-and-socket joint permitting flexion, extension, abduction, adduction, circumduction, and rotation. Muscles effecting these movements of the thigh are among the most powerful muscles of the body.

For the most part, the thigh *flexors* pass in front of the hip joint. The most important of these are the **iliopsoas, tensor fasciae latae,**

and **rectus femoris** (Figure 10.19a). They are assisted in this action by the **adductor muscles** of the medial thigh and the straplike **sartorius.** The prime mover of thigh flexion is the iliopsoas.

Thigh *extension* is effected primarily by the massive **hamstring muscles** of the posterior thigh (Figure 10.20a), and, during forceful extension, the **gluteus maximus** of the buttock is activated. Buttock muscles that lie lateral to the hip joint (**gluteus medius** and **minimus**) *abduct* the thigh (Figure 10.20c). Thigh adduction is the role of the adductor muscles of the medial thigh. Abduction and adduction of the thighs are extremely important during walking to shift the trunk from side to side so that the body's weight is balanced over the limb that is on the ground. Many different muscles bring about medial and lateral rotation of the thigh.

At the knee joint, flexion and extension are the main movements. The sole knee *extensor* is the **quadriceps femoris** muscle of the anterior thigh, the most powerful muscle in the body (Figure 10.19a). The quadriceps is antagonized by the hamstrings of the posterior compartment, which are the prime movers of knee flexion.

The actions of these muscles are further summarized in Table 10.17 (Part I).

MUSCLE	DESCRIPTION	ORIGIN (O) AND INSERTION (I)	ACTION	NERVE SUPPLY
PART I: ANTERIOR AND MEDIAL MUSCLES (FIGURE 10.19)				
ORIGIN ON THE PELVIS OR SPINE				
Iliopsoas (il"e-o-so'us)	Iliopsoas is a composite of two closely related muscles (iliacus and psoas major) whose fibers pass under the inguinal ligament (see Figure 10.11) to insert via a common tendon on the femur.			
▪ **Iliacus** (il-e-ak'us) (*iliac* = ilium)	Large, fan-shaped, more lateral muscle	O—iliac fossa and crest, ala of sacrum I—lesser trochanter of femur via iliopsoas tendon	Iliopsoas is the prime mover for flexing thigh or for flexing trunk on thigh during a bow	Femoral nerve (L_2 and L_3)
▪ **Psoas major** (so'us) (*psoa* = loin muscle; *major* = larger)	Longer, thicker, more medial muscle of the pair (butchers refer to this muscle as the tenderloin)	O—by fleshy slips from transverse processes, bodies, and discs of lumbar vertebrae and T_{12} I—lesser trochanter of femur via iliopsoas tendon	As above; also effects lateral flexion of vertebral column; important postural muscle	Ventral rami (L_1–L_3)
Sartorius (sar-tor'e-us) (*sartor* = tailor)	Straplike superficial muscle running obliquely across anterior surface of thigh to knee; longest muscle in body; crosses both hip and knee joints	O—anterior superior iliac spine I—winds around medial aspect of knee and inserts into medial aspect of proximal tibia	Flexes, abducts, and laterally rotates thigh; flexes knee; produces the cross-legged position	Femoral nerve

10

➤

TABLE 10.14 Muscles Crossing the Hip and Knee Joints: Movements of the Thigh and Leg (Figures 10.19 and 10.20) *(continued)*

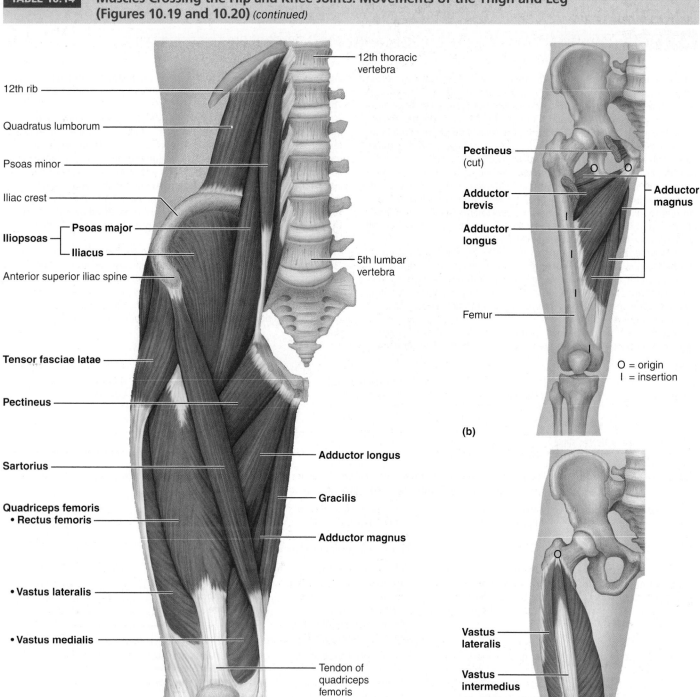

Figure 10.19 Anterior and medial muscles promoting movements of the thigh and leg.
(See *A Brief Atlas of the Human Body,* Figure 40.) **(a)** Anterior view of the deep muscles of the pelvis and superficial muscles of the right thigh. **(b)** Adductor muscles of the medial compartment of the thigh, isolated. **(c)** Vastus muscles of the quadriceps group, isolated.

MUSCLE GALLERY

TABLE 10.14 *(continued)*

MUSCLES OF THE MEDIAL COMPARTMENT OF THE THIGH

Adductors (ah-duk′torz)	Large muscle mass consisting of three muscles (magnus, longus, and brevis) forming medial aspect of thigh; arise from inferior part of pelvis and insert at various levels on femur. All are used in movements that press thighs together, as when astride a horse; important in pelvic tilting movements that occur during walking and in fixing the hip when the knee is flexed and the foot is off the ground. Entire group innervated by obturator nerve. Strain or stretching of this muscle group is called a "pulled groin."			
▪ **Adductor magnus** (mag′nus) (*adduct* = move toward midline; *magnus* = large)	A triangular muscle with a broad insertion; is a composite muscle that is part adductor and part hamstring in action	O—ischial and pubic rami and ischial tuberosity I—linea aspera and adductor tubercle of femur	Anterior part adducts and medially rotates and flexes thigh; posterior part is a synergist of hamstrings in thigh extension	Obturator nerve and sciatic nerve (L$_2$–L$_4$)
▪ **Adductor longus** (*longus* = long)	Overlies middle aspect of adductor magnus; most anterior of adductor muscles	O—pubis near pubic symphysis I—linea aspera	Adducts, flexes, and medially rotates thigh	Obturator nerve (L$_2$–L$_4$)
▪ **Adductor brevis** (*brevis* = short)	In contact with obturator externus muscle; largely concealed by adductor longus and pectineus	O—body and inferior ramus of pubis I—linea aspera above adductor longus	Adducts and medially rotates thigh	Obturator nerve
Pectineus (pek-tin′e-us) (*pecten* = comb)	Short, flat muscle; overlies adductor brevis on proximal thigh; abuts adductor longus medially	O—pubis (and superior ramus) I—from lesser trochanter inferior to the linea aspera on posterior aspect of femur	Adducts, flexes, and medially rotates thigh	Femoral and sometimes obturator nerve
Gracilis (grah-si′lis) (*gracilis* = slender)	Long, thin, superficial muscle of medial thigh	O—inferior ramus and body of pubis and adjacent ischial ramus I—medial surface of tibia just inferior to its medial condyle	Adducts thigh, flexes and medially rotates leg, especially during walking	Obturator nerve

MUSCLES OF THE ANTERIOR COMPARTMENT OF THE THIGH

Quadriceps femoris (kwod′rĭ-seps fem′o-ris)	Arises from four separate heads (*quadriceps* = four heads) that form the flesh of front and sides of thigh; these heads (rectus femoris, and lateral, medial, and intermediate vasti muscles) have a common insertion tendon, the *quadriceps tendon*, which inserts into the patella and then via the *patellar ligament* into tibial tuberosity. The quadriceps is a powerful knee extensor used in climbing, jumping, running, and rising from seated position. The group is innervated by femoral nerve; the tone of quadriceps plays important role in strengthening the knee joint.			
▪ **Rectus femoris** (rek′tus) (*rectus* = straight; *femoris* = femur)	Superficial muscle of anterior thigh; runs straight down thigh; longest head and only muscle of group to cross hip joint	O—anterior inferior iliac spine and superior margin of acetabulum I—patella and tibial tuberosity via patellar ligament	Extends knee and flexes thigh at hip	Femoral nerve (L$_2$–L$_4$)
▪ **Vastus lateralis** (vas′tus lat″er-a′lis) (*vastus* = large; *lateralis* = lateral)	Largest head of the group, forms lateral aspect of thigh; a common intramuscular injection site, particularly in infants (who have poorly developed buttock and arm muscles)	O—greater trochanter, intertrochanteric line, linea aspera I—as for rectus femoris	Extends and stabilizes knee	Femoral nerve
▪ **Vastus medialis** (me″de-a′lis) (*medialis* = medial)	Forms inferomedial aspect of thigh	O—linea aspera, intertrochanteric and medial supracondylar lines I—as for rectus femoris	Extends knee	Femoral nerve

MUSCLE GALLERY

TABLE 10.14	Muscles Crossing the Hip and Knee Joints: Movements of the Thigh and Leg (Figures 10.19 and 10.20) *(continued)*

MUSCLE	DESCRIPTION	ORIGIN (O) AND INSERTION (I)	ACTION	NERVE SUPPLY
▪ **Vastus intermedius** (in"ter-me′de-us) (*intermedius* = intermediate)	Obscured by rectus femoris; lies between vastus lateralis and vastus medialis on anterior thigh	O—anterior and lateral surfaces of proximal femur shaft I—as for rectus femoris	Extends knee	Femoral nerve
Tensor fasciae latae (ten′sor fǎ′she-e la′te) (*tensor* = to make tense; *fascia* = band; *lata* = wide)	Enclosed between fascia layers of anterolateral aspect of thigh; functionally associated with medial rotators and flexors of thigh	O—anterior aspect of iliac crest and anterior superior iliac spine I—iliotibial tract*	Steadies the knee and trunk on thigh by making iliotibial tract taut; flexes and abducts thigh; rotates thigh medially	Superior gluteal nerve (L_4 and L_5)

PART II: POSTERIOR MUSCLES (FIGURE 10.20)

GLUTEAL MUSCLES—ORIGIN ON PELVIS

MUSCLE	DESCRIPTION	ORIGIN (O) AND INSERTION (I)	ACTION	NERVE SUPPLY
Gluteus maximus (gloo′te-us mak′sĭ-mus) (*glutos* = buttock; *maximus* = largest)	Largest and most superficial of gluteus muscles; forms bulk of buttock mass; fibers are thick and coarse; important site of intramuscular injection (dorsal gluteal site); overlies large sciatic nerve; covers ischial tuberosity only when standing; when sitting, moves superiorly, leaving ischial tuberosity exposed in the subcutaneous position	O—dorsal ilium, sacrum, and coccyx I—gluteal tuberosity of femur; iliotibial tract	Major extensor of thigh; complex, powerful, and most effective when thigh is flexed and force is necessary, as in rising from a forward flexed position and in thrusting the thigh posteriorly in climbing stairs and running; generally inactive during standing and walking; laterally rotates and abducts thigh	Inferior gluteal nerve (L_5, S_1, and S_2)
Gluteus medius (me′de-us) (*medius* = middle)	Thick muscle largely covered by gluteus maximus; important site for intramuscular injections (ventral gluteal site); considered safer than dorsal gluteal site because there is less chance of injuring sciatic nerve	O—between anterior and posterior gluteal lines on lateral surface of ilium I—by short tendon into lateral aspect of greater trochanter of femur	Abducts and medially rotates thigh; steadies pelvis; its action is extremely important in walking; e.g., muscle of limb planted on ground tilts or holds pelvis in abduction so that pelvis on side of swinging limb does not sag; the foot of swinging limb can thus clear the ground	Superior gluteal nerve (L_5, S_1)
Gluteus minimus (mĭ′nĭ-mus) (*minimus* = smallest)	Smallest and deepest of gluteal muscles	O—between anterior and inferior gluteal lines on external surface of ilium I—anterior border of greater trochanter of femur	As for gluteus medius	Superior gluteal nerve (L_5, S_1)

LATERAL ROTATORS

MUSCLE	DESCRIPTION	ORIGIN (O) AND INSERTION (I)	ACTION	NERVE SUPPLY
Piriformis (pir′ĭ-form-is) (*piri* = pear; *forma* = shape)	Pyramidal muscle located on posterior aspect of hip joint; inferior to gluteus minimus; issues from pelvis via greater sciatic notch	O—anterolateral surface of sacrum (opposite greater sciatic notch) I—superior border of greater trochanter of femur	Rotates extended thigh laterally; because inserted above head of femur, can also assist in abduction of thigh when hip is flexed; stabilizes hip joint	S_1 and S_2, L_5

*The iliotibial tract is a thickened lateral portion of the *fascia lata* (the fascia that ensheathes all the muscles of the thigh). It extends as a tendinous band from the iliac crest to the knee (see Figure 10.20a).

MUSCLE GALLERY

TABLE 10.14 *(continued)*

MUSCLE	DESCRIPTION	ORIGIN (O) AND INSERTION (I)	ACTION	NERVE SUPPLY

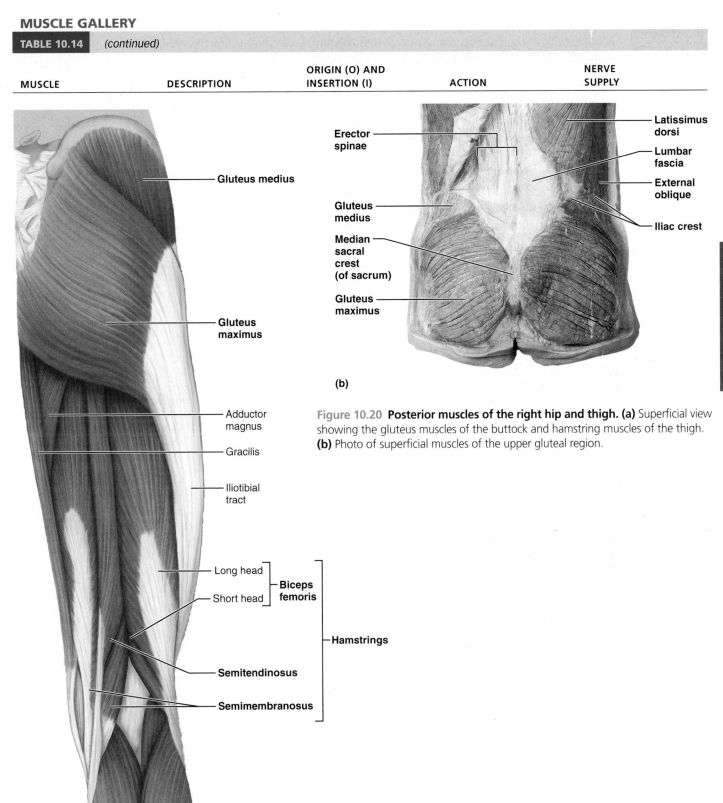

(a)

(b)

Figure 10.20 **Posterior muscles of the right hip and thigh. (a)** Superficial view showing the gluteus muscles of the buttock and hamstring muscles of the thigh. **(b)** Photo of superficial muscles of the upper gluteal region.

MUSCLE GALLERY

TABLE 10.14	Muscles Crossing the Hip and Knee Joints: Movements of the Thigh and Leg (Figures 10.19 and 10.20) *(continued)*

MUSCLE	DESCRIPTION	ORIGIN (O) AND INSERTION (I)	ACTION	NERVE SUPPLY
Obturator externus (ob″tu-ra′tor ek-ster′nus) (*obturator* = obturator foramen; *externus* = outside)	Flat, triangular muscle deep in superomedial aspect of thigh	O—outer surfaces of obturator membrane, pubis, and ischium, margins of obturator foramen I—by a tendon into trochanteric fossa of posterior femur	As for piriformis	Obturator nerve
Obturator internus (in-ter′nus) (*internus* = inside)	Surrounds obturator foramen within pelvis; leaves pelvis via lesser sciatic notch and turns acutely forward to insert in femur	O—inner surface of obturator membrane, greater sciatic notch, and margins of obturator foramen I—greater trochanter in front of piriformis	As for piriformis	L_5 and S_1
Gemellus (jĕ-mĕ′lis)— superior and inferior (*gemin* = twin, double; *superior* = above; *inferior* = below)	Two small muscles with common insertions and actions; considered extrapelvic portions of obturator internus	O—ischial spine (superior); ischial tuberosity (inferior) I—greater trochanter of femur	As for piriformis	L_5 and S_1
Quadratus femoris (*quad* = four-sided square)	Short, thick muscle; most inferior of lateral rotator muscles; extends laterally from pelvis	O—ischial tuberosity I—intertrochanteric crest of femur	Rotates thigh laterally and stabilizes hip joint	L_5 and S_1

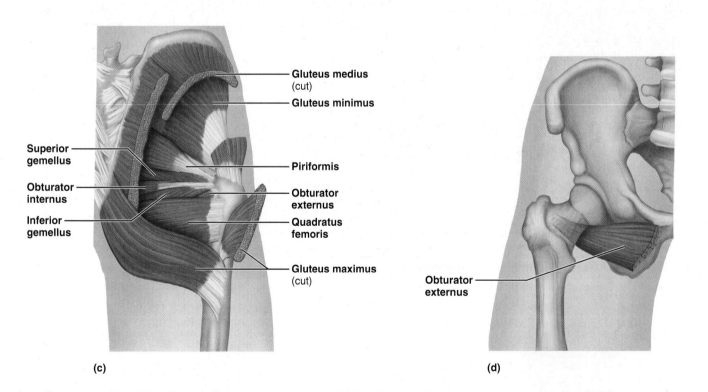

(c)

(d)

Figure 10.20 *(continued)* **Posterior muscles of the right hip and thigh. (c)** Deep muscles of the gluteal region, which act primarily to rotate the thigh laterally. **(d)** Anterior view of the isolated obturator externus muscle.

MUSCLE GALLERY

TABLE 10.14   *(continued)*

MUSCLE	DESCRIPTION	ORIGIN (O) AND INSERTION (I)	ACTION	NERVE SUPPLY

MUSCLES OF THE POSTERIOR COMPARTMENT OF THE THIGH

Hamstrings — The hamstrings are fleshy muscles of the posterior thigh (biceps femoris, semitendinosus, and semimembranosus). They cross both the hip and knee joints and are prime movers of thigh extension and knee flexion. The group has a common origin site and is innervated by sciatic nerve (actually two nerves, the tibial and common fibular nerves wrapped in a common sheath). Ability of hamstrings to act on one of the two joints spanned depends on which joint is fixed; i.e., if knee is fixed (extended), they promote hip extension; if hip is extended, they promote knee flexion. However, when hamstrings are stretched, they tend to restrict full accomplishment of antagonistic movements; e.g., if knees are fully extended, it is difficult to flex the hip fully (and touch your toes), and when the thigh is fully flexed as in kicking a football, it is almost impossible to extend the knee fully at the same time (without considerable practice). Name of this muscle group comes from old butchers' practice of using their tendons to hang hams for smoking. "Pulled hamstrings" are common sports injuries in those who run very hard, e.g., football halfbacks.

MUSCLE	DESCRIPTION	ORIGIN (O) AND INSERTION (I)	ACTION	NERVE SUPPLY
▪ **Biceps femoris** (*biceps* = two heads)	Most lateral muscle of the group; arises from two heads	O—ischial tuberosity (long head); linea aspera, lateral supracondylar line, and distal femur (short head) I—common tendon passes downward and laterally (forming lateral border of popliteal fossa) to insert into head of fibula and lateral condyle of tibia	Extends thigh and flexes knee; laterally rotates leg, especially when knee is flexed	Sciatic nerve—tibial nerve to long head, common fibular nerve to short head (L_5–S_2)
▪ **Semitendinosus** (sem″e-ten″dĭ-no′sus) (*semi* = half; *tendinosus* = tendon)	Lies medial to biceps femoris; although its name suggests that this muscle is largely tendinous, it is quite fleshy; its long slender tendon begins about two-thirds of the way down thigh	O—ischial tuberosity in common with long head of biceps femoris I—medial aspect of upper tibial shaft	Extends thigh and flexes knee; with semimembranosus, medially rotates leg	Sciatic nerve— tibial nerve portion (L_5–S_2)
▪ **Semimembranosus** (sem″e-mem″-brah-no′sus) (*membranosus* = membrane)	Deep to semitendinosus	O—ischial tuberosity I—medial condyle of tibia; via oblique popliteal ligament to lateral condyle of femur	Extends thigh and flexes knee; medially rotates leg	Sciatic nerve— tibial nerve portion (L_5–S_2)

10

MUSCLE GALLERY

TABLE 10.15 **Muscles of the Leg: Movements of the Ankle and Toes** (Figures 10.21 to 10.23)

The deep fascia of the leg is continuous with the fascia lata that ensheathes the thigh. Like a snug "knee sock" beneath the skin, the leg fascia binds the leg muscles tightly, helping to prevent excessive swelling of muscles during exercise and aiding venous return. Its inward extensions segregate the leg muscles into *anterior, lateral,* and *posterior compartments* (see Figure 10.25b), each with its own nerve and blood supply. Distally the leg fascia thickens to form the **flexor, extensor,** and **fibular** (or **peroneal**) **retinacula,** "ankle brackets" that hold the tendons in place where they run to the foot (Figure 10.21a, 10.22a).

The various muscles of the leg promote movements at the ankle joint (dorsiflexion and plantar flexion), at the intertarsal joints (inversion and eversion of the foot), and/or at the toes (flexion and extension). Muscles in the *anterior extensor compartment of the leg* are primarily toe extensors and ankle dorsiflexors. Although dorsiflexion

is not a powerful movement, it is important in preventing the toes from dragging during walking. Lateral compartment muscles are the **fibular,** formerly *peroneal* (*peron* = fibula), **muscles** that plantar flex and evert the foot. Muscles of the *posterior flexor compartment* primarily plantar flex the foot and flex the toes (Figure 10.23b–d). Plantar flexion is the most powerful movement of the ankle (and foot) because it lifts the entire weight of our body. It is essential for standing on tiptoe and provides the forward thrust when walking and running. The **popliteus muscle,** which crosses the knee, has a unique function. It "unlocks" the extended knee in preparation for flexion (Figure 10.23b, f).

We consider the tiny intrinsic muscles of the sole of the foot (lumbricals, interossei, and others) in Table 10.16.

The actions of the muscles in this table are summarized in Table 10.17 (Part II).

MUSCLE	DESCRIPTION	ORIGIN (O) AND INSERTION (I)	ACTION	NERVE SUPPLY
PART I: MUSCLES OF THE ANTERIOR COMPARTMENT (FIGURES 10.21 AND 10.22)	All muscles of the anterior compartment are dorsiflexors of the ankle and have a common innervation, the deep fibular nerve. Paralysis of the anterior muscle group causes *foot drop,* which requires that the leg be lifted unusually high during walking to prevent tripping over one's toes. One cause of "shin splints," also called anterior compartment syndrome, is a painful inflammatory condition of the muscles of the anterior compartment.			
Tibialis anterior (tib"e-a'lis) (*tibial* = tibia; *anterior* = toward the front)	Superficial muscle of anterior leg; laterally parallels sharp anterior margin of tibia	O—lateral condyle and upper 2/3 of tibial shaft; interosseous membrane I—by tendon into inferior surface of medial cuneiform and first metatarsal bone	Prime mover of dorsiflexion; inverts foot; assists in supporting medial longitudinal arch of foot	Deep fibular nerve (L_4 and L_5)
Extensor digitorum longus (*extensor* = increases angle at a joint; *digit* = finger or toe; *longus* = long)	Unipennate muscle on anterolateral surface of leg; lateral to tibialis anterior muscle	O—lateral condyle of tibia; proximal 3/4 of fibula; interosseous membrane I—middle and distal phalanges of toes 2–5 via extensor expansion	Prime mover of toe extension (acts mainly at metatarsophalangeal joints); dorsiflexes foot	Deep fibular nerve (L_5 and S_1)
Fibularis (peroneus) tertius (fib-u-lar'ris ter'shus) (*fibular* = fibula; *tertius* = third)	Small muscle; usually continuous and fused with distal part of extensor digitorum longus; not always present	O—distal anterior surface of fibula and interosseous membrane I—tendon inserts on dorsum of fifth metatarsal	Dorsiflexes and everts foot	Deep fibular nerve (L_5 and S_1)
Extensor hallucis longus (hal'yu-kis) (*hallux* = great toe)	Deep to extensor digitorum longus and tibialis anterior; narrow origin	O—anteromedial fibula shaft and interosseous membrane I—tendon inserts on distal phalanx of great toe	Extends great toe; dorsiflexes foot	Deep fibular nerve (L_5 and S_1)

MUSCLE GALLERY

TABLE 10.15 *(continued)*

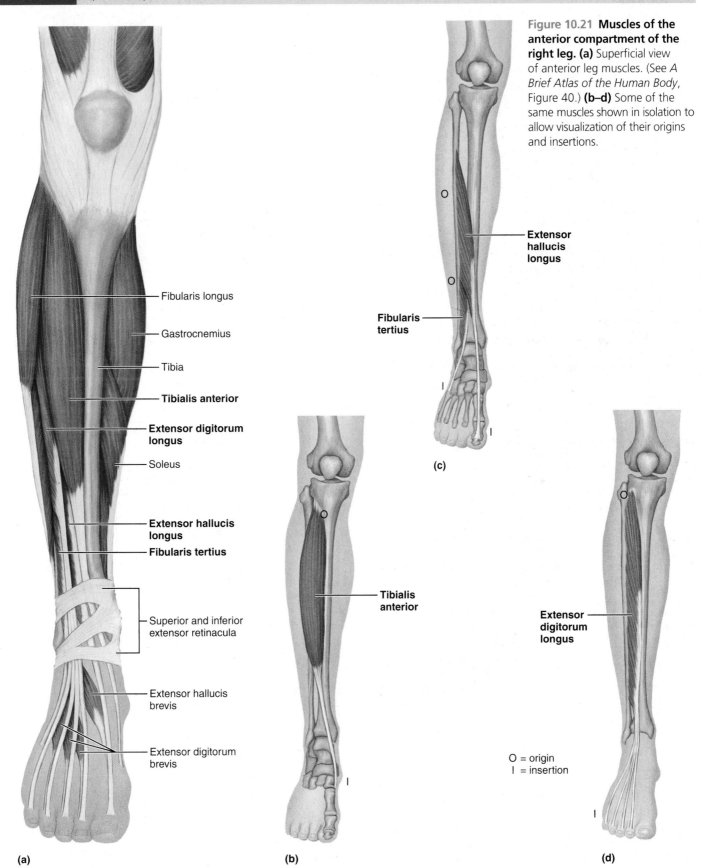

Figure 10.21 Muscles of the anterior compartment of the right leg. (a) Superficial view of anterior leg muscles. (See *A Brief Atlas of the Human Body*, Figure 40.) **(b–d)** Some of the same muscles shown in isolation to allow visualization of their origins and insertions.

(a)

Fibularis longus

Gastrocnemius

Tibia

Tibialis anterior

Extensor digitorum longus

Soleus

Extensor hallucis longus

Fibularis tertius

Superior and inferior extensor retinacula

Extensor hallucis brevis

Extensor digitorum brevis

(b)

Tibialis anterior

(c)

O

O

Extensor hallucis longus

Fibularis tertius

I

I

(d)

O

Extensor digitorum longus

O = origin
I = insertion

I

10

MUSCLE GALLERY

TABLE 10.15   **Muscles of the Leg: Movements of the Ankle and Toes (Figures 10.21 to 10.23)** *(continued)*

10

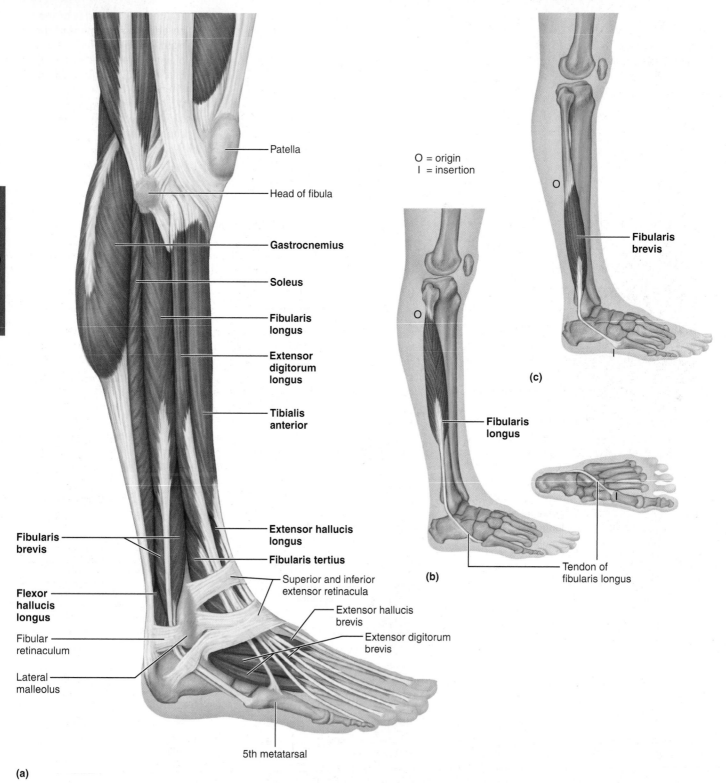

O = origin
I = insertion

Patella

Head of fibula

Gastrocnemius

Soleus

Fibularis longus

Extensor digitorum longus

Tibialis anterior

Extensor hallucis longus

Fibularis tertius

Superior and inferior extensor retinacula

Extensor hallucis brevis

Extensor digitorum brevis

Fibularis brevis

Flexor hallucis longus

Fibular retinaculum

Lateral malleolus

5th metatarsal

(a)

O

Fibularis brevis

(c)

O

Fibularis longus

(b)

Tendon of fibularis longus

I

Figure 10.22 Muscles of the lateral compartment of the right leg. (a) Superficial view of lateral aspect of the leg, illustrating positions of lateral compartment muscles (fibularis longus and brevis) relative to anterior and posterior leg muscles. **(b)** Isolated view of fibularis longus; inset illustrates the insertion of the fibularis longus on the plantar surface of the foot. **(c)** Isolated view of fibularis brevis. (See *A Brief Atlas of the Human Body,* Figure 42.)

MUSCLE GALLERY

TABLE 10.15 *(continued)*

MUSCLE	DESCRIPTION	ORIGIN (O) AND INSERTION (I)	ACTION	NERVE SUPPLY

PART II: MUSCLES OF THE LATERAL COMPARTMENT (FIGURES 10.22 AND 10.23) These muscles have a common innervation, the superficial fibular nerve. Besides plantar flexion and foot eversion, these muscles stabilize the lateral ankle and lateral longitudinal arch of the foot.

MUSCLE	DESCRIPTION	ORIGIN (O) AND INSERTION (I)	ACTION	NERVE SUPPLY
Fibularis (peroneus) longus (See also Figure 10.21)	Superficial lateral muscle; overlies fibula	O—head and upper portion of lateral fibula I—by long tendon that curves under foot to first metatarsal and medial cuneiform	Plantar flexes and everts foot; may help keep foot flat on ground	Superficial fibular nerve (L_5–S_2)
Fibularis (peroneus) brevis (*brevis* = short)	Smaller muscle; deep to fibularis longus; enclosed in a common sheath	O—distal fibula shaft I—by tendon running behind lateral malleolus to insert on proximal end of fifth metatarsal	Plantar flexes and everts foot	Superficial fibular nerve (L_5–S_2)

PART III: MUSCLES OF THE POSTERIOR COMPARTMENT (FIGURE 10.23) The muscles of the posterior compartment have a common innervation, the tibial nerve. They act in concert to plantar flex the ankle.

SUPERFICIAL MUSCLES

MUSCLE	DESCRIPTION	ORIGIN (O) AND INSERTION (I)	ACTION	NERVE SUPPLY
Triceps surae (tri"seps sur'e) (See also Figure 10.22)	Refers to muscle pair (gastrocnemius and soleus) that shapes the posterior calf and inserts via a common tendon into the calcaneus of the heel; this *calcaneal* or *Achilles tendon* is the largest tendon in the body. Prime movers of ankle plantar flexion.			
▪ **Gastrocnemius** (gas"truk-ne'me-us) (*gaster* = belly; *kneme* = leg)	Superficial muscle of pair; two prominent bellies that form proximal curve of calf	O—by two heads from medial and lateral condyles of femur I—posterior calcaneus via calcaneal tendon	Plantar flexes foot when knee is extended; because it also crosses knee joint, it can flex knee when foot is dorsiflexed	Tibial nerve (S_1, S_2)
▪ **Soleus** (so'le-us) (*soleus* = fish)	Broad, flat muscle, deep to gastrocnemius on posterior surface of calf	O—extensive origin from superior tibia, fibula, and interosseous membrane I—as for gastrocnemius	Plantar flexes foot; important locomotor and postural muscle during walking, running, and dancing	Tibial nerve
Plantaris (plan-tar'is) (*planta* = sole of foot)	Generally a small, feeble muscle, but varies in size and extent; may be absent	O—posterior femur above lateral condyle I—via a long, thin tendon into calcaneus or its tendon	Assists in knee flexion and plantar flexion of foot	Tibial nerve

DEEP MUSCLES (FIGURE 10.23c–f)

MUSCLE	DESCRIPTION	ORIGIN (O) AND INSERTION (I)	ACTION	NERVE SUPPLY
Popliteus (pop-lit'e-us) (*poplit* = back of knee)	Thin, triangular muscle at posterior knee; passes inferomedially to tibial surface	O—lateral condyle of femur and lateral meniscus I—proximal tibia	Flexes and rotates leg medially to unlock extended knee when flexion begins; with tibia fixed, rotates thigh laterally	Tibial nerve (L_4–S_1)
Flexor digitorum longus (*flexor* = decreases angle at a joint)	Long, narrow muscle; runs medial to and partially overlies tibialis posterior	O—extensive origin on the posterior tibia I—tendon runs behind medial malleolus and inserts into distal phalanges of toes 2–5	Plantar flexes and inverts foot; flexes toes; helps foot "grip" ground	Tibial nerve (L_5–S_2)
Flexor hallucis longus (See also Figure 10.22)	Bipennate muscle; lies lateral to inferior aspect of tibialis posterior	O—midshaft of fibula; interosseous membrane I—tendon runs under foot to distal phalanx of great toe	Plantar flexes and inverts foot; flexes great toe at all joints; "push off" muscle during walking	Tibial nerve (L_5–S_2)
Tibialis posterior (*posterior* = toward the back)	Thick, flat muscle deep to soleus; placed between posterior flexors	O—superior tibia and fibula and interosseous membrane I—tendon passes behind medial malleolus and under arch of foot; inserts into several tarsals and metatarsals 2–4	Prime mover of foot inversion; plantar flexes foot; stabilizes medial longitudinal arch of foot (as during ice skating)	Tibial nerve (L_4 and L_5)

MUSCLE GALLERY

| TABLE 10.15 | Muscles of the Leg: Movements of the Ankle and Toes (Figures 10.21 to 10.23) *(continued)* |

10

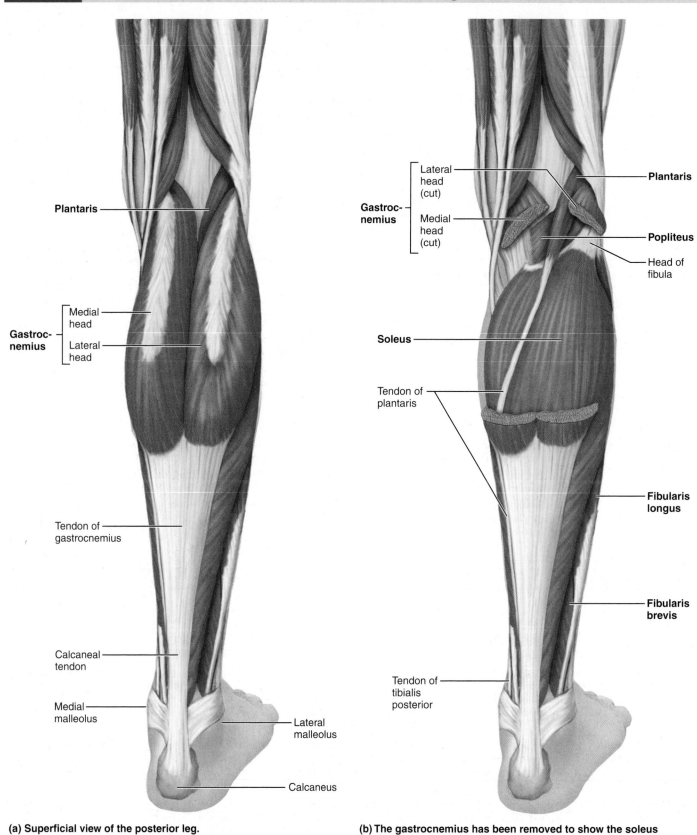

Plantaris

Gastroc-
nemius
  Medial
  head
  Lateral
  head

Tendon of
gastrocnemius

Calcaneal
tendon

Medial
malleolus

Lateral
malleolus

Calcaneus

(a) Superficial view of the posterior leg.

Lateral
head
(cut)

Gastroc-
nemius

Medial
head
(cut)

Plantaris

Popliteus

Head of
fibula

Soleus

Tendon of
plantaris

Fibularis
longus

Fibularis
brevis

Tendon of
tibialis
posterior

**(b) The gastrocnemius has been removed to show the soleus
immediately deep to it.**

Figure 10.23 **Muscles of the posterior compartment of the right leg.**

MUSCLE GALLERY

TABLE 10.15 *(continued)*

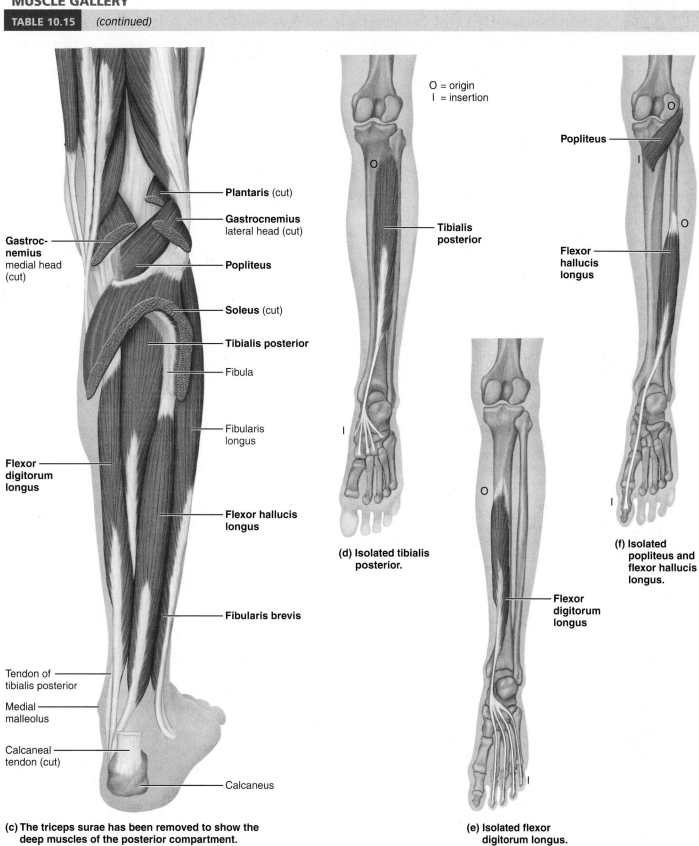

O = origin
I = insertion

Plantaris (cut)

Gastrocnemius lateral head (cut)

Popliteus

Gastroc-nemius medial head (cut)

Soleus (cut)

Tibialis posterior

Fibula

Fibularis longus

Flexor digitorum longus

Flexor hallucis longus

Fibularis brevis

Tendon of tibialis posterior

Medial malleolus

Calcaneal tendon (cut)

Calcaneus

(c) The triceps surae has been removed to show the deep muscles of the posterior compartment.

Tibialis posterior

(d) Isolated tibialis posterior.

Flexor digitorum longus

(e) Isolated flexor digitorum longus.

Popliteus

Flexor hallucis longus

(f) Isolated popliteus and flexor hallucis longus.

10

Figure 10.23 *(continued)*

MUSCLE GALLERY

TABLE 10.16   **Intrinsic Muscles of the Foot: Toe Movement and Arch Support** (Figure 10.24)

The intrinsic muscles of the foot help to flex, extend, abduct, and adduct the toes. Collectively, along with the tendons of some leg muscles that enter the sole, the foot muscles help support the arches of the foot. There is a single muscle on the foot's dorsum (superior aspect),

and several muscles on the plantar aspect (the sole). The plantar muscles occur in four layers, from superficial to deep. Overall, the foot muscles are remarkably similar to those in the palm of the hand.

MUSCLE	DESCRIPTION	ORIGIN (O) AND INSERTION (I)	ACTION	NERVE SUPPLY
MUSCLES ON DORSUM OF FOOT				
Extensor digitorum brevis (Figures 10.21a and 10.22a)	Small, four-part muscle on dorsum of foot; deep to the tendons of extensor digitorum longus; corresponds to the extensor indicis and extensor pollicis muscles of forearm.	O—anterior part of calcaneus bone; extensor retinaculum I—base of proximal phalanx of great toe; extensor expansions on toes 2–5	Helps extend toes at metatarsophalangeal joints	Deep fibular nerve (L_5 and S_1)
MUSCLES ON SOLE OF FOOT—FIRST LAYER (MOST SUPERFICIAL) (FIGURE 10.24)				
Flexor digitorum brevis	Bandlike muscle in middle of sole; corresponds to flexor digitorum superficialis of forearm and inserts into digits in the same way	O—calcaneal tuberosity I—middle phalanx of toes 2–4	Helps flex toes	Medial plantar nerve (a branch of tibial nerve, S_1 and S_2)
Abductor hallucis (hal'yu-kis) (*hallux* = great toe)	Lies medial to flexor digitorum brevis (recall the similar thumb muscle, abductor pollicis brevis)	O—calcaneal tuberosity and flexor retinaculum I—proximal phalanx of great toe, medial side, in the tendon of flexor hallucis brevis (see below)	Abducts great toe	Medial plantar nerve
Abductor digiti minimi	Most lateral of the three superficial sole muscles (recall similar abductor muscle in palm)	O—calcaneal tuberosity I—lateral side of base of little toe's proximal phalanx	Abducts and flexes little toe	Lateral plantar nerve (a branch of tibial nerve, S_1, S_2, and S_3)
MUSCLES ON SOLE OF FOOT—SECOND LAYER				
Flexor accessorius (quadratus plantae)	Rectangular muscle just deep to flexor digitorum brevis in posterior half of sole; two heads (see also Figure 10.24c)	O—medial and lateral sides of calcaneus I—tendon of flexor digitorum longus in midsole	Straightens out the oblique pull of flexor digitorum longus	Lateral plantar nerve
Lumbricals	Four little "worms" (like lumbricals in hand)	O—from each tendon of flexor digitorum longus I—extensor expansion on proximal phalanx of toes 2–5, medial side	By pulling on extensor expansion, flex toes at metatarsophalangeal joints and extend toes at interphalangeal joints	Medial plantar nerve (first lumbrical) and lateral plantar nerve (second to fourth lumbrical)

MUSCLE GALLERY

TABLE 10.16   (continued)

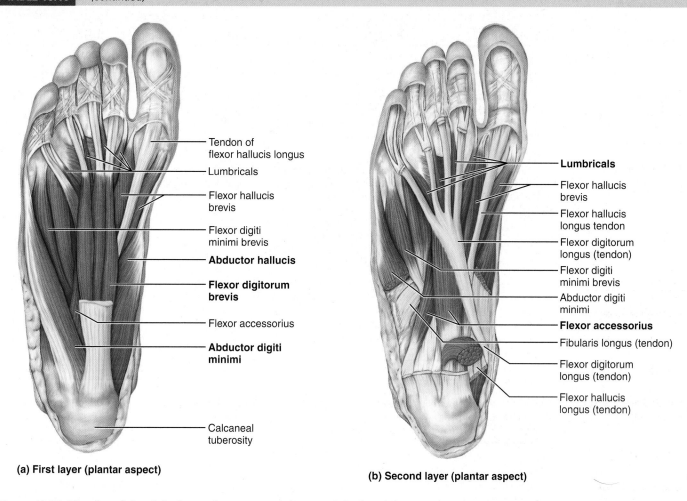

(a) First layer (plantar aspect)

Tendon of
flexor hallucis longus

Lumbricals

Flexor hallucis
brevis

Flexor digiti
minimi brevis

Abductor hallucis

**Flexor digitorum
brevis**

Flexor accessorius

**Abductor digiti
minimi**

Calcaneal
tuberosity

(b) Second layer (plantar aspect)

Lumbricals

Flexor hallucis
brevis

Flexor hallucis
longus tendon

Flexor digitorum
longus (tendon)

Flexor digiti
minimi brevis

Abductor digiti
minimi

Flexor accessorius

Fibularis longus (tendon)

Flexor digitorum
longus (tendon)

Flexor hallucis
longus (tendon)

Figure 10.24 Muscles of the right foot, plantar aspect. (See *A Brief Atlas of the Human Body,* Figure 43.)

10

MUSCLE GALLERY

| TABLE 10.16 | Intrinsic Muscles of the Foot: Toe Movement and Arch Support (Figure 10.24) *(continued)* |

MUSCLE	DESCRIPTION	ORIGIN (O) AND INSERTION (I)	ACTION	NERVE SUPPLY
MUSCLES ON SOLE OF FOOT—THIRD LAYER				
Flexor hallucis brevis	Covers metatarsal 1; splits into two bellies—recall flexor pollicis brevis of thumb	O—lateral cuneiform and cuboid bones I—via two tendons onto base of the proximal phalanx of great toe	Flexes great toe's metatarsophalangeal joint	Medial plantar nerve
Adductor hallucis	Oblique and transverse heads; deep to lumbricals (recall adductor pollicis in thumb)	O—from bases of metatarsals 2–4 and from fibularis longus tendon sheath (oblique head); from a ligament across metatarsophalangeal joints (transverse head) I—base of proximal phalanx of great toe, lateral side	Helps maintain the transverse arch of foot; weak adductor of great toe	Lateral plantar nerve (S_2 and S_3)
Flexor digiti minimi brevis	Covers metatarsal 5 (recall same muscle in hand)	O—base of metatarsal 5 and tendon sheath of fibularis longus I—base of proximal phalanx of toe 5	Flexes little toe at metatarsophalangeal joint	Lateral plantar nerve
MUSCLES ON SOLE OF FOOT—FOURTH LAYER (DEEPEST)				
Plantar (3) and dorsal interossei (4)	Similar to the palmar and dorsal interossei of hand in locations, attachments, and actions; however, the long axis of foot around which these muscles orient is the second digit, not the third	See palmar and dorsal interossei (Table 10.13)	See palmar and dorsal interossei (Table 10.13)	Lateral plantar nerve

MUSCLE GALLERY

TABLE 10.16 *(continued)*

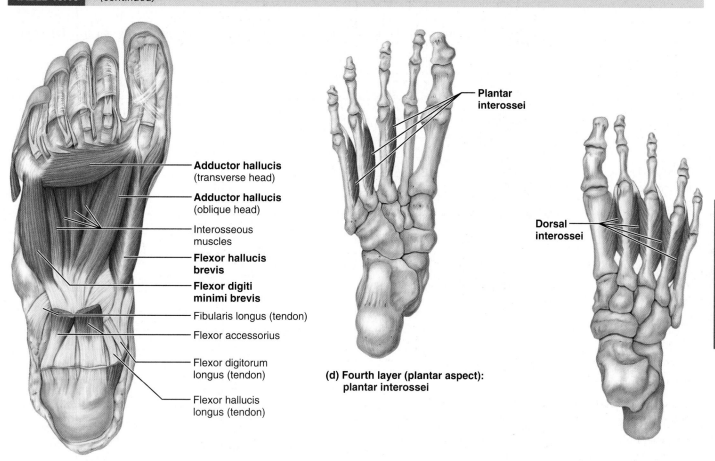

(c) Third layer (plantar aspect)

Adductor hallucis (transverse head)
Adductor hallucis (oblique head)
Interosseous muscles
Flexor hallucis brevis
Flexor digiti minimi brevis
Fibularis longus (tendon)
Flexor accessorius
Flexor digitorum longus (tendon)
Flexor hallucis longus (tendon)

Plantar interossei

(d) Fourth layer (plantar aspect): plantar interossei

Dorsal interossei

(e) Fourth layer (dorsal aspect): dorsal interossei

Figure 10.24 *(continued)* **Muscles of the right foot, plantar aspect.**

TABLE 10.17 Summary of Major Actions of Muscles Acting on the Thigh, Leg, and Foot (Figure 10.25)

Part I: Muscles Acting on the Thigh and Leg (PM = prime mover)	ACTIONS AT THE HIP JOINT						ACTIONS AT THE KNEE	
	Flexion	Extension	Abduction	Adduction	Medial Rotation	Lateral Rotation	Flexion	Extension
Anterior and Medial Muscles								
Iliopsoas	× (PM)							
Sartorius	×		×			×	×	
Tensor fasciae latae	×		×		×			
Rectus femoris	×							× (PM)
Vasti muscles								× (PM)
Adductor magnus		×		×	×			
Adductor longus	×			×	×			
Adductor brevis	×			×	×			
Pectineus	×			×	×			
Gracilis				×	×		×	
Posterior Muscles								
Gluteus maximus		× (PM)	×			×		
Gluteus medius			× (PM)		×			
Gluteus minimus			×		×			
Piriformis			×			×		
Obturator internus						×		
Obturator externus						×		
Gemelli						×		
Quadratus femoris						×		
Biceps femoris		× (PM)					× (PM)	
Semitendinosus		×					× (PM)	
Semimembranosus		×					× (PM)	
Gastrocnemius							×	
Plantaris							×	
Popliteus							× (and rotates leg medially)	

Part II: Muscles Acting on the Ankle and Toes	ACTIONS AT THE ANKLE JOINT				ACTIONS AT THE TOES	
	Plantar Flexion	Dorsiflexion	Inversion	Eversion	Flexion	Extension
Anterior Compartment						
Tibialis anterior		× (PM)	×			
Extensor digitorum longus		×				× (PM)
Fibularis tertius		×		×		
Extensor hallucis longus		×	× (weak)			× (great toe)
Lateral Compartment						
Fibularis longus and brevis	×			×		
Posterior Compartment						
Gastrocnemius	× (PM)					
Soleus	× (PM)					
Plantaris	×					
Flexor digitorum longus	×		×		× (PM)	
Flexor hallucis longus	×		×		× (great toe)	
Tibialis posterior	×		× (PM)			

MUSCLE GALLERY

TABLE 10.17 *(continued)*

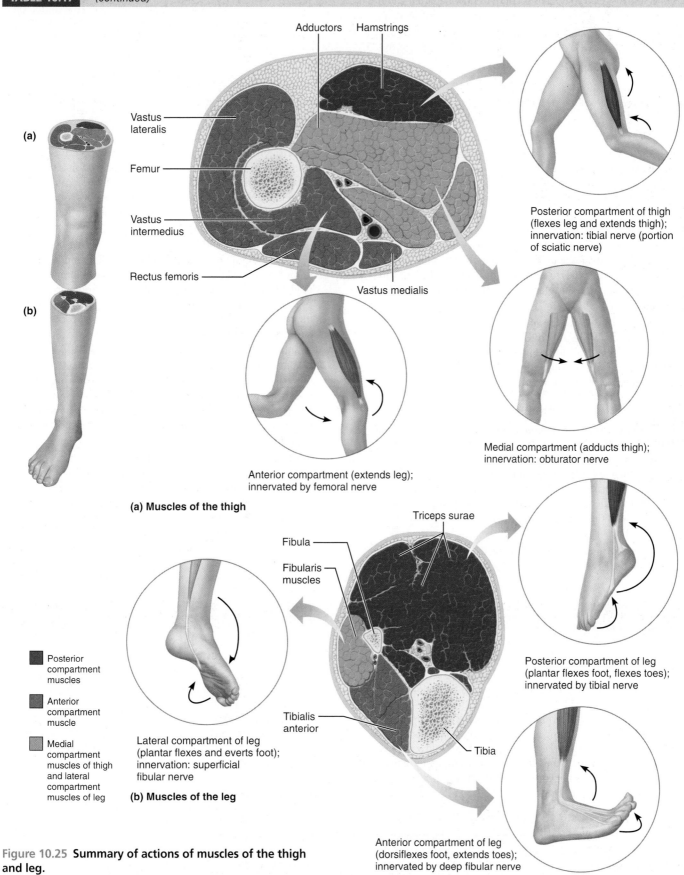

(a)

(b)

Adductors Hamstrings

Vastus lateralis

Femur

Vastus intermedius

Rectus femoris

Vastus medialis

Posterior compartment of thigh (flexes leg and extends thigh); innervation: tibial nerve (portion of sciatic nerve)

Anterior compartment (extends leg); innervated by femoral nerve

Medial compartment (adducts thigh); innervation: obturator nerve

(a) Muscles of the thigh

Triceps surae

Fibula

Fibularis muscles

Tibialis anterior

Tibia

Posterior compartment of leg (plantar flexes foot, flexes toes); innervated by tibial nerve

Anterior compartment of leg (dorsiflexes foot, extends toes); innervated by deep fibular nerve

Lateral compartment of leg (plantar flexes and everts foot); innervation: superficial fibular nerve

Posterior compartment muscles

Anterior compartment muscle

Medial compartment muscles of thigh and lateral compartment muscles of leg

(b) Muscles of the leg

10

Figure 10.25 Summary of actions of muscles of the thigh and leg.

CHECK YOUR UNDERSTANDING

6. As John listened to Roger's account of how he flirted with his neighbor, he raised his eyebrows and then winked at Sarah. What facial muscles was he using?

7. What muscles would you contract to make a "sad clown's face"?

8. How can the deltoid muscles both extend and flex the arm? Aren't these antagonistic movements?

9. Which of the thenar muscles does *not* have an insertion on bones of the thumb?

For answers, see Appendix G.

RELATED CLINICAL TERMS

Charley horse A muscle contusion, i.e., tearing of muscle followed by bleeding into the tissues (hematoma) and severe, prolonged pain; a common contact sports injury; a charley horse of the quadriceps muscle of the thigh occurs frequently in football players.

Electromyography Recording and interpretation of graphic records of the electrical activity of contracting muscles. Electrodes inserted into the muscles record the impulses that pass over muscle-cell membranes to stimulate contraction. The best and most important technique for determining the functions of muscles and muscle groups.

Hernia An abnormal protrusion of abdominal contents (typically coils of the small intestine) through a weak point in the muscles of the abdominal wall. Most often caused by increased intra-abdominal pressure during lifting or straining. The hernia penetrates the muscle wall but not the skin and so appears as a visible bulge in the body surface. Common abdominal hernias include the inguinal and umbilical hernias.

Quadriceps and hamstring strains Also called quad and hamstring pulls, these conditions involve tearing of these muscles or their tendons; happen mainly in athletes who do not warm up properly and then fully extend their hip (quad pull) or knee (hamstring pull) quickly or forcefully (e.g., sprinters, tennis players); not painful at first, but pain intensifies within three to six hours (30 minutes if the tearing is severe). After a week of rest, stretching is the best therapy.

Rupture of the calcaneal tendon Although the calcaneal (Achilles) tendon is the largest, strongest tendon in the body, its rupture is surprisingly common, particularly in older people as a result of stumbling and in young sprinters when the tendon is traumatized during the takeoff. The rupture is followed by abrupt pain; a gap is seen just above the heel, and the calf bulges as the triceps surae are released from their insertion. Plantar flexion is weak or impossible, but dorsiflexion is exaggerated. Surgical repair of the tendon is usually performed.

Shin splints Common term for pain in the anterior compartment of the leg caused by irritation of the tibialis anterior muscle as might follow extreme or unusual exercise without adequate prior conditioning. Because it is tightly wrapped by fascia, the inflamed tibialis anterior cuts off its own circulation as it swells and presses painfully on its own nerves.

Tennis elbow Tenderness due to trauma or overuse of the tendon of origin of the forearm extensor muscles at the lateral epicondyle of the humerus. Caused and aggravated when these muscles contract forcefully to extend the hand at the wrist—as in executing a tennis backhand or lifting a loaded snow shovel. Despite its name, tennis elbow does not involve the elbow joint; most cases caused by work activities.

Torticollis (tor″tĭ-kol′is; *tort* = twisted) A twisting of the neck in which there is a chronic rotation and tilting of the head to one side, due to injury of the sternocleidomastoid muscle on one side; also called wryneck. Sometimes present at birth when the muscle fibers are torn during difficult delivery. Exercise that stretches the affected muscle is the usual treatment.

CHAPTER SUMMARY

Interactions of Skeletal Muscles in the Body (p. 321)

1. Skeletal muscles are arranged in opposing groups across body joints so that one group can reverse or modify the action of the other.

2. Muscles are classified as prime movers, or agonists (bear the chief responsibility for producing movement); antagonists (reverse, or oppose, the action of another muscle); synergists (aid a prime mover by effecting the same action, stabilizing joints, or preventing undesirable movements); and fixators (function to immobilize a bone or a muscle's origin).

Naming Skeletal Muscles (pp. 321–322)

1. Criteria used to name muscles include a muscle's location, shape, relative size, fiber (fascicle) direction, number of origins, attachment sites (origin/insertion), and action. Several criteria are combined to name some muscles.

Muscle Mechanics: Importance of Fascicle Arrangement and Leverage (pp. 322–324)

1. Common patterns of fascicle arrangement are parallel, fusiform, pennate, convergent, and circular. Muscles with fibers that run parallel to the long axis of the muscle shorten most; stocky pennate muscles shorten little but are the most powerful muscles.

2. A lever is a bar that moves on a fulcrum. When an effort is applied to the lever, a load is moved. In the body, bones are the levers, joints are the fulcrums, and the effort is exerted by skeletal muscles at their insertions.

3. When the effort is farther from the fulcrum than is the load, the lever operates at a mechanical advantage (is slow and strong). When the effort is exerted closer to the fulcrum than is the load, the lever operates at a mechanical disadvantage (is fast and promotes a large degree of movement).

4. First-class levers (effort-fulcrum-load) may operate at a mechanical advantage or disadvantage. Second-class levers (fulcrum-load-effort) all operate at a mechanical advantage. Third-class levers (fulcrum-effort-load) always operate at a mechanical disadvantage. Most skeletal muscles of the body act in third-class lever systems.

Major Skeletal Muscles of the Body   (pp. 324–382)

1. Muscles of the head that produce facial expression tend to be small and to insert into soft tissue (skin and other muscles) rather than into bone. These muscles open and close the eyes and mouth, compress the cheeks, allow smiling and other types of facial language (see Table 10.1*).
2. Muscles of the head involved in mastication include the masseter and temporalis that elevate the mandible and two deep muscle pairs that promote grinding and sliding jaw movements (see Table 10.2*). Extrinsic muscles of the tongue anchor the tongue and control its movements.
3. Deep muscles of the anterior neck promote swallowing movements, including elevation/depression of the hyoid bone, closure of the respiratory passages, and peristalsis of the pharynx (see Table 10.3*).
4. Neck muscles and deep muscles of the vertebral column promote head and trunk movements (see Table 10.4*). The deep muscles of the posterior trunk can extend large regions of the vertebral column (and head) simultaneously. Head flexion and rotation are effected by the anteriorly located sternocleidomastoid and scalene muscles.
5. Movements of quiet breathing are promoted by the diaphragm and the external intercostal muscles of the thorax (see Table 10.5*). Downward movement of the diaphragm increases intra-abdominal pressure.
6. The four muscle pairs forming the abdominal wall are layered like plywood to form a natural muscular girdle that protects, supports, and compresses abdominal contents. These muscles also flex and laterally rotate the trunk (see Table 10.6*).
7. Muscles of the pelvic floor and perineum (see Table 10.7*) support the pelvic viscera, resist increases in intra-abdominal pressure, inhibit urination and defecation, and aid erection.
8. Except for the pectoralis major and the latissimus dorsi, the superficial muscles of the thorax act to fix or promote movements of the scapula (see Table 10.8*). Scapular movements are effected primarily by posterior thoracic muscles.
9. Nine muscles cross the shoulder joint to effect movements of the humerus (see Table 10.9*). Of these, seven originate on the scapula and two arise from the axial skeleton. Four muscles contribute to the "rotator cuff" helping to stabilize the multiaxial shoulder joint. Generally speaking, muscles located anteriorly flex, rotate, and adduct the arm. Those located posteriorly extend, rotate, and adduct the arm. The deltoid muscle of the shoulder is the prime mover of shoulder abduction.
10. Muscles causing movements of the forearm form the flesh of the arm (see Table 10.10*). Anterior arm muscles are forearm flexors; posterior muscles are forearm extensors.
11. Movements of the wrist, hand, and fingers are effected mainly by muscles originating on the forearm (see Table 10.11*). Except for the two pronator muscles, the anterior forearm muscles are wrist and/or finger flexors; those of the posterior compartment are wrist and finger extensors.
12. The intrinsic muscles of the hand aid in precise movements of the fingers (Table 10.13*) and in opposition, which helps us grip things in our palms. These small muscles are divided into thenar, hypothenar, and midpalmar groups.
13. Muscles crossing the hip and knee joints effect thigh and leg movements (see Table 10.14*). Anteromedial muscles include thigh flexors and/or adductors and knee extensors. Muscles of the posterior gluteal region extend and rotate the thigh. Posterior thigh muscles extend the hip and flex the knee.
14. Muscles in the leg act on the ankle and toes (see Table 10.15*). Anterior compartment muscles are largely ankle dorsiflexors. Lateral compartment muscles are plantar flexors and foot everters. Those of the posterior leg are plantar flexors.
15. The intrinsic muscles of the foot (Table 10.17*) support the foot arches and help move the toes. Most occur in the sole, arranged in four layers. They resemble the small muscles in the palm of the hand.

*See specific table cited for detailed description of each muscle in the group.

REVIEW QUESTIONS

Multiple Choice/Matching

(Some questions have more than one correct answer. Select the best answer or answers from the choices given.)

1. A muscle that assists an agonist by causing a like movement or by stabilizing a joint over which an agonist acts is (**a**) an antagonist, (**b**) a prime mover, (**c**) a synergist, (**d**) an agonist.
2. The arrangement of muscle fibers in which the fibers are arranged at an angle to a central longitudinal tendon is: (**a**) circular, (**b**) longitudinal, (**c**) pennate, (**d**) parallel.
3. Match the muscle names in column B to the facial muscles described in column A.

Column A	Column B
—— (**1**) squints the eyes	(**a**) corrugator supercilii
—— (**2**) raises the eyebrows	(**b**) depressor anguli oris
—— (**3**) smiling muscle	(**c**) frontal belly of epicranius
—— (**4**) puckers the lips	(**d**) occipital belly of epicranius
—— (**5**) pulls the scalp posteriorly	(**e**) orbicularis oculi
	(**f**) orbicularis oris
	(**g**) zygomaticus

4. The prime mover of inspiration is the (**a**) diaphragm, (**b**) internal intercostals, (**c**) external intercostals, (**d**) abdominal wall muscles.
5. The arm muscle that both flexes the elbow and supinates the forearm is the (**a**) brachialis, (**b**) brachioradialis, (**c**) biceps brachii, (**d**) triceps brachii.

6. The chewing muscles that protrude the mandible and produce side-to-side grinding movements are the (**a**) buccinators, (**b**) masseters, (**c**) temporalis, (**d**) pterygoids.

7. Muscles that depress the hyoid bone and larynx include all but the (**a**) sternohyoid, (**b**) omohyoid, (**c**) geniohyoid, (**d**) sternothyroid.

8. Intrinsic muscles of the back that promote extension of the spine (or head) include all but (**a**) splenius muscles, (**b**) semispinalis muscles, (**c**) scalene muscles, (**d**) erector spinae.

9. Several muscles act to move and/or stabilize the scapula. Which of the following are small rectangular muscles that square the shoulders as they act together to retract the scapula? (**a**) levator scapulae, (**b**) rhomboids, (**c**) serratus anterior, (**d**) trapezius.

10. The quadriceps include all but (**a**) vastus lateralis, (**b**) vastus intermedius, (**c**) vastus medialis, (**d**) biceps femoris, (**e**) rectus femoris.

11. A prime mover of hip flexion is the (**a**) rectus femoris, (**b**) iliopsoas, (**c**) vasti muscles, (**d**) gluteus maximus.

12. The prime mover of hip extension *against* resistance is the (**a**) gluteus maximus, (**b**) gluteus medius, (**c**) biceps femoris, (**d**) semimembranosus.

13. Muscles that cause plantar flexion include all but the (**a**) gastrocnemius, (**b**) soleus, (**c**) tibialis anterior, (**d**) tibialis posterior, (**e**) fibularis muscles.

14. In walking, which two lower limb muscles keep the forward-swinging foot from dragging on the ground? (**a**) pronator teres and popliteus, (**b**) flexor digitorum longus and popliteus, (**c**) adductor longus and abductor digiti minimi in foot, (**d**) gluteus medius and tibialis anterior.

15. What criterion (or criteria) are used in naming the gluteus medius? (**a**) relative size, (**b**) muscle location, (**c**) muscle shape, (**d**) action, (**e**) number of origins.

16. Which of the following is a large, deep muscle that protracts the scapula during punching? (**a**) serratus anterior, (**b**) rhomboids, (**c**) levator scapulae, (**d**) subscapularis.

Short Answer Essay Questions

17. Name four criteria used in naming muscles, and provide an example (other than those used in the text) that illustrates each criterion.

18. Differentiate between the arrangement of elements (load, fulcrum, and effort) in first-, second-, and third-class levers.

19. What does it mean when we say that a lever operates at a mechanical disadvantage, and what benefits does such a lever system provide?

20. What muscles act to propel a food bolus down the length of the pharynx to the esophagus?

21. Name and describe the action of muscles used to shake your head no; to nod yes.

22. (a) Name the four muscle pairs that act in unison to compress the abdominal contents. (b) How does their arrangement (fiber direction) contribute to the strength of the abdominal wall? (c) Which of these muscles can effect lateral rotation of the spine? (d) Which can act alone to flex the spine?

23. List all (six) possible movements that can occur at the shoulder joint and name the prime mover(s) of each movement. Then name their antagonists.

24. (a) Name two forearm muscles that are powerful extensors and abductors of the wrist. (b) Name the sole forearm muscle that can flex the distal interphalangeal joints.

25. Name the muscles usually grouped together as the lateral rotators of the hip.

26. Name three thigh muscles that help you keep your seat astride a horse.

27. (a) Name three muscles or muscle groups used as sites for intramuscular injections. (b) Which of these is used most often in infants, and why?

28. Name two muscles in each of the following compartments or regions: (a) thenar eminence (ball of thumb), (b) posterior compartment of forearm, (c) anterior compartment of forearm—deep muscle group, (d) anterior muscle group in the arm, (e) muscles of mastication, (f) third muscle layer of the foot, (g) posterior compartment of leg, (h) medial compartment of thigh, (i) posterior compartment of thigh.

Critical Thinking and Clinical Application Questions

1. Assume you have a 10-lb weight in your right hand. Explain why it is easier to flex the right elbow when your forearm is supinated than when it is pronated.

2. When Mrs. O'Brien returned to her doctor for a follow-up visit after childbirth, she complained that she was having problems controlling her urine flow (was incontinent) when she sneezed. The physician asked his nurse to give Mrs. O'Brien instructions on how to perform exercises to strengthen the muscles of the pelvic floor. To what muscles was he referring?

3. Mr. Ahmadi, an out-of-shape 45-year-old man, was advised by his physician to lose weight and to exercise on a regular basis. He followed his diet faithfully and began to jog daily. One day, while on his morning jog, he heard a snapping sound that was immediately followed by a severe pain in his right lower calf. When his leg was examined, a gap was seen between his swollen upper calf region and his heel, and he was unable to plantar flex that ankle. What do you think happened? Why was the upper part of his calf swollen?

4. As Peter watched Sue walk down the runway at the fashion show, he contracted his right orbicularis oculi muscle, raised his arm, and contracted his opponens pollicis. Was he pleased or displeased with her performance? How do you know?

5. What type of lever system is described by the following activities? (a) The soleus muscle plantar flexes the foot. (b) The deltoid abducts the arm. (c) The triceps brachii is strained while doing pushups.

6. While riding an unusually large horse, Chao Jung had to spread her thighs widely to span its back and she pulled the muscles in her medial thighs. Which muscles were these and what might this condition be called?

11

Functions and Divisions of the Nervous System (pp. 386–388)

Histology of Nervous Tissue (pp. 388–395)

Neuroglia (pp. 388–389)

Neurons (pp. 389–395)

Membrane Potentials (pp. 395–406)

Basic Principles of Electricity (p. 395)

The Resting Membrane Potential (pp. 396–398)

Membrane Potentials That Act as Signals (pp. 398–406)

The Synapse (pp. 406–413)

Electrical Synapses (p. 406)

Chemical Synapses (pp. 407–408)

Postsynaptic Potentials and Synaptic Integration (pp. 408–413)

Neurotransmitters and Their Receptors (pp. 413–420)

Classification of Neurotransmitters by Chemical Structure (pp. 414–419)

Classification of Neurotransmitters by Function (pp. 419–420)

Neurotransmitter Receptors (pp. 420–421)

Basic Concepts of Neural Integration (pp. 421–423)

Organization of Neurons: Neuronal Pools (pp. 421–422)

Types of Circuits (p. 422)

Patterns of Neural Processing (pp. 422–423)

Developmental Aspects of Neurons (pp. 423–424)

Fundamentals of the Nervous System and Nervous Tissue

Y ou are driving down the freeway, and a horn blares to your right. You immediately swerve to your left. Charlie leaves a note on the kitchen table: "See you later. Have the stuff ready at 6." You know the "stuff" is chili with taco chips. You are dozing but you awaken instantly as your infant son makes a soft cry.

What do these three events have in common? They are all everyday examples of the functioning of your nervous system, which has your body cells humming with activity nearly all the time.

The **nervous system** is the master controlling and communicating system of the body. Every thought, action, and emotion reflects its activity. Its cells communicate by electrical and chemical signals, which are rapid and specific, and usually cause almost immediate responses.

We begin this chapter with a brief overview of the functions and organization of the nervous system. Then we focus on the functional anatomy of nervous tissue, especially that of nerve cells, or *neurons*, which are the key to neural communication.

Functions and Divisions of the Nervous System

▶ List the basic functions of the nervous system.

▶ Explain the structural and functional divisions of the nervous system.

The nervous system has three overlapping functions, illustrated by the example of a thirsty person seeing and then lifting a glass of drinking water in **Figure 11.1**:

1. **Sensory input.** The nervous system uses its millions of sensory receptors to monitor changes occurring both inside and outside the body. The gathered information is called **sensory input**.
2. **Integration.** The nervous system processes and interprets sensory input and decides what should be done at each moment—a process called **integration**.
3. **Motor output.** The nervous system causes a *response*, called **motor output**, by activating *effector organs*—the muscles and glands.

In another example, when you are driving and see a red light ahead (sensory input), your nervous system integrates this information (red light means "stop"), and your foot goes for the brake (motor output).

We have only one highly integrated nervous system. For convenience, it can be divided into two principal parts. The **central nervous system (CNS)** consists of the *brain* and *spinal cord*, which occupy the dorsal body cavity. The CNS is the integrating and command center of the nervous system. It interprets sensory input and dictates motor responses based on reflexes, current conditions, and past experience **(Figure 11.2)**.

The **peripheral nervous system (PNS)** is the part of the nervous system *outside* the CNS. The PNS consists mainly of the

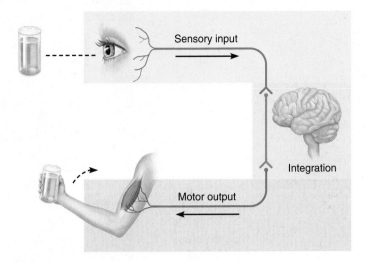

Figure 11.1 The nervous system's functions.

nerves (bundles of axons) that extend from the brain and spinal cord. *Spinal nerves* carry impulses to and from the spinal cord, and *cranial nerves* carry impulses to and from the brain. These peripheral nerves serve as the communication lines that link all parts of the body to the CNS.

The PNS has two functional subdivisions, as Figure 11.2 shows. The **sensory**, or **afferent**, **division** (af′er-ent; "carrying toward") consists of nerve fibers (axons) that convey impulses *to* the central nervous system from sensory receptors located throughout the body (see the blue fibers in Figure 11.2). Sensory fibers conveying impulses from the skin, skeletal muscles, and joints are called *somatic afferent fibers* (*soma* = body), and those transmitting impulses from the visceral organs (organs within the ventral body cavity) are called *visceral afferent fibers*. The sensory division keeps the CNS constantly informed of events going on both inside and outside the body.

The **motor**, or **efferent**, **division** (ef′er-ent; "carrying away") of the PNS transmits impulses *from* the CNS to effector organs, which are the muscles and glands (see the red fibers in Figure 11.2). These impulses activate muscles to contract and glands to secrete. In other words, they *effect* (bring about) a motor response.

The motor division also has two main parts:

1. The **somatic nervous system** is composed of somatic motor nerve fibers that conduct impulses from the CNS to skeletal muscles. It is often referred to as the **voluntary nervous system** because it allows us to consciously control our skeletal muscles.
2. The **autonomic nervous system (ANS)** consists of visceral motor nerve fibers that regulate the activity of smooth muscles, cardiac muscles, and glands. *Autonomic* means "a law unto itself," and because we generally cannot control such activities as the pumping of our heart or the movement of food through our digestive tract, the ANS is also referred to as the **involuntary nervous system**. As we will describe in Chapter 14 and as Figure 11.2 shows, the ANS

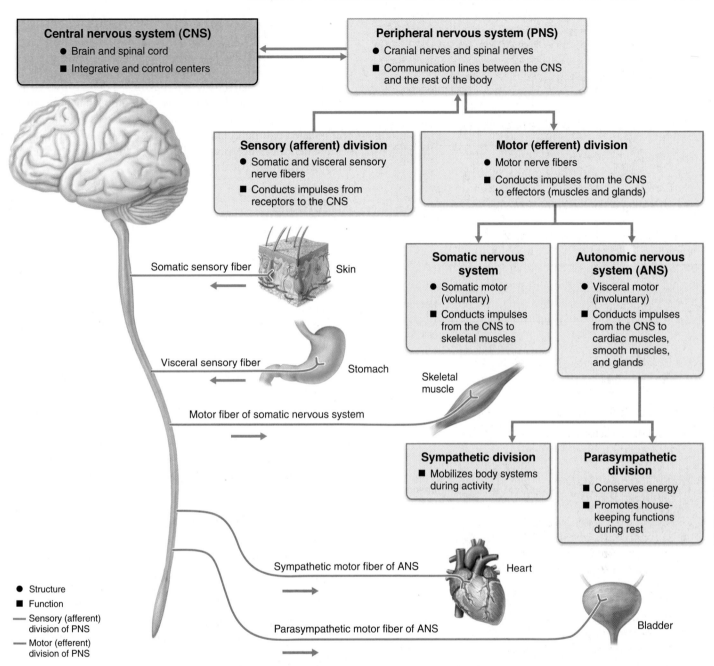

Figure 11.2 Schematic of levels of organization in the nervous system. Visceral organs (primarily located in the ventral body cavity) are served by visceral sensory fibers and by motor fibers of the autonomic nervous system. The somata (limbs and body wall) are served by motor fibers of the somatic nervous system and by somatic sensory fibers. Arrows indicate the direction of nerve impulses. (Connections to spinal cord are not anatomically accurate.)

has two functional subdivisions, the **sympathetic division** and the **parasympathetic division**, which typically work in opposition to each other—what one subdivision stimulates, the other inhibits.

CHECK YOUR UNDERSTANDING

1. What is meant by integration, and does it primarily occur in the CNS or the PNS?

2. Which subdivision of the PNS is involved in (a) relaying the feeling of a "full stomach" after a meal, (b) contracting the muscles to lift your arm, and (c) increasing your heart rate.

For answers, see Appendix G.

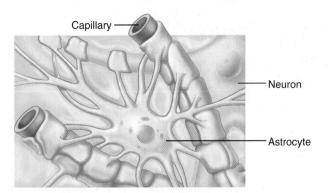

Capillary

Neuron

Astrocyte

(a) Astrocytes are the most abundant CNS neuroglia.

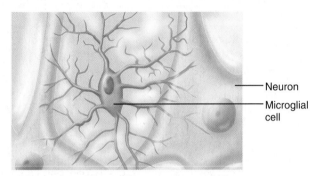

Neuron

Microglial cell

(b) Microglial cells are defensive cells in the CNS.

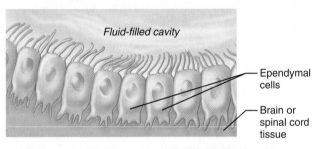

Fluid-filled cavity

Ependymal cells

Brain or spinal cord tissue

(c) Ependymal cells line cerebrospinal fluid–filled cavities.

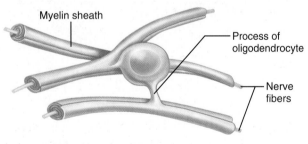

Myelin sheath

Process of oligodendrocyte

Nerve fibers

(d) Oligodendrocytes have processes that form myelin sheaths around CNS nerve fibers.

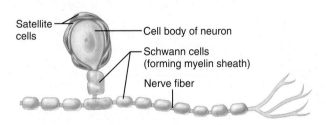

Satellite cells

Cell body of neuron

Schwann cells (forming myelin sheath)

Nerve fiber

(e) Satellite cells and Schwann cells (which form myelin) surround neurons in the PNS.

Histology of Nervous Tissue

The nervous system consists mostly of nervous tissue, which is highly cellular. For example, less than 20% of the CNS is extracellular space, which means that the cells are densely packed and tightly intertwined. Although it is very complex, nervous tissue is made up of just two principal types of cells: (1) *supporting cells* called neuroglia, smaller cells that surround and wrap the more delicate neurons, and (2) *neurons*, the excitable nerve cells that transmit electrical signals.

Neuroglia

▶ List the types of neuroglia and cite their functions.

Neurons associate closely with much smaller cells called **neuroglia** (nu-rog′le-ah; "nerve glue") or simply **glial cells** (gle′al). There are six types of neuroglia—four in the CNS and two in the PNS **(Figure 11.3)**. Each type has a unique function, but in general, these cells provide a supportive scaffolding for neurons. Some produce chemicals that guide young neurons to the proper connections, and promote neuron health and growth. Others wrap around and insulate neuronal processes to speed up action potential conduction.

Neuroglia in the CNS

Neuroglia in the CNS include *astrocytes, microglia, ependymal cells,* and *oligodendrocytes* (Figure 11.3a–d). Like neurons, most glial cells have branching processes (extensions) and a central cell body. Neuroglia can be distinguished, however, by their much smaller size and by their darker-staining nuclei. They outnumber neurons in the CNS by about 10 to 1, and make up about half the mass of the brain.

Shaped like delicate branching sea anemones, **astrocytes** (as′tro-sītz; "star cells") are the most abundant and most versatile glial cells. Their numerous radiating processes cling to neurons and their synaptic endings, and cover nearby capillaries, supporting and bracing the neurons and anchoring them to their nutrient supply lines, the blood capillaries (Figure 11.3a). Astrocytes have a role in making exchanges between capillaries and neurons, in helping to determine capillary permeability, in guiding the migration of young neurons, and in synapse formation. They also control the chemical environment around neurons, where their most important job is "mopping up" leaked potassium ions and recapturing (and recycling) released neurotransmitters. Furthermore, astrocytes have been shown to respond to nearby nerve impulses and released neurotransmitters. Astrocytes are connected together by gap junctions and signal

Figure 11.3 Neuroglia. (a–d) Supporting cells of the CNS. **(e)** Supporting cells of the PNS.

each other both by taking in calcium, creating slow-paced intracellular calcium pulses (calcium sparks), and by releasing extracellular chemical messengers. According to recent research, astrocytes also influence neuronal functioning and therefore participate in information processing in the brain.

Microglia (mi-kro′gle-ah) are small ovoid cells with relatively long "thorny" processes (Figure 11.3b). Their processes touch nearby neurons, monitoring their health, and when they sense that certain neurons are injured or in other trouble, the microglia migrate toward them. Where invading microorganisms or dead neurons are present, the microglia transform into a special type of macrophage that phagocytizes the microorganisms or neuronal debris. This protective role of the microglia is important because cells of the immune system are denied access to the CNS.

Ependymal cells (ě-pen′dĭ-mul; "wrapping garment") range in shape from squamous to columnar, and many are ciliated. They line the central cavities of the brain and the spinal cord, where they form a fairly permeable barrier between the cerebrospinal fluid that fills those cavities and the tissue fluid bathing the cells of the CNS. The beating of their cilia helps to circulate the cerebrospinal fluid that cushions the brain and spinal cord (Figure 11.3c).

Though they also branch, the **oligodendrocytes** (ol″ĭ-go-den′dro-sīts) have fewer processes (*oligo* = few; *dendr* = branch) than astrocytes. Oligodendrocytes line up along the thicker neuron fibers in the CNS and wrap their processes tightly around the fibers, producing insulating coverings called *myelin sheaths* (Figure 11.3d).

Neuroglia in the PNS

The two kinds of PNS neuroglia—*satellite cells* and *Schwann cells*—differ mainly in location. **Satellite cells** surround neuron cell bodies located in the peripheral nervous system (Figure 11.3e), and are thought to have many of the same functions in the PNS as astrocytes do in the CNS. Their name comes from a fancied resemblance to the moons (satellites) around a planet.

Schwann cells (also called *neurolemmocytes*) surround and form myelin sheaths around the larger nerve fibers in the peripheral nervous system (Figures 11.3e and 11.4b). In this way, they are functionally similar to oligodendrocytes. (We describe the formation of myelin sheaths later in this chapter.) Schwann cells are vital to regeneration of damaged peripheral nerve fibers.

CHECK YOUR UNDERSTANDING

3. Which type of neuroglia controls the extracellular fluid environment around neuron cell bodies in the CNS? In the PNS?

4. Which two types of neuroglia form insulating coverings called myelin sheaths?

For answers, see Appendix G.

Neurons

▶ Define neuron, describe its important structural components, and relate each to a functional role.

▶ Differentiate between a nerve and a tract, and between a nucleus and a ganglion.

▶ Explain the importance of the myelin sheath and describe how it is formed in the central and peripheral nervous systems.

The billions of **neurons**, also called **nerve cells**, are the structural units of the nervous system. They are highly specialized cells that conduct messages in the form of nerve impulses from one part of the body to another. Besides their ability to conduct nerve impulses, neurons have some other special characteristics:

1. They have *extreme longevity*. Given good nutrition, neurons can function optimally for a lifetime (over 100 years).
2. They are *amitotic*. As neurons assume their roles as communicating links of the nervous system, they lose their ability to divide. We pay a high price for this neuron feature because they cannot be replaced if destroyed. There *are* exceptions to this rule. For example, olfactory epithelium and some hippocampal regions contain stem cells that can produce new neurons throughout life. (The hippocampus is a brain region involved in memory.)
3. They have an exceptionally *high metabolic rate* and require continuous and abundant supplies of oxygen and glucose. Neurons cannot survive for more than a few minutes without oxygen.

Neurons are typically large, complex cells. Although they vary in structure, they all have a *cell body* and one or more slender *processes* (Figure 11.4). The plasma membrane of neurons is the site of electrical signaling, and it plays a crucial role in cell-to-cell interactions that occur during development.

Cell Body

The **neuron cell body** consists of a spherical nucleus with a conspicuous nucleolus surrounded by cytoplasm. Also called the **perikaryon** (*peri* = around, *kary* = nucleus) or **soma**, the cell body ranges in diameter from 5 to 140 μm. The cell body is the major *biosynthetic center* of a neuron and it contains the usual organelles.

The neuron cell body's protein- and membrane-making machinery, consisting of clustered free ribosomes and rough endoplasmic reticulum (ER), is probably the most active and best developed in the body. This rough ER, referred to as **Nissl bodies** (nis′l) or **chromatophilic substance** (*chromatophilic* = color loving), stains darkly with basic dyes. The Golgi apparatus is also well developed and forms an arc or a complete circle around the nucleus.

Mitochondria are scattered among the other organelles. Microtubules and **neurofibrils**, which are bundles of intermediate filaments (*neurofilaments*), are important in maintaining cell shape and integrity. They form a network throughout the cell body.

The cell body of some neurons also contains pigment inclusions. For example, some contain a black melanin, a red iron-containing pigment, or a golden-brown pigment called *lipofuscin* (lip″o-fu′sin). Lipofuscin, a harmless by-product of

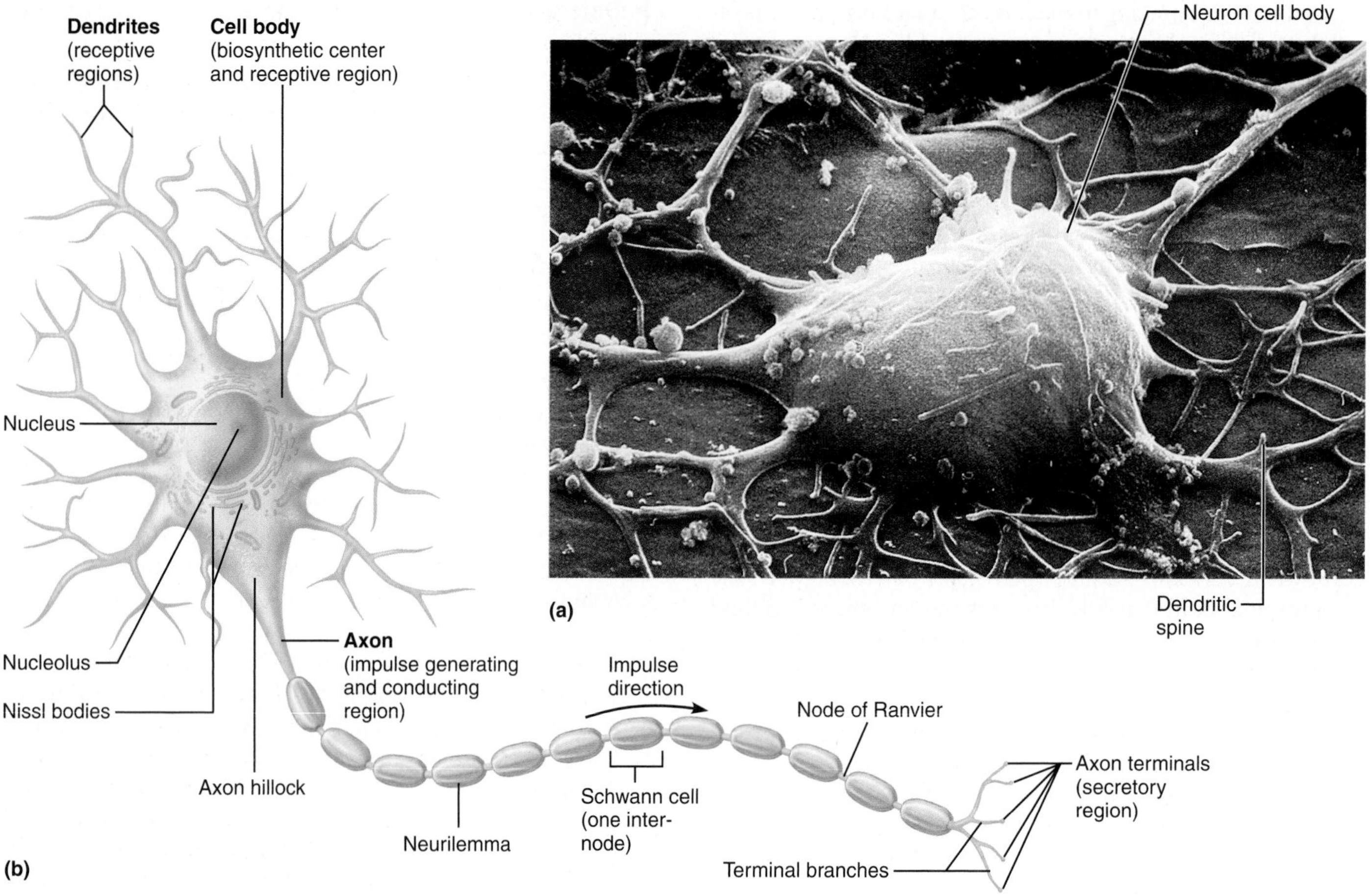

Figure 11.4 **Structure of a motor neuron. (a)** Scanning electron micrograph showing the cell body and dendrites with obvious dendritic spines (2000×). **(b)** Diagrammatic view.

lysosomal activity, is sometimes called the "aging pigment" because it accumulates in neurons of elderly individuals.

The cell body is the focal point for the outgrowth of neuron processes during embryonic development. In most neurons, the plasma membrane of the cell body also acts as *part of the receptive region* that receives information from other neurons (as shown in Table 11.1, pp. 393–394).

Most neuron cell bodies are located in the CNS, where they are protected by the bones of the skull and vertebral column. Clusters of cell bodies in the CNS are called **nuclei**, whereas those that lie along the nerves in the PNS are called **ganglia** (gang′gle-ah; *ganglion* = "knot on a string," "swelling").

Processes

Armlike **processes** extend from the cell body of all neurons. The brain and spinal cord (CNS) contain both neuron cell bodies and their processes. The PNS, for the most part, consists chiefly of neuron processes. Bundles of neuron processes are called **tracts** in the CNS and **nerves** in the PNS.

The two types of neuron processes, *dendrites* and *axons* (ak′sonz), differ from each other in the structure and function of their plasma membranes. The convention is to describe these processes using a motor neuron as an example of a typical neu-

ron. We shall follow this practice, but keep in mind that many sensory neurons and some tiny CNS neurons differ from the "typical" pattern we present here.

Dendrites **Dendrites** of motor neurons are short, tapering, diffusely branching extensions. Typically, motor neurons have hundreds of twiglike dendrites clustering close to the cell body. Virtually all organelles present in the cell body also occur in dendrites.

Dendrites are the main **receptive** or **input regions** (Table 11.1). They provide an enormous surface area for receiving signals from other neurons. In many brain areas, the finer dendrites are highly specialized for information collection. They bristle with thorny appendages having bulbous or spiky ends called *dendritic spines*, which represent points of close contact (synapses) with other neurons (Figure 11.4a).

Dendrites convey incoming messages *toward* the cell body. These electrical signals are usually *not* action potentials (nerve impulses) but are short-distance signals called *graded potentials*, as we will describe shortly.

The Axon Each neuron has a single **axon** (*axo* = axis, axle). The initial region of the axon arises from a cone-shaped area of the cell body called the **axon hillock** ("little hill") and then narrows to form a slender process that is uniform in diameter for the rest of its length (Figure 11.4b). In some neurons, the axon is very short or absent, but in others it is long and accounts for nearly the entire length of the neuron. For example, axons of the motor neurons controlling the skeletal muscles of your great toe extend from the lumbar region of your spine to your foot, a distance of a meter or more (3–4 feet), making them among the longest cells in the body. Any long axon is called a **nerve fiber**.

Each neuron has only one axon, but axons may have occasional branches along their length. These branches, called **axon collaterals**, extend from the axon at more or less right angles. Whether an axon is undivided or has collaterals, it usually branches profusely at its end (terminus): 10,000 or more **terminal branches**, or **telodendria**, per neuron is not unusual. The knoblike distal endings of the terminal branches are variously called **axon terminals**, **synaptic knobs**, or **boutons** (boo-tonz; "buttons"). Take your pick!

Functionally, the axon is the **conducting region** of the neuron (Table 11.1). It *generates nerve impulses* and *transmits them*, typically away from the cell body, along the plasma membrane, or **axolemma** (ak″so-lem′ah). In motor neurons, the nerve impulse is generated at the junction of the axon hillock and axon (which for this reason is called the *trigger zone*) and conducted along the axon to the axon terminals, which are the **secretory region** of the neuron. When the impulse reaches the axon terminals, it causes *neurotransmitters*, signaling chemicals stored in vesicles there, to be released into the extracellular space. The neurotransmitters either excite or inhibit neurons (or effector cells) with which the axon is in close contact. Because each neuron both receives signals from and sends signals to scores of other neurons, it carries on "conversations" with many different neurons at the same time.

An axon contains the same organelles found in the dendrites and cell body with two important exceptions—it lacks Nissl bodies and a Golgi apparatus, the structures involved with protein synthesis and packaging. Consequently, an axon depends (1) on its cell body to renew the necessary proteins and membrane components, and (2) on efficient transport mechanisms to distribute them. Axons quickly decay if cut or severely damaged.

Because axons are often very long, the task of moving molecules along their length might appear difficult. However, through the cooperative effort of several types of cytoskeletal elements (microtubules, actin filaments, and so on), substances travel continuously along the axon both away from and toward the cell body. Movement toward the axon terminals is *anterograde movement*, and that in the opposite direction is *retrograde movement*.

Substances moved in the anterograde direction include mitochondria, cytoskeletal elements, membrane components used to renew the axon plasma membrane, and enzymes needed for synthesis of certain neurotransmitters. (Some neurotransmitters are synthesized in the cell body and then transported to the axon terminals.)

Substances transported through the axon in the retrograde direction are mostly organelles being returned to the cell body for degradation or recycling. Retrograde transport is also an important means of intracellular communication for "advising" the cell body of conditions at the axon terminals, and for delivering to the cell body vesicles containing signal molecules (like nerve growth factor, which activates certain nuclear genes promoting growth).

A single bidirectional transport mechanism appears to be responsible for axonal transport. It uses ATP-dependent "motor" proteins such as kinesin, dynein, and myosin. These proteins propel cellular components along the microtubules like trains along tracks at speeds up to 40 cm (15 inches) per day.

HOMEOSTATIC IMBALANCE

Certain viruses and bacterial toxins that damage neural tissues use retrograde axonal transport to reach the cell body. This transport mechanism has been demonstrated for polio, rabies, and herpes simplex viruses and for tetanus toxin. Its use as a tool to treat genetic diseases by introducing viruses containing "corrected" genes or microRNA to suppress defective genes is under investigation. ■

Myelin Sheath and Neurilemma Many nerve fibers, particularly those that are long or large in diameter, are covered with a whitish, fatty (protein-lipoid), segmented **myelin sheath** (mi′ĕ-lin). Myelin protects and electrically insulates fibers, and it increases the speed of transmission of nerve impulses. **Myelinated fibers** (axons bearing a myelin sheath) conduct nerve impulses rapidly, whereas **unmyelinated fibers** conduct impulses quite slowly. Note that myelin sheaths are associated only with axons. Dendrites are *always* unmyelinated.

Myelin sheaths in the PNS are formed by Schwann cells, which indent to receive an axon and then wrap themselves around it in a jelly roll fashion (Figure 11.5). Initially the wrapping is loose, but the Schwann cell cytoplasm is gradually squeezed from between the membrane layers. When the wrapping process is complete, many concentric layers of Schwann cell plasma membrane enclose the axon, much like gauze wrapped around an injured finger. This tight coil of wrapped membranes is the myelin sheath, and its thickness depends on the number of spirals.

Plasma membranes of myelinating cells contain much less protein than the plasma membranes of most body cells. Channel and carrier proteins are notably absent, a characteristic that makes myelin sheaths exceptionally good electrical insulators. Another unique characteristic of these membranes is the presence of specific protein molecules that interlock to form a sort of molecular Velcro between adjacent myelin membranes.

The nucleus and most of the cytoplasm of the Schwann cell end up as a bulge just external to the myelin sheath. This portion of the Schwann cell, which includes the exposed part of its plasma membrane, is called the **neurilemma** ("neuron husk") (Figure 11.5b). Adjacent Schwann cells along an axon do not touch one another, so there are gaps in the sheath. These gaps, called **nodes of Ranvier** (ran′vē-ā″) or **myelin sheath gaps**, occur at regular intervals (about 1 mm apart) along the myelinated axon. Axon collaterals can emerge from the axon at these nodes.

11

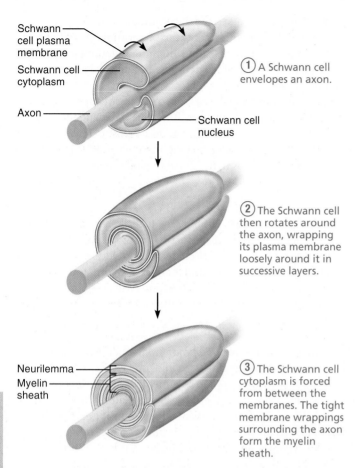

Schwann cell plasma membrane
Schwann cell cytoplasm
Axon
Schwann cell nucleus

① A Schwann cell envelopes an axon.

② The Schwann cell then rotates around the axon, wrapping its plasma membrane loosely around it in successive layers.

Neurilemma
Myelin sheath

③ The Schwann cell cytoplasm is forced from between the membranes. The tight membrane wrappings surrounding the axon form the myelin sheath.

(a) Myelination of a nerve fiber (axon)

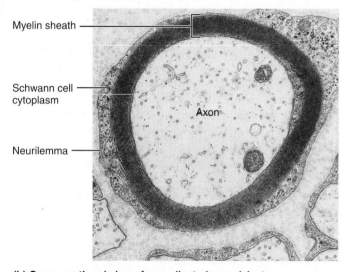

Myelin sheath
Schwann cell cytoplasm
Axon
Neurilemma

(b) Cross-sectional view of a myelinated axon (electron micrograph 24,000×)

Figure 11.5 Nerve fiber myelination by Schwann cells in the PNS.

Sometimes Schwann cells surround peripheral nerve fibers but the coiling process does not occur. In such instances, a single Schwann cell can partially enclose 15 or more axons, each of which occupies a separate recess in the Schwann cell surface. Nerve fibers associated with Schwann cells in this manner are said to be *unmyelinated* and are typically thin fibers.

Both myelinated and unmyelinated axons are also found in the central nervous system. However, oligodendrocytes are the cells that form CNS myelin sheaths (Figure 11.3d). In contrast to Schwann cells, each of which forms only one segment (internode) of a myelin sheath, oligodendrocytes have multiple flat processes that can coil around as many as 60 axons at the same time. As in the PNS, adjacent sections of an axon's myelin sheath are separated by nodes of Ranvier. CNS myelin sheaths lack a neurilemma because cell extensions are doing the coiling and the squeezed-out cytoplasm is forced not peripherally but back toward the centrally located nucleus. As in the PNS, the smallest-diameter axons are unmyelinated. These unmyelinated axons are covered by the long extensions of adjacent glial cells.

Regions of the brain and spinal cord containing dense collections of myelinated fibers are referred to as **white matter** and are primarily fiber tracts. **Gray matter** contains mostly nerve cell bodies and unmyelinated fibers.

CHECK YOUR UNDERSTANDING

5. Which part of the neuron is its fiber? How do nerve fibers differ from the fibers of connective tissue (see Chapter 4) and the fibers in muscle (see Chapter 9)?
6. How is a nucleus within the brain different from a nucleus within a neuron?
7. How is a myelin sheath formed in the CNS, and what is its function?

For answers, see Appendix G.

Classification of Neurons

▶ Classify neurons structurally and functionally.

Neurons are classified both structurally and functionally. We describe both classifications here but use the functional classification in most discussions.

Structural Classification Neurons are grouped structurally according to the number of processes extending from their cell body. Three major neuron groups make up this classification: multipolar (*polar* = end, pole), bipolar, and unipolar neurons. (**Table 11.1** is organized according to these three neuron types, and their structures are shown in the top row.)

Multipolar neurons have three or more processes—one axon and the rest dendrites. They are the most common neuron type in humans, with more than 99% of neurons belonging to this class. Multipolar neurons are the major neuron type in the CNS.

Bipolar neurons have two processes—an axon and a dendrite—that extend from opposite sides of the cell body. These rare neurons are found in some of the special sense organs. Examples include some neurons in the retina of the eye and in the olfactory mucosa.

Unipolar neurons have a single short process that emerges from the cell body and divides T-like into proximal and distal

TABLE 11.1	Comparison of Structural Classes of Neurons		
	NEURON TYPE		
MULTIPOLAR	**BIPOLAR**	**UNIPOLAR (PSEUDOUNIPOLAR)**	

Structural Class: Neuron Type According to the Number of Processes Extending from the Cell Body

Many processes extend from the cell body; all are dendrites except for a single axon.	Two processes extend from the cell body: One is a fused dendrite, the other is an axon.	One process extends from the cell body and forms central and peripheral processes, which together comprise an axon.
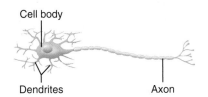	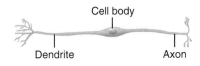	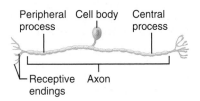

Relationship of Anatomy to the Three Functional Regions

☐ Receptive region (receives stimulus). Plasma membrane exhibits chemically gated ion channels.	☐ Conducting region (generates/transmits action potential). Plasma membrane exhibits voltage-gated Na⁺ and K⁺ channels.	☐ Secretory region (axon terminals release neurotransmitters). Plasma membrane exhibits voltage-gated Ca⁺ channels.
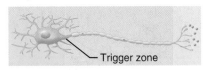	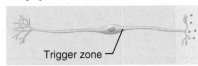	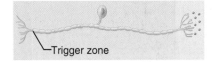
	(Many bipolar neurons do not generate action potentials and, in those that do, the location of the trigger zone is not universal.)	

Relative Abundance and Location in Human Body

Most abundant in body. Major neuron type in the CNS.	Rare. Found in some special sensory organs (olfactory mucosa, eye, ear).	Found mainly in the PNS. Common only in dorsal root ganglia of the spinal cord and sensory ganglia of cranial nerves.

Structural Variations

Multipolar	Bipolar	Unipolar
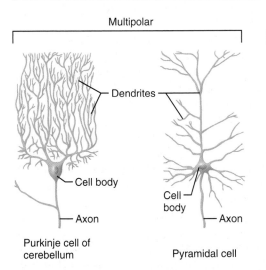	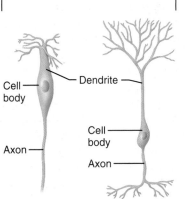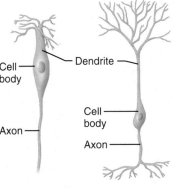	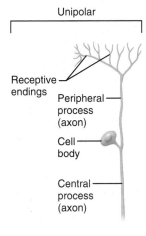
Purkinje cell of cerebellum Pyramidal cell	Olfactory cell Retinal cell	Dorsal root ganglion cell

TABLE 11.1	Comparison of Structural Classes of Neurons *(continued)*	
	NEURON TYPE	
MULTIPOLAR	**BIPOLAR**	**UNIPOLAR (PSEUDOUNIPOLAR)**
Functional Class: Neuron Type According to Direction of Impulse Conduction		
1. Most multipolar neurons are **interneurons (association neurons)** that conduct impulses within the CNS, integrating sensory input or motor output; may be one of a chain of CNS neurons, or a single neuron connecting sensory and motor neurons. 2. Some multipolar neurons are **motor neurons** that conduct impulses along the efferent pathways from the CNS to an effector (muscle/gland).	Essentially all bipolar neurons are **sensory neurons** that are located in some special sense organs. For example, bipolar cells of the retina are involved with the transmission of visual inputs from the eye to the brain (via an intermediate chain of neurons).	Most unipolar neurons are **sensory neurons** that conduct impulses along afferent pathways to the CNS for interpretation. (These sensory neurons are called primary or first-order sensory neurons.)
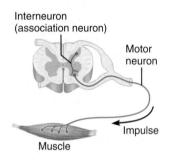	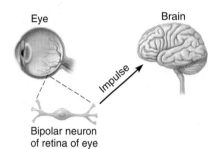	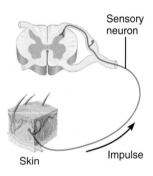

branches. The more distal process, which is often associated with a sensory receptor, is the **peripheral process**, whereas that entering the CNS is the **central process** (Table 11.1). Unipolar neurons are more accurately called **pseudounipolar neurons** (*pseudo* = false) because they originate as bipolar neurons. Then, during early embryonic development, the two processes converge and partially fuse to form the short single process that issues from the cell body. Unipolar neurons are found chiefly in ganglia in the PNS, where they function as sensory neurons.

The fact that the fused peripheral and central processes of unipolar neurons are continuous and function as a single fiber might make you wonder whether they are axons or dendrites. The central process is definitely an axon because it conducts impulses away from the cell body (one definition of axon). However, the peripheral process is perplexing. Three facts favor classifying it as an axon: (1) It generates and conducts an impulse (functional definition of axon); (2) when large, it is heavily myelinated; and (3) it has a uniform diameter and is indistinguishable microscopically from an axon. However, the older definition of a dendrite as a process that transmits impulses *toward* the cell body interferes with that conclusion.

So which is it? In this book, we have chosen to emphasize the newer definition of an axon as generating and transmitting an impulse. For *unipolar neurons*, we will refer to the combined length of the peripheral and central process as an axon. In place of "dendrites," unipolar neurons have *receptive endings* (sensory terminals) at the end of the peripheral process.

Functional Classification This scheme groups neurons according to the direction in which the nerve impulse travels relative to the central nervous system. Based on this criterion, there are sensory neurons, motor neurons, and interneurons (Table 11.1, last row).

Sensory, or **afferent**, **neurons** transmit impulses from sensory receptors in the skin or internal organs *toward* or *into* the central nervous system. Except for certain neurons found in some special sense organs, virtually all sensory neurons are unipolar, and their cell bodies are located in sensory ganglia *outside* the CNS. Only the most distal parts of these unipolar neurons act as impulse receptor sites, and the peripheral processes are often very long. For example, fibers carrying sensory impulses from the skin of your great toe travel for more than a meter before they reach their cell bodies in a ganglion close to the spinal cord.

The receptive endings of some sensory neurons are naked, in which case those terminals themselves function as sensory receptors, but many sensory neuron endings bear receptors that include other cell types. We describe the various types of general sensory receptor end organs, such as those of the skin, in Chapter 13. The special sensory receptors (of the ear, eye, etc.) are the topic of Chapter 15.

Motor, or **efferent**, **neurons** carry impulses *away from* the CNS to the effector organs (muscles and glands) of the body periphery. Motor neurons are multipolar. Except for some neurons of the autonomic nervous system, their cell bodies are located in the CNS.

Interneurons, or **association neurons**, lie between motor and sensory neurons in neural pathways and shuttle signals through CNS pathways where integration occurs. Most interneurons are confined within the CNS. They make up over 99% of the neurons of the body, including most of those in the CNS. Almost all interneurons are multipolar, but there is considerable diversity in both size and fiber-branching patterns. The Purkinje and pyramidal cells illustrated as structural variations in Table 11.1 are just two examples of their variety.

CHECK YOUR UNDERSTANDING

8. Which structural and functional type of neuron is activated first when you burn your finger? Which type is activated last to move your finger away from the source of heat?

For answers, see Appendix G.

Membrane Potentials

Neurons are highly *irritable* or *excitable* (responsive to stimuli). When a neuron is adequately stimulated, an electrical impulse is generated and conducted along the length of its axon. This response, called the *action potential* or *nerve impulse*, is always the same, regardless of the source or type of stimulus, and it underlies virtually all functional activities of the nervous system.

In this section, we will consider how neurons become excited or inhibited and how they communicate with other cells. First, however, we need to explore some basic principles of electricity and revisit the resting membrane potential.

Basic Principles of Electricity

The human body is electrically neutral—it has the same number of positive and negative charges. However, there are areas where one type of charge predominates, making such regions positively or negatively charged. Because opposite charges attract each other, energy must be used (work must be done) to separate them. On the other hand, the coming together of opposite charges liberates energy that can be used to do work. For this reason, situations in which there are separated electrical charges of opposite sign have potential energy.

Some Definitions: Voltage, Resistance, Current

The measure of potential energy generated by separated charge is called **voltage** and is measured in either *volts* (V) or *millivolts* (1 mV = 0.001 V). Voltage is always measured between two points and is called the **potential difference** or simply the **potential** between the points. The greater the difference in charge between two points, the higher the voltage.

The flow of electrical charge from one point to another is called a **current**, and it can be used to do work—for example, to power a flashlight. The amount of charge that moves between the two points depends on two factors: voltage and resistance. **Resistance** is the hindrance to charge flow provided by substances through which the current must pass. Substances with high electrical resistance are called *insulators*, and those with low resistance are called *conductors*.

The relationship between voltage, current, and resistance is given by **Ohm's law**:

$$\text{Current } (I) = \frac{\text{voltage } (V)}{\text{resistance} (R)}$$

which tells us that current (I) is directly proportional to voltage. This means that the greater the voltage (potential difference), the greater the current. This relationship also tells us there is no net current flow between points that have the same potential, as you can see by inserting a value of 0 V into the equation. A third thing Ohm's law tells us is that current is inversely related to resistance: The greater the resistance, the smaller the current.

In the body, electrical currents reflect the flow of ions (rather than free electrons) across cellular membranes. (Unlike the electrons flowing along your house wiring, there are no free electrons "running around" in a living system.) As we described in Chapter 3, there is a slight difference in the numbers of positive and negative ions on the two sides of cellular plasma membranes (there is a charge separation), so there is a potential across those membranes. The resistance to current flow is provided by the plasma membranes.

Role of Membrane Ion Channels

Recall that plasma membranes are peppered with a variety of membrane proteins that act as *ion channels*. Each of these channels is selective as to the type of ion (or ions) it allows to pass. For example, a potassium ion channel allows only potassium ions to pass.

Membrane channels are large proteins, often with several subunits, whose amino acid chains snake back and forth across the membrane. Some channels, **leakage** or **nongated channels**, are always open. In other channels, part of the protein forms a molecular "gate" that changes shape to open and close the channel in response to specific signals. These are called *gated* channels.

Chemically gated, or **ligand-gated**, **channels** open when the appropriate chemical (in this case a neurotransmitter) binds (Figure 11.6a). **Voltage-gated channels** open and close in response to changes in the membrane potential (Figure 11.6b). **Mechanically gated channels** open in response to physical deformation of the receptor (as in sensory receptors for touch and pressure).

When gated ion channels are open, ions diffuse quickly across the membrane following their electrochemical gradients, creating electrical currents and voltage changes across the membrane according to the rearranged Ohm's law equation:

$$\text{Voltage } (V) = \text{current } (I) \times \text{resistance } (R)$$

Ions move along chemical *concentration gradients* when they diffuse passively from an area of their higher concentration to an area of lower concentration, and along *electrical gradients* when they move toward an area of opposite electrical charge. Together, electrical and concentration gradients constitute the **electrochemical gradient**. It is ion flows along electrochemical gradients that underlie all electrical phenomena in neurons.

11

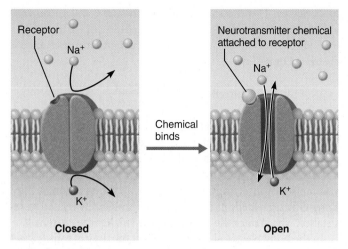

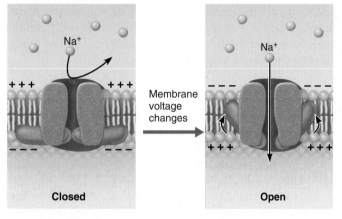

(a) Chemically (ligand) gated ion channels open when the appropriate neurotransmitter binds to the receptor, allowing (in this case) simultaneous movement of Na⁺ and K⁺.

(b) Voltage-gated ion channels open and close in response to changes in membrane voltage.

Figure 11.6 **Operation of gated channels.**

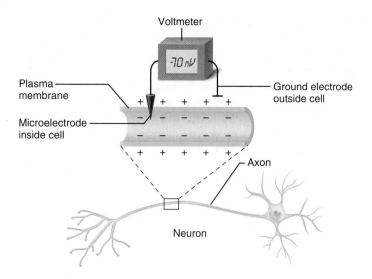

Figure 11.7 **Measuring membrane potential in neurons.** The potential difference between an electrode inside a neuron and the ground electrode in the extracellular fluid is approximately −70 mV (inside negative).

The Resting Membrane Potential

▶ Define resting membrane potential and describe its electrochemical basis.

The potential difference between two points is measured with a voltmeter. When one microelectrode of the voltmeter is inserted into the neuron and the other is in the extracellular fluid, a voltage across the membrane of approximately −70 mV is recorded **(Figure 11.7)**. The minus sign indicates that the cytoplasmic side (inside) of the membrane is negatively charged relative to the outside. This potential difference in a resting neuron (V_r) is called the **resting membrane potential**, and the membrane is said to be **polarized**. The value of the resting membrane potential varies (from −40 mV to −90 mV) in different types of neurons.

The resting potential exists only across the membrane. In other words, the bulk solutions inside and outside the cell are electrically neutral. The resting membrane potential is generated by differences in the ionic makeup of the intracellular and

extracellular fluids and by the differential permeability of the plasma membrane to those ions.

First, let's look at differences in ionic makeup of the intracellular and extracellular fluids, as shown in *Focus on Resting Membrane Potential* **(Figure 11.8)**. The cell cytosol contains a lower concentration of Na⁺ and a higher concentration of K⁺ than the extracellular fluid. Negatively charged (anionic) proteins (A⁻) help to balance the positive charges of intracellular cations (primarily K⁺). In the extracellular fluid, the positive charges of Na⁺ and other cations are balanced chiefly by chloride ions (Cl⁻). Although there are many other solutes (glucose, urea, and other ions) in both fluids, potassium (K⁺) plays the most important role in generating the membrane potential.

Next, let's consider the differential permeability of the membrane to various ions (Figure 11.8, bottom). At rest the membrane is impermeable to the large anionic cytoplasmic proteins, very slightly permeable to sodium, approximately 75 times more permeable to potassium than to sodium, and quite freely permeable to chloride ions. These resting permeabilities reflect the properties of the leakage ion channels in the membrane. Potassium ions diffuse out of the cell along their *concentration gradient* much more easily than sodium ions can enter the cell along theirs. K⁺ flowing out of the cell causes the cell to become more negative inside. Na⁺ trickling into the cell makes the cell just slightly more positive than it would be if only K⁺ flowed. Therefore, at resting membrane potential, the negative interior of the cell is due to much greater diffusion of K⁺ out of the cell than Na⁺ diffusion into the cell.

Because some K⁺ is always leaking out of the cell and some Na⁺ is always leaking in, you might think that the concentration gradients would eventually "run down," resulting in equal concentrations of Na⁺ and K⁺ inside and outside the cell. This does not happen because the ATP-driven **sodium-potassium pump** first ejects three Na⁺ from the cell and then transports two K⁺ back into the cell. In other words, the sodium-potassium pump

Figure 11.8   FOCUS Resting Membrane Potential

**Generating a resting membrane potential depends on
(1) differences in K⁺ and Na⁺ concentrations inside and
outside cells, and (2) differences in permeability of the
plasma membrane to these ions.**

**The concentrations of Na⁺ and K⁺ on each side of the
membrane are different.**

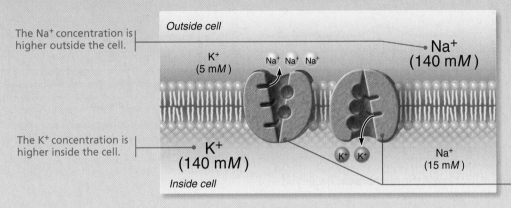

Outside cell

The Na⁺ concentration is higher outside the cell.

K⁺ (5 mM)   Na⁺ Na⁺ Na⁺

Na⁺ (140 mM)

The K⁺ concentration is higher inside the cell.

K⁺ (140 mM)   K⁺ K⁺   Na⁺ (15 mM)

Inside cell

Na⁺-K⁺ ATPases (pumps) maintain the concentration gradients of Na⁺ and K⁺ across the membrane.

**The permeabilities of Na⁺ and K⁺ across the membrane
are different.** In the next three panels, we will build the
resting membrane potential step by step.

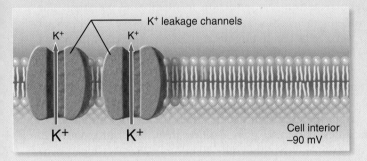

K⁺ leakage channels

K⁺   K⁺

K⁺   K⁺

Cell interior
–90 mV

Suppose a cell has only K⁺ channels...

**K⁺ loss through abundant leakage channels
establishes a negative membrane potential.** K⁺ flows
down its large concentration gradient because the
membrane is highly permeable to K⁺. As the positive K⁺
ions leak out, the negative voltage that develops on the
membrane interior counteracts the concentration gradient,
pulling K⁺ back into the cell. At –90 mV, the concentration
and electrical gradients for K⁺ are balanced.

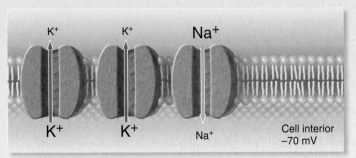

K⁺   K⁺   Na⁺

K⁺   K⁺   Na⁺

Cell interior
–70 mV

Now, let's add some Na⁺ channels to our cell...

**Na⁺ entry through leakage channels reduces the
negative membrane potential slightly.** Na⁺ flows down
its large concentration gradient, but the membrane is only
slightly permeable to Na⁺. As a result, Na⁺ entering the
cell makes the membrane potential slightly less negative
than if there were only K⁺ channels.

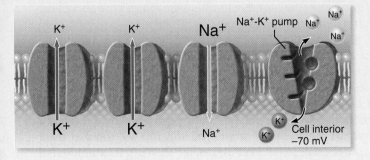

K⁺   K⁺   Na⁺   Na⁺-K⁺ pump Na⁺   Na⁺

Na⁺

K⁺   K⁺   Na⁺   K⁺   K⁺ Cell interior
–70 mV

Finally, let's add a pump to compensate for leaking ions.

**Na⁺-K⁺ ATPases (pumps) maintain the concentration
gradients, resulting in the resting membrane potential.**
A cell at rest is like a leaky boat that is constantly leaking
K⁺ out and Na⁺ in through open channels. The "bailing
pump" for this boat is the **Na⁺-K⁺ ATPase** (Na⁺-K⁺ pump),
which counteracts the leaks by transporting Na⁺ out and
K⁺ in.

A&P Flix   *View this animation at myA&P*

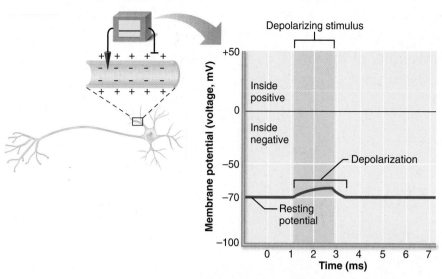

Depolarizing stimulus

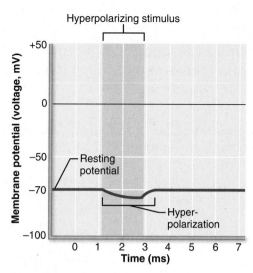

Hyperpolarizing stimulus

(a) Depolarization: The membrane potential moves toward 0 mV, the inside becoming less negative (more positive).

(b) Hyperpolarization: The membrane potential increases, the inside becoming more negative.

Figure 11.9 Depolarization and hyperpolarization of the membrane. The resting membrane potential is approximately −70 mV (inside negative) in neurons.

stabilizes the resting membrane potential by maintaining the concentration gradients for sodium and potassium.

CHECK YOUR UNDERSTANDING

9. For an open channel, what factors determine in which direction ions will move through that channel?

10. For which cation is there the greatest amount of leakage (through leakage channels) across the plasma membrane?

For answers, see Appendix G.

Membrane Potentials That Act as Signals

▶ Compare and contrast graded potentials and action potentials.

▶ Explain how action potentials are generated and propagated along neurons.

▶ Define absolute and relative refractory periods.

▶ Define saltatory conduction and contrast it to conduction along unmyelinated fibers.

Neurons use changes in their membrane potential as communication signals for receiving, integrating, and sending information. A change in membrane potential can be produced by (1) anything that alters ion concentrations on the two sides of the membrane or (2) anything that changes membrane permeability to any ion. However, only permeability changes are important for information transfer.

Changes in membrane potential can produce two types of signals: *graded potentials*, which are usually incoming signals operating over short distances, and *action potentials*, which are long-distance signals of axons.

The terms *depolarization* and *hyperpolarization* describe membrane potential changes *relative to resting membrane potential*. It is important to clearly understand these terms. **Depolarization** is a reduction in membrane potential: The inside of the membrane becomes *less negative* (moves closer to zero) than the resting potential. For instance, a change in resting potential from −70 mV to −65 mV is a depolarization (Figure 11.9a). By convention, depolarization also includes events in which the membrane potential reverses and moves above zero to become positive.

Hyperpolarization occurs when the membrane potential increases, becoming *more negative* than the resting potential. For example, a change from −70 mV to −75 mV is hyperpolarization (Figure 11.9b). As we will describe shortly, depolarization increases the probability of producing nerve impulses, whereas hyperpolarization reduces this probability.

Graded Potentials

Graded potentials are short-lived, localized changes in membrane potential that can be either depolarizations or hyperpolarizations. These changes cause current flows that decrease in magnitude with distance. Graded potentials are called "graded" because their magnitude varies directly with stimulus strength. The stronger the stimulus, the more the voltage changes and the farther the current flows.

Graded potentials are triggered by some change (a stimulus) in the neuron's environment that causes gated ion channels to open. Graded potentials are given different names, depending on where they occur and the functions they perform. When the receptor of a sensory neuron is excited by some form of energy (heat, light, or other), the resulting graded potential is called a *receptor potential* or *generator potential*. We will consider these types of graded potentials in Chapter 13. When the stimulus is a neurotransmitter released by another neuron, the graded potential is called a *postsynaptic potential*, because the neurotransmitter is released into a fluid-filled gap called a synapse and influences the neuron beyond (post) the synapse.

Fluids inside and outside cells are fairly good conductors, and current, carried by ions, flows through these fluids whenever voltage changes occur. Let us assume that a small area of a neuron's plasma membrane has been depolarized by a stimulus (Figure 11.10a). Current (ions) will flow on both sides of the membrane between the depolarized (active) membrane area and the adjacent polarized (resting) areas. Positive ions migrate toward more negative areas (the direction of cation movement is the direction of current flow), and negative ions simultaneously move toward more positive areas (Figure 11.10b).

For our patch of plasma membrane, positive ions (mostly K^+) inside the cell move away from the depolarized area and accumulate on the neighboring membrane areas, where they neutralize negative ions. Meanwhile, positive ions on the outer membrane face are moving toward the region of reversed membrane polarity (the depolarized region), which is momentarily less positive. As these positive ions move, their "places" on the membrane become occupied by negative ions (such as Cl^- and HCO_3^-), sort of like ionic musical chairs. In this way, at regions abutting the depolarized region, the inside becomes less negative and the outside becomes less positive. In other words, the depolarization spreads as the neighboring membrane is, in turn, depolarized.

As just explained, the flow of current to adjacent membrane areas changes the membrane potential there as well. However, the plasma membrane is permeable like a leaky water hose, and most of the charge is quickly lost through leakage channels. Consequently, the current dies out within a few millimeters of its origin and is said to be *decremental* (Figure 11.10c).

Because the current dissipates quickly and dies out (decays) with increasing distance from the site of initial depolarization, graded potentials can act as signals only over very short distances. Nonetheless, they are essential in initiating action potentials, the long-distance signals.

Action Potentials

The principal way neurons send signals over long distances is by generating and propagating action potentials (APs), and only cells with *excitable membranes*—neurons and muscle cells—can generate action potentials. An **action potential (AP)** is a brief reversal of membrane potential with a total amplitude (change in voltage) of about 100 mV (from −70 mV to +30 mV). A depolarization phase is followed by a repolarization phase and often a short period of hyperpolarization. The whole event is over in a few milliseconds. Unlike graded potentials, action potentials do not decrease in strength with distance.

The events of action potential generation and transmission are identical in skeletal muscle cells and neurons. As we have noted, in a neuron, an AP is also called a **nerve impulse**, and is typically generated *only in axons*. A neuron transmits a nerve impulse only when it is adequately stimulated. The stimulus changes the permeability of the neuron's membrane by opening specific voltage-gated channels on the axon. These channels open

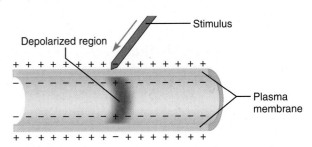

(a) Depolarization: A small patch of the membrane (red area) has become depolarized.

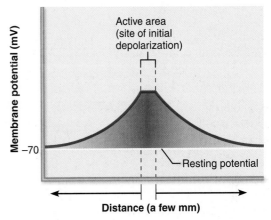

(b) Spread of depolarization: The local currents (black arrows) that are created depolarize adjacent membrane areas and allow the wave of depolarization to spread.

Active area
(site of initial
depolarization)

Membrane potential (mV)

−70

Resting potential

Distance (a few mm)

(c) Decay of membrane potential with distance: Because current is lost through the "leaky" plasma membrane, the voltage declines with distance from the stimulus (the voltage is *decremental*). Consequently, graded potentials are short-distance signals.

Figure 11.10 **The spread and decay of a graded potential.**

and close in response to changes in the membrane potential and are activated by local currents (graded potentials) that spread toward the axon along the dendritic and cell body membranes.

In many neurons, the transition from local graded potential to long-distance action potential takes place at the axon hillock. In sensory neurons, the action potential is generated by the peripheral (axonal) process just proximal to the receptor region. However, for simplicity, we will just use the term *axon* in our discussion. We'll look first at the generation of an action potential and then at its propagation.

Generation of an Action Potential *Focus on an Action Potential* (Figure 11.11) on pp. 400–401 describes the generation of an action potential. Generating an action potential involves three consecutive but overlapping changes in membrane permeability

Figure 11.11 **FOCUS** | Action Potential

The AP (action potential) is a brief change in membrane potential in a "patch" of membrane that is depolarized by local currents.

The big picture

This graph shows how voltage changes over time at a given point inside an axon during the course of an action potential.

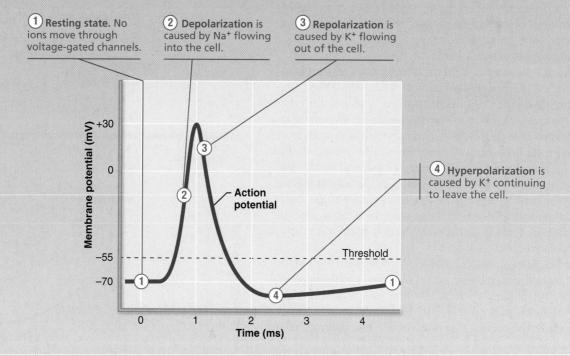

① **Resting state.** No ions move through voltage-gated channels.

② **Depolarization** is caused by Na⁺ flowing into the cell.

③ **Repolarization** is caused by K⁺ flowing out of the cell.

④ **Hyperpolarization** is caused by K⁺ continuing to leave the cell.

The AP is caused by permeability changes in the plasma membrane:

Relative membrane permeability tells you the relative number of ion channels that are open for each ion. Remember that open ion channels make the plasma membrane permeable to those ions.

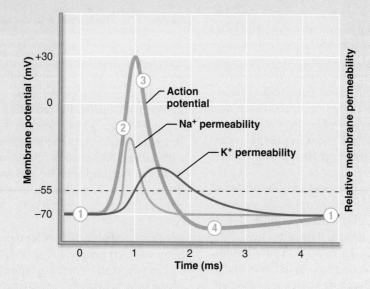

The key players

Voltage-gated Na⁺ channels have two gates and alternate between three different states.

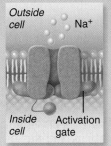
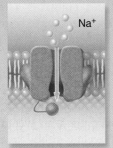
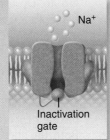

Outside cell Na⁺

Inside cell Activation gate

Na⁺

Na⁺

Inactivation gate

Closed at the resting state, so no Na⁺ enters the cell through them

Opened by depolarization, allowing Na⁺ to enter the cell

Inactivated— channels automatically blocked by inactivation gates soon after they open

Voltage-gated K⁺ channels have one gate and two states.

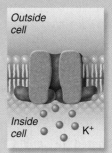
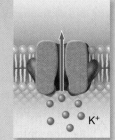

Outside cell

Inside cell K⁺

K⁺

Closed at the resting state, so no K⁺ exits the cell through them

Opened by depolarization, after a delay, allowing K⁺ to exit the cell

The events

Each step corresponds to one part of the AP graph.

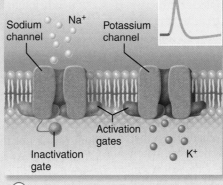

Sodium channel Na⁺ Potassium channel

Activation gates

Inactivation gate

K⁺

① **Resting state:** All gated Na⁺ and K⁺ channels are closed.

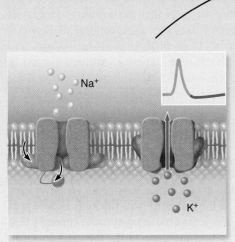

Na⁺

K⁺

④ **Hyperpolarization:** Some K⁺ channels remain open, and Na⁺ channels reset.

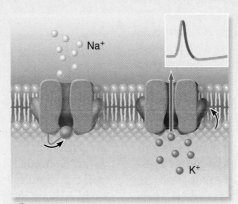

Na⁺

K⁺

③ **Repolarization:** Na⁺ channels are inactivating, and K⁺ channels open.

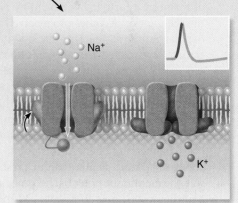

Na⁺

K⁺

② **Depolarization:** Na⁺ channels open.

resulting from the opening and closing of voltage-gated ion channels, all induced by depolarization of the axon membrane. These permeability changes are a transient increase in Na^+ permeability (Na^+ channels open), followed by restoration of Na^+ impermeability (described below), together with a short-lived increase in K^+ permeability (K^+ channels open, then close).

The first two permeability changes mark the beginning and the end of the *depolarization phase* of action potential generation, indicated by the upward-rising part of the AP curve or spike on the first graph in Figure 11.11. The third permeability change is responsible for both the *repolarization* (the downward part of the AP spike) and *hyperpolarization phases* shown in the graph. Let's examine each of these phases more carefully, starting with a neuron in the resting (polarized) state.

① **Resting state: All gated Na^+ and K^+ channels are closed.** Only the leakage channels are open, maintaining resting membrane potential.

Each Na^+ channel has two gates: a voltage-sensitive *activation gate* that is closed at rest and responds to depolarization by opening, and an *inactivation gate* that blocks the channel once it is open. Thus, *depolarization opens and then inactivates sodium channels.* Both gates must be open in order for Na^+ to enter, but the closing of *either* gate effectively closes the channel. By contrast, each active potassium channel has a single voltage-sensitive gate that is closed in the resting state and opens slowly in response to depolarization.

② **Depolarizing phase: Na^+ channels open.** As the axon membrane is depolarized by local currents, the voltage-gated sodium channels open and Na^+ rushes into the cell. This influx of positive charge depolarizes that local "patch" of membrane further, opening more Na^+ channels so that the cell interior becomes progressively less negative. When depolarization at the stimulation site reaches a certain critical level called **threshold** (often between -55 and -50 mV), depolarization becomes self-generating, urged on by positive feedback. That is, after being initiated by the stimulus, depolarization is driven by the ionic currents created by Na^+ influx. As more Na^+ enters, the membrane depolarizes further and opens still more channels until all Na^+ channels are open. At this point, Na^+ permeability is about 1000 times greater than in a resting neuron. As a result, the membrane potential becomes less and less negative and then overshoots to about $+30$ mV as Na^+ rushes in along its electrochemical gradient. This rapid depolarization and polarity reversal produces the sharply upward *spike* of the action potential.

Earlier, we stated that membrane potential depends on membrane permeability, but here we are saying that membrane permeability depends on membrane potential. Can both statements be true? Yes, because these two relationships establish a *positive feedback* cycle (increased Na^+ permeability due to increased channel openings leads to greater depolarization, which leads to increased Na^+ permeability, and so on). This explosive positive feedback cycle

is responsible for the rising (depolarizing) phase of action potentials and puts the "action" in the action potential.

③ **Repolarizing phase: Na^+ channels are inactivating, and K^+ channels open.** The explosively rising phase of the action potential persists for only about 1 ms. It is self-limiting because the slow inactivation gates of the Na^+ channels begin to close at this point. As a result, the membrane permeability to Na^+ declines to resting levels, and the net influx of Na^+ stops completely. Consequently, the AP spike stops rising.

As Na^+ entry declines, the slow voltage-gated K^+ channels open and K^+ rushes out of the cell, following its electrochemical gradient. Consequently, internal negativity of the resting neuron is restored, an event called **repolarization**. Both the abrupt decline in Na^+ permeability and the increased permeability to K^+ contribute to repolarization.

④ **Hyperpolarization: Some K^+ channels remain open, and Na^+ channels reset.** The period of increased K^+ permeability typically lasts longer than needed to restore the resting state. As a result of the excessive K^+ efflux, an **after-hyperpolarization**, also called the *undershoot*, is seen on the AP curve as a slight dip following the spike (and before the potassium gates close). Also at this point, the Na^+ channels begin to reset back to their original position by changing shape to reopen their inactivation gates and close their activation gates.

Repolarization restores resting electrical conditions, but it does *not* restore resting ionic conditions. The ion redistribution is accomplished by the *sodium-potassium pump* following repolarization. While it might appear that tremendous numbers of Na^+ and K^+ ions change places during action potential generation, this is not the case. Only small amounts of sodium and potassium cross the membrane. (The Na^+ influx required to reach threshold produces only a 0.012% change in intracellular Na^+ concentration.) These small ionic changes are quickly corrected because an axon membrane has thousands of Na^+-K^+ pumps.

Propagation of an Action Potential If it is to serve as the neuron's signaling device, an AP must be **propagated** (sent or transmitted) along the axon's entire length. As we have seen, the AP is generated by the influx of Na^+ through a given area of the membrane. This influx establishes local currents that depolarize adjacent membrane areas in the forward direction (away from the origin of the nerve impulse), which opens voltage-gated channels and triggers an action potential there (Figure 11.12).

Because the area where the AP originated has just generated an AP, the sodium channels in that area are inactivated and no new AP is generated there. For this reason, the AP propagates away from its point of origin. (If an *isolated* axon is stimulated by an electrode, the nerve impulse will move away from the point of stimulus in all directions along the membrane.) In the body, APs are initiated at one end of the axon and conducted away from that point toward the axon's terminals. Once initiated,

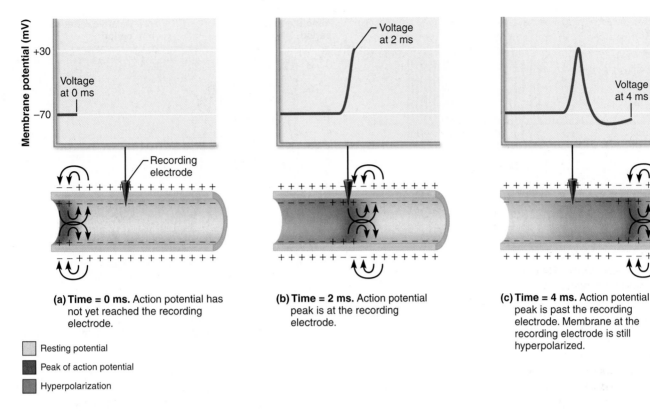

(a) **Time = 0 ms.** Action potential has not yet reached the recording electrode.

(b) **Time = 2 ms.** Action potential peak is at the recording electrode.

(c) **Time = 4 ms.** Action potential peak is past the recording electrode. Membrane at the recording electrode is still hyperpolarized.

Resting potential

Peak of action potential

Hyperpolarization

Figure 11.12 Propagation of an action potential (AP). Recordings at three successive times as an AP propagates along an axon (from left to right). The arrows show the direction of local current flow generated by the movement of positive ions. This current brings the resting membrane at the leading edge of the AP to threshold, propagating the AP forward.

an AP is *self-propagating* and continues along the axon at a constant velocity—something like a domino effect.

Following depolarization, each segment of axon membrane repolarizes, which restores the resting membrane potential in that region. Because these electrical changes also set up local currents, the repolarization wave chases the depolarization wave down the length of the axon.

The propagation process we have just described occurs on unmyelinated axons. On p. 405, we will describe propagation along myelinated axons, called *saltatory conduction.*

Although the phrase *conduction of a nerve impulse* is commonly used, nerve impulses are not really conducted in the same way that an insulated wire conducts current. In fact, neurons are fairly poor conductors, and as noted earlier, local current flows decline with distance because the charges leak through the membrane. The expression *propagation of a nerve impulse* is more accurate, because the AP is *regenerated anew* at each membrane patch, and every subsequent AP is identical to the one that was generated initially.

Threshold and the All-or-None Phenomenon Not all local depolarization events produce APs. The depolarization must reach threshold values if an axon is to "fire." What determines the *threshold point*? One explanation is that threshold is the membrane potential at which the outward current created by K^+ movement is exactly equal to the inward current created by

Na^+ movement. Threshold is typically reached when the membrane has been depolarized by 15 to 20 mV from the resting value. This depolarization status represents an unstable equilibrium state. If one more Na^+ enters, further depolarization occurs, opening more Na^+ channels and allowing more Na^+ entry. If, on the other hand, one more K^+ leaves, the membrane potential is driven away from threshold, Na^+ channels close, and K^+ continues to diffuse outward until the potential returns to its resting value.

Recall that local depolarizations are graded potentials and that their magnitude increases with increasing stimulus intensity. Brief weak stimuli (*subthreshold stimuli*) produce subthreshold depolarizations that are not translated into nerve impulses. On the other hand, stronger *threshold stimuli* produce depolarizing currents that push the membrane potential toward and beyond the threshold voltage. As a result, Na^+ permeability is increased to such an extent that entering sodium ions "swamp" (exceed) the outward movement of K^+, allowing the positive feedback cycle to become established and generating an AP.

The critical factor here is the total amount of current that flows through the membrane during a stimulus (electrical charge × time). Strong stimuli depolarize the membrane to threshold quickly. Weaker stimuli must be applied for longer periods to provide the crucial amount of current flow. Very weak stimuli do not trigger an AP because the local current

11

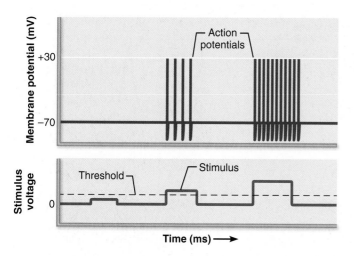

Figure 11.13 **Relationship between stimulus strength and action potential frequency.** APs are shown as vertical lines in the upper trace. The lower trace shows the intensity of the applied stimulus. A subthreshold stimulus does not generate an AP, but once threshold voltage is reached, the stronger the stimulus, the more frequently APs are generated.

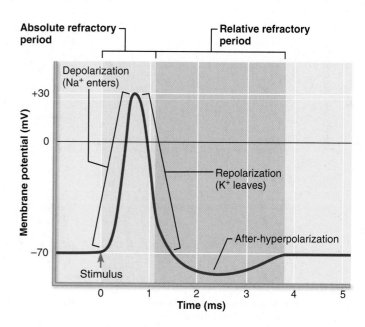

Figure 11.14 **Absolute and relative refractory periods in an AP.**

flows they produce are so slight that they dissipate long before threshold is reached.

The AP is an **all-or-none phenomenon**: It either happens completely or doesn't happen at all. Generation of an AP can be compared to lighting a match under a small dry twig. The changes occurring where the twig is heated are analogous to the change in membrane permeability that initially allows more Na⁺ to enter the cell. When that part of the twig becomes hot enough (when enough Na⁺ has entered the cell), the flash point (threshold) is reached and the flame consumes the entire twig, even if you blow out the match (the AP is generated and propagated whether or not the stimulus continues). But if the match is extinguished just before the twig has reached the critical temperature, ignition will not take place. Likewise, if the number of Na⁺ ions entering the cell is too low to achieve threshold, no AP will occur.

Coding for Stimulus Intensity Once generated, all APs are independent of stimulus strength, and all APs are alike. So how can the CNS determine whether a particular stimulus is intense or weak—information it needs to initiate an appropriate response? The answer is really quite simple: Strong stimuli cause nerve impulses to be generated more *often* in a given time interval than do weak stimuli. In this way, stimulus intensity is coded for by the number of impulses per second—that is, by the *frequency of action potentials*—rather than by increases in the strength (amplitude) of the individual APs **(Figure 11.13)**.

Refractory Periods When a patch of neuron membrane is generating an AP and its voltage-gated sodium channels are open, the neuron cannot respond to another stimulus, no matter how strong. This period, from the opening of the Na⁺ channels until the Na⁺ channels begin to reset to their original resting state, is called the **absolute refractory period** **(Figure 11.14)**. It

ensures that each AP is a separate, *all-or-none event* and enforces one-way transmission of the AP.

The **relative refractory period** is the interval following the absolute refractory period. During the relative refractory period, most Na⁺ channels have returned to their resting state, some K⁺ channels are still open, and repolarization is occurring. During this time, the axon's threshold for AP generation is substantially elevated. A stimulus that would normally have generated an AP is no longer sufficient, but an exceptionally strong stimulus can reopen the Na⁺ channels that have already returned to their resting state and allow another AP to be generated. Strong stimuli cause more frequent generation of APs by intruding into the relative refractory period.

Conduction Velocity How fast do APs travel? Conduction velocities of neurons vary widely. Nerve fibers that transmit impulses most rapidly (100 m/s or more) are found in neural pathways where speed is essential, such as those that mediate some postural reflexes. Axons that conduct impulses more slowly typically serve internal organs (the gut, glands, blood vessels), where slower responses are not a handicap. The rate of impulse propagation depends largely on two factors:

1. **Axon diameter.** Axons vary considerably in diameter and, as a rule, the larger the axon's diameter, the faster it conducts impulses. Larger axons conduct more rapidly because they offer less resistance to the flow of local currents, and so adjacent areas of the membrane can more quickly be brought to threshold.

2. **Degree of myelination.** Action potentials propagate because they are regenerated by voltage-gated channels in the membrane **(Figure 11.15a, b)**. On unmyelinated axons, these channels are immediately adjacent to each other and conduction is relatively slow, a type of AP propagation called **continuous conduction**. The presence of a myelin

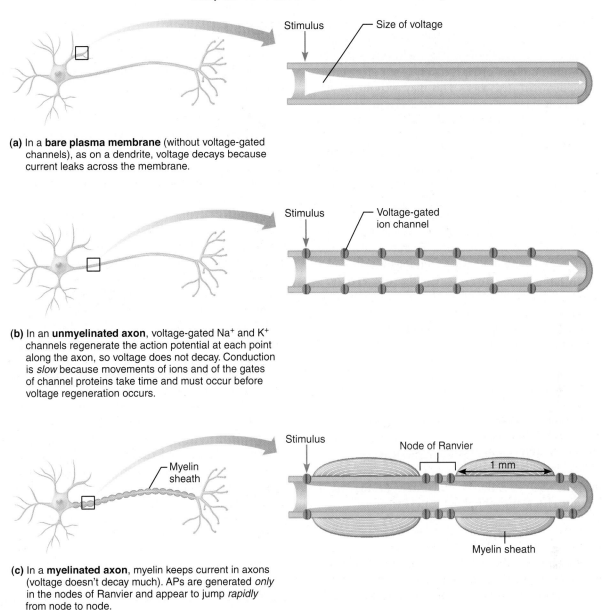

(a) In a **bare plasma membrane** (without voltage-gated channels), as on a dendrite, voltage decays because current leaks across the membrane.

(b) In an **unmyelinated axon**, voltage-gated Na⁺ and K⁺ channels regenerate the action potential at each point along the axon, so voltage does not decay. Conduction is *slow* because movements of ions and of the gates of channel proteins take time and must occur before voltage regeneration occurs.

(c) In a **myelinated axon**, myelin keeps current in axons (voltage doesn't decay much). APs are generated *only* in the nodes of Ranvier and appear to jump *rapidly* from node to node.

Figure 11.15 Action potential propagation in unmyelinated and myelinated axons.

sheath dramatically increases the rate of AP propagation because myelin acts as an insulator, both preventing almost all leakage of charge from the axon and allowing the membrane voltage to change more rapidly. Current can pass through the membrane of a myelinated axon *only* at the nodes of Ranvier, where the myelin sheath is interrupted and the axon is bare, and essentially all the voltage-gated Na⁺ channels are concentrated at the nodes.

When an AP is generated in a myelinated fiber, the local depolarizing current does not dissipate through the adjacent membrane regions, which are nonexcitable. Instead, the current is maintained and moves rapidly to the next node, a distance of approximately 1 mm, where it triggers another AP. Consequently, APs are triggered only at the nodes, a type of conduction called **saltatory conduction** (*saltare* = to leap) because the electrical signal

jumps from node to node along the axon (Figure 11.15c). Saltatory conduction is about 30 times faster than continuous conduction.

HOMEOSTATIC IMBALANCE

The importance of myelin to nerve transmission is painfully clear to people with demyelinating diseases such as **multiple sclerosis (MS)**. This autoimmune disease affects mostly young adults. Common symptoms are visual disturbances (including blindness), problems controlling muscles (weakness, clumsiness, and ultimately paralysis), speech disturbances, and urinary incontinence. In this disease, myelin sheaths in the CNS are gradually destroyed, reduced to nonfunctional hardened lesions called *scleroses*. The loss of myelin (a result of the immune system's attack on myelin proteins) causes such substantial shunting and short-circuiting of the current that successive nodes are excited more and more slowly, and eventually impulse conduction ceases. However, the axons themselves are not damaged and growing numbers of Na^+ channels appear spontaneously in the demyelinated fibers. This may account for the remarkably variable cycles of relapse (disability) and remission (symptom-free periods) typical of this disease.

The advent of drugs that modify the immune system's activity [such as interferons and glatiramer (Copaxone)] have improved the lives of people with MS. These drugs seem to hold the symptoms at bay, reducing complications and the disability that often occurs with MS. ■

Nerve fibers may be classified according to diameter, degree of myelination, and conduction speed. **Group A fibers** are mostly somatic sensory and motor fibers serving the skin, skeletal muscles, and joints. They have the largest diameter and thick myelin sheaths, and conduct impulses at speeds ranging up to 150 m/s (over 300 miles per hour).

In the B and C fiber groups are autonomic nervous system motor fibers serving the visceral organs; visceral sensory fibers; and the smaller somatic sensory fibers transmitting afferent impulses from the skin (such as pain and small touch fibers). **Group B fibers**, lightly myelinated fibers of intermediate diameter, transmit impulses at an average rate of 15 m/s (about 30 mi/h). **Group C fibers** have the smallest diameter and are unmyelinated. Consequently, they are incapable of saltatory conduction and conduct impulses at a leisurely pace—1 m/s (2 mi/h) or less.

What happens when an action potential arrives at the end of a neuron's axon? That is the subject of the next section.

⚖ HOMEOSTATIC IMBALANCE

A number of chemical and physical factors impair impulse propagation. Local anesthetics like those used by your dentist act by blocking voltage-gated Na^+ channels. As we have seen, no Na^+ entry—no AP.

Cold and continuous pressure interrupt blood circulation, hindering the delivery of oxygen and nutrients to neuron processes and impairing their ability to conduct impulses. For example, your fingers get numb when you hold an ice cube for more than a few seconds, and your foot "goes to sleep" when you sit on it. When you remove the cold object or pressure, impulses are transmitted again, leading to an unpleasant prickly feeling. ■

CHECK YOUR UNDERSTANDING

11. Comparing graded potentials and action potentials, which is bigger? Which travels farthest? Which initiates the other?
12. An action potential does not get smaller as it propagates along an axon. Why not?
13. Why is conduction of action potentials faster in myelinated than in unmyelinated axons?
14. If an axon receives two stimuli close together in time, only one AP occurs. Why?

For answers, see Appendix G.

The Synapse

▶ Define synapse. Distinguish between electrical and chemical synapses by structure and by the way they transmit information.

The operation of the nervous system depends on the flow of information through chains of neurons functionally connected by synapses. A **synapse** (sin'aps), from the Greek *syn*, "to clasp or join," is a junction that mediates information transfer from one neuron to the next or from a neuron to an effector cell—it's where the action is.

Synapses between the axon endings of one neuron and the dendrites of other neurons are **axodendritic synapses**. Those between axon endings of one neuron and cell bodies (soma) of other neurons are **axosomatic synapses** (Figure 11.16). Less common (and far less understood) are synapses between axons (*axoaxonic*), between dendrites (*dendrodendritic*), or between dendrites and cell bodies (*dendrosomatic*).

The neuron conducting impulses toward the synapse is the **presynaptic neuron**, and the neuron transmitting the electrical signal away from the synapse is the **postsynaptic neuron**. At a given synapse, the presynaptic neuron is the information sender, and the postsynaptic neuron is the information receiver. As you might anticipate, most neurons function as both presynaptic and postsynaptic neurons. Neurons have anywhere from 1000 to 10,000 axon terminals making synapses and are stimulated by an equal number of other neurons. Outside the central nervous system, the postsynaptic cell may be either another neuron or an effector cell (a muscle cell or gland cell).

Now let's look at the two varieties of synapses: *electrical* and *chemical*.

Electrical Synapses

Electrical synapses, the less common variety, consist of gap junctions like those found between certain other body cells. They contain protein channels, called connexons, that intimately connect the cytoplasm of adjacent neurons and allow ions and small molecules to flow directly from one neuron to the next. Neurons joined in this way are said to be *electrically coupled*, and transmission across these synapses is very rapid. Depending on the nature of the synapse, communication may be unidirectional or bidirectional.

A key feature of electrical synapses between neurons is that they provide a simple means of synchronizing the activity of all interconnected neurons. In adults, electrical synapses are found in regions of the brain responsible for certain stereotyped movements, such as the normal jerky movements of the eyes, and in axoaxonic synapses in the hippocampus, a brain region intimately involved in emotions and memory. Electrical synapses are far more abundant in embryonic nervous tissue, where they permit exchange of guiding cues during early neuronal development so that neurons can connect properly with one another. As the nervous system develops, some electrical synapses are replaced by chemical synapses. Gap junctions also exist between glial cells of the CNS.

11

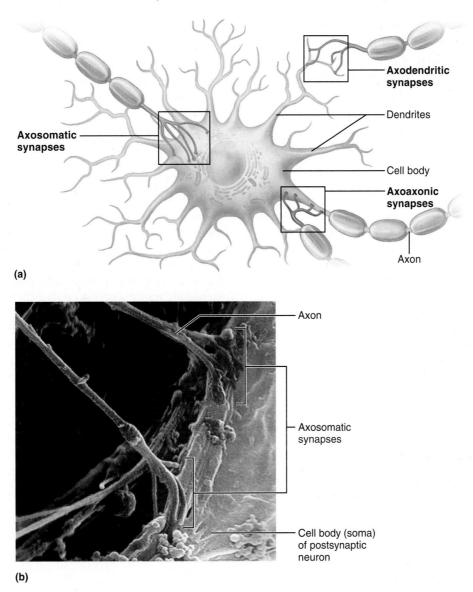

(a)

(b)

Figure 11.16 Synapses. (a) Axodendritic, axosomatic, and axoaxonic synapses. **(b)** Scanning electron micrograph of incoming fibers at axosomatic synapses (5300×).

Chemical Synapses

In contrast to electrical synapses, which are specialized to allow the flow of ions between neurons, **chemical synapses** are specialized for release and reception of chemical neurotransmitters. A typical chemical synapse is made up of two parts:

1. A knoblike *axon terminal* of the presynaptic neuron, which contains many tiny, membrane-bounded sacs called **synaptic vesicles**, each containing thousands of neurotransmitter molecules
2. A neurotransmitter *receptor region* on the membrane of a dendrite or the cell body of the postsynaptic neuron

Although close to each other, presynaptic and postsynaptic membranes are always separated by the **synaptic cleft**, a fluid-filled space approximately 30 to 50 nm (about one-millionth of an inch) wide. (If an electrical synapse is like the threshold of a doorway between neurons, a synaptic cleft is like a good-size lake intervening between them.)

Because the current from the presynaptic membrane dissipates in the fluid-filled cleft, chemical synapses effectively prevent a nerve impulse from being *directly* transmitted from one neuron to another. Instead, transmission of signals across these synapses is a *chemical event* that depends on the release, diffusion, and receptor binding of neurotransmitter molecules and results in *unidirectional communication* between neurons. In short, transmission of nerve impulses along an axon and across electrical synapses is a purely electrical event, while chemical synapses convert the electrical signals to chemical signals (neurotransmitters) that travel across the synapse to the postsynaptic cells, where they are converted back into electrical signals.

Information Transfer Across Chemical Synapses

In Chapter 9 we introduced a specialized chemical synapse called a neuromuscular junction (p. 285). The chain of events that occurs at the neuromuscular junction is simply one example of the general process that we will discuss next and show in *Focus on a Chemical Synapse* (Figure 11.17):

① **Action potential arrives at axon terminal.** The process of neurotransmission at a chemical synapse begins with the arrival of an action potential at the presynaptic axon terminal.

② **Voltage-gated Ca^{2+} channels open and Ca^{2+} enters the axon terminal.** Depolarization of the membrane by the action potential opens not only Na^+ channels but voltage-gated Ca^{2+} channels as well. During the brief time the Ca^{2+} channels are open, Ca^{2+} floods down its electrochemical gradient into the terminal from the extracellular fluid.

③ **Ca^{2+} entry causes neurotransmitter-containing vesicles to release their contents by exocytosis.** The surge of Ca^{2+} into the axon terminal acts as an intracellular messenger. A Ca^{2+}-sensing protein (*synaptotagmin*) binds Ca^{2+} and interacts with the SNARE proteins that control membrane fusion (see Figure 3.14). As a result, synaptic vesicles fuse with the axon membrane and empty their contents by exocytosis into the synaptic cleft. Ca^{2+} is then quickly removed from the terminal—either taken up into the mitochondria or ejected from the neuron by an active Ca^{2+} pump.

For each nerve impulse reaching the presynaptic terminal, many vesicles (perhaps 300) are emptied into the synaptic cleft. The higher the impulse frequency (that is, the more intense the stimulus), the greater the number of synaptic vesicles that fuse and spill their contents, and the greater the effect on the postsynaptic cell.

④ **Neurotransmitter diffuses across the synaptic cleft and binds to specific receptors on the postsynaptic membrane.**

⑤ **Binding of neurotransmitter opens ion channels, resulting in graded potentials.** When neurotransmitter binds to the receptor protein, this receptor changes its three-dimensional shape. This change in turn causes ion channels to open and creates graded potentials. Postsynaptic membranes often contain receptor proteins and ion channels packaged together as chemically gated ion channels. Depending on the receptor protein to which the neurotransmitter binds and the type of channel the receptor controls, the postsynaptic neuron may be either excited or inhibited.

⑥ **Neurotransmitter effects are terminated.** The binding of a neurotransmitter to its receptor is reversible. As long as it is bound to a postsynaptic receptor, a neurotransmitter continues to affect membrane permeability and to block reception of additional signals from presynaptic neurons. For this reason, some means of "wiping the postsynaptic slate clean" is necessary. The effects of neurotransmitters generally last a few milliseconds before being terminated in one of three ways, depending on the particular neurotransmitter:

- *Reuptake* by astrocytes or the presynaptic terminal, where the neurotransmitter is stored or destroyed by enzymes, as with norepinephrine
- *Degradation* by enzymes associated with the postsynaptic membrane or present in the synapse, as with acetylcholine
- *Diffusion* away from the synapse

Synaptic Delay

An impulse may travel at speeds of up to 150 m/s (300 mi/h) down an axon, but neural transmission across a chemical synapse is comparatively slow. It reflects the time required for neurotransmitter release, diffusion across the synaptic cleft, and binding to receptors. Typically, this **synaptic delay** lasts 0.3–5.0 ms, making transmission across the chemical synapse the *rate-limiting* (slowest) step of neural transmission. Synaptic delay helps explain why transmission along neural pathways involving only two or three neurons occurs rapidly, but transmission along multisynaptic pathways typical of higher mental functioning occurs much more slowly. However, in practical terms these differences are not noticeable.

CHECK YOUR UNDERSTANDING

15. What is the structure that joins two neurons at an electrical synapse?

16. Events at a chemical synapse usually involve opening of both voltage-gated ion channels and chemically gated ion channels. Where are these ion channels located and what causes each to open?

For answers, see Appendix G.

Postsynaptic Potentials and Synaptic Integration

▶ Distinguish between excitatory and inhibitory postsynaptic potentials.

▶ Describe how synaptic events are integrated and modified.

Many receptors on postsynaptic membranes at chemical synapses are specialized to open ion channels, in this way converting chemical signals to electrical signals. Unlike the voltage-gated ion channels responsible for APs, however, these chemically gated channels are relatively insensitive to changes in membrane potential. Consequently, channel opening at postsynaptic membranes cannot possibly become self-amplifying or self-generating. Instead, neurotransmitter receptors mediate graded potentials—local changes in membrane potential that are *graded* (or varied in strength) according to the amount of neurotransmitter released and the time it remains in the area. APs are compared with graded potentials in **Table 11.2**.

Figure 11.17 **FOCUS** **Chemical Synapse**

Chemical synapses transmit signals from one neuron to another using neurotransmitters.

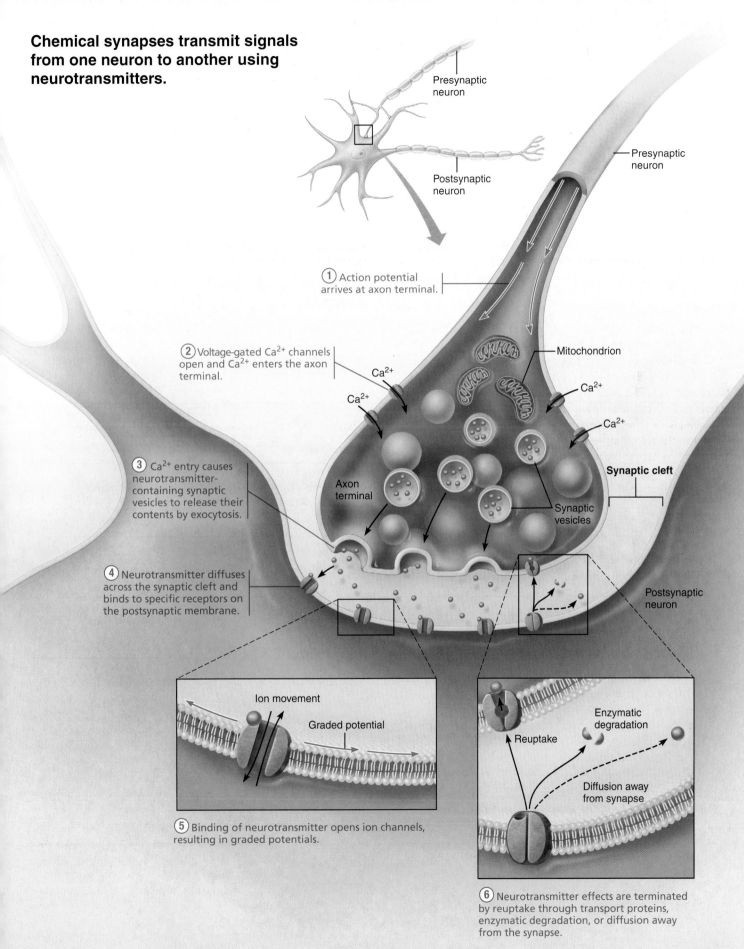

Presynaptic neuron

Postsynaptic neuron

Presynaptic neuron

① Action potential arrives at axon terminal.

② Voltage-gated Ca²⁺ channels open and Ca²⁺ enters the axon terminal.

Ca^{2+}

Ca^{2+}

Mitochondrion

Ca^{2+}

Ca^{2+}

Synaptic cleft

③ Ca²⁺ entry causes neurotransmitter-containing synaptic vesicles to release their contents by exocytosis.

Axon terminal

Synaptic vesicles

④ Neurotransmitter diffuses across the synaptic cleft and binds to specific receptors on the postsynaptic membrane.

Postsynaptic neuron

Ion movement

Graded potential

Enzymatic degradation

Reuptake

Diffusion away from synapse

⑤ Binding of neurotransmitter opens ion channels, resulting in graded potentials.

⑥ Neurotransmitter effects are terminated by reuptake through transport proteins, enzymatic degradation, or diffusion away from the synapse.

A&P Flix   *View this animation at mvA&P*

TABLE 11.2	Comparison of Action Potentials with Graded Potentials	
	GRADED POTENTIAL (GP)	**ACTION POTENTIAL (AP)**
Location of event	Cell body and dendrites, typically	Axon hillock and axon

Dendrites · Cell body · Axon hillock · Axon

Distance traveled	Short distance—typically within cell body to axon hillock (0.1–1.0 mm)	Long distance—from axon hillock through entire length of axon (a few mm to over a meter)

Axon hillock · Short distance · Long distance

Amplitude (size)	Various sizes (graded); declines with distance	Always the same size (all-or-none); does not decline with distance
Stimulus for opening of ion channels	Chemical (neurotransmitter) or sensory stimulus (e.g., light, pressure, temperature)	Voltage (depolarization, triggered by GP reaching threshold)
Positive feedback cycle	Absent	Present
Repolarization	Voltage independent; occurs when stimulus is no longer present	Voltage regulated; occurs when Na^+ channels inactivate and K^+ channels open
Summation	Stimulus responses can be summed to increase amplitude of graded potential	Does not occur; an all-or-none phenomenon

Temporal: increased frequency of stimuli · Spatial: stimuli from multiple sources

TABLE 11.2	(continued)		
	GRADED POTENTIAL (GP)		**ACTION POTENTIAL (AP)**
	POSTSYNAPTIC POTENTIAL (A TYPE OF GP)		
	EXCITATORY (EPSP)	**INHIBITORY (IPSP)**	
Function	Short-distance signaling; depolarization that spreads to axon hillock; moves membrane potential *toward* threshold for generation of AP	Short-distance signaling; hyperpolarization that spreads to axon hillock; moves membrane potential *away from* threshold for generation of AP	Long-distance signaling; constitutes the nerve impulse
Initial effect of stimulus	Opens channels that allow simultaneous Na^+ and K^+ fluxes	Opens K^+ or Cl^- channels	First opens Na^+ channels, then K^+ channels
Peak membrane potential	Becomes depolarized; moves toward 0 mV	Becomes hyperpolarized; moves toward −90 mV	+30 to +50 mV

Chemical synapses are either excitatory or inhibitory, depending on how they affect the membrane potential of the postsynaptic neuron.

Excitatory Synapses and EPSPs

At excitatory synapses, neurotransmitter binding causes depolarization of the postsynaptic membrane. However, in contrast to what happens on axon membranes, a single type of *chemically gated* ion channel opens on postsynaptic membranes (those of dendrites and neuronal cell bodies). This channel allows Na^+ and K^+ to diffuse *simultaneously* through the membrane in opposite directions. Although this two-way cation flow may appear to be self-defeating when depolarization is the goal, remember that the electrochemical gradient for sodium is much steeper than that for potassium. As a result, Na^+ influx is greater than K^+ efflux, and *net* depolarization occurs.

If enough neurotransmitter binds, depolarization of the postsynaptic membrane can reach 0 mV, which is well above an axon's threshold (about −50 mV) for "firing off" an AP. However, *postsynaptic membranes generally do not generate APs*, unlike axons, which have voltage-gated channels that make an AP possible. The dramatic polarity reversal seen in axons never occurs in membranes containing *only* chemically gated channels because the opposite movements of K^+ and Na^+ prevent accumulation of excessive positive charge inside the cell. For this reason, instead of APs, local graded depolarization events called **excitatory postsynaptic potentials** (**EPSPs**) occur at excitatory postsynaptic membranes (Figure 11.18a).

Each EPSP lasts a few milliseconds and then the membrane returns to its resting potential. The only function of EPSPs is to help trigger an AP distally at the axon hillock of the postsynaptic neuron. Although currents created by individual EPSPs decline with distance, they can and often do spread all the way to

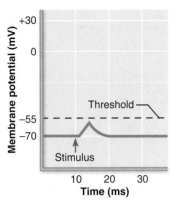

An EPSP is a local depolarization of the postsynaptic membrane that brings the neuron closer to AP threshold. Neurotransmitter binding opens chemically gated ion channels, allowing the simultaneous passage of Na⁺ and K⁺.

(a) Excitatory postsynaptic potential (EPSP)

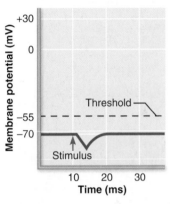

An IPSP is a local hyperpolarization of the postsynaptic membrane and drives the neuron away from AP threshold. Neurotransmitter binding opens K⁺ or Cl⁻ channels.

(b) Inhibitory postsynaptic potential (IPSP)

Figure 11.18 Postsynaptic potentials.

the axon hillock. If currents reaching the hillock are strong enough to depolarize the axon to threshold, axonal voltage-gated channels open and an AP is generated.

Inhibitory Synapses and IPSPs

Binding of neurotransmitters at inhibitory synapses *reduces* a postsynaptic neuron's ability to generate an AP. Most inhibitory neurotransmitters induce hyperpolarization of the postsynaptic membrane by making the membrane more permeable to K⁺ or Cl⁻. Sodium ion permeability is not affected.

If K⁺ channels are opened, K⁺ moves out of the cell. If Cl⁻ channels are opened, Cl⁻ moves in. In either case, the charge on the inner face of the membrane becomes more negative. As the membrane potential increases and is driven farther from the axon's threshold, the postsynaptic neuron becomes *less and less likely* to "fire," and larger depolarizing currents are required to induce an AP. Such changes in potential are called **inhibitory postsynaptic potentials** (IPSPs) (Figure 11.18b).

Integration and Modification of Synaptic Events

Summation by the Postsynaptic Neuron   A single EPSP cannot induce an AP in the postsynaptic neuron **(Figure 11.19a)**. But if thousands of excitatory axon terminals are firing on the same postsynaptic membrane, or if a smaller number of terminals are delivering impulses rapidly, the probability of reaching threshold

depolarization increases greatly. EPSPs can add together, or **summate**, to influence the activity of a postsynaptic neuron. Nerve impulses would never be initiated if this were not so.

Two types of summation occur. **Temporal summation** (*temporal* = time) occurs when one or more presynaptic neurons transmit impulses in rapid-fire order and bursts of neurotransmitter are released in quick succession. The first impulse produces a small EPSP, and before it dissipates, successive impulses trigger more EPSPs. These summate, producing a much greater depolarization of the postsynaptic membrane than would result from a single EPSP (Figure 11.19b).

Spatial summation occurs when the postsynaptic neuron is stimulated at the same time by a large number of terminals from the same or, more commonly, different neurons. Huge numbers of its receptors bind neurotransmitter and simultaneously initiate EPSPs, which summate and dramatically enhance depolarization (Figure 11.19c).

Although we have focused on EPSPs here, IPSPs also summate, both temporally and spatially. In this case, the postsynaptic neuron is inhibited to a greater degree.

Most neurons receive both excitatory and inhibitory inputs from thousands of other neurons. Additionally, the same axon may form different types of synapses (in terms of biochemical and electrical characteristics) with different types of target neurons. How is all this conflicting information sorted out?

Each neuron's axon hillock keeps a running account of all the signals it receives. Not only do EPSPs summate and IPSPs summate, but also EPSPs summate with IPSPs. If the stimulatory effects of EPSPs dominate the membrane potential enough to reach threshold, the neuron will fire. If summation yields only subthreshold depolarization or hyperpolarization, the neuron fails to generate an AP (Figure 11.19d). However, partially depolarized neurons are **facilitated**—that is, more easily excited by successive depolarization events—because they are already near threshold. Thus, axon hillock membranes function as *neural integrators*, and their potential at any time reflects the sum of all incoming neural information.

Because EPSPs and IPSPs are graded potentials that diminish in strength the farther they spread, the most effective synapses are those closest to the axon hillock. Specifically, inhibitory synapses are most effective when located between the site of excitatory inputs and the site of action potential generation (the axon hillock). Accordingly, inhibitory synapses occur most often on the cell body and excitatory synapses occur most often on the dendrites (Figure 11.19d).

Synaptic Potentiation   Repeated or continuous use of a synapse (even for short periods) enhances the presynaptic neuron's ability to excite the postsynaptic neuron, producing larger-than-expected postsynaptic potentials. This phenomenon is called **synaptic potentiation**. The presynaptic terminals at such synapses contain relatively high Ca²⁺ concentrations, a condition that (presumably) triggers the release of more neurotransmitter, which in turn produces larger EPSPs.

Furthermore, synaptic potentiation brings about Ca²⁺ influx via dendritic spines into the postsynaptic neuron as well. Brief high-frequency stimulation partially depolarizes the postsynaptic membrane. This partial depolarization causes certain

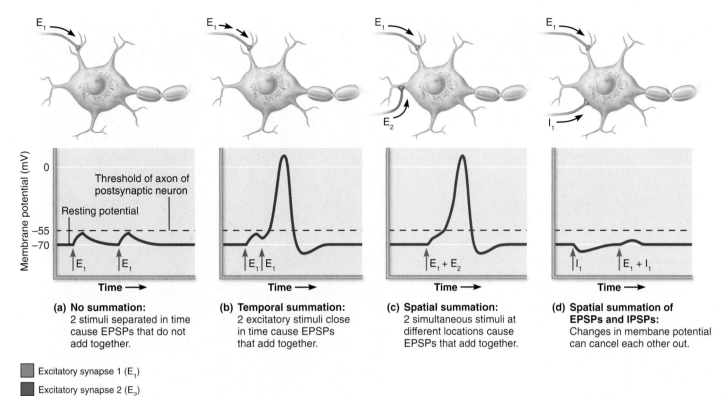

(a) No summation:
2 stimuli separated in time cause EPSPs that do not add together.

(b) Temporal summation:
2 excitatory stimuli close in time cause EPSPs that add together.

(c) Spatial summation:
2 simultaneous stimuli at different locations cause EPSPs that add together.

(d) Spatial summation of EPSPs and IPSPs:
Changes in membane potential can cancel each other out.

☐ Excitatory synapse 1 (E_1)
☐ Excitatory synapse 2 (E_2)
☐ Inhibitory synapse (I_1)

Figure 11.19 Neural integration of EPSPs and IPSPs.

chemically gated channels called *NMDA* (*N-methyl-D-aspartate*) *receptors* to allow Ca^{2+} entry, something that only happens when the membrane is depolarized. As Ca^{2+} floods into the cell, it activates certain kinase enzymes that promote changes that result in more effective responses to subsequent stimuli.

In some neurons, APs generated at the axon hillock propagate back up into the dendrites. This current flow may alter the effectiveness of synapses by causing voltage-gated Ca^{2+} channels to open, again allowing Ca^{2+} into the dendrites and promoting synaptic potentiation.

Synaptic potentiation can be viewed as a learning process that increases the efficiency of neurotransmission along a particular pathway. Indeed, the hippocampus of the brain, which plays a special role in memory and learning, exhibits an important type of synaptic plasticity called *long-term potentiation* (LTP).

Presynaptic Inhibition Postsynaptic activity can also be influenced by events occurring at the presynaptic membrane. **Presynaptic inhibition** occurs when the release of excitatory neurotransmitter by one neuron is inhibited by the activity of another neuron via an axoaxonic synapse. More than one mechanism is involved, but the end result is that less neurotransmitter is released and bound, and smaller EPSPs are formed.

Notice that this is the opposite of what we see with synaptic potentiation. In contrast to postsynaptic inhibition by IPSPs, which decreases the excitability of the postsynaptic neuron, presynaptic inhibition reduces excitatory stimulation of the postsynaptic neuron. In this way, presynaptic inhibition is like a functional synaptic "pruning."

CHECK YOUR UNDERSTANDING

17. Which ions flow through chemically gated channels to produce IPSPs? EPSPs?

18. What is the difference between temporal summation and spatial summation?

For answers, see Appendix G.

Neurotransmitters and Their Receptors

▶ Define neurotransmitter and name several classes of neurotransmitters.

Neurotransmitters, along with electrical signals, are the "language" of the nervous system—the means by which each neuron communicates with others to process and send messages to the rest of the body. Sleep, thought, rage, hunger, memory, movement, and even your smile reflect the "doings" of these versatile molecules. Most factors that affect synaptic transmission do so by enhancing or inhibiting neurotransmitter release or destruction, or by blocking their binding to receptors. Just as speech defects may hinder interpersonal communication, interferences with neurotransmitter activity may short-circuit the brain's "conversations" or internal talk (see *A Closer Look* on pp. 414–415).

At present, more than 50 neurotransmitters or neurotransmitter candidates have been identified. Although some neurons

A CLOSER LOOK
Pleasure Me, Pleasure Me!

Sex! Drugs! Rock 'n' roll! Eat, drink, and be merry! Why do we find these activities so compelling? Our brains are wired to reward us with pleasure when we engage in behavior that is necessary for our own and our species' survival. This reward system consists of dopamine-releasing neurons in areas of the brain called the *ventral tegmental area* (VTA), the *nucleus accumbens*, and the *amygdala*.

Our ability to "feel good" involves brain neurotransmitters in this reward system. For example, the ecstasy of romantic love may be just a brain bath of glutamate and norepinephrine, which act on the reward system to release dopamine. Unfortunately, this powerful system can be subverted by drugs of abuse. The 1930s songwriter Cole Porter knew what he was talking about when he wrote "I get a kick out of you," because these neurotransmitters are chemical cousins of the amphetamines. People who use "crystal meth" (methamphetamine) artificially stimulate their brains to provide their highly addictive pleasure flush. However, their pleasure is short-lived, because when the brain is flooded with neurotransmitter-like chemicals from the outside, it makes less of its own (why bother?).

Cocaine, another reward system titillater, has been around since ancient times. Once a toy of the rich, its granular form is inhaled, or "snorted." The laws of supply and demand have now brought cheaper cocaine to the masses, notably "crack"—a cheaper, more potent, smokable form of cocaine. For $50 or so, a novice user can experience a rush of intense pleasure. But crack is treacherous and intensely addictive. It produces not only a higher high than the inhaled form of cocaine, but also a deeper crash that leaves the user desperate for more.

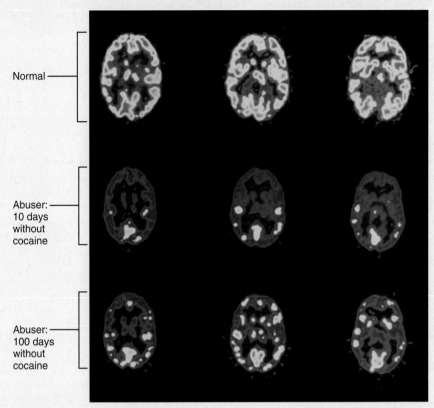

Normal

Abuser: 10 days without cocaine

Abuser: 100 days without cocaine

PET scans show that normal levels of brain activity (yellow and red) are depressed in cocaine users long after drug use has stopped.

How does cocaine produce its effects? Basically, the drug stimulates the reward system and then "squeezes it dry." Cocaine produces its rush by hooking up to the dopamine reuptake transporter protein, blocking the reabsorption of dopamine. The neurotransmitter remains in the synapse and stimulates the postsynaptic receptor cells again and again, allowing the body to feel its effects over a prolonged period. This sensation is accompanied by increases in heart rate, blood pressure, and sexual appetite.

As dopamine uptake continues to be blocked by repeated doses of cocaine, the system releases less and less dopamine and the reward system effectively goes dry. The cocaine user becomes anxious and, in a very real sense, unable to experience pleasure without the drug. Consequently, the postsynaptic cells become hypersensitive and sprout new receptors

produce and release only one kind of neurotransmitter, most make two or more and may release any one or all of them. It appears that in most cases, different neurotransmitters are released at different stimulation frequencies, a restriction that avoids producing a jumble of nonsense messages. However, co-release of two neurotransmitters from the same vesicles has been documented. The coexistence of more than one neurotransmitter in a single neuron makes it possible for that cell to exert several influences rather than one discrete effect.

Neurotransmitters are classified chemically and functionally. **Table 11.3** provides a fairly detailed overview of neurotransmit-

ters, and we describe some of them here. No one expects you to memorize this table at this point, but it will be a handy reference for you to look back at when neurotransmitters are mentioned in subsequent chapters.

Classification of Neurotransmitters by Chemical Structure

Neurotransmitters fall into several chemical classes based on molecular structure.

in a desperate effort to pick up dopamine signals. A vicious cycle of addiction begins: Cocaine is needed to experience pleasure, but using it suppresses dopamine release even more.

The dopamine effect alone is not enough to establish addiction. Another neurotransmitter, glutamate, which plays an important role in learning, is required to maintain addiction. Glutamate signaling seems to cause more permanent changes in the brain (synaptic potentiation) that lead to compulsive drug-seeking behaviors elicited by external cues. Take, for example, mice genetically engineered to lack a particular glutamate receptor (GluR5). These mice are perfectly willing to try cocaine but never become addicted. (Of course, no GluR5 means they're none too bright, either.)

Current thinking, then, is that the rush of pleasure on taking cocaine is due to dopamine. Glutamate, on the other hand, is thought to be responsible for the learning that makes true the perception "once an addict, always an addict." So strong is the combined dopamine and glutamate system that, even years later, certain settings can trigger intense cravings for the drug.

These out-of-control, desperate cravings are notoriously difficult to manage. Drug abusers call it "jonesing." Traditional antiaddiction drugs take so long to reduce the cravings that users commonly drop out of treatment programs.

How can we break this cycle of addiction? One way is to prevent cocaine from ever reaching the brain. Promising results have been obtained from a vaccine that prompts the immune system to bind cocaine molecules, preventing them from entering the brain. In a clinical trial, this vaccine dampened addicts' pleasurable responses to cocaine and reduced their use of the drug. Another approach to breaking the addiction cycle is to even out the highs and lows experienced by the drug user. Clinical trials are under way with a drug (vanoxerine) that slowly binds the dopamine reuptake transporter and inhibits it in a more long-lasting manner than cocaine does. This results in a leveling-out of brain dopamine levels and keeps the user from "crashing" so badly.

A final approach to breaking the addiction cycle is to interrupt the learned reinforcement that brings on cravings. An effective ancient African folk remedy called ibogaine may do exactly this. However, ibogaine itself is too toxic for clinical use, as some unfortunate "underground" users have discovered. A close synthetic cousin, 18-methoxycoronaridine (18-MC) is much less toxic and promises to be effective against not only cocaine but also a number of other abused drugs. Future studies will show if it is truly effective.

The craving for drugs has made some who depend on them into very creative home pharmacologists, willing to experiment with practically anything, no matter how toxic or dangerous, to get the "buzz" they need. A cheap mixture of cold medications, match heads, and iodine in acetone yields crystal meth—the highly addictive and once-again popular drug that wrecks people's lives and often explodes their home laboratories. Another creative mixture, with the street name of "ill face" or "illy," involves dipping marijuana in formaldehyde, drying and then smoking it. Other remarkable combinations are the "H-bomb" (ecstasy mixed with heroin), "A-bomb" (marijuana with heroin or opium), "sextasy" [ecstasy mixed with sildenafil (Viagra)], "octane" (PCP laced with gasoline), and "ozone" (marijuana,

PCP, and crack in a cigarette). Formaldehyde is a known cancer-causing agent and gasoline damages the liver, but the real damage comes from the drugs themselves.

Take, for example, ecstasy, a drug that many of its users believe to be innocuous. In reality, ecstasy (MDMA) targets serotonin-releasing neurons. The "rush" of pleasure and energy that users feel is due to release of serotonin and other neurotransmitters. However, it damages and may destroy these neurons, causing the loss of verbal and spatial memory. Depression, sleeplessness, and memory problems may be permanent consequences—a high price for a few moments of pleasure!

People who want pure, effective, and "safe" drugs of abuse don't get them on the street. They get them from doctors or "pill ladies" [female senior citizens who sell oxycodone (OxyContin), a powerful prescription opioid with effects similar to heroin]. Even people who would never dream of taking the illicit drugs can be caught in the addictive cycle of prescription drugs. Prescribed legitimately to relieve severe pain, oxycodone is meant to be swallowed whole. Abusers crush the tablets and snort the powder or dissolve it in water and inject the solution. Abuse of oxycodone and its chemical cousin hydrocodone is spreading rapidly. Medical examiners across North America report soaring rates of oxycodone-related emergency room visits and deaths.

The brain, with its complex biochemistry, always circumvents attempts to keep it in a euphoric haze. Perhaps this means that pleasure must be transient by nature, experienced only against a background of its absence.

Acetylcholine

Acetylcholine (ACh) (as″ĕ-til-ko′lēn) was the first neurotransmitter identified. It is still the best understood because it is released at neuromuscular junctions, which are much easier to study than synapses buried in the CNS. ACh is synthesized from acetic acid (as acetyl CoA) and choline by the enzyme *choline acetyltransferase*. The newly synthesized ACh is then transported into synaptic vesicles for later release. Once released by the presynaptic terminal, ACh binds briefly to the postsynaptic receptors. Then it is released and degraded to acetic acid and choline by the enzyme **acetylcholinesterase (AChE)**, located in the synaptic cleft and on postsynaptic membranes. The released choline is recaptured by the presynaptic terminals and reused to synthesize more ACh.

ACh is released by all neurons that stimulate skeletal muscles and by some neurons of the autonomic nervous system. ACh-releasing neurons are also found in the CNS.

Biogenic Amines

The **biogenic amines** (bi″o-jen′ik) include the **catecholamines** (kat″ĕ-kol′ah-mēnz), such as dopamine, norepinephrine (NE), and epinephrine, and the **indolamines**, which include serotonin

TABLE 11.3	Neurotransmitters and Neuromodulators		
NEUROTRANSMITTER	**FUNCTIONAL CLASSES**	**SITES WHERE SECRETED**	**COMMENTS**

Acetylcholine

• At *nicotinic ACh receptors* (on skeletal muscles, autonomic ganglia, and in the CNS)	Excitatory Direct action	CNS: widespread throughout cerebral cortex, hippocampus, and brain stem	Effects prolonged, leading to tetanic muscle spasms, when AChE blocked by nerve gas and organophosphate insecticides (malathion). Release inhibited by botulinum toxin; binding to nicotinic ACh receptors inhibited by curare (a muscle paralytic agent) and to muscarinic ACh receptors by atropine. ACh levels decreased in certain brain areas in Alzheimer's disease; nicotinic ACh receptors destroyed in myasthenia gravis. Binding of nicotine to nicotinic receptors in the brain enhances dopamine release, which may account for the behavioral effects of nicotine in smokers.
• At *muscarinic ACh receptors* (on visceral effectors and in the CNS)	Excitatory or inhibitory depending on subtype of muscarinic receptor Indirect action via second messengers	PNS: all neuromuscular junctions with skeletal muscle; some autonomic motor endings (all preganglionic and parasympathetic postganglionic fibers)	

$$H_3C-\overset{\overset{\displaystyle O}{\|}}{C}-O-CH_2-CH_2-\overset{+}{N}-(CH_3)_3$$

Biogenic Amines

Norepinephrine	Excitatory or inhibitory depending on receptor type bound Indirect action via second messengers	CNS: brain stem, particularly in the locus coeruleus of the midbrain; limbic system; some areas of cerebral cortex PNS: main neurotransmitter of ganglionic neurons in the sympathetic nervous system	A "feeling good" neurotransmitter. Release enhanced by amphetamines; removal from synapse blocked by tricyclic antidepressants [amitriptyline (Elavil) and others] and cocaine. Brain levels reduced by reserpine (an antihypertensive drug), leading to depression.

(Norepinephrine structure: benzene ring with two HO groups, $-CH-CH_2-NH_2$ with OH below)

Dopamine	Excitatory or inhibitory depending on the receptor type bound Indirect action via second messengers	CNS: substantia nigra of midbrain; hypothalamus; is the principal neurotransmitter of extrapyramidal system PNS: some sympathetic ganglia	A "feeling good" neurotransmitter. Release enhanced by L-dopa and amphetamines; reuptake blocked by cocaine. Deficient in Parkinson's disease; dopamine neurotransmission increased in schizophrenia.

(Dopamine structure: benzene ring with two HO groups, $-CH_2-CH_2-NH_2$)

Serotonin (5-HT)	Mainly inhibitory Indirect action via second messengers; direct action at 5-HT$_3$ receptors	CNS: brain stem, especially midbrain; hypothalamus; limbic system; cerebellum; pineal gland; spinal cord	May play a role in sleep, appetite, nausea, migraine headaches, and regulation of mood. Drugs that block its uptake [fluoxetine (Prozac)] relieve anxiety and depression. Activity blocked by LSD and enhanced by ecstasy (MDMA).

(Serotonin structure: indole ring with HO group, $-C=CH-CH_2-CH_2-NH_2$)

Histamine	Excitatory or inhibitory depending on receptor type bound Indirect action via second messengers	CNS: hypothalamus	Involved in wakefulness, appetite control, and learning and memory. Also a paracrine (local signal) released from stomach (causes acid secretion) and connective tissue mast cells (mediates inflammation and vasodilation).

(Histamine structure: imidazole ring, $HC=C-CH_2-CH_2-NH_2$)

11

TABLE 11.3	(continued)		
NEUROTRANSMITTER	**FUNCTIONAL CLASSES**	**SITES WHERE SECRETED**	**COMMENTS**
Amino Acids			
GABA (γ-aminobutyric acid) $H_2N—CH_2—CH_2—CH_2—COOH$	Generally inhibitory Direct and indirect actions via second messengers	CNS: cerebral cortex, hypothalamus, Purkinje cells of cerebellum, spinal cord, granule cells of olfactory bulb, retina	Principal inhibitory neurotransmitter in the brain; important in presynaptic inhibition at axoaxonic synapses. Inhibitory effects augmented by alcohol, antianxiety drugs of the benzodiazepine class (e.g., Valium), and barbiturates, resulting in impaired motor coordination. Substances that block its synthesis, release, or action induce convulsions.

Glutamate
 	
$H_2N—CH—CH_2—CH_2—COOH$
        $|$
      $COOH$
	Generally excitatory
	
	Direct action
		CNS: spinal cord; widespread in brain where it represents the major excitatory neurotransmitter	Important in learning and memory. The "stroke neurotransmitter": excessive release produces excitotoxicity—neurons literally stimulated to death; most commonly caused by ischemia (oxygen deprivation, usually due to a blocked blood vessel). When released by gliomas, aids tumor advance.

Glycine $H_2N—CH_2—COOH$	Generally inhibitory Direct action	CNS: spinal cord and brain stem, retina	Principal inhibitory neurotransmitter of the spinal cord. Strychnine blocks glycine receptors, resulting in uncontrolled convulsions and respiratory arrest.
Peptides			
Endorphins, e.g., dynorphin, enkephalins (illustrated) Tyr Gly Gly Phe Met	Generally inhibitory Indirect action via second messengers	CNS: widely distributed in brain; hypothalamus; limbic system; pituitary; spinal cord	Natural opiates; inhibit pain by inhibiting substance P. Effects mimicked by morphine, heroin, and methadone.
Tachykinins: Substance P (illustrated), neurokinin A (NKA) Arg Pro Lys Pro Gln Gln Phe Phe Gly Leu Met	Excitatory Indirect action via second messengers	CNS: basal nuclei, midbrain, hypothalamus, cerebral cortex PNS: certain sensory neurons of dorsal root ganglia (pain afferents), enteric neurons	Substance P mediates pain transmission in the PNS. In the CNS, tachykinins are involved in respiratory and cardiovascular controls and in mood.
Somatostatin Ala Gly Cys Lys Asn Phe Phe Trp Cys Ser Thr Phe Thr Lys	Generally inhibitory Indirect action via second messengers	CNS: hypothalamus, septum, basal nuclei, hippocampus, cerebral cortex Pancreas	Often released with GABA. A gut-brain peptide hormone. Inhibits growth hormone release.
Cholecystokinin (CCK) Asp Tyr Met Gly Trp Met Asp Phe SO_4	Generally excitatory Indirect action via second messengers	Throughout CNS Small intestine	Involved in anxiety, pain, memory. A gut-brain peptide hormone. Inhibits appetite.

11

TABLE 11.3	Neurotransmitters and Neuromodulators (continued)		
NEUROTRANSMITTER	**FUNCTIONAL CLASSES**	**SITES WHERE SECRETED**	**COMMENTS**
Purines			
ATP	Excitatory or inhibitory depending on receptor type bound	CNS: basal nuclei, induces Ca^{2+} wave propagation in astrocytes	ATP released by sensory neurons (as well as that released by injured cells) provokes pain sensation.
	Direct and indirect actions via second messengers	PNS: dorsal root ganglion neurons	
Adenosine	Generally inhibitory	Throughout CNS	Caffeine (coffee), theophylline (tea), and theobromine (chocolate) stimulate by blocking brain adenosine receptors. May be involved in sleep-wake cycle and terminating seizures. Dilates arterioles, increasing blood flow to heart and other tissues as needed.
	Indirect action via second messengers		

Gases And Lipids			
Nitric oxide (NO)	Excitatory	CNS: brain, spinal cord	Its release potentiates stroke damage. Some types of male impotence treated by enhancing NO action [e.g., with sildenafil (Viagra)].
	Indirect action via second messengers	PNS: adrenal gland; nerves to penis	
Carbon monoxide (CO)	Excitatory	Brain and some neuromuscular and neuroglandular synapses	
	Indirect action via second messengers		
Endocannabinoids, e.g., 2-arachidonoylglycerol (illustrated), anandamide	Inhibitory	Throughout CNS	Involved in memory (as a retrograde messenger), appetite control, nausea and vomiting, neuronal development. Receptors also found on immune cells.
	Indirect action via second messengers		

and histamine. *Dopamine* and *NE* are synthesized from the amino acid tyrosine in a common pathway consisting of several steps. The same pathway is used by the epinephrine-releasing cells of the brain and the adrenal medulla. *Serotonin* is synthesized from the amino acid tryptophan. *Histamine* is synthesized from the amino acid histidine.

Biogenic amine neurotransmitters are broadly distributed in the brain, where they play a role in emotional behavior and help regulate the biological clock. Additionally, catecholamines (particularly NE) are released by some motor neurons of the autonomic nervous system. Imbalances of these neurotransmitters are associated with mental illness. For example, overactive dopamine signaling occurs in schizophrenia. Additionally, certain psychoactive drugs (LSD and mescaline) can bind to biogenic amine receptors and induce hallucinations.

Amino Acids

It is difficult to prove a neurotransmitter role when the suspect is an amino acid, because amino acids occur in all cells of the body and are important in many biochemical reactions. The amino acids for which a neurotransmitter role is certain include **gamma (γ)-aminobutyric acid (GABA)**, **glycine**, **aspartate**, and **glutamate**, but there may be others.

Peptides

The **neuropeptides**, essentially strings of amino acids, include a broad spectrum of molecules with diverse effects. For example, a neuropeptide called **substance P** is an important mediator of pain signals. By contrast, **endorphins**, which include **beta endorphin**, **dynorphin**, and **enkephalins** (en-kef'ah-linz), act as natural opiates, reducing our perception of pain under certain stressful conditions. Enkephalin activity increases dramatically in pregnant women in labor. Endorphin release is enhanced when an athlete gets a so-called second wind and is probably responsible for the "runner's high." Additionally, some researchers claim that the placebo effect is due to endorphin release. These painkilling neurotransmitters remained undiscovered until investigators began to ask why morphine and other opiates reduce anxiety and pain, and found that these drugs attach to the same receptors that bind natural opiates, producing similar but stronger effects.

Some neuropeptides, such as somatostatin and cholecystokinin, are also produced by nonneural body tissues and are widespread in the gastrointestinal tract. Such peptides are commonly referred to as **gut-brain peptides**.

Purines

Like amino acids, another ubiquitous cellular component, **adenosine triphosphate (ATP**, the universal form of energy), is now recognized as a major neurotransmitter (perhaps the most primitive one) in both the CNS and PNS. Like glutamate and acetylcholine, it produces a fast excitatory response at certain receptors. Depending on the ATP receptor type it binds to, ATP can mediate fast excitatory responses or trigger slow, second-messenger responses. Upon binding to receptors on astrocytes, it mediates Ca^{2+} influx.

In addition to the neurotransmitter action of extracellular ATP, **adenosine**, a part of ATP, also acts outside of cells on adenosine receptors. Adenosine is a potent inhibitor in the brain. Caffeine's well-known stimulatory effects result from its block of these adenosine receptors.

Gases and Lipids

Not so long ago, it would have been scientific suicide to suggest that nitric oxide and carbon monoxide—two ubiquitous molecules—might be neurotransmitters. Nonetheless, the discovery of these unlikely messengers has opened up a whole new chapter in the story of neurotransmission.

Nitric oxide (NO), a short-lived toxic gas, defies all the official descriptions of neurotransmitters. Rather than being stored in vesicles and released by exocytosis, it is synthesized on demand and diffuses out of the cells making it. Instead of attaching to surface receptors, it zooms through the plasma membrane of nearby cells to bind with a peculiar intracellular receptor—iron in *guanylyl cyclase*, the enzyme that makes the second messenger *cyclic GMP*. NO participates in a variety of processes in the brain, including the formation of new memories by increasing the strength of certain synapses. In this process, neurotransmitter binding to the postsynaptic receptors indirectly causes the activation of *nitric oxide synthase* (*NOS*), the enzyme that makes NO. The newly synthesized NO diffuses out of the postsynaptic cell back to the presynaptic terminal, where it activates guanylyl cyclase. In this way NO is thought to act as a retrograde messenger that sends a signal to increase synaptic strength. Excessive release of NO contributes to much of the brain damage seen in stroke patients (see pp. 464–465). In the myenteric plexus of the intestine, NO causes intestinal smooth muscle to relax.

NO is the first member of a class of signaling gases that pass swiftly into cells, bind briefly to metal-containing enzymes, and then vanish. **Carbon monoxide (CO)**, another airy messenger, also stimulates synthesis of cyclic GMP. NO and CO are found in different brain regions and appear to act in different pathways, but their mode of action is similar.

Just as there are natural opiate neurotransmitters in the brain, our brains make natural neurotransmitters that act at the same receptors as the active ingredient in marijuana, tetrahydrocannabinol (THC). Surprisingly, this **endocannabinoid** (en″do-kă-nă′bĭ-noid) class of neurotransmitter has only recently been discovered. We now know that their receptors, the *cannabinoid receptors*, are the most common G protein–coupled receptors in the brain. Like NO, the endocannabinoids are lipid soluble and are synthesized on demand, rather than stored and released from vesicles. Endocannabinoids are formed by clipping the cell's own plasma membrane lipids. The newly synthesized endocannabinoids diffuse freely from the postsynaptic neuron to their receptors on presynaptic terminals where they act as a retrograde messenger to decrease neurotransmitter release. Like NO, they are thought to be involved in learning and memory. We are only beginning to understand the many other processes these neurotransmitters may be involved in, which include neuronal development, control of appetite, and suppression of nausea.

Classification of Neurotransmitters by Function

In this text we can only sample the incredible diversity of functions that neurotransmitters mediate. We limit our discussion here to two broad ways of classifying neurotransmitters according to function, adding more details in subsequent chapters.

Effects: Excitatory Versus Inhibitory

We can summarize this classification scheme by saying that some neurotransmitters are excitatory (cause depolarization), some are inhibitory (cause hyperpolarization), and others exert both effects, depending on the specific receptor types with which they interact. For example, the amino acids GABA and glycine are usually inhibitory, whereas glutamate is typically excitatory (Table 11.3). On the other hand, ACh and NE each bind to at least two receptor types that cause opposite effects. For example, acetylcholine is excitatory at neuromuscular junctions in skeletal muscle and inhibitory in cardiac muscle.

Actions: Direct Versus Indirect

Neurotransmitters that bind to and open ion channels are said to act *directly*. These neurotransmitters provoke rapid responses in postsynaptic cells by promoting changes in membrane potential. ACh and the amino acid neurotransmitters are typically direct-acting neurotransmitters.

Neurotransmitters that act *indirectly* tend to promote broader, longer-lasting effects by acting through intracellular

11

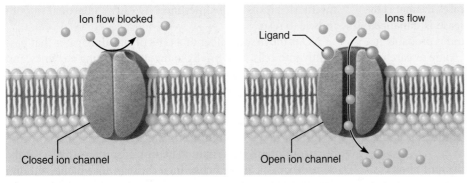

(a) Channel-linked receptors open in response to binding of ligand (ACh in this case).

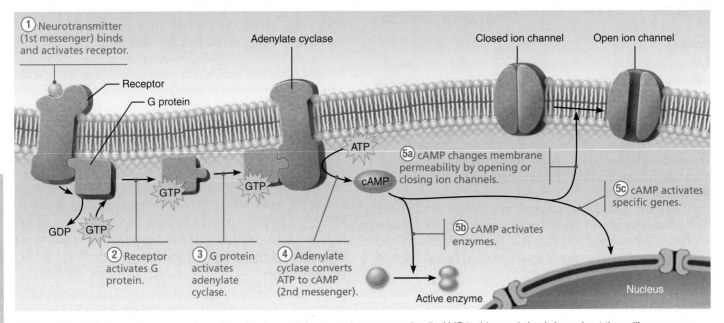

(b) G-protein linked receptors cause formation of an intracellular second messenger (cyclic AMP in this case) that brings about the cell's response.

Figure 11.20 Direct and indirect neurotransmitter receptor mechanisms (cAMP = cyclic AMP).

second-messenger molecules, typically via G protein pathways (see Figure 3.16). In this way their action is similar to that of many hormones. The biogenic amines, neuropeptides, and the dissolved gases are indirect neurotransmitters.

Neuromodulator is a term used to describe a chemical messenger released by a neuron that does not directly cause EPSPs or IPSPs but instead affects the strength of synaptic transmission. A neuromodulator may act presynaptically to influence the synthesis, release, degradation, or reuptake of neurotransmitter. Alternatively, a neuromodulator may act postsynaptically by altering the sensitivity of the postsynaptic membrane to neurotransmitter.

Receptors for neuromodulators are not necessarily found at a synapse. Instead, a neuromodulator may be released from one cell to act at many cells in its vicinity in the manner typical of paracrines (chemical messengers that act locally and are quickly destroyed). The distinction between neurotransmitters and neuromodulators is fuzzy, but chemical messengers such as NO,

adenosine, and a number of neuropeptides are often referred to as neuromodulators.

Neurotransmitter Receptors

In Chapter 3, we introduced the various receptors involved in cell signaling. Now we are ready to pick up that thread again as we examine the action of receptors that bind neurotransmitters. For the most part, neurotransmitter receptors are either channel-linked receptors, which mediate fast synaptic transmission, or G protein–linked receptors, which oversee slow synaptic responses.

Mechanism of Action of Channel-Linked Receptors

Channel-linked receptors are ligand-gated ion channels that mediate direct transmitter action. Also called *ionotropic receptors*, they are composed of several protein subunits arranged in a "rosette" around a central pore. As the ligand binds to one (or more) receptor subunits, the proteins change shape. This event opens the central channel and allows ions to pass (Figure 11.20a). As a result, the membrane potential of the target cell changes.

Channel-linked receptors are always located precisely opposite sites of neurotransmitter release, and their ion channels open instantly upon ligand binding and remain open 1 ms or less while the ligand is bound. At excitatory receptor sites (nicotinic ACh channels and receptors for glutamate, aspartate, and ATP), the channel-linked receptors are cation channels that allow small cations (Na^+, K^+, Ca^{2+}) to pass, but Na^+ entry contributes most to membrane depolarization. Channel-linked receptors that respond to GABA and glycine, and allow Cl^- to pass, mediate fast inhibition (hyperpolarization).

Mechanism of Action of G Protein–Linked Receptors

Unlike responses to neurotransmitter binding at channel-linked receptors, which are immediate, simple, and brief, the activity mediated by **G protein–linked receptors** is indirect, complex, slow (hundreds of milliseconds or more), and often prolonged—ideal as a basis for some types of learning. Receptors in this class are transmembrane protein complexes. They include muscarinic ACh receptors and those that bind the biogenic amines and neuropeptides. Because their effects tend to bring about widespread metabolic changes, G protein–linked receptors are commonly called *metabotropic receptors*.

When a neurotransmitter binds to a G protein–linked receptor, the G protein is activated. (You might like to refer back to the simpler G protein explanation in Figure 3.16 on p. 82 to orient yourself.) Activated G proteins typically work by controlling the production of second messengers such as **cyclic AMP**, **cyclic GMP**, **diacylglycerol**, or **Ca^{2+}**. These second messengers, in turn, act as go-betweens to regulate (open or close) ion channels or activate kinase enzymes that initiate a cascade of enzymatic reactions in the target cells. Some second messengers modify (activate or inactivate) other proteins, including channel proteins, by attaching phosphate groups to them. Others interact with nuclear proteins that activate genes and induce synthesis of new proteins in the target cell (Figure 11.20b).

CHECK YOUR UNDERSTANDING

19. ACh excites skeletal muscle and yet it inhibits heart muscle. How can this be?

20. Why is cyclic AMP called a second messenger?

For answers, see Appendix G.

Basic Concepts of Neural Integration

Until now, we have been concentrating on the activities of individual neurons, but neurons function in groups, and each group contributes to still broader neural functions. In this way, the organization of the nervous system is hierarchical.

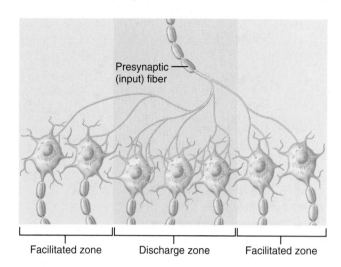

Presynaptic (input) fiber

Facilitated zone   Discharge zone   Facilitated zone

Figure 11.21 Simple neuronal pool. Center neurons have more synapses and are more likely to discharge (generate APs). Outer neurons have fewer synapses and are facilitated (brought closer to threshold).

Any time you have a large number of *anything*—people included—there must be *integration*. In other words, the parts must be fused into a smoothly operating whole. In this section, we look at the first level of **neural integration**, which is *neuronal pools* and their patterns of communicating with other parts of the nervous system. We discuss the highest levels of neural integration—how we think and remember—in Chapter 12. With this understanding of the basics and of the larger picture, in Chapter 13 we examine how sensory inputs interface with motor activity.

Organization of Neurons: Neuronal Pools

▶ Describe common patterns of neuronal organization and processing.

The billions of neurons in the CNS are organized into **neuronal pools**, functional groups of neurons that integrate incoming information received from receptors or different neuronal pools and then forward the processed information to other destinations.

In a simple type of neuronal pool, shown in Figure 11.21, one incoming presynaptic fiber branches profusely as it enters the pool and then synapses with several different neurons in the pool. When the incoming fiber is excited, it will excite some postsynaptic neurons and facilitate others. Neurons most likely to generate impulses are those closely associated with the incoming fiber, because they receive the bulk of the synaptic contacts. Those neurons are said to be in the *discharge zone* of the pool.

Neurons farther from the center are not usually excited to threshold by EPSPs induced by this incoming fiber, but they are facilitated and can easily be brought to threshold by stimuli from another source. For this reason, the periphery of the pool is the *facilitated zone*. Keep in mind, however, that our figure is a gross oversimplification. Most neuronal pools consist of

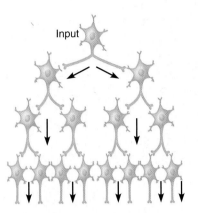

(a) Divergence in same pathway

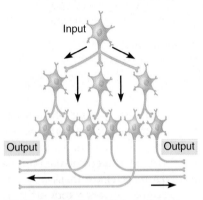

(b) Divergence to multiple pathways

11

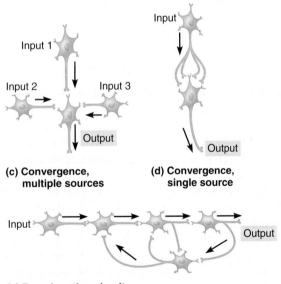

(c) Convergence, multiple sources

(d) Convergence, single source

(e) Reverberating circuit

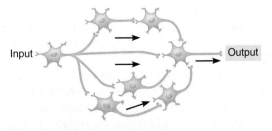

(f) Parallel after-discharge circuit

Figure 11.22 Types of circuits in neuronal pools.

thousands of neurons and include inhibitory as well as excitatory neurons.

Types of Circuits

Individual neurons in a neuronal pool both send and receive information, and synaptic contacts may cause either excitation or inhibition. The patterns of synaptic connections in neuronal pools are called **circuits**, and they determine the pool's functional capabilities. Four basic circuit patterns are shown in simplified form in **Figure 11.22**.

In **diverging circuits**, one incoming fiber triggers responses in ever-increasing numbers of neurons farther and farther along in the circuit. So, diverging circuits are often *amplifying* circuits. Divergence can occur along a single pathway or along several (Figure 11.22a and b). These circuits are common in both sensory and motor systems. For example, impulses traveling from a single neuron of the brain can activate a hundred or more motor neurons in the spinal cord and, consequently, thousands of skeletal muscle fibers.

The pattern of **converging circuits** is opposite that of diverging circuits, but they too are common in both sensory and motor pathways. In a converging circuit, the pool receives inputs from several presynaptic neurons, and the circuit has a funneling, or *concentrating*, effect. Incoming stimuli may converge from many different areas or from one area, resulting in strong stimulation or inhibition (Figure 11.22c and d). Convergence from different areas helps to explain how different types of sensory stimuli can have the same ultimate effect. For instance, seeing the smiling face of their infant, smelling the baby's freshly powdered skin, or hearing the baby gurgle can all trigger a flood of loving feelings in parents.

In **reverberating**, or **oscillating**, **circuits**, the incoming signal travels through a chain of neurons, each of which makes collateral synapses with neurons in a previous part of the pathway (Figure 11.22e). As a result of the positive feedback, the impulses *reverberate* (are sent through the circuit again and again), giving a continuous output signal until one neuron in the circuit fails to fire. Reverberating circuits are involved in control of rhythmic activities, such as the sleep-wake cycle, breathing, and certain motor activities (such as arm swinging when walking). Some researchers believe that such circuits underlie short-term memory. Depending on the specific circuit, reverberating circuits may continue to oscillate for seconds, hours, or (in the case of the circuit controlling the rhythm of breathing) a lifetime.

In **parallel after-discharge circuits**, the incoming fiber stimulates several neurons arranged in parallel arrays that eventually stimulate a common output cell (Figure 11.22f). Impulses reach the output cell at different times, creating a burst of impulses called an *after-discharge* that lasts 15 ms or more after the initial input has ended. This type of circuit has no positive feedback, and once all the neurons have fired, circuit activity ends. Parallel after-discharge circuits may be involved in complex, exacting types of mental processing.

Patterns of Neural Processing

▶ Distinguish between serial and parallel processing.

Input processing is both *serial* and *parallel*. In serial processing, the input travels along one pathway to a specific destination. In parallel processing, the input travels along several different pathways to be integrated in different CNS regions. Each mode has unique advantages in the overall scheme of neural functioning, but as an information processor, the brain derives its power from its ability to process in parallel.

Serial Processing

In **serial processing**, the whole system works in a predictable all-or-nothing manner. One neuron stimulates the next, which stimulates the next, and so on, eventually causing a specific, anticipated response. The most clear-cut examples of serial processing are spinal reflexes, but straight-through sensory pathways from receptors to the brain are also examples. Because reflexes are the functional units of the nervous system, it is important that you understand them early on.

Reflexes are rapid, automatic responses to stimuli, in which a particular stimulus always causes the same response. Reflex activity, which produces the simplest of behaviors, is stereotyped and dependable. For example, jerking away your hand after touching a hot object is the norm, and an object approaching the eye triggers a blink. Reflexes occur over neural pathways called **reflex arcs** that have five essential components—receptor, sensory neuron, CNS integration center, motor neuron, and effector (Figure 11.23).

Parallel Processing

In **parallel processing**, inputs are segregated into many pathways, and information delivered by each pathway is dealt with simultaneously by different parts of the neural circuitry. For example, smelling a pickle (the input) may cause you to remember picking cucumbers on a farm; or it may remind you that you don't like pickles or that you must buy some at the market; or perhaps it will call to mind *all* these thoughts. For each person, parallel processing triggers some pathways that are unique. The same stimulus—pickle smell, in our example—promotes many responses beyond simple awareness of the smell. Parallel processing is not repetitious because the circuits do different things with the information, and each pathway or "channel" is decoded in relation to all the others to produce a total picture.

Think, for example, about what happens when you step on something sharp while walking barefoot. The serially processed withdrawal reflex causes instantaneous removal of your injured foot from the sharp object (painful stimulus). At the same time, pain and pressure impulses are speeding up to the brain along parallel pathways that allow you to decide whether to simply rub the hurt spot to soothe it or to seek first aid.

Parallel processing is extremely important for higher-level mental functioning—for putting the parts together to understand the whole. For example, you can recognize a dollar bill in a split second, a task that takes a serial-based computer a fairly long time. Your recognition is quick because you use parallel processing, which allows a single neuron to send information along several pathways instead of just one, so a large amount of information is processed much more quickly.

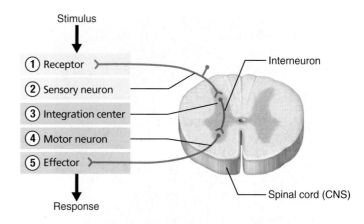

Figure 11.23 A simple reflex arc. Receptors detect changes in the internal or external environment. Effectors are muscles or glands.

CHECK YOUR UNDERSTANDING

21. What types of neural circuits would give a prolonged output after a single input?

22. What pattern of neural processing occurs when we blink as an object comes toward the eye? What is this response called?

23. What pattern of neural processing occurs when we smell freshly baked apple pie and remember Thanksgiving at our grandparents' house, the odor of freshly cooked turkey, and other such memories?

For answers, see Appendix G.

11

Developmental Aspects of Neurons

▶ Describe how neurons develop and form synapses.

We cover the nervous system in several chapters, so we limit our attention here to the development of neurons, beginning with the questions, How do nerve cells originate? and How do they mature?

The nervous system originates from a dorsal *neural tube* and the *neural crest*, formed from surface ectoderm (see Figure 12.1 ③, ④, p. 430). The neural tube, whose walls begin as a layer of *neuroepithelial* cells, becomes the CNS. The neuroepithelial cells then begin a three-phase process of differentiation, which occurs largely in the second month of development. (1) They *proliferate* to produce the appropriate number of cells needed for nervous system development. (2) The potential neurons, **neuroblasts**, become amitotic and *migrate* externally into their characteristic positions. (3) The neuroblasts sprout axons to *connect with* their functional targets and in so doing become neurons.

How does a neuroblast's growing axon "know" where to go—and once it gets there, where to make the proper connection? The growth of an axon toward an appropriate target requires multiple steps and is guided by multiple signals. The growing tip of an axon, called a **growth cone**, is a prickly, fanlike structure that gives an axon the ability to interact with its

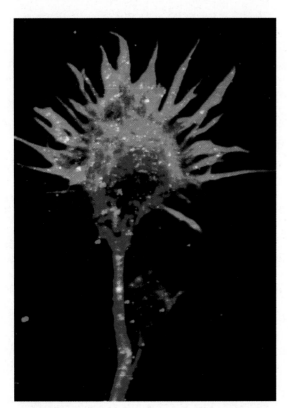

Figure 11.24 A neuronal growth cone. Fluorescent stains show the locations of cannabinoid receptors (green), tubulin (blue), and actin (pink) in this photomicrograph (1400×).

environment **(Figure 11.24)**. Extracellular and cell surface adhesion proteins such as laminin, integrin, and *nerve cell adhesion molecule* (*N-CAM*) provide anchor points for the growth cone, saying, "It's okay to grow here." *Neurotropins* are chemicals that signal to the growth cone "come this way" (netrin) or "go away" (ephrin, slit) or "stop here" (semaphorin). Throughout this growth and development, neurotrophic factors such as *nerve growth factor* (*NGF*) must be present to keep the neuroblast alive. Failure of any of these guiding signals results in catastrophic developmental problems. For example, lack of N-CAM action causes developing neural tissue to fall into a tangled, spaghetti-like mass and hopelessly impairs neural function.

The growth cone gropes along like an amoeba, with oozing processes called *filopodia* which detect the guiding signals in the surrounding environment. Receptors for these signals generate various second messengers that cause the filopodia to move by rearranging their actin protein cores. Once the axon has reached its target area, it must select the right site on the target cell to form a synapse. Special cell adhesion molecules couple the presynaptic and postsynaptic membranes together and generate intracellular signals that recruit vesicles containing preformed synaptic components. This results in the rapid formation of a synapse. In the brain and spinal cord, astrocytes seem to provide both physical support and the cholesterol essential for constructing synapses. Both dendrites and astrocytes are active partners in the process of synapse formation. In the presence of thrombospondin released by astrocytes, dendrites actually reach out and grasp migrating axons, and synapses begin sprouting.

Neurons that fail to make appropriate or functional synaptic contacts act as if they have been deprived of some essential nutrient and die. Besides cell death resulting from unsuccessful synapse formation, *apoptosis* (programmed cell death) also appears to be a normal part of the developmental process. Of the neurons formed during the embryonic period, perhaps two-thirds die before we are born. Those that remain constitute most of our neural endowment for life. The generally amitotic nature of neurons is important because their activity depends on the synapses they've formed, and if neurons were to divide, their connections might be hopelessly disrupted. This aside, there *do* appear to be some specific neuronal populations where stem cells are found and new neurons can be formed—notably olfactory neurons and some cells of the hippocampus, a brain region involved in learning and memory.

CHECK YOUR UNDERSTANDING

24. What is the name of the growing tip of an axon that "sniffs out" where to go during development? What is the general name for the chemicals that tell it where to go?

For answers, see Appendix G.

In this chapter, we have examined how the amazingly complex neurons, via electrical and chemical signals, serve the body in a variety of ways: Some serve as "lookouts," others process information for immediate use or for future reference, and still others stimulate the body's muscles and glands into activity. With this background, we are ready to study the most sophisticated mass of neural tissue in the entire body—the brain (and its continuation, the spinal cord), the focus of Chapter 12.

RELATED CLINICAL TERMS

Neuroblastoma (nu″ro-blas-to′mah; *oma* = tumor) A malignant tumor in children; arises from cells that retain a neuroblast-like structure. These tumors sometimes arise in the brain, but most occur in the peripheral nervous system.

Neurologist (nu-rol′o-jist) A medical specialist in the study of the nervous system, its functions, and its disorders.

Neuropathy (nu-rop′ah-the) Any disease of nervous tissue, but particularly degenerative disease of nerves.

Neuropharmacology (nu″ro-far″mah-kol′o-je) Scientific study of the effects of drugs on the nervous system.

Neurotoxin Substance that is poisonous or destructive to nervous tissue, e.g., botulinum and tetanus toxins.

Rabies (*rabies* = madness) A viral infection of the nervous system transmitted by the bite of an infected mammal (such as a dog, bat, or skunk). After entry, the virus travels via axonal transport in peripheral nerve axons to the CNS, where it causes brain inflammation, delirium, and death. A vaccine- and antibody-based treatment is effective if given before symptoms appear; rabies in humans is very rare in the United States.

Shingles (herpes zoster) A viral infection of sensory neurons serving the skin. Characterized by scaly, painful blisters usually confined to a narrow strip of skin, often on one side of the body trunk. Caused by the varicella-zoster virus, which causes chicken pox (generally during childhood); during this initial infection the virus is transported from the skin lesions to the sensory cell bodies in the sensory ganglia. Typically, the virus is held in check by the immune system and remains dormant until the immune system is weakened, often by stress. Then viral particles multiply and travel back to the skin, producing the characteristic rash. Attacks last several weeks, alternating between periods of healing and relapse. Seen mostly in those over 50 years old.

CHAPTER SUMMARY

Media study tools that could provide you additional help in reviewing specific key topics of Chapter 11 are referenced below.

iP = *Interactive Physiology*

Functions and Divisions of the Nervous System   (pp. 386–388)

1. The nervous system bears a major responsibility for maintaining body homeostasis. Its chief functions are to monitor, integrate, and respond to information in the environment.
2. The nervous system is divided anatomically into the central nervous system (brain and spinal cord) and the peripheral nervous system (mainly cranial and spinal nerves).
3. The major functional divisions of the PNS are the sensory (afferent) division, which conveys impulses to the CNS, and the motor (efferent) division, which conveys impulses from the CNS.
4. The efferent division includes the somatic (voluntary) system, which serves skeletal muscles, and the autonomic (involuntary) system, which innervates smooth and cardiac muscle and glands.

Histology of Nervous Tissue   (pp. 388–395)

Neuroglia   (pp. 388–389)

1. Neuroglia (supporting cells) segregate and insulate neurons and assist neurons in various other ways.
2. CNS neuroglia include astrocytes, microglia, ependymal cells, and oligodendrocytes. Schwann cells and satellite cells are neuroglia found in the PNS.

Neurons   (pp. 389–395)

3. Neurons have a cell body and cytoplasmic processes called axons and dendrites.
4. A bundle of nerve fibers is called a tract in the CNS and a nerve in the PNS. A collection of cell bodies is called a nucleus in the CNS and a ganglion in the PNS.
5. The cell body is the biosynthetic (and receptive) center of the neuron. Except for those found in ganglia, cell bodies are found in the CNS.
6. Most neurons have many dendrites, receptive processes that conduct signals from other neurons toward the nerve cell body. With few exceptions, all neurons have one axon, which generates and conducts nerve impulses away from the nerve cell body. Terminal endings of axons release neurotransmitter.
7. Bidirectional transport along axons uses ATP-dependent motor proteins "walking" along microtubule tracks. It moves vesicles, mitochondria, and cytosolic proteins toward the axon terminals and conducts substances destined for degradation back to the cell body.
8. Large nerve fibers (axons) are myelinated. The myelin sheath is formed in the PNS by Schwann cells and in the CNS by oligo-

dendrocytes. The sheath has gaps called nodes of Ranvier. Unmyelinated fibers are surrounded by supporting cells, but the membrane-wrapping process does not occur.
9. Anatomically, neurons are classified according to the number of processes issuing from the cell body as multipolar, bipolar, or unipolar.
10. Functionally, neurons are classified according to the direction of nerve impulse conduction. Sensory neurons conduct impulses toward the CNS, motor neurons conduct away from the CNS, and interneurons (association neurons) lie between sensory and motor neurons in the neural pathways.

iP Nervous System I; Topic: Anatomy Review, pp. 1–12.

Membrane Potentials   (pp. 395–406)

Basic Principles of Electricity   (p. 395)

1. The measure of the potential energy of separated electrical charges is called voltage (V) or potential. Current (I) is the flow of electrical charge from one point to another. Resistance (R) is hindrance to current flow. The relationship among these is given by Ohm's law: $I = V/R$.
2. In the body, electrical charges are provided by ions; cellular plasma membranes provide resistance to ion flow. The membranes contain leakage channels (nongated, always open) and gated channels.

iP Nervous System I; Topic: Ion Channels, pp. 1–10.

The Resting Membrane Potential   (pp. 396–398)

3. A resting neuron exhibits a resting membrane potential, which is −70 mV (inside negative). It is due both to differences in sodium and potassium ion concentrations inside and outside the cell and to differences in permeability of the membrane to these ions.
4. The ionic concentration differences result from the operation of the sodium-potassium pump, which ejects $3Na^+$ from the cell for each $2K^+$ transported in.

iP Nervous System I; Topic: The Membrane Potential, pp. 1–16.

Membrane Potentials That Act as Signals   (pp. 398–406)

5. Depolarization is a reduction in membrane potential (inside becomes less negative); hyperpolarization is an increase in membrane potential (inside becomes more negative).
6. Graded potentials are small, brief, local changes in membrane potential that act as short-distance signals. The current produced dissipates with distance.
7. An action potential (AP), or nerve impulse, is a large, but brief, depolarization signal (and polarity reversal) that underlies long-distance neural communication. It is an all-or-none phenomenon.

11

8. An AP has three underlying phases of membrane permeability. (1) Increase in sodium permeability: Local depolarization opens voltage-gated Na^+ channels; at threshold, depolarization becomes self-generating (driven by Na^+ influx). The membrane potential is reversed to approximately $+30$ mV (inside positive). (2) Decrease in sodium permeability. (3) Increase in potassium permeability. Repolarization occurs during phases 2 and 3.

9. In nerve impulse propagation, each AP provides the depolarizing stimulus for triggering an AP in the next membrane patch. Regions that have just generated APs are refractory; for this reason, the nerve impulse is propagated in one direction only.

10. If threshold is reached, an AP is generated; if not, depolarization remains local.

11. APs are independent of stimulus strength: Strong stimuli cause APs to be generated more frequently but not with greater amplitude.

12. During the absolute refractory period, a neuron cannot respond to another stimulus because it is already generating an AP. During the relative refractory period, the neuron's threshold is elevated because repolarization is ongoing.

13. In unmyelinated fibers, APs are produced in a wave all along the axon, that is, by continuous conduction. In myelinated fibers, APs are generated only at nodes of Ranvier and are propagated more rapidly by saltatory conduction.

iP Nervous System I; Topic: The Action Potential, pp. 1–18.

The Synapse   (pp. 406–413)

1. A synapse is a functional junction between neurons. The information-transmitting neuron is the presynaptic neuron; the information-receiving neuron is the postsynaptic neuron.

Electrical Synapses   (p. 406)

2. Electrical synapses allow ions to flow directly from one neuron to another; the cells are electrically coupled.

Chemical Synapses   (pp. 407–408)

3. Chemical synapses are sites of neurotransmitter release and binding. When the impulse reaches the presynaptic axon terminals, voltage-gated Ca^{2+} channels open, and Ca^{2+} enters the cell and mediates neurotransmitter release. Neurotransmitters diffuse across the synaptic cleft and attach to postsynaptic membrane receptors, opening ion channels. After binding, the neurotransmitters are removed from the synapse by enzymatic breakdown or by reuptake into the presynaptic terminal or astrocytes.

iP Nervous System II; Topics: Anatomy Review, pp. 1–9, Ion Channels, pp. 1–8, Synaptic Transmission, pp. 1–7.

Postsynaptic Potentials and Synaptic Integration   (pp. 408–413)

4. Binding of neurotransmitter at excitatory chemical synapses results in local graded potentials called EPSPs, caused by the opening of channels that allow simultaneous passage of Na^+ and K^+.

5. Neurotransmitter binding at inhibitory chemical synapses results in hyperpolarizations called IPSPs, caused by the opening of K^+ or Cl^- channels. IPSPs drive the membrane potential farther from threshold.

6. EPSPs and IPSPs summate temporally and spatially. The membrane of the axon hillock acts as a neuronal integrator.

7. Synaptic potentiation, in which the postsynaptic neuron's response is enhanced, is produced by intense repeated stimulation. Ionic calcium appears to mediate such effects, which may be the basis of learning.

8. Presynaptic inhibition is mediated by axoaxonic synapses that reduce the amount of neurotransmitter released by the inhibited neuron.

iP Nervous System II; Topic: Synaptic Potentials and Cellular Integration, pp. 1–10.

Neurotransmitters and Their Receptors   (pp. 413–421)

Classification of Neurotransmitters by Chemical Structure   (pp. 414–419)

1. The major classes of neurotransmitters based on chemical structure are acetylcholine, biogenic amines, amino acids, peptides, purines, dissolved gases, and lipids.

Classification of Neurotransmitters by Function   (pp. 419–420)

2. Functionally, neurotransmitters are classified as (1) inhibitory or excitatory (or both) and (2) direct or indirect action. Direct-acting neurotransmitters bind to and open ion channels. Indirect-acting neurotransmitters act through second messengers. Neuromodulators also act indirectly presynaptically or postsynaptically to change synaptic strength.

Neurotransmitter Receptors   (pp. 420–421)

3. Neurotransmitter receptors are either channel-linked receptors that open ion channels, leading to fast changes in membrane potential, or G protein–linked receptors that oversee slow synaptic responses mediated by G proteins and intracellular second messengers. Second messengers most often activate kinases, which in turn act on ion channels or activate other proteins.

iP Nervous System II; Topic: Synaptic Transmission, pp. 6–15.

Basic Concepts of Neural Integration   (pp. 421–423)

Organization of Neurons: Neuronal Pools   (pp. 421–422)

1. CNS neurons are organized into several types of neuronal pools, each with distinguishing patterns of synaptic connections called circuits.

Types of Circuits   (p. 422)

2. The four basic circuit types are diverging, converging, reverberating, and parallel after-discharge.

Patterns of Neural Processing   (pp. 422–423)

3. In serial processing, one neuron stimulates the next in sequence, producing specific, predictable responses, as in spinal reflexes. A reflex is a rapid, involuntary motor response to a stimulus.

4. Reflexes are mediated over neural pathways called reflex arcs. The minimum number of elements in a reflex arc is five: receptor, sensory neuron, integration center, motor neuron, and effector.

5. In parallel processing, which underlies complex mental functions, impulses are sent along several pathways to different integration centers.

Developmental Aspects of Neurons   (pp. 423–424)

1. Neuron development involves proliferation, migration, and the formation of interconnections. The formation of interconnections involves axons finding their targets and forming synapses, and the synthesis of specific neurotransmitters.

2. Axon outgrowth and synapse formation are guided by other neurons, glial cells, and chemicals (such as N-CAM and nerve growth factor). Neurons that do not make appropriate synapses die, and approximately two-thirds of neurons formed in the embryo undergo programmed cell death before birth.

11

REVIEW QUESTIONS

Multiple Choice/Matching

(Some questions have more than one correct answer. Select the best answer or answers from the choices given.)

1. Which of the following structures is not part of the central nervous system? (**a**) the brain, (**b**) a nerve, (**c**) the spinal cord, (**d**) a tract.

2. Match the names of the supporting cells found in column B with the appropriate descriptions in column A.

Column A	Column B
____ (**1**) myelinates nerve fibers in the CNS	(**a**) astrocyte
____ (**2**) lines brain cavities	(**b**) ependymal cell
____ (**3**) myelinates nerve fibers in the PNS	(**c**) microglia
____ (**4**) CNS phagocytes	(**d**) oligodendrocyte
	(**e**) satellite cell
____ (**5**) helps regulate the ionic composition of CNS extracellular fluid	(**f**) Schwann cell

3. What type of current flows through the axolemma during the steep phase of repolarization? (**a**) chiefly a sodium current, (**b**) chiefly a potassium current, (**c**) sodium and potassium currents of approximately the same magnitude.

4. Assume that an EPSP is being generated on the dendritic membrane. Which will occur? (**a**) specific Na^+ channels will open, (**b**) specific K^+ channels will open, (**c**) a single type of channel will open, permitting simultaneous flow of Na^+ and K^+, (**d**) Na^+ channels will open first and then close as K^+ channels open.

5. The velocity of nerve impulse conduction is greatest in (**a**) heavily myelinated, large-diameter fibers, (**b**) myelinated, small-diameter fibers, (**c**) unmyelinated, small-diameter fibers, (**d**) unmyelinated, large-diameter fibers.

6. Chemical synapses are characterized by all of the following except (**a**) the release of neurotransmitter by the presynaptic membranes, (**b**) postsynaptic membranes bearing receptors that bind neurotransmitter, (**c**) ions flowing through protein channels from the presynaptic to the postsynaptic neuron, (**d**) a fluid-filled gap separating the neurons.

7. Biogenic amine neurotransmitters include all but (**a**) norepinephrine, (**b**) acetylcholine, (**c**) dopamine, (**d**) serotonin.

8. The neuropeptides that act as natural opiates are (**a**) substance P, (**b**) somatostatin, (**c**) cholecystokinin, (**d**) enkephalins.

9. Inhibition of acetylcholinesterase by poisoning blocks neurotransmission at the neuromuscular junction because (**a**) ACh is no longer released by the presynaptic terminal, (**b**) ACh synthesis in the presynaptic terminal is blocked, (**c**) ACh is not degraded, hence prolonged depolarization is enforced on the postsynaptic cell, (**d**) ACh is blocked from attaching to the postsynaptic ACh receptors.

10. The anatomical region of a multipolar neuron that has the lowest threshold for generating an AP is the (**a**) soma, (**b**) dendrites, (**c**) axon hillock, (**d**) distal axon.

11. An IPSP is inhibitory because (**a**) it hyperpolarizes the postsynaptic membrane, (**b**) it reduces the amount of neurotransmitter released by the presynaptic terminal, (**c**) it prevents calcium ion entry into the presynaptic terminal, (**d**) it changes the threshold of the neuron.

12. Identify the neuronal circuits described by choosing the correct response from the key.

Key: (**a**) converging   (**c**) parallel after-discharge
        (**b**) diverging   (**d**) reverberating

____ (**1**) Impulses continue around and around the circuit until one neuron stops firing.
____ (**2**) One or a few inputs ultimately influence large numbers of neurons.
____ (**3**) Many neurons influence a few neurons.
____ (**4**) May be involved in exacting types of mental activity.

Short Answer Essay Questions

13. Explain both the anatomical and functional divisions of the nervous system. Include the subdivisions of each.

14. (**a**) Describe the composition and function of the cell body. (**b**) How are axons and dendrites alike? In what ways (structurally and functionally) do they differ?

15. (**a**) What is myelin? (**b**) How does the myelination process differ in the CNS and PNS?

16. (**a**) Contrast unipolar, bipolar, and multipolar neurons structurally. (**b**) Indicate where each is most likely to be found.

17. What is the polarized membrane state? How is it maintained? (Note the relative roles of both passive and active mechanisms.)

18. Describe the events that must occur to generate an AP. Relate the sequence of changes in permeability to changes in the ion channels, and explain why the AP is an all-or-none phenomenon.

19. Since all APs generated by a given nerve fiber have the same magnitude, how does the CNS "know" whether a stimulus is strong or weak?

20. (**a**) Explain the difference between an EPSP and an IPSP. (**b**) What specifically determines whether an EPSP or IPSP will be generated at the postsynaptic membrane?

21. Since at any moment a neuron is likely to have thousands of neurons releasing neurotransmitters at its surface, how is neuronal activity (to fire or not to fire) determined?

22. The effects of neurotransmitter binding are very brief. Explain.

23. During a neurobiology lecture, a professor repeatedly refers to group A and group B fibers, absolute refractory period, and nodes of Ranvier. Define these terms.

24. Distinguish between serial and parallel processing.

25. Briefly describe the three stages of neuron development.

26. What factors appear to guide the outgrowth of an axon and its ability to make the "correct" synaptic contacts?

Critical Thinking and Clinical Application Questions

1. Mr. Miller is hospitalized for cardiac problems. Somehow, medical orders are mixed up and Mr. Miller is infused with a K^+-enhanced intravenous solution meant for another patient who is taking potassium-wasting diuretics (i.e., drugs that cause excessive loss of potassium from the body in urine). Mr. Miller's potassium levels are normal before the IV is administered. What do you think will happen to Mr. Miller's resting membrane potentials? To his neurons' ability to generate APs?

2. Local anesthetics block voltage-gated Na^+ channels. General anesthetics are thought to activate chemically gated Cl^- channels,

thereby rendering the nervous system quiescent while surgery is performed. What specific process do anesthetics impair, and how does this interfere with nerve impulse transmission?

3. When admitted to the emergency room, John was holding his right hand, which had a deep puncture hole in its palm. He explained that he had fallen on a nail while exploring a barn. John was given an antitetanus shot to prevent neural complications. Tetanus bacteria fester in deep, dark wounds, but how do their toxins travel in neural tissue?

4. Rochelle developed multiple sclerosis when she was 27. After eight years she had lost a good portion of her ability to control her skeletal muscles. How did this happen?

5. In the Netherlands a young man named Jan was admitted to the emergency room. He and his friends had been to a rave. His friends say he started twitching and having muscle spasms which progressed until he was "stiff as a board." On examination, staff found a marked increase in muscle tone and hyperreflexia involving facial and limb muscles. In his pocket, he had unmarked dark yellow tablets with dark flecks. Analysis of the tablets showed them to contain a mixture of ecstasy and strychnine. Ecstasy would not cause this clinical picture, but strychnine, which blocks glycine receptors, could. Explain how.

Access everything you need to practice, review, and self-assess for both your A&P lecture and lab courses at **myA&P** (www.myaandp.com). There, you'll find powerful online resources, including chapter quizzes and tests, games, A&P Flix animations with quizzes, *Interactive Physiology*® with quizzes, MP3 Tutor Sessions, Practice Anatomy Lab™, and more to help you get a better grade in your course.

11

12

The Brain (pp. 430–453)

Embryonic Development (pp. 430–431)

Regions and Organization (p. 431)

Ventricles (pp. 431–433)

Cerebral Hemispheres (pp. 433–441)

Diencephalon (pp. 441–445)

Brain Stem (pp. 445–450)

Cerebellum (pp. 450–451)

Functional Brain Systems (pp. 451–453)

Higher Mental Functions (pp. 453–460)

Brain Wave Patterns and the EEG (pp. 453–455)

Consciousness (p. 455)

Sleep and Sleep-Wake Cycles (pp. 455–457)

Language (p. 457)

Memory (pp. 457–460)

Protection of the Brain (pp. 460–466)

Meninges (pp. 461–463)

Cerebrospinal Fluid (p. 463)

Blood-Brain Barrier (pp. 463–464)

Homeostatic Imbalances of the Brain (pp. 464–466)

The Spinal Cord (pp. 466–477)

Embryonic Development (p. 466)

Gross Anatomy and Protection (pp. 466–468)

Cross-Sectional Anatomy (pp. 468–476)

Spinal Cord Trauma and Disorders (pp. 476–477)

Diagnostic Procedures for Assessing CNS Dysfunction (p. 477)

Developmental Aspects of the Central Nervous System (pp. 477–478)

The Central Nervous System

Historically, the **central nervous system (CNS)**—brain and spinal cord—has been compared to the central switchboard of a telephone system that interconnects and directs a dizzying number of incoming and outgoing calls. Nowadays, many people compare it to a supercomputer. These analogies may explain some workings of the spinal cord, but neither does justice to the fantastic complexity of the human brain. Whether we view the brain as an evolved biological organ, an impressive computer, or simply a miracle, it is one of the most amazing things known.

During the course of animal evolution, **cephalization** (sĕ″fah-lĭ-za′shun) has occurred. That is, there has been an elaboration of the *rostral* ("toward the snout"), or anterior, portion of the CNS, along with an increase in the number of neurons in the head. This phenomenon reaches its highest level in the human brain.

In this chapter, we examine the structure of the CNS and the functions associated with its various regions. We also touch on complex integrative functions, such as sleep-wake cycles and memory.

The Brain

The unimpressive appearance of the human **brain** gives few hints of its remarkable abilities. It is about two good fistfuls of quivering pinkish gray tissue, wrinkled like a walnut, with a consistency somewhat like cold oatmeal. The average adult man's brain has a mass of about 1600 g (3.5 lb); that of a woman averages 1450 g (3.2 lb). In terms of brain mass per body mass, however, males and females have equivalent brain sizes.

Embryonic Development

▶ Describe the process of brain development.

▶ Name the major regions of the adult brain.

▶ Name and locate the ventricles of the brain.

We begin our study of the brain with brain embryology, as the terminology used for the structural divisions of the adult brain is easier to follow when you understand brain development.

The earliest phase of brain development is shown in **Figure 12.1**. Starting in the three-week-old embryo, the *ectoderm* (cell layer at the dorsal surface) thickens along the dorsal midline axis of the embryo to form the **neural plate**. The neural plate then invaginates, forming a groove flanked by **neural folds**. As this **neural groove** deepens, the superior edges of the neural folds fuse, forming the **neural tube**, which soon detaches from the surface ectoderm and sinks to a deeper position.

The neural tube, formed by the fourth week of pregnancy, differentiates rapidly into the CNS. The brain forms rostrally (anteriorly), and the spinal cord develops from the *caudal* ("toward the tail") or posterior portion of the neural tube. Small groups of neural fold cells migrate laterally from between the surface ectoderm and the neural tube, forming the **neural crest** (Figure 12.1, ③). Neural crest cells give rise (among other things) to some neurons destined to reside in ganglia.

As soon as the neural tube forms, its anterior end begins to expand and constrictions appear that mark off the three **primary brain vesicles** (**Figure 12.2b**): the **prosencephalon** (pros″en-sef′ah-lon), or **forebrain**; the **mesencephalon** (mes″en-sef′ah-lon), or **midbrain**; and the **rhombencephalon** (romb″en-sef′ah-lon), or **hindbrain**. (Note that *encephalo* means "brain.") The remainder of the neural tube becomes the spinal cord, which we will discuss later in the chapter.

In week 5, the primary vesicles give rise to the **secondary brain vesicles** (Figure 12.2c). The forebrain divides into the **telencephalon** ("endbrain") and **diencephalon** ("interbrain"), and the hindbrain constricts, forming the **metencephalon**

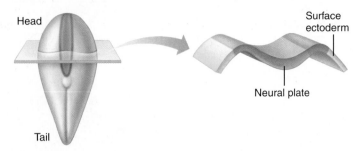

① The neural plate forms from surface ectoderm.

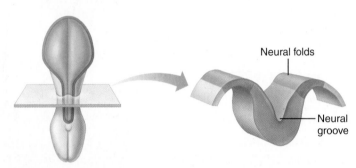

② The neural plate invaginates, forming the neural groove, flanked by neural folds.

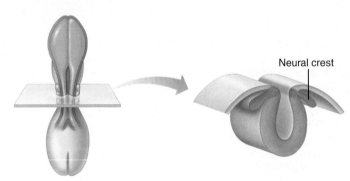

③ Neural fold cells migrate to form the neural crest, which will form much of the PNS and many other structures.

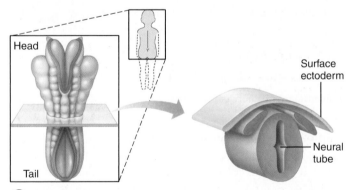

④ The neural groove becomes the neural tube, which will form CNS structures.

Figure 12.1 Development of the neural tube from embryonic ectoderm. Left: dorsal surface views of the embryo; right: transverse sections at days 17, 19, 20, and 22.

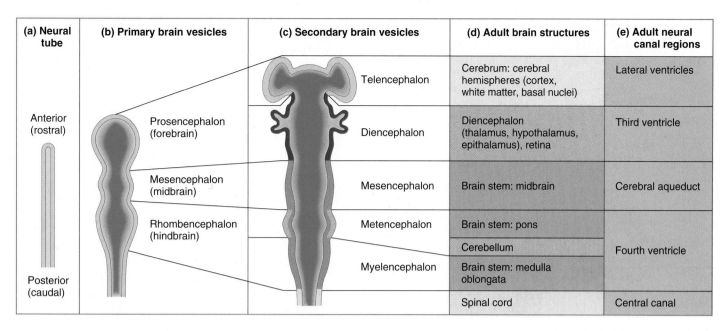

(a) Neural tube	(b) Primary brain vesicles	(c) Secondary brain vesicles	(d) Adult brain structures	(e) Adult neural canal regions
Anterior (rostral)	Prosencephalon (forebrain)	Telencephalon	Cerebrum: cerebral hemispheres (cortex, white matter, basal nuclei)	Lateral ventricles
		Diencephalon	Diencephalon (thalamus, hypothalamus, epithalamus), retina	Third ventricle
	Mesencephalon (midbrain)	Mesencephalon	Brain stem: midbrain	Cerebral aqueduct
	Rhombencephalon (hindbrain)	Metencephalon	Brain stem: pons	Fourth ventricle
			Cerebellum	
		Myelencephalon	Brain stem: medulla oblongata	
Posterior (caudal)			Spinal cord	Central canal

Figure 12.2 Embryonic development of the human brain. (a) Formed by week 4, the neural tube quickly subdivides into **(b)** the primary brain vesicles, which subsequently form **(c)** the secondary brain vesicles by week 5. These five vesicles differentiate into **(d)** the adult brain structures. **(e)** The adult structures derived from the neural canal.

("afterbrain") and **myelencephalon** ("spinal brain"). The midbrain remains undivided.

Each of the five secondary vesicles then develops rapidly to produce the major structures of the adult brain (Figure 12.2d). The greatest change occurs in the telencephalon, which sprouts two lateral swellings that look like Mickey Mouse's ears. These become the two *cerebral hemispheres*, referred to collectively as the **cerebrum** (ser′ĕ-brum). The diencephalon part of the forebrain specializes to form the *hypothalamus* (hi″po-thal′ah-mus), *thalamus*, *epithalamus*, and *retina* of the eye. Less dramatic changes occur in the mesencephalon, metencephalon, and myelencephalon as these regions are transformed into the *midbrain*, the *pons* and *cerebellum*, and the *medulla oblongata*, respectively. All these midbrain and hindbrain structures, except the cerebellum, form the **brain stem**. The central cavity of the neural tube remains continuous and enlarges in four areas to form the fluid-filled *ventricles* (*ventr* = little belly) of the brain (Figure 12.2e). We will describe the ventricles shortly.

Because the brain grows more rapidly than the membranous skull that contains it, two major flexures develop—the *midbrain* and *cervical flexures*—which move the forebrain toward the brain stem (Figure 12.3a). A second consequence of restricted space is that the cerebral hemispheres are forced to take a horseshoe-shaped course and grow posteriorly and laterally (indicated by black arrows in Figure 12.3b and c). As a result, they grow back over and almost completely envelop the diencephalon and midbrain. By week 26, the continued growth of the cerebral hemispheres causes their surfaces to crease and fold (Figure 12.3c and d), producing *convolutions* and increasing their surface area, which allows more neurons to occupy the limited space.

Regions and Organization

Some textbooks discuss brain anatomy in terms of the *embryonic scheme* (see Figure 12.2c), but in this text, we will consider the brain in terms of the medical scheme and the adult brain regions shown in Figure 12.3d: (1) cerebral hemispheres, (2) diencephalon, (3) brain stem (midbrain, pons, and medulla), and (4) cerebellum.

The basic pattern of the CNS consists of a central cavity surrounded by gray matter (mostly neuron cell bodies), external to which is white matter (myelinated fiber tracts). The brain exhibits this basic design but has additional regions of gray matter not present in the spinal cord (Figure 12.4). Both the cerebral hemispheres and the cerebellum have an outer layer or "bark" of gray matter called a *cortex*. This pattern changes with descent through the brain stem—the cortex disappears, but scattered gray matter nuclei are seen within the white matter. At the caudal end of the brain stem, the basic pattern is evident.

Ventricles

As noted earlier, the brain **ventricles** arise from expansions of the lumen (cavity) of the embryonic neural tube. They are continuous with one another and with the central canal of the spinal cord (Figure 12.5). The hollow ventricular chambers are filled with cerebrospinal fluid and lined by *ependymal cells*, a type of neuroglia (see Figure 11.3c on p. 388).

The paired **lateral ventricles**, one deep within each cerebral hemisphere, are large C-shaped chambers that reflect the pattern of cerebral growth. Anteriorly, the lateral ventricles lie close together, separated only by a thin median membrane called the

12

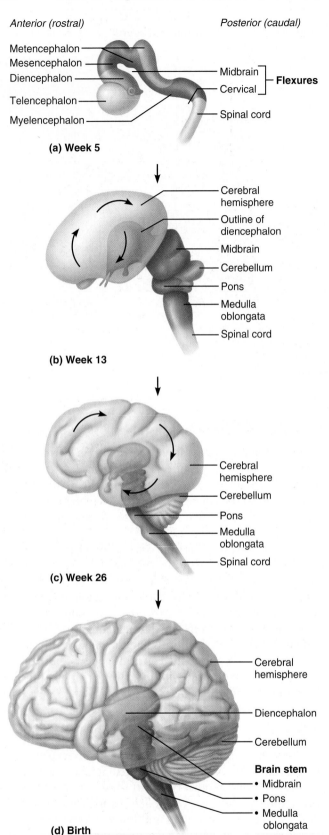

(a) Week 5

Anterior (rostral)

Posterior (caudal)

- Metencephalon
- Mesencephalon
- Diencephalon
- Telencephalon
- Myelencephalon

- Midbrain
- Cervical — **Flexures**
- Spinal cord

(b) Week 13

- Cerebral hemisphere
- Outline of diencephalon
- Midbrain
- Cerebellum
- Pons
- Medulla oblongata
- Spinal cord

(c) Week 26

- Cerebral hemisphere
- Cerebellum
- Pons
- Medulla oblongata
- Spinal cord

(d) Birth

- Cerebral hemisphere
- Diencephalon
- Cerebellum
- **Brain stem**
  - Midbrain
  - Pons
  - Medulla oblongata

Figure 12.3 Effect of space restriction on brain development. **(a)** Formation of two major flexures by week 5 of development causes the telencephalon and diencephalon to angle toward the brain stem. Development of the cerebral hemispheres at **(b)** 13 weeks, **(c)** 26 weeks, and **(d)** birth. Initially, the cerebral surface is smooth. The folding begins in month 6, and convolutions become more obvious as development continues. The posterolateral growth of the cerebral hemispheres ultimately encloses the diencephalon and superior aspect of the brain stem (seen through the cerebral hemispheres in this see-through view).

septum pellucidum (pĕ-lu′sid-um; "transparent wall"). (See Figure 12.12, p. 443.)

Each lateral ventricle communicates with the narrow **third ventricle** in the diencephalon via a channel called an **interventricular foramen** (*foramen of Monro*).

The third ventricle is continuous with the **fourth ventricle** via the canal-like **cerebral aqueduct** that runs through the midbrain. The fourth ventricle lies in the hindbrain dorsal to the

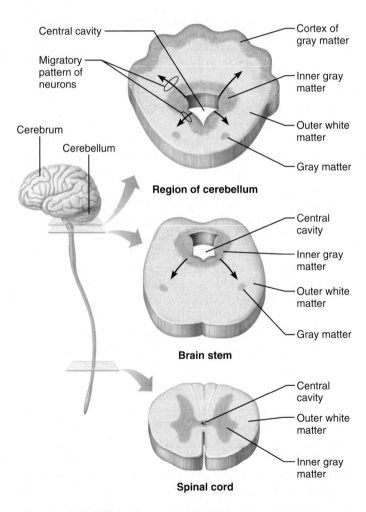

- Central cavity
- Migratory pattern of neurons
- Cortex of gray matter
- Inner gray matter
- Outer white matter
- Gray matter

Region of cerebellum

- Cerebrum
- Cerebellum

- Central cavity
- Inner gray matter
- Outer white matter
- Gray matter

Brain stem

- Central cavity
- Outer white matter
- Inner gray matter

Spinal cord

Figure 12.4 Pattern of gray and white matter in the CNS (highly simplified). In each cross section, the dorsal aspect is at the top. In general, white matter lies external to gray matter. In the developing brain, collections of gray matter migrate externally into the white matter (see black arrows). The cerebrum resembles the cerebellum in its external cortex of gray matter.

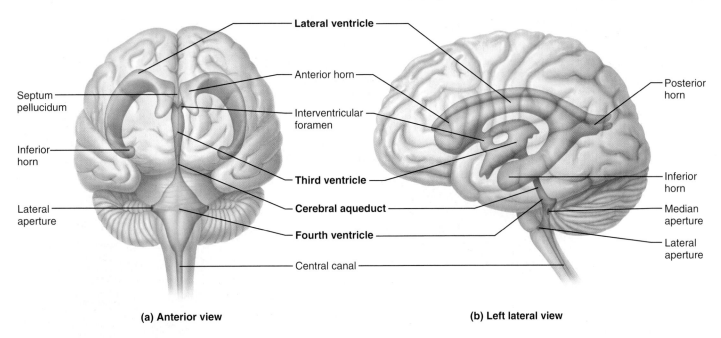

(a) Anterior view

(b) Left lateral view

Figure 12.5 Ventricles of the brain. Different regions of the large lateral ventricles are labeled anterior horn, posterior horn, and inferior horn.

pons and superior medulla. It is continuous with the central canal of the spinal cord inferiorly. Three openings mark the walls of the fourth ventricle: the paired **lateral apertures** in its side walls and the **median aperture** in its roof. These apertures connect the ventricles to the *subarachnoid space* (sub″ah-rak′noid), a fluid-filled space surrounding the brain.

CHECK YOUR UNDERSTANDING

1. Which ventricle is surrounded by the diencephalon?
2. Which two areas of the adult brain have an outside layer of gray matter in addition to central gray matter and surrounding white matter?
3. What is the function of convolutions of the brain?

For answers, see Appendix G.

Cerebral Hemispheres

▶ List the major lobes, fissures, and functional areas of the cerebral cortex.

▶ Explain lateralization of hemisphere function.

▶ Differentiate between commissures, association fibers, and projection fibers.

▶ Describe the general function of the basal nuclei (basal ganglia).

The **cerebral hemispheres** form the superior part of the brain **(Figure 12.6)**. Together they account for about 83% of total brain mass and are the most conspicuous parts of an intact brain. Picture how a mushroom cap covers the top of its stalk, and you have a fairly good idea of how the paired cerebral

hemispheres cover and obscure the diencephalon and the top of the brain stem (see Figure 12.3d).

Nearly the entire surface of the cerebral hemispheres is marked by elevated ridges of tissue called **gyri** (ji′ri; "twisters"), separated by shallow grooves called **sulci** (sul′ki; "furrows"). The singular forms of these terms are *gyrus* and *sulcus*. Deeper grooves, called **fissures**, separate large regions of the brain (Figure 12.6a).

The more prominent gyri and sulci are similar in all people and are important anatomical landmarks. The median **longitudinal fissure** separates the cerebral hemispheres (Figure 12.6c). Another large fissure, the **transverse cerebral fissure**, separates the cerebral hemispheres from the cerebellum below (Figure 12.6a, d).

Several sulci divide each hemisphere into five lobes—frontal, parietal, temporal, occipital, and insula (Figure 12.6a, b). All but the last are named for the cranial bones that overlie them (see Figure 7.5, pp. 203–204). The **central sulcus**, which lies in the frontal plane, separates the **frontal lobe** from the **parietal lobe**. Bordering the central sulcus are the **precentral gyrus** anteriorly and the **postcentral gyrus** posteriorly. More posteriorly, the **occipital lobe** is separated from the parietal lobe by the **parieto-occipital sulcus** (pah-ri″ĕ-to-ok-sip′ĭ-tal), located on the medial surface of the hemisphere.

The deep **lateral sulcus** outlines the flaplike **temporal lobe** and separates it from the parietal and frontal lobes. A fifth lobe of the cerebral hemisphere, the **insula** (in′su-lah; "island"), is buried deep within the lateral sulcus and forms part of its floor (Figure 12.6b). The insula is covered by portions of the temporal, parietal, and frontal lobes.

The cerebral hemispheres fit snugly in the skull. Rostrally, the frontal lobes lie in the anterior cranial fossa (see Figure 7.2b, c, p. 201). The anterior parts of the temporal lobes fill the

12

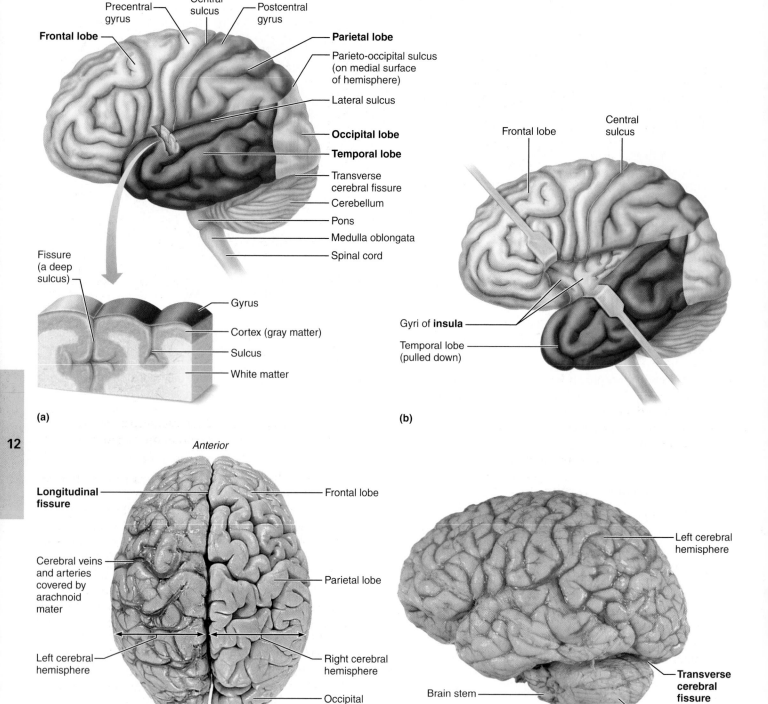

Figure 12.6 **Lobes and fissures of the cerebral hemispheres. (a)** Diagram of the lobes and major sulci and fissures of the brain. **(b)** Cortex of insula revealed by pulling back frontal and temporal lobes. **(c)** Superior surface of cerebral hemispheres; arachnoid matter has been removed from the right half. **(d)** Left lateral view of the brain.

middle cranial fossa. The posterior cranial fossa, however, houses the brain stem and cerebellum. The occipital lobes are located well superior to that cranial fossa.

Each cerebral hemisphere has three basic regions: a superficial *cortex* of gray matter, which looks gray in fresh brain tissue; an internal *white matter*; and the *basal nuclei*, islands of gray matter situated deep within the white matter. We consider these regions next.

Cerebral Cortex

The **cerebral cortex** is the "executive suite" of the nervous system, where our *conscious mind* is found. It enables us to be aware of ourselves and our sensations, to communicate, remember, and understand, and to initiate voluntary movements. The cerebral cortex is composed of gray matter: neuron cell bodies, dendrites, associated glia and blood vessels, but no fiber tracts. It contains billions of neurons arranged in six layers. Although it is only 2–4 mm (about 1/8 inch) thick, it accounts for roughly 40% of total brain mass. Its many convolutions effectively triple its surface area.

In the late 1800s, anatomists mapped subtle variations in the thickness and structure of the cerebral cortex. Most successful in these efforts was K. Brodmann, who in 1906 produced an elaborate numbered mosaic of 52 cortical areas, now called **Brodmann areas**.

With a structural map emerging, early neurologists were eager to localize *functional* regions of the cortex as well. Modern imaging techniques allow us to see the brain in action—PET scans show maximal metabolic activity in the brain, and functional MRI scans reveal blood flow (Figure 12.7). They have shown that specific motor and sensory functions are localized in discrete cortical areas called *domains*. However, many higher mental functions, such as memory and language, appear to have overlapping domains and are spread over large areas of the cortex.

Before we examine the functional regions of the cerebral cortex, let's consider some generalizations about this region of the brain:

1. The cerebral cortex contains three kinds of functional areas: *motor areas, sensory areas,* and *association areas*. As you read about these areas, do not confuse the sensory and motor areas of the cortex with sensory and motor neurons. All neurons in the cortex are interneurons.
2. Each hemisphere is chiefly concerned with the sensory and motor functions of the opposite (contralateral) side of the body.
3. Although largely symmetrical in structure, the two hemispheres are not entirely equal in function. Instead, there is a lateralization (specialization) of cortical functions.
4. The final, and perhaps most important, generalization to keep in mind is that our approach is a gross oversimplification; no functional area of the cortex acts alone, and conscious behavior involves the entire cortex in one way or another.

Motor Areas As shown in Figure 12.8a (dark and light red areas), the following **motor areas** of the cortex, which control

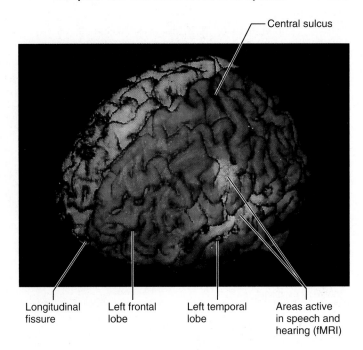

Central sulcus

Longitudinal fissure | Left frontal lobe | Left temporal lobe | Areas active in speech and hearing (fMRI)

Figure 12.7 Functional neuroimaging (fMRI) of the cerebral cortex. Speaking and hearing increases activity (blood flow, yellow and orange areas) in the posterior frontal and superior temporal lobes, respectively.

voluntary movement, lie in the posterior part of the frontal lobes: primary motor cortex, premotor cortex, Broca's area, and the frontal eye field.

1. **Primary motor cortex.** The **primary (somatic) motor cortex** is located in the precentral gyrus of the frontal lobe of each hemisphere (Figure 12.8, dark red area). Large neurons, called **pyramidal cells**, in these gyri allow us to consciously control the precise or skilled voluntary movements of our skeletal muscles. Their long axons, which project to the spinal cord, form the massive voluntary motor tracts called the *pyramidal tracts*, or *corticospinal tracts* (kor″tĭ-ko-spi′nal). All other descending motor tracts issue from brain stem nuclei and consist of chains of two or more neurons.

   The entire body is represented spatially in the primary motor cortex of each hemisphere. For example, the pyramidal cells that control foot movements are in one place and those that control hand movements are in another. Such a mapping of the body in CNS structures is called **somatotopy** (so″mah-to-to′pe).

   As illustrated in Figure 12.9 (p. 438), the body is represented upside down—with the head at the inferolateral part of the precentral gyrus, and the toes at the superomedial end. Most of the neurons in these gyri control muscles in body areas having the most precise motor control—that is, the face, tongue, and hands. Consequently, these regions of the caricature-like **motor homunculi** (ho-mung′ku-li; singular: homunculus; "little man") drawn in Figure 12.9 are disproportionately large. The motor innervation of the

12

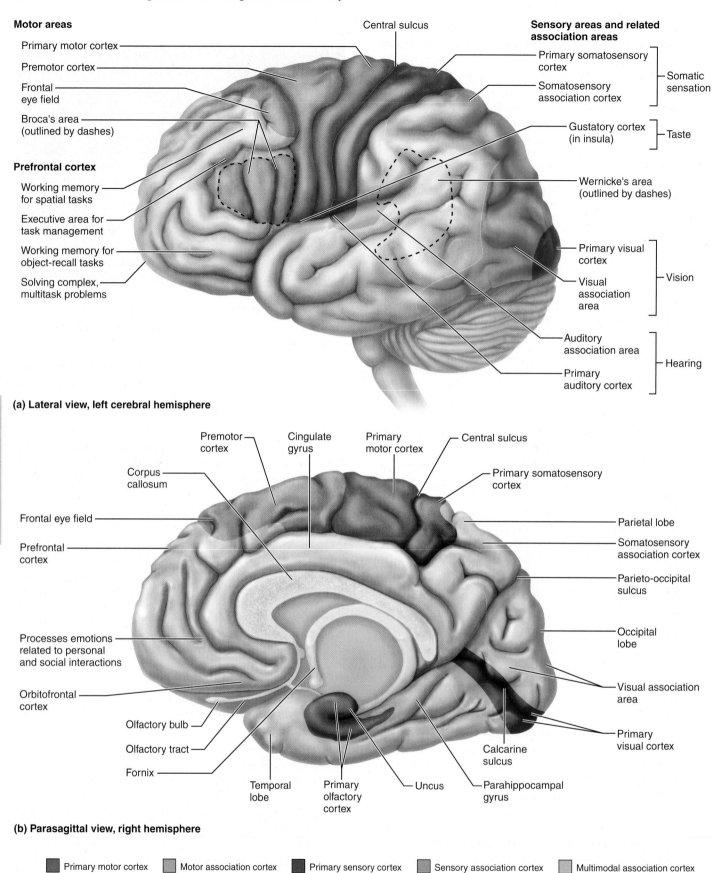

Motor areas

- Primary motor cortex
- Premotor cortex
- Frontal eye field
- Broca's area (outlined by dashes)

Prefrontal cortex

- Working memory for spatial tasks
- Executive area for task management
- Working memory for object-recall tasks
- Solving complex, multitask problems

Central sulcus

Sensory areas and related association areas

- Primary somatosensory cortex
- Somatosensory association cortex } Somatic sensation
- Gustatory cortex (in insula) } Taste
- Wernicke's area (outlined by dashes)
- Primary visual cortex
- Visual association area } Vision
- Auditory association area
- Primary auditory cortex } Hearing

(a) Lateral view, left cerebral hemisphere

- Premotor cortex
- Cingulate gyrus
- Primary motor cortex
- Central sulcus
- Corpus callosum
- Frontal eye field
- Prefrontal cortex
- Processes emotions related to personal and social interactions
- Orbitofrontal cortex
- Olfactory bulb
- Olfactory tract
- Fornix
- Temporal lobe
- Primary olfactory cortex
- Uncus
- Parahippocampal gyrus
- Calcarine sulcus
- Primary visual cortex
- Visual association area
- Occipital lobe
- Parieto-occipital sulcus
- Somatosensory association cortex
- Parietal lobe
- Primary somatosensory cortex

(b) Parasagittal view, right hemisphere

■ Primary motor cortex ■ Motor association cortex ■ Primary sensory cortex ■ Sensory association cortex ■ Multimodal association cortex

Figure 12.8 **Functional and structural areas of the cerebral cortex.**

body is contralateral: In other words, the left primary motor gyrus controls muscles on the right side of the body, and vice versa.

The *motor homunculus* view of the primary motor cortex, shown at the left in Figure 12.9, implies a one-to-one correspondence between certain cortical neurons and the muscles they control, but this is somewhat misleading. Current research indicates that a given muscle is controlled by multiple spots on the cortex and that individual cortical neurons actually send impulses to more than one muscle. In other words, individual pyramidal motor neurons control muscles that work together in a synergistic way to perform a given movement.

For example, reaching forward with one arm involves some muscles acting at the shoulder and some acting at the elbow. Instead of the discrete map offered by the motor homunculus, the primary motor cortex map is an orderly but fuzzy map with neurons arranged in useful ways to control and coordinate sets of muscles. Neurons controlling the arm, for instance, are intermingled and overlap with those controlling the hand and shoulder. However, neurons controlling unrelated movements, such as those controlling the arm and those controlling body trunk muscles, do not cooperate in motor activity. Thus, the motor homunculus is useful to show that broad areas of the primary cortex are devoted to the leg, arm, torso, and head, but neuron organization within those broad areas is much more diffuse than initially imagined.

2. **Premotor cortex.** Just anterior to the precentral gyrus in the frontal lobe is the **premotor cortex** (see Figure 12.8, light red area). This region controls learned motor skills of a repetitive or patterned nature, such as playing a musical instrument and typing. The premotor cortex coordinates the movement of several muscle groups either simultaneously or sequentially, mainly by sending activating impulses to the primary motor cortex. However, the premotor cortex also influences motor activity more directly by supplying about 15% of pyramidal tract fibers. Think of this region as the memory bank for skilled motor activities.

The premotor cortex also appears to be involved in planning movements. Using highly processed sensory information received from other cortical areas, it can control voluntary actions that depend on sensory feedback, such as moving an arm through a maze to grasp a hidden object.

3. **Broca's area.** Broca's area (bro′kahz) lies anterior to the inferior region of the premotor area. It has long been considered to be (1) present in one hemisphere only (usually the left) and (2) a special *motor speech area* that directs the muscles involved in speech production. However, recent studies using PET scans to watch active areas of the brain "light up" indicate that Broca's area also becomes active as we prepare to speak and even as we think about (plan) many voluntary motor activities other than speech.

4. **Frontal eye field.** The **frontal eye field** is located partially in and anterior to the premotor cortex and superior to Broca's area. This cortical region controls voluntary movement of the eyes.

HOMEOSTATIC IMBALANCE

Damage to localized areas of the *primary motor cortex* (as from a stroke) paralyzes the body muscles controlled by those areas. If the lesion is in the right hemisphere, the left side of the body will be paralyzed. Only *voluntary* control is lost, however, as the muscles can still contract reflexively.

Destruction of the *premotor cortex*, or part of it, results in a loss of the motor skill(s) programmed in that region, but muscle strength and the ability to perform the discrete individual movements are not hindered. For example, if the premotor area controlling the flight of your fingers over a computer keyboard were damaged, you couldn't type with your usual speed, but you could still make the same movements with your fingers. Reprogramming the skill into another set of premotor neurons would require practice, just as the initial learning process did. ■

Sensory Areas Areas concerned with conscious awareness of sensation, the **sensory areas** of the cortex, occur in the parietal, insular, temporal, and occipital lobes (see Figure 12.8, dark and light blue areas).

1. **Primary somatosensory cortex.** The **primary somatosensory cortex** resides in the postcentral gyrus of the parietal lobe, just posterior to the primary motor cortex. Neurons in this gyrus receive information from the general (somatic) sensory receptors in the skin and from proprioceptors (position sense receptors) in skeletal muscles, joints, and tendons. The neurons then identify the body region being stimulated, an ability called **spatial discrimination**.

As with the primary motor cortex, the body is represented spatially and upside-down according to the site of stimulus input, and the right hemisphere receives input from the left side of the body. The amount of sensory cortex devoted to a particular body region is related to that region's sensitivity (that is, to how many receptors it has), not to the size of the body region. In humans, the face (especially the lips) and fingertips are the most sensitive body areas. For this reason, these regions are the largest parts of the **somatosensory homunculus** shown in the right half of Figure 12.9.

2. **Somatosensory association cortex.** The **somatosensory association cortex** lies just posterior to the primary somatosensory cortex and has many connections with it. The major function of this area is to integrate sensory inputs (temperature, pressure, and so forth) relayed to it via the primary somatosensory cortex to produce an understanding of an object being felt: its size, texture, and the relationship of its parts. For example, when you reach into your pocket, your somatosensory association cortex draws upon stored memories of past sensory experiences to perceive the objects you feel as coins or keys. Someone with damage to this area could not recognize these objects without looking at them.

3. **Visual areas.** The **primary visual (striate) cortex** is seen on the extreme posterior tip of the occipital lobe, but most of it is buried deep in the *calcarine sulcus* in the medial as-

12

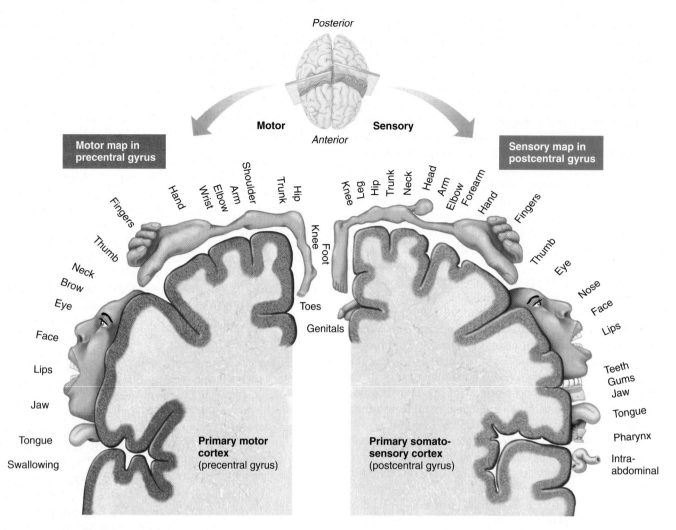

Figure 12.9 Body maps in the primary motor cortex and somatosensory cortex of the cerebrum. The relative amount and location of cortical tissue devoted to each function is proportional to the distorted body diagrams (homunculi).

pect of the occipital lobe (Figure 12.8b). The largest of all cortical sensory areas, the primary visual cortex receives visual information that originates on the retina of the eye. There is a contralateral map of visual space on the primary visual cortex, analogous to the body map on the somatosensory cortex.

The **visual association area** surrounds the primary visual cortex and covers much of the occipital lobe. Communicating with the primary visual cortex, the visual association area uses past visual experiences to interpret visual stimuli (color, form, and movement), enabling us to recognize a flower or a person's face and to appreciate what we are seeing. We do our "seeing" with these cortical neurons. However, experiments on monkeys and humans indicate that complex visual processing involves the entire posterior half of the cerebral hemispheres. Particularly important are two visual "streams"—one running along the top of the brain and handling spatial relationships and object location, the other taking the lower road and focusing on object identity (recognizing faces, words, and objects).

4. **Auditory areas.** Each **primary auditory cortex** is located in the superior margin of the temporal lobe abutting the lateral sulcus. Sound energy exciting the hearing receptors of the inner ear causes impulses to be transmitted to the primary auditory cortex, where they are interpreted as pitch, loudness, and location.

   The more posterior **auditory association area** then permits the perception of the sound stimulus, which we "hear" as speech, a scream, music, thunder, noise, and so on. Memories of sounds heard in the past appear to be stored here for reference. Wernicke's area, which we describe later, includes parts of the auditory cortex.

5. **Olfactory cortex.** The primary **olfactory (smell) cortex** lies on the medial aspect of the temporal lobe in a small region called the *piriform lobe* which is dominated by the hooklike *uncus* (Figure 12.8b). Afferent fibers from smell receptors in the superior nasal cavities send impulses along the olfactory tracts that are ultimately relayed to the olfactory cortices. The outcome is conscious awareness of different odors.

The olfactory cortex is part of the primitive **rhinencephalon** (ri″nen-sef′ah-lon; "nose brain"), which includes all parts of the cerebrum that receive olfactory signals—the orbitofrontal cortex, the uncus and associated regions located on or in the medial aspects of the temporal lobes, and the protruding olfactory tracts and bulbs that extend to the nose. During the course of evolution, most of the "old" rhinencephalon has taken on new functions concerned chiefly with emotions and memory. It has become part of the "newer" emotional brain, called the *limbic system*, which we will consider later in this chapter. The only portions of the human rhinencephalon still devoted to smell are the olfactory bulbs and tracts (described in Chapter 13) and the greatly reduced olfactory cortices.

6. **Gustatory cortex.** The **gustatory (taste) cortex** (gus′tah-tor-e), a region involved in the perception of taste stimuli, is located in the insula just deep to the temporal lobe (Figure 12.8a).

7. **Visceral sensory area.** The cortex of the insula just posterior to the gustatory cortex is involved in conscious perception of visceral sensations. These include upset stomach, full bladder, and the feeling that your lungs will burst when you hold your breath too long.

8. **Vestibular (equilibrium) cortex.** It has been difficult to pin down the part of the cortex responsible for conscious awareness of balance, that is, of the position of the head in space. However, imaging studies now locate this region in the posterior part of the insula and adjacent parietal cortex.

HOMEOSTATIC IMBALANCE

Damage to the *primary visual cortex* (Figure 12.8) results in functional blindness. By contrast, individuals with damage to the visual association area can see, but they do not comprehend what they are looking at. ■

Multimodal Association Areas The association areas that we have considered so far (colored light red or light blue in Figure 12.8) have all been tightly tied to one kind of primary motor or sensory cortex (colored dark red or dark blue). Most of the cortex, though, is more complexly connected, receiving inputs from multiple senses and sending outputs to multiple areas. We call these areas **multimodal association areas** (colored light violet in Figure 12.8).

In general, information flows from sensory receptors to the appropriate primary sensory cortex, then to a sensory association cortex and then on to the multimodal association cortex. Multimodal association cortex allows us to give meaning to the information that we receive, store it in memory if needed, tie it to previous experience and knowledge, and decide what action to take. Once the course of action has been decided, those decisions are relayed to the premotor cortex, which in turn communicates with the motor cortex. The multimodal association cortex seems to be where sensations, thoughts, and emotions become conscious. It is what makes us who we are.

Suppose, for example, you drop a bottle of acid in the chem lab and it splashes on you. You see the bottle shatter; hear the crash; feel your skin burning; and smell the acid fumes. These individual perceptions come together in the multimodal association areas. Along with feelings of panic, these perceptions are woven into a seamless whole, which (hopefully) recalls instructions about what to do in this situation. As a result your premotor and primary motor cortices direct your legs to propel you to the safety shower. The multimodal association areas can be broadly divided into three parts, which we describe next.

1. **Anterior association area.** The **anterior association area** in the frontal lobe, also called the **prefrontal cortex**, is the most complicated cortical region of all (Figure 12.8). It is involved with intellect, complex learning abilities (called cognition), recall, and personality. It contains working memory, which is necessary for the production of abstract ideas, judgment, reasoning, persistence, and planning. These abilities develop slowly in children, which implies that the prefrontal cortex matures slowly and depends heavily on positive and negative feedback from one's social environment.

2. **Posterior association area.** The **posterior association area** is a large region encompassing parts of the temporal, parietal, and occipital lobes. This area plays a role in recognizing patterns and faces, localizing us and our surroundings in space, and in binding different sensory inputs into a coherent whole. In the spilled acid example above, your awareness of the entire scene originates from this area. Attention to an area of space or an area of one's own body is also a function of this part of the brain. Many parts of this area (including Wernicke's area, Figure 12.8a) are also involved in understanding written and spoken language.

3. **Limbic association area.** The **limbic association area** includes the cingulate gyrus, the parahippocampal gyrus, and the hippocampus (see Figures 12.8b and 12.18). It is part of the limbic system, which we describe later. The limbic association area provides the emotional impact that makes a scene important to us. In our example above, it provides the sense of "danger" when the acid splashes on our legs. The hippocampus establishes memories that allow us to remember this incident. More on this later.

HOMEOSTATIC IMBALANCE

Tumors or other lesions of the *anterior association area* may cause mental and personality disorders including loss of judgment, attentiveness, and inhibitions. The affected individual may be oblivious to social restraints, perhaps becoming careless about personal appearance, or rashly attacking a 7-foot opponent rather than running.

On the other hand, individuals with lesions in the posterior parietal region of the posterior association area, which provides for awareness of self in space, may refuse to wash or dress the side of their body opposite to the lesion because "that doesn't belong to me." ■

Lateralization of Cortical Functioning We use both cerebral hemispheres for almost every activity, and the hemispheres appear nearly identical. Nonetheless, there is a division of labor,

12

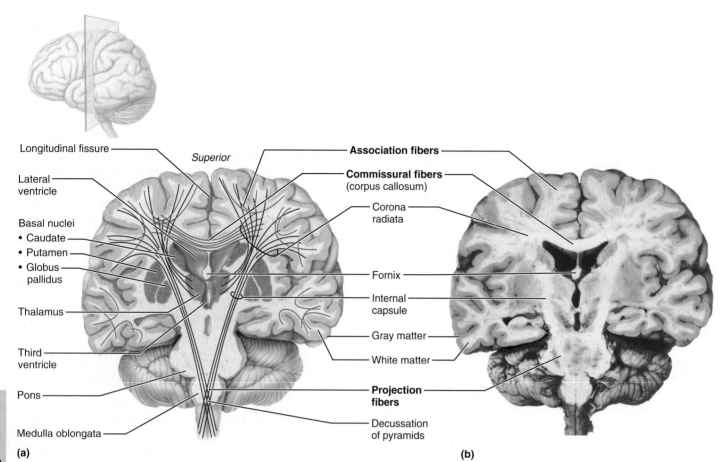

Longitudinal fissure

Superior

Association fibers

Commissural fibers
(corpus callosum)

Lateral
ventricle

Corona
radiata

Basal nuclei
• Caudate
• Putamen
• Globus
  pallidus

Fornix

Internal
capsule

Thalamus

Gray matter

White matter

Third
ventricle

Pons

**Projection
fibers**

Medulla oblongata

Decussation
of pyramids

(a)

(b)

12

Figure 12.10 Types of fiber tracts in white matter. (a) Frontal section showing commissural, projection, and association fibers running within the cerebrum and between the cerebrum and lower CNS centers. Notice the tight band of projection fibers called the internal capsule that passes between the thalamus and the basal nuclei, and then fans out as the corona radiata. **(b)** Photo of the same view as (a).

and each hemisphere has unique abilities not shared by its partner. This phenomenon is called **lateralization**. Although one cerebral hemisphere or the other "dominates" each task, the term **cerebral dominance** designates the hemisphere that is *dominant for language*. In most people (about 90%), the left hemisphere has greater control over language abilities, math, and logic. This so-called dominant hemisphere is working when we compose a sentence, balance a checkbook, and memorize a list. The other hemisphere (usually the right) is more free-spirited, involved in visual-spatial skills, intuition, emotion, and artistic and musical skills. It is the poetic, creative, and the "Ah-ha!" (insightful) side of our nature, and it is far better at recognizing faces. Most individuals with left cerebral dominance are right-handed.

In the remaining 10% of people, the roles of the hemispheres are reversed or the hemispheres share their functions equally. Typically, right-cerebral-dominant people are left-handed and male. Some "lefties" who have a cerebral cortex that functions bilaterally are ambidextrous. The reading disorder *dyslexia*, in which otherwise intelligent people reverse the order of letters in words (and the order of words in sentences) was once thought to be more common in left-handed males. This led to speculation that it might be the result of cerebral confusion ("Is it your

turn, or mine?"). However, dyslexia is equally common in right and left handers, and is now thought to be the result of processing errors within one hemisphere.

The two cerebral hemispheres have perfect and almost instantaneous communication with one another via connecting fiber tracts, as well as complete functional integration. Furthermore, although lateralization means that each hemisphere is better than the other at certain functions, neither side is better at everything.

Cerebral White Matter

The second of the three basic regions of each cerebral hemisphere is the internal **cerebral white matter**. From what we have already described, you know that communication within the brain is extensive. The white matter deep to the cortical gray matter is responsible for communication between cerebral areas and between the cerebral cortex and lower CNS centers. White matter consists largely of myelinated fibers bundled into large tracts. These fibers and tracts are classified according to the direction in which they run as *commissural, association,* or *projection* (**Figure 12.10**).

Commissures (kom'ĭ-shūrz), composed of **commissural fibers**, connect corresponding gray areas of the two hemispheres, enabling them to function as a coordinated whole. The largest commissure is the **corpus callosum** (kah-lo'sum; "thickened body"), which lies superior to the lateral ventricles, deep within the longitudinal fissure. Less prominent examples are the **anterior** and **posterior commissures** (see Figure 12.12, p. 443).

Association fibers connect different parts of the same hemisphere. Short association fibers connect adjacent gyri. Long association fibers are bundled into tracts and connect different cortical lobes.

Projection fibers either enter the cerebral cortex from lower brain or cord centers or descend from the cortex to lower areas. Sensory information reaches the cerebral cortex and motor output leaves it through these projection fibers. They tie the cortex to the rest of the nervous system and to the body's receptors and effectors. In contrast to commissural and association fibers, which run horizontally, projection fibers run vertically, as Figure 12.10a shows.

At the top of the brain stem, the projection fibers on each side form a compact band, the **internal capsule**, that passes between the thalamus and some of the basal nuclei. Beyond that point, the fibers radiate fanlike through the cerebral white matter to the cortex. This distinctive arrangement of projection tract fibers is known as the **corona radiata** ("radiating crown").

Basal Nuclei

Deep within the cerebral white matter is the third basic region of each hemisphere, a group of subcortical nuclei called the **basal nuclei** or **basal ganglia**.* Although the definition of the precise structures forming the basal nuclei is controversial, most anatomists agree that the **caudate nucleus** (kaw'dāt), **putamen** (pu-ta'men), and **globus pallidus** (glo'bis pal'ĭ-dus) constitute most of the mass of each group of basal nuclei (Figure 12.11).

Together, the putamen ("pod") and globus pallidus ("pale globe") form a lens-shaped mass, the **lentiform nucleus**, that flanks the internal capsule laterally. The comma-shaped caudate nucleus arches superiorly over the diencephalon. Collectively, the lentiform and caudate nuclei are called the **corpus striatum** (stri-a'tum) because the fibers of the internal capsule that course past and through them give them a striped appearance.

The basal nuclei are functionally associated with the *subthalamic nuclei* (located in the lateral "floor" of the diencephalon) and the *substantia nigra* of the midbrain (see Figure 12.16a).

The basal nuclei receive input from the entire cerebral cortex, as well as from other subcortical nuclei and each other. Via relays through the thalamus, the output nucleus of the basal nu-

clei (globus pallidus) and the substantia nigra project to the premotor and prefrontal cortices and so influence muscle movements directed by the primary motor cortex. The basal nuclei have no direct access to motor pathways.

The precise role of the basal nuclei has been elusive because of their inaccessible location and because their functions overlap with those of the cerebellum. Their role in motor control is complex and there is evidence they play a part in regulating attention and in cognition. The basal nuclei are particularly important in starting, stopping, and monitoring the intensity of movements executed by the cortex, especially those that are relatively slow or stereotyped, such as arm-swinging during walking. Additionally, they inhibit antagonistic or unnecessary movements. Their input seems necessary to our ability to perform several activities at once. Disorders of the basal nuclei result in either too much or too little movement as exemplified by Huntington's disease and Parkinson's disease, respectively (see pp. 465–466).

CHECK YOUR UNDERSTANDING

4. What anatomical landmark of the cerebral cortex separates primary motor areas from somatosensory areas?
5. Mike, who is left-handed, decided to wear his favorite T-shirt to his anatomy class. On his T-shirt were the words "Only left-handed people are in their right minds." What does this statement mean?
6. Which type of fibers allows the two cerebral hemispheres to "talk to each other"?
7. Name the components of the basal nuclei.

For answers, see Appendix G.

Diencephalon

▶ Describe the location of the diencephalon, and name its subdivisions and functions.

Forming the central core of the forebrain and surrounded by the cerebral hemispheres, the **diencephalon** consists largely of three paired structures—the thalamus, hypothalamus, and epithalamus. These gray matter areas collectively enclose the third ventricle (Figure 12.12).

Thalamus

The **thalamus** consists of bilateral egg-shaped nuclei, which form the superolateral walls of the third ventricle (Figures 12.10 and 12.12). In most people, the nuclei are connected at the midline by an **interthalamic adhesion (intermediate mass)**. *Thalamus* is a Greek word meaning "inner room," which well describes this deep, well-hidden brain region that makes up 80% of the diencephalon.

The thalamus is *the* relay station for information coming into the cerebral cortex. Within the thalamus are a large number of nuclei, most named according to their relative location

---

*Because a nucleus is a collection of nerve cell bodies within the CNS, the term *basal nuclei* is technically correct. The more frequently used but misleading historical term *basal ganglia* is a misnomer and should be abandoned, because ganglia are PNS structures.

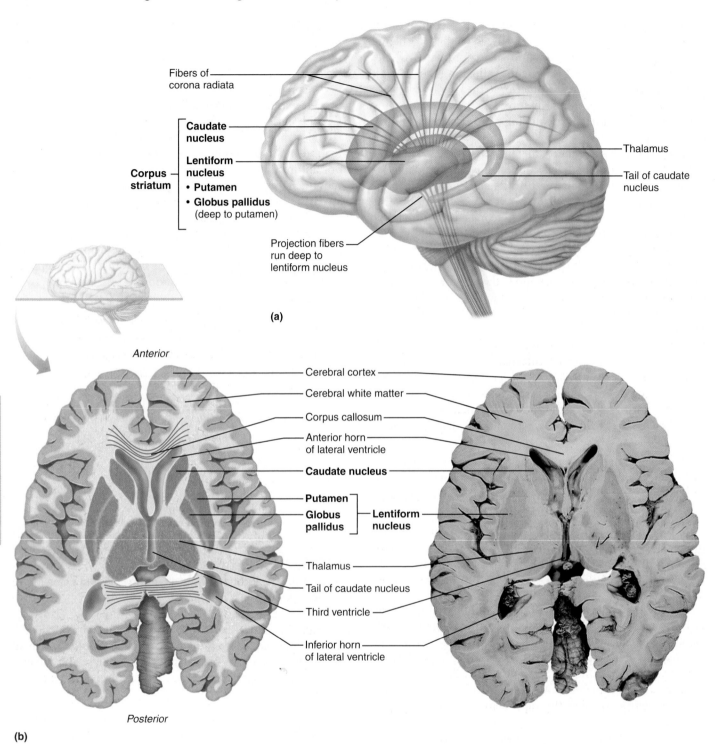

Figure 12.11 **Basal nuclei. (a)** Three-dimensional view of the basal nuclei (basal ganglia), showing their position in the cerebrum. **(b)** Transverse section of cerebrum and diencephalon showing the relationship of the basal nuclei to the thalamus and the lateral and third ventricles.

(Figure 12.13a). Each nucleus has a functional specialty, and each projects fibers to and receives fibers from a specific region of the cerebral cortex. Afferent impulses from all senses and all parts of the body converge on the thalamus and synapse with at least one of its nuclei. For example, the *ventral posterolateral nuclei* receive impulses from the general somatic sensory receptors (touch, pressure, pain, etc.), and the *lateral* and *medial geniculate*

bodies (jě-nik′u-lāt; "knee shaped") are important visual and auditory relay centers, respectively.

Within the thalamus, information is sorted out and "edited." Impulses having to do with similar functions are relayed as a group via the internal capsule to the appropriate area of the sensory cortex as well as to specific cortical association areas. As the afferent impulses reach the thalamus, we have a crude recogni-

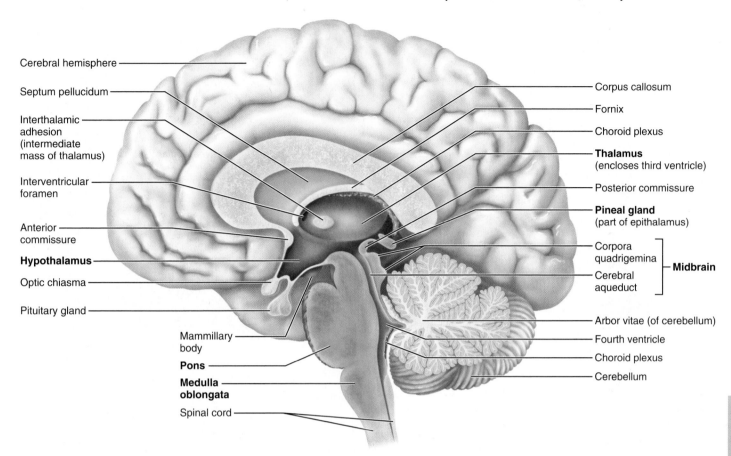

Cerebral hemisphere

Septum pellucidum

Interthalamic adhesion (intermediate mass of thalamus)

Interventricular foramen

Anterior commissure

Hypothalamus

Optic chiasma

Pituitary gland

Mammillary body

Pons

Medulla oblongata

Spinal cord

Corpus callosum

Fornix

Choroid plexus

Thalamus (encloses third ventricle)

Posterior commissure

Pineal gland (part of epithalamus)

Corpora quadrigemina

Cerebral aqueduct

Midbrain

Arbor vitae (of cerebellum)

Fourth ventricle

Choroid plexus

Cerebellum

Figure 12.12 Midsagittal section of the brain illustrating the diencephalon (purple) and brain stem (green).

tion of the sensation as pleasant or unpleasant. However, specific stimulus localization and discrimination occur in the cerebral cortex.

In addition to sensory inputs, virtually *all* other inputs ascending to the cerebral cortex funnel through thalamic nuclei. These inputs include impulses participating in the regulation of emotion and visceral function from the hypothalamus (via the anterior nuclei), and impulses that help direct the activity of the motor cortices from the cerebellum and basal nuclei (via the ventral lateral and ventral anterior nuclei, respectively). Several thalamic nuclei (pulvinar, lateral dorsal, and lateral posterior nuclei) are involved in integration of sensory information and project to specific association cortices. In summary, the thalamus plays a key role in mediating sensation, motor activities, cortical arousal, learning, and memory. It is truly the gateway to the cerebral cortex.

Hypothalamus

Named for its position below (*hypo*) the thalamus, the **hypothalamus** caps the brain stem and forms the inferolateral walls of the third ventricle (Figure 12.12). Merging into the midbrain inferiorly, the hypothalamus extends from the optic chiasma (crossover point of the optic nerves) to the posterior margin of the mammillary bodies. The **mammillary bodies** (mam′mil-er-e; "little breast"), paired pealike nuclei that bulge

anteriorly from the hypothalamus, are relay stations in the olfactory pathways. Between the optic chiasma and mammillary bodies is the **infundibulum** (in″fun-dib′u-lum), a stalk of hypothalamic tissue that connects the **pituitary gland** to the base of the hypothalamus. Like the thalamus, the hypothalamus contains many functionally important nuclei (Figure 12.13b).

Despite its small size, the hypothalamus is the main visceral control center of the body and is vitally important to overall body homeostasis. Few tissues in the body escape its influence. Its chief homeostatic roles are

1. **Autonomic control center.** As you will remember, the autonomic nervous system (ANS) is a system of peripheral nerves that regulates cardiac and smooth muscle and secretion by the glands. The hypothalamus regulates ANS activity by controlling the activity of centers in the brain stem and spinal cord. In this role, the hypothalamus influences blood pressure, rate and force of heartbeat, digestive tract motility, eye pupil size, and many other visceral activities.

2. **Center for emotional response.** The hypothalamus lies at the "heart" of the limbic system (the emotional part of the brain). Nuclei involved in the perception of pleasure, fear, and rage, as well as those involved in biological rhythms and drives (such as the sex drive), are found in the hypothalamus.

12

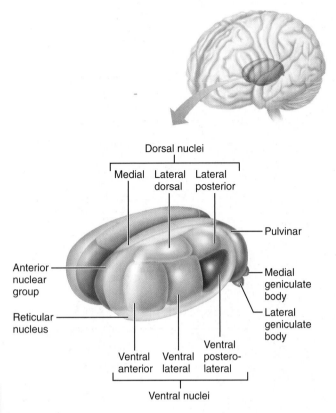

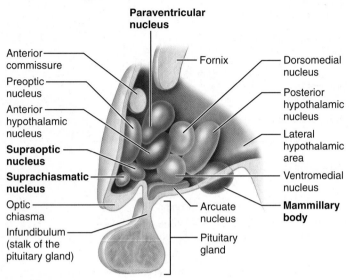

(a) **The main thalamic nuclei.** (The reticular nuclei that "cap" the thalamus laterally are depicted as curving translucent structures.)

(b) **The main hypothalamic nuclei.**

Figure 12.13 Selected structures of the diencephalon.

The hypothalamus acts through ANS pathways to initiate most physical expressions of emotion. For example, a fearful person has a pounding heart, high blood pressure, pallor, sweating, and a dry mouth.

3. **Body temperature regulation.** The body's thermostat is in the hypothalamus. Hypothalamic neurons monitor blood temperature and receive input from other thermoreceptors in the brain and body periphery. Accordingly, the hypothalamus initiates cooling (sweating) or heat-generating actions (shivering) as needed to maintain a relatively constant body temperature.

4. **Regulation of food intake.** In response to changing blood levels of certain nutrients (glucose and perhaps amino acids) or hormones [cholecystokinin (CCK) and others], the hypothalamus regulates feelings of hunger and satiety.

5. **Regulation of water balance and thirst.** When body fluids become too concentrated, hypothalamic neurons called *osmoreceptors* are activated. These neurons excite hypothalamic nuclei that trigger the release of antidiuretic hormone (ADH) from the posterior pituitary. ADH causes the kidneys to retain water. The same conditions also stimulate hypothalamic neurons in the *thirst center*, causing us to feel thirsty and, therefore, to drink more fluids.

6. **Regulation of sleep-wake cycles.** Acting with other brain regions, the hypothalamus helps regulate sleep. Through the operation of its *suprachiasmatic nucleus* (our biological clock), it sets the timing of the sleep cycle in response to daylight-darkness cues received from the visual pathways.

7. **Control of endocrine system functioning.** The hypothalamus acts as the helmsman of the endocrine system in two important ways. First, its *releasing and inhibiting hormones* control the secretion of hormones by the anterior pituitary gland. Second, its *supraoptic* and *paraventricular nuclei* produce the hormones ADH and oxytocin.

HOMEOSTATIC IMBALANCE

Hypothalamic disturbances cause a number of disorders including severe body wasting, obesity, sleep disturbances, dehydration, and a broad range of emotional imbalances. For example, the hypothalamus is implicated in *failure to thrive*, a condition characterized by a delay in a child's growth or development, that occurs when infants are deprived of a warm, nurturing relationship. ∎

Epithalamus

The **epithalamus** is the most dorsal portion of the diencephalon and forms the roof of the third ventricle. Extending from its posterior border and visible externally is the **pineal gland** or **body** (pin′e-al; "pine cone shaped") (see Figures 12.12 and 12.15c). The pineal gland secretes the hormone *melatonin* (a sleep-

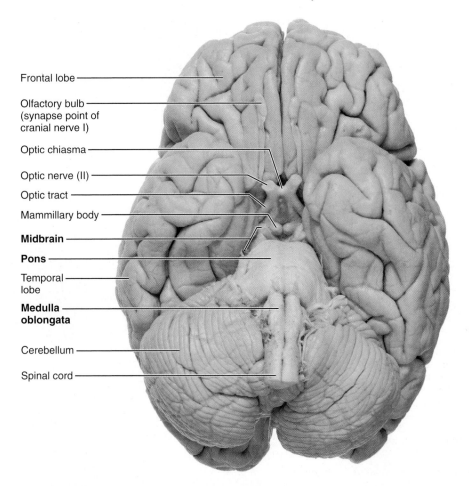

Frontal lobe

Olfactory bulb (synapse point of cranial nerve I)

Optic chiasma

Optic nerve (II)

Optic tract

Mammillary body

Midbrain

Pons

Temporal lobe

Medulla oblongata

Cerebellum

Spinal cord

Figure 12.14 Inferior view of the brain, showing the three parts of the brain stem: midbrain, pons, and medulla oblongata. Only a small portion of the midbrain can be seen; the rest is surrounded by other brain regions. (See *A Brief Atlas of the Human Body,* Figure 49.)

12

inducing signal and antioxidant; see Chapter 16) and, along with hypothalamic nuclei, helps regulate the sleep-wake cycle.

CHECK YOUR UNDERSTANDING

8. Why is the thalamus sometimes called the "gateway to the cerebral cortex"?
9. The hypothalamus oversees a branch of the peripheral nervous system. Which branch?

For answers, see Appendix G.

Brain Stem

▶ Identify the three major regions of the brain stem, and note the functions of each area.

From superior to inferior, the brain stem regions are midbrain, pons, and medulla oblongata (Figures 12.12, 12.14, and 12.15). Each roughly an inch long, collectively they account for only 2.5% of total brain mass. Histologically, the organization of the brain stem is similar (but not identical) to that of the spinal cord—deep gray matter surrounded by white matter fiber tracts

(see Figure 12.4). However, the brain stem has nuclei of gray matter embedded in the white matter, a feature not found in the spinal cord.

Brain stem centers produce the rigidly programmed, automatic behaviors necessary for survival. Positioned between the cerebrum and the spinal cord, the brain stem also provides a pathway for fiber tracts running between higher and lower neural centers. Additionally, brain stem nuclei are associated with 10 of the 12 pairs of cranial nerves (which we will describe in Chapter 13), so it is heavily involved with innervation of the head.

Midbrain

The **midbrain** is located between the diencephalon and the pons (**Figure 12.14** and **Figure 12.15**). On its ventral aspect two bulging **cerebral peduncles** (pĕ-dung′klz) form vertical pillars that seem to hold up the cerebrum, hence their name meaning "little feet of the cerebrum" (Figure 12.15a, b, and **Figure 12.16a**). The *crus cerebri* ("leg of the cerebrum") of each peduncle contains a large pyramidal (corticospinal) motor tract descending toward the spinal cord. The *superior cerebellar peduncles*, also fiber tracts, connect the midbrain to the cerebellum dorsally (Figure 12.15b, c).

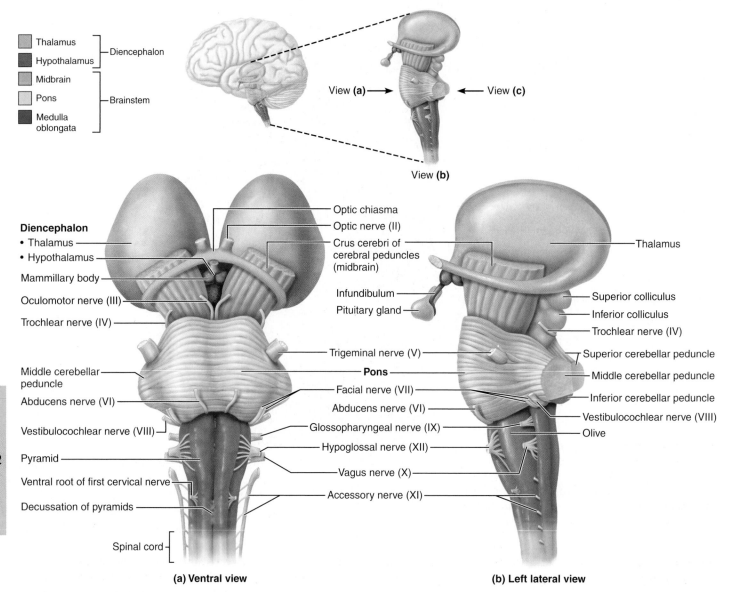

Thalamus ⎤
Hypothalamus ⎦ Diencephalon

Midbrain ⎤
Pons ⎥ Brainstem
Medulla ⎦
oblongata

View **(a)** → ← View **(c)**

View **(b)**

Diencephalon
- Thalamus
- Hypothalamus
Mammillary body
Oculomotor nerve (III)
Trochlear nerve (IV)

Middle cerebellar peduncle
Abducens nerve (VI)
Vestibulocochlear nerve (VIII)
Pyramid
Ventral root of first cervical nerve
Decussation of pyramids
Spinal cord

Optic chiasma
Optic nerve (II)
Crus cerebri of cerebral peduncles (midbrain)
Infundibulum
Pituitary gland
Trigeminal nerve (V)
Pons
Facial nerve (VII)
Abducens nerve (VI)
Glossopharyngeal nerve (IX)
Hypoglossal nerve (XII)
Vagus nerve (X)
Accessory nerve (XI)

Thalamus
Superior colliculus
Inferior colliculus
Trochlear nerve (IV)
Superior cerebellar peduncle
Middle cerebellar peduncle
Inferior cerebellar peduncle
Vestibulocochlear nerve (VIII)
Olive

(a) Ventral view

(b) Left lateral view

Figure 12.15 Three views of the brain stem (green) and the diencephalon (purple).

Running through the midbrain is the hollow *cerebral aqueduct*, which connects the third and fourth ventricles (Figures 12.12 and 12.16a). It delineates the cerebral peduncles ventrally from the *tectum*, the midbrain's roof. Surrounding the aqueduct is the *periaqueductal gray matter*, which is involved in pain suppression and serves as the link between the fear-perceiving amygdala and ANS pathways that control the "fight-or-flight" response. The periaqueductal gray matter also includes nuclei that control two cranial nerves, the *oculomotor* and the *trochlear nuclei* (trok′le-ar).

Nuclei are also scattered in the surrounding white matter of the midbrain. The largest of these are the **corpora quadrigemina** (kor′por-ah kwod″ri-jem′i-nah; "quadruplets"), which raise four domelike protrusions on the dorsal midbrain surface (Figures 12.12 and 12.15c). The superior pair, the **superior colliculi** (kŏ-lik′u-li), are visual reflex centers that coordinate head and eye movements when we visually follow a moving object, even if we are not consciously looking at the object. The **inferior**

colliculi are part of the auditory relay from the hearing receptors of the ear to the sensory cortex. They also act in reflexive responses to sound, such as in the *startle reflex*, which causes you to turn your head toward an unexpected sound.

Also embedded in each side of the midbrain white matter are two pigmented nuclei, the substantia nigra and red nucleus. The bandlike **substantia nigra** (sub-stan′she-ah ni′grah) is located deep to the cerebral peduncle (Figure 12.16a). Its dark (*nigr* = black) color reflects a high content of melanin pigment, a precursor of the neurotransmitter (dopamine) released by these neurons. The substantia nigra is functionally linked to the basal nuclei (its axons project to the putamen), and is considered part of the basal nuclear complex by many authorities. Degeneration of the dopamine-releasing neurons of the substantia nigra is the ultimate cause of Parkinson's disease.

The oval **red nucleus** lies deep to the substantia nigra (Figure 12.16a). Its reddish hue is due to its rich blood supply and to

12

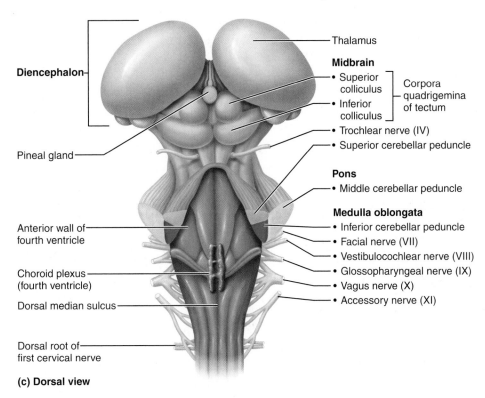

Diencephalon

Pineal gland

Anterior wall of
fourth ventricle

Choroid plexus
(fourth ventricle)

Dorsal median sulcus

Dorsal root of
first cervical nerve

Thalamus

Midbrain
- Superior colliculus ⎤ Corpora
- Inferior colliculus ⎦ quadrigemina of tectum
- Trochlear nerve (IV)
- Superior cerebellar peduncle

Pons
- Middle cerebellar peduncle

Medulla oblongata
- Inferior cerebellar peduncle
- Facial nerve (VII)
- Vestibulocochlear nerve (VIII)
- Glossopharyngeal nerve (IX)
- Vagus nerve (X)
- Accessory nerve (XI)

(c) Dorsal view

Figure 12.15 *(continued)*

the presence of iron pigment in its neurons. The red nuclei are relay nuclei in some descending motor pathways that effect limb flexion, and they are embedded in the *reticular formation,* a system of small nuclei scattered through the core of the brain stem (see pp. 452–453).

Pons

The **pons** is the bulging brain stem region wedged between the midbrain and the medulla oblongata (see Figures 12.12, 12.14, and 12.15). Dorsally, it forms part of the anterior wall of the fourth ventricle.

As its name suggests (*pons* = bridge), the pons is chiefly composed of conduction tracts. They are oriented in two different directions. The deep projection fibers run longitudinally and complete the pathway between higher brain centers and the spinal cord. The more superficial ventral fibers are oriented transversely and dorsally. They form the *middle cerebellar peduncles* and connect the pons bilaterally with the two sides of the cerebellum dorsally (Figure 12.15). These fibers issue from numerous *pontine nuclei*, which act as relays for "conversations" between the motor cortex and cerebellum.

Several cranial nerve pairs issue from pontine nuclei. They include the *trigeminal* (tri-jem′ĭ-nal), the *abducens* (ab-du′senz), and the *facial nerves* (Figures 12.15a, b and 12.16b). We discuss the cranial nerves and their functions in Chapter 13. Other important pontine nuclei are part of the reticular formation and some help the medulla maintain the normal rhythm of breathing.

Medulla Oblongata

The conical **medulla oblongata** (mě-dul′ah ob″long-gah′tah), or simply **medulla**, is the most inferior part of the brain stem. It blends imperceptibly into the spinal cord at the level of the foramen magnum of the skull (Figures 12.12 and 12.14; see Figure 7.6, p. 205). The central canal of the spinal cord continues upward into the medulla, where it broadens out to form the cavity of the fourth ventricle. Together, the medulla and the pons form the ventral wall of the fourth ventricle. [The dorsal ventricular wall is formed by a thin capillary-rich membrane called a choroid plexus which abuts the cerebellum dorsally (Figure 12.12).]

Flanking the midline on the medulla's ventral aspect are two longitudinal ridges called **pyramids,** formed by the large pyramidal (corticospinal) tracts descending from the motor cortex (Figure 12.16c). Just above the medulla–spinal cord junction, most of these fibers cross over to the opposite side before continuing into the spinal cord. This crossover point is called the **decussation of the pyramids** (de″kus-sa′shun; "a crossing"). As we mentioned earlier, the consequence of this crossover is that each cerebral hemisphere chiefly controls the voluntary movements of muscles on the opposite side of the body.

Also visible externally are several other structures. The *inferior cerebellar peduncles* are fiber tracts that connect the medulla to the cerebellum dorsally. Situated lateral to the pyramids, the **olives** are oval swellings (which *do* resemble olives) (Figure 12.15b). These swellings are caused mainly by the wavy folds of gray matter of the underlying **inferior olivary nuclei** (Figure 12.16c). These nuclei relay sensory information on the

12

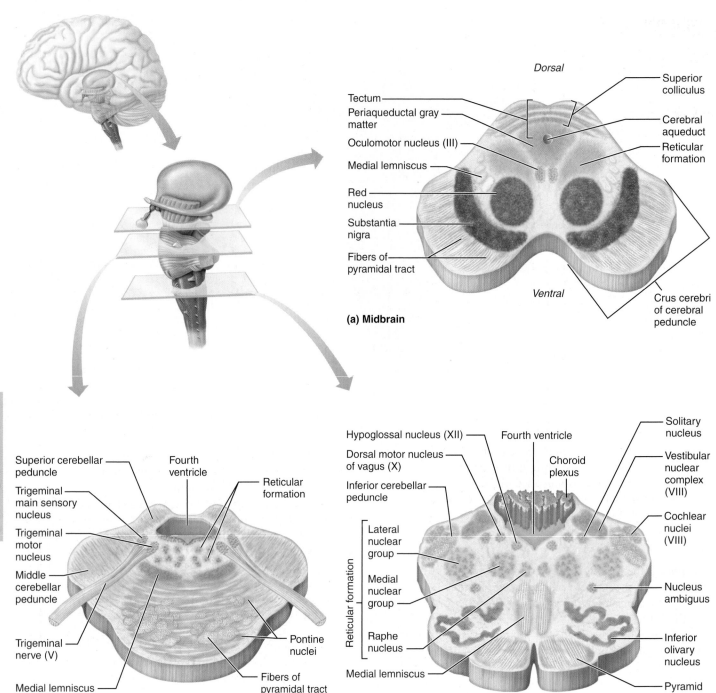

Figure 12.16 Cross sections through different regions of the brain stem.

Within the figure:

(a) Midbrain
- Dorsal
- Tectum
- Periaqueductal gray matter
- Oculomotor nucleus (III)
- Medial lemniscus
- Red nucleus
- Substantia nigra
- Fibers of pyramidal tract
- Superior colliculus
- Cerebral aqueduct
- Reticular formation
- Ventral
- Crus cerebri of cerebral peduncle

(b) Pons
- Superior cerebellar peduncle
- Trigeminal main sensory nucleus
- Trigeminal motor nucleus
- Middle cerebellar peduncle
- Trigeminal nerve (V)
- Medial lemniscus
- Fourth ventricle
- Reticular formation
- Pontine nuclei
- Fibers of pyramidal tract

(c) Medulla oblongata
- Hypoglossal nucleus (XII)
- Dorsal motor nucleus of vagus (X)
- Inferior cerebellar peduncle
- Reticular formation: Lateral nuclear group, Medial nuclear group, Raphe nucleus
- Medial lemniscus
- Fourth ventricle
- Choroid plexus
- Solitary nucleus
- Vestibular nuclear complex (VIII)
- Cochlear nuclei (VIII)
- Nucleus ambiguus
- Inferior olivary nucleus
- Pyramid

state of stretch of muscles and joints to the cerebellum. The rootlets of the *hypoglossal nerves* emerge from the groove between the pyramid and olive on each side of the brain stem. Other cranial nerves associated with the medulla are the *glossopharyngeal nerves* and *vagus nerves*. Additionally, the fibers of the *vestibulocochlear nerves* (ves-tib″u-lo-kok′le-ar) synapse with the **cochlear nuclei** (auditory relays), and with numerous vestibular nuclei in both the pons and medulla. Collectively, the vestibular nuclei, called the **vestibular nuclear complex**, mediate responses that maintain equilibrium.

Also housed in the medulla are several nuclei associated with ascending sensory tracts. The most prominent are the dorsally located **nucleus gracilis** (grah-sĭ′lis) and **nucleus cuneatus** (ku′ne-āt-us), associated with a tract called the *medial lemniscus* (Figure 12.16). These serve as relay nuclei in a pathway by which general somatic sensory information ascends from the spinal cord to the somatosensory cortex.

The small size of the medulla belies its crucial role as an autonomic reflex center involved in maintaining body homeo-

TABLE 12.1	**Functions of Major Brain Regions**
REGION	**FUNCTION**

Cerebral Hemispheres (pp. 433–441)

Cortical gray matter: Localizes and interprets sensory inputs, controls voluntary and skilled skeletal muscle activity, and functions in intellectual and emotional processing.

Basal nuclei (ganglia): Subcortical motor centers important in initiation of skeletal muscle movements.

Diencephalon (pp. 441–445)

Thalamic nuclei: Relay stations in conduction of (1) sensory impulses to cerebral cortex for interpretation, and (2) impulses to and from cerebral motor cortex and lower (subcortical) motor centers, including cerebellum. The thalamus is also involved in memory processing.

Hypothalamus: Chief integration center of autonomic (involuntary) nervous system; it functions in regulation of body temperature, food intake, water balance, thirst, and biological rhythms and drives. It regulates hormonal output of anterior pituitary gland and is an endocrine organ in its own right (produces ADH and oxytocin). Part of limbic system.

Limbic system (p. 452)

A functional system involving cerebral and diencephalon structures that mediates emotional response; also involved in memory processing.

Brain Stem (pp. 445–449)

Midbrain: Conduction pathway between higher and lower brain centers (e.g., cerebral peduncles contain the fibers of the pyramidal tracts). Its superior and inferior colliculi are visual and auditory reflex centers; substantia nigra and red nuclei are subcortical motor centers; contains nuclei for cranial nerves III and IV.

Pons: Conduction pathway between higher and lower brain centers; pontine nuclei relay information from the cerebrum to the cerebellum. Its respiratory nuclei cooperate with the medullary respiratory centers to control respiratory rate and depth. Houses nuclei of cranial nerves V–VII.

Medulla oblongata: Conduction pathway between higher brain centers and spinal cord, and site of decussation of the pyramidal tracts. Houses nuclei of cranial nerves VIII–XII. Contains nuclei cuneatus and gracilis (synapse points of ascending sensory pathways transmitting sensory impulses from skin and proprioceptors), and visceral nuclei controlling heart rate, blood vessel diameter, respiratory rate, vomiting, coughing, etc. Its inferior olivary nuclei provide the sensory relay to the cerebellum.

Reticular formation (pp. 452–453)

A functional brain stem system that maintains cerebral cortical alertness (reticular activating system) and filters out repetitive stimuli. Its motor nuclei help regulate skeletal and visceral muscle activity.

Cerebellum (pp. 450–451)

Processes information from cerebral motor cortex and from proprioceptors and visual and equilibrium pathways, and provides "instructions" to cerebral motor cortex and subcortical motor centers that result in proper balance and posture and smooth, coordinated skeletal muscle movements.

stasis, as summarized in **Table 12.1.** Important visceral motor nuclei found in the medulla include the following:

1. **Cardiovascular center.** This includes the *cardiac center*, which adjusts the force and rate of heart contraction to meet the body's needs, and the *vasomotor center*, which changes blood vessel diameter to regulate blood pressure.
2. **Respiratory centers.** These generate the respiratory rhythm and (in concert with pontine centers) control the rate and depth of breathing.

3. **Various other centers.** Additional centers regulate such activities as vomiting, hiccuping, swallowing, coughing, and sneezing.

Notice that many functions listed above are also attributed to the hypothalamus (pp. 443–444). The overlap is easily explained. The hypothalamus exerts its control over many visceral functions by relaying its instructions through medullary reticular centers, which carry them out.

10. What are the pyramids of the medulla? What is the result of decussation of the pyramids?
11. Which region of the brain stem is associated with the cerebral peduncles and the superior and inferior colliculi?

For answers, see Appendix G.

Cerebellum

▶ Describe the structure and function of the cerebellum.

The cauliflower-like **cerebellum** (ser″ĕ-bel′um; "small brain"), exceeded in size only by the cerebrum, accounts for about 11% of total brain mass. The cerebellum is located dorsal to the pons and medulla (and to the intervening fourth ventricle). It protrudes under the occipital lobes of the cerebral hemispheres, from which it is separated by the transverse cerebral fissure (see Figure 12.6d).

By processing inputs received from the cerebral motor cortex, various brain stem nuclei, and sensory receptors, the cerebellum provides the precise timing and appropriate patterns of skeletal muscle contraction for smooth, coordinated movements and agility needed for our daily living—driving, typing, and for some of us, playing the tuba. Cerebellar activity occurs subconsciously—we have no awareness of its functioning.

Anatomy

The cerebellum is bilaterally symmetrical. Its two apple-sized **cerebellar hemispheres** are connected medially by the wormlike **vermis** (Figure 12.17). Its surface is heavily convoluted, with fine, transversely oriented pleatlike gyri known as **folia** ("leaves"). Deep fissures subdivide each hemisphere into **anterior**, **posterior**, and **flocculonodular lobes** (flok″u-lo-nod′u-lar). The small propeller-shaped flocculonodular lobes, situated deep to the vermis and posterior lobe, cannot be seen in a surface view.

Like the cerebrum, the cerebellum has a thin outer cortex of gray matter, internal white matter, and small, deeply situated, paired masses of gray matter, the most familiar of which are the *dentate nuclei*. Several types of neurons populate the cerebellar cortex, including **Purkinje cells** (see Table 11.1 on p. 393). These large cells, with their extensively branched dendrites, are the only cortical neurons that send axons through the white matter to synapse with the central nuclei of the cerebellum. The distinctive pattern of white matter in the cerebellum resembles a branching tree, a pattern fancifully called the **arbor vitae** (ar′bor vi′te; "tree of life") (Figure 12.17a, b).

The anterior and posterior lobes of the cerebellum, which coordinate body movements, have three sensory maps of the entire body as indicated by the homunculi in Figure 12.17d. The part of the cerebellar cortex that receives sensory input from a body region influences motor output to that region. The medial portions influence the motor activities of the trunk and girdle muscles. The intermediate parts of each hemisphere are more concerned with the distal parts of the limbs and skilled movements. The lateralmost parts of each hemisphere integrate information from the association areas of the cerebral cortex and appear to play a role in planning rather than executing

movements. The flocculonodular lobes receive inputs from the equilibrium apparatus of the inner ears, and adjust posture to maintain balance.

Cerebellar Peduncles

As noted earlier, three paired fiber tracts—the cerebellar peduncles—connect the cerebellum to the brain stem (see Figures 12.15 and 12.17b). Unlike the contralateral fiber distribution to and from the cerebral cortex, virtually all fibers entering and leaving the cerebellum are **ipsilateral** (*ipsi* = same)—from and to the same side of the body. The **superior cerebellar peduncles** connecting cerebellum and midbrain carry instructions from neurons in the deep cerebellar nuclei to the cerebral motor cortex via thalamic relays. Like the basal nuclei, the cerebellum has no *direct* connections to the cerebral cortex.

The **middle cerebellar peduncles** carry one-way communication from the pons to the cerebellum, advising the cerebellum of voluntary motor activities initiated by the motor cortex (via relays in the pontine nuclei). The **inferior cerebellar peduncles** connect medulla and cerebellum. These peduncles convey sensory information to the cerebellum from (1) muscle proprioceptors throughout the body and (2) the vestibular nuclei of the brain stem, which are concerned with equilibrium and balance.

Cerebellar Processing

The functional scheme of cerebellar processing for motor activity seems to be as follows:

1. The motor areas of the cerebral cortex, via relay nuclei in the brain stem, notify the cerebellum of their intent to initiate voluntary muscle contractions.
2. At the same time, the cerebellum receives information from proprioceptors throughout the body (regarding tension in the muscles and tendons, and joint position) and from visual and equilibrium pathways. This information enables the cerebellum to evaluate body position and momentum, that is, where the body is and where it is going.
3. The cerebellar cortex calculates the best way to coordinate the force, direction, and extent of muscle contraction to prevent overshoot, maintain posture, and ensure smooth, coordinated movements.
4. Then, via the superior peduncles, the cerebellum dispatches to the cerebral motor cortex its "blueprint" for coordinating movement. Cerebellar fibers also send information to brain stem nuclei, which in turn influence motor neurons of the spinal cord.

Just as an automatic pilot compares a plane's instrument readings with the planned course, the cerebellum continually compares the body's performance with the higher brain's intention and sends out messages to initiate the appropriate corrective measures. Cerebellar injury results in loss of muscle tone and clumsy, unsure movements.

Cognitive Function of the Cerebellum

Functional imaging studies indicate that the cerebellum plays a role in cognition. The cerebellum recognizes and predicts se-

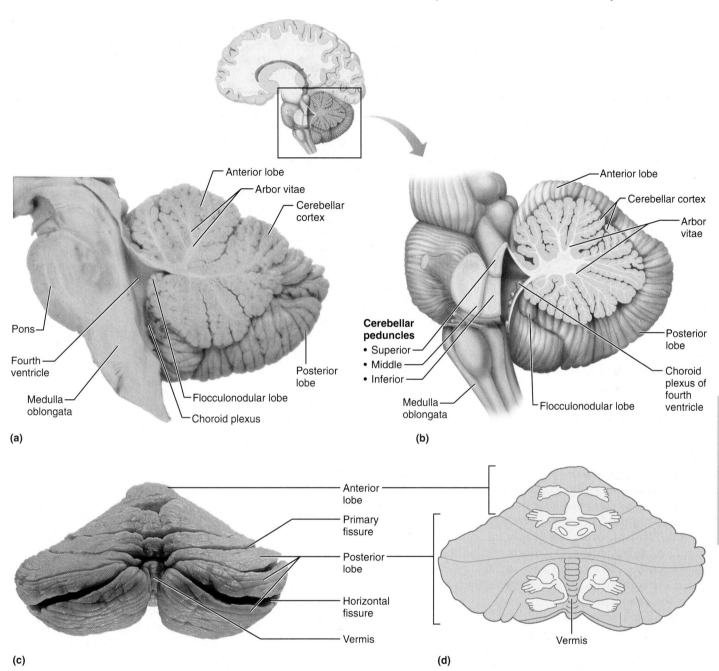

Figure 12.17 Cerebellum. (a) Photo of midsagittal section. **(b)** Drawing of parasagittal section. **(c)** Photograph of the posterior aspect of the cerebellum. **(d)** Three body maps of the cerebellar cortex (in the form of homunculi).

quences of events so that it may adjust for the multiple forces exerted on a limb during complex movements involving several joints. Some nonmotor functions, including word association and puzzle solving, also appear to involve the cerebellum.

CHECK YOUR UNDERSTANDING

12. In what ways are the cerebellum and the cerebrum similar? In what ways are they different?

For answers, see Appendix G.

Functional Brain Systems

▶ Locate the limbic system and the reticular formation, and explain the role of each functional system.

Functional brain systems are networks of neurons that work together but span relatively large distances in the brain, so they cannot be localized to specific brain regions. The *limbic system* and the *reticular formation* are excellent examples. Table 12.1 (p. 449) summarizes their functions, as well as those of the cerebral hemispheres, diencephalon, brain stem, and cerebellum.

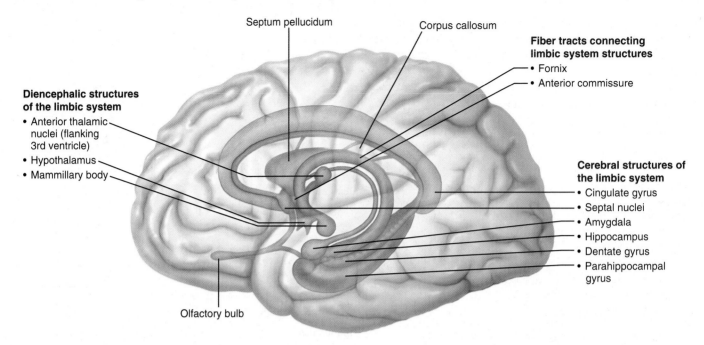

Figure 12.18 The limbic system. Lateral view of the brain, showing some of the structures of the limbic system, the emotional-visceral brain. The brain stem is not illustrated.

The Limbic System

The **limbic system** is a group of structures located on the medial aspect of each cerebral hemisphere and diencephalon. Its cerebral structures encircle (*limbus* = ring) the upper part of the brain stem (Figure 12.18). Included are parts of the rhinencephalon (*septal nuclei, cingulate gyrus, parahippocampal gyrus, dentate gyrus*, and C-shaped *hippocampus*), and the **amygdala** (ah-mig′dah-lah), an almond-shaped nucleus that sits on the tail of the caudate nucleus. In the diencephalon, the main limbic structures are the *hypothalamus* and the *anterior thalamic nuclei.* The **fornix** ("arch") and other fiber tracts link these limbic system regions together.

The limbic system is our *emotional,* or *affective* (feelings), *brain.* Two parts seem especially important in emotions—the amygdala and the anterior part of the **cingulate gyrus**. The amygdala recognizes angry or fearful facial expressions, assesses danger, and elicits the fear response. The cingulate gyrus plays a role in expressing our emotions through gestures and in resolving mental conflicts when we are frustrated.

Odors often trigger emotional reactions and memories. These responses reflect the origin of much of the limbic system in the primitive "smell brain" (rhinencephalon). Our reactions to odors are rarely neutral (a skunk smells *bad* and repulses us), and odors often recall memories of emotion-laden events.

Extensive connections between the limbic system and lower and higher brain regions allow the system to integrate and respond to a variety of environmental stimuli. Most limbic system output is relayed through the hypothalamus. Because the hypothalamus is the neural clearinghouse for both autonomic (visceral) function and emotional response, it is not surprising that some people under acute or unrelenting emotional stress fall prey to visceral illnesses, such as high blood pressure and heartburn. Such emotion-induced illnesses are called **psychosomatic illnesses**.

Because the limbic system interacts with the prefrontal lobes, there is an intimate relationship between our feelings (mediated by the emotional brain) and our thoughts (mediated by the cognitive brain). As a result, we (1) react emotionally to things we consciously understand to be happening, and (2) are consciously aware of the emotional richness of our lives. Communication between the cerebral cortex and limbic system explains why emotions sometimes override logic and, conversely, why reason can stop us from expressing our emotions in inappropriate situations. Particular limbic system structures—the **hippocampus** and amygdala—also play a role in memory.

The Reticular Formation

The **reticular formation** extends through the central core of the medulla oblongata, pons, and midbrain (Figure 12.19). It is composed of loosely clustered neurons in what is otherwise white matter. These neurons form three broad columns along the length of the brain stem (Figure 12.16c): (1) the midline **raphe nuclei** (ra′fe; *raphe* = seam or crease), which are flanked laterally by (2) the **medial (large cell) group** and then (3) the **lateral (small cell) group of nuclei**.

The outstanding feature of the reticular neurons is their far-flung axonal connections. Individual reticular neurons project to the hypothalamus, thalamus, cerebral cortex, cerebellum, and spinal cord, making reticular neurons ideal for governing the arousal of the brain as a whole. For example, certain reticular neurons, unless inhibited by other brain areas, send a continuous stream of impulses to the cerebral cortex, keeping the cortex alert and conscious and enhancing its excitability. This arm of the reticular formation is known as the **reticular activating system (RAS)**. Impulses from all the great ascending sensory tracts synapse with RAS neurons, keeping them active and enhancing their arousing effect on the cerebrum. (This may explain why many students, stimulated by a bustling environment, like to study in a crowded cafeteria.)

The RAS also acts like a filter for this flood of sensory inputs. Repetitive, familiar, or weak signals are filtered out, but unusual, significant, or strong impulses do reach consciousness. For example, you are probably unaware of your watch encircling your wrist, but would immediately notice it if the clasp broke. Between them, the RAS and the cerebral cortex disregard perhaps 99% of all sensory stimuli as unimportant. If this filtering did not occur, the sensory overload would drive us crazy. The drug LSD interferes with these sensory dampers, promoting an often overwhelming sensory overload.

- Take a moment to become aware of all the stimuli in your environment. Notice all the colors, shapes, odors, sounds, and so on. How many of these sensory stimuli are you usually aware of?

The RAS is inhibited by sleep centers located in the hypothalamus and other neural regions, and is depressed by alcohol, sleep-inducing drugs, and tranquilizers. Severe injury to this system, as might follow a knockout punch that twists the brain stem, results in permanent unconsciousness (irreversible *coma*). Although the RAS is central to wakefulness, some of its nuclei are also involved in sleep, which we will discuss later in this chapter.

The reticular formation also has a *motor* arm. Some of its motor nuclei project to motor neurons in the spinal cord via the *reticulospinal tracts*, and help control skeletal muscles during coarse limb movements. Other reticular motor nuclei, such as the vasomotor, cardiac, and respiratory centers of the medulla, are autonomic centers that regulate visceral motor functions.

CHECK YOUR UNDERSTANDING

13. The limbic system is sometimes called the emotional-visceral brain. Which part of the limbic system is responsible for the visceral connection?

14. When Taylor begins to feel drowsy while driving, she opens her window, turns up the volume of the car stereo, and has sips of her ice-cold water. How do these actions keep her awake?

For answers, see Appendix G.

Higher Mental Functions

During the last four decades, an exciting exploration of our "inner space," or what we commonly call *the mind*, has been going on. But researchers in the field of cognition are still struggling to understand how the mind's presently incomprehensible

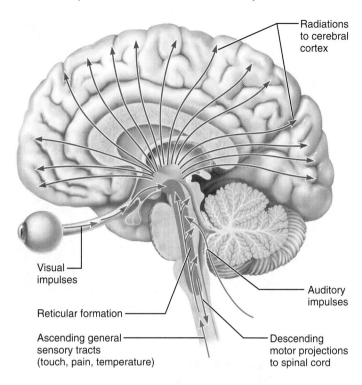

Radiations to cerebral cortex

Visual impulses

Reticular formation

Ascending general sensory tracts (touch, pain, temperature)

Auditory impulses

Descending motor projections to spinal cord

Figure 12.19 The reticular formation. This functional brain system extends the length of the brain stem. Part of this formation, the reticular activating system (RAS), maintains alert wakefulness of the cerebral cortex. Ascending blue arrows indicate input of sensory systems to the RAS. Purple arrows indicate reticular output (some via thalamic relays) to the cerebral cortex. Descending red arrow represents motor output involved in regulating muscle tone.

qualities might spring from living tissue and electrical impulses. Souls and synapses are hard to reconcile!

Because brain waves reflect the electrical activity on which higher mental functions are based, we will consider them first, along with the related topics of consciousness and sleep. We will then examine language and memory, an area of ongoing research that is of particular interest to our aging population.

Brain Wave Patterns and the EEG

▶ Define EEG and distinguish between alpha, beta, theta, and delta brain waves.

Normal brain function involves continuous electrical activity of neurons. An **electroencephalogram** (e-lek″tro-en-sef′ah-logram), or **EEG**, records some aspects of this activity. An EEG is made by placing electrodes on the scalp and then connecting the electrodes to an apparatus that measures electrical potential differences between various cortical areas **(Figure 12.20a)**. The patterns of neuronal electrical activity recorded, called **brain waves**, are generated by synaptic activity at the surface of the cortex, rather than by action potentials in the white matter.

Each of us has a brain wave pattern that is as unique as our fingerprints. For simplicity, however, we can group brain waves into the four frequency classes shown in Figure 12.20b. Each wave is a continuous train of peaks and troughs, and the wave

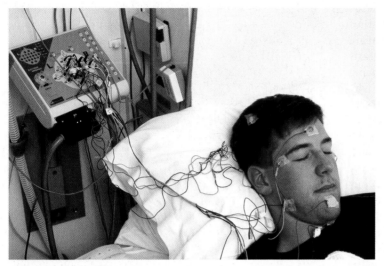

(a) Scalp electrodes are used to record brain wave activity (EEG).

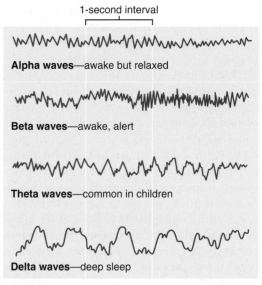

1-second interval

Alpha waves—awake but relaxed

Beta waves—awake, alert

Theta waves—common in children

Delta waves—deep sleep

(b) Brain waves shown in EEGs fall into four general classes.

Figure 12.20   Electroencephalography and brain waves.

frequency, expressed in hertz (Hz), is the number of peaks in one second. A frequency of 1 Hz means that one peak occurs each second.

The amplitude or intensity of any wave is represented by how high the wave peaks rise and how low the troughs dip. The amplitude of brain waves reflects the synchronous activity of many neurons and not the degree of electrical activity of individual neurons. Usually, brain waves are complex and low amplitude. During some stages of sleep, neurons tend to fire synchronously, producing similar, high-amplitude brain waves.

- **Alpha waves** (8–13 Hz) are relatively regular and rhythmic, low-amplitude, synchronous waves. In most cases, they indicate a brain that is "idling"—a calm, relaxed state of wakefulness.
- **Beta waves** (14–30 Hz) are also rhythmic, but they are not as regular as alpha waves and have a higher frequency. Beta waves occur when we are mentally alert, as when concentrating on some problem or visual stimulus.
- **Theta waves** (4–7 Hz) are still more irregular. Though common in children, theta waves are uncommon in awake adults but may appear when concentrating.
- **Delta waves** (4 Hz or less) are high-amplitude waves seen during deep sleep and when the reticular activating system is damped, such as during anesthesia. In awake adults, they indicate brain damage.

Brain waves change with age, sensory stimuli, brain disease, and the chemical state of the body. EEGs are used for diagnosing epilepsy and sleep disorders, and in research on brain function. Interference with cerebral cortical functions is suggested when the frequency of brain waves is too high or too low, and unconsciousness occurs at both extremes. Because spontaneous brain waves are always present, even during unconsciousness and coma, their absence—called a "flat EEG"—is clinical evidence of brain death.

HOMEOSTATIC IMBALANCE

Almost without warning, a victim of epilepsy may lose consciousness and fall stiffly to the ground, body wracked by uncontrollable jerking. These **epileptic seizures** reflect a torrent of electrical discharges of groups of brain neurons, and while their uncontrolled activity is occurring, no other messages can get through. Epilepsy, manifested by one out of 100 of us, is not associated with, nor does it cause, intellectual impairment. Some cases of epilepsy are induced by genetic factors, but it can also result from brain injuries caused by blows to the head, stroke, infections, high fever, or tumors.

Epileptic seizures can vary tremendously in their expression and severity. *Absence seizures*, formerly known as *petit mal*, are mild forms in which the expression goes blank for a few seconds as consciousness disappears. These are typically seen in young children and usually disappear by the age of 10. In the most severe, convulsive form of epileptic seizures, *tonic-clonic* (formerly called *grand mal*), the person loses consciousness. Bones are often broken during the intense convulsions, showing the incredible strength of the muscle contractions that occur. Loss of bowel and bladder control and severe biting of the tongue are common. The seizure lasts for a few minutes, then the muscles relax and the person awakens but remains disoriented for several minutes. Many seizure sufferers experience a sensory hallucination, such as a taste, smell, or flashes of light, just before the seizure begins. This phenomenon, called an **aura**, is helpful because it gives the person time to lie down and avoid falling to the floor.

Epilepsy can usually be controlled by anticonvulsive drugs. Newer on the scene is the *vagus nerve stimulator*, which is implanted under the skin of the chest and delivers pulses via the vagus nerve to the brain at predetermined intervals to keep the electrical activity of the brain from becoming chaotic. A current line of research seeks to use electrodes implanted in the brain to

12

detect coming seizures in time to deliver programmed electrical stimulation to avert the seizure. ■

Consciousness

▶ Describe consciousness clinically.

Consciousness encompasses conscious perception of sensations, voluntary initiation and control of movement, and capabilities associated with higher mental processing (memory, logic, judgment, perseverance, and so on). Clinically, consciousness is defined on a continuum that grades behavior in response to stimuli as (1) *alertness*, (2) *drowsiness* or *lethargy* (which proceeds to sleep), (3) *stupor*, and (4) *coma*. Alertness is the highest state of consciousness and cortical activity, and coma the most depressed.

Consciousness is difficult to define. And to be perfectly frank, reducing our response to the palette of a Key West sunset to a series of interactions between dendrites, axons, and neurotransmitters does not capture what makes that event so special. A sleeping person obviously lacks something that he or she has when awake, and we call this "something" consciousness.

The current suppositions about consciousness are as follows:

1. **It involves simultaneous activity of large areas of the cerebral cortex.**
2. **It is superimposed on other types of neural activity.** At any time, specific neurons and neuronal pools are involved both in localized activities (such as motor control) and in cognition.
3. **It is holistic and totally interconnected.** Information for "thought" can be claimed from many locations in the cerebrum simultaneously. For example, retrieval of a specific memory can be triggered by several routes—a smell, a place, a particular person, and so on.

HOMEOSTATIC IMBALANCE

Except when a person is sleeping, unconsciousness is always a signal that brain function is impaired. A brief loss of consciousness is called **fainting** or **syncope** (sing′ko-pe; "cut short"). Most often, it indicates inadequate cerebral blood flow due to low blood pressure, as might follow hemorrhage or sudden emotional stress.

Total unresponsiveness to sensory stimuli for an extended period is called **coma**. Coma is *not* deep sleep. During sleep, the brain is active and oxygen consumption resembles that of the waking state. In coma patients, in contrast, oxygen use is always below normal resting levels.

Blows to the head may induce coma by causing widespread cerebral or brain stem trauma. Tumors or infections that invade the brain stem may also produce coma. Metabolic disturbances such as hypoglycemia (abnormally low blood sugar levels), drug overdose, or liver or kidney failure interfere with overall brain function and can result in coma. Strokes rarely cause coma unless they are massive and accompanied by extreme swelling of the brain, or are located in the brain stem.

When the brain has suffered irreparable damage, irreversible coma occurs, even though life-support measures may have re-

stored vitality to other body organs. The result is **brain death**, a dead brain in an otherwise living body. Because life support can be removed only after death, physicians must determine whether a patient in an irreversible coma is legally alive or dead. ■

Sleep and Sleep-Wake Cycles

▶ Compare and contrast the events and importance of slow-wave and REM sleep, and indicate how their patterns change through life.

Sleep is defined as a state of partial unconsciousness from which a person can be aroused by stimulation. This distinguishes sleep from coma, a state of unconsciousness from which a person *cannot* be aroused by even the most vigorous stimuli. For the most part, cortical activity is depressed during sleep, but brain stem functions, such as control of respiration, heart rate, and blood pressure, continue. Even environmental monitoring continues to some extent, as illustrated by the fact that strong stimuli ("things that go bump in the night") immediately arouse us. In fact, people who sleepwalk can avoid objects and navigate stairs while truly asleep.

Types of Sleep

The two major types of sleep, which alternate through most of the sleep cycle, are **non–rapid eye movement (NREM) sleep** and **rapid eye movement (REM) sleep**, defined in terms of their EEG patterns. During the first 30 to 45 minutes of the sleep cycle, we pass through the first two stages of NREM sleep and into NREM stages 3 and 4, also called **slow-wave sleep** (Figure 12.21b). As we pass through these stages and slip into deeper and deeper sleep, the frequency of the EEG waves declines, but their amplitude increases (Figure 12.21). Blood pressure and heart rate also decrease with deeper sleep.

About 90 minutes after sleep begins, after NREM stage 4 has been achieved, the EEG pattern changes abruptly. It becomes very irregular and appears to backtrack quickly through the stages until alpha waves (more typical of the awake state) appear, indicating the onset of REM sleep. This brain wave change is coupled with increases in heart rate, respiratory rate, and blood pressure and a decrease in gastrointestinal motility. Oxygen use by the brain is tremendous during REM—greater than during the awake state.

Although the eyes move rapidly under the lids during REM, most of the body's skeletal muscles are actively inhibited and go limp. This temporary paralysis prevents us from acting out our dreams. Most dreaming occurs during REM sleep, and some suggest that the flitting eye movements are following the visual imagery of our dreams. (Note, however, that most nightmares and night terrors occur during NREM stages 3 and 4.) In adolescents and adults, REM episodes are frequently associated with erection of the penis or engorgement of the clitoris.

Sleep Patterns

The alternating cycles of sleep and wakefulness reflect a natural *circadian*, or 24-hour, *rhythm*. The hypothalamus is responsible

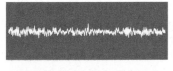

Awake

REM: Skeletal muscles (except ocular muscles and diaphragm) are actively inhibited; most dreaming occurs.

NREM stage 1: Relaxation begins; EEG shows alpha waves, arousal is easy.

NREM stage 2: Irregular EEG with sleep spindles (short high-amplitude bursts); arousal is more difficult.

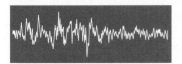

NREM stage 3: Sleep deepens; theta and delta waves appear; vital signs decline.

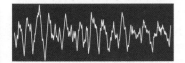

NREM stage 4: EEG is dominated by delta waves; arousal is difficult; bed-wetting, night terrors, and sleepwalking may occur.

(a) Typical EEG patterns

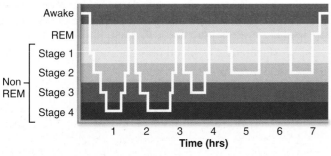

(b) Typical progression of an adult through one night's sleep stages

Figure 12.21 Types and stages of sleep. The four stages of non–rapid eye movement (NREM) sleep and rapid eye movement (REM) sleep are shown.

for the timing of the sleep cycle. Its *suprachiasmatic nucleus* (a biological clock) regulates its *preoptic nucleus* (a sleep-inducing center). By inhibiting the brain stem's reticular activating system (RAS; see Figure 12.19), the preoptic nucleus puts the cerebral cortex to sleep. However, sleep is much more than simply turning off the arousal system. RAS centers not only help maintain the awake state but also mediate some sleep stages, especially dreaming sleep.

In young and middle-aged adults, a typical night's sleep starts with the four stages of NREM sleep and then alternates between REM and NREM sleep with occasional partial arousals. Following each REM episode, the sleeper descends toward stage 4 again.

REM recurs about every 90 minutes, with each REM period getting longer. The first REM of the night lasts 5–10 minutes and the final one 20 to 50 minutes (Figure 12.21b). Consequently, our longest dreams occur at the end of the sleep period. Just before we wake, hypothalamic neurons release peptides called *orexins*, which in this situation act as "wake-up" chemicals. As a result, certain neurons of the brain stem reticular formation fire at maximal rates, arousing the sleepy cortex.

The slow theta and delta waves of deep sleep are the result of synchronized firing of thalamic neurons that is normally inhibited during wakefulness by the RAS of the pons. Some pontine neurons of the reticular formation control the transition from NREM sleep to REM sleep, and others suppress motor activity, inducing paralysis. A large number of chemical substances in the body cause sleepiness, but the relative importance of these various sleep-inducing substances is not known.

Importance of Sleep

Why do we sleep? Slow-wave (NREM stages 3 and 4) and REM sleep seem to be important in different ways. Slow-wave sleep is presumed to be restorative—the time when most neural activity can wind down to basal levels. When deprived of sleep, we spend more time than usual in slow-wave sleep during the next sleep episode.

A person persistently deprived of REM sleep becomes moody and depressed, and exhibits various personality disorders. REM sleep may give the brain an opportunity to analyze the day's events and to work through emotional problems in dream imagery. Another idea is that REM sleep is reverse learning. According to this hypothesis, accidental, repetitious, and meaningless communications continually occur, and they must be eliminated from the neural networks by dreaming if the cortex is to remain a well-behaved and efficient thinking system. In other words, we dream to forget.

Alcohol and some sleep medications (barbiturates and others) suppress REM sleep but not slow-wave sleep. On the other hand, certain tranquilizers, such as diazepam (Valium) reduce slow-wave sleep much more than REM sleep.

Whatever its importance, a person's daily sleep requirement declines steadily from 16 hours or so in infants to approximately 7½ to 8½ hours in early adulthood. It then levels off before declining once again in old age. Sleep patterns also change throughout life. REM sleep occupies about half the total sleeping time in infants and then declines until the age of 10 years, when it stabilizes at about 25%. In contrast, stage 4 sleep declines steadily from birth and often disappears completely in those over 60.

HOMEOSTATIC IMBALANCE

People with **narcolepsy** lapse abruptly into REM sleep from the awake state. These sleep episodes last about 15 minutes, can occur without warning at any time, and are often triggered by a pleasurable event—a good joke, a game of poker. In most patients with narcolepsy, an emotionally intense experience can also trigger *cataplexy*, a sudden loss of voluntary muscle control similar to that seen during REM sleep. During cataplectic attacks, lasting seconds to minutes, the patient remains fully conscious but unable to move. Obviously this can be extremely hazardous when a person is driving a car or swimming! It appears that the brains of patients with narcolepsy have fewer cells in the hypothalamus that secrete peptides called orexins (hypocretins), the peptides mentioned above as a wake-up chemical. This finding may be a key to future treatments. Conversely, drugs that block the actions of orexin have been shown to promote sleep and so may help treat an entirely different sleep disorder, insomnia.

Insomnia is a chronic inability to obtain the *amount* or *quality* of sleep needed to function adequately during the day. Sleep requirements vary from four to nine hours a day in healthy people, so there is no way to determine the "right" amount. Insomniacs tend to overestimate the extent of their sleeplessness, and some come to rely on hypnotics (sleep medications), which can exacerbate the problem.

True insomnia often reflects normal age-related changes, but perhaps the most common cause is psychological disturbance. We have difficulty falling asleep when we are anxious or upset, and depression is often accompanied by early awakening.

Sleep apnea, a temporary cessation of breathing during sleep, is scary. The victim awakes abruptly due to hypoxia (lack of oxygen)—a condition that may occur repeatedly throughout the night. Obstructive sleep apnea, the most common form, occurs when the loss of muscle tone during sleep allows excess fatty tissue or other structural abnormalities to block the upper airway. It is associated with obesity and made worse by alcohol and other depressants. Aside from weight loss, effective treatments are either a mask that allows air to be blown in through the nose, keeping the airway open, or surgery to correct the problem. ■

CHECK YOUR UNDERSTANDING

15. When would you see delta waves in an EEG?
16. Which two states of consciousness are between alertness and coma?
17. During which sleep stage are most skeletal muscles actively inhibited?

For answers, see Appendix G.

Language

Language is such an important function of the brain that practically all of the association cortex on the left side is involved in one way or another. Pioneering studies of patients with *aphasias* (the loss of language abilities due to damage to specific areas of the brain) pointed to two regions that are critically important for language, Broca's area and Wernicke's area (see areas outlined by dashes in Figure 12.8a). Patients with lesions involving **Broca's area** can understand language but have difficulty speaking (and sometimes cannot write or type or use sign language). On the other hand, patients with lesions involving **Wernicke's area** are able to speak but produce a type of nonsense often referred to as a "word salad." They also have great difficulty understanding language.

Recent functional studies of the brain indicate that this picture is clinically useful, but oversimplified. In fact, Broca's and Wernicke's areas together with the basal nuclei form a single language implementation system that analyzes incoming and produces outgoing word sounds and grammatical structures. A surrounding set of cortical areas forms a bridge between this system and the regions of cortex that hold concepts and ideas, which are distributed throughout the remainder of the association cortices.

The corresponding areas in the right or non-language-dominant hemisphere are involved in "body language"—the nonverbal emotional (affective) components of language. These areas allow the lilt or tone of our voice and our gestures to express our emotions when we speak, and permit us to comprehend the emotional content of what we hear. For example, a soft, melodious response to your question conveys quite a different meaning than a sharp reply.

Memory

▶ Compare and contrast the stages and categories of memory.

▶ Describe the relative roles of the major brain structures believed to be involved in declarative and procedural memories.

Memory is the storage and retrieval of information. Memories are essential for learning and incorporating our experiences into behavior and are part and parcel of our consciousness. Stored somewhere in your 3 pounds of wrinkled brain are zip codes, the face of your grandfather, and the taste of yesterday's pizza. Your memories reflect your lifetime.

Stages of Memory

Memory storage involves two distinct stages: short-term memory and long-term memory **(Figure 12.22)**. **Short-term memory (STM)**, also called *working memory*, is the preliminary step, as well as the power that lets you look up a telephone number, dial it, and then never think of it again. The capacity of STM is limited to seven or eight chunks of information, such as the digits of a telephone number or the sequence of words in an elaborate sentence.

In contrast, **long-term memory (LTM)** seems to have a limitless capacity. Although our STM cannot recall numbers much longer than a telephone number, we can remember scores of telephone numbers by committing them to LTM. However, long-term memories can be forgotten, and so our memory bank continually changes with time. Furthermore, our ability to store and to retrieve information declines with aging.

Figure 12.22 shows how information is processed for storage. We do not remember or even consciously notice much of what is going on around us. As sensory inputs flood into our cerebral cortex, they are processed (yellow box in Figure 12.22). Some 5% of this information is selected for transfer to STM (light green box in Figure 12.22). STM serves as a sort of temporary holding bin for data that we may or may not want to retain.

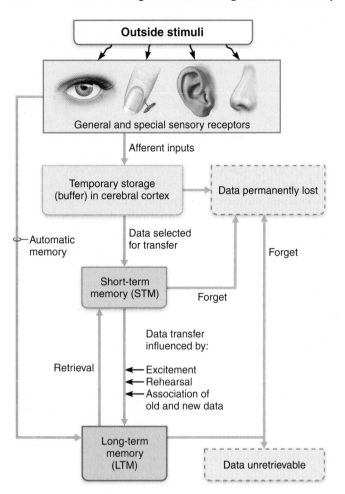

Figure 12.22 Memory processing.

Information is then transferred from STM to LTM (dark green box in Figure 12.22). This transfer is affected by many factors, including

1. **Emotional state.** We learn best when we are alert, motivated, surprised, and aroused. For example, when we witness shocking events, transferal is almost immediate. Norepinephrine, a neurotransmitter involved in memory processing of emotionally charged events, is released when we are excited or "stressed out," which helps to explain this phenomenon.
2. **Rehearsal.** Rehearsal or repetition of the material enhances memory.
3. **Association.** Tying "new" information to "old" information already stored in LTM appears to be important in remembering facts.
4. **Automatic memory.** Not all impressions that become part of LTM are consciously formed. A student concentrating on a lecturer's speech may record an automatic memory of the pattern of the lecturer's tie.

Memories transferred to LTM take time to become permanent. The process of **memory consolidation** apparently involves fitting new facts into the various categories of knowledge already stored in the cerebral cortex.

Categories of Memory

The brain distinguishes between factual knowledge and skills, and we process and store these different kinds of information in different ways. **Declarative (fact) memory** entails learning explicit information, such as names, faces, words, and dates. It is related to our conscious thoughts and our ability to manipulate symbols and language. When fact memories are committed to LTM, they are usually filed along with the context in which they were learned. For instance, when you think of your new acquaintance Joe, you probably picture him at the basketball game where you met him.

Nondeclarative memory is less conscious or even unconscious learning. Categories of nondeclarative memory are **procedural (skills) memory** (piano playing), **motor memory** (riding a bike), and **emotional memory** (your pounding heart when you hear a rattlesnake nearby). These kinds of memory are acquired through experience and usually repetition. They do not preserve the circumstances of learning, and in fact, they are best remembered in the doing. You do not have to think through how to tie your shoes. Once learned, nondeclarative memories are hard to unlearn.

Brain Structures Involved in Memory

Much of what scientists know about learning and memory comes from experiments with macaque monkeys, and functional imaging and studies of amnesia in humans. Such studies have revealed that different brain structures are involved in the two categories of memory.

It appears that specific pieces of each memory are stored near regions of the brain that need them so that new inputs can be quickly associated with the old. Accordingly, visual memories are stored in the occipital cortex, memories of music in the temporal cortex, and so on.

But how do we create new memories? It seems that different types of memory are created in different parts of the brain. A proposed scheme of information flow for declarative memory is shown in **Figure 12.23a**. When sensory input is processed in the association cortices, the cortical neurons dispatch impulses to the medial temporal lobe, which includes the hippocampus and surrounding temporal cortical areas. These temporal lobe areas play a major role in memory consolidation and memory access by communicating with the thalamus and the prefrontal cortex. The prefrontal cortex and medial temporal lobe receive input from acetylcholine-releasing neurons in the basal forebrain. The sprinkling of acetylcholine (ACh) onto these structures is thought to prime them to allow the formation of memories. The loss of this ACh input, for example in Alzheimer's disease, seems to disrupt both the formation of new memories and the retrieval of old ones. Memories are retrieved when the same sets of neurons that were initially involved in memory formation are stimulated.

HOMEOSTATIC IMBALANCE

Damage to the hippocampus and surrounding medial temporal lobe structures on either side results in only slight memory loss, but bilateral destruction causes widespread amnesia.

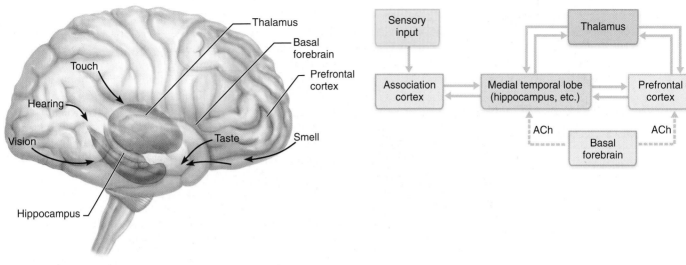

(a) Declarative memory circuits

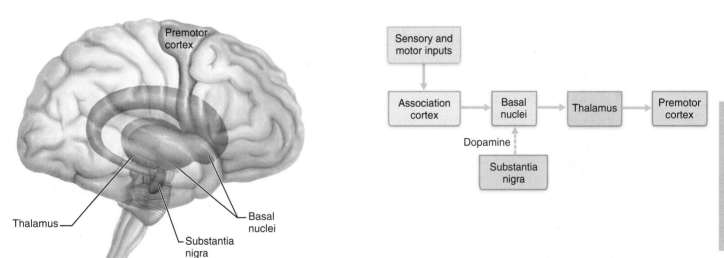

(b) Procedural (skills) memory circuits

Figure 12.23 Proposed memory circuits.
(a) Essential structures of declarative memory formation and flowchart showing how these structures may interact. Information from association cortices flows to the medial temporal lobe (including the hippocampus), which communicates with the thalamus and prefrontal cortex. The medial temporal lobe structures then feed back to the association cortices. Acetylcholine, released from the basal forebrain, is necessary for this circuit to function. **(b)** Essential structures of procedural (skills) memory. Sensory and motor input flows through the association cortices and is relayed via the basal nuclei through the thalamus to the premotor cortex. Dopamine, released from the substantia nigra, is necessary for this circuit to function.

Consolidated memories are not lost, but new sensory inputs cannot be associated with old, and the person lives in the here and now from that point on. This condition is called *anterograde amnesia* (an'ter-o-grād"), in contrast to *retrograde amnesia*, which is the loss of memories formed in the distant past. You could carry on an animated conversation with a person with anterograde amnesia, excuse yourself, return five minutes later, and that person would not remember you. ■

Individuals suffering from anterograde amnesia can still learn skills such as drawing, which means a different learning circuit must be used for procedural memory. As Figure 12.23b shows, the basal nuclei (pink) are key players for procedural memory. Sensory and motor inputs pass through the association cortex to the basal nuclei. These inputs are then relayed via the thalamus to the premotor cortex. Note that the basal nuclei receive input from dopamine-releasing neurons in the substantia nigra of the midbrain. Just as acetylcholine is necessary for declarative memory, dopamine appears to be necessary for this procedural memory circuit to function. The loss of this dopamine input, as in Parkinson's disease, interferes with procedural memory.

The two other kinds of nondeclarative memory involve yet other brain regions. The cerebellum is involved in motor

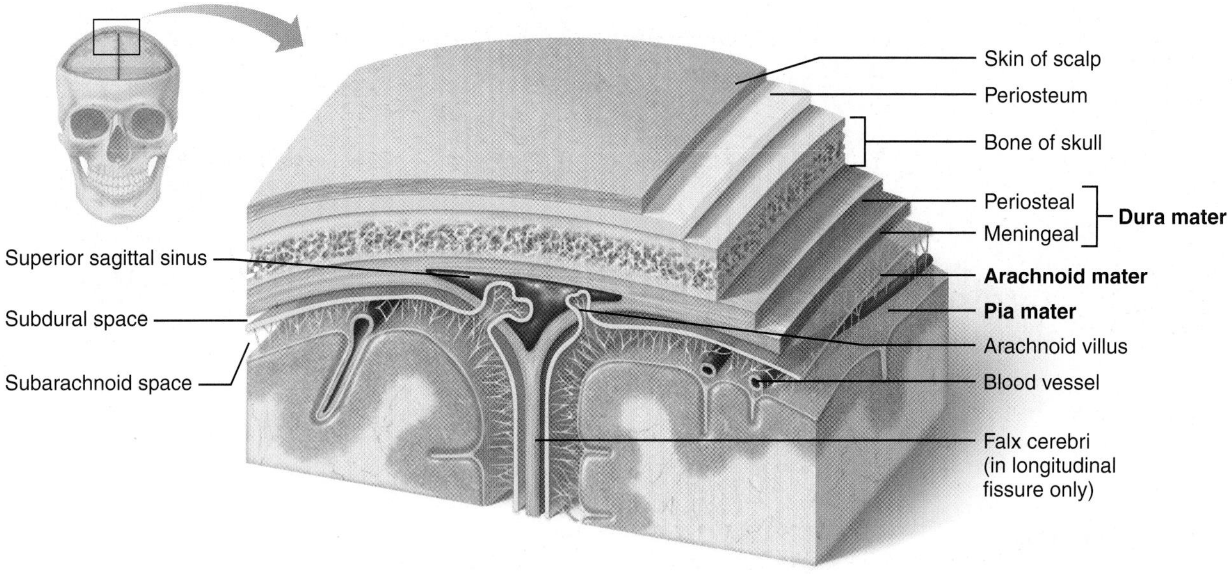

Figure 12.24 Meninges: dura mater, arachnoid mater, and pia mater. The meningeal dura forms the falx cerebri fold. A dural sinus, the superior sagittal sinus, is enclosed by the dural membranes superiorly. Arachnoid villi, which return cerebrospinal fluid to the dural sinus, are also shown. (Frontal section.)

memory, while the amygdala is crucial for emotional memory (see Figure 12.18). We will not describe these pathways here.

Molecular Basis of Memory

We have looked at brain structures involved in memory, but what happens at the molecular level when we form memories? Human memory is notoriously difficult to study. Animal experimental studies reveal that during learning, (1) neuronal RNA content is altered and newly synthesized mRNAs are delivered to axons and dendrites, (2) dendritic spines change shape, (3) unique extracellular proteins are deposited at synapses involved in LTM, (4) the number and size of presynaptic terminals may increase, and (5) more neurotransmitter is released by the presynaptic neurons.

Each one of these changes is an aspect of **long-term potentiation (LTP)**, a persistent increase in synaptic strength that has been shown to be crucial for memory formation. LTP was first identified in hippocampal neurons that use the amino acid glutamate as a neurotransmitter. One kind of glutamate receptor, the *NMDA receptor*, can act as a calcium channel and initiate the cellular changes that bring about LTP.

Normally, NMDA receptors are blocked, preventing calcium entry. When the postsynaptic terminal is depolarized by binding of glutamate to different receptors, as would happen upon the rapid arrival of action potentials at the synapse, this NMDA block is removed and calcium flows into the postsynaptic cell.

Calcium influx triggers activation of enzymes that carry out two main tasks. First, they modify the proteins in the postsynaptic terminal, and also in the presynaptic terminal via retrograde messengers such as nitric oxide and endocannabinoids. These changes strengthen the response to subsequent stimuli. Second,

they cause the activation of genes in the postsynaptic neuron's nucleus, which leads to synthesis of synaptic proteins.

The molecular messenger that brings the news to the nucleus that more protein is needed is a molecule called CREB (cAMP response-element binding protein). A neurotrophic factor called BDNF (brain-derived neurotrophic factor) is required for the protein synthesis phase of LTP. Together, these changes create long-lasting increases in synaptic strength that are believed to underlie memory.

The events underlying memory at a cellular level suggest several approaches to enhancing memory formation. Currently several drugs to improve memory are undergoing clinical trials. Among these are drugs that enhance CREB production—the more CREB, the more protein synthesis and the stronger the synapse becomes.

CHECK YOUR UNDERSTANDING

18. Name three factors that can enhance transfer of information from STM to LTM.

19. What functional areas of the cerebrum are involved in the formation of procedural (skills) memory, but *not* involved in declarative memory formation?

For answers, see Appendix G.

Protection of the Brain

▶ Describe how meninges, cerebrospinal fluid, and the blood-brain barrier protect the CNS.

▶ Describe the formation of cerebrospinal fluid, and follow its circulatory pathway.

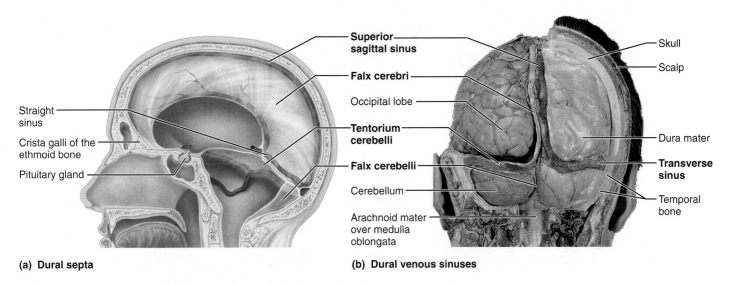

(a) Dural septa

(b) Dural venous sinuses

Figure 12.25 Dural septa and dural venous sinuses. (a) Dural septa are partitioning folds of dura mater in the craninal cavity. **(b)** Posterior view of the brain in place. Dural venous sinuses are spaces between the periosteal and meningeal dura containing venous blood.

▶ Describe the cause (if known) and major signs and symptoms of cerebrovascular accidents, Alzheimer's disease, Parkinson's disease, and Huntington's disease.

Nervous tissue is soft and delicate, and neurons are injured by even slight pressure. However, the brain is protected by bone (the skull), membranes (the meninges), and a watery cushion (cerebrospinal fluid). Furthermore, the brain is protected from harmful substances in the blood by the blood-brain barrier. We described the cranium, the brain's bony encasement, in Chapter 7. Here we will consider the other protective elements.

Meninges

The **meninges** (mĕ-nin′jēz; *mening* = membrane) are three connective tissue membranes that lie just external to the CNS organs. They (1) cover and protect the CNS, (2) protect blood vessels and enclose venous sinuses, (3) contain cerebrospinal fluid, and (4) form partitions in the skull. From external to internal, the meninges (singular: **meninx**) are the dura mater, arachnoid mater, and pia mater **(Figure 12.24)**.

Dura Mater

The leathery **dura mater** (du′rah ma′ter), meaning "tough mother," is the strongest meninx. Where it surrounds the brain, it is a two-layered sheet of fibrous connective tissue. The more superficial *periosteal layer* is attached to the inner surface of the skull (the periosteum). (There is no dural periosteal layer surrounding the spinal cord.) The deeper *meningeal layer* forms the true external covering of the brain and continues caudally in the vertebral canal as the spinal dura mater. The brain's two dural layers are fused together except in certain areas, where they separate to enclose **dural venous sinuses** that collect venous blood from the brain and direct it into the internal jugular veins of the neck **(Figure 12.25b)**.

In several places, the meningeal dura mater extends inward to form flat partitions that subdivide the cranial cavity. These **dural septa**, which limit excessive movement of the brain within the cranium, include the following (Figure 12.25a):

- **Falx cerebri** (falks ser′ĕ-bri). A large sickle-shaped (*falx* = sickle) fold that dips into the longitudinal fissure between the cerebral hemispheres. Anteriorly, it attaches to the crista galli of the ethmoid bone.
- **Falx cerebelli** (ser″ĕ-bel′i). Continuing inferiorly from the posterior falx cerebri, this small midline partition runs along the vermis of the cerebellum.
- **Tentorium cerebelli** (ten-to′re-um; "tent"). Resembling a tent over the cerebellum, this nearly horizontal dural fold extends into the transverse fissure between the cerebral hemispheres (which it helps to support) and the cerebellum.

Arachnoid Mater

The middle meninx, the **arachnoid mater**, or simply the **arachnoid** (ah-rak′noid), forms a loose brain covering, never dipping into the sulci at the cerebral surface. It is separated from the dura mater by a narrow serous cavity, the **subdural space**, which contains a film of fluid. Beneath the arachnoid membrane is the wide **subarachnoid space**. Weblike extensions span this space and secure the arachnoid mater to the underlying pia mater. (*Arachnida* means "spider," and this membrane was named for its weblike extensions.) The subarachnoid space is filled with cerebrospinal fluid and also contains the largest blood vessels serving the brain. Because the arachnoid is fine and elastic, these blood vessels are poorly protected.

Knoblike projections of the arachnoid mater called **arachnoid villi** (vil′i) protrude superiorly through the dura mater and into the superior sagittal sinus (see Figure 12.24). Cerebrospinal fluid is absorbed into the venous blood of the sinus by these valvelike villi.

12

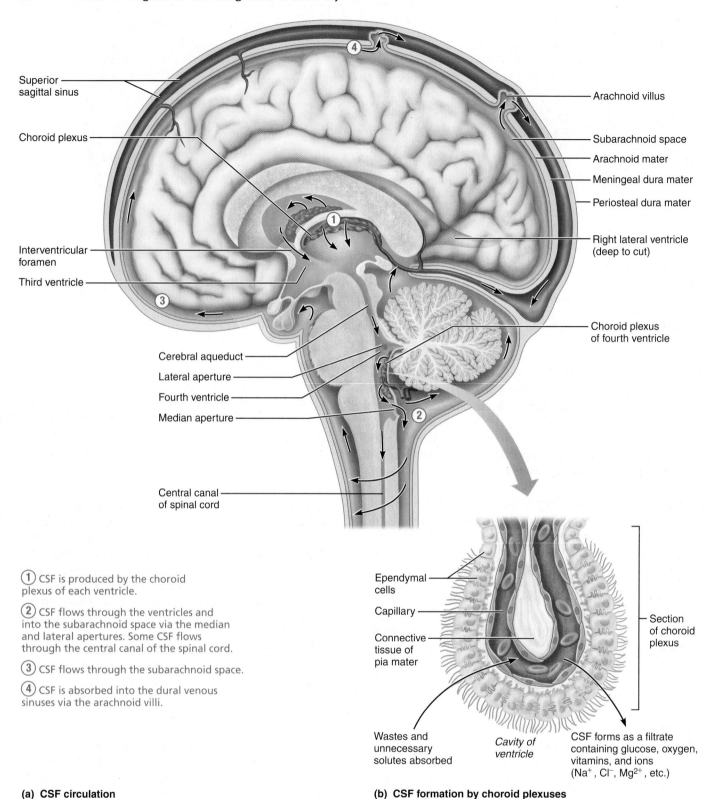

Superior sagittal sinus

Choroid plexus

Interventricular foramen

Third ventricle

Arachnoid villus

Subarachnoid space

Arachnoid mater

Meningeal dura mater

Periosteal dura mater

Right lateral ventricle (deep to cut)

Choroid plexus of fourth ventricle

Cerebral aqueduct

Lateral aperture

Fourth ventricle

Median aperture

Central canal of spinal cord

① CSF is produced by the choroid plexus of each ventricle.

② CSF flows through the ventricles and into the subarachnoid space via the median and lateral apertures. Some CSF flows through the central canal of the spinal cord.

③ CSF flows through the subarachnoid space.

④ CSF is absorbed into the dural venous sinuses via the arachnoid villi.

(a) CSF circulation

Ependymal cells

Capillary

Connective tissue of pia mater

Section of choroid plexus

Wastes and unnecessary solutes absorbed

Cavity of ventricle

CSF forms as a filtrate containing glucose, oxygen, vitamins, and ions (Na^+, Cl^-, Mg^{2+}, etc.)

(b) CSF formation by choroid plexuses

Figure 12.26 Formation, location, and circulation of CSF. (a) Location and circulatory pattern of cerebrospinal fluid (CSF). Arrows indicate the direction of flow. **(b)** Each choroid plexus consists of a knot of porous capillaries surrounded by a single layer of ependymal cells joined by tight junctions and bearing long cilia. Fluid leaking from porous capillaries is processed by the ependymal cells to form the CSF in the ventricles.

Pia Mater

The **pia mater** (pi′ah), meaning "gentle mother," is composed of delicate connective tissue and is richly invested with tiny blood vessels. It is the only meninx that clings tightly to the brain like cellophane wrap, following its every convolution. Small arteries entering the brain tissue carry ragged sheaths of pia mater inward with them for short distances.

HOMEOSTATIC IMBALANCE

Meningitis, inflammation of the meninges, is a serious threat to the brain because a bacterial or viral meningitis may spread to the CNS. Brain inflammation is called *encephalitis* (en-sef′ah-li′tis). Meningitis is usually diagnosed by obtaining a sample of cerebrospinal fluid via a lumbar tap (see Figure 12.30, p. 468) and examining it for microbes. ∎

Cerebrospinal Fluid

Cerebrospinal fluid (CSF), found in and around the brain and spinal cord, forms a liquid cushion that gives buoyancy to the CNS structures. By floating the jellylike brain, the CSF effectively reduces brain weight by 97% and prevents the delicate brain from crushing under its own weight. CSF also protects the brain and spinal cord from blows and other trauma. Additionally, although the brain has a rich blood supply, CSF helps nourish the brain, and there is some evidence that it carries chemical signals (such as hormones and sleep- and appetite-inducing molecules) from one part of the brain to another.

CSF is a watery "broth" similar in composition to blood plasma, from which it is formed. However, it contains less protein than plasma and its ion concentrations are different. For example, CSF contains more Na^+, Cl^-, and H^+ than does blood plasma, and less Ca^{2+} and K^+.

The **choroid plexuses** that hang from the roof of each ventricle form CSF. These plexuses are frond-shaped clusters of broad, thin-walled capillaries (*plex* = interwoven) enclosed first by pia mater and then by a layer of ependymal cells lining the ventricles (Figure 12.26b). These capillaries are fairly permeable, and tissue fluid filters continuously from the bloodstream. However, the choroid plexus ependymal cells are joined by tight junctions, and they have ion pumps that allow them to modify this filtrate by actively transporting only certain ions across their membranes into the CSF pool. This careful regulation of CSF composition is important because CSF mixes with the extracellular fluid bathing neurons and influences the composition of this fluid. Ion pumping also sets up ionic gradients that cause water to diffuse into the ventricles.

In adults, the total CSF volume of about 150 ml (about half a cup) is replaced every 8 hours or so. About 500 ml of CSF is formed daily. The choroid plexuses also help cleanse the CSF by removing waste products and unnecessary solutes.

Once produced, CSF moves freely through the ventricles. Some CSF circulates into the central canal of the spinal cord, but most enters the subarachnoid space via the lateral and median apertures in the walls of the fourth ventricle (Figure 12.26a). The long cilia of the ependymal cells lining the ventricles help to

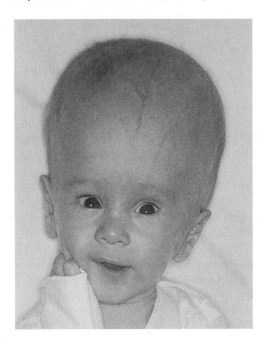

Figure 12.27 Hydrocephalus in a newborn.

keep the CSF in constant motion. In the subarachnoid space, CSF bathes the outer surfaces of the brain and spinal cord and then returns to the blood in the dural sinuses via the arachnoid villi.

HOMEOSTATIC IMBALANCE

Ordinarily, CSF is produced and drained at a constant rate. However, if something (such as a tumor) obstructs its circulation or drainage, CSF accumulates and exerts pressure on the brain. This condition is called *hydrocephalus* ("water on the brain"). Hydrocephalus in a newborn baby causes its head to enlarge (Figure 12.27). This enlargement is possible because the newborn's skull bones have not yet fused. In adults, however, hydrocephalus is likely to damage the brain because the skull is rigid and hard, and accumulating fluid compresses blood vessels serving the brain and crushes the soft nervous tissue. Hydrocephalus is treated by inserting a shunt into the ventricles to drain the excess fluid into the abdominal cavity. ∎

Blood-Brain Barrier

The **blood-brain barrier** is a protective mechanism that helps maintain a stable environment for the brain. No other body tissue is so absolutely dependent on a constant internal environment as is the brain. In other body regions, the extracellular concentrations of hormones, amino acids, and ions are in constant flux, particularly after eating or exercise. If the brain were exposed to such chemical variations, the neurons would fire uncontrollably, because some hormones and amino acids serve as neurotransmitters and certain ions (particularly K^+) modify the threshold for neuronal firing.

Bloodborne substances in the brain's capillaries must pass through three layers before they reach the neurons: (1) the endothelium of the capillary wall, (2) a relatively thick basal lamina surrounding the external face of each capillary, and (3) the bulbous "feet" of the astrocytes clinging to the capillaries. Which of these layers constitutes the blood-brain barrier? As you might expect, the astrocyte "feet" play a role but they are not themselves the barrier. Instead, they supply required signals to the endothelial cells, causing them to make *tight junctions*. These tight junctions seamlessly join together the endothelial cells, forming the blood-brain barrier and making these the least permeable capillaries in the body.

The blood-brain barrier is selective, rather than absolute. Nutrients such as glucose, essential amino acids, and some electrolytes move passively by facilitated diffusion through the endothelial cell membranes. Bloodborne metabolic wastes, proteins, certain toxins, and most drugs are denied entry to brain tissue. Small nonessential amino acids and potassium ions not only are prevented from entering the brain, but also are actively pumped from the brain across the capillary endothelium.

The barrier is ineffective against fats, fatty acids, oxygen, carbon dioxide, and other fat-soluble molecules that diffuse easily through all plasma membranes. This explains why bloodborne alcohol, nicotine, and anesthetics can affect the brain.

The structure of the blood-brain barrier is not completely uniform. The capillaries of the choroid plexuses are very porous, but the ependymal cells surrounding them have tight junctions. In some brain areas surrounding the third and fourth ventricles, the blood-brain barrier is entirely absent and the capillary endothelium is quite permeable, allowing bloodborne molecules easy access to the neural tissue.

One such region is the vomiting center of the brain stem, which monitors the blood for poisonous substances. Another is in the hypothalamus, which regulates water balance, body temperature, and many other metabolic activities. Lack of a blood-brain barrier here is essential to allow the hypothalamus to sample the chemical composition of the blood. The barrier is incomplete in newborn and premature infants, and potentially toxic substances can enter the CNS and cause problems not seen in adults.

Injury to the brain, whatever the cause, may result in a localized breakdown of the blood-brain barrier. Most likely, this breakdown reflects some change in the capillary endothelial cells or their tight junctions.

Homeostatic Imbalances of the Brain

Brain dysfunctions are unbelievably varied and extensive. We have mentioned some of them already, but here we will focus on traumatic brain injuries, cerebrovascular accidents, and degenerative brain disorders.

Traumatic Brain Injury

Head injuries are a leading cause of accidental death in North America. Consider, for example, what happens if you forget to fasten your seat belt and then rear-end another car. Your head is moving and then is suddenly stopped as it hits the windshield.

Brain damage is caused not only by localized injury at the site of the blow (the *coup* injury), but also by the ricocheting effect as the brain hits the opposite end of the skull (the *contrecoup* injury).

A **concussion** is an alteration in brain function, usually temporary, following a blow to the head. The victim may be dizzy or lose consciousness. Although typically mild and short-lived, even a seemingly mild concussion can be damaging, and multiple concussions over time have been shown to produce cumulative damage. More serious concussions can cause bruising of the brain and permanent neurological damage, a condition called a **contusion**. In cortical contusions, the individual may remain conscious, but severe brain stem contusions always cause coma, lasting from hours to a lifetime because of injury to the reticular activating system.

Following a head blow, death may result from **subdural** or **subarachnoid hemorrhage** (bleeding from ruptured vessels into those spaces). Individuals who are initially lucid and then begin to deteriorate neurologically are, in all probability, hemorrhaging intracranially. Blood accumulating in the skull increases intracranial pressure and compresses brain tissue. If the pressure forces the brain stem inferiorly through the foramen magnum, control of blood pressure, heart rate, and respiration is lost. Intracranial hemorrhages are treated by surgical removal of the hematoma (localized blood mass) and repair of the ruptured vessels.

Another consequence of traumatic head injury is **cerebral edema**, swelling of the brain. At best, this cerebral edema aggravates the injury—at worst, it can be fatal in and of itself.

Cerebrovascular Accidents

The single most common nervous system disorder and the third leading cause of death in North America are **cerebrovascular accidents (CVAs)** (ser″ĕ-bro-vas′ku-lar), also called *strokes*. CVAs occur when blood circulation to a brain area is blocked and brain tissue dies. [Deprivation of blood supply to any tissue is called **ischemia** (is-ke′me-ah; "to hold back blood") and results in deficient oxygen and nutrient delivery to cells.] The most common cause of CVA is blockage of a cerebral artery by a blood clot. Other causes include compression of brain tissue by hemorrhage or edema and narrowing of brain vessels by atherosclerosis.

Those who survive a CVA are typically paralyzed on one side of the body (*hemiplegia*). Many exhibit sensory deficits or have difficulty in understanding or vocalizing speech. Even so, the picture is not hopeless. Some patients recover at least part of their lost faculties, because undamaged neurons sprout new branches that spread into the injured area and take over some lost functions. Physical therapy is usually started as soon as possible to prevent muscle contractures (abnormal shortening of muscles due to differences in strength between opposing muscle groups).

Not all strokes are "completed." Temporary episodes of reversible cerebral ischemia, called **transient ischemic attacks (TIAs)**, are common. TIAs last from 5 to 50 minutes and are characterized by temporary numbness, paralysis, or impaired speech. These deficits are not permanent, but TIAs do constitute "red flags" that warn of impending, more serious CVAs.

CVAs are like undersea earthquakes. It's not the initial temblor that does most of the damage, it's the tsunami that floods the coast later. Similarly, the initial vascular blockage during a stroke is not usually disastrous because there are many blood vessels in the brain that can pick up the slack. Rather, it's the events that lead to killing of neurons not in the initial ischemic zone that wreak the most havoc.

Experimental evidence indicates that the main culprit is *glutamate*, an excitatory neurotransmitter also involved in learning and memory. Normally, glutamate binding to NMDA receptors opens NMDA channels that allow Ca^{2+} to enter the stimulated neuron. After brain injury, neurons totally deprived of oxygen begin to disintegrate, unleashing the cellular equivalent of "buckets" of glutamate. Under these conditions, glutamate acts as an *excitotoxin*, literally exciting surrounding cells to death. The initial events in excitotoxicity are identical to those in LTP— Ca^{2+} flows in through NMDA receptor channels (see p. 460). In excitotoxicity, however, the amount of Ca^{2+} swamps the cell's ability to cope and Ca^{2+} homeostasis breaks down. High levels of Ca^{2+} lead to cell death in two ways. First, Ca^{2+} damages mitochondria, causing them to produce the free radical superoxide, which can damage cells directly and can also cause programmed cell death (apoptosis). Second, Ca^{2+} turns on the synthesis of certain proteins. Some of these promote apoptosis while others are enzymes that produce the free radical NO and other powerful inflammatory agents.

Although the NMDA receptor and the enzyme that makes NO are attractive targets for drug therapies to decrease damage around the stroke epicenter, clinical trials so far have all failed. At present, the most successful treatment for stroke is tissue plasminogen activator (tPA), which dissolves blood clots in the brain. A newly approved mechanical device drills into a blood clot and pulls it from a vessel like a cork from a bottle. Other approaches currently under study focus on recovering function after a stroke. One method implants immature neurons into stroke-damaged brain regions in the hope that they will take on properties of the nearby mature neurons. Another tries to coax adult brain stem cells to replace damaged neurons. Mice with strokes can generate new tissue and recover motor function when treated with a combination of growth factors during a critical time following injury. Hopefully, this will be true for humans, too.

Degenerative Brain Disorders

Alzheimer's Disease Alzheimer's disease (AD) (altz′hi-merz) is a progressive degenerative disease of the brain that ultimately results in dementia (mental deterioration). Alzheimer's patients represent nearly half of the people living in nursing homes. Between 5 and 15% of people over 65 develop this condition, and for up to half of those over 85 it is a major contributing cause in their deaths.

Its victims exhibit memory loss (particularly for recent events), shortened attention span, disorientation, and eventual language loss. Over a period of several years, formerly good-natured people may become irritable, moody, and confused. Ultimately, hallucinations occur.

Examinations of brain tissue reveal senile plaques littering the brain like shrapnel between the neurons. The plaques consist of extracellular aggregations of *beta-amyloid peptide*, which has been cut from a normal membrane precursor protein (APP) by enzymes. One form of Alzheimer's disease is caused by an inherited mutation in the gene for APP, which suggests that beta-amyloid may be toxic. Some researchers believe that small clusters of these protein fragments kill cells by forming holes in their plasma membranes. Unfortunately, clinical trials of vaccines to stimulate an immune response to clear away beta-amyloid peptide have not yet been successful.

Another hallmark of Alzheimer's disease is the presence of *neurofibrillary tangles* inside neurons. These tangles involve a protein called tau, which functions like railroad ties to bind microtubule "tracks" together. In the brains of AD victims, tau abandons its microtubule-stabilizing role and grabs onto other tau molecules, forming spaghetti-like neurofibrillary tangles, which kill the neurons by disrupting their transport mechanisms.

As the brain cells die, the brain shrinks. Particularly vulnerable brain areas include the hippocampus and the basal forebrain, regions involved in thinking and memory (see Figure 12.23). Loss of neurons in the basal forebrain is associated with a shortage of the neurotransmitter acetylcholine, and drugs that inhibit breakdown of acetylcholine slightly enhance cognitive function in AD patients. Interestingly, a drug that blocks NMDA receptors, memantine, also slightly improves thinking in more advanced stages of AD, suggesting that glutamate excitotoxicity is also involved in this disease.

Parkinson's Disease Typically striking people in their 50s and 60s, **Parkinson's disease** results from a degeneration of the dopamine-releasing neurons of the substantia nigra. As those neurons deteriorate, the dopamine-deprived basal nuclei they target become overactive, causing the well-known symptoms of the disease. Afflicted individuals have a persistent tremor at rest (exhibited by head nodding and a "pill-rolling" movement of the fingers), a forward-bent walking posture and shuffling gait, and a stiff facial expression. They are slow in initiating and executing movement.

The cause of Parkinson's disease is still unknown, but the interaction of multiple factors is thought to lead to the death of dopamine-releasing neurons. Recent evidence points to abnormalities in a dopamine transport regulator and in certain mitochondrial proteins. The drug L-dopa often helps to alleviate some symptoms. It passes through the blood-brain barrier and is then converted into dopamine. However, it is not curative, and as more and more neurons die off, L-dopa becomes ineffective. Mixing L-dopa with drugs that inhibit the breakdown of dopamine (for example, deprenyl), can prolong the effectiveness of L-dopa. In addition, deprenyl by itself, early in the disease, slows the neurological deterioration to some extent and delays the need to administer L-dopa for up to 18 months.

Deep brain stimulation via implanted electrodes shuts down abnormal brain activity and has proved helpful in alleviating tremors. This treatment (for patients who no longer respond to drug therapy) is delicate, expensive, and risky. Another possibility is to use gene therapy to insert genes into adult brain cells, causing them to secrete the inhibitory neurotransmitter GABA. GABA then inhibits the abnormal brain activity just as the electrical stimulation does. Replacing dead or damaged cells by implanting embryonic or fetal cells also shows great promise. However, the use of embryonic or fetal tissue is controversial and riddled with ethical and legal roadblocks.

Huntington's Disease **Huntington's disease** is a fatal hereditary disorder that strikes during middle age. Mutant *huntingtin* protein accumulates in brain cells and the tissue dies, leading to massive degeneration of the basal nuclei and later of the cerebral cortex. Its initial symptoms in many are wild, jerky, almost continuous "flapping" movements called *chorea* (Greek for "dance"). Although the movements appear to be voluntary they are not. Late in the disease, marked mental deterioration occurs. Huntington's disease is progressive and usually fatal within 15 years of onset of symptoms.

The hyperkinetic manifestations of Huntington's disease are essentially the opposite of those of Parkinson's disease (overstimulation rather than inhibition of the motor drive). Huntington's is usually treated with drugs that block, rather than enhance, dopamine's effects. As with Parkinson's disease, fetal tissue implants may provide promise for its treatment in the future.

CHECK YOUR UNDERSTANDING

20. What is CSF? Where is it produced? What are its functions?
21. What is a transient ischemic attack (TIA) and how is it different from a stroke?
22. Mrs. Lee, a neurology patient, seldom smiles, has a shuffling stooped gait, and often spills her coffee. What degenerative brain disorder might she have?

For answers, see Appendix G.

The Spinal Cord

▶ Describe the embryonic development of the spinal cord.

▶ Describe the gross and microscopic structure of the spinal cord.

▶ List the major spinal cord tracts, and classify each as a motor or sensory tract.

Embryonic Development

The spinal cord develops from the caudal portion of the embryonic neural tube (see Figure 12.2 on p. 431). By the sixth week, each side of the developing cord has two recognizable clusters of neuroblasts that have migrated outward from the original neural tube: a dorsal **alar plate** (a′lar) and a ventral **basal plate** (Figure 12.28).

Alar plate neuroblasts become interneurons. The basal plate neuroblasts develop into motor neurons and sprout axons that

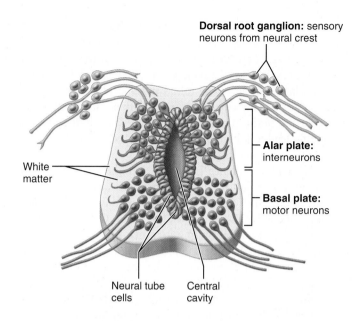

Figure 12.28 **Structure of the embryonic spinal cord.** At six weeks of development, aggregations of gray matter called the alar plates (future interneurons) and basal plates (future motor neurons) have formed. Dorsal root ganglia (future sensory neurons) have arisen from neural crest cells.

grow out to the effector organs. Axons that emerge from alar plate cells (and some basal plate cells) form the white matter of the cord by growing along the length of the cord. As development progresses, these plates expand dorsally and ventrally to produce the H-shaped central mass of gray matter of the adult spinal cord.

Neural crest cells that come to lie alongside the cord form the *dorsal root ganglia* containing sensory neuron cell bodies. These sensory neurons send their axons into the dorsal aspect of the cord.

Gross Anatomy and Protection

The spinal cord, enclosed in the vertebral column, extends from the foramen magnum of the skull to the level of the first or second lumbar vertebra, just inferior to the ribs (Figure 12.29). About 42 cm (17 inches) long and 1.8 cm (3/4 of an inch) thick, the glistening-white **spinal cord** provides a two-way conduction pathway to and from the brain. It is a major reflex center: Spinal reflexes are initiated and completed at the spinal cord level. We discuss reflex functions and motor activity of the cord in subsequent chapters. In this section we focus on the anatomy of the cord and on the location and naming of its ascending and descending tracts.

Like the brain, the spinal cord is protected by bone, meninges, and cerebrospinal fluid. The single-layered **spinal dura mater** (Figure 12.29c) is not attached to the bony walls of the vertebral column. Between the bony vertebrae and the spinal dura mater is an **epidural space** filled with a soft padding of fat and a network of veins (see Figure 12.31a). Cerebrospinal fluid fills the subarachnoid space between the *arachnoid* and *pia mater* meninges.

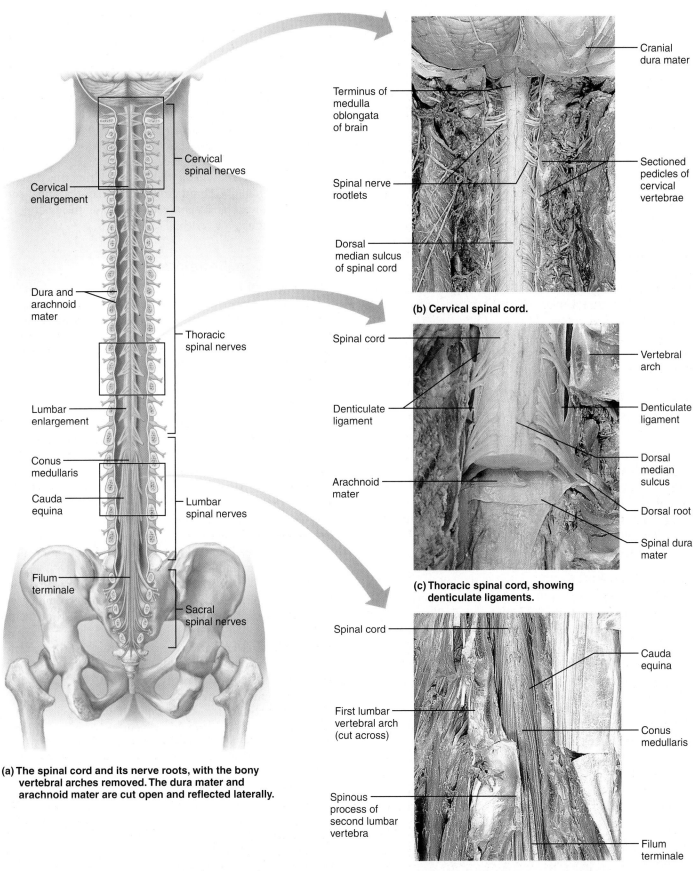

Cranial dura mater

Terminus of medulla oblongata of brain

Spinal nerve rootlets

Sectioned pedicles of cervical vertebrae

Dorsal median sulcus of spinal cord

(b) Cervical spinal cord.

Spinal cord

Vertebral arch

Denticulate ligament

Denticulate ligament

Dorsal median sulcus

Arachnoid mater

Dorsal root

Spinal dura mater

(c) Thoracic spinal cord, showing denticulate ligaments.

Cervical spinal nerves

Cervical enlargement

Dura and arachnoid mater

Thoracic spinal nerves

Lumbar enlargement

Conus medullaris

Cauda equina

Lumbar spinal nerves

Filum terminale

Sacral spinal nerves

(a) The spinal cord and its nerve roots, with the bony vertebral arches removed. The dura mater and arachnoid mater are cut open and reflected laterally.

Spinal cord

Cauda equina

First lumbar vertebral arch (cut across)

Conus medullaris

Spinous process of second lumbar vertebra

Filum terminale

(d) Inferior end of spinal cord, showing conus medullaris, cauda equina, and filum terminale.

Figure 12.29 Gross structure of the spinal cord, dorsal view.
(See *A Brief Atlas of the Human Body,* Figures 52, 53, and 55.)

12

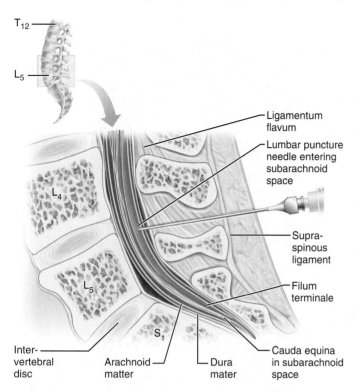

Figure 12.30 Diagrammatic view of a lumbar tap.

Inferiorly, the dural and arachnoid membranes extend to the level of S_2, well beyond the end of the spinal cord. The spinal cord typically ends between L_1 and L_2 (Figure 12.29a). For this reason, the subarachnoid space within the meningeal sac inferior to that point provides a nearly ideal spot for removing cerebrospinal fluid for testing, a procedure called a **lumbar puncture** or **tap** (Figure 12.30). Because the spinal cord is absent there and the delicate nerve roots drift away from the point of needle insertion, there is little or no danger of damaging the cord (or spinal roots) beyond L_3.

Inferiorly, the spinal cord terminates in a tapering cone-shaped structure called the **conus medullaris** (ko′nus me″dul-ar′is). The **filum terminale** (fi′lum ter″mĭ-nah′le; "terminal filament"), a fibrous extension of the conus covered by pia mater, extends inferiorly from the conus medullaris to the coccyx, where it anchors the spinal cord in place so it is not jostled by body movements (Figure 12.29a, d). Furthermore, the spinal cord is secured to the tough dura mater meninx throughout its length by saw-toothed shelves of pia mater called **denticulate ligaments** (den-tik′u-lāt; "toothed") (Figure 12.29c).

In humans, 31 pairs of *spinal nerves* attach to the cord by paired roots. Each nerve exits from the vertebral column by passing superior to its corresponding vertebra via the intervertebral foramen, and travels to the body region it serves. While each nerve pair defines a segment of the cord, the spinal cord is, in fact, continuous throughout its length and its internal structure changes gradually.

The spinal cord is about the width of a thumb for most of its length, but it has obvious enlargements in the cervical and lum-

bosacral regions, where the nerves serving the upper and lower limbs arise. These enlargements are the **cervical** and **lumbar enlargements**, respectively (Figure 12.29a).

Because the cord does not reach the end of the vertebral column, the lumbar and sacral spinal nerve roots angle sharply downward and travel inferiorly through the vertebral canal for some distance before reaching their intervertebral foramina. The collection of nerve roots at the inferior end of the vertebral canal is named the **cauda equina** (kaw′da e-kwi′nuh) because of its resemblance to a horse's tail (Figure 12.29a, c). This strange arrangement reflects the fact that during fetal development, the vertebral column grows faster than the spinal cord, forcing the lower spinal nerve roots to "chase" their exit points inferiorly through the vertebral canal.

Cross-Sectional Anatomy

The spinal cord is somewhat flattened from front to back and two grooves mark its surface: the **ventral (anterior) median fissure** and the shallower **dorsal (posterior) median sulcus** (Figure 12.31b). These grooves run the length of the cord and partially divide it into right and left halves. The gray matter of the cord is located in its core, the white matter outside.

Gray Matter and Spinal Roots

In cross section the gray matter of the cord looks like the letter H or like a butterfly (Figure 12.31b). It consists of mirror-image lateral gray masses connected by a crossbar of gray matter, the **gray commissure**, that encloses the central canal. The two dorsal projections of the gray matter are the **dorsal (posterior) horns**, and the ventral pair are the **ventral (anterior) horns**. In 3-D, these horns form columns of gray matter that run the entire length of the spinal cord. An additional pair of gray matter columns, the small **lateral horns**, is present in the thoracic and superior lumbar segments of the cord.

All neurons whose cell bodies are in the spinal cord gray matter are multipolar. The dorsal horns consist entirely of interneurons. The ventral horns have some interneurons but mainly house cell bodies of somatic motor neurons. These motor neurons send their axons out to the skeletal muscles (their effector organs) via the *ventral rootlets* that fuse together to become the **ventral roots** of the spinal cord (Figure 12.31b).

The amount of ventral gray matter present at a given level of the spinal cord reflects the amount of skeletal muscle innervated at that level. As a result, the ventral horns are largest in the limb-innervating cervical and lumbar regions of the cord and are responsible for the cord enlargements seen in those regions.

The lateral horn neurons are autonomic (sympathetic division) motor neurons that serve visceral organs. Their axons leave the cord via the ventral root along with those of the somatic motor neurons. Because the ventral roots contain both somatic and autonomic efferents, they serve both motor divisions of the peripheral nervous system (Figure 12.32).

Afferent fibers carrying impulses from peripheral sensory receptors form the **dorsal roots** of the spinal cord that fan out as

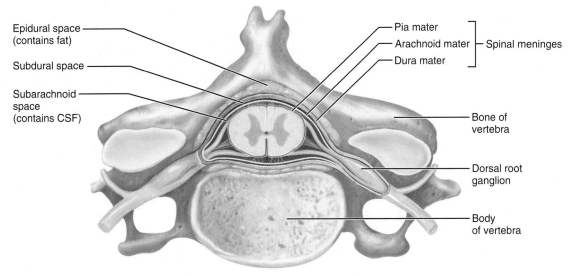

Epidural space (contains fat)

Subdural space

Subarachnoid space (contains CSF)

Pia mater

Arachnoid mater — Spinal meninges

Dura mater

Bone of vertebra

Dorsal root ganglion

Body of vertebra

(a) Cross section of spinal cord and vertebra

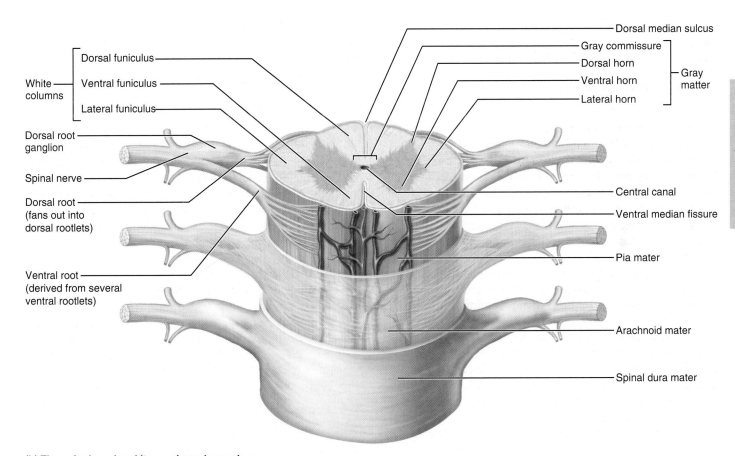

Dorsal median sulcus

Gray commissure

Dorsal horn

Ventral horn — Gray matter

Lateral horn

Dorsal funiculus

White columns — Ventral funiculus

Lateral funiculus

Dorsal root ganglion

Spinal nerve

Dorsal root (fans out into dorsal rootlets)

Ventral root (derived from several ventral rootlets)

Central canal

Ventral median fissure

Pia mater

Arachnoid mater

Spinal dura mater

12

(b) The spinal cord and its meningeal coverings

Figure 12.31 Anatomy of the spinal cord. (a) Cross section through the spinal cord illustrating its relationship to the surrounding vertebral column. **(b)** Anterior view of the spinal cord and its meningeal coverings.

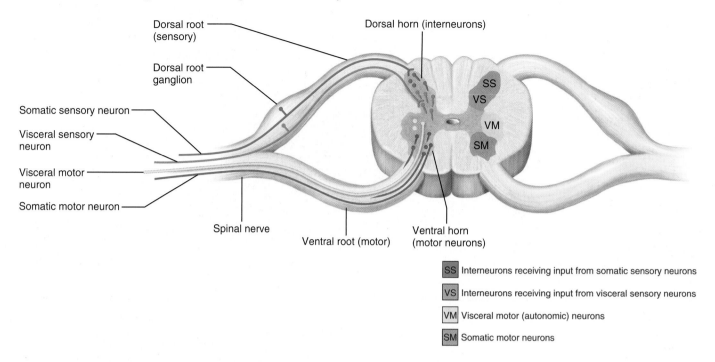

Figure 12.32 **Organization of the gray matter of the spinal cord.** The gray matter of the spinal cord is divided into a sensory half dorsally and a motor half ventrally. Note that the dorsal and ventral roots are part of the PNS, not of the spinal cord.

the *dorsal rootlets* before they enter the spinal cord (Figure 12.31). The cell bodies of the associated sensory neurons are found in an enlarged region of the dorsal root called the **dorsal root ganglion** or **spinal ganglion**. After entering the cord, the axons of these neurons may take a number of routes. Some enter the dorsal white matter of the cord directly and travel to synapse at higher cord or brain levels. Others synapse with interneurons in the dorsal horns of the spinal cord gray matter at their entry level.

The dorsal and ventral roots are very short and fuse laterally to form the **spinal nerves**. The spinal nerves, which are part of the peripheral nervous system, are considered further in Chapter 13.

The spinal gray matter can be divided further according to its neurons' relative involvement in the innervation of the somatic and visceral regions of the body. The following four zones are evident within this gray matter: **somatic sensory (SS)**, **visceral (autonomic) sensory (VS)**, **visceral motor (VM)**, **somatic motor (SM)** (Figure 12.32).

White Matter

The white matter of the spinal cord is composed of myelinated and unmyelinated nerve fibers that allow communication between different parts of the spinal cord and between the cord and brain. These fibers run in three directions: (1) *ascending*—up to higher centers (sensory inputs), (2) *descending*—down to the cord from the brain or within the cord to lower levels (motor outputs), and (3) *transversely*—across from one side of the cord to the other (commissural fibers). Ascending and descending tracts make up most of the white matter.

The white matter on each side of the cord is divided into three **white columns**, or **funiculi** (fu-nik′u-li; "long ropes"), named according to their position as **dorsal (posterior)**, **lateral**, and **ventral (anterior) funiculi** (Figure 12.31b). Each funiculus contains several fiber tracts, and each tract is made up of axons with similar destinations and functions. With a few exceptions, the names of the spinal tracts reveal both their origin and destination. The principal ascending and descending tracts of the spinal cord are illustrated schematically in the cross-sectional view of the spinal cord in **Figure 12.33**.

All major spinal tracts are *part of multineuron pathways* that connect the brain to the body periphery. These great ascending and descending pathways contain not only spinal cord neurons but also parts of peripheral neurons and neurons in the brain. Before we get specific about the individual tracts, we will make some generalizations about them and the pathways to which they contribute:

1. **Decussation.** Most pathways cross from one side of the CNS to the other (decussate) at some point along their journey.
2. **Relay.** Most pathways consist of a chain of two or three neurons (a relay) that contribute to successive tracts of the pathway.
3. **Somatotopy.** Most pathways exhibit *somatotopy*, a precise spatial relationship among the tract fibers that reflects the orderly mapping of the body. For example, in an ascending sensory tract, somatotopy refers to the fact that fibers transmitting inputs from sensory receptors in the superior parts of the body lie lateral to those conveying sensory information from inferior body regions.

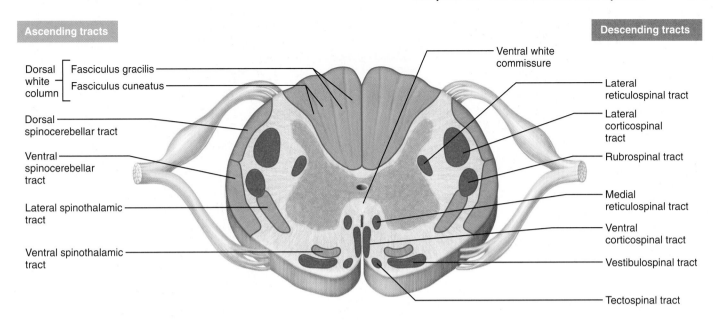

Figure 12.33 Major ascending (sensory) and descending (motor) tracts of the spinal cord, cross-sectional view.

4. Symmetry. All pathways and tracts are paired symmetrically (right and left), with a member of the pair present on each side of the spinal cord or brain.

Ascending Pathways to the Brain

The ascending pathways conduct sensory impulses upward, typically through chains of three successive neurons (first-, second-, and third-order neurons) to various areas of the brain. Note that both second- and third-order neurons are interneurons.

■ **First-order neurons**, whose cell bodies reside in a ganglion (dorsal root or cranial), conduct impulses from the cutaneous receptors of the skin and from proprioceptors to the spinal cord or brain stem, where they synapse with second-order neurons. Impulses from the facial area are transmitted by cranial nerves, and spinal nerves conduct somatic sensory impulses from the rest of the body to the CNS. First-order neurons entering the spinal cord are shown at the bottom of Figure 12.34.

■ **Second-order neurons** are shown in the middle of Figure 12.34. Their cell bodies reside in the dorsal horn of the spinal cord or in medullary nuclei, and they transmit impulses to the thalamus or to the cerebellum where they synapse.

■ **Third-order neurons** have cell bodies in the thalamus (shown in the top of Figure 12.34). They relay impulses to the somatosensory cortex of the cerebrum. (There are no third-order neurons in the cerebellum.)

In general, somatosensory information is conveyed along three main pathways on each side of the spinal cord. Two of these pathways (the *dorsal column–medial lemniscal* and *spinothalamic pathways*) transmit impulses via the thalamus to the sensory cortex for conscious interpretation. Collectively the inputs of these sister tracts provide *discriminative touch* and

conscious proprioception. Both pathways decussate—the first in the medulla and the second in the spinal cord.

The third pathway, the *spinocerebellar pathway*, terminates in the cerebellum, and does not contribute to sensory perception. Let's examine these pathways more closely.

1. **Dorsal column–medial lemniscal pathways.** The **dorsal column–medial lemniscal pathways** (lem-nis′kul; "ribbon") mediate precise, straight-through transmission of inputs from a single type (or a few related types) of sensory receptor that can be localized precisely on the body surface, such as discriminative touch and vibrations. These pathways are formed by the paired tracts of the **dorsal white column** of the spinal cord—**fasciculus cuneatus** and **fasciculus gracilis**—and the **medial lemniscus**. The medial lemniscus arises in the medulla and terminates in the thalamus (Figure 12.34a and **Table 12.2**). From the thalamus, impulses are forwarded to specific areas of the somatosensory cortex.

2. **Anterolateral pathways.** The **anterolateral pathways** [named for their location in the ventral (anterior) and lateral white columns of the spinal cord] receive input from many different types of sensory receptors and make multiple synapses in the brain stem. These pathways are largely formed by the **lateral** and **ventral (anterior) spinothalamic tracts** (see Figure 12.34b and Table 12.2). Their fibers cross over in the spinal cord.

   Most of the fibers in these pathways transmit pain, temperature, and coarse touch impulses, sensations that we are aware of but have difficulty localizing precisely on the body surface.

3. **Spinocerebellar tracts.** The last pair of ascending pathways, the **ventral (anterior)** and **dorsal (posterior) spinocerebellar tracts**, convey information about muscle or tendon stretch to the cerebellum, which uses this information to

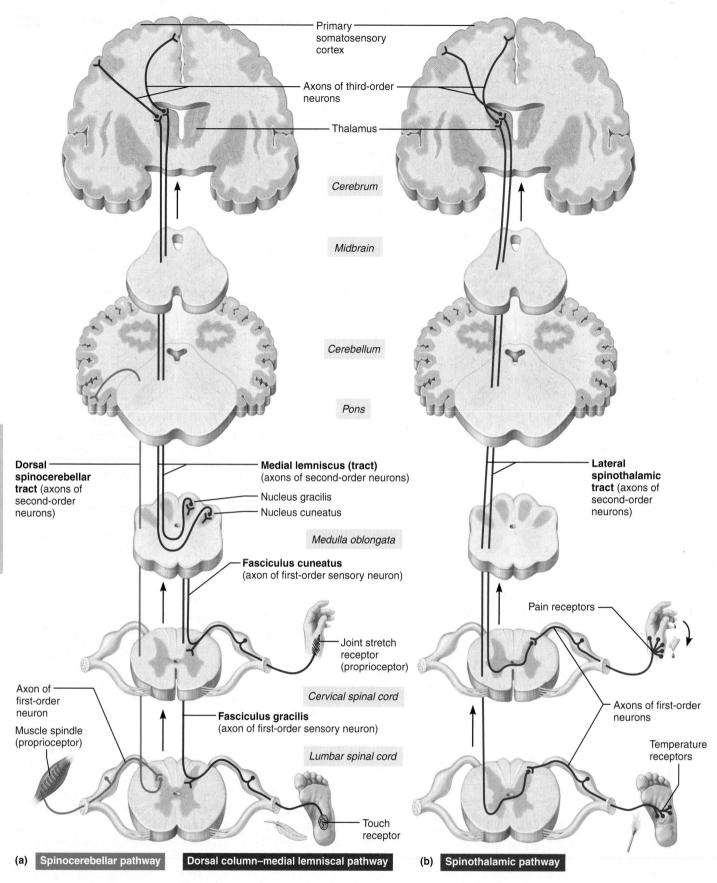

12

(a) Spinocerebellar pathway Dorsal column–medial lemniscal pathway   **(b)** Spinothalamic pathway

Figure 12.34 Pathways of selected ascending spinal cord tracts. Cross sections up to the cerebrum, which is shown in frontal section. **(a)** The spinocerebellar pathway (left) transmits proprioceptive information only to the cerebellum, and so is subconscious. The dorsal column–medial lemniscal pathway transmits discriminative touch and conscious proprioception signals to the cerebral cortex. **(b)** The lateral spinothalamic pathway transmits pain and temperature. The ventral spinothalamic pathway (not shown) transmits crude touch and pressure.

TABLE 12.2	Major Ascending (Sensory) Pathways and Spinal Cord Tracts				
SPINAL CORD TRACT	**LOCATION (FUNICULUS)**	**ORIGIN**	**TERMINATION**	**FUNCTION**	
Dorsal Column–Medial Lemniscal Pathways					
Fasciculus cuneatus and fasciculus gracilis (dorsal white column)	Dorsal	Central axons of sensory (first-order) neurons enter dorsal root of the spinal cord and branch; branches enter dorsal white column on same side without synapsing	By synapse with second-order neurons in nucleus cuneatus and nucleus gracilis in medulla; fibers of medullary neurons cross over and ascend in medial lemniscus to thalamus, where they synapse with third-order neurons; thalamic neurons then transmit impulses to somatosensory cortex	Both tracts transmit sensory impulses from general sensory receptors of skin and proprioceptors, which are interpreted as discriminative touch, pressure, and "body sense" (limb and joint position) in opposite somatosensory cortex. Cuneatus transmits afferent impulses from upper limbs, upper trunk, and neck. Gracilis carries impulses from lower limbs and inferior body trunk.	
Anterolateral Pathways					
Lateral spinothalamic	Lateral	Interneurons (second-order neurons) of dorsal horn; fibers cross to opposite side before ascending	By synapse with third-order neurons in thalamus; impulses then conveyed to somatosensory cortex by thalamic neurons	Transmits impulses concerned with pain and temperature to opposite side of brain for interpretation by somatosensory cortex.	
Ventral spinothalamic	Ventral	Interneurons (second-order neurons) in dorsal horns; fibers cross to opposite side before ascending	By synapse with third-order neurons in thalamus; impulses eventually conveyed to somatosensory cortex by thalamic neurons	Transmits impulses concerned with crude touch and pressure to opposite side of brain for interpretation by somatosensory cortex.	
Spinocerebellar Pathways					
Dorsal spinocerebellar*	Lateral (dorsal part)	Interneurons (second-order neurons) in dorsal horn on same side of cord; fibers ascend without crossing	By synapse in cerebellum	Transmits impulses from trunk and lower limb proprioceptors on one side of body to same side of cerebellum for subconscious proprioception.	
Ventral spinocerebellar*	Lateral (ventral part)	Interneurons (second-order neurons) of dorsal horn; contains crossed fibers that cross back to the opposite side in the pons	By synapse in cerebellum	Transmits impulses from the trunk and lower limb on the same side of body to cerebellum for subconscious proprioception.	

*These spinocerebellar tracts carry information from the lower limbs and trunk only. The corresponding tracts for the upper limb and neck (rostral spinocerebellar and others) are beyond the scope of this book.

coordinate skeletal muscle activity (see Figure 12.34a and Table 12.2). As noted earlier, these pathways do not contribute to conscious sensation. The fibers of the spinocerebellar pathways either do not decussate or else cross over twice (thus "undoing" the decussation).

Descending Pathways and Tracts

The descending tracts that deliver efferent impulses from the brain to the spinal cord are divided into two groups: (1) the *direct pathways* equivalent to the pyramidal tracts and (2) the *indirect pathways*, essentially all others. Motor pathways involve two

TABLE 12.3	Major Descending (Motor) Pathways and Spinal Cord Tracts			
SPINAL CORD TRACT	**LOCATION (FUNICULUS)**	**ORIGIN**	**TERMINATION**	**FUNCTION**
Direct (Pyramidal)				
Lateral corticospinal	Lateral	Pyramidal neurons of motor cortex of the cerebrum; decussate in pyramids of medulla	By synapse with ventral horn interneurons that influence motor neurons and occasionally with ventral horn motor neurons directly	Transmits motor impulses from cerebrum to spinal cord motor neurons (which activate skeletal muscles on opposite side of body). A voluntary motor tract.
Ventral corticospinal	Ventral	Pyramidal neurons of motor cortex; fibers cross over at the spinal cord level	Ventral horn (as above)	Same as lateral corticospinal tract.
Indirect (Extrapyramidal) Pathways				
Tectospinal	Ventral	Superior colliculus of midbrain of brain stem (fibers cross to opposite side of cord)	Ventral horn (as above)	Turns neck so eyes can follow a moving object.
Vestibulospinal	Ventral	Vestibular nuclei in medulla of brain stem (fibers descend without crossing)	Ventral horn (as above)	Transmits motor impulses that maintain muscle tone and activate ipsilateral limb and trunk extensor muscles and muscles that move head; in this way it helps maintain balance during standing and moving.
Rubrospinal	Lateral	Red nucleus of midbrain of brain stem (fibers cross to opposite side just inferior to the red nucleus)	Ventral horn (as above)	In experimental animals, transmits motor impulses concerned with muscle tone of distal limb muscles (mostly flexors) on opposite side of body. In humans, functions are largely assumed by corticospinal tracts.
Reticulospinal (ventral, medial, and lateral)	Ventral and lateral	Reticular formation of brain stem (medial nuclear group of pons and medulla); both crossed and uncrossed fibers	Ventral horn (as above)	Transmits impulses concerned with muscle tone and many visceral motor functions. May control most unskilled movements.

neurons, referred to as the upper and lower motor neurons. The pyramidal cells of the motor cortex, as well as the neurons in subcortical motor nuclei that give rise to other descending motor pathways, are called *upper motor neurons*. The ventral horn motor neurons, which actually innervate the skeletal muscles (their effectors), are called *lower motor neurons*. We briefly overview these tracts here and provide more information in **Table 12.3**.

The Direct (Pyramidal) System The direct pathways originate mainly with the pyramidal neurons located in the precentral gyri. These neurons send impulses through the brain stem via the large **pyramidal (corticospinal) tracts** (Figure 12.35a). The direct pathways are so called because their axons descend without synapsing from the pyramidal neurons to the spinal cord. There they synapse either with interneurons or with ventral horn motor neurons. Stimulation of the ventral horn neurons activates the skeletal muscles with which they are associated. The direct pathway primarily regulates fast and fine (or skilled) movements such as doing needlework and writing.

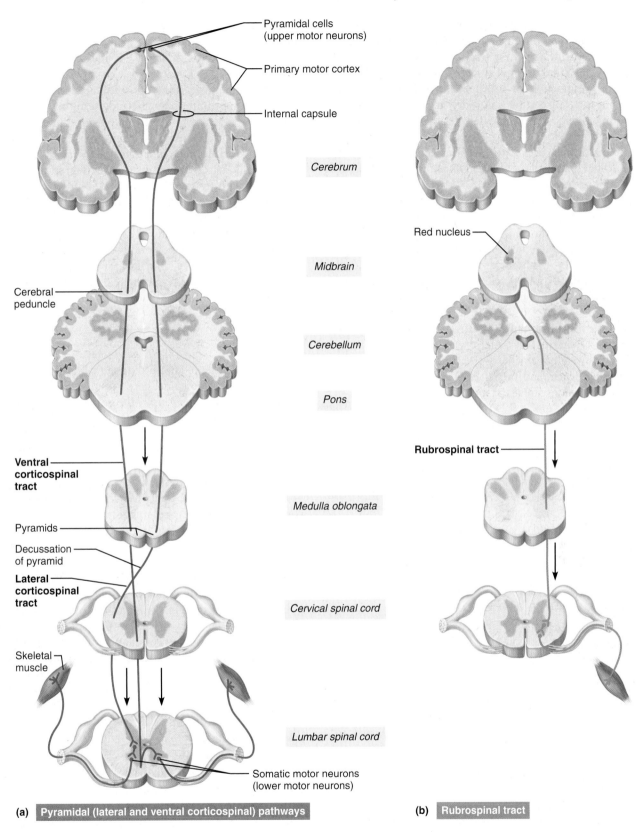

Pyramidal cells (upper motor neurons)

Primary motor cortex

Internal capsule

Cerebrum

Red nucleus

Midbrain

Cerebral peduncle

Cerebellum

Pons

Rubrospinal tract

Ventral corticospinal tract

Medulla oblongata

Pyramids

Decussation of pyramid

Lateral corticospinal tract

Cervical spinal cord

Skeletal muscle

Lumbar spinal cord

Somatic motor neurons (lower motor neurons)

(a) Pyramidal (lateral and ventral corticospinal) pathways

(b) Rubrospinal tract

Figure 12.35 Three descending pathways by which the brain influences movement.
Cross sections up to the cerebrum, which is shown in frontal section. **(a)** Pyramidal (lateral and ventral corticospinal pathways) are direct pathways that control skilled voluntary movements. **(b)** The rubrospinal tract, one of the indirect (or extrapyramidal) pathways, helps regulate muscle tone.

The Indirect (Extrapyramidal) System   The indirect system includes brain stem motor nuclei and *all motor pathways except* the pyramidal pathways. These tracts were formerly lumped together as the **extrapyramidal system** because their nuclei of origin were presumed to be independent of ("extra to") the pyramidal tracts. This term is still widely used clinically. However, pyramidal tract neurons are now known to project to and influence the activity of most "extrapyramidal" nuclei, so modern anatomists prefer to use the term **indirect**, or **multineuronal**, **pathways**, or even just the names of the individual motor pathways.

These motor pathways are complex and multisynaptic. They are most involved in regulating (1) the axial muscles that maintain balance and posture, (2) the muscles controlling coarse limb movements, and (3) head, neck, and eye movements that follow objects in the visual field. Many of the activities controlled by subcortical motor nuclei depend heavily on reflex activity. One of these tracts, the rubrospinal tract, is illustrated in Figure 12.35b.

Overall, the **reticulospinal** and **vestibulospinal tracts** maintain balance by varying the tone of postural muscles (Table 12.3). The **rubrospinal tracts** control flexor muscles, whereas the **tectospinal tracts** and the *superior colliculi* mediate head movements in response to visual stimuli.

CHECK YOUR UNDERSTANDING

23. What functional type of neuron is derived from the alar plate? From the basal plate?

24. What is the explanation for the cervical and lumber enlargements of the spinal cord?

25. Where are the cell bodies of the first-, second-, and third-order sensory neurons in the spinothalamic pathway located?

For answers, see Appendix G.

Spinal Cord Trauma and Disorders

▶ Distinguish between flaccid and spastic paralysis, and between paralysis and paresthesia.

Spinal Cord Trauma

The spinal cord is elastic, stretching with every turn of the head or bend of the trunk, but it is exquisitely sensitive to direct pressure. Any localized damage to the spinal cord or its roots leads to some functional loss, either **paralysis** (loss of motor function) or **paresthesias** (par″es-the′ze-ahz) (sensory loss). Severe damage to ventral root or ventral horn cells results in a **flaccid paralysis** (flak′sid) of the skeletal muscles served. Nerve impulses do not reach these muscles, which consequently cannot move either voluntarily or involuntarily. Without stimulation, the muscles atrophy.

When only the upper motor neurons of the primary motor cortex are damaged, **spastic paralysis** occurs. In this case, the spinal motor neurons remain intact and the muscles continue to be stimulated irregularly by spinal reflex activity. As a result, the muscles remain healthy longer, but their movements are no longer subject to voluntary control. In many such cases, the muscles become permanently shortened.

Transection (cross sectioning) of the spinal cord at any level results in total motor and sensory loss in body regions inferior to the site of damage. If the transection occurs between T_1 and L_1, both lower limbs are affected, resulting in **paraplegia** (par″ah-ple′je-ah; *para* = beside, *plegia* = a blow). If the injury occurs in the cervical region, all four limbs are affected and the result is **quadriplegia**. *Hemiplegia*, paralysis of one side of the body, usually reflects brain injury rather than spinal cord injury.

Anyone with traumatic spinal cord injury must be watched for symptoms of **spinal shock**, a transient period of functional loss that follows the injury. Spinal shock results in immediate depression of all reflex activity caudal to the lesion site. Bowel and bladder reflexes stop, blood pressure falls, and all muscles (somatic and visceral alike) below the injury are paralyzed and insensitive. Neural function usually returns within a few hours following injury. If function does not resume within 48 hours, paralysis is permanent in most cases.

Poliomyelitis

Poliomyelitis (po″le-o-mi″ĕ-li′tis; *polio* = gray matter; *myelitis* = inflammation of the spinal cord) results from destruction of ventral horn motor neurons by the poliovirus. Early symptoms include fever, headache, muscle pain and weakness, and loss of certain somatic reflexes. Later, paralysis develops and the muscles served atrophy. The victim may die from paralysis of the respiratory muscles or from cardiac arrest if neurons in the medulla oblongata are destroyed.

In most cases, the poliovirus enters the body in feces-contaminated water (such as might occur in a public swimming pool), and the incidence of the disease has traditionally been highest in children and during the summer months. Fortunately, vaccines have nearly eliminated this disease and a global effort is ongoing to eradicate it completely from the world.

However, many of the "recovered" survivors of the great polio epidemic of the late 1940s and 1950s have begun to experience extreme lethargy, sharp burning pains in their muscles, and progressive muscle weakness and atrophy. These disturbing symptoms are referred to as **postpolio syndrome**. The cause of postpolio syndrome is not known, but a likely explanation is that its victims, like the rest of us, continue to lose neurons throughout life. While a healthy nervous system can recruit nearby neurons to compensate for the losses, polio survivors have already drawn on that "pool" and have few neurons left to take over. Ironically, those who worked hardest to overcome their disease are its newest victims.

Amyotrophic Lateral Sclerosis

Amyotrophic lateral sclerosis (ALS) (ah-mi″o-trof′ik), also called Lou Gehrig's disease, is a devastating neuromuscular condition that involves progressive destruction of ventral horn motor neurons and fibers of the pyramidal tracts. As the disease progresses, the sufferer loses the ability to speak, swallow, and breathe. Death typically occurs within five years. For 90% of cases, the cause of ALS is unknown, although ALS patients appear to have excess extracellular glutamate. Researchers now believe that motor neurons are killed as a result of glutamate excitotoxicity, attack by the immune system, or possibly a combination of the two. Riluzole, the only advance in pharmacological treatment of ALS in 50 years, prolongs life, apparently by inhibiting glutamate release.

Diagnostic Procedures for Assessing CNS Dysfunction

▶ List and explain several techniques used to diagnose brain disorders.

Anyone who has had a routine physical examination is familiar with the reflex tests done to assess neural function. A tap with a reflex hammer stretches your quadriceps tendon and your anterior thigh muscles contract, which results in the knee-jerk response. This response shows that the spinal cord and upper brain centers are functioning normally. Abnormal reflex test responses may indicate such serious disorders as intracranial hemorrhage, multiple sclerosis, or hydrocephalus and suggest that more sophisticated neurological tests are needed to identify the problem.

New imaging techniques have revolutionized the diagnosis of brain lesions (see *A Closer Look*, pp. 18–19). Together the various *CT* and *MRI scanning techniques* allow most tumors, intracranial lesions, multiple sclerosis plaques, and areas of dead brain tissue (infarcts) to be identified quickly. PET scans can localize brain lesions that generate seizures (epileptic tissue) and diagnose Alzheimer's disease.

Take, for example, a patient arriving in emergency with a stroke. A race against time to save the affected area of the patient's brain begins. The first step is to determine if the stroke is due to a clot or a bleed by imaging the brain, most often with CT. If the stroke is due to a clot, then the clot-busting drug tPA can be used, but only within the first hours. tPA is usually given intravenously, but a longer time window can be obtained if tPA is applied directly to the clot using a catheter guided into position. In order to visualize the location of the catheter with respect to the clot, dye is injected to make arteries stand out in an X ray, a procedure called *cerebral angiography*.

Cerebral angiography is also used for patients who have had a warning stroke or TIA. The carotid arteries of the neck feed most of the cerebral vessels and often become narrowed with age, which can lead to strokes. Cheaper and less invasive than angiography, ultrasound can be used to quickly examine the carotid arteries and even measure the flow of blood through them.

CHECK YOUR UNDERSTANDING

26. Roy was tackled while playing football. After hitting the ground, he was unable to move his lower limbs. What is this condition called? What level of his spinal cord do you think was injured (cervical, thoracic, lumbar, or sacral)? Is this a permanent injury? What diagnostic procedures might be helpful?

For answers, see Appendix G.

Developmental Aspects of the Central Nervous System

▶ Indicate several maternal factors that can impair development of the nervous system in an embryo.

▶ Explain the effects of aging on the brain.

Induced by several organizer centers and established during the first month of development, the brain and spinal cord continue to grow and mature throughout the prenatal period. During development, gender-specific areas appear in both the brain and the spinal cord. For example, certain hypothalamic nuclei concerned with regulating typical male sexual behavior and clusters of neurons in the spinal cord that serve the external genitals are much larger in males. Females have a larger corpus callosum, and gender differences are seen in the language and auditory areas of the cerebral cortex. The key to this CNS gender-specific development is whether or not testosterone is being secreted by the fetus. If it is, the male pattern develops.

Maternal exposure to radiation, various drugs (alcohol, opiates, and others), and infections can harm a developing infant's nervous system, particularly during the initial formative stages. For example, rubella (German measles) often leads to deafness and other types of CNS damage in the newborn. Smoking decreases the amount of oxygen in the blood, and lack of oxygen for even a few minutes causes death of neurons. This means that a smoking mother may be sentencing her infant to some degree of brain damage.

⚖ HOMEOSTATIC IMBALANCE

In difficult deliveries, a temporary lack of oxygen may lead to **cerebral palsy**, but any of the factors listed above may also be a cause. Cerebral palsy is a neuromuscular disability in which the voluntary muscles are poorly controlled or paralyzed as a result of brain damage. In addition to spasticity, speech difficulties, and other motor impairments, about half of cerebral palsy victims have seizures, half are mentally retarded, and about a third have some degree of deafness. Visual impairments are also common. Cerebral palsy does not get worse over time, but its deficits are irreversible. It is the largest single cause of physical disability in children, affecting three out of every 1000 births.

The CNS is plagued by a number of other congenital malformations triggered by genetic or environmental factors during early development. The most serious are congenital hydrocephalus (discussed previously), anencephaly, and spina bifida.

In **anencephaly** (an″en-sef′ah-le; "without brain") the cerebrum and part of the brain stem never develop, because the neural folds fail to fuse rostrally. The child is totally vegetative, unable to see, hear, or process sensory inputs. Muscles are flaccid, and no voluntary movement is possible. Mental life as we know it does not exist. Mercifully, death occurs soon after birth.

Spina bifida (spi′nah bif′ĭ-dah; "forked spine") results from incomplete formation of the vertebral arches and typically involves the lumbosacral region. The technical definition is that laminae and spinous processes are missing on at least one

see 465

12

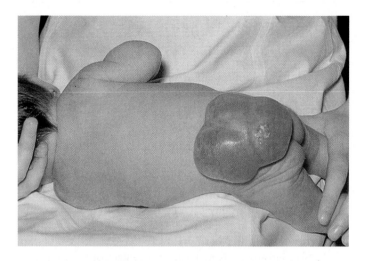

Figure 12.36 Newborn with a lumbar myelomeningocele.

vertebra. If the condition is severe, neural deficits occur as well. *Spina bifida occulta*, the least serious type, involves one or only a few vertebrae and causes no neural problems. Other than a small dimple or tuft of hair over the site of nonfusion, it has no external manifestations. In the more common and severe form, *spina bifida cystica*, a saclike cyst protrudes dorsally from the child's spine. The cyst may contain meninges and cerebrospinal fluid [a *meningocele* (mě-ning′go-sēl)], or even portions of the spinal cord and spinal nerve roots (a *myelomeningocele*, "spinal cord in a meningeal sac," shown in Figure 12.36). The larger the cyst and the more neural structures it contains, the greater the neurological impairment. In the worst case, where the inferior spinal cord is functionless, bowel incontinence, bladder muscle paralysis (which predisposes the infant to urinary tract infection and renal failure), and lower limb paralysis occur. Problems with infection are continual because the cyst wall is thin and porous and tends to rupture or leak. Spina bifida cystica is accompanied by hydrocephalus in 90% of all cases.

In the past, up to 70% of cases of spina bifida were caused by inadequate amounts of the B vitamin folic acid in the maternal diet. Recently, the number of spina bifida cases has dropped significantly in countries (such as the U.S.) where mandatory supplementation of folic acid in bread, flour, and pasta products has been introduced. ■

One of the last CNS areas to mature is the hypothalamus. Since the hypothalamus contains body temperature regulatory centers, premature babies have problems controlling their loss of body heat and must be kept in temperature-controlled environments. PET scans have revealed that the thalamus and somatosensory cortex are active in a 5-day-old baby, but that the visual cortex is not. This explains why infants of this age respond to touch but have poor vision. By 11 weeks, more of the cortex is active, and the baby can reach for a rattle. By 8 months, the cortex is very active and the child can think about what he or she sees. Growth and maturation of the nervous system continue throughout childhood and largely reflect progressive myelination. As described in Chapter 9, neuromuscular coordination progresses in a superior-to-inferior direction and in a proximal-to-distal direction, and we know that myelination also occurs in this sequence.

The brain reaches its maximum weight in the young adult. Over the next 60 years or so, neurons are damaged and die, and brain weight and volume steadily decline. However, the number of neurons lost over the decades is normally only a small percentage of the total, and the remaining neurons can change their synaptic connections, providing for continued learning throughout life.

Although age brings some cognitive declines in spatial ability, speed of perception, decision making, reaction time, and working memory, these losses are not significant in the *healthy individual* until after the seventh decade. Then the brain becomes increasingly fragile, presumably due to less efficient calcium clearance in aging neurons (as we have seen, elevated Ca^{2+} levels are neurotoxic), and a fairly rapid decline occurs in some, but not all, of these abilities. Ability to build on experience, mathematical skills, and verbal fluency do not decline with age, and many people continue to enjoy intellectual lives and to work at mentally demanding tasks their entire life. Fewer than 5% of people over 65 demonstrate true dementia. Sadly, many cases of "reversible dementia" are caused by prescription drug effects, low blood pressure, poor nutrition, hormone imbalances, depression, and/or dehydration that go undiagnosed. The best way to maintain one's mental abilities in old age may be to seek regular medical checkups throughout life.

Although eventual shrinking of the brain is normal and accelerates in old age, alcoholics and professional boxers hasten the process. Whether a boxer wins the match or not, the likelihood of brain damage and atrophy increases with every blow. Everyone recognizes that alcohol profoundly affects both the mind and the body. CT scans of alcoholics reveal a reduction in brain size and density appearing at a fairly early age. Both boxers and alcoholics exhibit signs of mental deterioration unrelated to the aging process.

CHECK YOUR UNDERSTANDING

27. Premature babies have problems controlling their body temperature. Why?

28. List several causes of reversible dementia in the elderly.

For answers, see Appendix G.

The human cerebral hemispheres—our "thinking caps"—are awesome in their complexity. But no less amazing are the brain regions that oversee our subconscious, autonomic body functions—the diencephalon and brain stem—particularly when you consider their relatively insignificant size. The spinal cord, which acts as a reflex center and a communication link between the brain and body periphery, is equally important to body homeostasis.

We have introduced a good deal of new terminology in this chapter, and much of it will come up again in one or more of the remaining nervous system chapters. Chapter 13, your next challenge, considers the structures of the peripheral nervous system that work hand in hand with the CNS to keep it informed and to deliver its orders to the effectors of the body.

RELATED CLINICAL TERMS

Autism A complex developmental neurological disorder that typically appears in the first three years of life and is characterized by difficulty in communicating, forming relationships with others, and responding appropriately to the environment. No single cause has been determined although a number of genes are thought to play a role and structural brain abnormalities are present. Occurs in about two per 1000 people, and early behavioral intervention is beneficial.

Cordotomy (kor-dot′o-me) A procedure in which a tract in the spinal cord is severed surgically; usually done to relieve unremitting pain.

Encephalopathy (en-sef″ah-lop′ah-the; *enceph* = brain; *path* = disease) Any disease or disorder of the brain.

Functional brain disorders Psychological disorders for which no structural cause can be found; include neuroses and psychoses (see entries in this list).

Hypersomnia (*hyper* = excess; *somnus* = sleep) A condition in which affected individuals sleep as much as 15 hours daily.

Microcephaly (mi″kro-sef′ah-le; *micro* = small) Congenital condition involving the formation of a small brain, as evidenced by reduced skull size; most microcephalic children are mentally retarded.

Myelitis (mi″ĕ-li′tis; *myel* = spinal cord; *itis* = inflammation) Inflammation of the spinal cord.

Myelogram (*gram* = recording) X ray of the spinal cord after injection of a contrast medium.

Myoclonus (mi″o-klo′nus; *myo* = muscle; *clon* = violent motion, tumult) Sudden contraction of a muscle or muscle part, usually involving muscles of the limbs. Myoclonal jerks can occur in normal individuals as they are falling asleep; others may be due to diseases of the reticular formation or cerebellum.

Neuroses (nu-ro′sēs) A less debilitating class of mental illness; examples include severe anxiety (panic attacks), phobias (irrational fears), and obsessive-compulsive behaviors (e.g., washing one's hands every few minutes); the affected individual, however, retains contact with reality.

Pallidectomy ("cutting the pallidus") Surgically lesioning part of the globus pallidus of the basal nuclei to relieve some symptoms of Parkinson's disease.

Psychoses (si-ko′sēs) A class of severe mental illness in which affected individuals lose touch with reality and exhibit bizarre behaviors; the *legal* word for psychotic behavior is *insanity*. Psychoses include *schizophrenia* (skit-so-fre′ne-ah), *bipolar disorder,* and some forms of *depression*.

CHAPTER SUMMARY

The Brain   (pp. 430–453)

1. The brain provides for voluntary movements, interpretation and integration of sensation, consciousness, and cognitive function.

Embryonic Development   (pp. 430–431)

2. The brain develops from the rostral portion of the embryonic neural tube.

3. Early brain development yields the three primary brain vesicles: the prosencephalon (cerebral hemispheres and diencephalon), mesencephalon (midbrain), and rhombencephalon (pons, medulla, and cerebellum).

4. Cephalization results in the envelopment of the diencephalon and superior brain stem by the cerebral hemispheres.

Regions and Organization   (p. 431)

5. In a widely used system, the adult brain is divided into the cerebral hemispheres, diencephalon, brain stem, and cerebellum.

6. The cerebral hemispheres and cerebellum have gray matter nuclei surrounded by white matter and an outer cortex of gray matter. The diencephalon and brain stem lack a cortex.

Ventricles   (pp. 431–433)

7. The brain contains four ventricles filled with cerebrospinal fluid. The lateral ventricles are in the cerebral hemispheres; the third ventricle is in the diencephalon; the fourth ventricle is between the brain stem and the cerebellum and connects with the central canal of the spinal cord.

Cerebral Hemispheres   (pp. 433–441)

8. The two cerebral hemispheres exhibit gyri, sulci, and fissures. The longitudinal fissure partially separates the hemispheres; other fissures or sulci subdivide each hemisphere into lobes.

9. Each cerebral hemisphere consists of the cerebral cortex, the cerebral white matter, and basal nuclei (ganglia).

10. Each cerebral hemisphere receives sensory impulses from, and dispatches motor impulses to, the opposite side of the body. The body is represented in an upside-down fashion in the sensory and motor cortices.

11. Functional areas of the cerebral cortex include (1) motor areas: primary motor and premotor cortices of the frontal lobe, the frontal eye field, and Broca's area in the frontal lobe of one hemisphere (usually the left); (2) sensory areas: primary somatosensory cortex and somatosensory association cortex in the parietal lobe; visual areas in the occipital lobe; olfactory and auditory areas in the temporal lobe; gustatory, visceral, and vestibular areas in the insula; (3) association areas: anterior association area in the frontal lobe, and posterior and limbic association areas spanning several lobes.

12. The cerebral hemispheres show lateralization of cortical function. In most people, the left hemisphere is dominant (i.e., specialized for language and mathematical skills); the right hemisphere is more concerned with visual-spatial skills and creative endeavors.

13. Fiber tracts of the cerebral white matter include commissures, association fibers, and projection fibers.

14. The paired basal nuclei (also called basal ganglia) include the lentiform nucleus (globus pallidus and putamen) and caudate nucleus. The basal nuclei are subcortical nuclei that help control muscular movements. Functionally they are closely associated with the substantia nigra of the midbrain.

Diencephalon   (pp. 441–445)

15. The diencephalon includes the thalamus, hypothalamus, and epithalamus and encloses the third ventricle.

12

16. The thalamus is the major relay station for (1) sensory impulses ascending to the sensory cortex, (2) inputs from subcortical motor nuclei and the cerebellum traveling to the cerebral motor cortex, and (3) impulses traveling to association cortices from lower centers.

17. The hypothalamus is an important autonomic nervous system control center and a pivotal part of the limbic system. It maintains water balance and regulates thirst, eating behavior, gastrointestinal activity, body temperature, and the activity of the anterior pituitary gland.

18. The epithalamus includes the pineal gland, which secretes the hormone melatonin.

Brain Stem (pp. 445–450)

19. The brain stem includes the midbrain, pons, and medulla oblongata.

20. The midbrain contains the corpora quadrigemina (visual and auditory reflex centers), the red nucleus (subcortical motor centers), and the substantia nigra. The periaqueductal gray matter is involved in pain suppression and contains the motor nuclei of cranial nerves III and IV. The cerebral peduncles on its ventral face house the pyramidal fiber tracts. The midbrain surrounds the cerebral aqueduct.

21. The pons is mainly a conduction area. Its nuclei contribute to regulation of respiration and cranial nerves V–VII.

22. The pyramids (descending corticospinal tracts) form the ventral face of the medulla oblongata; these fibers cross over (decussation of the pyramids) before entering the spinal cord. Important nuclei in the medulla regulate respiratory rhythm, heart rate, and blood pressure and serve cranial nerves VIII–XII. The olivary nuclei and cough, sneezing, swallowing, and vomiting centers are also in the medulla.

Cerebellum (pp. 450–451)

23. The cerebellum consists of two hemispheres, marked by convolutions and separated by the vermis. It is connected to the brain stem by superior, middle, and inferior peduncles.

24. The cerebellum processes and interprets impulses from the motor cortex and sensory pathways and coordinates motor activity so that smooth, well-timed movements occur. It also plays a poorly understood role in cognition.

Functional Brain Systems (pp. 451–453)

25. The limbic system consists of numerous structures that encircle the brain stem. It is the "emotional-visceral brain." It also plays a role in memory.

26. The reticular formation is a diffuse network of neurons and nuclei spanning the length of the brain stem. It maintains the alert state of the cerebral cortex (RAS), and its motor nuclei serve both somatic and visceral motor activities.

Higher Mental Functions (pp. 453–460)

Brain Wave Patterns and the EEG (pp. 453–455)

1. Patterns of electrical activity of the brain are called brain waves; a record of this activity is an electroencephalogram (EEG). Brain wave patterns, identified by their frequencies, include alpha, beta, theta, and delta waves.

2. Epilepsy results from abnormal electrical activity of brain neurons. Involuntary muscle contractions and sensory auras are typical during such seizures.

Consciousness (p. 455)

3. Consciousness is described clinically on a continuum from alertness to drowsiness to stupor and finally to coma.

4. Human consciousness is thought to involve holistic information processing, which is (1) not localizable, (2) superimposed on other types of neural activity, and (3) totally interconnected.

5. Fainting (syncope) is a temporary loss of consciousness that usually reflects inadequate blood delivery to the brain. Coma is loss of consciousness in which the victim is unresponsive to stimuli.

Sleep and Sleep-Wake Cycles (pp. 455–457)

6. Sleep is a state of partial consciousness from which a person can be aroused by stimulation. The two major types of sleep are non–rapid eye movement (NREM) sleep and rapid eye movement (REM) sleep.

7. During stages 1–4 of NREM sleep, brain wave frequency decreases and amplitude increases until delta wave sleep (stage 4) is achieved. REM sleep is indicated by a return to a stage 1 EEG. During REM, the eyes move rapidly under the lids. NREM and REM sleep alternate throughout the night.

8. Slow-wave sleep (stages 3 and 4 of NREM) appears to be restorative. REM sleep is important for emotional stability.

9. REM occupies half of an infant's sleep time and then declines to about 25% of sleep time by the age of 10 years. Time spent in slow-wave sleep declines steadily throughout life.

10. Narcolepsy is involuntary lapses into REM sleep that occur without warning during waking periods. Insomnia is a chronic inability to obtain the amount or quality of sleep needed to function adequately. Sleep apnea is a temporary cessation of breathing during sleep, causing hypoxia.

Language (p. 457)

11. In most people language is controlled by the left hemisphere. The language implementation system, which includes Broca's and Wernicke's areas and the basal nuclei, analyzes incoming and produces outgoing language. The opposite hemisphere deals with the emotional content of language.

Memory (pp. 457–460)

12. Memory is the storage and retrieval of information. It is essential for learning and is part of consciousness.

13. Memory storage has two stages: short-term memory (STM) and long-term memory (LTM). Transfer of information from STM to LTM takes minutes to hours, but more time is required for LTM consolidation.

14. Declarative memory is the ability to learn and consciously remember information. Procedural memory is the learning of motor skills, which are then performed without conscious thought.

15. Declarative memory appears to involve the medial temporal lobe (hippocampus and surrounding temporal cortical areas), thalamus, basal forebrain, and prefrontal cortex. Skill memory (a type of procedural memory) relies on the basal nuclei.

16. The nature of memory formation at the molecular level is not fully known, but NMDA receptors (essentially calcium channels), activated by depolarization and glutamate binding, play a major role in long-term potentiation (LTP). The calcium influx that follows NMDA receptor activation mobilizes enzymes that mediate events necessary for memory formation.

Protection of the Brain (pp. 460–466)

1. The delicate brain is protected by bone, meninges, cerebrospinal fluid, and the blood-brain barrier.

Meninges (pp. 461–463)

2. The meninges from superficial to deep are the dura mater, the arachnoid mater, and the pia mater. They enclose the brain and spinal cord and their blood vessels. Inward folds of the inner layer of the dura mater secure the brain to the skull.

Cerebrospinal Fluid (p. 463)

3. Cerebrospinal fluid (CSF), formed by the choroid plexuses from blood plasma, circulates through the ventricles and into the subarachnoid space. It returns to the dural venous sinuses via the arachnoid villi. CSF supports and cushions the brain and cord and helps to nourish them.

Blood-Brain Barrier (pp. 463–464)

4. The blood-brain barrier reflects the relative impermeability of the epithelium of capillaries of the brain. It allows water, respiratory gases, essential nutrients, and fat-soluble molecules to enter the neural tissue, but prevents entry of other, water-soluble, potentially harmful substances.

Homeostatic Imbalances of the Brain (pp. 464–466)

5. Head trauma may cause brain injuries called concussions or, in severe cases, contusions (bruising). When the brain stem is affected, unconsciousness (temporary or permanent) occurs. Trauma-induced brain injuries may be aggravated by intracranial hemorrhage or cerebral edema, both of which compress brain tissue.

6. Cerebrovascular accidents (strokes) result when blood circulation to brain neurons is impaired and brain tissue dies. The result may be hemiplegia, sensory deficits, or speech impairment.

7. Alzheimer's disease is a degenerative brain disease in which beta-amyloid peptide deposits and neurofibrillary tangles appear. Marked by a deficit of ACh, it results in slow, progressive loss of memory and motor control and increasing dementia.

8. Parkinson's disease and Huntington's disease are neurodegenerative disorders of the basal nuclei. Both involve abnormalities of the neurotransmitter dopamine (too little or too much secreted) and are characterized by abnormal movements.

The Spinal Cord (pp. 466–477)

Embryonic Development (p. 466)

1. The spinal cord develops from the neural tube. Its gray matter forms from the alar and basal plates. Fiber tracts form the outer white matter. The neural crest forms the sensory (dorsal root) ganglia.

Gross Anatomy and Protection (pp. 466–468)

2. The spinal cord, a two-way impulse conduction pathway and a reflex center, resides within the vertebral column and is protected by meninges and cerebrospinal fluid. It extends from the foramen magnum to the end of the first lumbar vertebra.

3. Thirty-one pairs of spinal nerves issue from the cord. The cord is enlarged in the cervical and lumbar regions, where spinal nerves serving the limbs arise.

Cross-Sectional Anatomy (pp. 468–476)

4. The central gray matter of the cord is H shaped. Ventral horns mainly contain somatic motor neurons. Lateral horns contain visceral (autonomic) motor neurons. Dorsal horns contain interneurons.

5. Axons of neurons of the lateral and ventral horns emerge in common from the cord via the ventral roots. Axons of sensory neurons (with cell bodies located in the dorsal root ganglion) enter the dorsal aspect of the cord and form the dorsal roots. The ventral and dorsal roots combine to form the spinal nerves.

6. Each side of the white matter of the cord has dorsal, lateral, and ventral columns (funiculi), and each funiculus contains a number of ascending and descending tracts. All tracts are paired and most decussate.

7. Ascending (sensory) tracts include the fasciculi gracilis and cuneatus, spinothalamic tracts, and spinocerebellar tracts.

8. The dorsal column–medial lemniscal pathway consists of the dorsal white column (fasciculus cuneatus, fasciculus gracilis) and the medial lemniscus, which are concerned with straight-through, precise transmission of one or a few related sensory modalities. The anterolateral pathways (mostly the spinothalamic tracts) are multimodal pathways that permit brain stem processing of ascending impulses. The spinocerebellar tracts, which terminate in the cerebellum, serve muscle sense, not conscious sensory perception.

9. Descending tracts include the pyramidal tracts (ventral and lateral corticospinal tracts) and a number of motor tracts originating from subcortical motor nuclei. These descending fibers issue from the brain stem motor areas [indirect (extrapyramidal) system] and cortical motor areas [direct (pyramidal) system].

Spinal Cord Trauma and Disorders (pp. 476–477)

10. Injury to the ventral horn neurons or the ventral roots results in flaccid paralysis. (Injury to the upper motor neurons in the brain results in spastic paralysis.) If the dorsal roots or sensory tracts are damaged, paresthesias occur.

11. Poliomyelitis results from inflammation and destruction of the ventral horn neurons by the poliovirus. Paralysis and muscle atrophy ensue.

12. Amyotrophic lateral sclerosis (ALS) results from destruction of the ventral horn neurons and the pyramidal tracts. The victim eventually loses the ability to swallow, speak, and breathe. Death generally occurs within five years.

Diagnostic Procedures for Assessing CNS Dysfunction (p. 477)

1. Diagnostic procedures used to assess neurological condition and function range from routine reflex testing to sophisticated techniques such as cerebral angiography, CT scans, MRI scans, and PET scans.

Developmental Aspects of the Central Nervous System (pp. 477–478)

1. Maternal and environmental factors may impair embryonic brain development, and oxygen deprivation destroys brain cells. Severe congenital brain diseases include cerebral palsy, anencephaly, hydrocephalus, and spina bifida.

2. Premature babies have trouble regulating body temperature because the hypothalamus is one of the last brain areas to mature prenatally.

3. Development of motor control indicates progressive myelination and maturation of a child's nervous system.

4. Brain growth ends in young adulthood. Neurons die throughout life and most are not replaced; brain weight and volume decline with age.

5. Healthy elders maintain nearly optimal intellectual function. Disease—particularly cardiovascular disease—is the major cause of declining mental function with age.

12

Multiple Choice/Matching

(Some questions have more than one correct answer. Select the best answer or answers from the choices given.)

1. The primary motor cortex, Broca's area, and the premotor cortex are located in which lobe? (a) frontal, (b) parietal, (c) temporal, (d) occipital.

2. The innermost layer of the meninges, delicate and closely apposed to the brain tissue, is the (a) dura mater, (b) corpus callosum, (c) arachnoid, (d) pia mater.

3. Cerebrospinal fluid is formed by (a) arachnoid villi, (b) the dura mater, (c) choroid plexuses, (d) all of these.

4. A patient has suffered a cerebral hemorrhage that has caused dysfunction of the precentral gyrus of his right cerebral cortex. As a result, (a) he cannot voluntarily move his left arm or leg, (b) he feels no sensation on the left side of his body, (c) he feels no sensation on his right side.

5. Choose the proper term from the key to respond to the statements describing various brain areas.
   Key:
(a) cerebellum	(d) striatum	(g) midbrain
(b) corpora quadrigemina	(e) hypothalamus	(h) pons
(c) corpus callosum	(f) medulla	(i) thalamus

   _____ (1) basal nuclei involved in fine control of motor activities
   _____ (2) region where there is a gross crossover of fibers of descending pyramidal tracts
   _____ (3) control of temperature, autonomic nervous system reflexes, hunger, and water balance
   _____ (4) houses the substantia nigra and cerebral aqueduct
   _____ (5) relay stations for visual and auditory stimuli input; found in midbrain
   _____ (6) houses vital centers for control of the heart, respiration, and blood pressure
   _____ (7) brain area through which all the sensory input is relayed to get to the cerebral cortex
   _____ (8) brain area most concerned with equilibrium, body posture, and coordination of motor activity

6. Which of the following tracts convey vibration and other specific sensations that can be precisely localized? (a) pyramidal tract, (b) medial lemniscus, (c) lateral spinothalamic tract, (d) reticulospinal tract.

7. Destruction of the ventral horn cells of the spinal cord results in loss of (a) integrating impulses, (b) sensory impulses, (c) voluntary motor impulses, (d) all of these.

8. Fiber tracts that allow neurons within the same cerebral hemisphere to communicate are (a) association tracts, (b) commissures, (c) projection tracts.

9. A number of brain structures are listed below. If an area is primarily gray matter, write a in the answer blank; if mostly white matter, respond with b.

   _____ (1) cerebral cortex
   _____ (2) corpus callosum and corona radiata
   _____ (3) red nucleus
   _____ (4) medial and lateral nuclear groups
   _____ (5) medial lemniscal tract
   _____ (6) cranial nerve nuclei
   _____ (7) spinothalamic tract
   _____ (8) fornix
   _____ (9) cingulate and precentral gyri

10. A professor unexpectedly blew a loud horn in his anatomy and physiology class. The students looked up, startled. The reflexive movements of their eyes were mediated by the (a) cerebral cortex, (b) inferior olives, (c) raphe nuclei, (d) superior colliculi, (e) nucleus gracilis.

11. Identify the stage of sleep described by using choices from the key. (Note that responses a–d refer to NREM sleep.)
    Key: (a) stage 1 (b) stage 2 (c) stage 3 (d) stage 4 (e) REM

    _____ (1) the stage when blood pressure and heart rate reach their lowest levels
    _____ (2) indicated by movement of the eyes under the lids; dreaming occurs
    _____ (3) when nightmares are likely to occur
    _____ (4) when the sleeper is very easily awakened; EEG shows alpha waves

12. All of the following descriptions refer to dorsal column–medial lemniscal ascending pathways except one: (a) they include the fasciculus gracilis and fasciculus cuneatus; (b) they include a chain of three neurons; (c) their connections are diffuse and polymodal; (d) they are concerned with precise transmission of one or a few related sensory modalities.

Short Answer Essay Questions

13. Make a diagram showing the three primary (embryonic) brain vesicles. Name each and then use clinical terminology to name the resulting adult brain regions.

14. (a) What is the advantage of having a cerebrum that is highly convoluted? (b) What term is used to indicate its grooves? Its outward folds? (c) What groove divides the cerebrum into two hemispheres? (d) What divides the parietal from the frontal lobe? The parietal from the temporal lobe?

15. (a) Make a rough drawing of the lateral aspect of the left cerebral hemisphere. (b) You may be thinking, "But I just can't draw!" So, name the hemisphere involved with most people's ability to draw. (c) On your drawing, locate the following areas and provide the major function of each: primary motor cortex, premotor cortex, somatosensory association cortex, primary somatosensory cortex, visual and auditory areas, prefrontal cortex, Wernicke's and Broca's areas.

16. (a) What does lateralization of cortical functioning mean? (b) Why is the term cerebral dominance a misnomer?

17. (a) What is the function of the basal nuclei? (b) Which basal nuclei form the lentiform nucleus? (c) Which arches over the diencephalon?

18. Explain how the cerebellum is physically connected to the brain stem.

19. Describe the role of the cerebellum in maintaining smooth, coordinated skeletal muscle activity.

20. (a) Where is the limbic system located? (b) What structures make up this system? (c) How is the limbic system important in behavior?

21. (a) Localize the reticular formation in the brain. (b) What does RAS mean, and what is its function?

22. What is an aura?

23. How do sleep patterns, extent of sleeping time, and amount of time spent in REM and NREM sleep change through life?

24. Compare and contrast short-term memory (STM) and long-term memory (LTM) relative to storage capacity and duration of the memory.

25. Define memory consolidation.
26. Compare and contrast declarative and procedural memory relative to the types of things remembered and the importance of conscious retrieval.
27. List four ways in which the CNS is protected.
28. (a) How is cerebrospinal fluid formed and drained? Describe its pathway within and around the brain. (b) What happens if CSF is not drained properly? Why is this consequence more harmful in adults?
29. What constitutes the blood-brain barrier?
30. A brain surgeon is about to make an incision. Name all the tissue layers that she cuts through from the skin to the brain.
31. (a) Define concussion and contusion. (b) Why does severe brain stem injury result in unconsciousness?
32. Describe the spinal cord, depicting its extent, its composition of gray and white matter, and its spinal roots.
33. How do the types of motor activity controlled by the direct (pyramidal) and indirect systems differ?
34. Describe the functional problems that would be experienced by a person in which these fiber tracts have been cut: (a) lateral spinothalamic, (b) ventral and dorsal spinocerebellar, (c) tecto-spinal.
35. Differentiate between spastic and flaccid paralysis.
36. How do the conditions paraplegia, hemiplegia, and quadriplegia differ?
37. (a) Define cerebrovascular accident or CVA. (b) Describe its possible causes and consequences.
38. (a) What factors account for brain growth after birth? (b) List some structural brain changes observed with aging.

 Critical Thinking and Clinical Application Questions

1. A 10-month-old infant has an enlarging head circumference and delayed overall development. She has a bulging anterior fontanelle and her CSF pressure is elevated. Based on these findings, answer the following questions: (a) What are the possible cause(s) of an enlarged head? (b) What tests might be helpful in obtaining information about this infant's problem? (c) Assuming the tests conducted showed the cerebral aqueduct to be constricted, which ventricles or CSF-containing areas would you expect to be enlarged? Which would likely not be visible? Respond to the same questions based on a finding of obstructed arachnoid villi.
2. Mrs. Jones has had a progressive decline in her mental capabilities in the last five or six years. At first her family attributed her occasional memory lapses, confusion, and agitation to grief over her husband's death six years earlier. When examined, Mrs. Jones was aware of her cognitive problems and was shown to have an IQ score approximately 30 points less than would be predicted by her work history. A CT scan showed diffuse cerebral atrophy. The physician prescribed an acetylcholinesterase inhibitor and Mrs. Jones showed slight improvement. What is Mrs. Jones's problem? Why did the acetylcholinesterase inhibitor help?

3. Robert, a brilliant computer analyst, suffered a blow to his anterior skull from a falling rock while mountain climbing. Shortly thereafter, it was obvious to his coworkers that his behavior had undergone a dramatic change. Although previously a smart dresser, he was now unkempt. One morning, he was observed defecating into the wastebasket. His supervisor ordered Robert to report to the company's doctor immediately. What region of Robert's brain was affected by the cranial blow?
4. Mrs. Adams is ready to deliver her first baby. Unfortunately, the baby appears to have a myelomeningocele. Would a vaginal or surgical (C-section) delivery be more appropriate and why?
5. The medical chart of a 68-year-old man includes the following notes: "Slight tremor of right hand at rest; stony facial expression; difficulty in initiating movements." (a) Based on your present knowledge, what is the diagnosis? (b) What brain areas are most likely involved in this man's disorder, and what is the deficiency? (c) How is this condition currently treated?
6. Cynthia, a 16-year-old girl, was rushed to the hospital after taking a bad spill off the parallel bars. After she had a complete neurological workup, her family was told that she would be permanently paralyzed from the waist down. The neurologist then outlined for Cynthia's parents the importance of preventing complications in such cases. Common complications include urinary infection, bed sores, and muscular spasms. Using your knowledge of neuroanatomy, explain the underlying reasons for these complications.
7. Mrs. Herrera suffered a stroke two weeks ago. Initially she was unable to move her right arm and the right side of her face, but her paralysis has decreased markedly. However, she still has a great deal of difficulty speaking. Mrs. Herrera's speech consists of very few words. She struggles to produce these words and they are distorted and separated by long pauses. Her comprehension of written and spoken language is unaltered. She is fully aware of what happened to her and is tearful much of the time. Which side of the brain and which particular area of the brain was affected by Mrs. Herrera's stroke?
8. Five-year-old Amy wakes her parents up at 3 AM crying and complaining of a sore neck, a severe headache, and feeling sick to her stomach. She has a temperature of 40°C (104°F) and hides her eyes, saying that the lights are too bright. The emergency physician suspects meningitis and performs a lumbar tap. Using your knowledge of neuroanatomy, explain into which space and at what level of the vertebral column the needle will be inserted to perform this test. Which fluid is being obtained and why?

12

13

PART 1
SENSORY RECEPTORS AND SENSATION

Sensory Receptors (pp. 485–488)

Sensory Integration: From Sensation to Perception (pp. 488–491)

PART 2
TRANSMISSION LINES: NERVES AND THEIR STRUCTURE AND REPAIR

Nerves and Associated Ganglia (pp. 491–492)

Cranial Nerves (pp. 493–501)

Spinal Nerves (pp. 502–511)

PART 3
MOTOR ENDINGS AND MOTOR ACTIVITY

Peripheral Motor Endings (p. 512)

Motor Integration: From Intention to Effect (pp. 512–513)

PART 4
REFLEX ACTIVITY

The Reflex Arc (p. 514)

Spinal Reflexes (pp. 514–520)

Developmental Aspects of the Peripheral Nervous System (p. 520)

The Peripheral Nervous System and Reflex Activity

▶ Define peripheral nervous system and list its components.

The human brain, for all its sophistication, would be useless without its links to the outside world. In one experiment that illustrates this point, blindfolded volunteers suspended in warm water in a sensory deprivation tank (a situation that limits sensory inputs) hallucinated. One saw charging pink and purple elephants. Another heard a chorus, still others had taste hallucinations. Our very sanity depends on a continuous flow of information from the outside.

No less important to our well-being are the orders sent from the CNS to voluntary muscles and other effectors of the body, which allow us to move and to take care of our own needs. The **peripheral nervous system (PNS)** provides these links from and to the world outside our bodies. Ghostly white nerves thread through virtually every part of the body, enabling the CNS to receive information and to carry out its decisions.

The PNS includes all neural structures outside the brain and spinal cord, that is, the *sensory receptors*, peripheral *nerves* and their associated *ganglia*, and efferent *motor endings*. Its basic components are diagrammed in Figure 13.1. In the first portion of this chapter we deal with the functional anatomy of each PNS element. Then we consider the components of reflex arcs and some important somatic reflexes, played out almost entirely in PNS structures, that help to maintain homeostasis.

PART **1**

SENSORY RECEPTORS AND SENSATION

Sensory Receptors

▶ Classify general sensory receptors by structure, stimulus detected, and body location.

Sensory receptors are specialized to respond to changes in their environment, which are called **stimuli**. Typically, activation of a sensory receptor by an adequate stimulus results in graded potentials that in turn trigger nerve impulses along the afferent PNS fibers coursing to the CNS. *Sensation* (awareness of the stimulus) and *perception* (interpretation of the meaning of the stimulus) occur in the brain. But we are getting ahead of ourselves here.

For now, let's just examine how sensory receptors are classified. Basically, there are three ways to classify sensory receptors: (1) by the type of stimulus they detect; (2) by their body location; and (3) by their structural complexity.

Classification by Stimulus Type

The receptor classes named according to the activating stimulus are easy to remember because the class name usually indicates the stimulus.

1. **Mechanoreceptors** respond to mechanical force such as touch, pressure (including blood pressure), vibration, and stretch.
2. **Thermoreceptors** are sensitive to temperature changes.
3. **Photoreceptors**, such as those of the retina of the eye, respond to light energy.
4. **Chemoreceptors** respond to chemicals in solution (molecules smelled or tasted, or changes in blood or interstitial fluid chemistry).
5. **Nociceptors** (no"se-sep'torz; *noci* = harm) respond to potentially damaging stimuli that result in pain. For example, searing heat, extreme cold, excessive pressure, and inflammatory chemicals are all interpreted as painful. These signals stimulate subtypes of thermoreceptors, mechanoreceptors, and chemoreceptors.

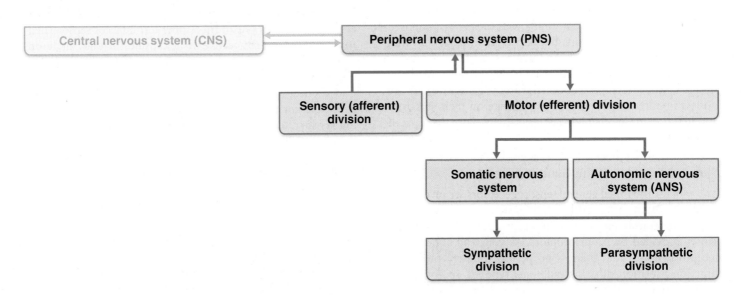

Figure 13.1 **Place of the PNS in the structural organization of the nervous system.**

Classification by Location

Three receptor classes are recognized according to either their location or the location of the activating stimulus.

1. **Exteroceptors** (ek″ster-o-sep′torz) are sensitive to stimuli arising outside the body (*extero* = outside), so most exteroceptors are near or at the body surface. They include touch, pressure, pain, and temperature receptors in the skin and most receptors of the special senses (vision, hearing, equilibrium, taste, smell).

2. **Interoceptors** (in″ter-o-sep′torz), also called *visceroceptors*, respond to stimuli within the body (*intero* = inside), such as from the internal viscera and blood vessels. They monitor a variety of stimuli, including chemical changes, tissue stretch, and temperature. Sometimes their activity causes us to feel pain, discomfort, hunger, or thirst. However, we are usually unaware of their workings.

3. **Proprioceptors** (pro″pre-o-sep′torz), like interoceptors, respond to internal stimuli; however, their location is much more restricted. Proprioceptors occur in skeletal muscles, tendons, joints, and ligaments and in connective tissue coverings of bones and muscles. (Some authorities include the equilibrium receptors of the inner ear in this class.) Proprioceptors constantly advise the brain of our body movements (*propria* = one's own) by monitoring how much the organs containing these receptors are stretched.

Classification by Structural Complexity

On the basis of overall receptor structure, there are **simple** and **complex receptors**, but the overwhelming majority are simple. The simple receptors are modified dendritic endings of sensory neurons. They are found throughout the body and monitor most types of general sensory information.

Complex receptors are actually **sense organs**, localized collections of cells (usually of many types) associated with the **special senses** (vision, hearing, equilibrium, smell, and taste). For example, the sense organ we know as the eye is composed not only of sensory neurons but also of nonneural cells that form its supporting wall, lens, and other associated structures.

Though the complex sense organs are most familiar to us, the simple sensory receptors associated with the **general senses** are no less important, and we will concentrate on their structure and function in this chapter. The special senses are the topic of Chapter 15.

Simple Receptors of the General Senses

The widely distributed general sensory receptors are involved in tactile sensation (a mix of touch, pressure, stretch, and vibration), temperature monitoring, and pain, as well as the "muscle sense" provided by proprioceptors. As you read about these receptors, notice that there is no perfect "one-receptor-one-function" relationship. Instead, one type of receptor can respond to several different kinds of stimuli. Likewise, different types of receptors can respond to similar stimuli. Anatomically, these receptors are either *unencapsulated* (*free*) *nerve endings* or

encapsulated nerve endings. The general sensory receptors are illustrated and classified in **Table 13.1**. You may find it helpful to refer to the illustrations in this table throughout the discussion that follows.

Unencapsulated Dendritic Endings **Free**, or **naked**, **nerve endings** of sensory neurons are present nearly everywhere in the body, but they are particularly abundant in epithelia and connective tissues. Most of these sensory fibers are unmyelinated, small-diameter C fibers, and their distal endings (the sensory terminals) usually have small knoblike swellings. They respond chiefly to temperature and painful stimuli, but some respond to tissue movements caused by pressure as well. Nerve endings that respond to cold (10–40°C) are located in the superficial dermis. Those responding to heat (32–48°C) are found deeper in the dermis.

Heat or cold outside the range of thermoreceptors activates nociceptors and is perceived as painful. Nociceptors also respond to pinch and chemicals released from damaged tissue. A recently discovered receptor (*vanilloid receptor*) in the plasma membrane of nociceptive free nerve endings is an ion channel that is opened by heat, low pH, and the substance found in red peppers called capsaicin.

Another sensation mediated by free nerve endings is itch. Located in the dermis, the *itch receptor* escaped detection until 1997 because of its thin diameter. A number of chemicals—notably histamine—present at inflamed sites activate these nerve endings.

Certain free nerve endings associate with enlarged, disc-shaped epidermal cells (*tactile* or *Merkel cells*) to form **tactile (Merkel) discs**, which lie in the deeper layers of the epidermis and function as light touch receptors. **Hair follicle receptors**, free nerve endings that wrap basketlike around hair follicles, are light touch receptors that detect bending of hairs. The tickle of a mosquito landing on your skin is mediated by hair follicle receptors.

Encapsulated Dendritic Endings All **encapsulated dendritic endings** consist of one or more fiber terminals of sensory neurons enclosed in a connective tissue capsule. Virtually all the encapsulated receptors are mechanoreceptors, but they vary greatly in shape, size, and distribution in the body.

The encapsulated receptors known as **Meissner's corpuscles** (mīs′nerz kor′pus″lz) are small receptors in which a few spiraling sensory terminals are surrounded by Schwann cells and then by a thin egg-shaped connective tissue capsule. Meissner's corpuscles are found just beneath the epidermis in the dermal papillae and are especially numerous in sensitive and hairless skin areas such as the nipples, fingertips, and soles of the feet. Also called **tactile corpuscles**, they are receptors for discriminative touch, and apparently play the same role in light touch reception in hairless skin as do the hair follicle receptors in hairy skin.

Pacinian corpuscles, also called **lamellated corpuscles**, are scattered deep in the dermis, and in subcutaneous tissue underlying the skin. Although they are mechanoreceptors stimulated by deep pressure, they respond only when the pressure is first

TABLE 13.1		General Sensory Receptors Classified by Structure and Function	
STRUCTURAL CLASS	**ILLUSTRATION**	**FUNCTIONAL CLASSES ACCORDING TO LOCATION (L) AND STIMULUS TYPE (S)**	**BODY LOCATION**
Unencapsulated			
Free nerve endings of sensory neurons		L: Exteroceptors, interoceptors, and proprioceptors S: Thermoreceptors (warm and cool), chemoreceptors (itch, pH, etc.), mechanoreceptors (pressure), nociceptors (pain, hot, cold, pinch, and chemicals)	Most body tissues; most dense in connective tissues (ligaments, tendons, dermis, joint capsules, periostea) and epithelia (epidermis, cornea, mucosae, and glands)
Modified free nerve endings: Tactile discs (Merkel discs)	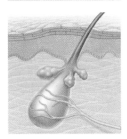Tactile cell	L: Exteroceptors S: Mechanoreceptors (light pressure); slowly adapting	Basal layer of epidermis
Hair follicle receptors		L: Exteroceptors S: Mechanoreceptors (hair deflection); rapidly adapting	In and surrounding hair follicles
Encapsulated			
Meissner's corpuscles (tactile corpuscles)		L: Exteroceptors S: Mechanoreceptors (light pressure, discriminative touch, vibration of low frequency); rapidly adapting	Dermal papillae of hairless skin, particularly nipples, external genitalia, fingertips, soles of feet, eyelids
Pacinian corpuscles (lamellated corpuscles)		L: Exteroceptors, interoceptors, and some proprioceptors S: Mechanoreceptors (deep pressure, stretch, vibration of high frequency); rapidly adapting	Dermis and hypodermis; periostea, mesentery, tendons, ligaments, joint capsules; most abundant on fingers, soles of feet, external genitalia, nipples
Ruffini endings		L: Exteroceptors and proprioceptors S: Mechanoreceptors (deep pressure and stretch); slowly or nonadapting	Deep in dermis, hypodermis, and joint capsules

13

applied, and thus are best suited to monitoring vibration (an "on/off" pressure stimulus). They are the largest corpuscular receptors. Some are over 3 mm long and half as wide and are visible to the naked eye as white, egg-shaped bodies. In section, a Pacinian corpuscle resembles a cut onion. Its single dendrite is surrounded by a capsule containing up to 60 layers of collagen fibers and flattened supporting cells.

Ruffini endings, which lie in the dermis, subcutaneous tissue, and joint capsules, contain a spray of receptor endings enclosed by a flattened capsule. They bear a striking resemblance to Golgi tendon organs (which monitor tendon stretch) and probably play a similar role in other dense connective tissues where they respond to deep and *continuous* pressure.

TABLE 13.1	General Sensory Receptors Classified by Structure and Function *(continued)*			
STRUCTURAL CLASS	**ILLUSTRATION**	**FUNCTIONAL CLASSES ACCORDING TO LOCATION (L) AND STIMULUS TYPE (S)**		**BODY LOCATION**
Encapsulated *(continued)*				
Muscle spindles	Intrafusal fibers	L: Proprioceptors S: Mechanoreceptors (muscle stretch, length)		Skeletal muscles, particularly those of the extremities
Golgi tendon organs		L: Proprioceptors S: Mechanoreceptors (tendon stretch, tension)		Tendons
Joint kinesthetic receptors		L: Proprioceptors S: Mechanoreceptors and nociceptors		Joint capsules of synovial joints

Muscle spindles are fusiform (spindle-shaped) proprioceptors found throughout the perimysium of a skeletal muscle. Each muscle spindle consists of a bundle of modified skeletal muscle fibers, called *intrafusal fibers* (in″trah-fu′zal), enclosed in a connective tissue capsule, as shown in Table 13.1. They detect muscle stretch and initiate a reflex that resists the stretch. Details of muscle spindle innervation are considered later when the stretch reflex is described (see p. 515).

Golgi tendon organs are proprioceptors located in tendons, close to the skeletal muscle insertion. They consist of small bundles of tendon (collagen) fibers enclosed in a layered capsule, with sensory terminals coiling between and around the fibers. When the tendon fibers are stretched by muscle contraction, the nerve endings are activated by compression. When Golgi tendon organs are activated, the contracting muscle is inhibited, which causes it to relax.

Joint kinesthetic receptors (kin″es-thet′ik) are proprioceptors that monitor stretch in the articular capsules that enclose synovial joints. At least four receptor types (Pacinian corpuscles, Ruffini endings, free nerve endings, and receptors resembling Golgi tendon organs) contribute to this receptor category. Together these receptors provide information on joint position and motion (*kines* = movement), a sensation of which we are highly conscious.

■ Close your eyes and flex and extend your fingers—you can *feel* exactly which joints are moving.

CHECK YOUR UNDERSTANDING

1. Your PNS mostly consists of nerves. What else belongs to your PNS?

2. You've cut your finger on a broken beaker in your A&P lab. Using stimulus type, location, and structural complexity, classify the sensory receptors that allow you to feel the pain.

For answers, see Appendix G.

Sensory Integration: From Sensation to Perception

▶ Outline the events that lead to sensation and perception.

▶ Describe receptor and generator potentials and sensory adaptation.

▶ Describe the main aspects of sensory perception.

Our survival depends not only on **sensation** (awareness of changes in the internal and external environments) but also on **perception** (conscious interpretation of those stimuli). For example, a pebble kicked up into my shoe causes the *sensation* of localized deep pressure, but my *perception* of it is an awareness of discomfort. Perception in turn determines how we will respond to stimuli. In the case of the pebble-in-my-shoe example, I'm taking off my shoe to get rid of the pesky pebble in a hurry.

General Organization of the Somatosensory System

The **somatosensory system**, or that part of the sensory system serving the body wall and limbs, receives inputs from exteroceptors, proprioceptors, and interoceptors. Consequently, it transmits information about several different sensory modalities.

As illustrated in **Figure 13.2**, three main levels of neural integration operate in the somatosensory (or any sensory) system:

(1) **Receptor level**: sensory receptors

(2) **Circuit level**: ascending pathways

(3) **Perceptual level**: neuronal circuits in the cerebral cortex

Sensory input is generally relayed toward the head, but note that it is also processed along the way.

Let's examine the events that must occur at each level along the pathway.

Processing at the Receptor Level

For sensation to occur, a stimulus must excite a receptor and action potentials must reach the CNS (Figure 13.2, (1)). For this to happen:

■ The stimulus energy must match the *specificity* of the receptor. For example, a given touch receptor may be sensitive to mechanical pressure, stretch, and vibration, but not to light energy (which is the province of receptors in the eye). The more complex the sensory receptor, the greater its specificity.

■ The stimulus must be applied within a sensory receptor's *receptive field*, the particular area monitored by the receptor. Typically, the smaller the receptive field, the greater the ability of the brain to accurately localize the stimulus site.

■ The stimulus energy must be converted into the energy of a *graded potential* called a **receptor potential**, a process called **transduction**. This receptor potential may be a depolarizing or hyperpolarizing graded potential similar to the EPSPs or IPSPs generated at postsynaptic membranes in response to neurotransmitter binding, as described in Chapter 11 (pp. 411–412). Membrane depolarizations that summate and directly lead to generation of action potentials in an afferent fiber are called **generator potentials**.

When the receptor region is part of a sensory neuron (as with free dendrites or the encapsulated receptors of most general sense receptors), the terms receptor potential and generator potential are synonymous. When the receptor is a separate cell, the receptor and generator potentials are completely separate events. Upon stimulation, such a depolarizing receptor cell produces a receptor potential causing neurotransmitter release. The released neurotransmitter, in turn, causes a generator potential in the associated afferent neuron.

■ A generator potential in the associated sensory neuron (a first-order neuron) must reach *threshold* so that voltage-gated sodium channels on the axon (usually located just proximal to the receptor membrane, often at the first node of Ranvier) are opened and nerve impulses are generated and propagated to the CNS.

Information about the stimulus—its strength, duration, and pattern—is encoded in the frequency of nerve impulses (the greater the frequency, the stronger the stimulus). Many but not all sensory receptors exhibit **adaptation**, a change in sensitivity

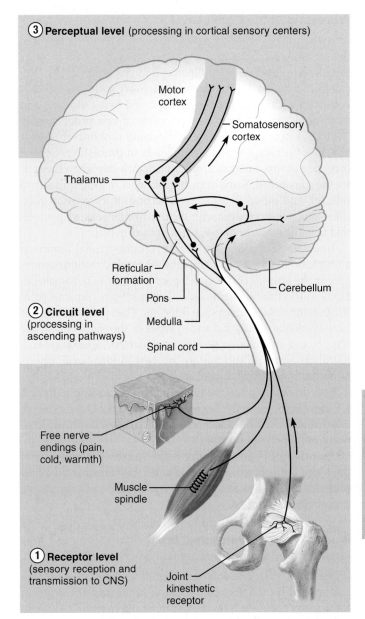

(3) **Perceptual level** (processing in cortical sensory centers)

Motor cortex

Somatosensory cortex

Thalamus

Reticular formation

Pons

Cerebellum

(2) **Circuit level** (processing in ascending pathways)

Medulla

Spinal cord

Free nerve endings (pain, cold, warmth)

Muscle spindle

(1) **Receptor level** (sensory reception and transmission to CNS)

Joint kinesthetic receptor

Figure 13.2 Three basic levels of neural integration in sensory systems.

(and nerve impulse generation) in the presence of a constant stimulus. For example, when you step into bright sunlight from a darkened room, your eyes are initially dazzled, but your photoreceptors rapidly adapt, allowing you to see both bright areas and dark areas in the scene.

Phasic receptors are *fast adapting*, often giving bursts of impulses at the beginning and at the end of the stimulus. These act mainly to report changes in the internal or external environment. Examples of phasic receptors are Pacinian and Meissner's corpuscles.

Tonic receptors provide a sustained response with little or no adaptation. Nociceptors and most proprioceptors are tonic receptors because of the protective importance of their information.

Processing at the Circuit Level

At the second level of integration, the circuit level, the task is to deliver impulses to the appropriate region of the cerebral cortex for stimulus localization and perception (Figure 13.2, ②). Recall from Chapter 12 that ascending sensory pathways typically consist of a chain of three neurons called first-, second-, and third-order sensory neurons. The axons of first-order sensory neurons, whose cell bodies are in the dorsal root or cranial ganglia, link the receptor and circuit levels of processing. Central processes of first-order neurons branch diffusely when they enter the spinal cord. Some branches take part in local spinal cord reflexes, and others synapse with second-order sensory neurons, which then synapse with the third-order sensory neurons that take the message to the cortex of the cerebrum.

Impulses sent along the dorsal column–medial lemniscal and spinothalamic ascending pathways reach conscious awareness in the sensory cortex (see Figure 12.34, p. 472). In general, fibers in the spinothalamic ascending pathways transmit pain, temperature, and coarse touch impulses. They give off branches to the reticular formation and synapse in the thalamus on the way up, and information sent to "headquarters" is fairly general, nondiscriminatory, and heavily involved in emotional aspects of perception (pleasure, pain, etc.).

The dorsal column–medial lemniscal ascending pathways are more involved in the discriminative aspects of touch (tactile discrimination), vibration, pressure, and conscious proprioception (limb and joint position).

Proprioceptive impulses conducted via the *spinocerebellar tracts* end at the cerebellum, which uses this information to coordinate skeletal muscle activity. These tracts do not contribute to conscious sensation.

Processing at the Perceptual Level

Interpretation of sensory input occurs in the cerebral cortex (Figure 13.2, ③). The ability to identify and appreciate sensations depends on the specific location of the target neurons in the sensory cortex, not on the nature of the message (which is, after all, just an action potential). Each sensory fiber is analogous to a "labeled line" that tells the brain "who" is calling—a taste bud or a pressure receptor—and from "where." The brain always interprets the activity of a specific sensory receptor ("who") as a specific sensation, no matter how it is activated. For example, pressing on your eyeball activates photoreceptors, but what you "see" is light. The exact point in the cortex that is activated always refers to the same "where," regardless of how it is activated, a phenomenon called **projection**. Electrically stimulating a particular spot in the visual cortex causes you to "see" light in a particular place.

The main aspects of sensory perception include the following:

- **Perceptual detection** is the ability to detect that a stimulus has occurred. This is the simplest level of perception. As a general rule, inputs from several receptors must be summed for perceptual detection to occur.
- **Magnitude estimation** is the ability to detect how *intense* the stimulus is. Because of frequency coding, perception increases as stimulus intensity increases (see Figure 11.13).

- **Spatial discrimination** allows us to identify the site or pattern of stimulation. A common tool for studying this quality in the laboratory is the **two-point discrimination test**. The test determines how close together two points on the skin can be and still be perceived as two points rather than as one. This test provides a crude map of the density of tactile receptors in the various regions of the skin. The distance between perceived points varies from less than 5 mm on highly sensitive body areas (tip of the tongue) to more than 50 mm on less sensitive areas (back).
- **Feature abstraction** is the mechanism by which a neuron or circuit is tuned to one feature in preference to others. Sensation usually involves an interplay of several stimulus properties or features. For example, one touch tells us that velvet is warm, compressible, and smooth but not completely continuous, each a feature that contributes to our perception of "velvet." Feature abstraction enables us to identify more complex aspects of a sensation.
- **Quality discrimination** is the ability to differentiate the submodalities of a particular sensation. Each sensory modality has several **qualities**, or submodalities. For example, the submodalities of taste include sweet and bitter.
- **Pattern recognition** is the ability to take in the scene around us and recognize a familiar pattern, an unfamiliar one, or one that has special significance for us. For example, a figure made of dots may be recognized as a familiar face, and when we listen to music, we hear the melody, not just a string of notes.

Perception of Pain

Everyone has suffered pain—the smart of a bee sting, the cruel persistence of a headache, or a cut finger. Although we may not appreciate it at the time, pain is invaluable because it warns us of actual or impending tissue damage and strongly motivates us to take protective action. Managing a patient's pain can be difficult because pain is an intensely personal experience that cannot be measured objectively.

Pain receptors are activated by extremes of pressure and temperature as well as a veritable soup of chemicals released from injured tissue. Histamine, K^+, ATP, acids, and bradykinin are among the most potent pain-producing chemicals. All of these chemicals act on small-diameter fibers.

When you cut your finger, you may have noticed that you first felt a sharp pain followed some time later by burning or aching pain. Sharp pain is carried by small myelinated A delta fibers, while burning pain is carried more slowly by small unmyelinated C fibers. Both types of fibers release the neurotransmitters *glutamate* and *substance P*, which activate second-order sensory neurons. Axons from these second-order neurons ascend to the brain via the spinothalamic tract and other anterolateral pathways.

If you cut your finger while fighting off an attacker, you might not notice the cut at all. How can that be? The brain has its own pain-suppressing analgesic systems in which the endogenous opioids (*endorphins* and *enkephalins*) play a key role. Descending cortical and hypothalamic pain-suppressing signals are relayed through various nuclei in the brain stem including the periaqueductal gray matter of the midbrain. Descending fibers activate interneurons in the spinal cord, which release the opioid neurotransmitters called enkephalins. Enkephalins are inhibitory neurotransmitters that quash the pain signals generated by the nociceptive neurons.

HOMEOSTATIC IMBALANCE

Normally a steady state is maintained that correlates injury and pain. Long-lasting or very intense pain inputs, such as limb amputation, can disrupt this system, leading to **hyperalgesia** (pain amplification), chronic pain, and **phantom limb pain**. Intense or long-duration pain causes activation of *NMDA receptors*, the same receptors that strengthen neural connections during certain kinds of learning. Essentially, the spinal cord *learns* hyperalgesia. In light of this, it is crucial that pain is effectively managed early to prevent the establishment of chronic pain. *Phantom limb pain* (pain perceived in tissue that is no longer present) is a curious example of hyperalgesia. Until recently, surgical limb amputations were conducted under general anesthesia only and the spinal cord still experienced the pain of amputation. Blocking neurotransmission in the spinal cord by additionally using epidural anesthetics greatly reduces the incidence of phantom limb pain. ■

CHECK YOUR UNDERSTANDING

3. What are the three levels of sensory integration?
4. What is the key difference between tonic and phasic receptors? Why are pain receptors tonic?
5. Your cortex decodes incoming action potentials from sensory pathways. How does it tell the difference between hot and cold? Between cool and cold? Between ice on your finger and ice on your foot?

For answers, see Appendix G.

PART 2

TRANSMISSION LINES: NERVES AND THEIR STRUCTURE AND REPAIR

Nerves and Associated Ganglia

▶ Define ganglion and indicate the general body location of ganglia.

▶ Describe the general structure of a nerve.

▶ Follow the process of nerve regeneration.

Structure and Classification

A **nerve** is a cordlike organ that is part of the peripheral nervous system. Nerves vary in size, but every nerve consists of parallel bundles of peripheral axons (some myelinated and some not) enclosed by successive wrappings of connective tissue (Figure 13.3).

Within a nerve, each axon is surrounded by **endoneurium** (en″do-nu′re-um), a delicate layer of loose connective tissue that also encloses the fiber's associated myelin sheath or neurilemma. Groups of fibers are bound into bundles or **fascicles** by a coarser connective tissue wrapping, the **perineurium**. Finally, all the fascicles are enclosed by a tough fibrous sheath, the **epineurium**, to form the nerve. Axons constitute only a small fraction of a nerve's bulk. The balance consists chiefly of myelin, the protective connective tissue wrappings, blood vessels, and lymphatic vessels.

Recall that the PNS is divided into *sensory* (afferent) and *motor* (efferent) divisions. So, too, nerves are classified according to the direction in which they transmit impulses. Nerves containing both sensory and motor fibers and transmitting impulses both to and from the central nervous system are called **mixed nerves**. Those that carry impulses only toward the CNS are **sensory (afferent) nerves**, and those carrying impulses only away from the CNS are **motor (efferent) nerves**. Most nerves are mixed. Pure sensory or motor nerves are rare.

Because mixed nerves often carry both somatic and autonomic (visceral) nervous system fibers, the fibers in them may be classified according to the region they innervate as *somatic afferent, somatic efferent, visceral afferent,* and *visceral efferent.*

For convenience, the peripheral nerves are classified as *cranial* or *spinal* depending on whether they arise from the brain or the spinal cord. Although we mention autonomic efferents of cranial nerves, in this chapter we will focus on somatic functions. We will defer the discussion of the autonomic nervous system and the visceral functions it serves to Chapter 14.

Ganglia are collections of neuron cell bodies associated with nerves in the PNS. Ganglia associated with *afferent* nerve fibers contain cell bodies of sensory neurons. (These are the *dorsal root ganglia* studied in Chapter 12.) Ganglia associated with *efferent* nerve fibers mostly contain cell bodies of autonomic motor neurons. We will describe these more complicated ganglia in Chapter 14.

Regeneration of Nerve Fibers

Damage to nervous tissue is serious because, as a rule, mature neurons do not divide. If the damage is severe or close to the cell body, the entire neuron may die, and other neurons that are normally stimulated by its axon may die as well. However, if the cell body remains intact, cut or compressed axons of peripheral nerves can regenerate successfully.

Almost immediately after a peripheral axon has been severed or crushed, the separated ends seal themselves off and then swell as substances being transported along the axon begin to accumulate in the sealed ends. Within a few hours, the axon and its myelin sheath distal to the injury site begin to disintegrate because they cannot receive nutrients from the cell body (Figure 13.4, ①). This process, **Wallerian degeneration**, spreads distally from the injury site, completely fragmenting the axon.

13

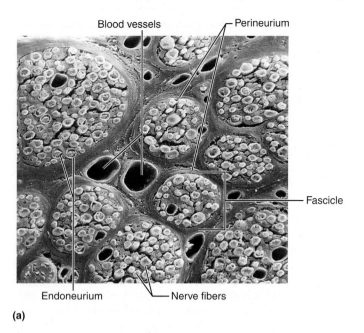

(a)

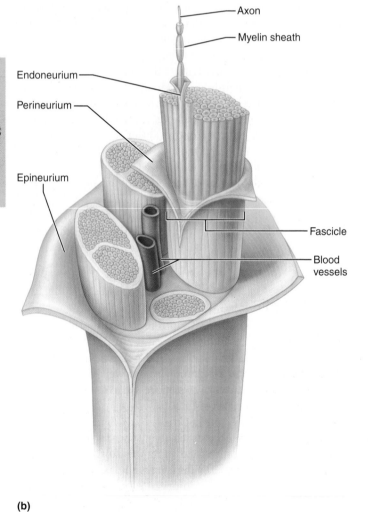

(b)

Figure 13.3 Structure of a nerve. (a) Scanning electron micrograph of a cross section of a portion of a nerve (1150×). **(b)** Three-dimensional view of a portion of a nerve, showing connective tissue wrappings.

SOURCE: (a) Kessel and Kardon/Visuals Unlimited.

Generally, the entire axon distal to the injury is degraded by phagocytes within a week, but the neurilemma remains intact within the endoneurium (Figure 13.4, ②). After the debris has been disposed of, surviving Schwann cells proliferate in response to mitosis-stimulating chemicals released by the macrophages, and migrate into the injury site. Once there, they release growth factors and begin to express cell adhesion molecules (CAMs) that encourage axonal growth. Additionally, they form a *regeneration tube*, a system of cellular cords that guide the regenerating axon "sprouts" across the gap and to their original contacts (Figure 13.4, ③ and ④). The same Schwann cells protect, support, and remyelinate the regenerating axons.

Changes also occur in the neuronal cell body after the axon has been destroyed. Within two days, its chromatophilic substance breaks apart, and then the cell body swells as protein synthesis revs up to support regeneration of its axon.

Axons regenerate at the approximate rate of 1.5 mm a day. The greater the distance between the severed endings, the less the chance of recovery because adjacent tissues block growth by protruding into the gaps, and axonal sprouts fail to find the regeneration tube. Neurosurgeons align cut nerve endings surgically to enhance the chance of successful regeneration, and scaffolding devices have been successful in guiding axon growth. Whatever the measures taken, post-trauma axon regrowth never exactly matches what existed before the injury. Much of the recovery protocol involves retraining the nervous system to respond appropriately so that stimulus and response are coordinated.

Unlike peripheral nerve fibers, most CNS fibers never regenerate. Consequently, damage to the brain or spinal cord has been viewed as irreversible. This difference in regenerative capacity seems to have less to do with the neurons themselves than with the "company they keep"—oligodendrocytes, their supporting cells. Oligodendrocytes are studded with growth-inhibiting proteins (Nogo and others) that act on inhibitory neuronal receptors. Consequently, the neuronal growth cone collapses and the fiber fails to regrow. Moreover, astrocytes at the site of injury form scar tissue rich in chondroitin sulfate (see p. 124) that blocks axonal regrowth. For the clinician treating spinal cord injury, this means that multiple inhibitory processes need to be blocked simultaneously to promote axon regrowth. To date, experimentally neutralizing the myelin-bound growth inhibitors, blocking their receptors, or enzymatically destroying chondroitin sulfate have yielded promising results.

CHECK YOUR UNDERSTANDING

6. What are ganglia?
7. What is in a nerve besides axons?
8. Bill's femoral nerve was crushed while clinicians tried to control bleeding from his femoral artery. This resulted in loss of function and sensation in his leg, which gradually returned over the course of a year. Which cells were important in his recovery?

For answers, see Appendix G.

Cranial Nerves

▶ Name the 12 pairs of cranial nerves; indicate the body region and structures innervated by each.

Twelve pairs of **cranial nerves** are associated with the brain (Figure 13.5). The first two pairs attach to the forebrain, and the rest are associated with the brain stem. Other than the vagus nerves, which extend into the abdomen, cranial nerves serve only head and neck structures.

In most cases, the names of the cranial nerves reveal either the structures they serve or their functions. The nerves are also generally numbered (using Roman numerals) from the most rostral to the most caudal. A mini-introduction to the cranial nerves follows.

I. Olfactory. These are the tiny sensory nerves (filaments) of smell, which run from the nasal mucosa to synapse with the olfactory bulbs. Note that the olfactory bulbs and tracts, shown in Figure 13.5a, are brain structures and not part of cranial nerve I. (See Table 13.2 art for the olfactory nerve filaments.)

II. Optic. Because this sensory nerve of vision develops as an outgrowth of the brain, it is really a brain tract.

III. Oculomotor. The name *oculomotor* means "eye mover." This nerve supplies four of the six extrinsic muscles that move the eyeball in the orbit.

IV. Trochlear. The name *trochlear* means "pulley" and it innervates an extrinsic eye muscle that loops through a pulley-shaped ligament in the orbit.

V. Trigeminal. Three (*tri*) branches spring from this, the largest of the cranial nerves. It supplies sensory fibers to the face and motor fibers to the chewing muscles.

VI. Abducens. This nerve controls the extrinsic eye muscle that *abducts* the eyeball (turns it laterally).

VII. Facial. A large nerve that innervates muscles of *facial* expression (among other things).

VIII. Vestibulocochlear. This sensory nerve for hearing and balance was formerly called the *auditory nerve.*

IX. Glossopharyngeal. The name *glossopharyngeal* means "tongue and pharynx," and reveals the structures that this nerve helps to innervate.

X. Vagus. This nerve's name means "wanderer" or "vagabond," and it is the only cranial nerve to extend beyond the head and neck to the thorax and abdomen.

XI. Accessory. Considered an *accessory* part of the vagus nerve, this nerve was formerly called the *spinal accessory nerve.*

XII. Hypoglossal. The name *hypoglossal* means under the tongue. This nerve runs inferior to the tongue and innervates the tongue muscles.

You might make up your own saying to remember the first letters of the cranial nerves in order, or use the following memory jog sent by a student: "**O**n **o**ccasion, **o**ur **t**rusty **t**ruck **a**cts **f**unny—**v**ery **g**ood **v**ehicle **a**ny**h**ow."

In the last chapter, we described how spinal nerves are formed by the fusion of ventral (motor) and dorsal (sensory)

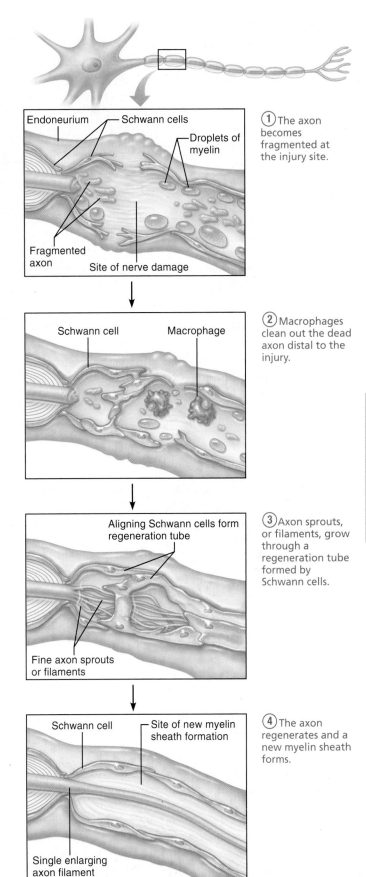

① The axon becomes fragmented at the injury site.

② Macrophages clean out the dead axon distal to the injury.

③ Axon sprouts, or filaments, grow through a regeneration tube formed by Schwann cells.

④ The axon regenerates and a new myelin sheath forms.

Figure 13.4 Regeneration of a nerve fiber in a peripheral nerve.

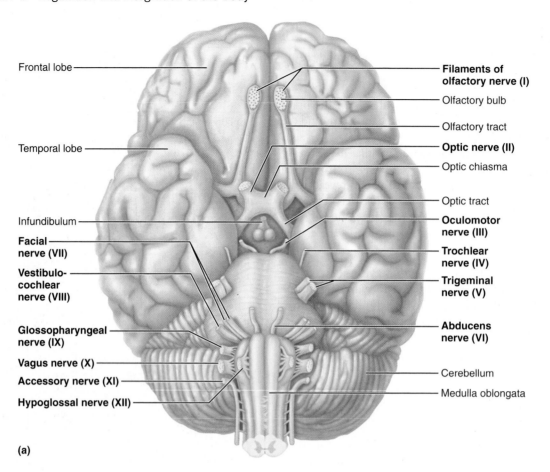

Frontal lobe

Filaments of olfactory nerve (I)

Olfactory bulb

Olfactory tract

Temporal lobe

Optic nerve (II)

Optic chiasma

Optic tract

Infundibulum

Oculomotor nerve (III)

Facial nerve (VII)

Trochlear nerve (IV)

Vestibulo-cochlear nerve (VIII)

Trigeminal nerve (V)

Glossopharyngeal nerve (IX)

Abducens nerve (VI)

Vagus nerve (X)

Accessory nerve (XI)

Cerebellum

Hypoglossal nerve (XII)

Medulla oblongata

(a)

Cranial nerves I – VI	Sensory function	Motor function	PS* fibers
I Olfactory	Yes (smell)	No	No
II Optic	Yes (vision)	No	No
III Oculomotor	No	Yes	Yes
IV Trochlear	No	Yes	No
V Trigeminal	Yes (general sensation)	Yes	No
VI Abducens	No	Yes	No

Cranial nerves VII – XII	Sensory function	Motor function	PS* fibers
VII Facial	Yes (taste)	Yes	Yes
VIII Vestibulocochlear	Yes (hearing and balance)	Some	No
IX Glossopharyngeal	Yes (taste)	Yes	Yes
X Vagus	Yes (taste)	Yes	Yes
XI Accessory	No	Yes	No
XII Hypoglossal	No	Yes	No

(b)

*PS = parasympathetic

Figure 13.5 Location and function of cranial nerves. (a) Ventral view of the human brain, showing the cranial nerves. **(b)** Summary of cranial nerves by function. Two cranial nerves (I and II) have sensory function only, no motor function. Four nerves (III, VII, IX, and X) carry parasympathetic fibers that serve visceral muscles and glands. All cranial nerves that innervate muscles also carry afferent fibers from proprioceptors in the muscles served; only sensory functions other than proprioception are indicated.

roots. Cranial nerves, on the other hand, vary markedly in their composition. Most cranial nerves are mixed nerves, as shown in Figure 13.5b. However, two nerve pairs (the olfactory and optic) associated with special sense organs are generally considered purely sensory. The cell bodies of the sensory neurons of the olfactory and optic nerves are located *within* their respective special sense organs. In other cases of sensory neurons contributing to cranial nerves (V, VII, IX, and X), the cell bodies are located in **cranial sensory ganglia** just outside the brain. Some cranial nerves have a single sensory ganglion, others have several, and still others have none.

Several of the mixed cranial nerves contain both somatic and autonomic motor fibers and hence serve both skeletal muscles and visceral organs. Except for some autonomic motor neurons located in ganglia, the cell bodies of motor neurons contributing to the cranial nerves are located in the ventral gray matter regions (nuclei) of the brain stem.

Having read this overview, you are now ready to tackle **Table 13.2**, which provides a more detailed description of the origin, course, and function of the cranial nerves. Notice that

(Text continues on p. 501.)

TABLE 13.2   Cranial Nerves

I The Olfactory Nerves (ol-fak′to-re)

Origin and course: Olfactory nerve fibers arise from olfactory receptor cells located in olfactory epithelium of nasal cavity and pass through cribriform plate of ethmoid bone to synapse in olfactory bulb. Fibers of olfactory bulb neurons extend posteriorly as olfactory tract, which runs beneath frontal lobe to enter cerebral hemispheres and terminates in primary olfactory cortex. See also Figure 15.21.

Function: Purely sensory; carry afferent impulses for sense of smell.

Clinical testing: Person is asked to sniff aromatic substances, such as oil of cloves and vanilla, and to identify each.

Homeostatic imbalance: Fracture of ethmoid bone or lesions of olfactory fibers may result in partial or total loss of smell, a condition known as *anosmia* (an-oz′me-ah). ■

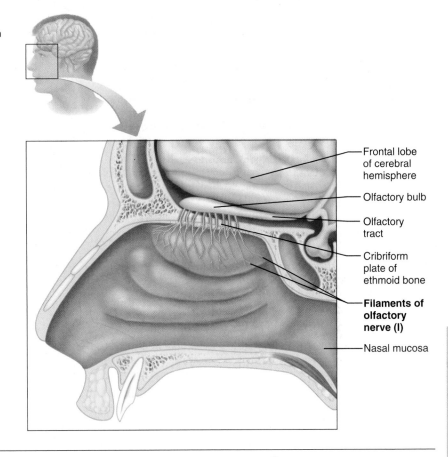

- Frontal lobe of cerebral hemisphere
- Olfactory bulb
- Olfactory tract
- Cribriform plate of ethmoid bone
- **Filaments of olfactory nerve (I)**
- Nasal mucosa

13

II The Optic Nerves

Origin and course: Fibers arise from retina of eye to form optic nerve, which passes through optic canal of orbit. The optic nerves converge to form the optic chiasma (ki-az′mah) where fibers partially cross over, continue on as optic tracts, enter thalamus, and synapse there. Thalamic fibers run (as the optic radiation) to occipital (visual) cortex, where visual interpretation occurs. See also Figure 15.19.

Function: Purely sensory; carry afferent impulses for vision.

Clinical testing: Vision and visual field are determined with eye chart and by testing the point at which the person first sees an object (finger) moving into the visual field. Fundus of eye viewed with ophthalmoscope to detect papilledema (swelling of optic disc, the site where the optic nerve leaves the eyeball), as well as for routine examination of the optic disc and retinal blood vessels.

Homeostatic imbalance: Damage to optic nerve results in blindness in eye served by nerve; damage to visual pathway beyond the optic chiasma results in partial visual losses; visual defects are called *anopsias* (ah-nop′se-ahz). ■

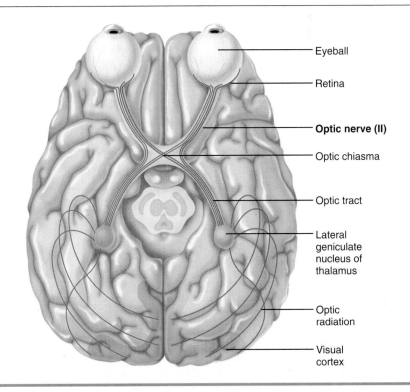

- Eyeball
- Retina
- **Optic nerve (II)**
- Optic chiasma
- Optic tract
- Lateral geniculate nucleus of thalamus
- Optic radiation
- Visual cortex

➤

TABLE 13.2	Cranial Nerves *(continued)*

III The Oculomotor Nerves (ok″u-lo-mo′tor)

Origin and course: Fibers extend from ventral midbrain (near its junction with pons) and pass through bony orbit, via superior orbital fissure, to eye.

Function: Chiefly motor nerves (*oculomotor* = motor to the eye); contain a few proprioceptive afferents. Each nerve includes the following:

- Somatic motor fibers to four of the six extrinsic eye muscles (inferior oblique and superior, inferior, and medial rectus muscles) that help direct eyeball, and to levator palpebrae superioris muscle, which raises upper eyelid.

- Parasympathetic (autonomic) motor fibers to sphincter pupillae (circular muscles of iris), which cause pupil to constrict, and to ciliary muscle, controlling lens shape for visual focusing. Some parasympathetic cell bodies are in the ciliary ganglia.

- Sensory (proprioceptor) afferents, which run from same four extrinsic eye muscles to midbrain.

Clinical testing: Pupils are examined for size, shape, and equality. Pupillary reflex is tested with penlight (pupils should constrict when illuminated). Convergence for near vision is tested, as is subject's ability to follow objects with the eyes.

Homeostatic imbalance: In oculomotor nerve paralysis, eye cannot be moved up, down, or inward, and at rest, eye rotates laterally [*external strabismus* (strah-biz′mus)] because the actions of the two extrinsic eye muscles not served by cranial nerves III are unopposed; upper eyelid droops (*ptosis*), and the person has double vision and trouble focusing on close objects. ■

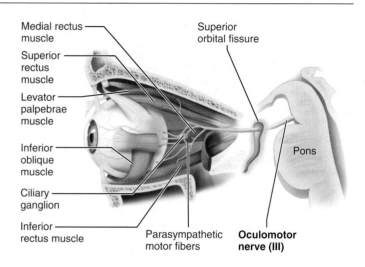

IV The Trochlear Nerves (trok′le-ar)

Origin and course: Fibers emerge from dorsal midbrain and course ventrally around midbrain to enter orbit through superior orbital fissure along with oculomotor nerves.

Function: Primarily motor nerves; supply somatic motor fibers to (and carry proprioceptor fibers from) one of the extrinsic eye muscles, the superior oblique muscle.

Clinical testing: Tested in common with cranial nerve III.

Homeostatic imbalance: Trauma to, or paralysis of, a trochlear nerve results in double vision and reduced ability to rotate eye inferolaterally. ■

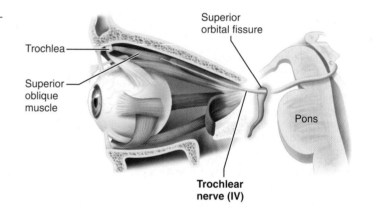

13

TABLE 13.2   *(continued)*

V The Trigeminal Nerves

Largest of cranial nerves; fibers extend from pons to face, and form three divisions (*trigemina* = threefold): ophthalmic, maxillary, and mandibular divisions. As major general sensory nerves of face, transmit afferent impulses from touch, temperature, and pain receptors. Cell bodies of sensory neurons of all three divisions are located in large *trigeminal ganglion.*

The mandibular division also contains motor fibers that innervate chewing muscles.

Dentists desensitize upper and lower jaws by injecting local anesthetic (such as Novocain) into alveolar branches of maxillary and mandibular divisions, respectively; since this blocks pain-transmitting fibers of teeth, the surrounding tissues become numb.

	Ophthalmic division (V_1)	Maxillary division (V_2)	Mandibular division (V_3)
Origin and course	Fibers run from face to pons via superior orbital fissure.	Fibers run from face to pons via foramen rotundum.	Fibers pass through skull via foramen ovale.
Function	Conveys sensory impulses from skin of anterior scalp, upper eyelid, and nose, and from nasal cavity mucosa, cornea, and lacrimal gland.	Conveys sensory impulses from nasal cavity mucosa, palate, upper teeth, skin of cheek, upper lip, lower eyelid.	Conveys sensory impulses from anterior tongue (except taste buds), lower teeth, skin of chin, temporal region of scalp. Supplies motor fibers to, and carries proprioceptor fibers from, muscles of mastication.
Clinical testing	Corneal reflex test: Touching cornea with wisp of cotton should elicit blinking.	Sensations of pain, touch, and temperature are tested with safety pin and hot and cold objects.	Motor branch assessed by asking person to clench his teeth, open mouth against resistance, and move jaw side to side.

Homeostatic imbalance: *Trigeminal neuralgia* (nu-ral'je-ah), or *tic douloureux* (tik doo"loo-roo'; *tic* = twitch, *douloureux* = painful), caused by inflammation of trigeminal nerve, is widely considered to produce most excruciating pain known; the stabbing pain lasts for a few seconds to a minute, but it can be relentless, occurring a hundred times a day. Usually provoked by some sensory stimulus, such as brushing teeth or even a passing breeze hitting the face. It is thought to be caused by compression of the trigeminal nerve by a loop of artery or vein close to its exit from the brain stem. Analgesics and carbamazepine (an anticonvulsant) are only partially effective. In severe cases, surgery relieves the agony—either by moving the compressing vessel or by destroying the nerve. Nerve destruction results in loss of sensation on that side of face. ■

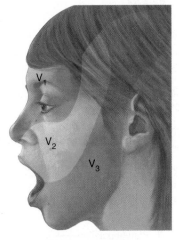

(b) Distribution of sensory fibers of each division

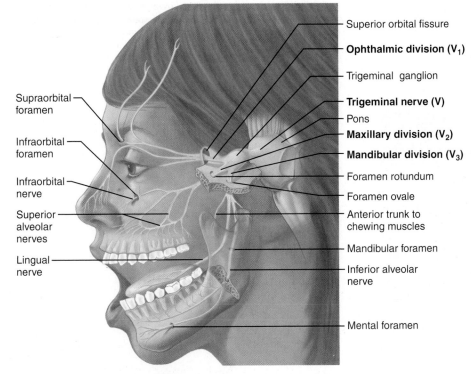

Supraorbital foramen

Infraorbital foramen

Infraorbital nerve

Superior alveolar nerves

Lingual nerve

Superior orbital fissure

Ophthalmic division (V_1)

Trigeminal ganglion

Trigeminal nerve (V)

Pons

Maxillary division (V_2)

Mandibular division (V_3)

Foramen rotundum

Foramen ovale

Anterior trunk to chewing muscles

Mandibular foramen

Inferior alveolar nerve

Mental foramen

(a) Distribution of the trigeminal nerve

Anterior trunk of mandibular division (V_3)

Temporalis muscle

Lateral pterygoid muscle

Medial pterygoid muscle

Masseter muscle

Anterior belly of digastric muscle

(c) Motor branches of the mandibular division (V_3)

13

TABLE 13.2	Cranial Nerves *(continued)*

VI The Abducens Nerves (ab-du'senz)

Origin and course: Fibers leave inferior pons and enter orbit via superior orbital fissure to run to eye.

Function: Primarily motor; supply somatic motor fibers to lateral rectus muscle, an extrinsic muscle of the eye; convey proprioceptor impulses from same muscle to brain.

Clinical testing: Tested in common with cranial nerve III.

Homeostatic imbalance: In abducens nerve paralysis, eye cannot be moved laterally; at rest, affected eyeball rotates medially (*internal strabismus*). ■

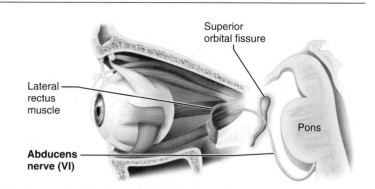

VII The Facial Nerves

Origin and course: Fibers issue from pons, just lateral to abducens nerves (see Figure 13.5), enter temporal bone via *internal acoustic meatus*, and run within bone (and through inner ear cavity) before emerging through *stylomastoid foramen*; nerve then courses to lateral aspect of face.

Function: Mixed nerves that are the chief motor nerves of face; have five major branches: temporal, zygomatic, buccal, mandibular, and cervical (see **c**).

- Convey motor impulses to skeletal muscles of face (muscles of facial expression), except for chewing muscles served by trigeminal nerves, and transmit proprioceptor impulses from same muscles to pons (see **b**).

- Transmit parasympathetic (autonomic) motor impulses to lacrimal (tear) glands, nasal and palatine glands, and submandibular and sublingual salivary glands. Some of the cell bodies of these parasympathetic motor neurons are in *ptery-*

gopalatine (ter"eh-go-pal'ah-tīn) and *submandibular ganglia* on the trigeminal nerve (see **a**).

- Convey sensory impulses from taste buds of anterior two-thirds of tongue; cell bodies of these sensory neurons are in *geniculate ganglion* (see **a**).

Clinical testing: Anterior two-thirds of tongue is tested for ability to taste sweet (sugar), salty, sour (vinegar), and bitter (quinine) substances. Symmetry of face is checked. Subject is asked to close eyes, smile, whistle, and so on. Tearing is assessed with ammonia fumes.

Homeostatic imbalance: *Bell's palsy*, characterized by paralysis of facial muscles on affected side and partial loss of taste sensation, may develop rapidly (often overnight). Most often caused by herpes simplex 1 viral infection, which causes swelling and inflammation of facial nerve. Lower eyelid droops, corner of mouth sags (making it difficult to eat or speak normally), tears drip continuously from eye and eye cannot be completely closed (conversely, dry-eye syndrome may occur). Condition may disappear spontaneously without treatment. ■

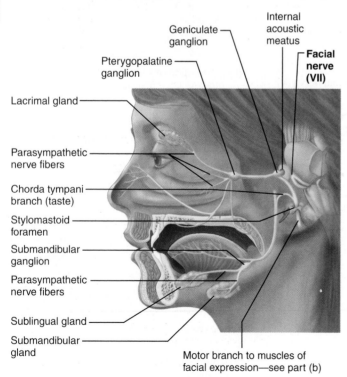

(a) Parasympathetic efferents and sensory afferents

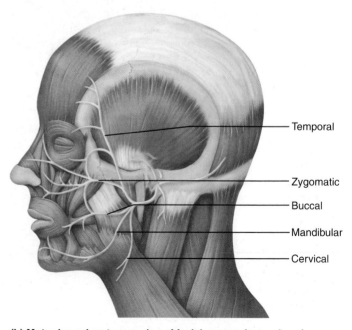

(b) Motor branches to muscles of facial expression and scalp muscles (see pp. 329–331)

TABLE 13.2	*(continued)*

VII The Facial Nerves *(continued)*

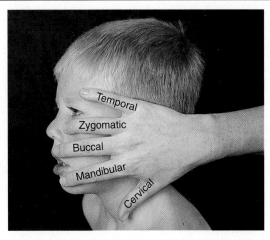

(c) A simple method of remembering the courses of the five major motor branches of the facial nerve

---

VIII The Vestibulocochlear Nerves (ves-tib″u-lo-kok′le-ar)

Origin and course: Fibers arise from hearing and equilibrium apparatus located within inner ear of temporal bone and pass through internal acoustic meatus to enter brain stem at pons-medulla border. Afferent fibers from hearing receptors in cochlea form the *cochlear division*; those from equilibrium receptors in semicircular canals and vestibule form the *vestibular division* (vestibular nerve); the two divisions merge to form vestibulocochlear nerve. See also Figure 15.27.

Function: Mostly sensory. Vestibular branch transmits afferent impulses for sense of equilibrium, and sensory nerve cell bodies are located in *vestibular ganglia.* Cochlear branch transmits afferent impulses for sense of hearing, and sensory nerve cell bodies are located in *spiral ganglion* within cochlea. Small motor component adjusts the sensitivity of sensory receptors. See also Figure 15.28c.

Clinical testing: Hearing is checked by air and bone conduction using tuning fork.

Homeostatic imbalance: Lesions of cochlear nerve or cochlear receptors result in *central* or *nerve deafness*, whereas damage to vestibular division produces dizziness, rapid involuntary eye movements, loss of balance, nausea, and vomiting. ■

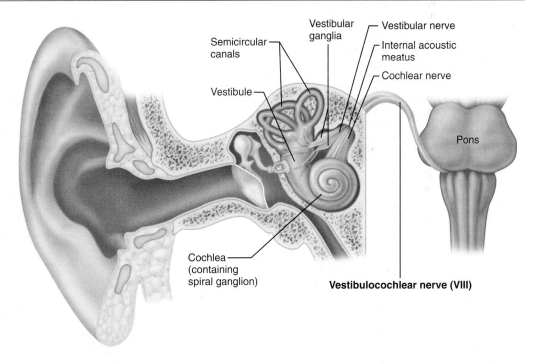

Vestibulocochlear nerve (VIII)

13

TABLE 13.2   Cranial Nerves *(continued)*

IX The Glossopharyngeal Nerves (glos"o-fah-rin'je-al)

Origin and course: Fibers emerge from medulla and leave skull via *jugular foramen* to run to throat.

Function: Mixed nerves that innervate part of tongue and pharynx. Provide somatic motor fibers to, and carry proprioceptor fibers from, a superior pharyngeal muscle called the *stylopharyngeus*, which elevates the pharynx in swallowing. Provide parasympathetic motor fibers to parotid salivary glands (some of the nerve cell bodies of these parasympathetic motor neurons are located in *otic ganglion*).

Sensory fibers conduct taste and general sensory (touch, pressure, pain) impulses from pharynx and posterior tongue, from chemoreceptors in the carotid body (which monitor O_2 and CO_2 levels in the blood and help regulate respiratory rate and depth), and from baroreceptors of carotid sinus (which monitor blood pressure). Sensory neuron cell bodies are located in *superior* and *inferior ganglia*.

Clinical testing: Position of the uvula is checked. Gag and swallowing reflexes are checked. Subject is asked to speak and cough. Posterior third of tongue may be tested for taste.

Homeostatic imbalance: Injury or inflammation of glossopharyngeal nerves impairs swallowing and taste. ■

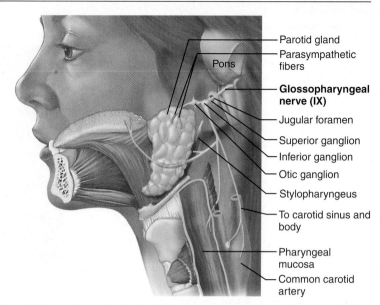

Parotid gland
Parasympathetic fibers
Pons
Glossopharyngeal nerve (IX)
Jugular foramen
Superior ganglion
Inferior ganglion
Otic ganglion
Stylopharyngeus
To carotid sinus and body
Pharyngeal mucosa
Common carotid artery

X The Vagus Nerves (va'gus)

Origin and course: The only cranial nerves to extend beyond head and neck region. Fibers emerge from medulla, pass through skull via jugular foramen, and descend through neck region into thorax and abdomen. See also Figure 14.4.

Function: Mixed nerves; nearly all motor fibers are parasympathetic efferents, except those serving skeletal muscles of pharynx and larynx (involved in swallowing). Parasympathetic motor fibers supply heart, lungs, and abdominal viscera and are involved in regulation of heart rate, breathing, and digestive system activity. Transmit sensory impulses from thoracic and abdominal viscera, from the aortic arch baroreceptors (for blood pressure) and the carotid and aortic bodies (chemoreceptors for respiration), and taste buds of posterior tongue and pharynx. Carry proprioceptor fibers from muscles of larynx and pharynx.

Clinical testing: As for cranial nerve IX (IX and X are tested in common, since they both innervate muscles of throat and mouth).

Homeostatic imbalance: Since nearly all muscles of the larynx ("voice box") are innervated by laryngeal branches of the vagus, vagal nerve paralysis can lead to hoarseness or loss of voice; other symptoms are difficulty swallowing and impaired digestive system motility. Total destruction of both vagus nerves is incompatible with life, because these parasympathetic nerves are crucial in maintaining normal state of visceral organ activity; without their influence, the activity of the sympathetic nerves, which mobilize and accelerate vital body processes (and shut down digestion), would be unopposed. ■

13

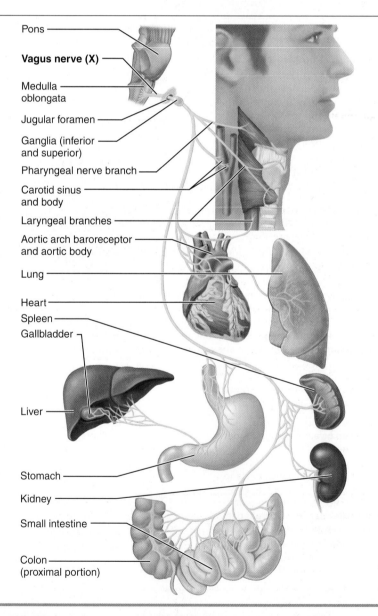

Pons
Vagus nerve (X)
Medulla oblongata
Jugular foramen
Ganglia (inferior and superior)
Pharyngeal nerve branch
Carotid sinus and body
Laryngeal branches
Aortic arch baroreceptor and aortic body
Lung
Heart
Spleen
Gallbladder
Liver
Stomach
Kidney
Small intestine
Colon (proximal portion)

TABLE 13.2	**Cranial Nerves** *(continued)*

XI The Accessory Nerves

Origin and course: Unique in that they are formed from ventral rootlets that emerge from the spinal cord, not the brain stem. These rootlets arise from superior region (C_1–C_5) of spinal cord, pass upward along spinal cord, and enter the skull as the accessory nerves via foramen magnum. The accessory nerves exit from skull through *jugular foramen* together with the vagus nerves, and supply two large neck muscles. Until recently, it was thought that the accessory nerves also received a contribution from cranial rootlets, but it has now been determined that in almost all people, these cranial rootlets are instead part of the vagus nerves. This raises an interesting question: Should the accessory nerves still be considered cranial nerves? Some anatomists say "yes" because they pass through the cranium. Others say "no" because they don't arise from the brain. Stay tuned!

Function: Mixed nerves, but primarily motor in function. Supply motor fibers to trapezius and sternocleidomastoid muscles, which together move head and neck, and convey proprioceptor impulses from same muscles.

Clinical testing: Sternocleidomastoid and trapezius muscles are checked for strength by asking person to rotate head and shrug shoulders against resistance.

Homeostatic imbalance: Injury to the spinal root of one accessory nerve causes head to turn toward injury side as result of sternocleidomastoid muscle paralysis; shrugging of that shoulder (role of trapezius muscle) becomes difficult. ■

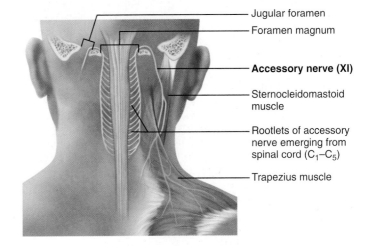

- Jugular foramen
- Foramen magnum
- **Accessory nerve (XI)**
- Sternocleidomastoid muscle
- Rootlets of accessory nerve emerging from spinal cord (C_1–C_5)
- Trapezius muscle

XII The Hypoglossal Nerves (hi″po-glos′al)

Origin and course: As their name implies (*hypo* = below; *glossal* = tongue), hypoglossal nerves mainly serve the tongue. Fibers arise by a series of roots from medulla and exit from skull via *hypoglossal canal* to travel to tongue. See also Figure 13.5.

Function: Mixed nerves, but primarily motor in function. Carry somatic motor fibers to intrinsic and extrinsic muscles of tongue, and proprioceptor fibers from same muscles to brain stem. Hypoglossal nerve control allows not only food mixing and manipulation by tongue during chewing, but also tongue movements that contribute to swallowing and speech.

Clinical testing: Person is asked to protrude and retract tongue. Any deviations in position are noted.

Homeostatic imbalance: Damage to hypoglossal nerves causes difficulties in speech and swallowing. If both nerves are impaired, the person cannot protrude tongue. If only one side is affected, tongue deviates (points) toward affected side; eventually paralyzed side begins to atrophy. ■

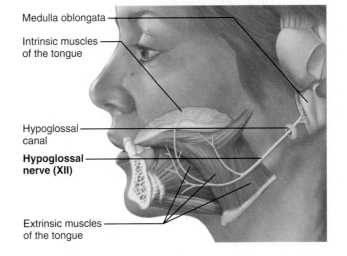

- Medulla oblongata
- Intrinsic muscles of the tongue
- Hypoglossal canal
- **Hypoglossal nerve (XII)**
- Extrinsic muscles of the tongue

13

the pathways of the purely or mostly sensory nerves (I, II, and VIII) are described from the receptors to the brain, while those of the other nerves are described in the opposite direction (from the brain distally). Remembering the primary functions of the cranial nerves (as **s**ensory, **m**otor, or **b**oth) can be a problem; this sentence might help: "**S**ome **s**ay **m**arry **m**oney, **b**ut **m**y **b**rother **b**elieves (it's) **b**ad **b**usiness (to) **m**arry **m**oney."

CHECK YOUR UNDERSTANDING

9. Name the cranial nerve(s) most involved in each of the following: moving your eyeball; sticking out your tongue; controlling your heart rate and digestive activity; shrugging your shoulders.

For answers, see Appendix G.

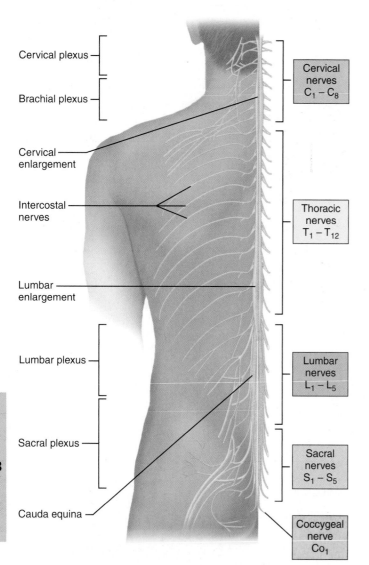

Cervical plexus

Brachial plexus

Cervical enlargement

Intercostal nerves

Lumbar enlargement

Lumbar plexus

Sacral plexus

Cauda equina

Cervical nerves $C_1 - C_8$

Thoracic nerves $T_1 - T_{12}$

Lumbar nerves $L_1 - L_5$

Sacral nerves $S_1 - S_5$

Coccygeal nerve Co_1

Figure 13.6 Spinal nerves. (Posterior view.) The short spinal nerves are shown at right; their ventral rami are shown at left. Most ventral rami form nerve plexuses (cervical, brachial, lumbar, and sacral).

Spinal Nerves

▶ Describe the formation of a spinal nerve and the general distribution of its rami.

▶ Define plexus. Name the major plexuses and describe the distribution and function of the peripheral nerves arising from each plexus.

Thirty-one pairs of **spinal nerves**, each containing thousands of nerve fibers, arise from the spinal cord and supply all parts of the body except the head and some areas of the neck. All are mixed nerves. As illustrated in **Figure 13.6**, these nerves are named according to their point of issue from the spinal cord. There are 8 pairs of cervical spinal nerves (C_1–C_8), 12 pairs of thoracic nerves (T_1–T_{12}), 5 pairs of lumbar nerves (L_1–L_5), 5 pairs of sacral nerves (S_1–S_5), and 1 pair of tiny coccygeal nerves (Co_1).

Notice that there are eight pairs of cervical nerves but only seven cervical vertebrae. This "discrepancy" is easily explained.

The first seven pairs exit the vertebral canal *superior to* the vertebrae for which they are named, but C_8 emerges *inferior to* the seventh cervical vertebra (between C_7 and T_1). Below the cervical level, each spinal nerve leaves the vertebral column *inferior to* the same-numbered vertebra.

As we mentioned in Chapter 12, each spinal nerve connects to the spinal cord by a dorsal root and a ventral root (**Figure 13.7**). Each root forms from a series of **rootlets** that attach along the length of the corresponding spinal cord segment (Figure 13.7a). The **ventral roots** contain *motor* (efferent) fibers that arise from ventral horn motor neurons and extend to and innervate the skeletal muscles. (In Chapter 14, we describe autonomic nervous system efferents that are also contained in the ventral roots.) **Dorsal roots** contain *sensory* (afferent) fibers that arise from sensory neurons in the dorsal root ganglia and conduct impulses from peripheral receptors to the spinal cord.

The spinal roots pass laterally from the cord and unite just distal to the dorsal root ganglion to form a spinal nerve before emerging from the vertebral column via their respective intervertebral foramina. Because motor and sensory fibers mingle in a spinal nerve, it contains both efferent and afferent fibers. The length of the spinal roots increases progressively from the superior to the inferior aspect of the cord. In the cervical region, the roots are short and run horizontally, but the roots of the lumbar and sacral nerves extend inferiorly for some distance through the lower vertebral canal as the *cauda equina* before exiting the vertebral column (Figure 13.6).

A spinal nerve is quite short (only 1–2 cm). Almost immediately after emerging from its foramen, it divides into a small **dorsal ramus**, a larger **ventral ramus** (ra′mus; "branch"), and a tiny **meningeal branch** (mĕ-nin′je-al) that reenters the vertebral canal to innervate the meninges and blood vessels within. Each ramus, like the spinal nerve itself, is mixed. Finally, joined to the base of the ventral rami of the thoracic spinal nerves are special rami called **rami communicantes**, which contain autonomic (visceral) nerve fibers.

Innervation of Specific Body Regions

The spinal nerve rami and their main branches supply the entire somatic region of the body (skeletal muscles and skin) from the neck down. The dorsal rami supply the posterior body trunk. The thicker ventral rami supply the rest of the trunk and the limbs.

To be clear, let's review the difference between roots and rami: Roots lie medial to and form the spinal nerves, and each root is strictly sensory or motor. Rami lie distal to and are lateral branches of the spinal nerves and, like spinal nerves, carry both sensory and motor fibers.

Before we get into the specifics of how the body is innervated, it is important for you to understand some points about the ventral rami of the spinal nerves. Except for T_2–T_{12}, all ventral rami branch and join one another lateral to the vertebral column, forming complicated interlacing nerve networks called **nerve plexuses** (Figure 13.6). Nerve plexuses occur in the cervical, brachial, lumbar, and sacral regions and primarily serve the limbs. Notice that *only ventral rami form plexuses.*

Within a plexus, fibers from the various ventral rami crisscross one another and become redistributed so that (1) each

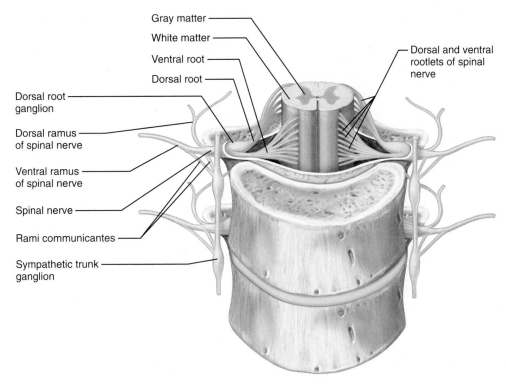

Gray matter

White matter

Ventral root

Dorsal root

Dorsal and ventral rootlets of spinal nerve

Dorsal root ganglion

Dorsal ramus of spinal nerve

Ventral ramus of spinal nerve

Spinal nerve

Rami communicantes

Sympathetic trunk ganglion

(a) Anterior view showing spinal cord, associated nerves, and vertebrae. The dorsal and ventral roots arise medially as rootlets and join laterally to form the spinal nerve.

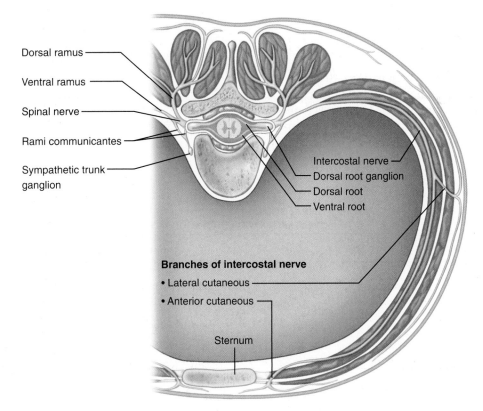

Dorsal ramus

Ventral ramus

Spinal nerve

Rami communicantes

Sympathetic trunk ganglion

Intercostal nerve

Dorsal root ganglion

Dorsal root

Ventral root

Branches of intercostal nerve

• Lateral cutaneous

• Anterior cutaneous

Sternum

(b) Cross section of thorax showing the main roots and branches of a spinal nerve.

Figure 13.7 Formation of spinal nerves and rami distribution. Notice in (b) the dorsal and ventral roots and rami, and the rami communicantes. In the thorax, each ventral ramus continues as an intercostal nerve. (The small meningeal branch is not illustrated.)

13

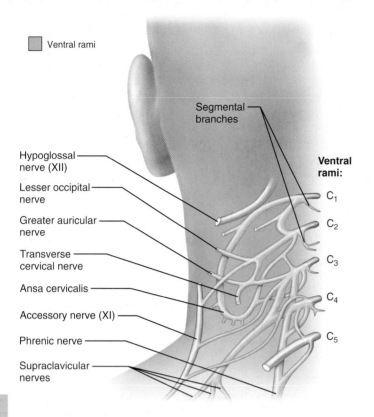

Ventral rami

Segmental branches

Hypoglossal nerve (XII)

Lesser occipital nerve

Greater auricular nerve

Transverse cervical nerve

Ansa cervicalis

Accessory nerve (XI)

Phrenic nerve

Supraclavicular nerves

Ventral rami:

C_1

C_2

C_3

C_4

C_5

Figure 13.8 The cervical plexus. The nerves colored gray connect to the plexus but do not belong to it. See Table 13.3 for structures served. (Posterior view.)

resulting branch of the plexus contains fibers from several spinal nerves and (2) fibers from each ventral ramus travel to the body periphery via several routes. As a result, each muscle in a limb receives its nerve supply from more than one spinal nerve. An advantage of this fiber regrouping is that damage to

one spinal segment or root cannot completely paralyze any limb muscle.

Throughout this section, we mention major groups of skeletal muscles served. For more specific information on muscle innervations, see Tables 10.1–10.17.

Back

The innervation of the posterior body trunk by the dorsal rami follows a neat, segmented plan. Via its several branches, each dorsal ramus innervates the narrow strip of muscle (and skin) in line with its emergence point from the spinal column (Figure 13.7b).

Anterolateral Thorax and Abdominal Wall

Only in the thorax are the ventral rami arranged in a simple segmental pattern corresponding to that of the dorsal rami. The ventral rami of T_1–T_{12} mostly course anteriorly, deep to each rib, as the **intercostal nerves**. Along their course, these nerves give off *cutaneous branches* to the skin (Figure 13.7b).

Two thoracic nerves are unusual: the tiny T_1 (most fibers enter the brachial plexus) and T_{12}, which lies inferior to the twelfth rib, making it a **subcostal nerve**. The intercostal nerves and their branches supply the intercostal muscles lying between the ribs, the muscle and skin of the anterolateral thorax, and most of the abdominal wall.

Cervical Plexus and the Neck

Buried deep in the neck under the sternocleidomastoid muscle, the looping **cervical plexus** is formed by the ventral rami of the first four cervical nerves (Figure 13.8). Its branches are summarized in **Table 13.3**. Most branches are **cutaneous nerves** that supply only the skin. They transmit sensory impulses from the skin of the neck, the ear area, the back of the head, and the shoulder. Other branches innervate muscles of the anterior neck.

TABLE 13.3	Branches of the Cervical Plexus (See Figure 13.8)	
NERVES	**SPINAL ROOTS (VENTRAL RAMI)**	**STRUCTURES SERVED**
Cutaneous Branches (Superficial)		
Lesser occipital	C_2 (C_3)	Skin on posterolateral aspect of neck
Greater auricular	C_2, C_3	Skin of ear, skin over parotid gland
Transverse cervical	C_2, C_3	Skin on anterior and lateral aspect of neck
Supraclavicular (medial, intermediate, and lateral)	C_3, C_4	Skin of shoulder and clavicular region
Motor Branches (Deep)		
Ansa cervicalis (superior and inferior roots)	C_1–C_3	Infrahyoid muscles of neck (omohyoid, sternohyoid, and sternothyroid)
Segmental and other muscular branches	C_1–C_5	Deep muscles of neck (geniohyoid and thyrohyoid) and portions of scalenes, levator scapulae, trapezius, and sternocleidomastoid muscles
Phrenic	C_3–C_5	Diaphragm (sole motor nerve supply)

13

The single most important nerve from this plexus is the **phrenic nerve** (fren′ik) (which receives fibers from C_3, C_4, and C_5). The phrenic nerve runs inferiorly through the thorax and supplies both motor and sensory fibers to the diaphragm (*phren* = diaphragm), which is the chief muscle causing breathing movements.

HOMEOSTATIC IMBALANCE

Irritation of the phrenic nerve causes spasms of the diaphragm, or hiccups. If both phrenic nerves are severed, or if the C_3–C_5 region of the spinal cord is crushed or destroyed, the diaphragm is paralyzed and respiratory arrest occurs. Victims are kept alive by mechanical respirators that force air into their lungs and do their breathing for them. ■

Brachial Plexus and Upper Limb

The large, important **brachial plexus**, situated partly in the neck and partly in the axilla, gives rise to virtually all the nerves that innervate the upper limb **(Table 13.4)**. It can be palpated (felt) in a living person just superior to the clavicle at the lateral border of the sternocleidomastoid muscle.

This plexus is formed by intermixing of ventral rami of C_5–C_8 and most of the T_1 ramus. Additionally, it often receives fibers from C_4 or T_2 or both.

The brachial plexus is very complex (some consider it to be the anatomy student's nightmare). Perhaps the simplest approach is to master the terms used for its four major groups of branches **(Figure 13.9a, d)**. From medial to lateral, these are (1) the ventral rami, misleadingly called *roots*, which form (2) *trunks*, which form (3) *divisions*, which form (4) *cords*. You might want to use the saying "**R**eally **t**ired? **D**rink **c**offee" to help you remember this branching sequence.

The five **roots** (ventral rami C_5–T_1) of the brachial plexus lie deep to the sternocleidomastoid muscle. At the lateral border of that muscle, these roots unite to form **upper**, **middle**, and **lower trunks**, each of which divides almost immediately into an **anterior** and a **posterior division**. These divisions, which generally indicate which fibers serve the front or back of the limb, pass deep to the clavicle and enter the axilla, where they give rise to three large fiber bundles called the **lateral**, **medial**, and **posterior cords**. (The cords are named for their relationship to the axillary artery, which runs through the axilla; see Figure 19.23.) All along the plexus, small nerves branch off. These supply the muscles and skin of the shoulder and superior thorax.

HOMEOSTATIC IMBALANCE

Injuries to the brachial plexus are common; when severe, they cause weakness or paralysis of the entire upper limb. Such injuries may occur when the upper limb is pulled hard and the plexus is stretched (as when a football tackler yanks the arm of the running back), and by blows to the top of the shoulder that force the humerus inferiorly (as when a cyclist is pitched headfirst off a motorcycle and his shoulder grinds into the pavement). ■

The brachial plexus ends in the axilla, where its three cords wind along the axillary artery and then give rise to the main nerves of the upper limb (Figure 13.9b, c). Five of these nerves are especially important: the axillary, musculocutaneous, median, ulnar, and radial nerves. Their distribution and targets are described briefly here, and in more detail in Table 13.4.

The **axillary nerve** branches off the posterior cord and runs posterior to the surgical neck of the humerus. It innervates the deltoid and teres minor muscles and the skin and joint capsule of the shoulder.

The **musculocutaneous nerve**, the major end branch of the lateral cord, courses inferiorly in the anterior arm, supplying motor fibers to the biceps brachii and brachialis muscles. Distal to the elbow, it provides for cutaneous sensation of the lateral forearm.

The **median nerve** descends through the arm to the anterior forearm, where it gives off branches to the skin and to most flexor muscles. On reaching the hand, it innervates five intrinsic muscles of the lateral palm. The median nerve activates muscles that pronate the forearm, flex the wrist and fingers, and oppose the thumb.

HOMEOSTATIC IMBALANCE

Median nerve injury makes it difficult to use the pincer grasp (opposed thumb and index finger) to pick up small objects. Because this nerve runs down the midline of the forearm and wrist, it is a frequent casualty of wrist-slashing suicide attempts. In carpal tunnel syndrome (see p. 231), the median nerve is compressed. ■

The **ulnar nerve** branches off the medial cord of the plexus. It descends along the medial aspect of the arm toward the elbow, swings behind the medial epicondyle, and then follows the ulna along the medial forearm. There it supplies the flexor carpi ulnaris and the medial part of the flexor digitorum profundus (the flexors not supplied by the median nerve). It continues into the hand, where it innervates most intrinsic hand muscles and the skin of the medial aspect of the hand. It produces wrist and finger flexion and (with the median nerve) adduction and abduction of the medial fingers.

HOMEOSTATIC IMBALANCE

Where it takes a superficial course, the ulnar nerve is very vulnerable to injury. Striking the "funny bone"—the spot where this nerve rests against the medial epicondyle—causes tingling of the little finger. Severe or chronic damage can lead to sensory loss, paralysis, and muscle atrophy. Affected individuals have trouble making a fist and gripping objects. As the little and ring fingers become hyperextended at the knuckles and flexed at the distal interphalangeal joints, the hand contorts into a *clawhand*. ■

The **radial nerve**, the largest branch of the brachial plexus, is a continuation of the posterior cord. This nerve wraps around the humerus (in the radial groove), and then runs anteriorly around the lateral epicondyle at the elbow. There it divides into a superficial branch that follows the lateral edge of the radius to the hand and a deep branch (not illustrated) that runs posteriorly. It supplies the posterior skin of the limb along its entire

13

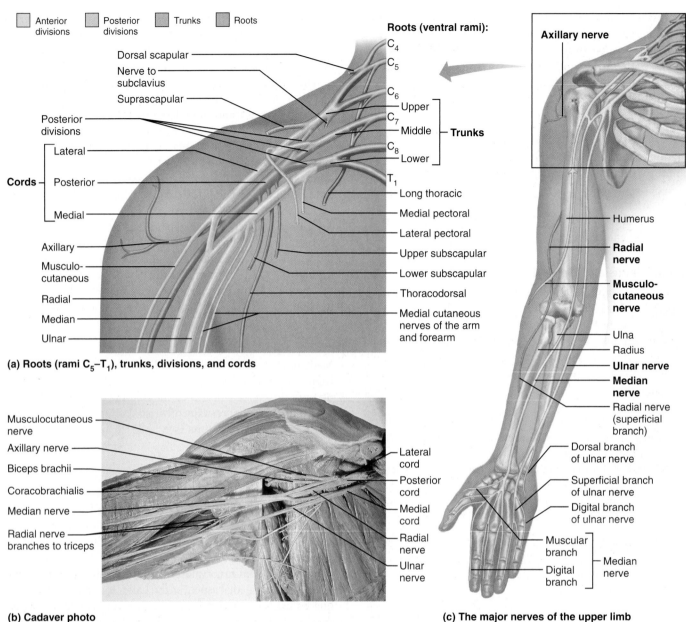

Anterior divisions | Posterior divisions | Trunks | Roots

Dorsal scapular
Nerve to subclavius
Suprascapular
Posterior divisions
Lateral
Cords
Posterior
Medial
Axillary
Musculo-cutaneous
Radial
Median
Ulnar

Roots (ventral rami):
C_4
C_5
C_6
C_7 — Upper
C_8 — Middle — **Trunks**
T_1 — Lower
Long thoracic
Medial pectoral
Lateral pectoral
Upper subscapular
Lower subscapular
Thoracodorsal
Medial cutaneous nerves of the arm and forearm

(a) Roots (rami C_5–T_1), trunks, divisions, and cords

Axillary nerve
Humerus
Radial nerve
Musculo-cutaneous nerve
Ulna
Radius
Ulnar nerve
Median nerve
Radial nerve (superficial branch)
Dorsal branch of ulnar nerve
Superficial branch of ulnar nerve
Digital branch of ulnar nerve
Muscular branch
Digital branch — Median nerve

(c) The major nerves of the upper limb

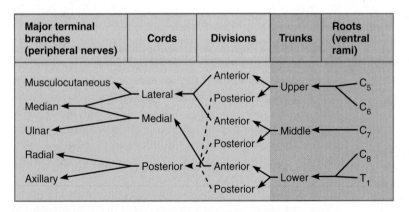

Musculocutaneous nerve
Axillary nerve
Biceps brachii
Coracobrachialis
Median nerve
Radial nerve branches to triceps

Lateral cord
Posterior cord
Medial cord
Radial nerve
Ulnar nerve

(b) Cadaver photo

Major terminal branches (peripheral nerves)	Cords	Divisions	Trunks	Roots (ventral rami)

Musculocutaneous
Median — Lateral
Ulnar — Medial
Radial — Posterior
Axillary

Anterior — Upper — C_5 / C_6
Posterior
Anterior — Middle — C_7
Posterior
Anterior
Posterior — Lower — C_8 / T_1

(d) Flowchart summarizing relationships within the brachial plexus

Figure 13.9 The brachial plexus. (Anterior view.)

13

TABLE 13.4	Branches of the Brachial Plexus (See Figure 13.9)	
NERVES	**CORD AND SPINAL ROOTS (VENTRAL RAMI)**	**STRUCTURES SERVED**
Musculocutaneous	Lateral cord (C_5–C_7)	Muscular branches: flexor muscles in anterior arm (biceps brachii, brachialis, coraco-brachialis) Cutaneous branches: skin on lateral forearm (extremely variable)
Median	By two branches, one from medial cord (C_8, T_1) and one from the lateral cord (C_5–C_7)	Muscular branches to flexor group of anterior forearm (palmaris longus, flexor carpi radialis, flexor digitorum superficialis, flexor pollicis longus, lateral half of flexor digitorum profundus, and pronator muscles); intrinsic muscles of lateral palm and digital branches to the fingers Cutaneous branches: skin of lateral two-thirds of hand, palm side and dorsum of fingers 2 and 3
Ulnar	Medial cord (C_8, T_1)	Muscular branches: flexor muscles in anterior forearm (flexor carpi ulnaris and medial half of flexor digitorum profundus); most intrinsic muscles of hand Cutaneous branches: skin of medial third of hand, both anterior and posterior aspects
Radial	Posterior cord (C_5–C_8, T_1)	Muscular branches: posterior muscles of arm and forearm (triceps brachii, anconeus, supinator, brachioradialis, extensors carpi radialis longus and brevis, extensor carpi ulnaris, and several muscles that extend the fingers) Cutaneous branches: skin of posterolateral surface of entire limb (except dorsum of fingers 2 and 3)
Axillary	Posterior cord (C_5, C_6)	Muscular branches: deltoid and teres minor muscles Cutaneous branches: some skin of shoulder region
Dorsal scapular	Branches of C_5 rami	Rhomboid muscles and levator scapulae
Long thoracic	Branches of C_5–C_7 rami	Serratus anterior muscle
Subscapular	Posterior cord; branches of C_5 and C_6 rami	Teres major and subscapularis muscles
Suprascapular	Upper trunk (C_5, C_6)	Shoulder joint; supraspinatus and infraspinatus muscles
Pectoral (lateral and medial)	Branches of lateral and medial cords (C_5–T_1)	Pectoralis major and minor muscles

course. Its motor branches innervate essentially all the extensor muscles of the upper limb. The radial nerve produces elbow extension, forearm supination, wrist and finger extension, and thumb abduction.

HOMEOSTATIC IMBALANCE
Trauma to the radial nerve results in *wrist drop*, an inability to extend the hand at the wrist. Improper use of a crutch or "Saturday night paralysis," in which an intoxicated person falls asleep with an arm draped over the back of a chair or sofa edge, causes radial nerve compression and ischemia (deprivation of blood supply). ■

Lumbosacral Plexus and Lower Limb
The sacral and lumbar plexuses overlap substantially. Because many fibers of the lumbar plexus contribute to the sacral plexus via the **lumbosacral trunk**, the two plexuses are often referred to as the **lumbosacral plexus**. Although the lumbosacral plexus serves mainly the lower limb, it also sends some branches to the abdomen, pelvis, and buttock.

Lumbar Plexus   The **lumbar plexus** arises from the spinal nerves L_1–L_4 and lies within the psoas major muscle (**Figure 13.10**). Its proximal branches innervate parts of the abdominal wall mus-

cles and the psoas muscle, but its major branches descend to innervate the anterior and medial thigh.

The **femoral nerve**, the largest terminal nerve of this plexus, runs deep to the inguinal ligament to enter the thigh and then divides into several large branches. The motor branches innervate anterior thigh muscles (quadriceps), which are the principal thigh flexors and knee extensors. The cutaneous branches serve the skin of the anterior thigh and the medial surface of the leg from knee to foot.

The **obturator nerve** (ob″tu-ra′tor) enters the medial thigh via the obturator foramen and innervates the adductor muscles. These and other smaller branches of the lumbar plexus are summarized in **Table 13.5**.

HOMEOSTATIC IMBALANCE
Compression of the spinal roots of the lumbar plexus, as by a herniated disc, results in gait problems because the femoral nerve serves the prime movers of both hip flexion and knee extension. Other symptoms are pain or anesthesia of the anterior thigh and of the medial thigh if the obturator nerve is impaired. ■

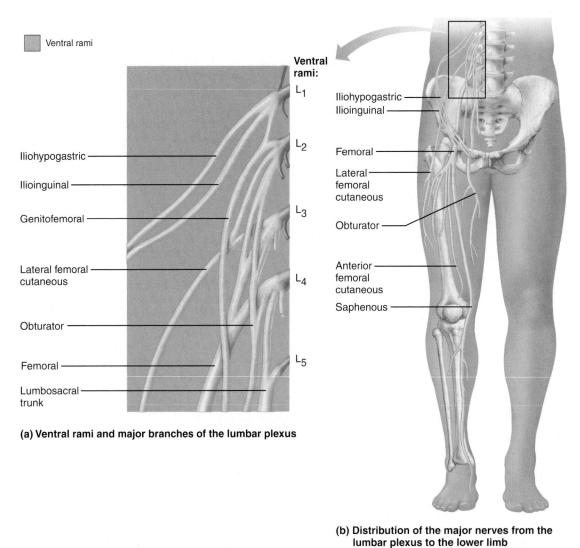

□ Ventral rami

Ventral rami:

L₁

Iliohypogastric

Ilioinguinal

Genitofemoral

L₂

Lateral femoral cutaneous

L₃

Obturator

Femoral

L₄

Lumbosacral trunk

L₅

(a) Ventral rami and major branches of the lumbar plexus

Ventral rami:

L₁

Iliohypogastric

Ilioinguinal

Femoral

Lateral femoral cutaneous

Obturator

Anterior femoral cutaneous

Saphenous

(b) Distribution of the major nerves from the lumbar plexus to the lower limb

Figure 13.10 The lumbar plexus. (Anterior view.)

TABLE 13.5	Branches of the Lumbar Plexus (See Figure 13.10)	
NERVES	**SPINAL ROOTS (VENTRAL RAMI)**	**STRUCTURES SERVED**
Femoral	L₂–L₄	Skin of anterior and medial thigh via *anterior femoral cutaneous* branch; skin of medial leg and foot, hip and knee joints via *saphenous* branch; motor to anterior muscles (quadriceps and sartorius) of thigh and to pectineus, iliacus
Obturator	L₂–L₄	Motor to adductor magnus (part), longus, and brevis muscles, gracilis muscle of medial thigh, obturator externus; sensory for skin of medial thigh and for hip and knee joints
Lateral femoral cutaneous	L₂, L₃	Skin of lateral thigh; some sensory branches to peritoneum
Iliohypogastric	L₁	Skin of lower abdomen and hip; muscles of anterolateral abdominal wall (internal obliques and transversus abdominis)
Ilioinguinal	L₁	Skin of external genitalia and proximal medial aspect of the thigh; inferior abdominal muscles
Genitofemoral	L₁, L₂	Skin of scrotum in males, of labia majora in females, and of anterior thigh inferior to middle portion of inguinal region; cremaster muscle in males

13

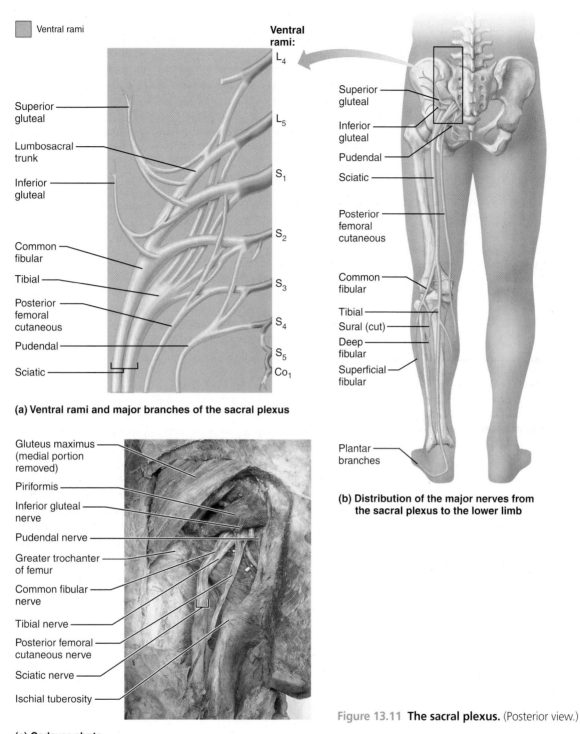

(a) Ventral rami and major branches of the sacral plexus

(b) Distribution of the major nerves from the sacral plexus to the lower limb

(c) Cadaver photo

Figure 13.11 The sacral plexus. (Posterior view.)

Sacral Plexus The **sacral plexus** arises from spinal nerves L_4–S_4 and lies immediately caudal to the lumbar plexus **(Figure 13.11)**. Some fibers of the lumbar plexus contribute to the sacral plexus via the *lumbosacral trunk*, as mentioned earlier. The sacral plexus has about a dozen named branches. About half of these serve the buttock and lower limb; the others innervate pelvic structures and the perineum. The most important branches are described here. **Table 13.6** summarizes all but the smallest ones.

The largest branch of the sacral plexus is the **sciatic nerve** (si-at′ik), the thickest and longest nerve in the body. It supplies the entire lower limb, except the anteromedial thigh.

The sciatic nerve is actually two nerves—the *tibial* and *common fibular*—wrapped in a common sheath. The sciatic nerve leaves the pelvis via the greater sciatic notch. It courses deep to the gluteus maximus muscle and enters the posterior thigh just medial to the hip joint (*sciatic* = of the hip). There it gives off motor branches to the hamstring muscles (all thigh extensors

TABLE 13.6	Branches of the Sacral Plexus (See Figure 13.11)	
NERVES	**SPINAL ROOTS (VENTRAL RAMI)**	**STRUCTURES SERVED**
Sciatic nerve	L_4, L_5, S_1–S_3	Composed of two nerves (tibial and common fibular) in a common sheath; they diverge just proximal to the knee
■ Tibial (including sural, medial and lateral plantar, and medial calcaneal branches)	L_4–S_3	Cutaneous branches: to skin of posterior surface of leg and sole of foot Motor branches: to muscles of back of thigh, leg, and foot [hamstrings (except short head of biceps femoris), posterior part of adductor magnus, triceps surae, tibialis posterior, popliteus, flexor digitorum longus, flexor hallucis longus, and intrinsic muscles of foot]
■ Common fibular (superficial and deep branches)	L_4–S_2	Cutaneous branches: to skin of anterior and lateral surface of leg and dorsum of foot Motor branches: to short head of biceps femoris of thigh, fibular muscles of lateral compartment of leg, tibialis anterior, and extensor muscles of toes (extensor hallucis longus, extensors digitorum longus and brevis)
Superior gluteal	L_4, L_5, S_1	Motor branches: to gluteus medius and minimus and tensor fasciae latae
Inferior gluteal	L_5–S_2	Motor branches: to gluteus maximus
Posterior femoral cutaneous	S_1–S_3	Skin of buttock, posterior thigh, and popliteal region; length variable; may also innervate part of skin of calf and heel
Pudendal	S_2–S_4	Supplies most of skin and muscles of perineum (region encompassing external genitalia and anus and including clitoris, labia, and vaginal mucosa in females, and scrotum and penis in males); external anal sphincter

and knee flexors) and to the adductor magnus. Immediately above the knee, the two divisions of the sciatic nerve diverge.

The **tibial nerve** courses through the popliteal fossa (the region just posterior to the knee joint) and supplies the posterior compartment muscles of the leg and the skin of the posterior calf and sole of the foot. In the vicinity of the knee, the tibial nerve gives off the **sural nerve**, which serves the skin of the posterolateral leg, and at the ankle the tibial nerve divides into the **medial** and **lateral plantar nerves**, which serve most of the foot. The **common fibular nerve**, or *common peroneal nerve* (*perone* = fibula), descends from its point of origin, wraps around the neck of the fibula, and then divides into superficial and deep branches. These branches innervate the knee joint, skin of the anterior and lateral leg and dorsum of the foot, and muscles of the anterolateral leg (the extensors that dorsiflex the foot).

The next largest sacral plexus branches are the **superior** and **inferior gluteal nerves**. Together, they innervate the buttock (gluteal) and tensor fasciae latae muscles. The **pudendal nerve** (pu-den'dal; "shameful") innervates the muscles and skin of the perineum, helps stimulate erection, and is involved in voluntary control of urination (see Table 10.7). Other branches of the sacral plexus supply the thigh rotators and muscles of the pelvic floor.

HOMEOSTATIC IMBALANCE

Injury to the proximal part of the sciatic nerve, as might follow a fall, disc herniation, or improper administration of an injection into the buttock, results in a number of lower limb impairments, depending on the precise nerve roots injured. *Sciatica* (si-at'ĭ-kah), characterized by stabbing pain radiating over the course of the sciatic nerve, is common. When the nerve is transected, the leg is nearly useless. The leg cannot be flexed (because the hamstrings are paralyzed), and all foot and ankle movement is lost. The foot drops into plantar flexion (it dangles), a condition called *footdrop*. Recovery from sciatic nerve injury is usually slow and incomplete.

If the lesion occurs below the knee, thigh muscles are spared. When the tibial nerve is injured, the paralyzed calf muscles cannot plantar flex the foot and a shuffling gait develops. The common fibular nerve is susceptible to injury largely because of its superficial location at the head and neck of the fibula. Even a tight leg cast, or remaining too long in a side-lying position on a firm mattress, can compress this nerve and cause footdrop. ■

Innervation of Skin: Dermatomes

The area of skin innervated by the cutaneous branches of a single spinal nerve is called a **dermatome** (der'mah-tōm; "skin segment"). Every spinal nerve except C_1 innervates dermatomes. In patients with spinal cord injuries, you can pinpoint which nerves are damaged and locate the injured region of the spinal cord by determining which dermatomes are affected.

Adjacent dermatomes on the body trunk are fairly uniform in width, almost horizontal, and in direct line with their spinal nerves (Figure 13.12). The dermatome arrangement in the limbs is less obvious. (It is also more variable and different clinicians have mapped a variety of areas for the same dermatomes.) The skin of the upper limbs is supplied by ventral rami of C_5–T_1 (or T_2). The lumbar nerves supply most of the anterior surfaces of the thighs and legs, and the sacral nerves serve most of the posterior surfaces of the lower limbs. (This distribution basically reflects the areas supplied by the lumbar and sacral plexuses, respectively.)

Adjacent dermatomes are not as cleanly separated as a typical dermatome map indicates. On the trunk, neighboring dermatomes overlap considerably (about 50%). As a result, destruction of a single spinal nerve will not cause complete

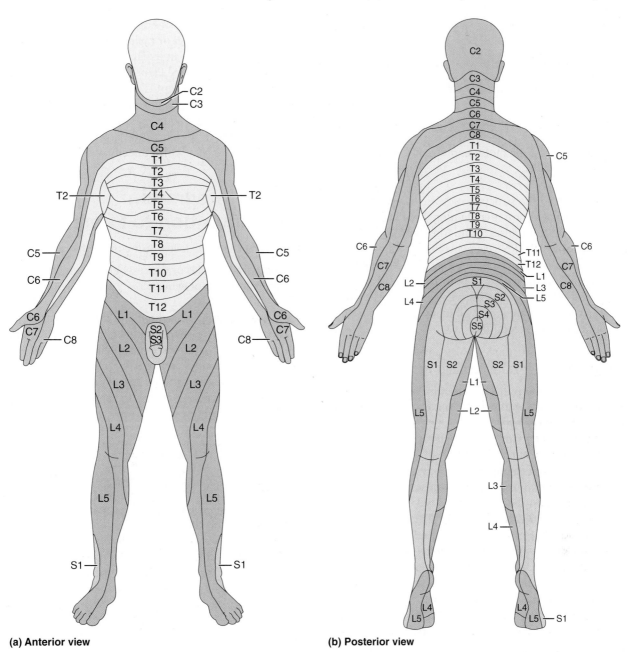

(a) Anterior view

(b) Posterior view

Figure 13.12 Map of dermatomes. Each dermatome is the skin segment innervated by the cutaneous sensory branches of a single spinal nerve. All spinal nerves but C_1 participate in the innervation of the dermatomes.

numbness anywhere. In the limbs, the overlap is less complete and some skin regions are innervated by just one spinal nerve.

Innervation of Joints

The easiest way to remember which nerves serve which synovial joint is to use **Hilton's law**, which says: *Any nerve serving a muscle that produces movement at a joint also innervates the joint and the skin over the joint.* Hence, once you learn which nerves serve the various major muscles and muscle groups, no new learning is necessary. For example, the knee is crossed by the quadriceps, gracilis, and hamstring muscles. The nerves to these muscles are the femoral nerve anteriorly and branches of the sciatic and

obturator nerves posteriorly. Consequently, these nerves innervate the knee joint as well.

CHECK YOUR UNDERSTANDING

10. Spinal nerves have both *dorsal roots* and *dorsal rami*. How are these different from each other in location and in functional composition?

11. After his horse-riding accident, the actor Christopher Reeve was unable to breathe on his own. Which spinal nerve roots, spinal nerve, and spinal nerve plexus were involved?

For answers, see Appendix G.

PART 3

MOTOR ENDINGS AND MOTOR ACTIVITY

Peripheral Motor Endings

▶ Compare and contrast the motor endings of somatic and autonomic nerve fibers.

So far we have covered the structure of sensory receptors that detect stimuli, and that of nerves containing the afferent and efferent fibers that deliver impulses to and from the CNS. We now turn to **motor endings**, the PNS elements that activate effectors by releasing neurotransmitters. Because we discussed that topic in Chapter 9 with the innervation of body muscles, all we need to do here is recap. To balance the overview of sensory function provided earlier in this chapter, we will follow the recap with a brief overview of motor integration.

Innervation of Skeletal Muscle

As illustrated in Figure 9.8 (p. 286), the terminals of somatic motor fibers that innervate voluntary muscles form elaborate **neuromuscular junctions** with their effector cells. As each axon branch reaches its target, a single muscle fiber, the ending splits into a cluster of *axon terminals* that branch treelike over the junctional folds of the sarcolemma of the muscle fiber. The axon terminals contain mitochondria and synaptic vesicles filled with the neurotransmitter acetylcholine (ACh).

When a nerve impulse reaches an axon terminal, ACh is released by exocytosis, diffuses across the fluid-filled synaptic cleft (about 50 nm wide), and attaches to ACh receptors on the highly infolded sarcolemma at the junction. ACh binding results in the opening of ligand-gated channels that allow both Na^+ and K^+ to pass. Because more Na^+ enters the cell than K^+ leaves, the muscle cell interior at that point depolarizes, producing a type of graded potential called an *end plate potential*. The end plate potential spreads to adjacent areas of the membrane where it triggers the opening of voltage-gated sodium channels. This event leads to propagation of an action potential along the sarcolemma that stimulates the muscle fiber to contract. The synaptic cleft at somatic neuromuscular junctions is filled with a glycoprotein-rich basal lamina, a structure not seen at other synapses. The basal lamina contains *acetylcholinesterase*, the enzyme that breaks down ACh almost immediately after it binds.

Innervation of Visceral Muscle and Glands

The junctions between autonomic motor endings and their effectors (which are smooth and cardiac muscle and glands) are much simpler than the junctions formed between somatic fibers and skeletal muscle cells. The autonomic motor axons branch repeatedly, each branch forming *synapses en passant* with its effector cells. Instead of a cluster of bulblike terminals, an axon ending serving smooth muscle or a gland (but not cardiac muscle) has a series of **varicosities**, knoblike swellings containing mitochondria and synaptic vesicles, that make it look like a string of beads (see Figure 9.27).

The autonomic synaptic vesicles typically contain either acetylcholine or norepinephrine, both of which act indirectly on their targets via second messengers. Consequently, the visceral motor responses tend to be slower than those induced by somatic motor fibers, which directly open ion channels.

Motor Integration: From Intention to Effect

▶ Outline the three levels of the motor hierarchy.

▶ Compare the roles of the cerebellum and basal nuclei in controlling motor activity.

How does integration in the motor system compare with integration in sensory systems? In the motor system, we have motor endings serving effectors (muscle fibers) instead of sensory receptors, descending efferent circuits instead of ascending afferent circuits, and motor behavior instead of perception. However, as in sensory systems, the basic mechanisms of motor systems operate at three levels.

Levels of Motor Control

The cerebral cortex is at the highest level of our conscious motor pathways, but it is *not* the ultimate planner and coordinator of complex motor activities. The cerebellum and basal nuclei (ganglia) play this role and are therefore at the top of the motor control hierarchy. Motor control exerted by lower levels is mediated by *reflex arcs* in some cases, but complex motor behavior, such as walking and swimming, appears to depend on more complex patterns. Currently, we define three levels of motor control: the *segmental level*, the *projection level*, and the *precommand level* (Figure 13.13).

The Segmental Level

The lowest level of the motor hierarchy, the **segmental level**, consists of the spinal cord circuits. A segmental circuit activates a network of ventral horn neurons in a group of cord segments, causing them to stimulate specific groups of muscles. Circuits that control locomotion and other specific and oft-repeated motor activities are called **central pattern generators (CPGs)**. CPGs consist of networks of oscillating inhibitory and excitatory neurons, which set crude rhythms and alternating patterns of movement.

The Projection Level

The spinal cord is under the direct control of the **projection level** of motor control. The projection level consists of *upper motor neurons* of the motor cortex, which initiate the *direct* (*pyramidal*) *system*, and of brain stem motor nuclei, which oversee the *indirect* (*extrapyramidal*) *system* (see Table 12.3 and pp. 473–476). Axons

13

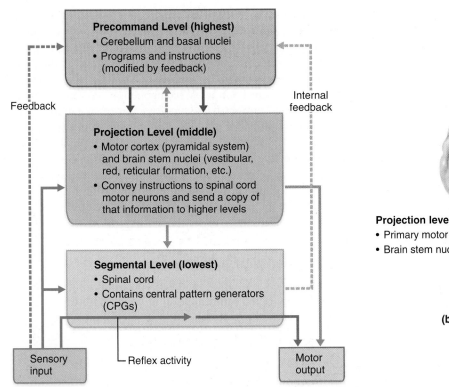

(a) Levels of motor control and their interactions

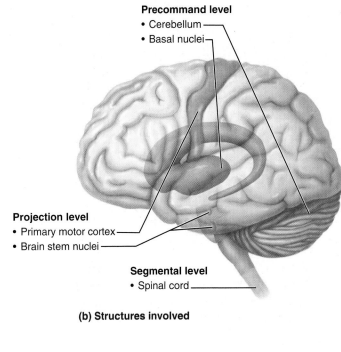

(b) Structures involved

Figure 13.13 **Hierarchy of motor control.**

of the direct system neurons produce discrete voluntary movements of the skeletal muscles. Axons of the indirect system help control reflex and CPG-controlled motor actions, modifying and controlling the activity of the segmental apparatus.

Projection motor pathways convey information to lower motor neurons, and send a copy of that information as *internal feedback* to higher command levels, continually informing them of what is happening. The direct and indirect systems provide separate and parallel pathways for controlling the spinal cord, but these systems are interrelated at all levels.

The Precommand Level

Two other systems of brain neurons, located in the cerebellum and basal nuclei, regulate motor activity. They precisely start or stop movements, coordinate movements with posture, block unwanted movements, and monitor muscle tone. Collectively called **precommand areas**, these systems *control the outputs* of the cortex and brain stem motor centers and stand at the highest level of the motor hierarchy.

The key center for "online" sensorimotor integration and control is the **cerebellum**. Remember the cerebellum is a target of ascending proprioceptor, tactile, equilibrium, and visual inputs—feedback that it needs for rapid correction of "errors" in motor activity. It also receives information via branches from descending pyramidal tracts, and from various brain stem nuclei. The cerebellum lacks direct connections to the spinal cord; it acts on motor pathways through the projection areas of

the brain stem and on the motor cortex via the thalamus to fine-tune motor activity.

The **basal nuclei** receive inputs from *all* cortical areas and send their output back mainly to premotor and prefrontal cortical areas via the thalamus. Compared to the cerebellum, the basal nuclei appear to be involved in more complex aspects of motor control. Under resting conditions, the basal nuclei inhibit various motor centers of the brain, but when the motor centers are released from inhibition, coordinated motions can begin.

Cells in both the basal nuclei and the cerebellum are involved in this unconscious planning and discharge *in advance* of willed movements. When you actually move your fingers, both the precommand areas and the primary motor cortex are active. At the risk of oversimplifying, it appears that the cortex says, "I want to do this," and then lets the precommand areas take over to provide the proper timing and patterns to execute the movements desired. The precommand areas control the motor cortex and provide its readiness to initiate a voluntary act. The conscious cortex then chooses to act or not act, but the groundwork has already been laid.

CHECK YOUR UNDERSTANDING

12. What are varicosities and where would you find them?

13. What parts of the nervous system ultimately plan and coordinate complex motor activities?

For answers, see Appendix G.

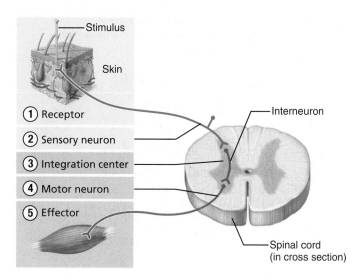

Figure 13.14 The five basic components of all reflex arcs. The reflex arc illustrated is polysynaptic.

PART **4**

REFLEX ACTIVITY

The Reflex Arc

▶ Name the components of a reflex arc and distinguish between autonomic and somatic reflexes.

Many of the body's control systems belong to a general category known as reflexes, which can be either inborn or learned. In the most restricted sense, an *inborn*, or *intrinsic, reflex* is a rapid, predictable motor response to a stimulus. It is unlearned, unpremeditated, and involuntary, and may be considered as built into our neural anatomy. Reflexes prevent us from having to *think* about all the little details of staying upright, intact, and alive—helping us maintain posture, avoid pain, and control visceral activities.

One example of an inborn reflex is what happens when you splash a pot of boiling water on your arm; you are likely to drop the pot instantly and involuntarily even before feeling any pain. This response is triggered by a spinal reflex without any help from the brain. In many cases we are aware of the final response of a basic reflex activity (you know you've dropped the pot of boiling water). In other cases, reflex activities go on without any awareness on our part. This is typical of many visceral reflexes, which are regulated by the subconscious lower regions of the CNS, specifically the brain stem and spinal cord.

In addition to these basic, inborn types of reflexes, there are *learned*, or *acquired, reflexes* that result from practice or repetition. Take, for instance, the complex sequence of reactions that occurs when an experienced driver drives a car. The process is largely automatic, but only because substantial time and effort were expended to acquire the driving skill. In reality, the distinction between inborn and learned reflexes is not clear-cut and most inborn reflex actions are subject to modification by learn-

ing and conscious effort. For instance, if a 3-year-old child was standing by your side when you scalded your arm, you most likely would set the pot down (rather than just letting go) because of your conscious recognition of the danger to the child.

Recall the discussion in Chapter 11 about serial and parallel processing of sensory input. What happens when you scald your arm is a good example of how these two processing modes work together. You drop the pot before feeling any pain, but the pain signals picked up by the interneurons of the spinal cord are quickly transmitted to the brain, so that within the next few seconds you *do* become aware of pain, and you also know what happened to cause it. The withdrawal reflex is serial processing mediated by the spinal cord, and pain awareness reflects simultaneous parallel processing of the sensory input.

Components of a Reflex Arc

As you learned in Chapter 11, reflexes occur over highly specific neural paths called **reflex arcs**, all of which have five essential components (Figure 13.14):

① **Receptor:** Site of the stimulus action.

② **Sensory neuron:** Transmits afferent impulses to the CNS.

③ **Integration center:** In simple reflex arcs, the integration center may be a single synapse between a sensory neuron and a motor neuron (**monosynaptic reflex**). More complex reflex arcs involve multiple synapses with chains of interneurons (**polysynaptic reflex**). The integration center for the reflexes we will describe in this chapter is within the CNS.

④ **Motor neuron:** Conducts efferent impulses from the integration center to an effector organ.

⑤ **Effector:** Muscle fiber or gland cell that responds to the efferent impulses (by contracting or secreting).

Reflexes are classified functionally as **somatic reflexes** if they activate skeletal muscle, or as **autonomic (visceral) reflexes** if they activate visceral effectors (smooth or cardiac muscle or glands). Here we describe some common somatic reflexes mediated by the spinal cord. We will consider autonomic reflexes in later chapters along with the visceral processes they help to regulate.

Spinal Reflexes

▶ Compare and contrast stretch, flexor, crossed-extensor, and Golgi tendon reflexes.

Somatic reflexes mediated by the spinal cord are called **spinal reflexes**. Many spinal reflexes occur without the direct involvement of higher brain centers. Generally, these reflexes are even present in animals whose brains have been destroyed as long as the spinal cord is still functional. However, the brain is "advised" of most spinal reflex activity and can facilitate, inhibit, or adapt it, depending on the circumstances (as we described in the example of the hot water–filled pot). Moreover, continuous facilitating signals from the brain are required for normal spinal reflex activity. As we saw in Chapter 12, *spinal shock* occurs when the spinal cord is transected, immediately depressing all functions controlled by the cord.

Testing of somatic reflexes is important clinically to assess the condition of the nervous system. Exaggerated, distorted, or absent reflexes indicate degeneration or pathology of specific nervous system regions, often before other signs are apparent.

Stretch and Golgi Tendon Reflexes

What information does your nervous system need in order to smoothly coordinate the activity of your skeletal muscles? Two types of information about the current state of a muscle are key. First, the nervous system needs to know the length of the muscle. The *muscle spindles*, found in skeletal muscles, supply this information. Second, it needs to know the amount of tension in the muscle and its associated tendons. *Golgi tendon organs*, located in the tendons, provide this information. These two types of proprioceptors play an important role in spinal reflexes and also provide essential feedback to the cerebral cortex and cerebellum. Let's take a closer look at the functional anatomy of these proprioceptors and their roles in certain spinal reflexes.

Functional Anatomy of Muscle Spindles

Each muscle spindle consists of three to ten modified skeletal muscle fibers called **intrafusal muscle fibers** (*intra* = within; *fusal* = the spindle) enclosed in a connective tissue capsule **(Figure 13.15)**. These fibers are less than one-quarter the size of the effector fibers of the muscle, called **extrafusal muscle fibers**.

The central regions of the intrafusal fibers lack myofilaments and are noncontractile. These regions are the receptive surfaces of the spindle. They are wrapped by two types of afferent endings that send sensory inputs to the CNS. The **primary sensory endings** of large **type Ia fibers**, which innervate the spindle center, are stimulated by both the rate and degree of stretch. The **secondary sensory endings** of small **type II fibers** supply the spindle ends and are stimulated only by degree of stretch.

The intrafusal muscle fibers have contractile regions at their ends, which are the only areas containing actin and myosin myofilaments. These regions are innervated by **gamma (γ) efferent fibers** that arise from small motor neurons in the ventral horn of the spinal cord. These γ motor fibers, which maintain spindle sensitivity (as described shortly), are distinct from the **alpha (α) efferent fibers** of the large **alpha (α) motor neurons** that stimulate the extrafusal muscle fibers to contract.

The muscle spindle is stretched (and excited) in one of two ways: (1) by applying an external force that lengthens the entire muscle, such as occurs when we carry a heavy weight or when antagonistic muscles contract (external stretch); or (2) by activating the γ motor neurons that stimulate the distal ends of the intrafusal fibers to contract, thereby stretching the middle of the spindle (internal stretch). Whenever the muscle spindle is stretched, its associated sensory neurons transmit impulses at higher frequency to the spinal cord **(Figure 13.16a, b)**.

During voluntary skeletal muscle contraction, the muscle shortens. If the intrafusal muscle fibers didn't contract along

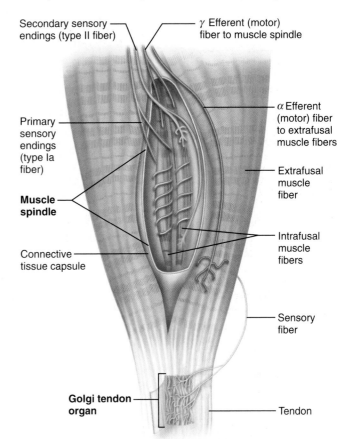

Figure 13.15 Anatomy of the muscle spindle and Golgi tendon organ. Notice the afferent fibers from and efferent fibers to the muscle spindle. Myelin has been omitted from all nerve fibers for clarity.

with the extrafusal fibers, then the muscle spindle would go slack and cease generating action potentials (Figure 13.16c). At this point it would be unable to signal further changes in muscle length, so it would be useless.

Fortunately, **α-γ coactivation** prevents this from happening. Descending fibers of motor pathways synapse with both α and γ motor neurons, and motor impulses are simultaneously sent to the large extrafusal fibers and to muscle spindle intrafusal fibers. Stimulating the intrafusal fibers maintains the spindle's tension (and sensitivity) during muscle contraction, so that the brain continues to be notified of conditions in the muscle (Figure 13.16d). Without such a system, information on changes in muscle length would cease to flow from contracting muscles.

The Stretch Reflex

By sending commands to the motor neurons, the brain essentially sets a muscle's length. The **stretch reflex** makes sure that the muscle stays at that length. For example, the **patellar** (pah-tel′ar) or **knee-jerk reflex** is a stretch reflex that helps keep your knees from buckling when you are standing upright. As your knees begin to buckle and the quadriceps lengthens, the stretch reflex causes the quadriceps to contract without your having to think about it. The stretch reflex and a specific example—the

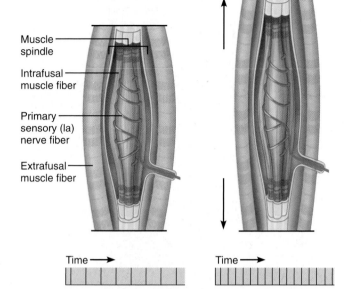
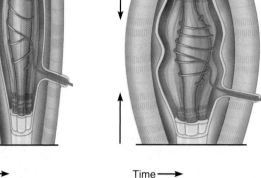
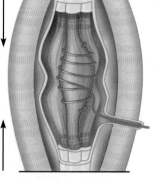
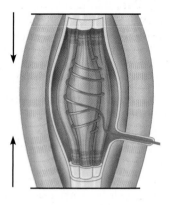

Muscle spindle
Intrafusal muscle fiber
Primary sensory (Ia) nerve fiber
Extrafusal muscle fiber

Time →

(a) Unstretched muscle. Action potentials (APs) are generated at a constant rate in the associated sensory (Ia) fiber.

(b) Stretched muscle. Stretching activates the muscle spindle, increasing the rate of APs.

(c) Only α motor neurons activated. Only the extrafusal muscle fibers contract. The muscle spindle becomes slack and no APs are fired. It is unable to signal further length changes.

(d) α-γ Coactivation. Both extrafusal and intrafusal muscle fibers contract. Muscle spindle tension is maintained and it can still signal changes in length.

Figure 13.16 Operation of the muscle spindle. The action potentials generated in the sensory (Ia) fibers are shown for each case as black lines in yellow bars.

13

knee-jerk reflex—are shown in *Focus on the Stretch Reflex* (Figure 13.17).

The stretch reflex is important for maintaining muscle tone and adjusting it reflexively. It is most important in the large extensor muscles that sustain upright posture and in postural muscles of the trunk. For example, contractions of the postural muscles of the spine are almost continuously regulated by stretch reflexes initiated first on one side of the spine and then on the other.

Let's look at how the stretch reflex works. As we've just seen in Figure 13.16, sensory neurons of muscle spindles activated by stretch transmit impulses at a higher frequency to the spinal cord. There the sensory neurons synapse directly with α motor neurons, which rapidly excite the extrafusal muscle fibers of the stretched muscle (Figure 13.17). The reflexive muscle contraction that follows (an example of serial processing) resists further muscle stretching.

Branches of the afferent fibers also synapse with interneurons that inhibit motor neurons controlling antagonistic muscles (parallel processing), and the resulting inhibition is called **reciprocal inhibition**. Consequently, the stretch stimulus causes the antagonists to relax so that they cannot resist the shortening of the "stretched" muscle caused by the main reflex arc. While this spinal reflex is occurring, information on muscle length and the speed of muscle shortening is being relayed (mainly via the dorsal white columns) to higher brain centers (more parallel processing).

The most familiar clinical example of a stretch reflex is the knee-jerk reflex we have just described. Stretch reflexes can be elicited in any skeletal muscle by a sudden jolt to the tendon or the muscle itself. All stretch reflexes are **monosynaptic** and **ipsilateral**. In other words, they involve a single synapse and motor activity on the same side of the body. Although stretch reflexes *themselves* are monosynaptic, the reflex arcs that inhibit the motor neurons serving the antagonistic muscles are polysynaptic.

A positive knee jerk (or a positive result for any other stretch reflex test) provides two important pieces of information. First, it proves that the sensory and motor connections between that muscle and the spinal cord are intact. Second, the vigor of the response indicates the degree of excitability of the spinal cord. When the spinal motor neurons are highly facilitated by impulses descending from higher centers, just touching the muscle tendon produces a vigorous reflex response. On the other hand, when the lower motor neurons are bombarded by inhibitory signals, even pounding on the tendon may fail to cause the reflex response.

HOMEOSTATIC IMBALANCE

Stretch reflexes tend to be either hypoactive or absent in cases of peripheral nerve damage or ventral horn injury involving the tested area. These reflexes are absent in those with chronic diabetes mellitus or neurosyphilis and during coma. However, they are hyperactive when lesions of the corticospinal tract reduce the inhibitory effect of the brain on the spinal cord (as in stroke patients). ∎

Figure 13.17 FOCUS **The Stretch Reflex**

Stretched muscle spindles initiate a stretch reflex, causing contraction of the stretched muscle and inhibition of its antagonist.

The events by which muscle stretch is damped

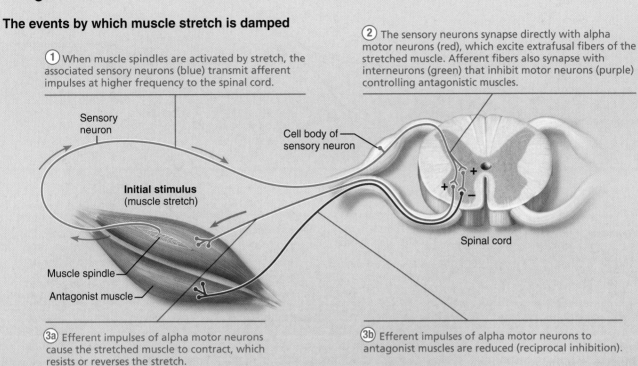

1 When muscle spindles are activated by stretch, the associated sensory neurons (blue) transmit afferent impulses at higher frequency to the spinal cord.

2 The sensory neurons synapse directly with alpha motor neurons (red), which excite extrafusal fibers of the stretched muscle. Afferent fibers also synapse with interneurons (green) that inhibit motor neurons (purple) controlling antagonistic muscles.

Sensory neuron

Cell body of sensory neuron

Initial stimulus (muscle stretch)

Spinal cord

Muscle spindle

Antagonist muscle

3a Efferent impulses of alpha motor neurons cause the stretched muscle to contract, which resists or reverses the stretch.

3b Efferent impulses of alpha motor neurons to antagonist muscles are reduced (reciprocal inhibition).

The patellar (knee-jerk) reflex – a specific example of a stretch reflex

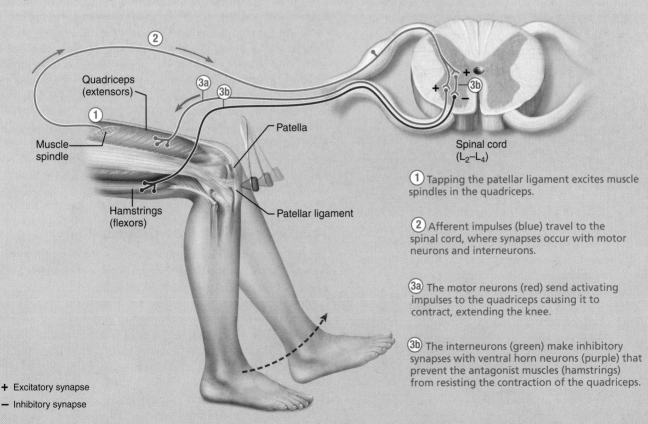

Quadriceps (extensors)

Muscle spindle

Hamstrings (flexors)

Patella

Patellar ligament

Spinal cord (L$_2$–L$_4$)

1 Tapping the patellar ligament excites muscle spindles in the quadriceps.

2 Afferent impulses (blue) travel to the spinal cord, where synapses occur with motor neurons and interneurons.

3a The motor neurons (red) send activating impulses to the quadriceps causing it to contract, extending the knee.

3b The interneurons (green) make inhibitory synapses with ventral horn neurons (purple) that prevent the antagonist muscles (hamstrings) from resisting the contraction of the quadriceps.

+ Excitatory synapse
− Inhibitory synapse

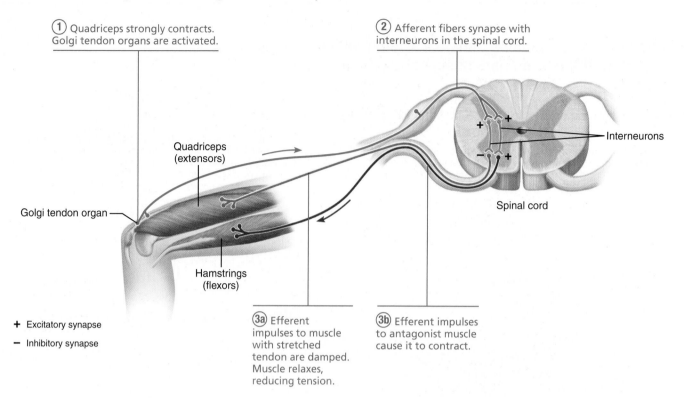

① Quadriceps strongly contracts. Golgi tendon organs are activated.

② Afferent fibers synapse with interneurons in the spinal cord.

Quadriceps (extensors)

Golgi tendon organ

Hamstrings (flexors)

Interneurons

Spinal cord

+ Excitatory synapse
− Inhibitory synapse

③a Efferent impulses to muscle with stretched tendon are damped. Muscle relaxes, reducing tension.

③b Efferent impulses to antagonist muscle cause it to contract.

Figure 13.18 The Golgi tendon reflex.

Adjusting Muscle Spindle Sensitivity

The motor supply to the muscle spindle allows the brain to voluntarily modify the stretch reflex response and the firing rate of α motor neurons. When the γ neurons are vigorously stimulated by impulses from the brain, the spindle is stretched and highly sensitive, and muscle contraction force is maintained or increased. When the γ motor neurons are inhibited, the spindle resembles a loose rubber band and is nonresponsive, and the extrafusal muscles relax.

The ability to modify the stretch reflex is important in many situations. As the speed and difficulty of a movement increases, the brain increases γ motor output to increase the sensitivity of the muscle spindles. For example, a gymnast on a balance beam needs to have highly sensitive muscle spindles or she'll fall off. On the other hand, if you want to wind up to pitch a baseball, it is essential to suppress the stretch reflex so that your muscles can produce a large degree of motion (i.e., circumduct your pitching arm). Other athletes who require movements of maximum force learn to stretch muscles as much and as quickly as possible just before the movement. This advantage is demonstrated by the crouch that athletes assume just before jumping or running.

As we have seen, muscle tone and smooth coordination of movement depends upon having intact stretch reflex pathways. Both afferent and efferent fibers to the muscle spindle are vitally important. If either afferent or efferent fibers are cut, the muscle immediately loses its tone and becomes flaccid.

The Golgi Tendon Reflex

Stretch reflexes cause muscle contraction in response to increased muscle length (stretch). The polysynaptic **Golgi tendon reflexes**,

on the other hand, produce exactly the opposite effect: muscle relaxation and lengthening in response to tension. When muscle tension increases substantially during contraction or passive stretching, high-threshold Golgi tendon organs in the tendon may be activated. Afferent impulses are transmitted to the spinal cord, and then to the cerebellum, where the information is used to adjust muscle tension. Simultaneously, motor neurons in spinal cord circuits supplying the contracting muscle are inhibited and antagonist muscles are activated, a phenomenon called **reciprocal activation**. As a result, the contracting muscle relaxes as its antagonist is activated (**Figure 13.18**).

Golgi tendon organs help to prevent muscles and tendons from tearing when they are subjected to possibly damaging stretching force. Golgi tendon organs also function at normal muscle tensions. In the normal range, Golgi tendon organs help to ensure smooth onset and termination of muscle contraction.

The Flexor and Crossed-Extensor Reflexes

The **flexor**, or **withdrawal**, **reflex** is initiated by a painful stimulus and causes automatic withdrawal of the threatened body part from the stimulus (**Figure 13.19**, left). The response that occurs when you prick your finger is a good example. Flexor reflexes are ipsilateral and polysynaptic, the latter a necessity when several muscles must be recruited to withdraw the injured body part. Because flexor reflexes are protective reflexes important to our survival, they override the spinal pathways and prevent any other reflexes from using them at the same time. However, this reflex, like other spinal reflexes, can be overridden by descending signals from the brain. This happens when you

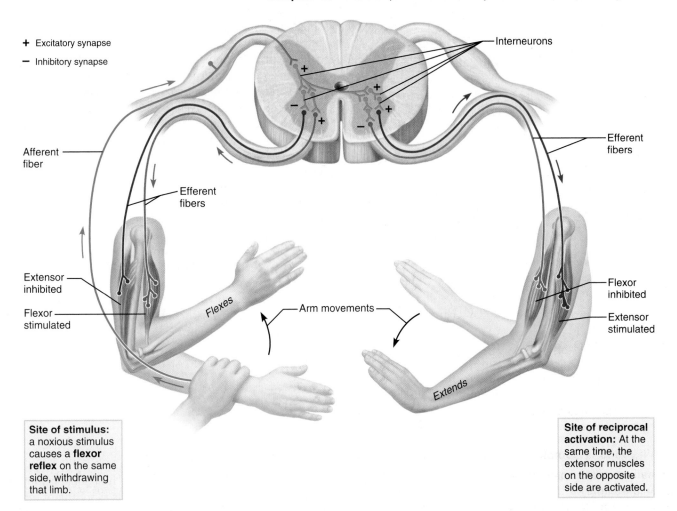

+ Excitatory synapse
− Inhibitory synapse

Interneurons

Afferent fiber

Efferent fibers

Efferent fibers

Extensor inhibited

Flexor stimulated

Flexer inhibited

Extensor stimulated

Flexes

Arm movements

Extends

Site of stimulus: a noxious stimulus causes a **flexor reflex** on the same side, withdrawing that limb.

Site of reciprocal activation: At the same time, the extensor muscles on the opposite side are activated.

Figure 13.19 The crossed-extensor reflex. In this example, a stranger suddenly grasps the right arm, which is reflexively withdrawn while the opposite (left) arm reflexively extends and pushes the stranger away.

are expecting a painful stimulus, for example a skin prick as a lab technician prepares to draw blood from a vein.

The **crossed-extensor reflex** often accompanies the flexor reflex in weight-bearing limbs and is particularly important in maintaining balance. It is a complex spinal reflex consisting of an ipsilateral withdrawal reflex and a contralateral extensor reflex. Incoming afferent fibers synapse with interneurons that control the flexor withdrawal response on the same side of the body and with other interneurons that control the extensor muscles on the opposite side.

This reflex is obvious when you step barefoot on broken glass. The ipsilateral response causes rapid lifting of the cut foot, while the contralateral response activates the extensor muscles of the opposite leg to support the weight suddenly shifted to it. The crossed-extensor reflex also occurs when someone unexpectedly grabs your arm. The grasped arm is withdrawn as the opposite arm pushes you away from the attacker (Figure 13.19).

Superficial Reflexes

Superficial reflexes are elicited by gentle cutaneous stimulation, such as that produced by stroking the skin with a tongue depres-

sor. These clinically important reflexes depend both on functional upper motor pathways and on cord-level reflex arcs. The best known of these are the plantar and abdominal reflexes.

The **plantar reflex** tests the integrity of the spinal cord from L_4 to S_2 and indirectly determines if the corticospinal tracts are functioning properly. It is elicited by drawing a blunt object downward along the lateral aspect of the plantar surface (sole) of the foot. The normal response is a downward flexion (curling) of the toes. However, if the primary motor cortex or corticospinal tract is damaged, the plantar reflex is replaced by an abnormal reflex called **Babinski's sign**, in which the great toe dorsiflexes and the smaller toes fan laterally. Infants exhibit Babinski's sign until they are about a year old because their nervous systems are incompletely myelinated. Despite its clinical significance, the physiological mechanism of Babinski's sign is not understood.

Stroking the skin of the lateral abdomen above, to the side, or below the umbilicus induces a reflex contraction of the abdominal muscles in which the umbilicus moves toward the stimulated site. These reflexes, called **abdominal reflexes**, check the integrity of the spinal cord and ventral rami from T_8 to T_{12}. The abdominal reflexes vary in intensity from one person to another. They are absent when corticospinal tract lesions are present.

13

14. Name the five components of a reflex arc.

15. What is the role of the stretch reflex? The flexor reflex?

16. Juan injured his back in a fall. When his ER physician stroked the bottom of Juan's foot, she noted that his big toe pointed up and his other toes fanned out. What is this response called and what does it indicate?

For answers, see Appendix G.

Developmental Aspects of the Peripheral Nervous System

▶ Describe the developmental relationship between the segmented arrangement of peripheral nerves, skeletal muscles, and skin dermatomes.

▶ List changes that occur in the peripheral nervous system with aging.

Most skeletal muscles derive from paired blocks of mesoderm (somites) distributed segmentally down the posteromedial aspect of the embryo. The spinal nerves branch from the developing spinal cord and adjacent neural crest and exit between the forming vertebrae, and each nerve becomes associated with the adjacent muscle mass. The spinal nerves supply both sensory and motor fibers to the developing muscles and help direct their maturation. Cranial nerves innervate muscles of the head in a comparable manner.

The distribution of cutaneous nerves to the skin follows a similar pattern. Most of the scalp and facial skin is innervated by the trigeminal nerves. Spinal nerves supply cutaneous branches to specific (adjacent) dermatomes that eventually become dermal segments. As a result, the distribution and growth of the spinal nerves correlate with the segmented body plan, which is established by the fourth week of embryonic development.

Growth of the limbs and unequal growth of other body areas result in an adult pattern of dermatomes with unequal sizes and shapes and varying degrees of overlap. Because embryonic muscle cells migrate extensively, much of the early segmental pattern is lost. Understanding the general pattern of sensory nerve distribution is critical for physicians. For example, in areas of substantial dermatome overlap, two or three spinal nerves must be blocked to perform local surgery.

Sensory receptors atrophy to some degree with age, and there is some lessening of muscle tone in the face and neck. Reflexes occur a bit more slowly during old age. This deterioration seems to reflect a general loss of neurons, fewer synapses per neuron, and a slowdown in central processing rather than any major changes in the peripheral nerve fibers. In fact, the peripheral nerves remain viable and normally functional throughout life unless subjected to traumatic injury or ischemia. The most common symptom of ischemia is a tingling sensation or numbness in the affected region.

CHECK YOUR UNDERSTANDING

17. Segmentation in the embryo gives rise to segmentation in the adult. Name two examples of segmentation in the adult body.

For answers, see Appendix G.

The PNS is an essential part of any functional nervous system. Without it, the CNS would lack its rich bank of information about events of the external and internal environments. Now that we have connected the CNS to both of these environments, we are ready to consider the autonomic nervous system, the topic of Chapter 14.

RELATED CLINICAL TERMS

Analgesia (an″al-je′zeah; *an* = without; *algos* = pain) Reduced ability to feel pain, not accompanied by loss of consciousness. An analgesic is a pain-relieving drug.

Dysarthria (dis-ar′thre-ah) Difficulty in speech articulation due to motor pathway disorders that result in weakness, uncoordinated motion, or altered respiration or rhythm. For example, lesions of cranial nerves IX, X, and XII result in nasal, breathy speech, and lesions in upper motor pathways produce a hoarse, strained voice. Not to be confused with *dysphasia* or *aphasia*, which are disorders of language processing.

Dystonia (dis-to′ne-ah) Impairment of muscle tone.

Nerve conduction studies Diagnostic tests that assess nerve integrity as indicated by their conduction velocities; the nerve is stimulated at one point, activity is recorded at a second point a known distance away, and the time required for the response to reach the recording electrode is measured; used to assess suspected peripheral neuropathies.

Neuralgia (nu-ral′je-ah; *neuro* = nerve) Sharp spasmlike pain along the course of one or more nerves; may be caused by inflammation or injury to the nerve(s) (for example, trigeminal neuralgia).

Neuritis (nu-ri′tis) Inflammation of a nerve; there are many forms with different effects (e.g., increased or decreased nerve sensitivity, paralysis of structure served, and pain).

Paresthesia (par″es-the′ze-ah) An abnormal sensation (burning, numbness, tingling) in the absence of stimuli; caused by a sensory nerve disorder.

Tabes dorsalis (ta′bēz dor-sa′lis) A slowly progressive condition caused by deterioration of the dorsal tracts (gracilis and cuneatus) and associated dorsal roots; a late sign of the neurological damage caused by the syphilis bacterium. Because joint proprioceptor tracts are destroyed, affected individuals have poor muscle coordination and an unstable gait. Bacterial invasion of the sensory (dorsal) roots results in pain, which ends when dorsal root destruction is complete.

CHAPTER SUMMARY

1. The peripheral nervous system consists of sensory receptors, nerves conducting impulses to and from the CNS, their associated ganglia, and motor endings.

PART 1: SENSORY RECEPTORS AND SENSATION

Sensory Receptors   (pp. 485–488)

1. Sensory receptors are specialized to respond to environmental changes (stimuli).
2. Sensory receptors include the simple (general) receptors for pain, touch, pressure, and temperature found in the skin, as well as those found in skeletal muscles and tendons and in the visceral organs. Complex receptors (sense organs), consisting of sensory receptors and other cells, serve the special senses (vision, hearing, equilibrium, smell, and taste).
3. Receptors are classified according to stimulus detected as mechanoreceptors, thermoreceptors, photoreceptors, chemoreceptors, and nociceptors, and according to location as exteroceptors, interoceptors, and proprioceptors.
4. The general sensory receptors are classified structurally as free or encapsulated nerve (receptor) endings of sensory neurons. The free endings are mainly receptors for temperature and pain, although two are for light touch (tactile discs and hair follicle receptors). The encapsulated endings, which are mechanoreceptors, include Meissner's corpuscles, Pacinian corpuscles, Ruffini endings, muscle spindles, Golgi tendon organs, and joint kinesthetic receptors.

Sensory Integration: From Sensation to Perception   (pp. 488–491)

1. Sensation is awareness of internal and external stimuli; perception is conscious interpretation of those stimuli.
2. The three levels of sensory integration are the receptor, circuit, and perceptual levels. These levels are functions of the sensory receptors, the ascending pathways, and the cerebral cortex, respectively.
3. Sensory receptors transduce (convert) stimulus energy via receptor or generator potentials into action potentials. Stimulus strength is frequency coded. Adaptation (decreased response to a continuous or unchanging stimulus) is seen in all general receptors except pain and proprioceptors.
4. Some sensory fibers entering the spinal cord act in local reflex arcs. Some synapse with the dorsal horn neurons (spinothalamic ascending pathways), and others continue upward to synapse in medullary nuclei (dorsal column–medial lemniscal ascending pathways). Second-order neurons of both dorsal column–medial lemniscal and spinothalamic ascending pathways terminate in the thalamus.
5. Perception—the internal, conscious image of the stimulus that serves as the basis for response—is the result of cortical processing.
6. The main aspects of sensory perception are detection, magnitude estimation, spatial discrimination, feature abstraction, quality discrimination, and pattern recognition.

PART 2: TRANSMISSION LINES: NERVES AND THEIR STRUCTURE AND REPAIR

Nerves and Associated Ganglia   (pp. 491–492)

1. A nerve is a bundle of axons in the PNS. Each fiber is enclosed by an endoneurium, fascicles of fibers are wrapped by a perineurium, and the whole nerve is bundled by the epineurium.
2. Nerves are classified according to the direction of impulse conduction as sensory, motor, or mixed; most nerves are mixed. The efferent fibers may be somatic or autonomic.
3. Ganglia are collections of neuron cell bodies associated with nerves in the PNS. Examples are the dorsal root (sensory) ganglia and autonomic (motor) ganglia.
4. Injured PNS fibers may regenerate if macrophages enter the area, phagocytize the debris, and promote Schwann cell proliferation. Schwann cells then form a channel and secrete chemicals to guide axon sprouts to their original contacts. Fibers in the CNS do not normally regenerate because the oligodendrocytes inhibit axonal sprouting and regrowth.

Cranial Nerves   (pp. 493–501)

1. Twelve pairs of cranial nerves issue through the skull to innervate the head and neck. Only the vagus nerves extend into the thoracic and abdominal cavities. All but the accessory nerve originate from the brain.
2. Cranial nerves are (generally) numbered from rostral to caudal in order of emergence from the brain. Their names reflect structures served or function or both. The cranial nerves include
   - The olfactory nerves (I): purely sensory; concerned with the sense of smell.
   - The optic nerves (II): purely sensory; transmit visual impulses from the retina to the thalamus.
   - The oculomotor nerves (III): primarily motor; emerge from the midbrain and serve four extrinsic eye muscles, the levator palpebrae superioris of the eyelid, and the intrinsic ciliary muscle of the eye and constrictor fibers of the iris. Also carry proprioceptive impulses from the skeletal muscles served.
   - The trochlear nerves (IV): primarily motor; emerge from the dorsal midbrain and carry motor and proprioceptor impulses to and from superior oblique muscles of the eyeballs.
   - The trigeminal nerves (V): mixed nerves; emerge from the lateral pons as the major general sensory nerves of the face. Each has three sensory divisions: ophthalmic, maxillary, and mandibular; the mandibular branch also contains motor fibers that innervate the chewing muscles.
   - The abducens nerves (VI): primarily motor; emerge from the pons and serve the motor and proprioceptive functions of the lateral rectus muscles of the eyeballs.
   - The facial nerves (VII): mixed nerves; emerge from the pons as the major motor nerves of the face. Also carry sensory impulses from the taste buds of anterior two-thirds of the tongue.
   - The vestibulocochlear nerves (VIII): mostly sensory; transmit impulses from the hearing and equilibrium receptors of the inner ears.
   - The glossopharyngeal nerves (IX): mixed nerves; issue from the medulla. Transmit sensory impulses from the taste buds of the posterior tongue, from the pharynx, and from chemo- and

13

baroreceptors of the carotid bodies and sinuses. Innervate some pharyngeal muscles and parotid glands.

- The vagus nerves (X): mixed nerves; arise from the medulla. Almost all motor fibers are autonomic parasympathetic fibers; motor efferents to, and sensory fibers from, the pharynx, larynx, and visceral organs of the thoracic and abdominal cavities.
- The accessory nerves (XI): primarily motor; arise as spinal rootlets from the cervical spinal cord and enter the foramen magnum. Supply somatic efferents to the trapezius and sterno-cleidomastoid muscles of the neck and carry proprioceptor afferents from the same muscles.
- The hypoglossal nerves (XII): primarily motor; issue from the medulla and carry somatic motor efferents to, and propriocep-tive fibers from, the tongue muscles.

Spinal Nerves   (pp. 502–511)

1. The 31 pairs of spinal nerves (all mixed nerves) are numbered suc-cessively according to the region of the spinal cord from which they issue.
2. Spinal nerves are formed by the union of dorsal and ventral roots of the spinal cord and are short, confined to the intervertebral foramina.
3. Branches of each spinal nerve include dorsal and ventral rami, and a meningeal branch, and in the thoracic region, rami com-municantes (ANS branches).
4. Ventral rami, except T_2–T_{12}, form plexuses that serve the limbs.
5. Dorsal rami serve the muscles and skin of the posterior body trunk. T_1–T_{12} ventral rami give rise to intercostal nerves that serve the thorax wall and abdominal surface.
6. The cervical plexus (C_1–C_4) innervates the muscles and skin of the neck and shoulder. Its phrenic nerve serves the diaphragm.
7. The brachial plexus serves the shoulder, some thorax muscles, and the upper limb. It arises primarily from C_5–T_1. Proximal to distal, the brachial plexus has roots, trunks, divisions, and cords. The main nerves arising from the cords are the axillary, musculo-cutaneous, median, radial, and ulnar nerves.
8. The lumbar plexus (L_1–L_4) provides the motor supply to the an-terior and medial thigh muscles and the cutaneous supply to the anterior thigh and part of the leg. Its chief nerves are the femoral and obturator.
9. The sacral plexus (L_4–S_4) supplies the posterior muscles and skin of the lower limb. Its principal nerve is the large sciatic nerve composed of the tibial and common fibular nerves.
10. Joints are innervated by the same nerves that serve the muscles acting at the joint. All spinal nerves except C_1 innervate specific segments of the skin called dermatomes.

PART 3: MOTOR ENDINGS AND MOTOR ACTIVITY

Peripheral Motor Endings   (p. 512)

1. Motor endings of somatic nerve fibers (axon terminals) help to form elaborate neuromuscular junctions with skeletal muscle cells. Axon terminals contain synaptic vesicles filled with acetyl-choline, which (when released) signals the muscle cell to contract. An elaborate basal lamina fills the synaptic cleft.
2. Autonomic motor endings, called varicosities, are functionally similar, but structurally simpler, beaded terminals that innervate smooth muscle and glands. They do not form specialized neuro-muscular junctions and the motor responses elicited are generally slower.

Motor Integration: From Intention to Effect   (pp. 512–513)

1. Motor mechanisms operate at the level of the effectors (muscle fibers), descending circuits, and control levels of motor behavior.
2. The motor control hierarchy consists of the segmental level, the projection level, and the precommand level.
3. The segmental level is the spinal cord circuitry that activates ven-tral horn motor neurons to stimulate the muscles. It consists of reflexes and central pattern generators (CPGs), segmental circuits controlling locomotion.
4. The projection level consists of descending fibers that project to and control the segmental level. These fibers issue from the brain stem motor areas [indirect (extrapyramidal) system] and corti-cal motor areas [direct (pyramidal) system]. Command neurons in the brain stem appear to turn CPGs on and off, or to modu-late them.
5. The cerebellum and basal nuclei constitute the precommand ar-eas that subconsciously integrate mechanisms mediated by the projection level.

PART 4: REFLEX ACTIVITY

The Reflex Arc   (p. 514)

1. A reflex is a rapid, involuntary motor response to a stimulus. The reflex arc has five elements: receptor, sensory neuron, integration center, motor neuron, and effector.

Spinal Reflexes   (pp. 514–520)

1. Testing of somatic spinal reflexes provides information on the in-tegrity of the reflex pathway and the degree of excitability of the spinal cord.
2. Somatic spinal reflexes include stretch, Golgi tendon, flexor, crossed-extensor, and superficial reflexes.
3. A stretch reflex, initiated by stretching of muscle spindles, causes contraction of the stimulated muscle and inhibits its antagonist. It is monosynaptic and ipsilateral. Stretch reflexes maintain mus-cle tone and body posture.
4. Golgi tendon reflexes, initiated by stimulation of Golgi tendon organs by excessive muscle tension, are polysynaptic reflexes. They cause relaxation of the stimulated muscle and contraction of its antagonist to prevent muscle and tendon damage.
5. Flexor reflexes are initiated by painful stimuli. They are polysyn-aptic, ipsilateral reflexes that are protective in nature.
6. Crossed-extensor reflexes consist of an ipsilateral flexor reflex and a contralateral extensor reflex.
7. Superficial reflexes (e.g., the plantar and abdominal reflexes) are elicited by cutaneous stimulation. They require functional cord reflex arcs and corticospinal pathways.

Developmental Aspects of the Peripheral Nervous System   (p. 520)

1. Each spinal nerve provides the sensory and motor supply of an adjacent muscle mass (destined to become skeletal muscles) and the cutaneous supply of a dermatome (skin segment).
2. Reflexes decline in speed with age; this probably reflects neuronal loss or sluggish CNS integration circuits.

REVIEW QUESTIONS

Multiple Choice/Matching

(Some questions have more than one correct answer. Select the best answer or answers from the choices given.)

1. The large onion-shaped receptors that are found deep in the dermis and in subcutaneous tissue and that respond to deep pressure are (**a**) tactile discs, (**b**) Pacinian corpuscles, (**c**) free nerve endings, (**d**) muscle spindles.

2. Proprioceptors include all of the following except (**a**) muscle spindles, (**b**) Golgi tendon organs, (**c**) tactile discs, (**d**) joint kinesthetic receptors.

3. The aspect of sensory perception by which the cerebral cortex identifies the site or pattern of stimulation is (**a**) perceptual detection, (**b**) feature abstraction, (**c**) pattern recognition, (**d**) spatial discrimination.

4. The neural machinery of the spinal cord is at the (**a**) precommand level, (**b**) projection level, (**c**) segmental level.

5. Dorsal root ganglia contain (**a**) cell bodies of somatic motor neurons, (**b**) axon terminals of somatic motor neurons, (**c**) cell bodies of autonomic motor neurons, (**d**) axon terminals of sensory neurons, (**e**) cell bodies of sensory neurons.

6. The connective tissue sheath that surrounds a fascicle of nerve fibers is the (**a**) epineurium, (**b**) endoneurium, (**c**) perineurium, (**d**) neurilemma.

7. Match the receptor type in column B to the correct description in column A.

Column A	Column B
____ (**1**) pain, itch, and temperature receptors	(**a**) Ruffini endings
____ (**2**) contains intrafusal fibers and type Ia and II sensory endings	(**b**) Golgi tendon organ
	(**c**) muscle spindle
	(**d**) free nerve endings
____ (**3**) discriminative touch receptor in hairless skin (fingertips)	(**e**) Pacinian corpuscle
	(**f**) Meissner's corpuscle
____ (**4**) contains receptor endings wrapped around thick collagen bundles	
____ (**5**) rapidly adapting deep-pressure receptor	
____ (**6**) slowly adapting deep-pressure receptor	

8. Match the names of the cranial nerves in column B to the appropriate description in column A.

Column A	Column B
____ (**1**) causes pupillary constriction	(**a**) abducens
____ (**2**) is the major sensory nerve of the face	(**b**) accessory
	(**c**) facial
____ (**3**) serves the sternocleidomastoid and trapezius muscles	(**d**) glossopharyngeal
	(**e**) hypoglossal
____ (**4**) are purely sensory (two nerves)	(**f**) oculomotor
	(**g**) olfactory
____ (**5**) serves the tongue muscles	(**h**) optic
	(**i**) trigeminal
	(**j**) trochlear
	(**k**) vagus

____ (**6**) allows you to chew your food   (**l**) vestibulocochlear

____ (**7**) is impaired in Bell's palsy

____ (**8**) helps to regulate heart activity

____ (**9**) helps you to hear and to maintain your balance

____, ____, ____, ____, (**10**) (contain parasympathetic motor fibers (four nerves)

9. For each of the following muscles or body regions, identify the plexus and the peripheral nerve(s) (or branch of one) involved. Use choices from keys A and B.

____ ; ____ (**1**) the diaphragm

____ ; ____ (**2**) muscles of the posterior leg

____ ; ____ (**3**) anterior thigh muscles

____ ; ____ (**4**) medial thigh muscles

____ ; ____ (**5**) anterior arm muscles that flex the forearm

____ ; ____ (**6**) muscles that flex the wrist and digits (two nerves)

____ ; ____ (**7**) muscles that extend the wrist and digits

____ ; ____ (**8**) skin and extensor muscles of the posterior arm

____ ; ____ (**9**) fibularis muscles, tibialis anterior, and toe extensors

____ ; ____ , ____ , ____ , ____ (**10**) elbow joint

Key A: Plexuses
(**a**) brachial
(**b**) cervical
(**c**) lumbar
(**d**) sacral

Key B: Nerves
(**1**) common fibular
(**2**) femoral
(**3**) median
(**4**) musculocutaneous
(**5**) obturator
(**6**) phrenic
(**7**) radial
(**8**) tibial
(**9**) ulnar

10. Characterize each receptor activity described below by choosing the appropriate letter and number(s) from keys A and B.

____ , ____ (**1**) You are enjoying an ice cream cone.

____ , ____ (**2**) You have just scalded yourself with hot coffee.

____ , ____ (**3**) The retinas of your eyes are stimulated.

____ , ____ (**4**) You bump (lightly) into someone.

____ , ____ (**5**) You are in a completely dark room and reaching toward the light switch.

____ , ____ (**6**) You feel uncomfortable after a large meal.

Key A:
(**a**) exteroceptor
(**b**) interoceptor
(**c**) proprioceptor

Key B:
(**1**) chemoreceptor
(**2**) mechanoreceptor
(**3**) nociceptor
(**4**) photoreceptor
(**5**) thermoreceptor

13

11. A reflex that causes reciprocal activation of the antagonist muscle is the **(a)** crossed-extensor, **(b)** flexor, **(c)** Golgi tendon, **(d)** muscle stretch.

Short Answer Essay Questions

12. What is the functional relationship of the peripheral nervous system to the central nervous system?

13. List the structural components of the peripheral nervous system, and describe the function of each component.

14. Differentiate clearly between sensation and perception.

15. Central pattern generators (CPGs) are found at the segmental level of motor control. (a) What is the job of the CPGs? (b) What controls them, and where is this control localized?

16. Make a diagram of the hierarchy of motor control. Position the CPGs, the command neurons, and the cerebellum and basal nuclei in this scheme.

17. Why are the cerebellum and basal nuclei called precommand areas?

18. Explain why damage to peripheral nerve fibers is often reversible, whereas damage to CNS fibers rarely is.

19. (a) Describe the formation and composition of a spinal nerve. (b) Name the branches of a spinal nerve (other than the rami communicantes), and indicate their distribution.

20. (a) Define plexus. (b) Indicate the spinal roots of origin of the four major nerve plexuses, and name the general body regions served by each.

21. Differentiate between ipsilateral and contralateral reflexes.

22. What is the homeostatic value of flexor reflexes?

23. Compare and contrast flexor and crossed-extensor reflexes.

24. Explain how a crossed-extensor reflex exemplifies both serial and parallel processing.

25. What clinical information can be gained by conducting somatic reflex tests?

26. What is the structural and functional relationship between spinal nerves, skeletal muscles, and dermatomes?

Critical Thinking and Clinical Application Questions

1. In 1962 a boy playing in a train yard fell under a train. His right arm was cut off cleanly by the train wheel. Surgeons reattached the arm, sewing nerves and vessels back together. The boy was told he should eventually regain the use of his arm but that it would never be strong enough to pitch a baseball. Explain why full recovery of strength was unlikely.

2. Jefferson, a football quarterback, suffered torn menisci in his right knee joint when tackled from the side. The same injury crushed his common fibular nerve against the head of the fibula. What locomotor problems did Jefferson have after this?

3. As Harry fell off a ladder, he grabbed a tree branch with his right hand, but unfortunately lost his grip and fell heavily to the ground. Days later, Harry complained that his upper limb was numb. What was damaged in his fall?

4. Mr. Frank, a former stroke victim who had made a remarkable recovery, suddenly began to have problems reading. He complained of seeing double and also had problems navigating steps. He was unable to move his left eye downward and laterally. What cranial nerve was the site of lesion? (Right or left?)

5. One of a group of rabbit hunters was accidentally sprayed with buckshot in both of his gluteal prominences. When his companions saw that he would survive, they laughed and joked about where he had been shot. They were horrified and ashamed a week later when it was announced that their friend would be permanently paralyzed and without sensation in both legs from the knee down, as well as on the back of his thighs. What had happened?

6. You are at a party at Mary's house. After you are blindfolded, an object (a key *or* a rabbit's foot) is placed in your hand. What spinal tracts carry the signals to the cortex that will allow you to differentiate between these objects, and what aspects of sensory perception are operating?

7. Fumiko, a 19-year-old nursing student, had had a runny nose and sore throat for several days. Upon waking, her face felt "twisted." When she examined her face in the mirror, she noticed that the right side looked "droopy" and she was unable to move the facial muscles on that side. This made it difficult to eat or speak clearly. Which cranial nerve was affected and on which side? What is a common cause of this condition?

13

14

The Autonomic Nervous System

Introduction (pp. 526–528)

Comparison of the Somatic and Autonomic Nervous Systems (pp. 526–527)

ANS Divisions (pp. 527–528)

ANS Anatomy (pp. 528–535)

Parasympathetic (Craniosacral) Division (pp. 529–530)

Sympathetic (Thoracolumbar) Division (pp. 530–534)

Visceral Reflexes (pp. 534–535)

ANS Physiology (pp. 535–540)

Neurotransmitters and Receptors (pp. 535–536)

The Effects of Drugs (p. 536)

Interactions of the Autonomic Divisions (pp. 536–539)

Control of Autonomic Functioning (pp. 539–540)

Homeostatic Imbalances of the ANS (pp. 540–541)

Developmental Aspects of the ANS (p. 541)

The human body is exquisitely sensitive to changes in its internal environment, and engages in a lifelong struggle to balance competing demands for resources under ever-changing conditions. Although all body systems contribute, the stability of our internal environment depends largely on the **autonomic nervous system (ANS)**, the system of motor neurons that innervates smooth and cardiac muscle and glands (Figure 14.1).

At every moment, signals stream from visceral organs into the CNS, and autonomic nerves make adjustments as necessary to ensure optimal support for body activities. In response to changing conditions, the ANS shunts blood to "needy" areas, speeds or slows heart rate, adjusts

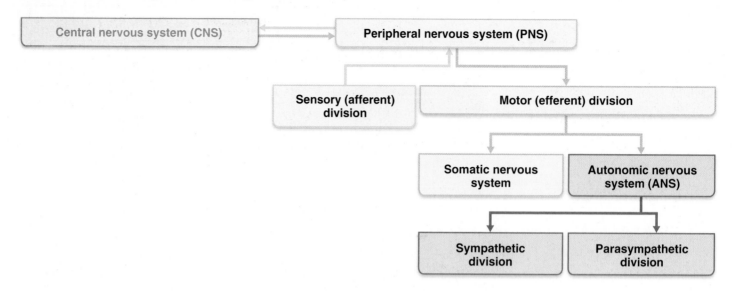

Figure 14.1 **Place of the ANS in the structural organization of the nervous system.**

blood pressure and body temperature, and increases or decreases stomach secretions.

Most of this fine-tuning occurs without our awareness or attention. Can you tell when your arteries are constricting or when your pupils are dilating? Probably not, but if you've ever been stuck in a checkout line, and your full bladder was contracting as if it had a mind of its own, you've been very aware of a visceral activity. These functions, both those we're aware of and those that occur without our awareness or attention, are controlled by the ANS. Indeed, as the term *autonomic* (*auto* = self; *nom* = govern) implies, this motor subdivision of the peripheral nervous system has a certain amount of functional independence. The ANS is also called the **involuntary nervous system**, which reflects its subconscious control, or the **general visceral motor system**, which indicates the location of most of its effectors.

Introduction

▶ Define autonomic nervous system and explain its relationship to the peripheral nervous system.

▶ Compare the somatic and autonomic nervous systems relative to effectors, efferent pathways, and neurotransmitters released.

▶ Compare and contrast the functions of the parasympathetic and sympathetic divisions.

Comparison of the Somatic and Autonomic Nervous Systems

In our previous discussions of motor nerves, we have focused largely on the activity of the somatic nervous system. So, before describing autonomic nervous system anatomy, we will point out the major differences between the somatic and autonomic systems as well as some areas of functional overlap.

Both systems have motor fibers, but the somatic and autonomic nervous systems differ (1) in their effectors, (2) in their efferent pathways, and (3) to some degree in target organ responses to their neurotransmitters. Consult Figure 14.2 for a summary of the differences as we discuss them next.

Effectors

The somatic nervous system stimulates skeletal muscles, whereas the ANS innervates cardiac and smooth muscle and glands. Differences in the physiology of the effector organs account for most of the remaining differences between somatic and autonomic effects on their target organs.

Efferent Pathways and Ganglia

In the somatic nervous system, the motor neuron cell bodies are in the CNS, and their axons extend in spinal or cranial nerves all the way to the skeletal muscles they activate. Somatic motor fibers are typically thick, heavily myelinated group A fibers that conduct nerve impulses rapidly.

In contrast, the ANS uses a *two-neuron chain* to its effectors. The cell body of the first neuron, the **preganglionic neuron**, resides in the brain or spinal cord. Its axon, the **preganglionic axon**, synapses with the second motor neuron, the **ganglionic neuron**, in an **autonomic ganglion** outside the CNS. The axon of the ganglionic neuron, called the **postganglionic axon**, extends to the effector organ. If you think about the meanings of all these terms while referring to Figure 14.2, understanding the rest of the chapter will be much easier.

Preganglionic axons are lightly myelinated, thin fibers, and postganglionic axons are even thinner and are unmyelinated. Consequently, conduction through the autonomic efferent chain is slower than conduction in the somatic motor system. For most of their course, many pre- and postganglionic fibers are incorporated into spinal or cranial nerves.

Keep in mind that autonomic ganglia are *motor* ganglia, containing the cell bodies of motor neurons. Technically, they are sites of synapse and information transmission from preganglionic to ganglionic neurons. Also, remember that the somatic

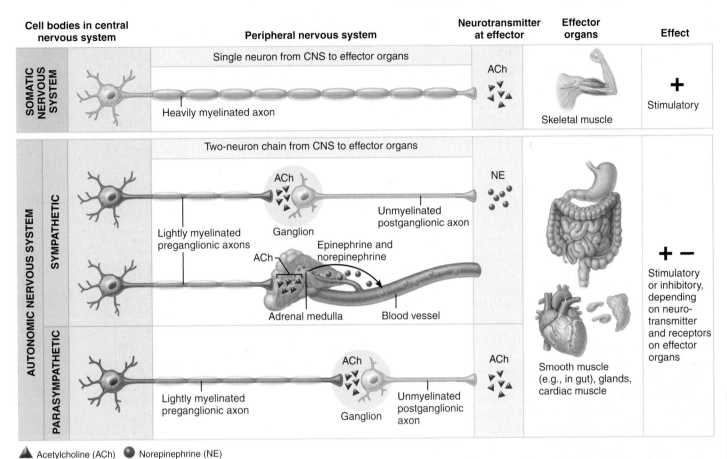

Cell bodies in central nervous system	Peripheral nervous system		Neurotransmitter at effector	Effector organs	Effect

SOMATIC NERVOUS SYSTEM

Single neuron from CNS to effector organs

Heavily myelinated axon

ACh

Skeletal muscle

+ Stimulatory

AUTONOMIC NERVOUS SYSTEM

SYMPATHETIC

Two-neuron chain from CNS to effector organs

ACh

Ganglion

Lightly myelinated preganglionic axons

Unmyelinated postganglionic axon

NE

ACh

Epinephrine and norepinephrine

Adrenal medulla   Blood vessel

PARASYMPATHETIC

Lightly myelinated preganglionic axon

ACh

Ganglion

Unmyelinated postganglionic axon

ACh

Smooth muscle (e.g., in gut), glands, cardiac muscle

+ − Stimulatory or inhibitory, depending on neurotransmitter and receptors on effector organs

▲ Acetylcholine (ACh)   ● Norepinephrine (NE)

Figure 14.2 Comparison of somatic and autonomic nervous systems.

motor division *lacks* ganglia entirely. The dorsal root ganglia are part of the sensory, not the motor, division of the PNS.

Neurotransmitter Effects

All somatic motor neurons release **acetylcholine (ACh)** at their synapses with skeletal muscle fibers. The effect is always *excitatory*, and if stimulation reaches threshold, the muscle fibers contract.

Neurotransmitters released onto visceral effector organs by postganglionic autonomic fibers include **norepinephrine (NE)** secreted by most sympathetic fibers, and ACh released by parasympathetic fibers. Depending on the type of receptors present on the target organ, the organ's response may be either excitation or inhibition (Figure 14.2; see Table 14.2 on p. 536).

Overlap of Somatic and Autonomic Function

Higher brain centers regulate and coordinate both somatic and autonomic motor activities, and nearly all spinal nerves (and many cranial nerves) contain both somatic and autonomic fibers. Moreover, most of the body's adaptations to changing internal and external conditions involve both skeletal muscle activity and enhanced responses of certain visceral organs. For example, when skeletal muscles are working hard, they need more oxygen and glucose and so autonomic control mecha-

nisms speed up heart rate and dilate airways to meet these needs and maintain homeostasis.

The ANS is only one part of our highly integrated nervous system, but according to convention we will consider it an individual entity and describe its role in isolation in the sections that follow.

ANS Divisions

The two arms of the ANS, the *parasympathetic* and *sympathetic divisions*, generally serve the same visceral organs but cause essentially opposite effects. If one division stimulates certain smooth muscles to contract or a gland to secrete, the other division inhibits that action. Through this **dual innervation**, the two divisions counterbalance each other's activities to keep body systems running smoothly. The sympathetic division mobilizes the body during activity, whereas the parasympathetic arm promotes maintenance functions and conserves body energy. Let's elaborate on these functional differences by focusing briefly on extreme situations in which each division is exerting primary control.

Role of the Parasympathetic Division

The **parasympathetic division**, sometimes called the "resting and digesting" system, keeps body energy use as low as possible, even as it directs vital "housekeeping" activities like digestion and elimination of feces and urine. (This explains why it is a good idea to relax after a heavy meal: so that digestion is not interfered with by sympathetic activity.) Parasympathetic activity is best illustrated in a person who relaxes after a meal and reads the newspaper. Blood pressure and heart rate are regulated at low normal levels, and the gastrointestinal tract is actively digesting food. In the eyes, the pupils are constricted and the lenses are accommodated for close vision to improve the clarity of the close-up image.

Role of the Sympathetic Division

The **sympathetic division** is often referred to as the "fight-or-flight" system. Its activity is evident when we are excited or find ourselves in emergency or threatening situations, such as being frightened by street toughs late at night. A rapidly pounding heart; deep breathing; dry mouth; cold, sweaty skin; and dilated eye pupils are sure signs of sympathetic nervous system mobilization. Not as obvious, but equally characteristic, are changes in brain wave patterns and in the electrical resistance of the skin (galvanic skin resistance)—events that are recorded during lie detector examinations.

During any type of vigorous physical activity, the sympathetic division also promotes a number of other adjustments. Visceral (and sometimes cutaneous) blood vessels are constricted, and blood is shunted to active skeletal muscles and the vigorously working heart. The bronchioles in the lungs dilate, increasing ventilation (and ultimately increasing oxygen delivery to body cells), and the liver releases more glucose into the blood to accommodate the increased energy needs of body cells.

At the same time, temporarily nonessential activities, such as gastrointestinal tract motility, are damped. If you are running from a mugger, digesting lunch can wait! It is far more important that your muscles be provided with everything they need to get you out of danger. In such active situations, the sympathetic division generates a head of steam that enables the body to cope with situations that threaten homeostasis. Its function is to provide the optimal conditions for an appropriate response to some threat, whether that response is to run, to see better, or to think more clearly.

We have just looked at two extreme situations in which one or the other branch of the ANS dominates. An easy way to remember the most important roles of the two ANS divisions is to think of the parasympathetic division as the **D** division [digestion, defecation, and diuresis (urination)], and the sympathetic division as the **E** division (exercise, excitement, emergency, embarrassment). A more detailed summary of the effects of each division on various organs is presented in Table 14.4 (p. 538).

Remember, however, that while we may find it easy to think of the two ANS divisions as working in an all-or-none fashion as described above, this is rarely the case. A dynamic antagonism exists between the divisions, and fine adjustments are made continuously by both.

CHECK YOUR UNDERSTANDING

1. Name the three types of effectors of the autonomic nervous system.

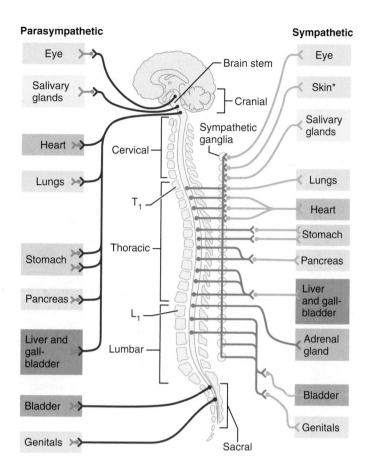

Figure 14.3 Overview of the subdivisions of the ANS. The parasympathetic and sympathetic divisions differ anatomically in (1) the sites of origin of their nerves, (2) the relative lengths of their preganglionic and postganglionic fibers, and (3) the locations of their ganglia (indicated here by synapse sites).

*Although sympathetic innervation to the skin is mapped to the cervical region here, all nerves to the periphery carry postganglionic sympathetic fibers.

2. Which relays instructions from the CNS to muscles more quickly, the somatic nervous system or the ANS? Explain why.

3. Which branch of the ANS would predominate if you were lying on the beach enjoying the sun and the sound of the waves? Which branch would predominate if you were on a surfboard and a shark appeared within a few feet of you?

For answers, see Appendix G.

ANS Anatomy

▶ For the parasympathetic and sympathetic divisions, describe the site of CNS origin, locations of ganglia, and general fiber pathways.

Anatomically, the sympathetic and parasympathetic divisions differ in

1. Their origin sites. Parasympathetic fibers emerge from the brain and sacral spinal cord (are craniosacral). Sympathetic fibers originate in the thoracolumbar region of the spinal cord.

2. **The relative lengths of their fibers.** The parasympathetic division has long preganglionic and short postganglionic fibers. The sympathetic division has the opposite condition.

3. **The location of their ganglia.** Most parasympathetic ganglia are located in the visceral effector organs. Sympathetic ganglia lie close to the spinal cord.

Note that these and other differences are illustrated in Figure 14.3 and summarized in **Table 14.1**, p. 534.

We begin our detailed exploration of the ANS with the anatomically simpler parasympathetic division.

Parasympathetic (Craniosacral) Division

The parasympathetic division is also called the **craniosacral division** because its preganglionic fibers spring from opposite ends of the CNS—the brain stem and the sacral region of the spinal cord (Figure 14.4). The preganglionic axons extend from the CNS nearly all the way to the structures to be innervated. There the axons synapse with ganglionic neurons located in **terminal ganglia** that lie very close to or within the target organs. Very short postganglionic axons issue from the terminal ganglia and synapse with effector cells in their immediate area.

Cranial Outflow

Preganglionic fibers run in the oculomotor, facial, glossopharyngeal, and vagus cranial nerves. Their cell bodies lie in associated motor cranial-nerve nuclei in the brain stem (see Figures 12.15 and 12.16). We describe the precise locations of the neurons of the cranial parasympathetics next.

1. **Oculomotor nerves (III).** The parasympathetic fibers of the oculomotor nerves innervate smooth muscles in the eyes that cause the pupils to constrict and the lenses to bulge— actions needed to focus on close objects. The preganglionic axons found in the oculomotor nerves issue from the *accessory oculomotor (Edinger-Westphal) nuclei* in the midbrain. The cell bodies of the ganglionic neurons are in the **ciliary ganglia** within the eye orbits (see Table 13.2, p. 496).

2. **Facial nerves (VII).** The parasympathetic fibers of the facial nerves stimulate many large glands in the head. Fibers that activate the nasal glands and the lacrimal glands of the eyes originate in the *lacrimal nuclei of the pons*. The preganglionic fibers synapse with ganglionic neurons in the **pterygopalatine ganglia** (ter″eh-go-pal′ah-tīn) just posterior to the maxillae. The preganglionic neurons that stimulate the submandibular and sublingual salivary glands originate in the *superior salivatory nuclei* of the pons and synapse with ganglionic neurons in the **submandibular ganglia**, deep to the mandibular angles (see Table 13.2, p. 498).

3. **Glossopharyngeal nerves (IX).** The parasympathetics in the glossopharyngeal nerves originate in the *inferior salivatory nuclei* of the medulla and synapse in the **otic ganglia**, located just inferior to the foramen ovale of the skull. The

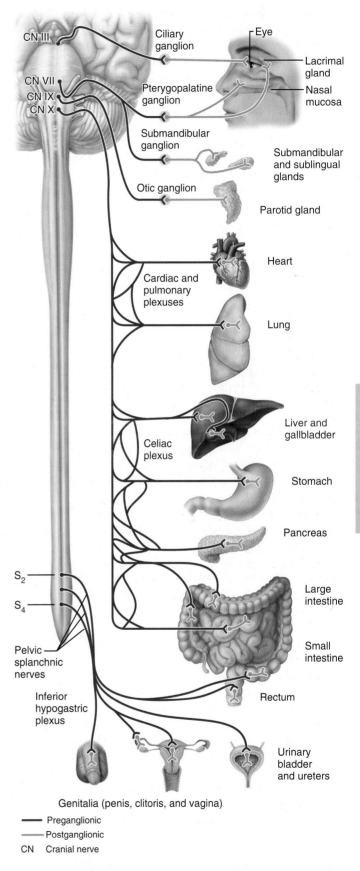

Figure 14.4 Parasympathetic division of the ANS.

postganglionic fibers course to and activate the parotid salivary glands anterior to the ears (see Table 13.2, p. 500).

Cranial nerves III, VII, and IX supply the entire parasympathetic innervation of the head; however, only the *preganglionic fibers* lie within these three pairs of cranial nerves—postganglionic fibers do not. Many of the postganglionic fibers "hitch a ride" with branches of the *trigeminal nerve* (V), taking advantage of its wide distribution, while others travel independently to their destinations.

4. **Vagus nerves (X).** The remaining and major portion of the parasympathetic cranial outflow is via the vagus (X) nerves. Between them, the two vagus nerves account for about 90% of all preganglionic parasympathetic fibers in the body. They provide fibers to the neck and to nerve plexuses (interweaving networks of nerves) that serve virtually every organ in the thoracic and abdominal cavities. The vagal nerve fibers (preganglionic axons) arise mostly from the *dorsal motor nuclei* of the medulla and synapse in terminal ganglia usually located in the walls of the target organ. Most terminal ganglia are not individually named. Instead they are collectively called *intramural ganglia*, literally, "ganglia within the walls."

As the vagus nerves pass into the thorax, they send branches to the **cardiac plexuses** supplying fibers to the heart that slow heart rate, the **pulmonary plexuses** serving the lungs and bronchi, and the **esophageal plexuses** (ĕ-sof″ah-je′al) supplying the esophagus.

When the main trunks of the vagus nerves reach the esophagus, their fibers intermingle, forming the **anterior** and **posterior vagal trunks**, each containing fibers from both vagus nerves. These vagal trunks then "ride" the esophagus down to the abdominal cavity. There they send fibers *through* the large **abdominal aortic plexus** [formed by a number of smaller plexuses (e.g., *celiac*, *superior mesenteric*, and *hypogastric*) that run along the aorta] before giving off branches to the abdominal viscera. The vagus nerves innervate the liver, gallbladder, stomach, small intestine, kidneys, pancreas, and the proximal half of the large intestine.

Sacral Outflow

The rest of the large intestine and the pelvic organs are served by the sacral outflow, which arises from neurons located in the lateral gray matter of spinal cord segments S_2–S_4. Axons of these neurons run in the ventral roots of the spinal nerves to the ventral rami and then branch off to form the **pelvic splanchnic nerves**, which pass through the **inferior hypogastric (pelvic) plexus** in the pelvic floor (Figure 14.4). Some preganglionic fibers synapse with ganglia in this plexus, but most synapse in intramural ganglia in the walls of the following organs: distal half of the large intestine, urinary bladder, ureters, and reproductive organs.

Sympathetic (Thoracolumbar) Division

The sympathetic division is anatomically more complex than the parasympathetic division, partly because it innervates more organs. It supplies not only the visceral organs in the internal body cavities but also all visceral structures in the superficial (somatic) part of the body. This sounds impossible, but there is an explanation—some glands and smooth muscle structures in the soma (sweat glands and the hair-raising arrector pili muscles of the skin) require autonomic innervation and are served only by sympathetic fibers. In addition, all arteries and veins (be they deep or superficial) have smooth muscle in their walls that is innervated by sympathetic fibers. But we will explain these matters later—let us get on with the anatomy of the sympathetic division.

All preganglionic fibers of the sympathetic division arise from cell bodies of preganglionic neurons in spinal cord segments T_1 through L_2 (Figure 14.3). For this reason, the sympathetic division is also referred to as the **thoracolumbar division** (tho″rah-ko-lum′bar). The presence of numerous preganglionic sympathetic neurons in the gray matter of the spinal cord produces the **lateral horns**—the so-called **visceral motor zones** (see Figures 12.31b, p. 469, and 12.32, p. 470). The lateral horns are just posterolateral to the ventral horns that house somatic motor neurons. (Parasympathetic preganglionic neurons in the sacral cord are far less abundant than the comparable sympathetic neurons in the thoracolumbar regions, and *lateral horns are absent* in the sacral region of the spinal cord. This is a major anatomical difference between the two divisions.)

After leaving the cord via the ventral root, preganglionic sympathetic fibers pass through a **white ramus communicans** [plural: **rami communicantes** (kom-mu′nĭ-kan″tēz)] to enter an adjoining **sympathetic trunk ganglion** forming part of the **sympathetic trunk** (or *sympathetic chain*, Figure 14.5). Looking like strands of glistening white beads, the sympathetic trunks flank each side of the vertebral column. The sympathetic trunk ganglia are also called *chain ganglia* or *paravertebral* ("near the vertebrae") *ganglia*.

Although the sympathetic *trunks* extend from neck to pelvis, sympathetic *fibers* arise only from the thoracic and lumbar cord segments, as shown in Figure 14.3. The ganglia vary in size, position, and number, but typically there are 23 in each sympathetic trunk—3 cervical, 11 thoracic, 4 lumbar, 4 sacral, and 1 coccygeal.

Once a preganglionic axon reaches a trunk ganglion, one of three things can happen to the axon, as shown by the three pathways in Figure 14.5b:

① The axon can synapse with a ganglionic neuron in the same trunk ganglion.

② The axon can ascend or descend the sympathetic trunk to synapse in another trunk ganglion. (These fibers running from one ganglion to another connect the ganglia together to form the sympathetic trunk.)

③ The axon can pass through the trunk ganglion and emerge from the sympathetic trunk without synapsing.

Preganglionic fibers following the third pathway help form several *splanchnic nerves* (splank′nik) that synapse in **collateral**, or **prevertebral**, **ganglia** located anterior to the vertebral column. Unlike sympathetic trunk ganglia, the collateral ganglia are neither paired nor segmentally arranged and occur only in the abdomen and pelvis.

14

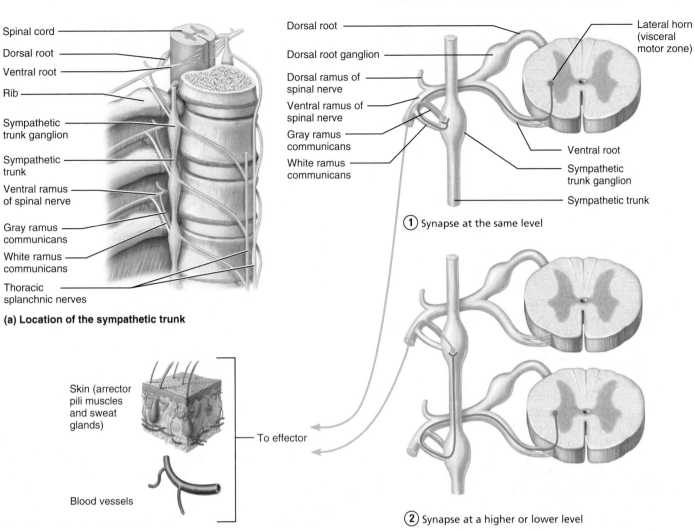

(a) Location of the sympathetic trunk

Spinal cord
Dorsal root
Ventral root
Rib
Sympathetic trunk ganglion
Sympathetic trunk
Ventral ramus of spinal nerve
Gray ramus communicans
White ramus communicans
Thoracic splanchnic nerves

Dorsal root
Dorsal root ganglion
Dorsal ramus of spinal nerve
Ventral ramus of spinal nerve
Gray ramus communicans
White ramus communicans
Lateral horn (visceral motor zone)
Ventral root
Sympathetic trunk ganglion
Sympathetic trunk

① Synapse at the same level

Skin (arrector pili muscles and sweat glands)

To effector

Blood vessels

② Synapse at a higher or lower level

Figure 14.5 Sympathetic trunks and pathways. (a) Diagram of the right sympathetic trunk in the posterior thorax, along the side of the vertebral column. **(b)** Synapses between preganglionic and ganglionic sympathetic neurons can occur at three different locations—either in a sympathetic trunk ganglion at the same or a different level, or in a collateral ganglion.

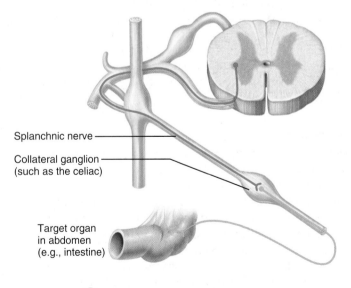

Splanchnic nerve
Collateral ganglion (such as the celiac)

Target organ in abdomen (e.g., intestine)

③ Synapse in a distant collateral ganglion anterior to the vertebral column

(b) Three pathways of sympathetic innervation

14

Regardless of where the synapse occurs, all sympathetic ganglia are close to the spinal cord, and their postganglionic fibers are typically much longer than their preganglionic fibers. Recall that the opposite condition exists in the parasympathetic division, an important anatomical distinction.

Pathways with Synapses in Trunk Ganglia

When synapses are made in sympathetic trunk ganglia, the postganglionic axons enter the ventral (or dorsal) ramus of the adjoining spinal nerves by way of communicating branches called **gray rami communicantes** (Figure 14.5). From there they travel via branches of the rami to their effectors, including sweat glands and arrector pili muscles of the skin. Anywhere along their path, the postganglionic axons may transfer over to nearby blood vessels and innervate the vascular smooth muscle all the way to their final branches.

Notice that the naming of the rami communicantes as *white* or *gray* reflects their appearance, revealing whether or not their fibers are myelinated (and has no relationship to the white and gray matter of the CNS). Preganglionic fibers composing the white rami are myelinated. Postganglionic axons forming the gray rami are not.

The white rami, which carry preganglionic axons to the sympathetic trunks, are found only in the T_1–L_2 cord segments, regions of sympathetic outflow. However, gray rami carrying postganglionic fibers headed for the periphery issue from every trunk ganglion from the cervical to the sacral region, allowing sympathetic output to reach all parts of the body. Note that *rami communicantes are associated only with the sympathetic division* and never carry parasympathetic fibers.

Pathways to the Head   Sympathetic preganglionic fibers serving the head emerge from spinal cord segments T_1–T_4 and ascend the sympathetic trunk to synapse with ganglionic neurons in the **superior cervical ganglion** (Figure 14.6). This ganglion contributes sympathetic fibers that run in several cranial nerves and with the upper three or four cervical spinal nerves. Besides serving the skin and blood vessels of the head, its fibers stimulate the dilator muscles of the irises of the eyes, inhibit the nasal and salivary glands (the reason your mouth goes dry when you are scared), and innervate the smooth (tarsal) muscle that lifts the upper eyelid. The superior cervical ganglion also sends direct branches to the heart.

Pathways to the Thorax   Sympathetic preganglionic fibers innervating the thoracic organs originate at T_1–T_6. From there the preganglionic fibers run to synapse in the cervical trunk ganglia. Postganglionic fibers emerging from the **middle** and **inferior cervical ganglia** enter cervical nerves C_4–C_8 (Figure 14.6). Some of these fibers innervate the heart via the cardiac plexus, and some innervate the thyroid gland, but most serve the skin. Additionally, some T_1–T_6 preganglionic fibers synapse in the nearest trunk ganglion, and the postganglionic fibers pass directly to the organ served. Fibers to the heart, aorta, lungs, and esophagus take this direct route. Along the way, they run into the plexuses associated with those organs.

Pathways with Synapses in Collateral Ganglia

Most of the preganglionic fibers from T_5 down synapse in collateral ganglia, and so most of these fibers enter and leave the sympathetic trunks without synapsing. They form several nerves called splanchnic nerves, including the thoracic **splanchnic nerves** (greater, lesser, and least) and the **lumbar** and **sacral splanchnic nerves**.

The splanchnic nerves contribute to a number of interweaving nerve plexuses known collectively as the *abdominal aortic plexus*, which clings to the surface of the abdominal aorta. This complex plexus contains several ganglia that together serve the abdominopelvic viscera (*splanchni* = viscera). From superior to inferior, the most important of these ganglia (and related subplexuses) are the **celiac**, **superior mesenteric**, and **inferior mesenteric**, named for the arteries with which they most closely associate (Figure 14.6). Postganglionic fibers issuing from these ganglia generally travel to their target organs in the company of the arteries serving these organs.

Pathways to the Abdomen   Sympathetic innervation of the abdomen is via preganglionic fibers from T_5 to L_2, which travel in the thoracic splanchnic nerves to synapse mainly at the celiac and superior mesenteric ganglia. Postganglionic fibers issuing from these ganglia serve the stomach, intestines (except the distal half of the large intestine), liver, spleen, and kidneys.

Pathways to the Pelvis   Preganglionic fibers innervating the pelvis originate from T_{10} to L_2 and then descend in the sympathetic trunk to the lumbar and sacral trunk ganglia. Some fibers synapse there and the postganglionic fibers run in lumbar and sacral splanchnic nerves to plexuses on the lower aorta and in the pelvis. Other preganglionic fibers pass directly to these autonomic plexuses and synapse in collateral ganglia, such as the inferior mesenteric ganglion. Postganglionic fibers proceed from these plexuses to the pelvic organs (the urinary bladder and reproductive organs) and also the distal half of the large intestine. For the most part, sympathetic fibers *inhibit* the activity of the muscles and glands in these visceral organs.

Pathways with Synapses in the Adrenal Medulla

Some fibers traveling in the thoracic splanchnic nerves pass through the celiac ganglion without synapsing and terminate by synapsing with the hormone-producing medullary cells of the adrenal gland (Figure 14.6). When stimulated by preganglionic fibers, the medullary cells secrete NE and *epinephrine* (also called *noradrenaline* and *adrenaline*, respectively) into the blood, producing the excitatory effects we have all felt as a "surge of adrenaline." Embryologically, sympathetic ganglia and the adrenal medulla arise from the same tissue. For this reason, the adrenal medulla is sometimes viewed as a "misplaced" sympathetic ganglion, and its hormone-releasing cells, although lacking nerve processes, are considered equivalent to ganglionic sympathetic neurons.

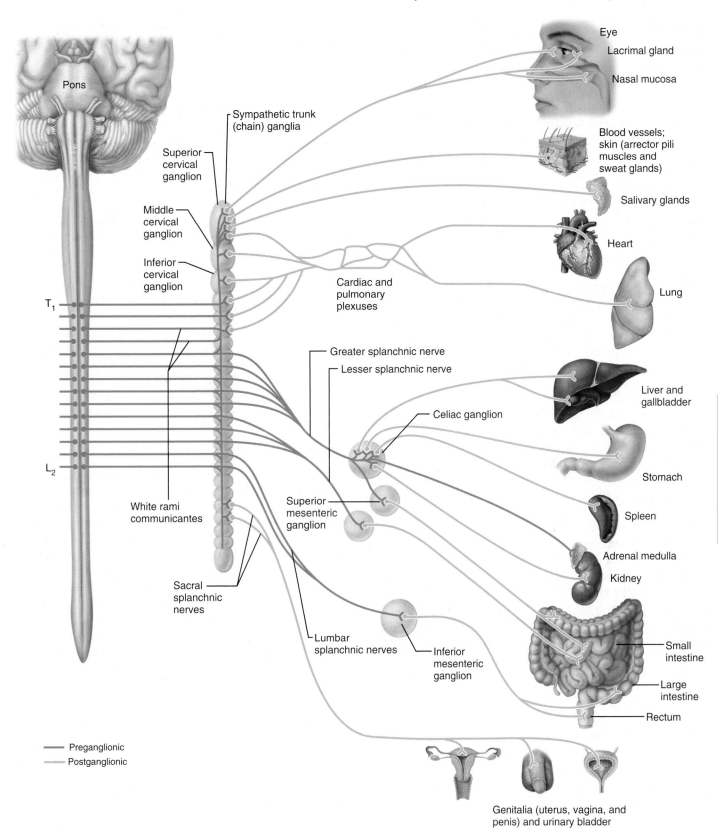

Figure 14.6 Sympathetic division of the ANS. Sympathetic innervation to peripheral structures (blood vessels, glands, and arrector pili muscles) occurs in all areas but is shown only in the cervical area.

TABLE 14.1	Anatomical and Physiological Differences Between the Parasympathetic and Sympathetic Divisions	
CHARACTERISTIC	PARASYMPATHETIC	SYMPATHETIC
Origin	Craniosacral outflow: brain stem nuclei of cranial nerves III, VII, IX, and X; spinal cord segments S_2–S_4.	Thoracolumbar outflow: lateral horns of gray matter of spinal cord segments T_1–L_2.
Location of ganglia	Ganglia (terminal ganglia) are within the visceral organ (intramural) or close to the organ served.	Ganglia are within a few centimeters of CNS: alongside vertebral column (sympathetic trunk ganglia) and anterior to vertebral column (collateral, or prevertebral, ganglia).
Relative length of pre- and postganglionic fibers	Long preganglionic; short postganglionic.	Short preganglionic; long postganglionic.
Rami communicantes	None.	Gray and white rami communicantes. White rami contain myelinated preganglionic fibers; gray contain unmyelinated postganglionic fibers.
Degree of branching of preganglionic fibers	Minimal.	Extensive.
Functional role	Maintenance functions; conserves and stores energy; "rest and digest."	Prepares body for activity; "fight-or-flight."
Neurotransmitters	All preganglionic and postganglionic fibers release ACh (are cholinergic fibers).	All preganglionic fibers release ACh. Most postganglionic fibers release norepinephrine (are adrenergic fibers); postganglionic fibers serving sweat glands and some blood vessels of skeletal muscles release ACh. Neurotransmitter activity is augmented by release of adrenal medullary hormones (norepinephrine and epinephrine).

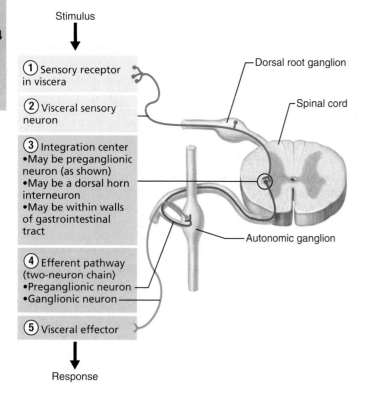

Stimulus

① Sensory receptor in viscera

② Visceral sensory neuron

③ Integration center
• May be preganglionic neuron (as shown)
• May be a dorsal horn interneuron
• May be within walls of gastrointestinal tract

④ Efferent pathway (two-neuron chain)
• Preganglionic neuron
• Ganglionic neuron

⑤ Visceral effector

Response

Dorsal root ganglion

Spinal cord

Autonomic ganglion

Figure 14.7 Visceral reflexes. Visceral reflex arcs have the same five elements as somatic reflex arcs. The visceral afferent (sensory) fibers are found both in spinal nerves (as depicted here) and in autonomic nerves.

Visceral Reflexes

Because most anatomists consider the ANS to be a visceral motor system, the presence of sensory fibers (mostly visceral pain afferents) is often overlooked. However, **visceral sensory neurons**, which send information concerning chemical changes, stretch, and irritation of the viscera, are the first link in autonomic reflexes. **Visceral reflex arcs** have essentially the same components as somatic reflex arcs—receptor, sensory neuron, integration center, motor neuron, effector—except that a visceral reflex arc has *two* neurons in its motor component (**Figure 14.7**; compare with Figure 13.14).

Nearly all the sympathetic and parasympathetic fibers we have described so far are accompanied by afferent fibers conducting sensory impulses from glands or muscles. This means that peripheral processes of visceral sensory neurons are found in cranial nerves VII, IX, and X, splanchnic nerves, and the sympathetic trunk, as well as in spinal nerves.

Like sensory neurons serving somatic structures (skeletal muscles and skin), the cell bodies of visceral sensory neurons are located either in the sensory ganglia of associated cranial nerves or in dorsal root ganglia of the spinal cord. Visceral sensory neurons are also found in sympathetic ganglia where preganglionic neurons synapse.

Furthermore, complete three-neuron reflex arcs (with sensory neurons, interneurons, and motor neurons) exist entirely within the walls of the gastrointestinal tract. Neurons composing these reflex arcs make up the *enteric nervous system*, which plays an important role in controlling gastrointestinal tract activity. We will discuss the enteric nervous system in more detail in Chapter 23.

The fact that visceral pain afferents travel along the same pathways as somatic pain fibers helps explain the phenomenon of **referred pain**, in which pain stimuli arising in the viscera are perceived as somatic in origin. For example, a heart attack may produce a sensation of pain that radiates to the superior thoracic wall and along the medial aspect of the left arm. Because the same spinal segments (T_1–T_5) innervate both the heart and the regions to which pain signals from heart tissue are referred, the brain interprets most such inputs as coming from the more common somatic pathway. Cutaneous areas to which visceral pain is commonly referred are shown in **Figure 14.8**.

CHECK YOUR UNDERSTANDING

4. State whether each of the following is a characteristic of the sympathetic or parasympathetic nervous system: short preganglionic fibers; origin from thoracolumbar region of spinal cord; terminal ganglia; collateral ganglia, innervates adrenal medulla.

5. How does a visceral reflex differ from a somatic reflex?

For answers, see Appendix G.

ANS Physiology

▶ Define cholinergic and adrenergic fibers, and list the different types of their receptors.

▶ Describe the clinical importance of drugs that mimic or inhibit adrenergic or cholinergic effects.

▶ State the effects of the parasympathetic and sympathetic divisions on the following organs: heart, blood vessels, gastrointestinal tract, lungs, adrenal medulla, and external genitalia.

▶ Describe autonomic nervous system controls.

Neurotransmitters and Receptors

The major neurotransmitters released by ANS neurons are *acetylcholine (ACh)* and *norepinephrine (NE)*. ACh, the same neurotransmitter secreted by somatic motor neurons, is released by (1) all ANS preganglionic axons and (2) all parasympathetic postganglionic axons at synapses with their effectors. ACh-releasing fibers are called **cholinergic fibers** (ko″lin-er′jik).

In contrast, most sympathetic postganglionic axons release NE and are classified as **adrenergic fibers** (ad″ren-er′jik). Some exceptions are sympathetic postganglionic fibers innervating sweat glands and some blood vessels in skeletal muscles. These fibers secrete ACh.

Unfortunately for memorization purposes, the effects of ACh and NE on their effectors are not consistently either excitation or inhibition. Why not? The response of visceral effectors to these neurotransmitters depends not only on the neurotransmitter but also on the receptor to which it attaches. The two or more kinds of receptors for each autonomic neurotransmitter allow it to exert different effects (activation or inhibition) at different body targets. **Table 14.2** provides a comprehensive summary of the receptor types that we introduce next.

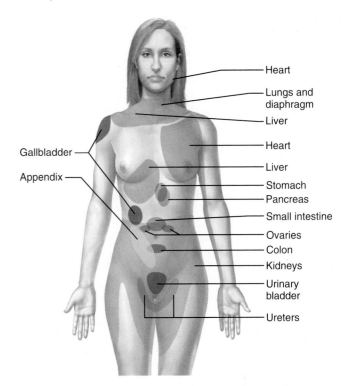

Figure 14.8 Map of referred pain. This map shows the anterior skin areas to which pain is referred from certain visceral organs.

Cholinergic Receptors

The two types of receptors that bind ACh are named for drugs that bind to them and mimic acetylcholine's effects. The first of these receptors identified were the **nicotinic receptors** (nik″o-tin′ik), which respond to nicotine. A mushroom poison, *muscarine* (mus′kah-rin), activates a different set of ACh receptors, named **muscarinic receptors**. All ACh receptors are either nicotinic or muscarinic.

Nicotinic receptors are found on (1) the sarcolemma of skeletal muscle cells at neuromuscular junctions (which, as you will recall, are somatic and not autonomic targets), (2) *all* ganglionic neurons, both sympathetic and parasympathetic, and (3) the hormone-producing cells of the adrenal medulla. The effect of ACh binding to nicotinic receptors anywhere is *always* stimulatory. Just as at the sarcolemma of skeletal muscle (examined in Chapter 9), ACh binding to any nicotinic receptor directly opens ion channels, depolarizing the postsynaptic cell.

Muscarinic receptors occur on all effector cells stimulated by postganglionic cholinergic fibers—that is, all parasympathetic target organs and a few sympathetic targets, such as eccrine sweat glands and some blood vessels of skeletal muscles. The effect of ACh binding to muscarinic receptors can be either inhibitory or stimulatory, depending on the subclass of muscarinic receptor found on the target organ. For example, binding of ACh to cardiac muscle receptors slows heart activity, whereas ACh binding to receptors on smooth muscle of the gastrointestinal tract increases its motility.

14

TABLE 14.2	Cholinergic and Adrenergic Receptors			
NEUROTRANSMITTER	RECEPTOR TYPE	MAJOR LOCATIONS*		EFFECT OF BINDING
Acetylcholine	**Cholinergic**			
	Nicotinic	All ganglionic neurons; adrenal medullary cells (also neuromuscular junctions of skeletal muscle)		Excitation
	Muscarinic	All parasympathetic target organs		Excitation in most cases; inhibition of cardiac muscle
		Limited sympathetic targets:		
			▪ Eccrine sweat glands	Activation
			▪ Blood vessels in skeletal muscles	Vasodilation (may not occur in humans)
Norepinephrine (and epinephrine released by adrenal medulla)	**Adrenergic**			
	β_1	Heart predominantly, but also kidneys and adipose tissue		Increases heart rate and strength; stimulates renin release by kidneys
	β_2	Lungs and most other sympathetic target organs; abundant on blood vessels serving the heart, liver and skeletal muscle		Effects mostly inhibitory; dilates blood vessels and bronchioles; relaxes smooth muscle walls of digestive and urinary visceral organs; relaxes uterus
	β_3	Adipose tissue		Stimulates lipolysis by fat cells
	α_1	Most importantly blood vessels serving the skin, mucosae, abdominal viscera, kidneys, and salivary glands; also, virtually all sympathetic target organs except heart		Constricts blood vessels and visceral organ sphincters; dilates pupils of the eyes
	α_2	Membrane of adrenergic axon terminals; pancreas; blood platelets		Inhibits NE release from adrenergic terminals; inhibits insulin secretion by pancreas; promotes blood clotting

* Note that all of these receptor subtypes are also found in the CNS.

Adrenergic Receptors

There are also two major classes of adrenergic (NE-binding) receptors: **alpha (α)** and **beta (β)**. These receptors are further divided into subclasses (α_1 and α_2; β_1, β_2, and β_3). Organs that respond to NE (or to epinephrine) have one or more of these receptor subtypes.

NE or epinephrine can have either excitatory or inhibitory effects on target organs depending on which subclass of receptor predominates in that organ. For example, binding of NE to the β_1 receptors of cardiac muscle prods the heart into more vigorous activity, whereas epinephrine binding to β_2 receptors in bronchiole smooth muscle causes it to relax, dilating the bronchiole.

The Effects of Drugs

Knowing the locations of the cholinergic and adrenergic receptor subtypes allows specific drugs to be prescribed to obtain the desired inhibitory or stimulatory effects on selected target organs. For example, *atropine* is an anticholinergic drug that blocks muscarinic ACh receptors. It is routinely administered before surgery to prevent salivation and to dry up respiratory system secretions. Ophthalmologists also use it to dilate the pupils for eye examination. The anticholinesterase drug *neostigmine* inhibits the enzyme acetylcholinesterase, preventing enzymatic breakdown of ACh and allowing it to accumulate in synapses. This drug is used to treat myasthenia gravis, a con-

dition in which skeletal muscle activity is impaired for lack of ACh stimulation.

As we described in Chapter 11, NE is one of our "feeling good" neurotransmitters, and drugs that prolong the activity of NE on the postsynaptic membrane help to relieve depression. Hundreds of over-the-counter drugs used to treat colds, coughs, allergies, and nasal congestion contain sympathomimetics (phenylephrine and others), sympathetic-mimicking drugs that stimulate α-adrenergic receptors.

Much pharmaceutical research is directed toward finding drugs that affect only one subclass of receptor without upsetting the whole adrenergic or cholinergic system. An important breakthrough was finding drugs that mainly activate β_2 receptors. People with asthma use such β_2 activators to dilate their lung bronchioles without activating β_1 receptors, which would increase their heart rate. Selected drug classes that influence ANS activity are summarized in **Table 14.3**.

Interactions of the Autonomic Divisions

As we mentioned earlier, most visceral organs receive *dual innervation*. Normally, both ANS divisions are partially active, producing a dynamic antagonism that allows visceral activity to be precisely controlled. However, one division or the other usually exerts the predominant effects in given circumstances, and in a few cases, the two divisions actually cooperate with each

TABLE 14.3	Selected Drug Classes That Influence the Activity of the Autonomic Nervous System			
DRUG CLASS	**RECEPTOR BOUND**	**EFFECTS**	**EXAMPLE**	**CLINICAL USE**
Nicotinic agents (little therapeutic value, but important because of presence of nicotine in tobacco)	Nicotinic ACh receptors on all ganglionic neurons and in CNS	Typically stimulation of sympathetic effects; blood pressure increases	Nicotine	Used in smoking cessation products
Parasympathomimetic agents (muscarinic agents)	Muscarinic ACh receptors	Mimic effects of ACh, enhance parasympathetic effects	Pilocarpine	Glaucoma (opens aqueous humor drainage pores)
			Bethanechol	Difficulty urinating (increases bladder contraction)
Acetylcholinesterase inhibitors	None; bind to the enzyme (AChE) that degrades ACh	Indirect effect at all ACh receptors; prolong the effect of ACh	Neostigmine	Myasthenia gravis, (increases availability of ACh)
			Sarin	Used as chemical warfare agent (similar to widely used insecticides)
Sympathomimetic agents	Adrenergic receptors	Enhance sympathetic activity by increasing NE release or binding to adrenergic receptors	Albuterol (Ventolin)	Asthma (dilates bronchioles by binding to β_2 receptors)
			Phenylephrine	Colds (nasal decongestant, binds to α_1 receptors)
Sympatholytic agents	Adrenergic receptors	Decrease sympathetic activity by blocking adrenergic receptors or inhibiting NE release	Propranolol	Hypertension (member of a class of drugs called *beta-blockers* that decrease heart rate and blood pressure)

14

other. **Table 14.4** contains an organ-by-organ summary of the differing effects of the two divisions.

Antagonistic Interactions

Antagonistic effects, described earlier, are most clearly seen on the activity of the heart, respiratory system, and gastrointestinal organs. In a fight-or-flight situation, the sympathetic division increases heart rate, dilates airways, and inhibits digestion and elimination. When the emergency is over, the parasympathetic division restores heart rate and airway diameter to resting levels and then attends to processes that refuel your body cells and discard wastes.

Sympathetic and Parasympathetic Tone

We have described the parasympathetic division as the "resting and digesting" division, but the sympathetic division is the major actor in controlling blood pressure, even at rest. With few exceptions, the vascular system is entirely innervated by sympathetic fibers that keep the blood vessels in a continual state of partial constriction called **sympathetic**, or **vasomotor**, **tone**. When a higher blood pressure is needed to maintain blood flow, the sympathetic fibers fire more rapidly, causing blood vessels to constrict and blood pressure to rise. When blood pressure is to be decreased, sympathetic fibers fire less rapidly and the vessels dilate. *Alpha-blockers*, drugs that interfere with the activity of these **vasomotor fibers**, are sometimes used to treat hypertension.

During circulatory shock (inadequate blood delivery to body tissues), or when more blood is needed to meet the increased needs of working skeletal muscles, blood vessels serving the skin and abdominal viscera are strongly constricted. This blood "shunting" helps maintain circulation to vital organs or enhance blood delivery to skeletal muscles.

On the other hand, parasympathetic effects normally dominate the heart and the smooth muscle of digestive and urinary tract organs. These organs exhibit **parasympathetic tone**. The parasympathetic division slows the heart and dictates the normal activity levels of the digestive and urinary tracts. However, the sympathetic division can override these parasympathetic effects during times of stress. Drugs that block parasympathetic responses increase heart rate and cause fecal and urinary retention. Except for the adrenal glands and sweat glands of the skin, most glands are activated by parasympathetic fibers.

Cooperative Effects

The best example of cooperative ANS effects is seen in controls of the external genitalia. Parasympathetic stimulation causes vasodilation of blood vessels in the external genitalia and is responsible for erection of the male penis or female clitoris during sexual excitement. (This may explain why sexual performance is sometimes impaired when people are anxious or upset and the sympathetic division is in charge.) Sympathetic stimulation

TABLE 14.4 **Effects of the Parasympathetic and Sympathetic Divisions on Various Organs**

TARGET ORGAN OR SYSTEM	PARASYMPATHETIC EFFECTS	SYMPATHETIC EFFECTS
Eye (iris)	Stimulates sphincter pupillae muscles; constricts pupils	Stimulates dilator pupillae muscles; dilates pupils
Eye (ciliary muscle)	Stimulates muscle, which results in bulging of the lens for close vision	Weakly inhibits muscle, which results in flattening of the lens for far vision
Glands (nasal, lacrimal, gastric, pancreas)	Stimulates secretory activity	Inhibits secretory activity; causes vasoconstriction of blood vessels supplying the glands
Salivary glands	Stimulates secretion of watery saliva	Stimulates secretion of thick, viscous saliva
Sweat glands	No effect (no innervation)	Stimulates copious sweating (cholinergic fibers)
Adrenal medulla	No effect (no innervation)	Stimulates medulla cells to secrete epinephrine and norepinephrine
Arrector pili muscles attached to hair follicles	No effect (no innervation)	Stimulates contraction (erects hairs and produces "goosebumps")
Heart (muscle)	Decreases rate; slows heart	Increases rate and force of heartbeat
Heart (coronary blood vessels)	No effect (no innervation)	Causes vasodilation*
Urinary bladder/urethra	Causes contraction of smooth muscle of bladder wall; relaxes urethral sphincter; promotes voiding	Causes relaxation of smooth muscle of bladder wall; constricts urethral sphincter; inhibits voiding
Lungs	Constricts bronchioles	Dilates bronchioles*
Digestive tract organs	Increases motility (peristalsis) and amount of secretion by digestive organs; relaxes sphincters to allow movement of foodstuffs along tract	Decreases activity of glands and muscles of digestive system and constricts sphincters (e.g., anal sphincter)
Liver	Increases glucose uptake from blood	Stimulates release of glucose to blood*
Gallbladder	Excites (gallbladder contracts to expel bile)	Inhibits (gallbladder is relaxed)
Kidney	No effect (no innervation)	Promotes renin release; causes vasoconstriction; decreases urine output
Penis	Causes erection (vasodilation)	Causes ejaculation
Vagina/clitoris	Causes erection (vasodilation) of clitoris; increases vaginal lubrication	Causes contraction of vagina
Blood vessels	Little or no effect	Constricts most vessels and increases blood pressure; constricts vessels of abdominal viscera and skin to divert blood to muscles, brain, and heart when necessary; NE constricts most vessels; epinephrine dilates vessels of the skeletal muscles during exercise*
Blood coagulation	No effect (no innervation)	Increases coagulation*
Cellular metabolism	No effect (no innervation)	Increases metabolic rate*
Adipose tissue	No effect (no innervation)	Stimulates lipolysis (fat breakdown)

*Effects are mediated by epinephrine release into the bloodstream from the adrenal medulla.

then causes ejaculation of semen by the penis or reflex contractions of a female's vagina.

HOMEOSTATIC IMBALANCE

Autonomic neuropathy (damage to autonomic nerves) is a common complication of diabetes mellitus. One of the earliest and most troubling symptoms is sexual dysfunction, with up to 75% of male diabetics experiencing erectile dysfunction. Women, on the other hand, often experience reduced vaginal lubrication. Other frequent manifestations of autonomic neuropathy include dizziness after standing suddenly (poor blood pressure control), urinary incontinence, sluggish eye pupil reactions, and impaired sweating. Just how the elevated blood glucose levels in diabetics damage nerves is still a mystery. ∎

Unique Roles of the Sympathetic Division

The adrenal medulla, sweat glands and arrector pili muscles of the skin, the kidneys, and most blood vessels receive only sympathetic fibers. It is easy to remember that the sympathetic system innervates these structures because most of us sweat under stress, our scalp "prickles" during fear, and our blood pressure skyrockets (from widespread vasoconstriction) when we get excited. We have already described how sympathetic control of blood vessels regulates blood pressure and shunting of blood in the vascular system. We will now consider several other uniquely sympathetic functions.

Thermoregulatory Responses to Heat The sympathetic division mediates reflexes that regulate body temperature. For example, applying heat to the skin causes reflexive dilation of blood vessels in that area. When systemic body temperature is elevated, sympathetic nerves cause the skin's blood vessels to dilate, allowing the skin to become flushed with warm blood, and activate the sweat glands to help cool the body. When body temperature falls, skin blood vessels are constricted, and, as a result, blood is restricted to deeper, more vital organs.

Release of Renin from the Kidneys Sympathetic impulses stimulate the kidneys to release *renin*, a hormone that promotes an increase in blood pressure. We describe this renin-angiotensin mechanism in Chapter 25.

Metabolic Effects Through both direct neural stimulation and release of adrenal medullary hormones, the sympathetic division promotes a number of metabolic effects not reversed by parasympathetic activity. It (1) increases the metabolic rate of body cells; (2) raises blood glucose levels; and (3) mobilizes fats for use as fuels. The medullary hormones also cause skeletal muscle to contract more strongly and quickly.

As a side effect, muscle spindles are stimulated more often and, consequently, nerve impulses traveling to the muscles occur more synchronously. These neural bursts, which put muscle contractions on a "hair trigger," are great if you have to make a quick jump or run, but they can be embarrassing or even disabling to the nervous musician or surgeon.

Localized Versus Diffuse Effects

In the parasympathetic division, one preganglionic neuron synapses with one (or at most a few) ganglionic neurons. Additionally, all parasympathetic fibers release ACh, which is quickly destroyed (hydrolyzed) by acetylcholinesterase. Consequently, the parasympathetic division exerts short-lived, highly localized control over its effectors.

In contrast, preganglionic sympathetic axons branch profusely as they enter the sympathetic trunk, and they synapse with ganglionic neurons at several levels. As a result, when the sympathetic division is activated, it responds in a diffuse and highly interconnected way. Indeed, the literal translation of sympathetic (*sym* = together; *pathos* = feeling) relates to the bodywide mobilization this division provokes. Nevertheless, parts of the sympathetic nervous system can be activated individually. For example, just because your eye pupils dilate in dim light doesn't necessarily mean that your heart rate speeds up.

Effects produced by sympathetic activation are much longer-lasting than parasympathetic effects. In contrast to the parasympathetic system's ACh, NE is inactivated more slowly because it must be taken back up into the presynaptic ending

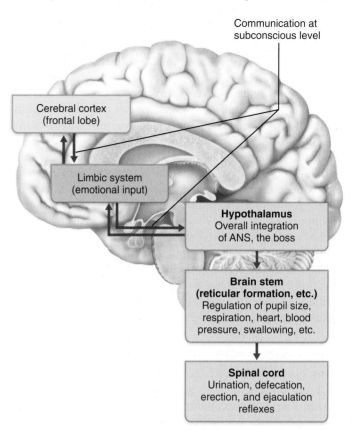

Figure 14.9 Levels of ANS control. The hypothalamus stands at the top of the control hierarchy as the integrator of ANS activity, but it is influenced by subconscious cerebral inputs via limbic system connections.

before being hydrolyzed or stored. More importantly, NE and epinephrine are secreted into the blood by adrenal medullary cells when the sympathetic division is mobilized. Although epinephrine is more potent at increasing heart rate and raising blood glucose levels and metabolic rate, these hormones have essentially the same effects as NE released by sympathetic neurons. In fact, circulating adrenal medullary hormones produce 25–50% of all the sympathetic effects acting on the body at a given time. These effects continue for several minutes until the hormones are destroyed by the liver.

In short, sympathetic nerve impulses act only briefly, but the hormonal effects they provoke linger. The widespread and prolonged effect of sympathetic activation helps explain why we need time to "come down" after an extremely stressful experience.

Control of Autonomic Functioning

Although the ANS is not usually considered to be under voluntary control, its activity is regulated by CNS controls in the spinal cord, brain stem, hypothalamus, and cerebral cortex (Figure 14.9). In general, the hypothalamus is the integrative center at the top of the ANS control hierarchy. From there, orders flow to lower and lower CNS centers for execution. Although the cerebral cortex may modify the workings of the ANS, it does so at the subconscious level and by acting through limbic system structures on hypothalamic centers.

Brain Stem and Spinal Cord Controls

The hypothalamus is the "boss," but the brain stem reticular formation appears to exert the most *direct* influence over autonomic functions (see Figure 12.16 on p. 448). For example, certain motor centers in the ventrolateral medulla (*cardiac* and *vasomotor centers*) reflexively regulate heart rate and blood vessel diameter. Other medullary regions oversee gastrointestinal activities. Most sensory impulses involved in eliciting these autonomic reflexes reach the brain stem via vagus nerve afferents. Although not considered part of the ANS, the medulla and pons also contain respiratory centers that mediate involuntary control of respiration and receive inputs from the hypothalamus. Midbrain centers (*oculomotor nuclei*) control the muscles concerned with pupil diameter and lens focus.

Defecation and micturition reflexes that promote emptying of the rectum and urinary bladder are integrated at the spinal cord level but are subject to conscious inhibition. We will describe all of these autonomic reflexes in later chapters in relation to the organ systems they serve.

Hypothalamic Controls

As we noted, the hypothalamus is the main integration center of the autonomic nervous system. In general, anterior hypothalamic regions direct parasympathetic functions, and posterior areas direct sympathetic functions. These centers exert their effects both directly and via relays through the *reticular formation*, which in turn influences the preganglionic motor neurons in the brain stem and spinal cord (Figure 14.9). The hypothalamus contains centers that coordinate heart activity, blood pressure, body temperature, water balance, and endocrine activity. It also contains centers that mediate various emotional states (rage, pleasure) and biological drives (thirst, hunger, sex).

The hypothalamus also mediates our reactions to fear via its associations with the amygdala and the periaqueductal gray matter. Emotional responses of the limbic system of the cerebrum to danger and stress signal the hypothalamus to activate the sympathetic system to fight-or-flight status. In this way, the hypothalamus serves as the keystone of the emotional and visceral brain, and through its centers emotions influence ANS functioning and behavior.

Cortical Controls

It was originally believed that the ANS is not subject to voluntary controls. However, we have all had occasions when remembering a frightening event made our heart race (sympathetic response) or just the thought of a favorite food, pecan pie for example, made our mouth water (a parasympathetic response). These inputs converge on the hypothalamus through its connections to the limbic lobe.

Additionally, studies have shown that voluntary cortical control of visceral activities is possible—a capability untapped by most people.

Influence of Biofeedback on Autonomic Function   During **biofeedback training**, subjects are connected to monitoring devices that provide an awareness of what is happening in their body. This awareness is called **biofeedback**. The devices detect and amplify changes in physiological processes such as heart rate and blood pressure, and these data are "fed back" in the form of flashing lights or audible tones. Subjects are asked to try to alter or control some "involuntary" function by concentrating on calming, pleasant thoughts. The monitor allows them to identify changes in the desired direction, so they can recognize the feelings associated with these changes and learn to produce the changes at will.

Biofeedback techniques have been successful in helping individuals plagued by migraine headaches. They are also used by cardiac patients to manage stress and reduce their risk of heart attack. However, biofeedback training is time-consuming and often frustrating, and the training equipment is expensive and difficult to use.

CHECK YOUR UNDERSTANDING

6. Name the division of the ANS that does each of the following: increases digestive activity; increases blood pressure; dilates bronchioles; decreases heart rate; stimulates the adrenal medulla to release its hormones; causes ejaculation.
7. Would you find nicotinic receptors on skeletal muscle? Smooth muscle? Eccrine sweat glands? The adrenal medulla? CNS neurons?
8. Which part of the brain is the main integration center of the ANS? Which part exerts the most direct influence over autonomic functions?

For answers, see Appendix G.

Homeostatic Imbalances of the ANS

▶ Explain the relationship of some types of hypertension, Raynaud's disease, and autonomic dysreflexia to disorders of autonomic functioning.

The ANS is involved in nearly every important process that goes on in the body, so it is not surprising that abnormalities of autonomic functioning can have far-reaching effects and threaten life itself. Most autonomic disorders reflect exaggerated or deficient controls of smooth muscle activity. Of these, the most devastating involve blood vessels and include conditions such as hypertension, Raynaud's disease, and autonomic dysreflexia.

Hypertension, or high blood pressure, may result from an overactive sympathetic vasoconstrictor response promoted by continuous high levels of stress. Hypertension is always serious because it increases the workload on the heart, which may precipitate heart disease, and increases the wear and tear on artery walls. Stress-induced hypertension can be treated with adrenergic receptor–blocking drugs.

Raynaud's disease is characterized by intermittent attacks causing the skin of the fingers and toes to become pale, then cyanotic and painful. Commonly provoked by exposure to cold or emotional stress, it is an exaggerated vasoconstriction response. The severity of this disease ranges from merely uncomfortable to such severe blood vessel constriction that ischemia and gangrene (tissue death) results. Vasodilators (for example, adrenergic blockers) usually suffice, but to treat very severe cases, preganglionic sympathetic fibers serving the affected regions are severed (a procedure called *sympathectomy*). The involved vessels then dilate, reestablishing adequate blood delivery to the region.

Autonomic dysreflexia is a life-threatening condition involving uncontrolled activation of autonomic neurons. It occurs in a majority of individuals with quadriplegia and in others with spinal cord injuries above the T_6 level, usually in the first year after injury. The usual trigger is a painful stimulus to the skin or overfilling of a visceral organ, such as the urinary bladder. Arterial blood pressure skyrockets to life-threatening levels, which may rupture a blood vessel in the brain, precipitating stroke. This may be accompanied by a headache, flushed face, sweating above the level of the injury, and cold, clammy skin below. The precise mechanism of autonomic dysreflexia is not yet clear.

CHECK YOUR UNDERSTANDING

9. Jackson works long, stress-filled shifts as an air traffic controller at a busy airport. His doctor has prescribed a beta-blocker. Why might his doctor have done this? What does a beta-blocker do?

For answers, see Appendix G.

Developmental Aspects of the ANS

▶ Describe some effects of aging on the autonomic nervous system.

ANS preganglionic neurons derive from the embryonic *neural tube*, as do somatic motor neurons. ANS structures in the PNS—ganglionic neurons, the adrenal medulla, and all autonomic ganglia—derive from the **neural crest** (along with all

sensory neurons) (see Figure 12.1, ③). Neural crest cells reach their ultimate destinations by migrating along growing axons. Forming ganglia receive axons from preganglionic neurons in the spinal cord or brain and send their axons to synapse with their effector cells in the body periphery. This process depends upon the presence of **nerve growth factor**, and is guided by a number of signaling chemicals similar to those acting in the CNS.

During youth, impairments of ANS function are usually due to injuries to the spinal cord or autonomic nerves. In old age the efficiency of the ANS begins to decline. At least part of the problem appears to be due to structural changes (bloating) of some preganglionic axon terminals, which become congested with neurofilaments.

Many elderly people complain of constipation (a result of reduced gastrointestinal tract motility), and of dry eyes and frequent eye infections (both a result of a diminished ability to form tears). Additionally, when they stand up they may have fainting episodes due to **orthostatic hypotension** (*ortho* = straight; *stat* = standing), a form of low blood pressure that occurs because the aging pressure receptors respond less to changes in blood pressure following changes in position, and because of slowed responses by aging sympathetic vasoconstrictor centers. These problems are distressing, but not usually life threatening, and most can be managed by lifestyle changes or artificial aids. For example, changing position slowly gives the sympathetic nervous system time to adjust the blood pressure, and eye drops (artificial tears) are available for the dry-eye problem.

CHECK YOUR UNDERSTANDING

10. Which embryonic structure gives rise to both the autonomic ganglia and the adrenal medulla?

For answers, see Appendix G.

In this chapter, we have described the structure and function of the ANS, one arm of the motor division of the peripheral nervous system. Because virtually every organ system still to be considered depends on autonomic controls, you will be hearing more about the ANS in chapters that follow. Now that we have explored most of the nervous system, this is a good time to examine how it interacts with the rest of the body as summarized in the *Making Connections* feature, pp. 542–543.

14

System Connections

Homeostatic Interrelationships Between the Nervous System and Other Body Systems

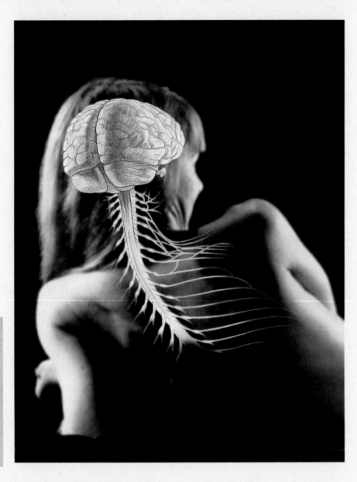

14

Endocrine System

- Sympathetic division of the ANS activates the adrenal medulla; hypothalamus helps regulate the activity of the anterior pituitary gland and produces the two posterior pituitary hormones
- Hormones influence neuronal metabolism

Cardiovascular System

- ANS helps regulate heart rate and blood pressure
- Cardiovascular system provides blood containing oxygen and nutrients to the nervous system and carries away wastes

Lymphatic System/Immunity

- Nerves innervate lymphoid organs; the brain plays a role in regulating immune function
- Lymphatic vessels carry away leaked tissue fluids from tissues surrounding nervous system structures; immune elements protect all body organs from pathogens (CNS has additional mechanisms as well)

Respiratory System

- Nervous system initiates and regulates respiratory rhythm and depth
- Respiratory system provides life-sustaining oxygen; disposes of carbon dioxide

Digestive System

- ANS (particularly the parasympathetic division) regulates digestive motility and glandular activity
- Digestive system provides nutrients needed for neuronal health

Urinary System

- ANS regulates bladder emptying and renal blood pressure
- Kidneys help to dispose of metabolic wastes and maintain proper electrolyte composition and pH of blood for neural functioning

Reproductive System

- ANS regulates sexual erection and ejaculation in males; erection of the clitoris in females
- Testosterone causes masculinization of the brain and underlies sex drive and aggressive behavior

Integumentary System

- Sympathetic division of the ANS regulates sweat glands and blood vessels of skin (therefore heat loss/retention)
- Skin serves as heat loss surface

Skeletal System

- Nerves innervate bones and joints, providing for pain and joint sense
- Bones serve as depot for calcium needed for neural function; skeletal system protects CNS structures

Muscular System

- Somatic division of nervous system activates skeletal muscles; maintains muscle health
- Skeletal muscles are the effectors of the somatic division

The Nervous System and Interrelationships with the Muscular, Respiratory, and Digestive Systems

The nervous system pokes its figurative nose into the activities of virtually every organ system of the body. Hence, trying to choose the most significant interactions comes pretty close to a lesson in futility. Which is more important: digestion, elimination of wastes, or motility? Your answer probably depends on whether you are hungry or need to make a "pit stop" at the bathroom when you read this. Since neural interactions with several other systems are thoroughly plumbed in chapters to come, here we will look at the all-important interactions between the nervous system and the muscular, respiratory, and digestive systems.

Muscular System

Most simply said, the muscular system would cease to function without the nervous system. Unlike visceral or cardiac muscles, both of which have other controlling systems, somatic motor fibers are *it* for skeletal muscle activation and regulation. Somatic nerve fibers "tell" skeletal muscles not only when to contract but also how strongly. Additionally, as the nervous system makes its initial synapses with skeletal muscle fibers, it determines their fate as fast or slow fibers, which forever after affects our potential for muscle speed and endurance. The interactions of the various brain regions (basal nuclei, cerebellum, premotor cortex, etc.) and inputs of stretch receptors also determine our grace—how smooth and coordinated we are. Nonetheless, keep in mind that as long as the skeletal muscle effector cells are healthy, they help determine the viability of the neurons synapsing with them. The relationship is truly synergistic.

Respiratory System

Another system that depends entirely on the nervous system for its function is the respiratory system, which continuously refreshes the blood with oxygen and unloads the carbon dioxide waste to the sea of air that surrounds us. Neural centers in the medulla and pons both initiate and maintain the tidelike rhythm of air flushing into and out of our lungs by activating skeletal muscles that change the volume (thus the gas pressure) within the lungs. Peripheral receptors supply information about gas concentrations, lung stretch, and skeletal muscle activity to these CNS respiratory centers.

Digestive System

Although the digestive system responds to many different types of controls—for example, hormones, local pH, and irritating chemicals—the parasympathetic nervous system is crucial to its normal functioning. Without the parasympathetic inputs, sympathetic neural activity, which inhibits normal digestion, would be unopposed. So important are parasympathetic controls that some of the parasympathetic neurons are actually located in the walls of the digestive organs, in what are called intrinsic plexuses. Thus, even if all extrinsic controls are severed, the intrinsic mechanisms can still maintain this crucial body function. The role the digestive system plays for the nervous system is the same one it offers to all body systems—it sees that ingested foodstuff gets digested and loaded into the blood for cell use.

14

Nervous System

Case study: On arrival at Holyoke Hospital, Jimmy Chin, a 10-year-old boy, is immobilized on a rigid stretcher so that he is unable to move his head or trunk. The paramedics report that when they found him some 50 feet from the bus, he was awake and alert, but crying and complaining that he couldn't "get up to find his mom" and that he had a "wicked headache." He has severe bruises on his upper back and head, and lacerations of his back and scalp. His blood pressure is low, body temperature is below normal, lower limbs are paralyzed, and he is insensitive to painful stimuli below the nipples. Although still alert on arrival, Jimmy soon begins to drift in and out of unconsciousness.

Jimmy is immediately scheduled for a CT scan, and an operating room is reserved.

Relative to Jimmy's condition:

1. Why were his head and torso immobilized for transport to the hospital?

2. What do his worsening neurological signs (drowsiness, incoherence, etc.) probably indicate? (Relate this to the type of surgery that will be performed.)

3. Assuming that Jimmy's sensory and motor deficits are due to a spinal cord injury, at what level do you expect to find a spinal cord lesion?

4. Two days after his surgery, Jimmy is alert and his MRI scan shows no residual brain injury, but pronounced swelling and damage to the spinal cord at T_4. On physical examination, Jimmy shows no reflex activity below the level of the spinal cord injury. His blood pressure is still low. Why are there no reflexes in his lower limbs and abdomen?

5. Over the next few days, his reflexes return in his lower limbs and become exaggerated. He is incontinent. Why is Jimmy hyperreflexive and incontinent?

On one occasion, Jimmy complains of a massive headache and his blood pressure is way above normal. On examination, he is sweating intensely above the nipples but has cold, clammy skin below the nipples and his heart rate is very slow.

6. What is this condition called and what precipitates it?

7. How does Jimmy's excessively high blood pressure put him at risk?

(Answers in Appendix G)

RELATED CLINICAL TERMS

Atonic bladder (ah-ton′ik; *a* = without; *ton* = tone, tension) A condition in which the urinary bladder becomes flaccid and overfills, allowing urine to dribble through the sphincters; results from temporary loss of the micturition reflex following spinal cord injury.

Horner's syndrome A condition due to damage to the superior sympathetic trunk on one side of the body; the affected person exhibits drooping of the upper eyelid (ptosis) and constricted pupil, and does not sweat on the affected side of the head.

Vagotomy (va-got′o-me) Cutting or severing of the vagus nerve to decrease secretion of gastric juice in those with peptic ulcers that do not respond to medication.

Vasovagal syncope Vasovagal syncope, also called *neurocardiogenic syncope*, is the most common cause of fainting. Although it may be provoked by emotional stress, pain, or dehydration, it typically occurs during prolonged standing. Fainting is due to a drop in blood pressure, which decreases blood flow to the brain and results in loss of consciousness.

CHAPTER SUMMARY

Media study tools that could provide you additional help in reviewing specific key topics of Chapter 14 are referenced below.

iP = *Interactive Physiology*

1. The autonomic nervous system (ANS) is the motor division of the PNS that controls visceral activities, with the goal of maintaining internal homeostasis.

Introduction (pp. 526–528)

Comparison of the Somatic and Autonomic Nervous Systems (pp. 526–527)

1. The somatic (voluntary) nervous system provides motor fibers to skeletal muscles. The autonomic (involuntary or visceral motor) nervous system provides motor fibers to smooth and cardiac muscles and glands.

2. In the somatic division, a single motor neuron forms the efferent pathway from the CNS to the effectors. The efferent pathway of the autonomic division consists of a two-neuron chain: the preganglionic neuron in the CNS and the ganglionic neuron in a ganglion.

3. Acetylcholine, the neurotransmitter of somatic motor neurons, is stimulatory to skeletal muscle fibers. Neurotransmitters released by autonomic motor neurons (acetylcholine and norepinephrine) may cause excitation or inhibition.

iP Nervous System II; Topic: Synaptic Transmission, pp. 8–11.

ANS Divisions (pp. 527–528)

4. The ANS consists of two divisions, the parasympathetic and sympathetic, which normally exert antagonistic effects on many of the same target organs.

5. The parasympathetic division (the resting-digesting system) conserves body energy and maintains body activities at basal levels.

6. Parasympathetic effects include pupillary constriction, glandular secretion, increased digestive tract motility, and smooth muscle activity leading to elimination of feces and urine.

7. The sympathetic division prepares the body for activity and is called the fight-or-flight system.

8. Sympathetic responses include dilated pupils, increased heart rate, increased blood pressure, dilation of the bronchioles of the lungs, increased blood glucose levels, and sweating. During exercise, sympathetic vasoconstriction shunts blood from the skin and digestive viscera to the heart, brain, and skeletal muscles.

ANS Anatomy (pp. 528–535)

Parasympathetic (Craniosacral) Division (pp. 529–530)

1. Parasympathetic preganglionic neurons arise from the brain stem and from the sacral (S_2–S_4) region of the spinal cord.

2. Preganglionic fibers synapse with ganglionic neurons in terminal ganglia located in (intramural ganglia) or close to their effector organs. Preganglionic fibers are long; postganglionic fibers are short.

3. Cranial fibers arise in the brain stem nuclei of cranial nerves III, VII, IX, and X and synapse in ganglia of the head, thorax, and abdomen. The vagus nerves serve virtually all organs of the thoracic and abdominal cavities.

4. Sacral fibers (S_2–S_4) issue from the lateral region of the cord and form pelvic splanchnic nerves that innervate the pelvic viscera. The preganglionic axons do not travel within rami communicantes.

Sympathetic (Thoracolumbar) Division (pp. 530–534)

5. Preganglionic sympathetic neurons arise from the lateral horns of the spinal cord from the level of T_1 through L_2.

6. Preganglionic axons leave the cord via white rami communicantes and enter the sympathetic trunk (chain) ganglia in the sympathetic trunk. An axon may synapse in a trunk ganglion at the same or at a different level, or it may issue from the sympathetic trunk without synapsing. Preganglionic fibers are short; postganglionic fibers are long.

7. When the synapse occurs in a trunk ganglion, the postganglionic fiber may enter the spinal nerve ramus via the gray ramus communicans to travel to the body periphery. Postganglionic fibers issuing from the cervical ganglia also serve visceral organs and blood vessels of the head, neck, and thorax.

8. When synapses do not occur in the trunk ganglia, the preganglionic fibers form splanchnic nerves (thoracic, lumbar, and sacral). Most splanchnic nerve fibers synapse in collateral ganglia, and the postganglionic fibers serve the abdominal viscera. Exceptions are that (1) some splanchnic nerve fibers synapse with cells of the adrenal medulla, and (2) some lumbar and sacral splanchnic nerve fibers *do* synapse in trunk ganglia.

Visceral Reflexes (pp. 534–535)

9. Visceral reflex arcs have the same components as somatic reflexes.

10. Cell bodies of visceral sensory neurons are located in dorsal root ganglia, sensory ganglia of cranial nerves, or autonomic ganglia. Visceral afferents are found in spinal nerves and in virtually all autonomic nerves.

ANS Physiology   (pp. 535–540)

Neurotransmitters and Receptors   (pp. 535–536)

1. Two major neurotransmitters, acetylcholine (ACh) and norepinephrine (NE), are released by autonomic motor neurons. On the basis of the neurotransmitter released, the fibers are classified as cholinergic or adrenergic.
2. ACh is released by all preganglionic fibers and all parasympathetic postganglionic fibers. NE is released by all sympathetic postganglionic fibers except those serving the sweat glands of the skin, and some blood vessels within skeletal muscles.
3. Neurotransmitter effects depend on the receptors to which the transmitter binds. Cholinergic (ACh) receptors are classified as nicotinic or muscarinic. Adrenergic (NE) receptors are classified as α_1 or α_2, or β_1, β_2, or β_3.

iP Nervous System II; Topic: Synaptic Transmission, pp. 8–11, 14.

The Effects of Drugs   (p. 536)

4. Drugs that mimic, enhance, or inhibit the action of ANS neurotransmitters are used to treat conditions caused by excessive, inadequate, or inappropriate ANS functioning. Some drugs bind with only one receptor subtype, allowing specific ANS-mediated activities to be enhanced or blocked.

Interactions of the Autonomic Divisions   (pp. 536–539)

5. Most visceral organs are innervated by both divisions; the divisions interact in various ways but usually exert a dynamic antagonism. Antagonistic interactions mainly involve the heart, respiratory system, and gastrointestinal organs. Sympathetic activity increases heart activity, dilates bronchioles, and depresses gastrointestinal activity. Parasympathetic activity reverses these effects.
6. Most blood vessels are innervated only by sympathetic fibers and exhibit vasomotor tone. Parasympathetic activity dominates the heart and muscles of the gastrointestinal tract (which normally exhibit parasympathetic tone) and glands.

7. The two ANS divisions exert cooperative effects on the external genitalia.
8. Roles unique to the sympathetic division are blood pressure regulation, shunting of blood in the vascular system, thermoregulatory responses, stimulation of renin release by the kidneys, and metabolic effects.
9. Activation of the sympathetic division can cause widespread, long-lasting mobilization of the fight-or-flight response. Parasympathetic effects are highly localized and short-lived.

Control of Autonomic Functioning   (pp. 539–540)

10. Autonomic function is controlled at several levels: (1) Reflex activity is mediated by the spinal cord and brain stem (particularly medullary) centers. (2) Hypothalamic integration centers interact with both higher and lower centers to orchestrate autonomic, somatic, and endocrine responses. (3) Cortical centers influence autonomic functioning via connections with the limbic system; conscious controls of autonomic function are rare but possible, as illustrated by biofeedback training.

Homeostatic Imbalances of the ANS   (pp. 540–541)

1. Most autonomic disorders reflect problems with smooth muscle control. Abnormalities in vascular control, such as occur in hypertension, Raynaud's disease, and autonomic dysreflexia, are most devastating.

Developmental Aspects of the ANS   (p. 541)

1. Preganglionic neurons develop from the neural tube; ganglionic neurons develop from the embryonic neural crest.
2. The efficiency of the autonomic nervous system declines in old age, as reflected by decreased glandular secretory activity, decreased gastrointestinal motility, and slowed sympathetic vasomotor responses to changes in position.

14

REVIEW QUESTIONS

Multiple Choice/Matching

(Some questions have more than one correct answer. Select the best answer or answers from the choices given.)

1. All of the following characterize the ANS except (a) two-neuron efferent chain, (b) presence of nerve cell bodies in the CNS, (c) presence of nerve cell bodies in the ganglia, (d) innervation of skeletal muscles.
2. Relate each of the following terms or phrases to either the sympathetic (S) or parasympathetic (P) division of the autonomic nervous system:
   _____ (1) short preganglionic, long postganglionic fibers
   _____ (2) intramural ganglia
   _____ (3) craniosacral outflow
   _____ (4) adrenergic fibers
   _____ (5) cervical ganglia
   _____ (6) otic and ciliary ganglia
   _____ (7) generally short-duration action
   _____ (8) increases heart rate and blood pressure
   _____ (9) increases gastric motility and secretion of lacrimal, salivary, and digestive juices
   _____ (10) innervates blood vessels

   _____ (11) most active when you are swinging in a hammock
   _____ (12) active when you are running in the Boston Marathon
3. Preganglionic neurons develop from (a) neural crest cells, (b) neural tube cells, (c) alar plate cells, (d) endoderm.
4. The white rami communicantes contain what kind of fibers? (a) preganglionic parasympathetic, (b) postganglionic parasympathetic, (c) preganglionic sympathetic, (d) postganglionic sympathetic.
5. Collateral sympathetic ganglia are involved with the innervation of the (a) abdominal organs, (b) thoracic organs, (c) head, (d) arrector pili, (e) all of these.

Short Answer Essay Questions

6. Briefly explain why the following terms are sometimes used to refer to the autonomic nervous system: involuntary nervous system and emotional-visceral system.
7. Describe the anatomical relationship of the white and gray rami communicantes to the spinal nerve, and indicate the kind of fibers found in each ramus type.
8. Indicate the results of sympathetic activation of the following structures: sweat glands, eye pupils, adrenal medulla, heart, bronchioles of the lungs, liver, blood vessels of vigorously working skeletal muscles, blood vessels of digestive viscera, salivary glands.

9. Which of the effects listed in response to question 8 would be reversed by parasympathetic activity?

10. Which ANS fibers release acetylcholine? Which release norepinephrine?

11. Describe the meaning and importance of sympathetic tone and parasympathetic tone.

12. List the receptor subtypes for ACh and NE, and indicate the major sites where each type is found.

13. What area of the brain is most directly involved in mediating autonomic reflexes?

14. Describe the importance of the hypothalamus in controlling the autonomic nervous system.

15. Describe the basis and uses of biofeedback training.

16. What manifestations of decreased autonomic nervous system efficiency are seen in elderly individuals?

17. Ganglionic neurons are also called postganglionic neurons. Why is this a misnomer?

 Critical Thinking and Clinical Application Questions

1. Mr. Johnson has been suffering from functional urinary retention and a hypoactive urinary bladder. Bethanechol, a drug that mimics acetylcholine's autonomic effects, is prescribed to manage his problem. First explain the rationale for prescribing bethanechol, and then predict which of the following adverse effects Mr. Johnson might experience while taking this drug (select all that apply): dizziness, low blood pressure, deficient tear formation, wheezing, increased mucus production in bronchi, deficient salivation, diarrhea, cramping, excessive sweating, undesirable erection of penis.

2. Mr. Jake was admitted to the hospital with excruciating pain in his left shoulder and arm. He was found to have suffered a heart attack. Explain the phenomenon of referred pain as exhibited by Mr. Jake.

3. A 32-year-old woman complains that she has been experiencing aching pains in the medial two fingers of both hands and that during such episodes, the fingers become blanched and then blue. Her history is taken, and it is noted that she is a heavy smoker. The physician advises her that she must stop smoking and states that he will not prescribe any medication until she has discontinued smoking for a month. What is this woman's problem, and why was she told to stop smoking?

4. Tiffany, a 21-year-old college student, had been having trouble sleeping, crying frequently, and having recurrent thoughts of suicide. She was prescribed an antidepressant. Like many such drugs, this antidepressant has anticholinergic side effects. What side effects might Tiffany experience in the first week of treatment?

5. As the aroma of freshly brewed coffee drifted by dozing Henry's nose, his mouth started to water and his stomach began to rumble. Explain his reactions in terms of ANS activity.

 Access everything you need to practice, review, and self-assess for both your A&P lecture and lab courses at **myA&P** (www.myaandp.com). There, you'll find powerful online resources, including chapter quizzes and tests, games, A&P Flix animations with quizzes, *Interactive Physiology*® with quizzes, MP3 Tutor Sessions, Practice Anatomy Lab™, and more to help you get a better grade in your course.

14

15

The Eye and Vision (pp. 548–569)

Accessory Structures of the Eye
(pp. 548–551)

Structure of the Eyeball (pp. 551–556)

Physiology of Vision (pp. 556–569)

The Chemical Senses: Taste and Smell (pp. 569–574)

The Olfactory Epithelium and the Sense of
Smell (pp. 569–571)

Taste Buds and the Sense of Taste
(pp. 571–573)

Homeostatic Imbalances of the Chemical
Senses (pp. 573–574)

The Ear: Hearing and Balance
(pp. 574–588)

Structure of the Ear (pp. 574–577)

Physiology of Hearing (pp. 577–583)

Homeostatic Imbalances of Hearing (p. 583)

Equilibrium and Orientation (pp. 584–588)

Developmental Aspects of the Special Senses (pp. 588–589)

Taste and Smell (p. 588)

Vision (p. 588)

Hearing and Balance (pp. 588–589)

The Special Senses

People are responsive creatures. The aroma of freshly baked bread makes our mouths water. A sudden clap of thunder makes us jump. These stimuli and many others continually greet us and are interpreted by our nervous systems.

We are usually told that we have five senses: touch, taste, smell, sight, and hearing. Actually, touch reflects the activity of the general senses that we considered in Chapter 13. The other four traditional senses— *smell, taste, sight,* and *hearing*—are called **special senses**. Receptors for a fifth special sense, *equilibrium*, are housed in the ear, along with the organ of hearing.

In contrast to the widely distributed general receptors (most of which are modified nerve endings of sensory neurons), the **special sensory receptors** are distinct *receptor cells*. These receptor cells are

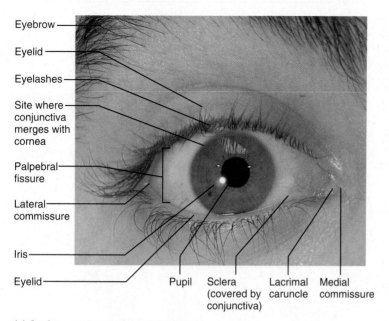

(a) Surface anatomy of the right eye

Figure 15.1 **The eye and accessory structures.**

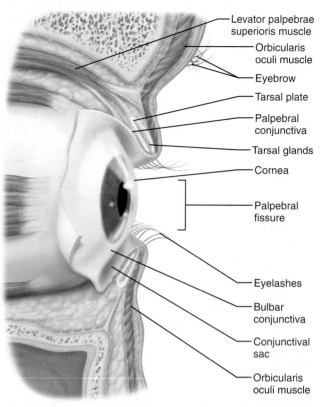

(b) Lateral view; some structures shown in sagittal section

confined to the head region and are highly localized, either housed within complex sensory organs (eyes and ears) or in distinct epithelial structures (taste buds and olfactory epithelium).

In this chapter we consider the functional anatomy of each of the five special senses. But keep in mind that our perceptions of sensory inputs are overlapping. What we finally experience—our "feel" of the world—is a blending of stimulus effects.

The Eye and Vision

▶ Describe the structure and function of accessory eye structures, eye layers, the lens, and humors of the eye.

▶ Outline the causes and consequences of cataracts and glaucoma.

Vision is our dominant sense: Some 70% of all the sensory receptors in the body are in the eyes, and nearly half of the cerebral cortex is involved in some aspect of visual processing.

The adult **eye** is a sphere with a diameter of about 2.5 cm (1 inch). Only the anterior one-sixth of the eye's surface is visible **(Figure 15.1a)**. The rest is enclosed and protected by a cushion of fat and the walls of the bony orbit. The fat pad occupies nearly all of the orbit not occupied by the eye itself. The eye is a complex structure and only a small portion of its tissues are actually involved in photoreception. Before turning our attention to the eye itself, let us consider the accessory structures that protect it or aid its functioning.

Accessory Structures of the Eye

The **accessory structures** of the eye include the eyebrows, eyelids, conjunctiva, lacrimal apparatus, and extrinsic eye muscles.

Eyebrows

The **eyebrows** are short, coarse hairs that overlie the supraorbital margins of the skull (Figure 15.1). They help shade the eyes from sunlight and prevent perspiration trickling down the forehead from reaching the eyes. Deep to the skin of the eyebrows are parts of the orbicularis oculi and corrugator muscles. Contraction of the orbicularis muscle depresses the eyebrow, whereas the corrugator moves the eyebrow medially.

Eyelids

Anteriorly, the eyes are protected by the mobile **eyelids** or **palpebrae** (pal′pĕ-bre). The eyelids are separated by the **palpebral fissure** ("eyelid slit") and meet at the medial and lateral angles of the eye—the **medial** and **lateral commissures** (*canthi*), respectively (Figure 15.1a).

The medial commissure sports a fleshy elevation called the **lacrimal caruncle** (kar′ung-kl; "a bit of flesh"). The caruncle contains sebaceous and sweat glands and produces the whitish, oily secretion (fancifully called the Sandman's eyesand) that sometimes collects at the medial commissure, especially during sleep. In most Asian peoples, a vertical fold of skin called the *epicanthic fold* commonly appears on both sides of the nose and sometimes covers the medial commissure.

The eyelids are thin, skin-covered folds supported internally by connective tissue sheets called **tarsal plates** (Figure 15.1b).

The tarsal plates also anchor the orbicularis oculi and **levator palpebrae superioris** muscles that run within the eyelid. The orbicularis muscle encircles the eye, and the eye closes when it contracts. Of the two eyelids, the larger, upper one is much more mobile, mainly because of the levator palpebrae superioris muscle, which raises that eyelid to open the eye.

The eyelid muscles are activated reflexively to cause blinking every 3–7 seconds and to protect the eye when it is threatened by foreign objects. Reflex blinking helps prevent drying of the eyes because each time we blink, accessory structure secretions (oil, mucus, and saline solution) are spread across the eyeball surface.

Projecting from the free margin of each eyelid are the **eyelashes**. The follicles of the eyelash hairs are richly innervated by nerve endings (hair follicle receptors), and anything that touches the eyelashes (even a puff of air) triggers reflex blinking.

Several types of glands are associated with the eyelids. The **tarsal glands** (*Meibomian glands*; mi-bo′me-an) are embedded in the tarsal plates (Figure 15.1b), and their ducts open at the eyelid edge just posterior to the eyelashes. These modified sebaceous glands produce an oily secretion that lubricates the eyelid and the eye and prevents the eyelids from sticking together. Associated with the eyelash follicles are a number of smaller, more typical sebaceous glands, and modified sweat glands called *ciliary glands* lie between the hair follicles (*cilium* = eyelash).

HOMEOSTATIC IMBALANCE

Infection of a tarsal gland results in an unsightly cyst called a *chalazion* (kah-la′ze-on; "swelling"). Inflammation of any of the smaller glands is called a *sty*. ■

Conjunctiva

The **conjunctiva** (kon″junk-ti′vah; "joined together") is a transparent mucous membrane. It lines the eyelids as the **palpebral conjunctiva** and reflects (folds back) over the anterior surface of the eyeball as the **bulbar conjunctiva** (Figure 15.1b). The bulbar conjunctiva covers only the white of the eye, not the cornea (the clear "window" over the iris and pupil). The bulbar conjunctiva is very thin, and blood vessels are clearly visible beneath it. (They are even more visible in irritated "bloodshot" eyes.)

When the eye is closed, a slitlike space occurs between the conjunctiva-covered eyeball and eyelids. This so-called **conjunctival sac** is where a contact lens lies, and eye medications are often administered into its inferior recess. The major function of the conjunctiva is to produce a lubricating mucus that prevents the eyes from drying out.

HOMEOSTATIC IMBALANCE

Inflammation of the conjunctiva, called *conjunctivitis*, results in reddened, irritated eyes. *Pinkeye*, a conjunctival infection caused by bacteria or viruses, is highly contagious. ■

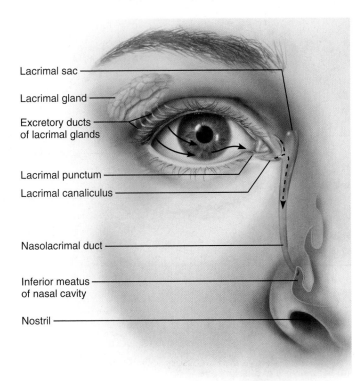

Figure 15.2 The lacrimal apparatus. Arrows indicate the flow of lacrimal fluid (tears) from the lacrimal gland to the nasal cavity.

Lacrimal Apparatus

The **lacrimal apparatus** (lak′rĭ-mal; "tear") consists of the lacrimal gland and the ducts that drain excess lacrimal secretions into the nasal cavity **(Figure 15.2)**. The **lacrimal gland** lies in the orbit above the lateral end of the eye and is visible through the conjunctiva when the lid is everted. It continually releases a dilute saline solution called **lacrimal secretion**—or, more commonly, **tears**—into the superior part of the conjunctival sac through several small excretory ducts.

Blinking spreads the tears downward and across the eyeball to the medial commissure, where they enter the paired **lacrimal canaliculi** via two tiny openings called **lacrimal puncta** (literally, "prick points"), visible as tiny red dots on the medial margin of each eyelid. From the lacrimal canaliculi, the tears drain into the **lacrimal sac** and then into the **nasolacrimal duct**, which empties into the nasal cavity at the inferior nasal meatus.

Lacrimal fluid contains mucus, antibodies, and **lysozyme**, an enzyme that destroys bacteria. Thus, it cleanses and protects the eye surface as it moistens and lubricates it. When lacrimal secretion increases substantially, tears spill over the eyelids and fill the nasal cavities, causing congestion and the "sniffles." This spillover (tearing) happens when the eyes are irritated and when we are emotionally upset. In the case of eye irritation, enhanced tearing serves to wash away or dilute the irritating substance. The importance of emotionally induced tears is poorly understood.

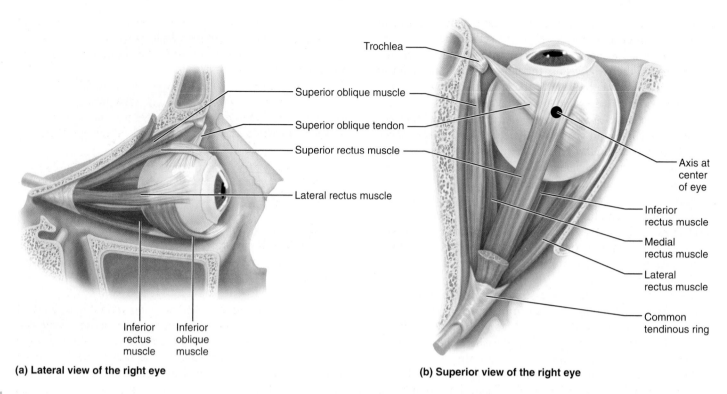

Trochlea
Superior oblique muscle
Superior oblique tendon
Superior rectus muscle
Lateral rectus muscle
Inferior rectus muscle
Inferior oblique muscle

(a) Lateral view of the right eye

Axis at center of eye
Inferior rectus muscle
Medial rectus muscle
Lateral rectus muscle
Common tendinous ring

(b) Superior view of the right eye

Muscle	Action	Controlling cranial nerve
Lateral rectus	Moves eye laterally	VI (abducens)
Medial rectus	Moves eye medially	III (oculomotor)
Superior rectus	Elevates eye and turns it medially	III (oculomotor)
Inferior rectus	Depresses eye and turns it medially	III (oculomotor)
Inferior oblique	Elevates eye and turns it laterally	III (oculomotor)
Superior oblique	Depresses eye and turns it laterally	IV (trochlear)

(c) Summary of muscle actions and innervating cranial nerves

Figure 15.3 Extrinsic eye muscles.

HOMEOSTATIC IMBALANCE

Because the nasal cavity mucosa is continuous with that of the lacrimal duct system, a cold or nasal inflammation often causes the lacrimal mucosa to become inflamed and swell. This swelling constricts the ducts and prevents tears from draining from the eye surface, causing "watery" eyes. ■

Extrinsic Eye Muscles

How do our eyes move? Six straplike **extrinsic eye muscles** control the movement of each eyeball. These muscles originate from the bony orbit and insert into the outer surface of the eyeball (Figure 15.3). They allow the eyes to follow a moving object, and provide external "guy-wires" that help to maintain the shape of the eyeball and hold it in the orbit.

The four *rectus muscles* originate from the **common tendinous ring** (or annular ring) at the back of the orbit and run straight to their insertion on the eyeball. Their locations and the movements that they promote are clearly indicated by

their names: **superior**, **inferior**, **lateral**, and **medial rectus muscles**.

The actions of the two *oblique muscles* are less easy to deduce because they take rather strange paths through the orbit. They move the eye in the vertical plane when the eyeball is already turned medially by the rectus muscles. The **superior oblique muscle** originates in common with the rectus muscles, runs along the medial wall of the orbit, and then makes a right-angle turn and passes through a fibrocartilaginous loop suspended from the frontal bone called the **trochlea** (trok′le-ah; "pulley") before inserting on the superolateral aspect of the eyeball. It rotates the eye downward and somewhat laterally.

The **inferior oblique muscle** originates from the medial orbit surface and runs laterally and obliquely to insert on the inferolateral eye surface. It rotates the eye up and laterally.

The four rectus muscles would seem to provide all the eye movements we require—medial, lateral, superior, and inferior—so why the two oblique muscles? The simplest way to answer this question is to point out that the superior and inferior recti cannot elevate or depress the eye *without also turning it medially* because they approach the eye from a posteromedial direction. For an eye to be *directly* elevated or depressed, the lateral pull of the oblique muscles is necessary to cancel the medial pull of the superior and inferior recti.

Except for the lateral rectus and superior oblique muscles, which are innervated respectively by the *abducens* and *trochlear nerves*, all extrinsic eye muscles are served by the *oculomotor nerves*. The actions and nerve supply of these muscles are summarized in Figure 15.3c. The courses of the associated cranial nerves are illustrated in Table 13.2.

The extrinsic eye muscles are among the most precisely and rapidly controlled skeletal muscles in the entire body. This precision reflects their high axon-to-muscle-fiber ratio: the motor units of these muscles contain only 8 to 12 muscle cells and in some cases as few as two or three.

HOMEOSTATIC IMBALANCE

When movements of the external muscles of the two eyes are not perfectly coordinated, a person cannot properly focus the images of the same area of the visual field from each eye and so sees two images instead of one. This condition is called **diplopia** (dǐ-plo′pe-ah), or *double vision*. It can result from paralysis or weakness of certain extrinsic muscles, or it may be a temporary consequence of acute alcohol intoxication.

Congenital weakness of the external eye muscles may cause **strabismus** (strah-biz′mus; "cross-eyed"), a condition in which the affected eye rotates medially or laterally. To compensate, the eyes may alternate in focusing on objects. In other cases, only the controllable eye is used, and the brain begins to disregard inputs from the deviant eye, which then becomes functionally blind. Strabismus is treated either with eye exercises to strengthen the weak muscles or by temporarily placing a patch on the stronger eye, which forces the child to use the weaker eye. Surgery is needed for unyielding conditions. ■

Structure of the Eyeball

The eye itself, commonly called the **eyeball**, is a slightly irregular hollow sphere (Figure 15.4). Because the eyeball is shaped roughly like the globe of the earth, it is said to have poles. Its most anterior point is the **anterior pole**, and its most posterior point is the **posterior pole**. Its wall is composed of three layers (formerly called tunics): the fibrous, vascular, and inner layers. Its internal cavity is filled with fluids called *humors* that help to maintain its shape. The lens, the adjustable focusing apparatus of the eye, is supported vertically within the eyeball, dividing it into *anterior* and *posterior segments*, or *cavities*.

Layers Forming the Wall of the Eyeball

Fibrous Layer   The outermost coat of the eye, the **fibrous layer**, is composed of dense avascular connective tissue. It has two obviously different regions: the sclera and the cornea. The **sclera** (skle′rah), forming the posterior portion and the bulk of the fibrous layer, is glistening white and opaque. Seen anteriorly as the "white of the eye," the tough, tendonlike sclera (*sclera* = hard)

protects and shapes the eyeball and provides a sturdy anchoring site for the extrinsic eye muscles. Posteriorly, where the sclera is pierced by the optic nerve, it is continuous with the dura mater of the brain.

The anterior sixth of the fibrous layer is modified to form the transparent **cornea**, which bulges anteriorly from its junction with the sclera. The crystal-clear cornea forms a window that lets light enter the eye, and is a major part of the light-bending apparatus of the eye.

The cornea is covered by epithelial sheets on both faces. The external sheet, a stratified squamous epithelium that helps protect the cornea from abrasion, merges with the bulbar conjunctiva at the sclera-cornea junction. Epithelial cells that continually renew the cornea are located here. The deep *corneal endothelium*, composed of simple squamous epithelium, lines the inner face of the cornea. Its cells have active sodium pumps that maintain the clarity of the cornea by keeping the water content of the cornea low.

The cornea is well supplied with nerve endings, most of which are pain receptors. (For this reason, some people can never adjust to wearing contact lenses.) When the cornea is touched, blinking and increased tearing occur reflexively. Even so, the cornea is the most exposed part of the eye and is very vulnerable to damage from dust, slivers, and the like. Luckily, its capacity for regeneration and repair is extraordinary. Furthermore, the cornea is the only tissue in the body that can be transplanted from one person to another with little or no possibility of rejection. Because it has no blood vessels, it is beyond the reach of the immune system.

Vascular Layer   The **vascular layer** forms the middle coat of the eyeball. Also called the *uvea* (u′ve-ah; "grape"), this pigmented layer has three regions: choroid, ciliary body, and iris (Figure 15.4).

The **choroid** is a blood vessel–rich, dark brown membrane (*choroids* = membranelike) that forms the posterior five-sixths of the vascular layer. Its blood vessels provide nutrition to all eye layers. Its brown pigment, produced by melanocytes, helps absorb light, preventing it from scattering and reflecting within the eye (which would cause visual confusion). The choroid is incomplete posteriorly where the optic nerve leaves the eye.

Anteriorly, the choroid becomes the **ciliary body**, a thickened ring of tissue that encircles the lens. The ciliary body consists chiefly of interlacing smooth muscle bundles called **ciliary muscles**, which are important in controlling lens shape. Near the lens, its posterior surface is thrown into radiating folds called **ciliary processes**, which contain the capillaries that secrete the fluid that fills the cavity of the anterior segment of the eyeball. The **ciliary zonule** (*suspensory ligament*) extends from the ciliary processes to the lens. This halo of fine fibers encircles and helps hold the lens in its upright position in the eye.

The **iris**, the visible colored part of the eye, is the most anterior portion of the vascular layer. Shaped like a flattened doughnut, it lies between the cornea and the lens and is continuous with the ciliary body posteriorly. Its round central opening, the **pupil**, allows light to enter the eye. The iris is made up of two smooth muscle layers with bunches of sticky elastic fibers that

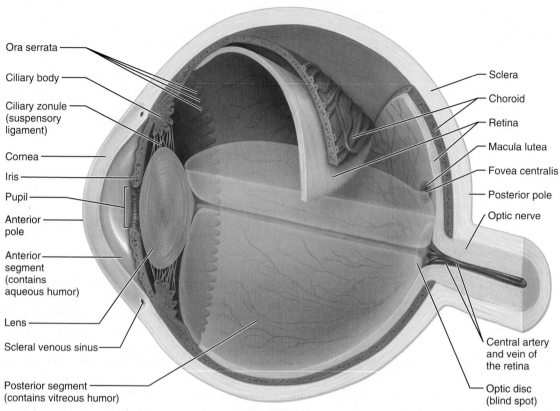

Ora serrata

Ciliary body

Ciliary zonule (suspensory ligament)

Cornea

Iris

Pupil

Anterior pole

Anterior segment (contains aqueous humor)

Lens

Scleral venous sinus

Posterior segment (contains vitreous humor)

Sclera

Choroid

Retina

Macula lutea

Fovea centralis

Posterior pole

Optic nerve

Central artery and vein of the retina

Optic disc (blind spot)

(a) Diagrammatic view. The vitreous humor is illustrated only in the bottom part of the eyeball.

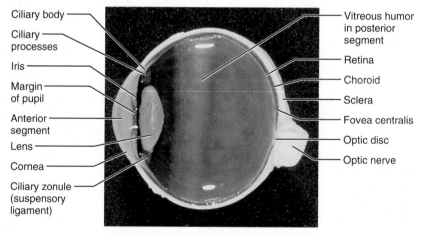

Ciliary body

Ciliary processes

Iris

Margin of pupil

Anterior segment

Lens

Cornea

Ciliary zonule (suspensory ligament)

Vitreous humor in posterior segment

Retina

Choroid

Sclera

Fovea centralis

Optic disc

Optic nerve

(b) Photograph of the human eye.

Figure 15.4 Internal structure of the eye (sagittal section).

congeal into a random pattern before birth. Its muscle fibers allow it to act as a reflexively activated diaphragm to vary pupil size (Figure 15.5). In close vision and bright light, the *sphincter pupillae* (circular muscles) contract and the pupil constricts. In distant vision and dim light, the *dilator pupillae* (radial muscles) contract and the pupil dilates, allowing more light to enter the eye. Pupillary dilation and constriction are controlled by sympathetic and parasympathetic fibers, respectively.

Changes in pupil size may also reflect our interests and emotional reactions to what we are seeing. Our pupils often dilate when the subject matter is appealing, in response to fear, and during problem solving. (Computing your taxes should make your pupils get bigger and bigger.) On the other hand, boredom or subject matter that is personally repulsive causes pupils to constrict.

Although irises come in different colors (*iris* = rainbow), they contain only brown pigment. When they have a lot of pigment, the eyes appear brown or black. If the amount of pigment is small and restricted to the posterior surface of the iris, the shorter wavelengths of light are scattered from the unpigmented parts, and the eyes appear blue, green, or gray. Most newborn babies' eyes are slate gray or blue because their iris pigment is not yet developed.

Inner Layer (Retina)   The innermost layer of the eyeball is the delicate, two-layered **retina** (ret′ĭ-nah). Its outer **pigmented layer**, a single-cell-thick lining, abuts the choroid, and extends anteriorly to cover the ciliary body and the posterior face of the iris. These pigmented epithelial cells, like those of the choroid, absorb light and prevent it from scattering in the eye. They also act as phagocytes to remove dead or damaged photoreceptor cells, and store vitamin A needed by the photoreceptor cells. The transparent inner **neural layer** extends anteriorly to the posterior margin of the ciliary body. This junction is called the **ora serrata**, literally, the saw-toothed margin (see Figure 15.4).

Originating as an outpocketing of the brain, the retina contains millions of photoreceptors that transduce (convert) light energy, other neurons involved in the processing of light stimuli, and glia. Although the pigmented and neural layers are very close together, they are not fused. Only the neural layer of the retina plays a direct role in vision.

From posterior to anterior, the neural layer is composed of three main types of neurons: **photoreceptors**, **bipolar cells**, and **ganglion cells** (Figure 15.6). Signals are produced in response to light and spread from the photoreceptors (abutting the pigmented layer) to the bipolar cells and then to the innermost ganglion cells, where action potentials are generated. The ganglion cell axons make a right-angle turn at the inner face of the retina, then leave the posterior aspect of the eye as the thick optic nerve. The retina also contains other types of neurons—horizontal cells and amacrine cells—which play a role in visual processing. The **optic disc**, where the optic nerve exits the eye, is a weak spot in the **fundus** (posterior wall) of the eye because it is not reinforced by the sclera. The optic disc is also called the **blind spot** because it lacks photoreceptors, so light focused on it cannot be seen. Nonetheless, we do not usually notice these gaps in our vision because the brain uses a sophisticated process called *filling in* to deal with absence of input.

The quarter-billion photoreceptors found in the neural retinas are of two types: rods and cones. The more numerous **rods** are our dim-light and peripheral vision receptors. They are far more sensitive to light than cones are, but they do not provide either sharp images or color vision. This is why colors are indistinct and edges of objects appear fuzzy in dim light and at the edges of our visual field. **Cones**, by contrast, operate in bright light and provide high-acuity color vision.

Lateral to the blind spot of each eye, and located precisely at the eye's posterior pole, is an oval region called the **macula lutea** (mak′u-lah lu′te-ah; "yellow spot") with a minute (0.4 mm) pit in its center called the **fovea centralis** (see Figure 15.4). In this region, the retinal structures abutting the vitreous humor are displaced to the sides. This allows light to pass almost directly to the photoreceptors rather than through several retinal layers, greatly enhancing visual acuity. The fovea contains only cones, the macula contains mostly cones, and from the edge of the macula toward the retina periphery, cone density declines gradually. The retina periphery contains mostly rods, which continuously decrease in density from there to the macula.

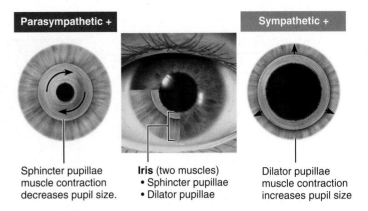

Sphincter pupillae muscle contraction decreases pupil size.

Iris (two muscles)
• Sphincter pupillae
• Dilator pupillae

Dilator pupillae muscle contraction increases pupil size

Figure 15.5 Pupil dilation and constriction, anterior view. (+ means activation.)

Only the foveae (plural of fovea) have a sufficient cone density to provide detailed color vision, so anything we wish to view critically is focused on the foveae. Because each fovea is only about the size of the head of a pin, not more than a thousandth of the entire visual field is in *hard focus* (foveal focus) at a given moment. Consequently, for us to visually comprehend a scene that is rapidly changing (as when we drive in traffic), our eyes must flick rapidly back and forth to provide the foveae with images of different parts of the visual field.

The neural retina receives its blood supply from two sources. The outer third (containing photoreceptors) is supplied by vessels in the choroid. The inner two-thirds is served by the **central artery** and **central vein of the retina**, which enter and leave the eye through the center of the optic nerve (see Figure 15.4a). Radiating outward from the optic disc, these vessels give rise to a rich vascular network that is clearly seen when the eyeball interior is examined with an ophthalmoscope (Figure 15.7). The fundus of the eye is the only place in the body where small blood vessels can be observed directly in a living person.

HOMEOSTATIC IMBALANCE

The pattern of vascularization of the retina makes it susceptible to *retinal detachment*. This condition, in which the pigmented and neural layers separate (detach) and allow the jellylike vitreous humor to seep between them, can cause permanent blindness because it deprives the photoreceptors of their nutrient source. It usually happens when the retina is torn during a traumatic blow to the head or when the head stops moving suddenly and then is jerked in the opposite direction (as in bungee jumping). The symptom that victims most often describe is "a curtain being drawn across the eye," but some people see sootlike spots or light flashes. If diagnosed early, it is often possible to reattach the retina with a laser before photoreceptor damage becomes permanent. ■

Internal Chambers and Fluids

As we noted earlier, the lens and its halolike ciliary zonule divide the eye into two segments, the anterior segment in front of the lens and the larger posterior segment behind it (see Figure 15.4a).

15

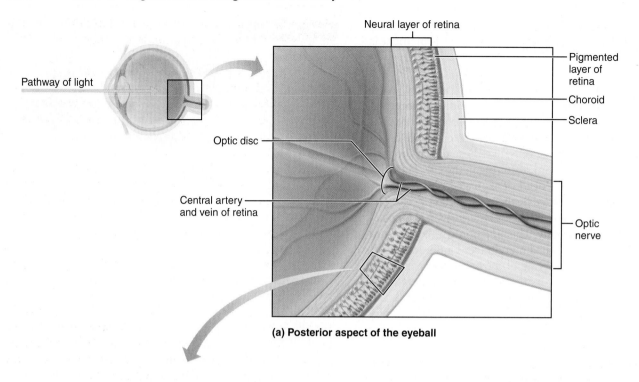

(a) Posterior aspect of the eyeball

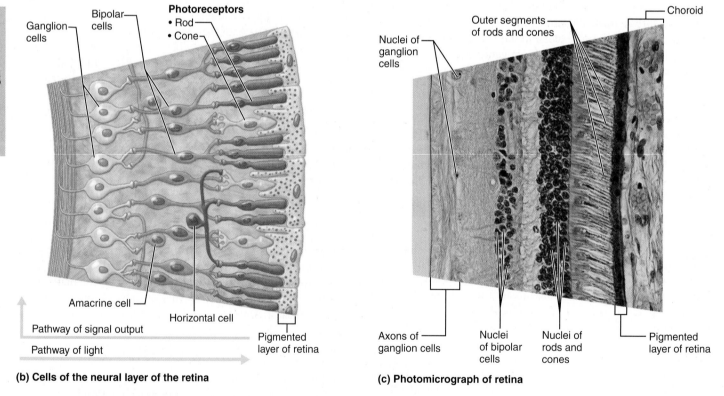

(b) Cells of the neural layer of the retina

(c) Photomicrograph of retina

Figure 15.6 Microscopic anatomy of the retina. (a) The axons of the ganglion cells form the optic nerve, which leaves the back of the eyeball at the optic disc. **(b)** Light (indicated by the yellow arrow) passes through the retina to excite the photoreceptor cells (rods and cones). Information (output signals) flows in the opposite direction via bipolar and ganglion cells. **(c)** Photomicrograph (150×).

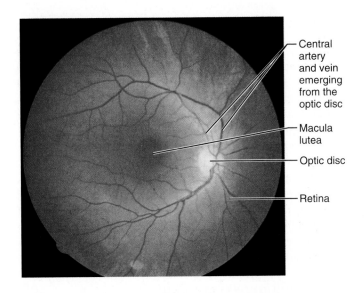

Figure 15.7 Part of the posterior wall (fundus) of the right eye as seen with an ophthalmoscope.

The **posterior segment** is filled with a clear gel called **vitreous humor** (*vitre* = glassy) that binds tremendous amounts of water. Vitreous humor (1) transmits light, (2) supports the posterior surface of the lens and holds the neural retina firmly against the pigmented layer, and (3) contributes to intraocular pressure, helping to counteract the pulling force of the extrinsic eye muscles. Vitreous humor forms in the embryo and lasts for a lifetime.

The **anterior segment** is partially subdivided by the iris into the **anterior chamber** (between the cornea and the iris) and the **posterior chamber** (between the iris and the lens) (Figure 15.8). The *entire* anterior segment is filled with **aqueous humor**, a clear fluid similar in composition to blood plasma. Unlike the vitreous humor, aqueous humor forms and drains continually and is in constant motion. It filters from the capillaries of the ciliary processes into the posterior chamber and a portion of it freely diffuses through the vitreous humor in the posterior segment while the remainder flows into the anterior chamber. After flowing through the pupil into the anterior chamber, it drains into the venous blood via the **scleral venous sinus** (*canal of Schlemm*), an unusual venous channel that encircles the eye in the angle at the sclera-cornea junction.

Normally, aqueous humor is produced and drained at the same rate, maintaining a constant intraocular pressure of about 16 mm Hg, which helps to support the eyeball internally. Aqueous humor supplies nutrients and oxygen to the lens and cornea and to some cells of the retina, and it carries away their metabolic wastes.

① Aqueous humor is formed by filtration from the capillaries in the ciliary processes.

② Aqueous humor flows from the posterior chamber through the pupil into the anterior chamber. Some also flows through the vitreous humor (not shown).

③ Aqueous humor is reabsorbed into the venous blood by the scleral venous sinus.

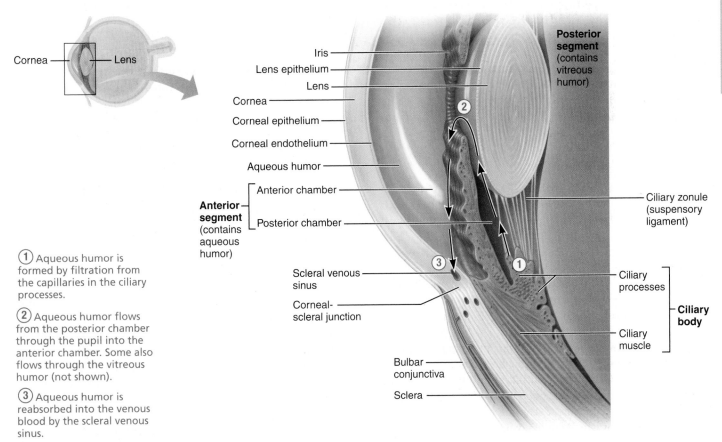

Figure 15.8 Circulation of aqueous humor. The arrows indicate the circulation pathway.

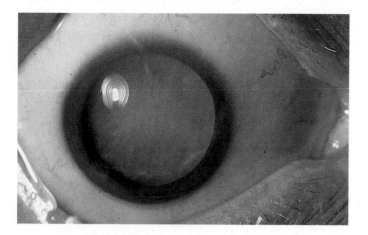

Figure 15.9 Photograph of a cataract. The lens is milky and opaque, not the cornea.

![HOMEOSTATIC IMBALANCE icon] **HOMEOSTATIC IMBALANCE**

If the drainage of aqueous humor is blocked, fluid backs up as in a clogged sink. Pressure within the eye may increase to dangerous levels and compress the retina and optic nerve—a condition called **glaucoma** (glaw-ko′mah). The eventual result is blindness (*glaucoma* = vision growing gray) unless the condition is detected early. Unfortunately, many forms of glaucoma steal sight so slowly and painlessly that people do not realize they have a problem until the damage is done. Late signs include seeing halos around lights and blurred vision.

The glaucoma examination is simple. The intraocular pressure is determined by directing a puff of air at the cornea and measuring the amount of corneal deformation it causes. This exam should be done yearly after the age of 40. The most common treatment is eye drops that increase the rate of aqueous humor drainage or decrease its production. Laser therapy or surgery can also be used. ■

Lens

The **lens** is a biconvex, transparent, flexible structure that can change shape to allow precise focusing of light on the retina. It is enclosed in a thin, elastic capsule and held in place just posterior to the iris by the ciliary zonule (Figure 15.8). Like the cornea, the lens is avascular; blood vessels interfere with transparency.

The lens has two regions: the **lens epithelium** and the lens fibers. The lens epithelium, confined to the anterior lens surface, consists of cuboidal cells that eventually differentiate into the **lens fibers** that form the bulk of the lens. The lens fibers, which are packed tightly together like the layers in an onion, contain no nuclei and few organelles. They do, however, contain transparent, precisely folded proteins called **crystallins** that form the body of the lens. Since new lens fibers are continually added, the lens enlarges throughout life, becoming denser, more convex, and less elastic, all of which gradually impair its ability to focus light properly.

![HOMEOSTATIC IMBALANCE icon] **HOMEOSTATIC IMBALANCE**

A **cataract** ("waterfall") is a clouding of the lens that causes the world to appear distorted, as if seen through frosted glass **(Figure 15.9)**. Some cataracts are congenital, but most result from age-related hardening and thickening of the lens or are a secondary consequence of diabetes mellitus. Heavy smoking and frequent exposure to intense sunlight increase the risk for cataracts, whereas long-term dietary supplementation with vitamin C may decrease the risk.

Whatever the promoting factors, the *direct* cause of cataracts seems to be inadequate delivery of nutrients to the deeper lens fibers. The metabolic changes that result promote clumping of the crystallin proteins. Fortunately, the offending lens can be surgically removed and an artificial lens implanted to save the patient's sight. ■

CHECK YOUR UNDERSTANDING

1. What are tears and what structure secretes them?
2. What is the blind spot and why is it blind?
3. Sam's optometrist tells him that his intraocular pressure is high. What is this condition called and which fluid does it involve?

For answers, see Appendix G.

Physiology of Vision

▶ Trace the pathway of light through the eye to the retina, and explain how light is focused for distant and close vision.

▶ Outline the causes and consequences of astigmatism, myopia, hyperopia, and presbyopia.

Overview: Light and Optics

To really comprehend the function of the eye as a photoreceptor organ, we need to understand the properties of light.

Wavelength and Color **Electromagnetic radiation** includes all energy waves, from long radio waves (with wavelengths measured in meters) to very short gamma (γ) waves and X rays with wavelengths of 1 nm and less. Our eyes respond to the part of the spectrum called **visible light**, which has a wavelength range of approximately 400–700 nm **(Figure 15.10a)**. (1 nm = 10^{-9} m, or one-billionth of a meter.)

Visible light travels in the form of waves, and its wavelengths can be measured very accurately. However, light can also be envisioned as small particles or packets of energy called **photons** or **quanta**. Attempts to reconcile these two findings have led to the present concept of light as packets of energy (photons) traveling in a wavelike fashion at very high speeds (300,000 km/s or about 186,000 mi/s). We can think of light as a vibration of pure energy ("a bright wiggle") rather than a material substance.

When visible light passes through a prism, each of its component waves bends to a different degree, so that the beam of light is dispersed and a **visible spectrum**, or band of colors, is

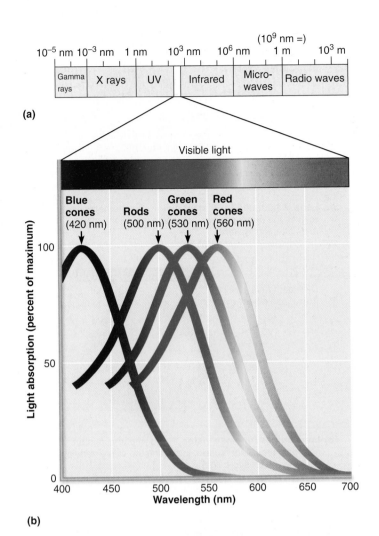

(a)

(b)

Figure 15.10 **The electromagnetic spectrum and photorecep-tor sensitivities. (a)** The electromagnetic spectrum, of which visible light constitutes only a small portion. (nm = nanometers.) **(b)** Sensitivities of rods and the three cone types to the different wavelengths of the visible spectrum.

Figure 15.11 **Refraction.** A spoon standing in a glass of water appears to be broken at the water-air interface. This occurs because light is bent toward the perpendicular when it travels from a less dense to a more dense medium, as from air to water in this example.

seen (Figure 15.10b). (In the same manner, the rainbow seen during a summer shower represents the collective prismatic effects of all the tiny water droplets suspended in air.) Red wave-lengths are the longest and have the lowest energy, whereas the violet wavelengths are the shortest and most energetic. Objects have color because they absorb some wavelengths and reflect others. Things that look white reflect all wavelengths of light, whereas black objects absorb them all. A red apple reflects mostly red light, while grass reflects more of the green.

Refraction and Lenses Light travels in straight lines and is blocked by any nontransparent object. Like sound, light can re-flect, or bounce, off a surface. This **reflection** of light by objects in our environment accounts for most of the light reaching our eyes.

When light travels in a given medium, its speed is constant. But when it passes from one transparent medium into another with a different density, its speed changes. Light speeds up as it passes into a less dense medium and slows as it passes into a denser medium. Because of these changes in speed, bending or

refraction of a light ray occurs when it meets the surface of a different medium at an oblique angle rather than at a right an-gle (perpendicular). The greater this angle, the greater the amount of bending. **Figure 15.11** shows refraction: A spoon in a glass of water appears to break at the air-water interface.

A lens is a transparent object curved on one or both surfaces. Since light hits the curve at an angle, it is refracted. If the lens surface is convex, that is, thickest in the center like a camera lens, the light rays are bent so that they converge (come together) or intersect at a single point called the **focal point (Figure 15.12a).** In general, the thicker (more convex) the lens, the more the light is bent and the shorter the focal distance (distance between the lens and focal point). The image formed by a convex lens, called a **real image**, is inverted—upside down and reversed from left to right (Figure 15.12b).

Concave lenses, which are thicker at the edges than at the center, diverge the light (bend it outward) so that the light rays move away from each other. Consequently, concave lenses pre-vent light from focusing and extend the focal distance.

Focusing of Light on the Retina

As light passes from air into the eye, it moves sequentially through the cornea, aqueous humor, lens, and vitreous humor, and then passes *through the entire thickness of the neural layer of the retina* to excite the photoreceptors that abut the pigmented layer (see Figures 15.4 and 15.6). During its passage, light is bent three times: as it enters the cornea and on entering and leaving the lens. The refractory power of the humors and cornea is

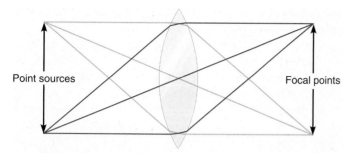

(a) Focusing of two points of light.

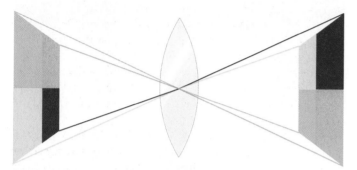

(b) The image is inverted—upside down and reversed.

Figure 15.12 Bending of light by a convex lens.

constant. On the other hand, the lens is highly elastic, and its curvature and light-bending power can be actively changed to allow fine focusing of the image.

Focusing for Distant Vision Our eyes are best adapted ("preset to focus") for distant vision. To look at distant objects, we need only aim our eyeballs so that they are both fixated on the same spot. The **far point of vision** is that distance beyond which no change in lens shape (accommodation) is needed for focusing. For the normal or **emmetropic** (em″ĕ-tro′pik) eye, the far point is 6 m (20 feet).

Any object being viewed can be said to consist of many small points, with light radiating outward in all directions from each point. However, because distant objects appear smaller, light from an object at or beyond the far point of vision approaches the eyes as nearly parallel rays and is focused precisely on the retina by the fixed refractory apparatus (cornea and humors) and the at-rest lens (Figure 15.13a).

During distant vision, the sphincterlike ciliary muscles are completely relaxed, and the lens is stretched flat by tension in the ciliary zonule. Consequently, the lens is as thin as it gets and is at its lowest refractory power. The ciliary muscles relax when sympathetic input to them increases and parasympathetic input decreases.

Focusing for Close Vision Light from close objects (less than 6 m away) diverges as it approaches the eyes and it comes to a focal point farther from the lens. For this reason, close vision demands that the eye make active adjustments. To restore focus, three processes must occur simultaneously: accommodation of the lenses, constriction of the pupils, and convergence of the

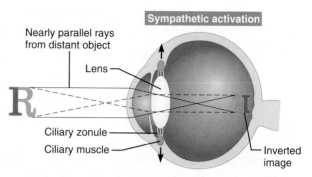

(a) Lens is flattened for distant vision. Sympathetic input relaxes the ciliary muscle, tightening the ciliary zonule, and flattening the lens.

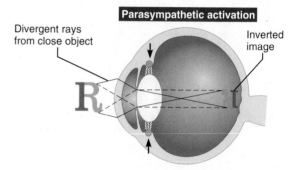

(b) Lens bulges for close vision. Parasympathetic input contracts the ciliary muscle, loosening the ciliary zonule, allowing the lens to bulge.

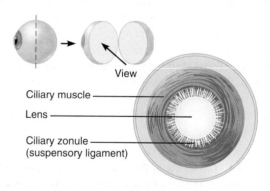

(c) The ciliary muscle and ciliary zonule are arranged sphincterlike around the lens. (Anterior segment as viewed from within the eye.)

Figure 15.13 Focusing for distant and close vision.

eyeballs. The signal that induces this trio of reflex responses appears to be a blurring of the retinal image.

1. **Accommodation of the lenses. Accommodation** is the process that increases the refractory power of the lens. As the ciliary muscles contract, the ciliary body is pulled anteriorly and inward toward the pupil and releases tension in the ciliary zonule. No longer stretched, the elastic lens recoils and bulges, providing the shorter focal length needed to focus the image of a close object on the retina

(Figure 15.13b). Contraction of the ciliary muscles is controlled mainly by the parasympathetic fibers of the oculomotor nerves.

The closest point on which we can focus clearly is called the **near point of vision**, and it represents the maximum bulge the lens can achieve. In young adults with emmetropic vision, the near point is 10 cm (4 inches) from the eye. However, it is closer in children and gradually recedes with age, explaining why children can hold their books very close to their faces while many elderly people must hold the newspaper at arm's length. The gradual loss of accommodation with age reflects the lens's decreasing elasticity. In many people over the age of 50, the lens is nonaccommodating, a condition known as **presbyopia** (pres″be-o′pe-ah), literally "old person's vision."

2. **Constriction of the pupils.** The sphincter pupillae muscles of the iris enhance the effect of accommodation by reducing the size of the pupil toward 2 mm (see Figure 15.5). This **accommodation pupillary reflex**, mediated by parasympathetic fibers of the oculomotor nerves, prevents the most divergent light rays from entering the eye. Such rays would pass through the extreme edge of the lens and would not be focused properly, and so would cause blurred vision.

3. **Convergence of the eyeballs.** The visual goal is always to keep the object being viewed focused on the retinal foveae. When we look at distant objects, both eyes are directed either straight ahead or to one side to the same degree, but when we fixate on a close object, our eyes converge. **Convergence**, controlled by somatic motor fibers of the oculomotor nerves, is medial rotation of the eyeballs by the medial rectus muscles so that each is directed toward the object being viewed. The closer that object, the greater the degree of convergence required. For example, when you focus on the tip of your nose, you "go cross-eyed."

Reading or other close work requires almost continuous accommodation, pupillary constriction, and convergence. This is why prolonged periods of reading tire the eye muscles and can result in eyestrain. When you read for an extended time, it is helpful to look up and stare into the distance occasionally to relax the intrinsic eye muscles.

HOMEOSTATIC IMBALANCE

Theoretically, visual problems related to refraction could result from a hyperrefractive (overconverging) or hyporefractive (underconverging) lens or from structural abnormalities of the eyeball. In practice, 99% of refractive problems are related to eyeball shape—either too long or too short.

Myopia (mi-o′pe-ah; "short vision") occurs when distant objects are focused in front of the retina, rather than on it (**Figure 15.14**, left). Myopic people see close objects without problems because they can focus them on the retina, but distant objects are blurred. The common name for myopia is *nearsightedness*. (Notice that this terminology names the aspect

of vision that is *unimpaired*.) Myopia typically results from an eyeball that is too long.

Correction has traditionally involved use of concave lenses that diverge the light before it enters the eye. Procedures to flatten the cornea slightly—laser procedures called PRK and LASIK—now offer other treatment options.

Hyperopia (hy′per-o″pe-ah; "far vision"), or *farsightedness*, occurs when the parallel light rays from distant objects are focused *behind* the retina (Figure 15.14, right). Hyperopic individuals can see distant objects perfectly well because their ciliary muscles contract almost continuously to increase the light-bending power of the lens, which moves the focal point forward onto the retina. However, diverging light rays from *nearby* objects are focused so far behind the retina that the lens cannot bring the focal point onto the retina even at its full refractory power. As a result, close objects appear blurry, and convex corrective lenses are needed to converge the light more strongly for close vision. Hyperopia usually results from an eyeball that is too short.

Unequal curvatures in different parts of the cornea or lens lead to blurry images. This refractory problem is **astigmatism** (*astigma* = not a point). Special cylindrically ground lenses, corneal implants, or laser procedures are used to correct this problem. ∎

CHECK YOUR UNDERSTANDING

4. Arrange the following in the order that light passes through them to reach the photoreceptors (rods and cones) in the retina: lens, bipolar cells, vitreous humor, cornea, aqueous humor, ganglion cells. (Hint: See Figure 15.6 if you need a reminder of where ganglion cells and bipolar cells are.)

5. You have been reading this book for a while now and your eyes are beginning to tire. Which intrinsic eye muscles are relaxing as you stare thoughtfully into the distance?

6. Why does your near point of vision move farther away as you age?

For answers, see Appendix G.

Photoreceptors and Phototransduction

▶ Describe the events involved in the stimulation of photoreceptors by light, and compare and contrast the roles of rods and cones in vision.

▶ Compare and contrast light and dark adaptation.

Once light is focused on the retina, the photoreceptors come into play. First, we will describe the functional anatomy of the rod and cone photoreceptor cells, then the chemistry and response of their visual pigments to light, and finally, photoreceptor activation and phototransduction. **Phototransduction** is the process by which light energy is converted into a graded receptor potential.

Functional Anatomy of the Photoreceptors Photoreceptors are modified neurons, but structurally they resemble tall

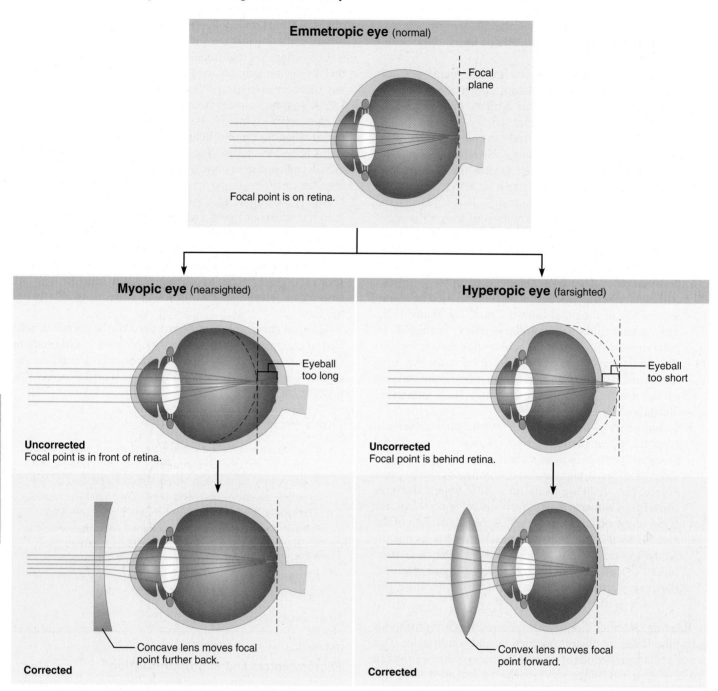

Figure 15.14 **Problems of refraction.** The refractive power of the cornea, which normally supplies about two-thirds of the light-bending power of the eye, is ignored here.

epithelial cells turned upside down with their "tips" immersed in the pigmented layer of the retina **(Figure 15.15a)**. These "tips" are the receptive regions of rods and cones and are called the **outer segments**. Moving from the pigmented layer into the neural layer, the outer segment of a rod or cone is joined to an **inner segment** by a connecting cilium. The inner segment then connects to the *cell body*, which is continuous with an *inner fiber* bearing *synaptic terminals*. In rods, the outer segment is slender and rod shaped (hence their name) and the inner segment connects to the cell body by the *outer fiber*. By contrast, the cones

have a short conical outer segment and the inner segment directly joins the cell body.

The outer segments contain an elaborate array of **visual pigments (photopigments)** that change shape as they absorb light. These pigments are embedded in areas of the plasma membrane that form discs (Figure 15.15b). Folding the plasma membrane into discs increases the surface area available for trapping light. In cones, the disc membranes are continuous with the plasma membrane, so the interiors of the cone discs are continuous with the extracellular space. In rods, the discs are

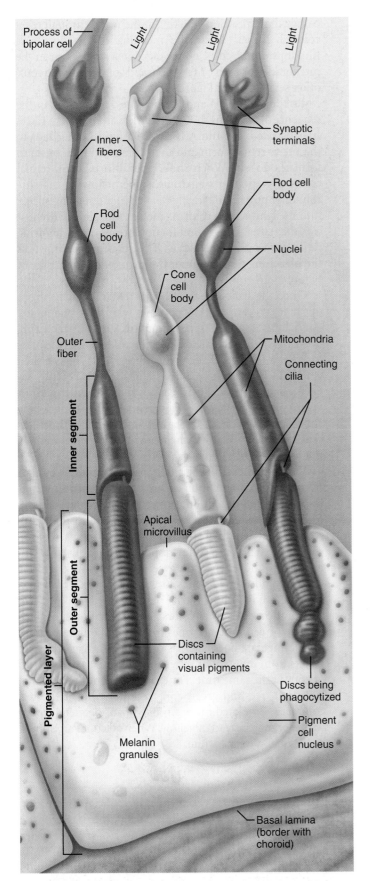

(a) **The outer segments of rods and cones are embedded in the pigmented layer of the retina.**

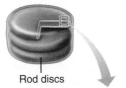

Rod discs

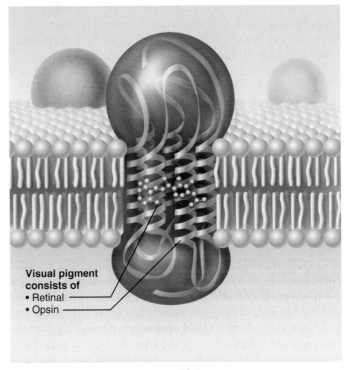

Visual pigment consists of
• **Retinal**
• **Opsin**

(b) **Rhodopsin, the visual pigment in rods, is embedded in the membrane that forms discs in the outer segment.**

Figure 15.15 **Photoreceptors of the retina.**

discontinuous—stacked inside a cylinder of plasma membrane like pennies in a coin wrapper.

The photoreceptor cells are highly vulnerable to damage and immediately begin to degenerate if the retina becomes detached. They are also destroyed by intense light, the very energy they are designed to detect. How is it, then, that we do not all gradually go blind? The answer lies in the photoreceptors' unique system for renewing their light-trapping outer segment. In rods, new discs are assembled at the proximal end of the outer segment from materials synthesized in the cell body at the end of each night. As new discs are made, they push the others peripherally. The discs at the tip of the outer segment continually fragment off and are phagocytized by cells of the pigmented layer. The tips of the outer segments of cones are also removed and renewed, but at the end of each day.

The rods and each of the three cone types contain unique visual pigments that absorb different wavelengths of light. Rods and cones also have different thresholds for activation. Rods, for example, (1) are very sensitive (respond to very dim light—a single photon), making them best suited for night vision and peripheral vision, and (2) contain a single kind of visual pigment so their inputs are perceived only in gray tones. Cones (1) need bright light for activation (have low sensitivity), but (2) have one of three different pigments that furnish a vividly colored view of the world.

Rods and cones are also "wired" differently to other retinal neurons. Rods participate in converging pathways, and as many as 100 rods may ultimately feed into each ganglion cell. As a result, rod effects are summated and considered collectively, resulting in vision that is fuzzy and indistinct. (The visual cortex has no way of knowing exactly *which* rods of the large number influencing a particular ganglion cell are actually activated.)

In contrast, each cone in the fovea (or at most a few) has a straight-through pathway via its "own personal bipolar cell" to a ganglion cell (see Figure 15.6b). Essentially, each cone has its own "labeled line" to the higher visual centers. This straight-through pathway accounts for the detailed, high-resolution views of very small areas of the visual field provided by cones.

Because rods are absent from the foveae and cones do not respond to low-intensity light, we see dimly lit objects best when we do not look at them directly, and we recognize them best when they move. If you doubt this, go out into your backyard on a moonlit evening and see how much you can actually discriminate.

The Chemistry of Visual Pigments

How does light affect the photoreceptors so that it is ultimately translated into electrical signals? The key is a light-absorbing molecule called **retinal** that combines with proteins called **opsins** to form four types of visual pigments. Depending on the type of opsin to which it is bound, retinal preferentially absorbs different wavelengths of the visible spectrum.

Retinal is chemically related to vitamin A and is made from it. The liver stores vitamin A and releases it as needed by the photoreceptors to make their visual pigments. The cells of the pigmented layer of the retina absorb vitamin A from the blood and serve as the local vitamin A depot for the rods and cones.

Retinal can assume a variety of distinct three-dimensional forms, each form called an isomer. When bound to opsin, retinal has a bent, or kinked, shape called **11-*cis*-retinal**, as shown at the top of Figure 15.16. However, when the pigment is struck by light and absorbs photons, retinal twists and snaps into a new configuration, **all-*trans*-retinal**, shown at the bottom of Figure 15.16. This change, in turn, causes opsin to change shape and assume its activated form.

The capture of light by visual pigments is the *only* light-dependent stage, and this simple photochemical event initiates a whole chain of chemical and electrical reactions in rods and cones that ultimately causes electrical impulses to be transmitted along the optic nerve. Let's look more closely at these events in rods and in cones.

Stimulation of the Photoreceptors

1. **Excitation of rods.** The visual pigment of rods is a deep purple pigment called **rhodopsin** (ro-dop′sin; *rhodo* = rose, *opsis* = vision). (Do you suppose the person who coined the expression "looking at the world through rose-colored glasses" knew the meaning of "rhodopsin"?) Rhodopsin molecules are arranged in a single layer in the membranes of each of the thousands of discs in the rods' outer segments (see Figure 15.15b).

Rhodopsin forms and accumulates in the dark in the sequence of reactions shown on the left side of Figure 15.16. As illustrated, vitamin A is oxidized (and isomerized) to the 11-*cis*-retinal form and then combined with opsin to form rhodopsin. When rhodopsin absorbs light, retinal changes shape to its all-*trans* isomer, allowing the surrounding protein to quickly relax like an uncoiling spring into its light-activated form (metarhodopsin II). Eventually, the retinal-opsin combination breaks down, allowing retinal and opsin to separate. This sequence is known as the **bleaching of the pigment**, shown on the right side of Figure 15.16.

Once the light-struck all-*trans*-retinal detaches from opsin, it is reconverted by enzymes within the pigmented epithelium to its 11-*cis* isomer in an ATP-requiring process. Then, retinal heads "homeward" again to the photoreceptor cells' outer segments. Rhodopsin is regenerated when 11-*cis*-retinal is rejoined to opsin.

2. **Excitation of cones.** The breakdown and regeneration of visual pigments in cones is essentially the same as for rhodopsin. However, cones are about a hundred times less sensitive than rods, which means that it takes higher-intensity (brighter) light to activate cones.

Visual pigments of the three types of cones, like those of rods, are a combination of retinal and opsins. However, the cone opsins differ both from the opsin of the rods and from one another. The naming of cones reflects the colors (that is, wavelengths) of light that each cone variety absorbs best. The blue cones respond maximally to wavelengths around 420 nm, the green cones to wavelengths of 530 nm, and the red cones to wavelengths at or close to 560 nm (see Figure 15.10b).

How do we see other colors? The absorption spectra of the blue, green, and red cones overlap, and our perception of intermediate hues, such as orange, yellow, and purple, results from differential activation of more than one type of cone at the same time. For example, yellow light stimulates both red and green cone receptors, but if the red cones are stimulated more strongly than the green cones, we see orange instead of yellow. When all cones are stimulated equally, we see white.

HOMEOSTATIC IMBALANCE

Color blindness is due to a congenital lack of one or more of the cone types. Inherited as an X-linked condition, it is far more common in males than in females. As many as 8–10% of males have some form of color blindness.

The most common type is red-green color blindness, resulting from a deficit or absolute absence of either red or green cones. Red and green are seen as the same color—either red or green, depending on the cone type present. Many color-blind

Figure 15.16 The formation and breakdown of rhodopsin. 11-*cis*-retinal can either be regenerated from all-*trans*-retinal or made from vitamin A.

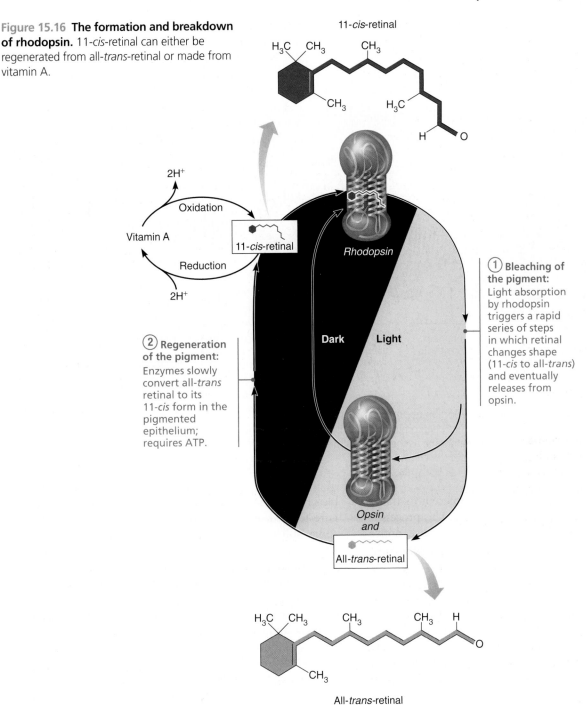

11-*cis*-retinal

① **Bleaching of the pigment:** Light absorption by rhodopsin triggers a rapid series of steps in which retinal changes shape (11-*cis* to all-*trans*) and eventually releases from opsin.

② **Regeneration of the pigment:** Enzymes slowly convert all-*trans* retinal to its 11-*cis* form in the pigmented epithelium; requires ATP.

2H⁺

Oxidation

Vitamin A

11-*cis*-retinal

Reduction

2H⁺

Rhodopsin

Dark **Light**

Opsin and

All-*trans*-retinal

All-*trans*-retinal

15

people are unaware of their condition because they have learned to rely on other cues—such as differences in intensities of the same color—to distinguish something green from something red, such as traffic signals. ■

Light Transduction Reactions What happens when light triggers pigment breakdown? An enzymatic cascade occurs that ultimately results in closing cation channels that are normally kept open in the dark. This process is illustrated in more detail in **Figure 15.17**, but in short, light-activated rhodopsin activates a G protein called **transducin**. Transducin, in turn, activates *PDE* (*phosphodiesterase*), the enzyme that breaks down **cyclic**

GMP (cGMP). In the dark, cGMP binds to cation channels in the outer segments of photoreceptor cells, holding them open. This allows Na^+ and Ca^{2+} to enter, depolarizing the cell to its *dark potential* of about -40 mV. In the light, cGMP breaks down, the cation channels close, Na^+ and Ca^{2+} stop entering the cell, and the cell hyperpolarizes to about -70 mV.

This arrangement can seem bewildering, to say the least. Here we have receptors built to detect light that depolarize in the dark and hyperpolarize when exposed to light! However, all that is required is a signal and hyperpolarization is just as good a signal as depolarization.

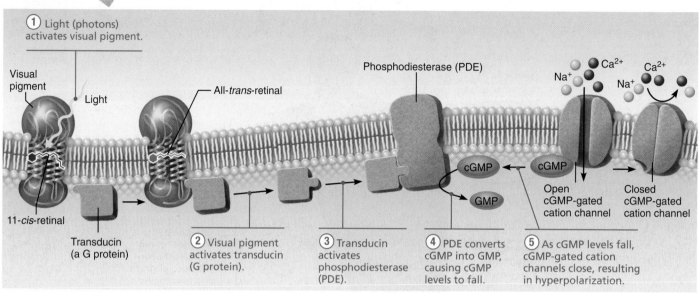

① Light (photons) activates visual pigment.

Visual pigment

Light

All-*trans*-retinal

Phosphodiesterase (PDE)

Na⁺ Ca²⁺ Ca²⁺
Na⁺

cGMP ← cGMP

GMP

Open cGMP-gated cation channel

Closed cGMP-gated cation channel

11-*cis*-retinal

Transducin (a G protein)

② Visual pigment activates transducin (G protein).

③ Transducin activates phosphodiesterase (PDE).

④ PDE converts cGMP into GMP, causing cGMP levels to fall.

⑤ As cGMP levels fall, cGMP-gated cation channels close, resulting in hyperpolarization.

Figure 15.17 Events of phototransduction. A portion of photoreceptor disc membrane is shown. The G protein conversion of GTP to GDP has been omitted for clarity. For simplicity, the cGMP-gated channels are shown on the same membrane as the visual pigment instead of in the plasma membrane.

15

How is the hyperpolarization of the photoreceptors transmitted through the retina and on to the brain? This process is illustrated in **Figure 15.18**. As you study this sequence, notice that the photoreceptors do not generate action potentials (APs), and neither do the bipolar cells that lie between them and the ganglion cells. Photoreceptors and bipolar cells only generate graded potentials—excitatory postsynaptic potentials (EPSPs) and inhibitory postsynaptic potentials (IPSPs). This is not surprising if you remember that the primary function of APs is to carry information rapidly over long distances. Retinal cells are small cells that are very close together. Graded potentials can serve quite adequately as signals that directly regulate neurotransmitter release at the synapse by opening or closing voltage-gated Ca^{2+} channels. As shown in the right panel of Figure 15.18, for example, light hyperpolarizes photoreceptors, which stop releasing their inhibitory neurotransmitter (glutamate). No longer inhibited, bipolar cells depolarize and release neurotransmitter onto ganglion cells. Once the signal reaches the ganglion cells, it is converted into an AP. This AP is transmitted to the brain along the ganglion cell axons that make up the optic nerve.

Light and Dark Adaptation Rhodopsin is amazingly sensitive. Even starlight causes some of the molecules to become bleached. As long as the light is low intensity, relatively little rhodopsin is bleached and the retina continues to respond to light stimuli. However, in high-intensity light there is wholesale

bleaching of the pigment, and rhodopsin is bleached as fast as it is re-formed. At this point, the rods are nonfunctional, but cones still respond. Hence, retinal sensitivity automatically adjusts to the amount of light present.

Light adaptation occurs when we move from darkness into bright light, as when leaving a movie matinee. We are momentarily dazzled—all we see is white light—because the sensitivity of the retina is still "set" for dim light. Both rods and cones are strongly stimulated, and large amounts of the visual pigments are broken down almost instantaneously, producing a flood of signals that accounts for the glare.

Under such conditions, compensations occur. The rod system turns off—all of the transducins "pack up and move" to the inner segment, uncoupling rhodopsin from the rest of the transduction cascade. Without transducin in the outer segment, light hitting rhodopsin cannot produce a signal. At the same time, the less sensitive cone system and other retinal neurons rapidly adapt, and retinal sensitivity decreases dramatically. Within about 60 seconds, the cones, initially overexcited by the bright light, are sufficiently desensitized to take over. Visual acuity and color vision continue to improve over the next 5–10 minutes. Thus, during light adaptation, retinal sensitivity (rod function) is lost, but visual acuity (the ability to resolve detail) is gained.

Dark adaptation is essentially the reverse of light adaptation. It occurs when we go from a well-lit area into a dark one. Initially, we see nothing but velvety blackness because (1) our

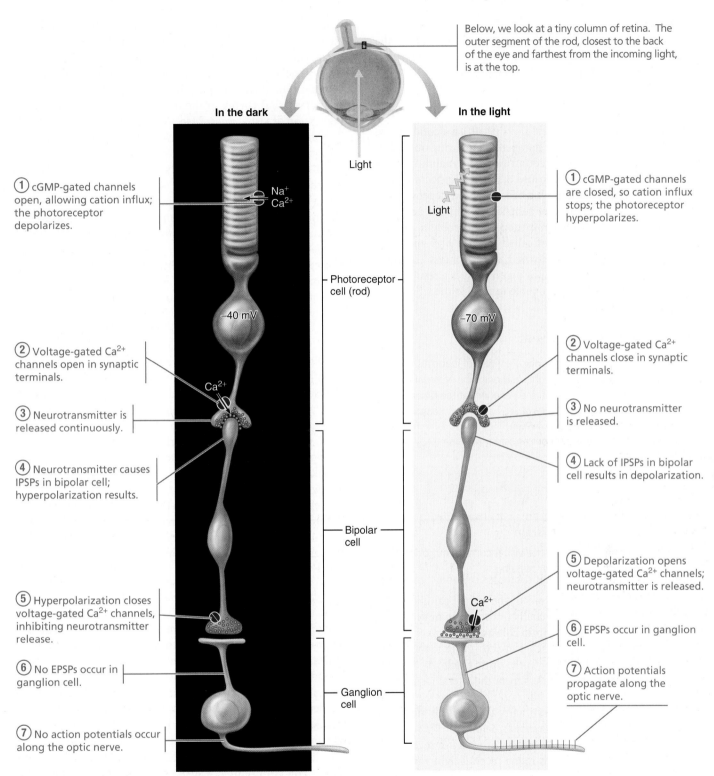

Below, we look at a tiny column of retina. The outer segment of the rod, closest to the back of the eye and farthest from the incoming light, is at the top.

In the dark

In the light

Light

Light

① cGMP-gated channels open, allowing cation influx; the photoreceptor depolarizes.

Na⁺
Ca²⁺

① cGMP-gated channels are closed, so cation influx stops; the photoreceptor hyperpolarizes.

Photoreceptor cell (rod)

−40 mV

−70 mV

② Voltage-gated Ca²⁺ channels open in synaptic terminals.

② Voltage-gated Ca²⁺ channels close in synaptic terminals.

Ca²⁺

③ Neurotransmitter is released continuously.

③ No neurotransmitter is released.

④ Neurotransmitter causes IPSPs in bipolar cell; hyperpolarization results.

④ Lack of IPSPs in bipolar cell results in depolarization.

Bipolar cell

⑤ Depolarization opens voltage-gated Ca²⁺ channels; neurotransmitter is released.

⑤ Hyperpolarization closes voltage-gated Ca²⁺ channels, inhibiting neurotransmitter release.

Ca²⁺

⑥ EPSPs occur in ganglion cell.

⑥ No EPSPs occur in ganglion cell.

⑦ Action potentials propagate along the optic nerve.

Ganglion cell

⑦ No action potentials occur along the optic nerve.

Figure 15.18 Signal transmission in the retina. EPSP = excitatory postsynaptic potential; IPSP = inhibitory postsynaptic potential.

cones stop functioning in low-intensity light, and (2) our rod pigments have been bleached out by the bright light, and the rods are still turned off. But once we are in the dark, rhodopsin accumulates, transducin returns to the outer segment, and retinal sensitivity increases. Dark adaptation is much slower than

light adaptation and can go on for hours. However, there is usually enough rhodopsin within 20–30 minutes to allow adequate dim-light vision.

During these adaptations, reflexive changes also occur in pupil size. Bright light shining in one or both eyes causes both pupils to constrict (elicits the *consensual* and *pupillary light reflexes*). These pupillary reflexes are mediated by the pretectal nucleus of the midbrain and by parasympathetic fibers. In dim light, the pupils dilate, allowing more light to enter the eye interior.

⚖ HOMEOSTATIC IMBALANCE

Night blindness, or *nyctalopia* (nic″tă-lo′pe-uh), is a condition in which rod function is seriously hampered, impairing one's ability to drive safely at night. In countries where malnutrition is common, the most common cause of night blindness is prolonged vitamin A deficiency, which leads to rod degeneration. Vitamin A supplements restore function if they are administered early. In countries where nutrition isn't a problem, a group of degenerative retinal diseases called *retinitis pigmentosa,* in which rods are selectively destroyed, are the most common causes of night blindness. Retinitis pigmentosa is a result of the pigment epithelial cells being unable to recycle the tips of the rods as they get sloughed off. ∎

CHECK YOUR UNDERSTANDING

7. For each of the following, indicate whether it applies to rods or cones: vision in bright light; only one type of visual pigment; most abundant in the periphery of the retina; many feed into one ganglion cell; color vision; higher sensitivity; higher acuity (ability to see detail).
8. What does bleaching of the pigment mean and when does it happen?

For answers, see Appendix G.

The Visual Pathway to the Brain

▶ Trace the visual pathway to the visual cortex, and briefly describe the steps in visual processing.

As we described earlier, the axons of the retinal ganglion cells issue from the back of the eyeballs in the **optic nerves (Figure 15.19)**. At the X-shaped **optic chiasma** (*chiasm* = cross), fibers from the medial aspect of each eye cross over to the opposite side and then continue on via the **optic tracts**. As a result, each optic tract (1) contains fibers from the lateral (temporal) aspect of the eye on the same side and fibers from the medial (nasal) aspect of the opposite eye, and (2) carries all the information from the same half of the visual field.

Notice that, because the lens system of each eye reverses all images, the medial half of each retina receives light rays from the *temporal* (lateralmost) part of the visual field (that is, from the far left or far right rather than from straight ahead), and the lateral half of each retina receives an image of the nasal (central) part of the visual field. Consequently, the left optic tract carries (and sends on) a complete representation of the right half of the visual field, and the opposite is true for the right optic tract.

The paired optic tracts sweep posteriorly around the hypothalamus and send most of their axons to synapse with neurons in the **lateral geniculate nuclei** (contained within the lateral geniculate bodies) of the thalamus. This thalamic nucleus maintains the fiber separation established at the chiasma, but balances and combines the retinal input for delivery to the visual cortex. Axons of the thalamic neurons project through the internal capsule to form the **optic radiation** of fibers in the cerebral white matter (Figure 15.19). These fibers project to the **primary visual cortex** in the occipital lobes, where conscious perception of visual images (seeing) occurs.

Some nerve fibers in the optic tracts send branches to the midbrain. One set of these fibers ends in the **superior colliculi**, visual reflex centers controlling the extrinsic muscles of the eyes. Another set comes from a small subset of ganglion cells in the retina that contain the visual pigment *melanopsin*, dubbed the circadian pigment. These ganglion cells respond directly to light stimuli and their fibers project to the **pretectal nuclei**, which mediate pupillary light reflexes, and to the **suprachiasmatic nucleus** of the hypothalamus, which functions as the "timer" to set our daily biorhythms.

Notice that both eyes are set anteriorly and look in approximately the same direction. Their visual fields, each about 170 degrees, overlap to a considerable extent, and each eye sees a slightly different view (Figure 15.19a). The visual cortex fuses the slightly different images delivered by the two eyes, providing us with **depth perception**, an accurate means of locating objects in space. This faculty is also called **three-dimensional vision**. In contrast, many animals (pigeons, rabbits, and others) have *panoramic vision*. Their eyes are placed more laterally on the head, so that the visual fields overlap very little, and crossover of the optic nerve fibers is almost complete. Consequently, each visual cortex receives input principally from a single eye and a totally different visual field.

Depth perception depends on the two eyes working together. If only one eye is used, depth perception is lost, and the person must learn to judge an object's position based on learned cues (for example, nearer objects appear larger, and parallel lines converge with distance).

⚖ HOMEOSTATIC IMBALANCE

The relationships described above explain patterns of blindness that follow damage to different visual structures. Loss of an eye or destruction of one optic nerve eliminates true depth perception, and peripheral vision is lost on the side of damage. For example, if the "left eye" in Figure 15.19 was lost in a hunting accident, nothing would be seen in the visual field area that is stippled yellow in that figure. If neural destruction occurs beyond the optic chiasma—in an optic tract, the thalamus, or visual cortex—then part or all of the opposite half of the visual field is lost. For example, a stroke affecting the left visual cortex leads to blindness in the right half of the visual field, but since the right (undamaged) visual cortex still receives inputs from both eyes, depth perception in the remaining half of the visual field is retained. ∎

Visual Processing

How does information received by the rods and cones become vision? In the past few decades, a tremendous amount of research has been devoted to this question. Here we present

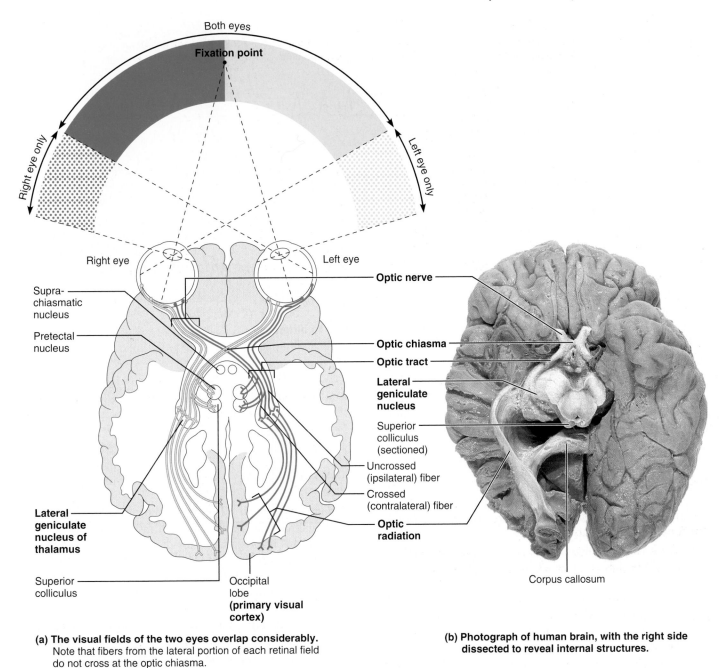

(a) **The visual fields of the two eyes overlap considerably.**
Note that fibers from the lateral portion of each retinal field
do not cross at the optic chiasma.

(b) **Photograph of human brain, with the right side
dissected to reveal internal structures.**

Figure 15.19 Visual pathway to the brain and visual fields, inferior view.

some of the more basic information that has come out of these studies.

Retinal Processing The dozen or so different types of retinal ganglion cells generate action potentials at a fairly steady rate (20–30 per second), even in the dark. Surprisingly, illuminating the entire retina evenly has no effect on that basal rate. However, the activity of individual ganglion cells changes dramatically when a particular pattern of light falls on certain portions of their receptive field. The *receptive field* of a ganglion cell consists of the area of the retina that, when stimulated, influences the activity of that ganglion cell (via the rods or cones that funnel their impulses to it). Different ganglion cells detect different light

patterns, some of which are complex—for example, lines at a particular angle, or moving in a particular direction at a particular velocity. The easiest pattern to understand, however, is a simple spot of light, and this is the pattern we will discuss next.

When researchers mapped the receptive fields of ganglion cells receiving inputs only from rods, they found two types of doughnut-shaped (circle-within-a-circle) receptive fields. These are called **on-center** and **off-center fields**, based on what happens to the ganglion cell when the center of its receptive field is illuminated with a spot of light. As the middle column in **Figure 15.20** shows, ganglion cells with on-center fields are stimulated (depolarized) by light hitting the field center (the "doughnut hole") and are inhibited by light hitting rods in the

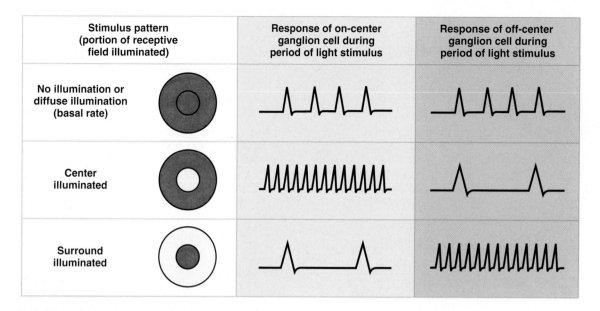

Figure 15.20 Responses of on-center and off-center retinal ganglion cells to different types of illumination. Intermediate amounts of illumination of the central and surround regions lead to intermediate rates of impulse transmission.

periphery (the doughnut itself). The opposite situation occurs in ganglion cells with off-center fields, as the right-hand column in Figure 15.20 shows. Equal illumination of "on" and "off" regions causes little change in the basal rate of ganglion cell firing.

We can summarize retinal processing as it is currently understood as follows:

1. The action of light on photoreceptors hyperpolarizes them.
2. Bipolar cells in the "on" regions are excited (depolarize) and excite the associated ganglion cell when the rods feeding into them are illuminated (and hyperpolarized). Bipolar cells in the "off" regions are inhibited (hyperpolarize) and inhibit the ganglion cell when the rods feeding into them are stimulated. These opposite responses of the bipolar cells in the "on" versus the "off" regions reflect the fact that they have different receptor types for glutamate.
3. Bipolar cells receiving signals from cones feed directly into excitatory synapses on ganglion cells. For this reason, cone inputs are perceived as sharp and clear (and in color).
4. Bipolar cells receiving inputs from rods excite amacrine cells via gap junctions. These local integrator neurons modify rod inputs and ultimately direct excitatory inputs to appropriate ganglion cells. In this way, rod inputs are not only summated but are also subject to "detours" before reaching the output (ganglion) cells. Together these factors provide a more smeary picture than cone inputs.
5. Inputs are also modified and subjected to a type of processing called *lateral inhibition* mediated by synaptic (gap junction) contacts with horizontal cells. These local integrator cells allow the retina to convert points of light into perceptually more meaningful contour (edge) information by accentuating bright/dark or color contrasts.
6. The two most common varieties of ganglion cells are the P cells and the M cells. P cells, the target of cone input,

relay information about small nonmoving objects in the center of the visual field—their color and details. M cells, which also receive rod input, respond best to large, moving objects at the edge of the image. Together, the various types of ganglion cells provide many parallel streams of information that are processed further in the brain.

Thalamic Processing The lateral geniculate nuclei (LGN) of the thalamus relay information on movement, segregate the retinal axons in preparation for depth perception, emphasize visual inputs from the cones, and sharpen the contrast information received from the retina. The separation of signals from the two eyes is relayed accurately to the visual cortex.

Cortical Processing Two types of areas for processing retinal inputs are found in the visual cortex. The *primary visual cortex*, also called the **striate cortex**, is thick with fibers coming in from the LGN. This area contains an accurate topographical map of the retina, with the left visual cortex receiving input from the right visual field and vice versa. Visual processing here occurs at a relatively basic level, with the processing neurons responding to dark and bright edges (contrast information) and object orientation.

The striate cortex also provides form, color, and motion inputs to *visual association areas* collectively called the **prestriate cortices**. The more anterior prestriate cortices are occipital lobe centers that continue the processing of visual information concerned with form, color, and movement.

Functional neuroimaging of humans has revealed that complex visual processing extends well forward into the temporal, parietal, and frontal lobes via two parallel streams: (1) The "what" processing stream extends through the ventral part of the temporal lobe and specializes in the identification of objects in the visual field. (2) The "where" processing stream takes a

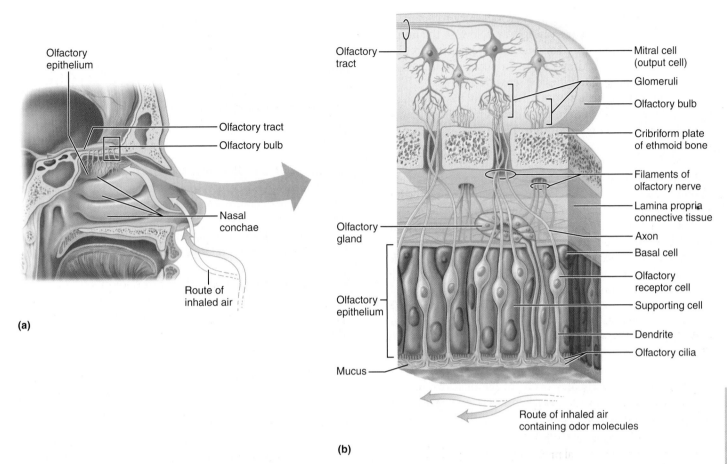

Figure 15.21 Olfactory receptors. (a) Site of olfactory epithelium in the superior nasal cavity. **(b)** An enlarged view of the olfactory epithelium showing the course of the fibers [filaments of the olfactory nerve (I)] through the ethmoid bone. These synapse in the glomeruli of the overlying olfactory bulb. The mitral cells are the output cells of the olfactory bulb.

dorsal path through the parietal cortex all the way to the postcentral gyrus and uses information from the primary visual cortex to assess the spatial location of objects. Output from both these regions then appears to pass to the frontal cortex, which uses that information to direct activities that, among other things, can guide movements such as reaching for a juicy peach.

CHECK YOUR UNDERSTANDING

9. What part of the visual field would be affected by a tumor in the right visual cortex? By a tumor compressing the right optic nerve?

For answers, see Appendix G.

The Chemical Senses: Taste and Smell

▶ Describe the location, structure, and afferent pathways of taste and smell receptors, and explain how these receptors are activated.

Taste and smell are gritty, primitive senses that alert us to whether that "stuff" nearby (or in our mouth) is to be savored or avoided. The receptors for taste (gustation) and smell (olfaction) are **chemoreceptors** (respond to chemicals in an aqueous solution). They complement each other and respond to different classes of chemicals. Taste receptors are excited by food chemicals dissolved in saliva, and smell receptors are excited by airborne chemicals that dissolve in fluids coating nasal membranes.

The Olfactory Epithelium and the Sense of Smell

Although our olfactory sense (*olfact* = to smell) is far less acute than that of many other animals, the human nose is still no slouch in picking up small differences in odors. Some people capitalize on this ability by becoming wine tasters.

Localization and Structure of Olfactory Receptors

Olfaction detects chemicals (*odorants*) in solution. The organ of smell is a yellow-tinged patch (about 5 cm^2) of pseudostratified epithelium, called the **olfactory epithelium**, located in the roof of the nasal cavity (**Figure 15.21a**). Air entering the nasal cavity

15

must make a hairpin turn to stimulate olfactory receptors before entering the respiratory passageway below, so the human olfactory epithelium is in a poor position for doing its job. (This is why sniffing, which draws more air superiorly across the olfactory epithelium, intensifies the sense of smell.)

The olfactory epithelium covers the superior nasal concha on each side of the nasal septum, and contains millions of bowling pin–shaped **olfactory receptor cells**. These are surrounded and cushioned by columnar **supporting cells**, which make up the bulk of the penny-thin epithelial membrane (Figure 15.21b). The supporting cells contain a yellow-brown pigment similar to lipofuscin, which gives the olfactory epithelium its yellow hue. At the base of the epithelium lie the short **basal cells**.

The olfactory receptor cells are unusual bipolar neurons. Each has a thin apical dendrite that terminates in a knob from which several long cilia radiate. These **olfactory cilia**, which substantially increase the receptive surface area, typically lie flat on the nasal epithelium and are covered by a coat of thin mucus produced by the supporting cells and by olfactory glands in the underlying connective tissue. This mucus is a solvent that "captures" and dissolves airborne odorants. Unlike other cilia in the body, which beat rapidly and in a coordinated manner, olfactory cilia are largely nonmotile.

The slender, unmyelinated axons of the olfactory receptor cells are gathered into small fascicles that collectively form the **filaments of the olfactory nerve** (cranial nerve I). They project superiorly through the openings in the cribriform plate of the ethmoid bone, where they synapse in the overlying olfactory bulbs.

Olfactory receptor cells are unusual in that they are one of the few types of *neurons* that undergo noticeable turnover throughout adult life. Their superficial location puts them at risk for damage. Their typical life span is 30–60 days, after which they are replaced by differentiation of the basal cells in the olfactory epithelium.

Specificity of the Olfactory Receptors

Smell is difficult to research because any given odor (say, tobacco smoke) may be made up of hundreds of different chemicals. Taste has been neatly packaged into five taste qualities, but science has yet to discover any similar means for classifying smell. Humans can distinguish 10,000 or so odors, but research suggests that our olfactory receptors are stimulated by different combinations of a more limited number of olfactory qualities.

Most promising in throwing light on this matter are the studies done in the early 1990s suggesting that there are at least 1000 "smell genes" that are active only in the nose. Each such gene encodes a unique receptor protein, and it appears that each of the receptor proteins responds to one or more different odors and each odor binds to several different receptor types. However, each receptor cell has only one type of receptor protein.

Olfactory neurons are exquisitely sensitive—in some cases, just a few molecules activate them. Some of what we call smell is really pain. The nasal cavities contain pain receptors that respond to irritants such as the sharpness of ammonia, the hotness of chili peppers, and the "chill" of menthol. Impulses from these pain receptors reach the central nervous system via afferent fibers of the trigeminal nerves.

Physiology of Smell

For us to smell a particular odorant, it must be *volatile*—that is, it must be in the gaseous state as it enters the nasal cavity. Additionally, it must dissolve in the fluid coating the olfactory epithelium.

Activation of the Olfactory Receptors Dissolved odorants stimulate the olfactory receptors by binding to receptor proteins in the olfactory cilium membranes, opening cation channels and generating a receptor potential. Ultimately (assuming threshold stimulation) an action potential is conducted to the first relay station in the olfactory bulb.

Smell Transduction Transduction of odorants uses a receptor linked to a G protein. The events that follow odorant binding will be easy for you to remember if you compare them to what you already know: general mechanisms of receptors and G proteins (see Figure 11.20) and phototransduction (see Figure 15.17).

As **Figure 15.22** shows, olfactory transduction begins when an odorant binds to a receptor. This event activates G protein (G_{olf}), which activates enzymes (adenylate cyclases) that synthesize cyclic AMP as a second messenger. Cyclic AMP then acts directly on a plasma membrane cation channel, causing it to open, allowing Na^+ and Ca^{2+} to enter.

Na^+ influx leads to depolarization and impulse transmission. Ca^{2+} influx causes the transduction process to adapt, decreasing its response to a sustained stimulus. This *olfactory adaptation* helps explain how a person working in a paper mill or sewage treatment plant can still enjoy lunch!

The Olfactory Pathway

As we have already noted, axons of the olfactory receptor cells form the olfactory nerves that synapse in the overlying **olfactory bulbs**, the distal ends of the olfactory tracts (see Table 13.2 on p. 495). There, the filaments of the olfactory nerves synapse with **mitral cells** (mi′tral), which are second-order neurons, in complex structures called **glomeruli** (glomer′u-li; "little balls") (see Figure 15.21).

Axons from neurons bearing the same kind of receptor converge on a given type of glomerulus. That is, each glomerulus represents a single aspect of an odor (like one note in a chord) but each odor activates a unique set of glomeruli (the chord itself). Different odors activate different subsets of glomeruli (making different chords which may have some of the same notes). The mitral cells refine the signal, amplify it, and then relay it. The olfactory bulbs also house *granule cells*, GABA-releasing cells that inhibit mitral cells (via dendrodendritic synapses), so that only highly excitatory olfactory impulses are transmitted.

When the mitral cells are activated, impulses flow from the olfactory bulbs via the **olfactory tracts** (composed mainly of

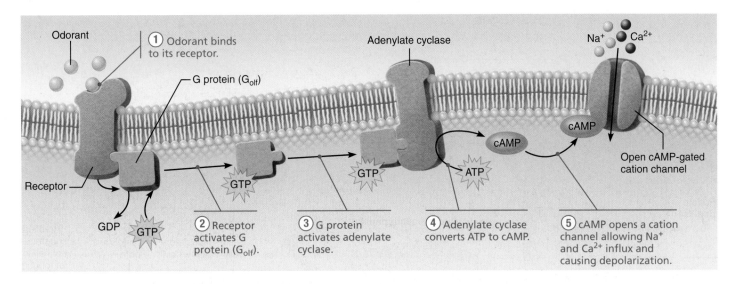

Figure 15.22 Olfactory transduction process. A portion of olfactory cilium membrane is shown.

mitral cell axons) to two main destinations. The first pathway travels via the thalamus to the piriform lobe of the olfactory cortex and the part of the frontal lobe just above the orbit, where smells are consciously interpreted and identified. Each olfactory cortical neuron receives input from up to 100 receptors to analyze.

The second pathway bypasses the thalamus and flows directly via the subcortical route to the hypothalamus, amygdala, and other regions of the limbic system, which elicits emotional responses to odors. Smells associated with danger—smoke, cooking gas, or skunk scent—trigger the sympathetic fight-or-flight response. Appetizing odors cause increased salivation and stimulation of the digestive tract, and unpleasant odors can trigger protective reflexes such as sneezing and choking.

Taste Buds and the Sense of Taste

The word *taste* comes from the Latin *taxare*, meaning "to touch, estimate, or judge." When we taste things, we are in fact intimately testing or judging our environment, and the sense of taste is considered by many to be the most pleasurable of the special senses.

Localization and Structure of Taste Buds

The **taste buds**, the sensory receptor organs for taste, are located primarily in the oral cavity. Of our 10,000 or so taste buds, most are on the tongue. A few taste buds are scattered on the soft palate, inner surface of the cheeks, pharynx, and epiglottis of the larynx, but most are found in **papillae** (pah-pil′e), peglike projections of the tongue mucosa that give the tongue surface a slightly abrasive feel. Taste buds are located mainly on the tops of the mushroom-shaped **fungiform papillae** (fun′jĭ-form) (which are scattered over the entire tongue surface) and in the epithelium of the side walls of the **foliate papillae** and of the large round **circumvallate** (ser″kum-val′āt), or simply **vallate, papillae**. The vallate papillae are the largest and least numerous

papillae, and 7 to 12 of these form an inverted V at the back of the tongue (Figure 15.23a, b).

Each flask-shaped taste bud consists of 50 to 100 *epithelial cells* of two major types: **gustatory**, or **taste**, **cells**, and basal cells (Figure 15.23c). Long microvilli called **gustatory hairs** project from the tips of all gustatory cells and extend through a **taste pore** to the surface of the epithelium, where they are bathed by saliva. The gustatory hairs are the sensitive portions (*receptor membranes*) of the gustatory cells. Coiling intimately around the gustatory cells are sensory dendrites that represent the initial part of the gustatory pathway to the brain. Each afferent fiber receives signals from several receptor cells within the taste bud. There are at least two kinds of gustatory cells. One kind forms traditional synapses with the sensory dendrites and releases the neurotransmitter serotonin. Another kind doesn't contain synaptic vesicles, but instead releases ATP that acts as a neurotransmitter.

Because of their location, taste bud cells are subjected to huge amounts of friction and are routinely burned by hot foods. Luckily, they are among the most dynamic cells in the body, and they are replaced every seven to ten days. The **basal cells** act as stem cells, dividing and differentiating into new gustatory cells.

Basic Taste Sensations

Normally, our taste sensations are complicated mixtures of qualities. However, when taste is tested with pure chemical compounds, taste sensations can all be grouped into one of five basic qualities: sweet, sour, salty, bitter, and umami.

- *Sweet* taste is elicited by many organic substances including sugars, saccharin, alcohols, some amino acids, and some lead salts (such as those found in lead paint).
- *Sour* taste is produced by acids, specifically their hydrogen ions (H^+) in solution.
- *Salty* taste is produced by metal ions (inorganic salts); table salt (sodium chloride) tastes the "saltiest."

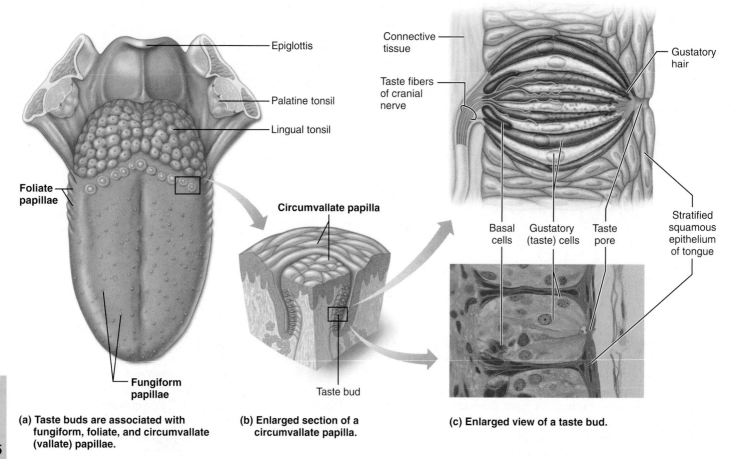

Epiglottis

Palatine tonsil

Lingual tonsil

Foliate papillae

Circumvallate papilla

Fungiform papillae

Taste bud

Connective tissue

Taste fibers of cranial nerve

Gustatory hair

Basal cells

Gustatory (taste) cells

Taste pore

Stratified squamous epithelium of tongue

(a) Taste buds are associated with fungiform, foliate, and circumvallate (vallate) papillae.

(b) Enlarged section of a circumvallate papilla.

(c) Enlarged view of a taste bud.

Figure 15.23 Location and structure of taste buds on the tongue. (See *A Brief Atlas of the Human Body,* Figure 62.)

15

- *Bitter* taste is elicited by alkaloids (such as quinine, nicotine, caffeine, morphine, and strychnine) as well as a number of nonalkaloid substances, such as aspirin.
- *Umami* (u-mam′e; "delicious"), a new taste discovered by the Japanese, is elicited by the amino acids glutamate and aspartate, which appear to be responsible for the "beef taste" of steak, the characteristic tang of aging cheese, and the flavor of the food additive monosodium glutamate.

Keep in mind that many substances produce a mixture of the basic taste sensations, and taste buds generally respond to all five taste qualities. However, it appears that a single taste cell has receptors for only one taste quality.

Taste maps that spatially assign sweet receptors to the tip of the tongue, salty and sour receptors to the sides, bitter receptors to the back, and umami receptors to the pharynx are common in older textbooks. However, researchers have known for years that these maps are dubious. Indeed, recent molecular and functional data show that all modalities of taste can be elicited from all areas that contain taste buds.

Taste likes and dislikes have homeostatic value. Umami guides the intake of proteins, and a liking for sugar and salt helps satisfy the body's need for carbohydrates and minerals (as well as some amino acids). Many sour, naturally acidic foods

(such as oranges, lemons, and tomatoes) are rich sources of vitamin C, an essential vitamin. On the other hand, intensely sour tastes warn us of spoilage. Likewise, many natural poisons and spoiled foods are bitter. Consequently, our dislike for sourness and bitterness is protective.

Physiology of Taste

For a chemical to be tasted it must dissolve in saliva, diffuse into the taste pore, and contact the gustatory hairs.

Activation of Taste Receptors The gustatory cells contain neurotransmitters, and binding of the food chemical, or *tastant*, to the receptors in the gustatory cell membrane induces a graded depolarizing potential that causes neurotransmitter release. Binding of the neurotransmitter to the associated sensory dendrites triggers generator potentials that elicit action potentials in these fibers.

The different gustatory cells have different thresholds for activation. In line with their protective nature, the bitter receptors detect substances present in minute amounts. The other receptors are less sensitive. Taste receptors adapt rapidly, with partial adaptation in 3–5 seconds and complete adaptation in 1–5 minutes.

Taste Transduction The mechanisms of taste transduction are only now beginning to become clear. Three different mechanisms underlie how we taste.

- Salty taste is due to Na^+ influx through Na^+ channels, which directly depolarizes the gustatory cell.
- Sour is mediated by H^+, which acts intracellularly to open channels that allow other cations to enter.
- Bitter, sweet, and umami responses share a common mechanism, but each occurs in a different cell. Each taste's unique receptor is coupled to a common G protein called *gustducin*. Activation leads to the release of Ca^{2+} from intracellular stores, which causes the opening of cation channels in the plasma membrane, thereby depolarizing the cell.

The Gustatory Pathway

Afferent fibers carrying taste information from the tongue are found primarily in two cranial nerve pairs. As Figure 15.24 shows, a branch of the **facial nerve** (VII), the *chorda tympani*, transmits impulses from taste receptors in the anterior two-thirds of the tongue. The lingual branch of the **glossopharyngeal nerve** (IX) services the posterior third and the pharynx just behind. Taste impulses from the few taste buds in the epiglottis and the lower pharynx are conducted primarily by the **vagus nerve** (X). These afferent fibers synapse in the **solitary nucleus** of the medulla, and from there impulses stream to the thalamus and ultimately to the *gustatory cortex* in the insula. Fibers also project to the hypothalamus and limbic system structures, regions that determine our appreciation of what we are tasting.

An important role of taste is to trigger reflexes involved in digestion. As taste impulses pass through the solitary nucleus, they initiate reflexes (via synapses with parasympathetic nuclei) that increase secretion of saliva into the mouth and of gastric juice into the stomach. Saliva contains mucus that moistens food and digestive enzymes that begin the digestion of starch. Acidic foods are particularly strong stimulants of the salivary reflex. Additionally, when we eat revolting or foul-tasting substances, gagging or even reflexive vomiting may be initiated.

Influence of Other Sensations on Taste

Taste is 80% smell. When the olfactory receptors in the nasal cavity are blocked by nasal congestion (or pinching your nostrils), food is bland. Without smell, our morning coffee would lack its richness and simply taste bitter.

The mouth also contains thermoreceptors, mechanoreceptors, and nociceptors, and the temperature and texture of foods can enhance or detract from their taste. "Hot" foods such as chili peppers actually bring about their pleasurable effects by exciting pain receptors in the mouth.

Homeostatic Imbalances of the Chemical Senses

Most olfactory disorders, or *anosmias* (an-oz′me-ahz; "without smells"), result from head injuries that tear the olfactory nerves, the aftereffects of nasal cavity inflammation, and aging.

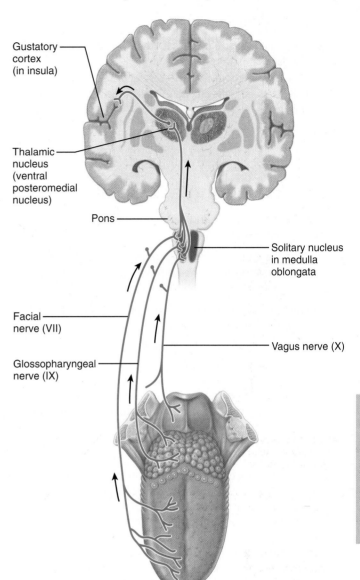

Figure 15.24 The gustatory pathway. Taste signals are relayed from the taste buds to the gustatory area of the cerebral cortex.

Brain disorders can distort the sense of smell. Some people have *uncinate fits* (uns′ih-nāt), olfactory hallucinations during which they experience a particular (usually unpleasant) odor, such as rotting meat. Some such cases are undeniably psychological, but many result from irritation of the olfactory pathway by brain surgery or head trauma. *Olfactory auras* experienced by some epileptics just before they have a seizure are transient uncinate fits.

Taste disorders are less common than disorders of smell, in part because the taste receptors are served by three different nerves and thus are less likely to be "put out of business" completely. Causes of taste disorders include upper respiratory tract infections, head injuries, chemicals or medications, or head and neck radiation for cancer treatment. Zinc supplements have been found to help in some cases of radiation-induced taste disorders.

10. Name the five taste modalities. Name the three types of papillae that have taste buds.
11. Olfactory receptor cells have cilia and taste cells have hairs. How do these structures help the cells perform their functions?

For answers, see Appendix G.

The Ear: Hearing and Balance

▶ Describe the structure and general function of the outer, middle, and internal ears.

▶ Describe the sound conduction pathway to the fluids of the internal ear, and follow the auditory pathway from the spiral organ (of Corti) to the temporal cortex.

▶ Explain how one is able to differentiate pitch and loudness, and localize the source of sounds.

▶ List possible causes and symptoms of otitis media, deafness, and Ménière's syndrome.

At first glance, the machinery for hearing and balance appears very crude. Fluids must be stirred to stimulate the mechanoreceptors of the internal ear. Nevertheless, our hearing apparatus allows us to hear an extraordinary range of sound, and our equilibrium receptors keep the nervous system continually informed of head movements and position. Although the organs serving these two senses are structurally interconnected within the ear, their receptors respond to different stimuli and are activated independently of one another.

Structure of the Ear

The ear is divided into three major areas: external ear, middle ear, and internal ear (Figure 15.25a). The external and middle ear structures are involved with hearing only and are rather simply engineered. The internal ear functions in both equilibrium and hearing and is extremely complex.

External Ear

The **external (outer) ear** consists of the auricle and the external acoustic meatus. The **auricle**, or **pinna**, is what most people call the ear—the shell-shaped projection surrounding the opening of the external acoustic meatus. The auricle is composed of elastic cartilage covered with thin skin and an occasional hair. Its rim, the **helix**, is somewhat thicker, and its fleshy, dangling **lobule** ("earlobe") lacks supporting cartilage. The function of the auricle is to direct sound waves into the external acoustic meatus.

The **external acoustic meatus** (auditory canal) is a short, curved tube (about 2.5 cm long by 0.6 cm wide) that extends from the auricle to the eardrum. Near the auricle, its framework is elastic cartilage; the remainder of the canal is carved into the temporal bone. The entire canal is lined with skin bearing hairs, sebaceous glands, and modified apocrine sweat glands called **ceruminous glands** (sĕ-roo′mĭ-nus). These glands secrete yellow-brown waxy **cerumen**, or earwax (*cere* = wax), which provides a sticky trap for foreign bodies and repels insects.

In many people, the ear is naturally cleansed as the cerumen dries and then falls out of the external acoustic meatus. Jaw movements as a person eats, talks, and so on, create an unnoticeable conveyor-belt effect that moves the wax out. In other people, cerumen builds up excessively and becomes compacted, a condition that can impair hearing.

Sound waves entering the external acoustic meatus eventually hit the **tympanic membrane**, or **eardrum** (*tympanum* = drum), the boundary between the outer and middle ears. The eardrum is a thin, translucent, connective tissue membrane, covered by skin on its external face and by a mucosa internally. It is shaped like a flattened cone, with its apex protruding medially into the middle ear. Sound waves make the eardrum vibrate. The eardrum, in turn, transfers the sound energy to the tiny bones of the middle ear and sets them into vibration.

Middle Ear

The **middle ear**, or **tympanic cavity**, is a small, air-filled, mucosa-lined cavity in the petrous portion of the temporal bone. It is flanked laterally by the eardrum and medially by a bony wall with two openings, the superior **oval (vestibular) window** and the inferior **round (cochlear) window**. Superiorly the tympanic cavity arches upward as the **epitympanic recess**, the "roof" of the middle ear cavity. The **mastoid antrum**, a canal in the posterior wall of the tympanic cavity, allows it to communicate with *mastoid air cells* housed in the mastoid process.

The anterior wall of the middle ear abuts the internal carotid artery (the main artery supplying the brain) and contains the opening of the **pharyngotympanic (auditory) tube**. This tube, formerly called the eustachian tube, runs obliquely downward to link the middle ear cavity with the nasopharynx (the superiormost part of the throat), and the mucosa of the middle ear is continuous with that lining the pharynx (throat).

Normally, the pharyngotympanic tube is flattened and closed, but swallowing or yawning opens it briefly to equalize pressure in the middle ear cavity with external air pressure. This is important because the eardrum vibrates freely only if the pressure on both of its surfaces is the same; otherwise sounds are distorted. The ear-popping sensation of the pressures equalizing is familiar to anyone who has flown in an airplane.

HOMEOSTATIC IMBALANCE

Otitis media (me′de-ah), or middle ear inflammation, is a fairly common result of a sore throat, especially in children, whose pharyngotympanic tubes are shorter and run more horizontally. Otitis media is the most frequent cause of hearing loss in children. In acute infectious forms, the eardrum bulges and becomes inflamed and red. Most cases of otitis media are treated with antibiotics. When large amounts of fluid or pus accumulate in the cavity, an emergency *myringotomy* (lancing of the eardrum) may be required to relieve the pressure, and a tiny tube implanted in the eardrum permits pus to drain into the external ear. The tube falls out by itself within the year. ∎

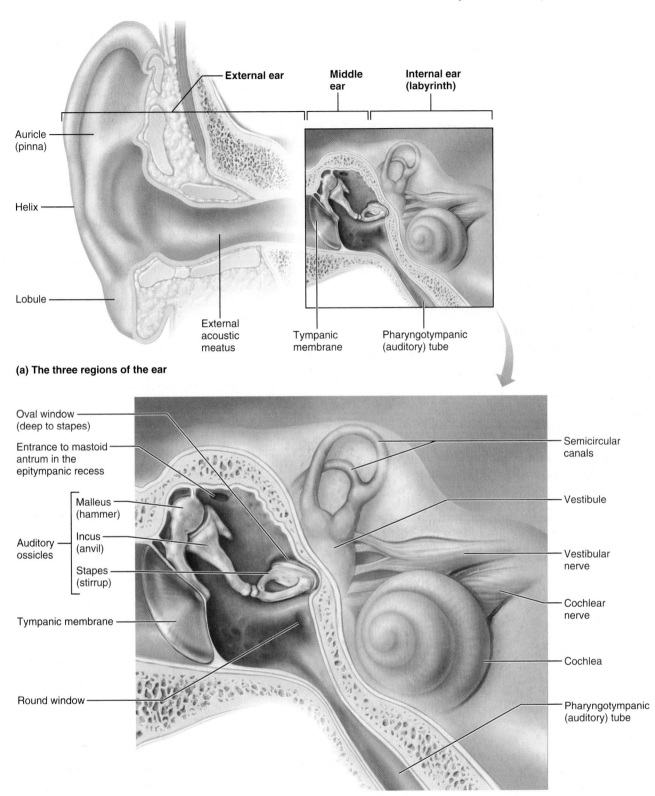

(a) The three regions of the ear

External ear | Middle ear | Internal ear (labyrinth)

Auricle (pinna)

Helix

Lobule

External acoustic meatus

Tympanic membrane

Pharyngotympanic (auditory) tube

Oval window (deep to stapes)

Entrance to mastoid antrum in the epitympanic recess

Auditory ossicles
- Malleus (hammer)
- Incus (anvil)
- Stapes (stirrup)

Tympanic membrane

Round window

Semicircular canals

Vestibule

Vestibular nerve

Cochlear nerve

Cochlea

Pharyngotympanic (auditory) tube

(b) Middle and internal ear

Figure 15.25 Structure of the ear. The inner ear structures in (b) appear as though they are veiled because they are cavities within the temporal bone.

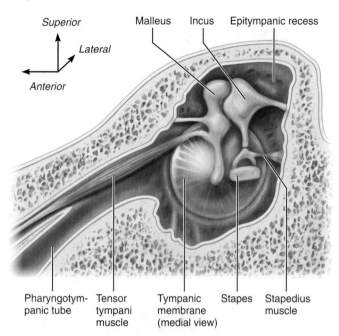

Superior

Lateral

Anterior

Malleus   Incus   Epitympanic recess

Pharyngotym-   Tensor   Tympanic   Stapes   Stapedius
panic tube   tympani   membrane   muscle
muscle   (medial view)

Figure 15.26 **The three auditory ossicles and associated skeletal muscles.** Right ear, medial view.

The tympanic cavity is spanned by the three smallest bones in the body: the **auditory ossicles** (Figure 15.25 and Figure 15.26). These bones, named for their shape, are the **malleus** (mal′e-us; "hammer"); the **incus** (ing′kus; "anvil"); and the **stapes** (sta′pēz; "stirrup"). The "handle" of the malleus is secured to the eardrum, and the base of the stapes fits into the oval window.

Tiny ligaments suspend the ossicles, and mini synovial joints link them together into a chain that spans the middle ear cavity. The incus articulates with the malleus laterally and the stapes medially. The ossicles transmit the vibratory motion of the eardrum to the oval window, which in turn sets the fluids of the internal ear into motion, eventually exciting the hearing receptors.

Two tiny skeletal muscles are associated with the ossicles (Figure 15.26). The **tensor tympani** (ten′sor tim′pah-ni) arises from the wall of the pharyngotympanic tube and inserts on the malleus. The **stapedius** (stah-pe′de-us) runs from the posterior wall of the middle ear cavity to the stapes. When the ears are assaulted by very loud sounds, these muscles contract reflexively to prevent damage to the hearing receptors. Specifically, the tensor tympani tenses the eardrum by pulling it medially; the stapedius checks vibration of the whole ossicle chain and limits the movement of the stapes in the oval window.

Internal Ear

The **internal (inner) ear** is also called the **labyrinth** ("maze") because of its complicated shape (see Figure 15.25). It lies deep in the temporal bone behind the eye socket and provides a secure site for all of the delicate receptor machinery housed there.

The internal ear has two major divisions: the bony labyrinth and the membranous labyrinth. The **bony**, or **osseous, labyrinth** is a system of tortuous channels worming through the bone. Its three regions are the *vestibule*, the *cochlea* (kok′le-ah), and the *semicircular canals*. The views of the bony labyrinth typically seen in textbooks, including this one, are somewhat misleading because we are talking about a *cavity* here. The representation in Figure 15.25 can be compared to a plaster of paris cast of the cavity or hollow space inside the bony labyrinth. The **membranous labyrinth** is a continuous series of membranous sacs and ducts contained within the bony labyrinth and (more or less) following its contours (Figure 15.27).

The bony labyrinth is filled with **perilymph**, a fluid similar to cerebrospinal fluid and continuous with it. The membranous labyrinth is suspended in the surrounding perilymph, and its interior contains **endolymph**, which is chemically similar to K$^+$-rich intracellular fluid. These two fluids conduct the sound vibrations involved in hearing and respond to the mechanical forces occurring during changes in body position and acceleration.

Vestibule   The **vestibule** is the central egg-shaped cavity of the bony labyrinth. It lies posterior to the cochlea, anterior to the semicircular canals, and flanks the middle ear medially. In its lateral wall is the oval window. Suspended in its perilymph and united by a small duct are two membranous labyrinth sacs, the **saccule** and **utricle** (u′trĭ-kl) (Figure 15.27). The smaller saccule is continuous with the membranous labyrinth extending anteriorly into the cochlea (the *cochlear duct*), whereas the utricle is continuous with the semicircular ducts extending into the semicircular canals posteriorly. The saccule and utricle house equilibrium receptor regions called *maculae* that respond to the pull of gravity and report on changes of head position.

Semicircular Canals   The **semicircular canals** lie posterior and lateral to the vestibule, and each of these canals defines about two-thirds of a circle. The cavities of the bony semicircular canals project from the posterior aspect of the vestibule, each oriented in one of the three planes of space. Accordingly, there is an *anterior*, *posterior*, and *lateral* semicircular canal in each internal ear. The anterior and posterior canals are oriented at right angles to each other in the vertical plane, whereas the lateral canal lies horizontally (Figure 15.27).

Snaking through each semicircular canal is a corresponding membranous **semicircular duct**, which communicates with the utricle anteriorly. Each of these ducts has an enlarged swelling at one end called an **ampulla**, which houses an equilibrium receptor region called a *crista ampullaris* (literally, crest of the ampulla). These receptors respond to angular (rotational) movements of the head.

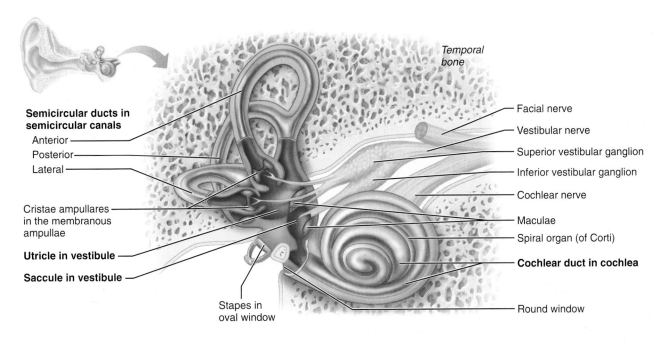

Semicircular ducts in
semicircular canals
Anterior
Posterior
Lateral

Cristae ampullares
in the membranous
ampullae

Utricle in vestibule

Saccule in vestibule

Stapes in
oval window

Temporal
bone

Facial nerve
Vestibular nerve
Superior vestibular ganglion
Inferior vestibular ganglion
Cochlear nerve
Maculae
Spiral organ (of Corti)
Cochlear duct in cochlea
Round window

Figure 15.27 Membranous labyrinth of the internal ear. The membranous labyrinth (blue) lies within the chambers of the bony labyrinth (tan). The locations of the sensory organs for hearing [spiral organ (of Corti)] and equilibrium (maculae and cristae ampullares) are shown in purple.

Cochlea   The **cochlea**, from the Latin "snail," is a spiral, conical, bony chamber about the size of a split pea. It extends from the anterior part of the vestibule and coils for about 2½ turns around a bony pillar called the **modiolus** (mo-di′o-lus) **(Figure 15.28a)**. Running through its center like a wedge-shaped worm is the membranous **cochlear duct**, which ends blindly at the cochlear apex. The cochlear duct houses the **spiral organ (of Corti)**, the receptor organ for hearing (Figures 15.27 and 15.28b).

The cochlear duct and the **osseous spiral lamina**, a thin shelflike extension of bone that spirals up the modiolus like the thread on a screw, together divide the cavity of the bony cochlea into three separate chambers or **scalae** (*scala* = ladder). The **scala vestibuli** (ska′lah věs-tĭ′bu-li), which lies superior to the cochlear duct, is continuous with the vestibule and abuts the oval window. The middle **scala media** is the cochlear duct itself. The **scala tympani**, which terminates at the round window, is inferior to the cochlear duct.

Since the scala media is part of the membranous labyrinth, it is filled with endolymph. The scala vestibuli and the scala tympani, both part of the bony labyrinth, contain perilymph. The perilymph-containing chambers are continuous with each other at the cochlear apex, a region called the **helicotrema** (hel″ĭ-ko-tre′mah; "the hole in the spiral").

The "roof" of the cochlear duct, separating the scala media from the scala vestibuli, is the **vestibular membrane** (Figure 15.28b). The duct's external wall, the **stria vascularis**, is composed of an unusual richly vascularized mucosa that secretes endolymph. The "floor" of the cochlear duct is composed of the bony spiral lamina and the flexible, fibrous **basilar membrane**, which supports the spiral organ (of Corti). (We will describe the spiral organ when we discuss hearing.) The basilar membrane,

which plays a critical role in sound reception, is narrow and thick near the oval window and gradually widens and thins as it approaches the cochlear apex. The *cochlear nerve*, a division of the *vestibulocochlear nerve* (VIII), runs from the spiral organ through the modiolus on its way to the brain.

Physiology of Hearing

The mechanics of human hearing can be summed up in a single sprawling sentence: Sounds set up vibrations in air that beat against the eardrum that pushes a chain of tiny bones that press fluid in the internal ear against membranes that set up shearing forces that pull on the tiny hair cells that stimulate nearby neurons that give rise to impulses that travel to the brain, which interprets them—and you hear. Before we unravel this intriguing sequence, let us describe sound, the stimulus for hearing.

Overview: Properties of Sound

Light can be transmitted through a vacuum (for instance, outer space), but sound depends on an *elastic* medium for its transmission. Sound also travels much more slowly than light. Its speed in dry air is only about 331 m/s (0.2 mi/s), as opposed to the about 300,000 km/s (186,000 mi/s) of light. A lightning flash is almost instantly visible, but the sound it creates (thunder) reaches our ears much more slowly. (For each second between the lightning bolt and the roll of thunder, the storm is 1/5 mile farther away.) The speed of sound is constant in a given medium. It is greatest in solids and lowest in gases, including air.

Sound is a pressure disturbance—alternating areas of high and low pressure—produced by a vibrating object and propagated

15

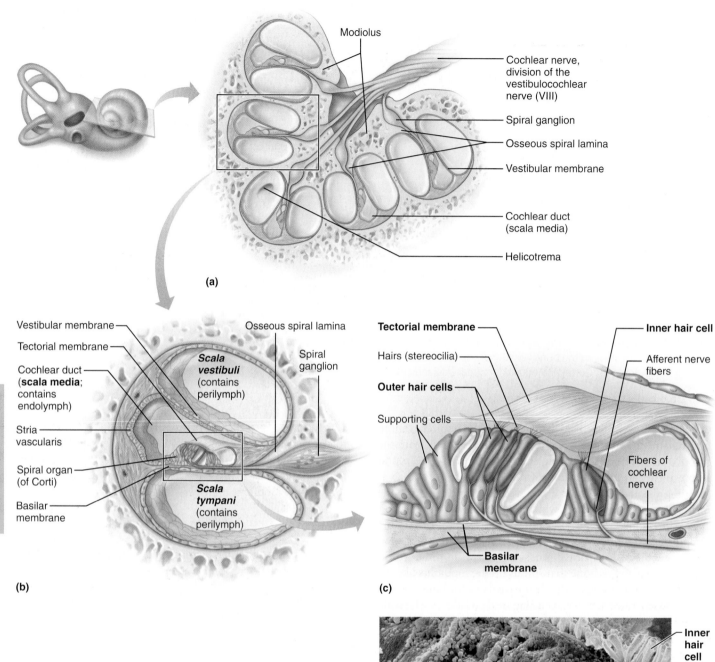

(a)

(b)

(c)

(d)

Figure 15.28 Anatomy of the cochlea. (a) A section through the cochlea, superior half removed. The area containing the helicotrema is at the apex of the cochlea. **(b)** Magnified cross section of one turn of the cochlea, showing the relationship of the three scalae. **(c)** Detailed structure of the spiral organ (of Corti). **(d)** Electron micrograph of cochlear hair cells (550×).

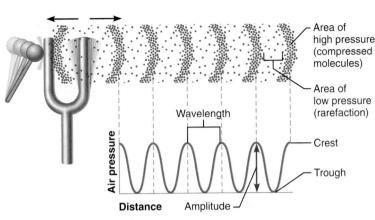

(a) A struck tuning fork alternately compresses and rarefies the air molecules around it, creating alternate zones of high and low pressure.

(b) Sound waves radiate outward in all directions.

Figure 15.29 Sound: source and propagation. The graph in (a) shows that plotting the oscillating air pressures yields a sine wave. The height (amplitude) of the crests is proportional to the energy, or intensity, of the sound wave. The distance between two corresponding points on the wave (crests or troughs) is the wavelength.

by the molecules of the medium. Consider a sound arising from a vibrating tuning fork **(Figure 15.29a)**. If the tuning fork is struck on the left, its prongs will move first to the right, creating an area of high pressure by compressing the air molecules there. Then, as the prongs rebound to the left, the air on the left will be compressed, and the region on the right will be a *rarefied*, or low-pressure, area (since most of its air molecules have been pushed farther to the right).

As the fork vibrates alternately from right to left, it produces a series of compressions and rarefactions, collectively called a *sound wave*, which moves outward in all directions (Figure 15.29b). However, the individual air molecules just vibrate back and forth for short distances as they bump other molecules and rebound. Because the outward-moving molecules give up kinetic energy to the molecules they bump, energy is always transferred in the direction the sound wave is traveling. For this reason, the energy of the wave declines with time and distance, and the sound dies a natural death.

We can illustrate a sound wave as an S-shaped curve, or *sine wave*, in which the compressed areas are crests and the rarefied areas are troughs (Figure 15.29a). Sound can be described in terms of two physical properties inferred from this sine wave graph: frequency and amplitude.

Frequency is defined as the number of waves that pass a given point in a given time. The sine wave of a pure tone is *periodic*. In other words, its crests and troughs repeat at definite distances. The distance between two consecutive crests (or troughs) is called the **wavelength** of the sound and is constant for a particular tone. The shorter the wavelength, the higher the frequency of the sound **(Figure 15.30a)**.

The frequency range of human hearing is from 20 to 20,000 waves per second, or *hertz (Hz)*. Our ears are most sensitive to frequencies between 1500 and 4000 Hz and, in that range, we

— High frequency (short wavelength) = high pitch
— Low frequency (long wavelength) = low pitch

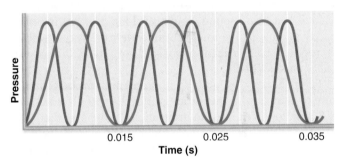

(a) Frequency is perceived as pitch.

— High amplitude = loud
— Low amplitude = soft

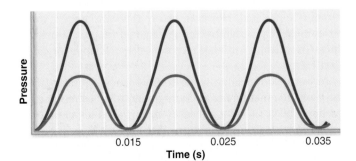

(b) Amplitude (size or intensity) is perceived as loudness.

Figure 15.30 Frequency and amplitude of sound waves.

can distinguish frequencies differing by only 2–3 Hz. We perceive different sound frequencies as differences in **pitch**: the higher the frequency, the higher the pitch.

A tuning fork produces a *tone*—a pure (but bland) sound with a single frequency—but most sounds are mixtures of several frequencies. This characteristic of sound, called **quality**, enables us to distinguish between the same musical note—say, high C—sung by a soprano and played on a piano or clarinet. Sound quality also provides the richness and complexity of sounds (and music) that we hear.

The **amplitude**, or height, of the sine wave crests reveals a sound's intensity, which is related to its energy, or the pressure differences between its compressed and rarefied areas (Figure 15.30b).

Loudness refers to our subjective interpretation of sound intensity. Because we can hear such an enormous range of intensities, from the proverbial pin drop to a jet engine 10 million times as intense, sound intensity (and loudness) is measured in logarithmic units called **decibels (dB)** (des′ĭ-belz). On a clinical audiometer, the decibel scale is arbitrarily set to begin at 0 dB, which is the threshold of hearing (barely audible sound) for normal ears. Each 10-dB increase represents a tenfold increase in sound intensity. A sound of 10 dB has 10 times more energy than one of 0 dB, and a 20-dB sound has 100 times (10×10) more energy than one of 0 dB. However, the same 10-dB increase represents only a twofold increase in loudness. In other words, most people would report that a 20-dB sound seems about twice as loud as a 10-dB sound. The normal range of hearing (from barely audible to the loudest sound we can process without excruciating pain) extends over a range of 120 dB. (The threshold of pain is 120 dB.)

Severe hearing loss occurs with frequent or prolonged exposure to sounds with intensities greater than 90 dB, and in the U.S., employees exposed to occupational noise over that range must wear ear (hearing) protection. That number becomes more meaningful when you realize that a normal conversation is in the 50-dB range, a noisy restaurant has 70-dB levels, and amplified rock music is 120 dB or more, far above the 90-dB danger zone.

Transmission of Sound to the Internal Ear

Hearing occurs when the auditory area of the temporal lobe cortex is stimulated. However, before this can happen, sound waves must be propagated through air, membranes, bones, and fluids to reach and stimulate receptor cells in the spiral organ (of Corti) **(Figure 15.31a)**.

Airborne sound entering the external acoustic meatus strikes the tympanic membrane and sets it vibrating at the same frequency. The greater the intensity, the farther the membrane is displaced in its vibratory motion. The motion of the tympanic membrane is amplified and transferred to the oval window by the ossicle lever system, which acts much like a hydraulic press or piston to transfer the same total force hitting the eardrum to the oval window.

Because the tympanic membrane is 17–20 times larger than the oval window, the pressure (force per unit area) actually exerted on the oval window is about 20 times that on the tympanic membrane. This increased pressure overcomes the stiffness and inertia of cochlear fluid and sets it into wave motion. This situation can be roughly compared to the difference in pressure relayed to the floor by the broad rubber heels of a man's shoes and a woman's tiny spike heels. The man's weight—say, 70 kg (about 150 pounds)—is spread over several square inches, and his heels will not make dents in a pliable vinyl floor. But spike heels will concentrate the same 70-kg force in an area of about 2.5 cm² (1 square inch) and *will* dent the floor.

Resonance of the Basilar Membrane

As the stapes rocks back and forth against the oval window, it sets the perilymph in the scala vestibuli into a similar back-and-forth motion, and a pressure wave travels through the perilymph from the basal end toward the helicotrema, much as a piece of rope held horizontally can be set into wave motion by movements initiated at one end. Sounds of very low frequency (below 20 Hz) create pressure waves that take the complete route through the cochlea—up the scala vestibuli, around the helicotrema, and back toward the round window through the scala tympani (Figure 15.31a). Such sounds do not activate the spiral organ and so are below the threshold of hearing.

In contrast, sounds with frequencies high enough to hear create pressure waves that take a "shortcut" and are transmitted through the cochlear duct into the perilymph of the scala tympani. Fluids cannot be compressed. Think of what happens when you sit on a water bed—you sit "here" and it bulges over "there." In a similar way, each time the fluid adjacent to the oval window is forced medially by the stapes, the membrane of the round window bulges laterally into the middle ear cavity and acts as a pressure valve.

As a pressure wave descends through the flexible cochlear duct, it sets the entire basilar membrane into vibration. Maximal displacement of the membrane occurs where the fibers of the basilar membranes are "tuned" to a particular sound frequency (Figure 15.31b). This characteristic of many natural substances is called *resonance*. The fibers of the basilar membrane span its width like the strings of a harp. The fibers near the oval window (cochlear base) are short and stiff, and they resonate in response to high-frequency pressure waves (Figure 15.31b). The longer, more floppy basilar membrane fibers near the cochlear apex resonate in time with lower-frequency pressure waves. As a result, sound signals are mechanically processed by the resonance of the basilar membrane, before ever reaching the receptors.

Excitation of Hair Cells in the Spiral Organ

The spiral organ (of Corti), which rests atop the basilar membrane, is composed of supporting cells and hearing receptor cells called *cochlear hair cells*. The hair cells are arranged functionally—specifically, one row of **inner hair cells** and three rows of **outer hair cells**—sandwiched between the tectorial and basilar membranes (see Figure 15.28c). Afferent fibers of the **cochlear nerve** [a division of the vestibulocochlear nerve (VIII)] are coiled about the bases of the hair cells.

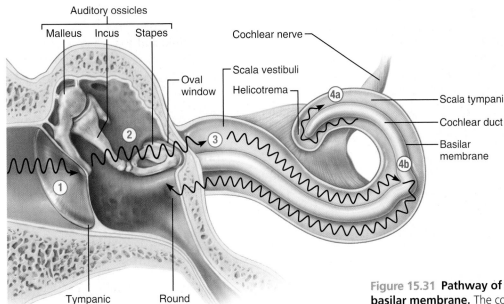

Auditory ossicles

Malleus   Incus   Stapes

Cochlear nerve

Oval window

Scala vestibuli

Helicotrema

Scala tympani

Cochlear duct

Basilar membrane

Tympanic membrane

Round window

(a) Route of sound waves through the ear

① Sound waves vibrate the tympanic membrane.

② Auditory ossicles vibrate. Pressure is amplified.

③ Pressure waves created by the stapes pushing on the oval window move through fluid in the scala vestibuli.

④a Sounds with frequencies below hearing travel through the helicotrema and do not excite hair cells.

④b Sounds in the hearing range go through the cochlear duct, vibrating the basilar membrane and deflecting hairs on inner hair cells.

Figure 15.31 Pathway of sound waves and resonance of the basilar membrane. The cochlea is depicted as if uncoiled. The graph in the bottom panel of (b) represents fibers that span the width of the basilar membrane. The stiffness of these fibers "tunes" specific regions of the basilar membrane to vibrate at specific frequencies.

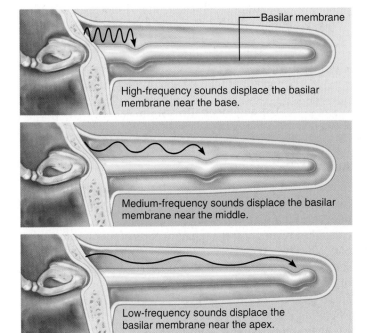

Basilar membrane

High-frequency sounds displace the basilar membrane near the base.

Medium-frequency sounds displace the basilar membrane near the middle.

Low-frequency sounds displace the basilar membrane near the apex.

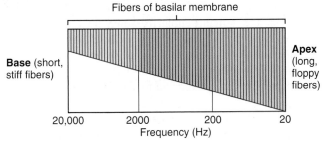

Fibers of basilar membrane

Base (short, stiff fibers)

Apex (long, floppy fibers)

20,000   2000   200   20

Frequency (Hz)

(b) Different sound frequencies cross the basilar membrane at different locations.

The hair cells have numerous *stereocilia* (actually long microvilli) and a single *kinocilium* (a true cilium) protruding from their apices. The "hairs" (stereocilia) of the hair cells are stiffened by actin filaments and linked together by fine fibers called *tip-links* **(Figure 15.32)**. They protrude into the K⁺-rich endolymph, and the longest of them are enmeshed in the overlying, stiff gel-like **tectorial membrane** (see Figure 15.28c).

Transduction of sound stimuli occurs after the trapped stereocilia of the hair cells are "tweaked" or deflected by localized movements of the basilar membrane. Bending the cilia toward the tallest cilium (the kinocilium) puts tension on the tip-links, which in turn opens cation channels in the adjacent shorter stereocilia like a rope pulling on a trap door. This results in an inward K⁺ (and Ca²⁺) current and a graded depolarization (receptor potential). Bending the cilia away from the tallest cilium relaxes the tip-links, closes the mechanically gated ion channels, and allows repolarization and even a graded hyperpolarization.

Depolarization increases intracellular Ca²⁺ and so increases the hair cells' release of neurotransmitter (glutamate), which causes the afferent cochlear fibers to transmit a faster stream of impulses to the brain for auditory interpretation. Hyperpolarization produces the exact opposite effect. As you might guess, activation of the hair cells occurs at points of vigorous basilar membrane vibration.

The outer hair cells, more numerous than the inner hair cells, send little information to the brain. Instead, they act on the basilar membrane itself. When outer hair cells depolarize and hyperpolarize as the basilar membrane moves, they contract and stretch in a type of cellular boogie called *fast motility*. Their strange behavior changes the stiffness of the basilar membrane, which alters its motion and amplifies the responsiveness of the inner hair cells—a kind of cochlear tuning.

15

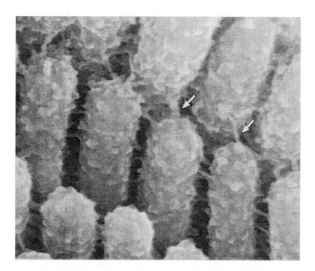

Figure 15.32 Photo of cochlear hair cell with its precise array of stereocilia. White arrows point to tip-links.

Outer hair cell motility is also responsible for producing ear sounds (*otoacoustic emissions*) that are so audible in some people that they can actually be heard by others. In clinical pediatrics, the ability to detect a stimulated otoacoustic emission has proven a quick, inexpensive way to screen newborns for hearing defects.

The vast majority of the sensory fibers of the spiral ganglia (90–95%) service the inner hair cells, which shoulder nearly the entire responsibility for sending auditory messages to the brain. By contrast, most fibers coiling around the outer hair cells are *efferent* fibers that convey messages from brain to ear. What is the brain "telling" the outer hair cells? Loud sounds activate a feedback loop from the brain stem to the outer hair cells that dampens the motion of the outer hair cells and causes the sound energy to be spread over a wider area of the basilar membrane. This may help protect the inner hair cells from damage by loud noise.

The Auditory Pathway to the Brain

The ascending auditory pathway transmits auditory information primarily from the cochlear receptors (the inner hair cells) to the cerebral cortex. Impulses generated in the cochlea pass through the **spiral ganglion**, where the auditory bipolar cells reside, and along the afferent fibers of the cochlear nerve to the **cochlear nuclei** of the medulla **(Figure 15.33)**.

From there, neurons project to the **superior olivary nucleus**, which lies at the junction of the medulla and pons. Beyond this, axons ascend in the **lateral lemniscus** (a fiber tract) to the **inferior colliculus** (auditory reflex center in the midbrain), which projects to the **medial geniculate nucleus** of the thalamus. Axons of the thalamic neurons then project to the **primary auditory cortex**, which provides for conscious awareness of sound.

The auditory pathway is unusual in that not all of the fibers from each ear cross over to the other side of the brain. For this reason, each auditory cortex receives impulses from both ears.

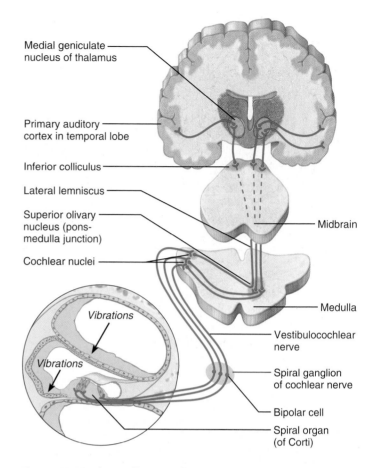

Figure 15.33 The auditory pathway. This simplified diagram shows only the pathway from the right ear.

Auditory Processing

If you are at a Broadway musical, the sound of the instruments, the actors' voices, rustling of clothing, and closing of doors are all intermingled in your awareness. Yet, the auditory cortex can distinguish the separate parts of this auditory jumble. Whenever the difference between sound wavelengths is sufficient for discrimination, you hear two separate and distinct tones. In fact, the analytic powers of the auditory cortex are so great that we are able to pick single instruments out of a whole orchestra.

Cortical processing of sound stimuli is complex. For example, certain cortical cells depolarize at the beginning of a particular tone, and others depolarize when the tone ends. Some cortical cells depolarize continuously, and others appear to have high thresholds (low sensitivity), and so on. Here we will concentrate on the more straightforward aspects of cortical perception of pitch, loudness, and sound location.

Perception of Pitch As we explained, hair cells in different positions along the length of the basilar membrane are activated by sound waves of different frequencies, and impulses from specific hair cells are interpreted as specific pitches. When the sound is composed of tones of many frequencies, several populations of cochlear hair cells and cortical cells are activated simultaneously, resulting in the perception of multiple tones.

Detection of Loudness   Louder sounds cause larger movements of the tympanic membrane, auditory ossicles, and oval window, and pressure waves of greater amplitude in the fluids of the cochlea. These larger waves in turn cause larger movements of the basilar membrane, larger deflections of the hairs on the hair cells, and larger graded potentials in the hair cells. As a result, more neurotransmitter is released and action potentials are generated more frequently. The brain interprets more frequent action potentials as greater loudness. In addition, as the release of neurotransmitter increases, more of the 10 or so bipolar cells connected to a given hair cell are recruited to fire action potentials.

Localization of Sound   Several brain stem nuclei (most importantly the superior olivary nuclei) help us localize a sound's source in space by means of two cues: the *relative intensity* and the *relative timing* of sound waves reaching the two ears. If the sound source is directly in front, in back, or over the midline of the head, the intensity and timing cues are the same for both ears. However, when sound comes from one side, the receptors of the nearer ear are activated slightly earlier and more vigorously (because of the greater intensity of the sound waves entering that ear).

CHECK YOUR UNDERSTANDING

12. Apart from the bony boundaries, what structure separates the external from the middle ear? What two (nonbone) structures separate the middle from the inner ear?
13. What structure inside the spiral organ allows us to differentiate sounds of different pitch?
14. If the brain stem did not receive input from both ears, what would you not be able to do?

For answers, see Appendix G.

Homeostatic Imbalances of Hearing

Deafness

Any hearing loss, no matter how slight, is **deafness** of some sort. Deafness is classified as conduction or sensorineural deafness, according to its cause.

Conduction deafness occurs when something hampers sound conduction to the fluids of the internal ear. For example, impacted earwax can block the external acoustic meatus, or a *perforated* (*ruptured*) eardrum can prevent sound conduction from the eardrum to the ossicles. But the most common causes of conduction deafness are middle ear inflammations (otitis media) and **otosclerosis** (o″to-sklĕ-ro′sis) of the ossicles. Otosclerosis ("hardening of the ear") occurs when overgrowth of bony tissue fuses the stapes foot plate to the oval window or welds the ossicles to one another. In such cases, sound is conducted to the receptors of that ear through vibrations of the skull bones, which is far less satisfactory. Otosclerosis is treated surgically.

Sensorineural deafness results from damage to neural structures at any point from the cochlear hair cells to and including the auditory cortical cells. This type of deafness typically results from the gradual loss of the hair cells throughout life. These cells can also be destroyed at an earlier age by a single explosively loud noise or prolonged exposure to high-intensity sounds, such as rock bands or airport noise, which literally tears off their cilia. Degeneration of the cochlear nerve, cerebral infarcts, and tumors in the auditory cortex are other causes.

For congenital defects or age- or noise-related cochlear damage, cochlear implants (devices that convert sound energy into electrical signals) can be inserted into a drilled recess in the temporal bone. The original cochlear implants made human voices sound tinny and robotlike, but modern versions are so effective that even children born deaf can hear well enough to learn to speak well.

Tinnitus

Tinnitus (tǐ-ni′tus) is a ringing or clicking sound in the ears in the absence of auditory stimuli. It is more a symptom of pathology than a disease. For example, tinnitus is one of the first symptoms of cochlear nerve degeneration. It may also result from inflammation of the middle or internal ears and is a side effect of some medications, such as aspirin.

Recent evidence suggests that tinnitus is analogous to phantom limb pain. In other words, it is "phantom cochlear noise" caused by destruction of some neurons of the auditory pathway and the subsequent ingrowth of nearby neurons whose signals are interpreted as noise by the CNS.

Ménière's Syndrome

Classic **Ménière's syndrome** (men″ē-ār′z) is a labyrinth disorder that seems to affect all three parts of the internal ear. The afflicted person has repeated attacks of vertigo, nausea, and vomiting. Balance is so disturbed that standing erect is nearly impossible. A "howling" tinnitus is common, so hearing is impaired (and ultimately lost) as well. The cause is uncertain, but it may result from distortion of the membranous labyrinth by excessive endolymph accumulation, or rupture of membranes which allows the perilymph and endolymph to mix.

Mild cases can usually be managed by antimotion drugs or a low-salt diet and diuretics to decrease endolymph fluid volume. In severe cases, draining the excess endolymph from the internal ear may help. A last resort is removal of the entire malfunctioning labyrinth, which is usually deferred until hearing loss is complete.

CHECK YOUR UNDERSTANDING

15. Six-year-old Mohammed has a cold and says his ears feel "full" and he "can't hear well." Explain what has happened in Mohammed's ears. Which type of deafness does Mohammed have—conduction or sensorineural?

For answers, see Appendix G.

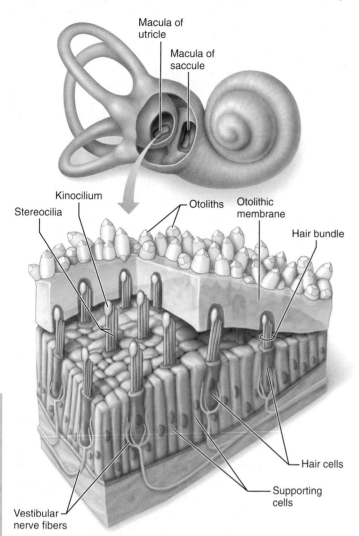

Figure 15.34 Structure of a macula. The "hairs" of the receptor cells of a macula project into the gelatinous otolithic membrane. Vestibular nerve fibers surround the base of the hair cells.

Equilibrium and Orientation

▶ Explain how the balance organs of the semicircular canals and the vestibule help maintain dynamic and static equilibrium.

The equilibrium sense is not easy to describe because it does not "see," "hear," or "feel," but responds (frequently without our awareness) to various head movements. Furthermore, this sense depends not only on inputs from the internal ear but also on vision and on information from stretch receptors of muscles and tendons.

Under normal conditions the equilibrium receptors in the semicircular canals and vestibule, collectively called the **vestibular apparatus**, send signals to the brain that initiate reflexes needed to make the simplest changes in position as well as to serve a tennis ball precisely to the right spot (your opponent's backhand). The equilibrium receptors of the internal ear can be divided into two functional arms, with the receptors in the vestibule and semicircular canals monitoring **static** and **dynamic equilibrium**, respectively.

The Maculae and Static Equilibrium

The sensory receptors for static equilibrium are the **maculae** (mak'u-le; "spots"), one in each saccule wall and one in each utricle wall (**Figure 15.34**). These receptors monitor the position of the head in space, and in so doing, they play a key role in control of posture. They respond to *linear* acceleration forces, that is, straight-line changes in speed and direction, but not to rotation.

Anatomy of the Maculae Each macula is a flat epithelial patch containing **hair cells**. These hair cells, like all those of the internal ear, have stereocilia plus one kinocilium that project into a gel-like mass. The macula's scattered hair cells are surrounded by **supporting cells** (Figure 15.34). The "hairs" of the hair cells are embedded in the overlying **otolithic membrane** (o'to-lith-ik), a jellylike mass studded with tiny stones (calcium carbonate crystals) called **otoliths** ("ear stones"). The otoliths, though small, are dense and they increase the membrane's weight and its inertia (resistance to change in motion).

In the utricle, the macula is horizontal, and the hairs are vertically oriented when the head is upright (Figure 15.34). For this reason, the utricular maculae respond best to acceleration in the horizontal plane and tilting the head to the side, because vertical (up-down) movements do not displace their horizontal otolithic membrane.

In the saccule, on the other hand, the macula is nearly vertical, and the hairs protrude horizontally into the otolithic membrane. The saccular maculae respond best to vertical movements, such as the sudden acceleration of an elevator.

The hair cells synapse with fibers of the **vestibular nerve**, whose endings coil around their bases. Like the cochlear nerve, the vestibular nerve is a subdivision of the vestibulocochlear nerve (VIII). The cell bodies of the sensory neurons are located in the nearby **superior** and **inferior vestibular ganglia** (see Figure 15.27).

Activating Maculae Receptors What happens in the maculae that leads to sensory transduction? When your head starts or stops moving in a linear direction, inertia causes the otolithic membrane to slide backward or forward like a greased plate over the hair cells, bending the hairs. For example, when you start to run, the otolithic membranes of the utricle maculae lag behind, bending the hairs backward. When you suddenly stop, the otolithic membrane slides abruptly forward (just as you slide forward in your car when you brake), bending the hair cells forward. Likewise, when you nod your head or fall, the otoliths roll inferiorly, bending the hairs of the maculae in the saccules.

The hair cells release neurotransmitter continuously but movement of their hairs modifies the amount they release. When the hairs are bent *toward the kinocilium*, the hair cells depolarize, stepping up their pace of neurotransmitter release, and a faster stream of impulses travels up the vestibular nerve to the

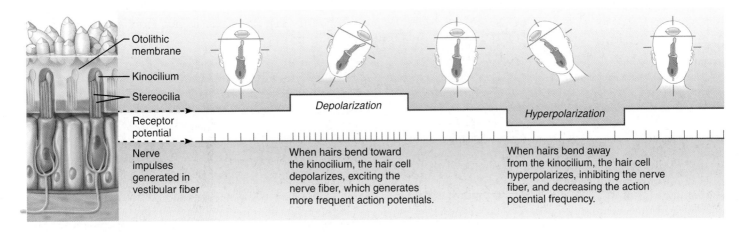

Figure 15.35 The effect of gravitational pull on a macula receptor cell in the utricle.

brain **(Figure 15.35)**. When the hairs are bent in the opposite direction, the receptors hyperpolarize, and neurotransmitter release and impulse generation decline. In either case, the brain is informed of the changing position of the head in space.

It is important to understand that the maculae respond *only to changes* in the velocity of head movement (acceleration or deceleration). Because the hair cells adapt quickly (resuming their basal level of neurotransmitter release), they do not report on unchanging head positions. In this way, the maculae help us to maintain normal head position with respect to gravity. They also contribute to dynamic equilibrium by responding to linear acceleration and deceleration.

The Crista Ampullaris and Dynamic Equilibrium

The receptor for dynamic equilibrium, called the **crista ampullaris**, or simply *crista*, is a minute elevation in the ampulla of each semicircular canal (see Figure 15.27). Like the maculae, the cristae are excited by head movement (acceleration and deceleration), but in this case the major stimuli are rotatory (angular) movements. When you twirl on the dance floor or suffer through a rough boat ride, these gyroscope-like receptors are working overtime. Since the semicircular canals are located in all three planes of space, all rotatory movements of the head disturb one or another *pair* of cristae (one in each ear).

Anatomy of the Crista Ampullaris   Each crista is composed of supporting cells and hair cells whose structure and function are basically the same as the hair cells of the cochlea and maculae. In this case, the gelled mass is a **cupula** (ku′pu-lah), which resembles a pointed cap **(Figure 15.36)**. The cupula is a delicate, loosely organized network of gelatinous strands that radiate outward to contact the "hairs" of each hair cell. Dendrites of vestibular nerve fibers encircle the base of the hair cells.

Activating Crista Ampullaris Receptors   The cristae respond to *changes* in the velocity of rotatory movements of the head. Because of its inertia, the endolymph in the semicircular ducts moves briefly in the direction *opposite* the body's rotation, deforming the crista in the duct. As the hairs are bent, the hair cells depolarize and impulses reach the brain at a faster rate

(Figure 15.36c, middle panel). Bending the cilia in the opposite direction causes hyperpolarization and reduces impulse generation. Because the axes of the hair cells in the complementary semicircular ducts are opposite, rotation in a given direction causes depolarization of the receptors in one ampulla of the pair, and hyperpolarization of the receptors in the other.

If the body continues to rotate at a constant rate, the endolymph eventually comes to rest—it moves along at the same speed as the body and stimulation of the hair cells ends. Consequently, if we are blindfolded, we cannot tell whether we are moving at a constant speed or not moving at all after the first few seconds of rotation. However, when we suddenly stop moving, the endolymph keeps on going, in effect reversing its direction within the canal. This sudden reversal in the direction of hair bending results in membrane voltage changes in the receptor cells and modifies the rate of impulse transmission, which tells the brain that we have slowed or stopped (Figure 15.36c, right panel).

The key point to remember when considering both types of equilibrium receptors is that the rigid bony labyrinth moves with the body, while the fluids (and gels) within the membranous labyrinth are free to move at various rates, depending on the forces (such as gravity, acceleration, and so on) acting on them.

Impulses transmitted from the semicircular canals are particularly important to reflex movements of the eyes. **Vestibular nystagmus** is a complex of rather strange eye movements that occurs during and immediately after rotation. As you rotate, your eyes slowly drift in the opposite direction, as though fixed on some object in the environment. This reaction relates to the backflow of endolymph in the semicircular canals. Then, because of CNS compensating mechanisms, the eyes jump rapidly toward the direction of rotation to establish a new fixation point. These alternating eye movements continue until the endolymph comes to rest. When you stop rotating, at first your eyes continue to move in the direction of the previous spin, and then they jerk rapidly in the opposite direction. This sudden change is caused by the change in the direction in which the cristae are bent after you stop. Nystagmus is often accompanied by vertigo.

15

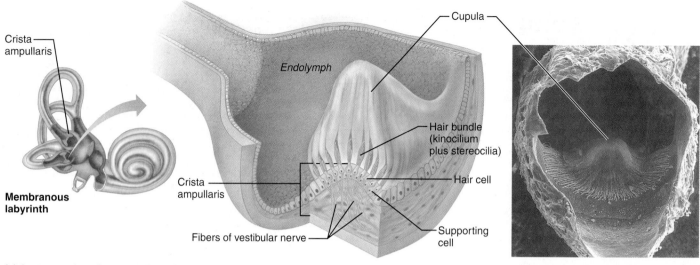

(a) Anatomy of a crista ampullaris in a semicircular canal

(b) Scanning electron micrograph of a crista ampullaris (200×)

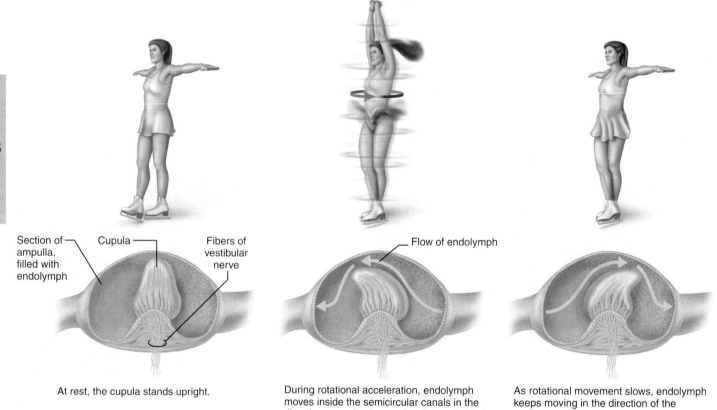

At rest, the cupula stands upright.

During rotational acceleration, endolymph moves inside the semicircular canals in the direction opposite the rotation (it lags behind due to inertia). Endolymph flow bends the cupula and excites the hair cells.

As rotational movement slows, endolymph keeps moving in the direction of the rotation, bending the cupula in the opposite direction from acceleration and inhibiting the hair cells.

(c) Movement of the cupula during rotational acceleration and deceleration

Figure 15.36 Location, structure, and function of a crista ampullaris in the internal ear.

The Equilibrium Pathway to the Brain

Our responses to body imbalance, such as during stumbling, must be fast and reflexive. By the time we "thought about" correcting our fall, we would already be on the ground. Accordingly, information from the balance receptors goes directly to reflex centers in the brain stem, rather than to the cerebral cortex as with the other special senses.

The nerve pathways connecting the vestibular apparatus with the brain are complex and poorly traced. The transmission sequence begins when the hair cells in the vestibular apparatus

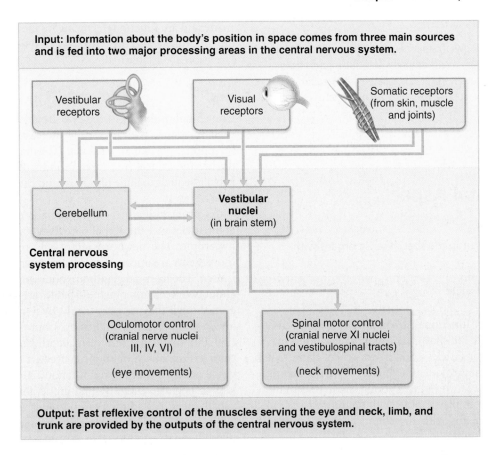

Input: Information about the body's position in space comes from three main sources and is fed into two major processing areas in the central nervous system.

Vestibular receptors

Visual receptors

Somatic receptors (from skin, muscle and joints)

Cerebellum

Vestibular nuclei (in brain stem)

Central nervous system processing

Oculomotor control (cranial nerve nuclei III, IV, VI)

(eye movements)

Spinal motor control (cranial nerve XI nuclei and vestibulospinal tracts)

(neck movements)

Output: Fast reflexive control of the muscles serving the eye and neck, limb, and trunk are provided by the outputs of the central nervous system.

Figure 15.37 **Pathways of the balance and orientation system.**

15

are activated. As depicted in Figure 15.37, impulses travel initially to one of two destinations: the **vestibular nuclei** in the brain stem or the **cerebellum**. The vestibular nuclei, the major integrative center for balance, also receive inputs from the visual and somatic receptors, particularly from proprioceptors in neck muscles that report on the position of the head. These nuclei integrate this information and then send commands to brain stem motor centers that control the extrinsic eye muscles (cranial nerve nuclei III, IV, and VI) and reflex movements of the neck, limb, and trunk muscles (via the vestibulospinal tracts). The ensuing reflex movements of the eyes and body allow us to remain focused on the visual field and to quickly adjust our body position to maintain or regain balance.

The cerebellum also integrates inputs from the eyes and somatic receptors (as well as from the cerebrum). It coordinates skeletal muscle activity and regulates muscle tone so that head position, posture, and balance are maintained, often in the face of rapidly changing inputs. Its "specialty" is fine control of delicate postural movements and timing.

Notice that the vestibular apparatus *does not automatically compensate* for forces acting on the body. Its job is to send warning signals to the central nervous system, which initiates the appropriate compensations (righting) to keep your body balanced, your weight evenly distributed, and your eyes focused on what you were looking at when the disturbance occurred.

HOMEOSTATIC IMBALANCE

Responses to equilibrium signals are totally reflexive, and usually we are aware of vestibular apparatus activity only when its functioning is impaired. Equilibrium problems are usually obvious and unpleasant. Nausea, dizziness, and loss of balance are common and there may be nystagmus in the absence of rotational stimuli.

Motion sickness has been difficult to explain, but it appears to be due to sensory input mismatch. For example, if you are inside a ship during a storm, visual inputs indicate that your body is fixed with reference to a stationary environment (your cabin). But as the ship is tossed about by the rough seas, your vestibular apparatus detects movement and sends impulses that disagree with the visual information. The brain thus receives conflicting information, and its "confusion" somehow leads to motion sickness. Warning signals, which precede nausea and vomiting, include excessive salivation, pallor, rapid deep breathing, and profuse sweating. Removal of the stimulus usually ends the symptoms. Over-the-counter antimotion drugs, such as meclizine (Bonine), depress vestibular inputs and help alleviate the symptoms. They are most effective when taken "before the fact." Scopolamine-containing timed-release skin patches are also used to head off motion sickness. ∎

16. For each of the following statements, indicate whether it applies to a macula or a crista ampullaris: inside a semicircular canal; contains otoliths; responds to linear acceleration and deceleration; has a cupula; responds to rotational acceleration and deceleration; inside a saccule.

For answers, see Appendix G.

Developmental Aspects of the Special Senses

▶ List changes that occur in the special sense organs with aging.

Taste and Smell

All the special senses are functional, to a greater or lesser degree, at birth. Smell and taste are sharp, and infants relish food that adults consider bland or tasteless. Some researchers claim that smell is just as important as touch in guiding newborn infants to their mother's breast. However, very young children seem indifferent to odors and can play happily with their own feces.

There are few problems with the chemical senses during childhood and young adulthood. Women generally have a more acute sense of smell than men, and nonsmokers have a sharper sense of smell than smokers. Beginning in the fourth decade of life, our ability to taste and smell declines due to the gradual loss of receptors, which are replaced more slowly than in younger people. More than half of people over the age of 65 years have serious problems detecting odors, which may explain why some tend to douse themselves with large amounts of cologne, or pay little attention to formerly disagreeable odors. Additionally, their sense of taste is poor. This along with the decline in the sense of smell makes food taste bland and contributes to loss of appetite.

Vision

By the fourth week of development, the beginnings of the eyes are seen in the **optic vesicles** that protrude from the diencephalon (see Figure 12.2c on p. 431). Soon these hollow vesicles indent to form double-layered **optic cups**, and their stalks form the optic nerves and provide a pathway for blood vessels to reach the eye interior. Once an optic vesicle reaches the overlying surface ectoderm, it induces the ectoderm to thicken and then form a **lens vesicle** that pinches off into the cavity of the optic cup, where it becomes the lens. The lining (internal layer) of the optic cup becomes the neural retina, and the outer layer forms the pigmented layer of the retina. The rest of the eye tissues and the vitreous humor are formed by mesenchymal cells derived from the mesoderm that surrounds the optic cup.

In the darkness of the uterus, the fetus cannot see. Nonetheless, even before the light-sensitive portions of the photoreceptors develop, the central nervous system connections have been made and are functional. During infancy, synaptic connections are fine-tuned, and the typical cortical fields that allow binocular vision are established.

HOMEOSTATIC IMBALANCE

Congenital problems of the eyes are relatively uncommon, but their incidence is dramatically increased by certain maternal infections, particularly rubella (German measles), occurring during the critical first three months of pregnancy. Common rubella sequels include blindness and cataracts. ■

As a rule, vision is the only special sense not fully functional at birth. Because the eyeballs are foreshortened, most babies are hyperopic. The newborn infant sees only in gray tones, eye movements are uncoordinated, and often only one eye at a time is used. The lacrimal glands are not completely developed until about two weeks after birth, so babies are tearless for this period, even though they may cry lustily. By 5 months, infants can follow moving objects with their eyes, but visual acuity is still poor (20/200). By the age of 5 years, depth perception is present and color vision is well developed. Because the eyeball has grown, visual acuity has improved to about 20/30, providing a readiness to begin reading. By first grade, the initial hyperopia has usually been replaced by emmetropia, and the eye reaches its adult size at 8–9 years of age. Emmetropia usually continues until presbyopia begins to set in around age 40 owing to decreasing lens elasticity.

With age, the lens loses its crystal clarity and discolors. As a result, it begins to scatter light, causing a glare that is distressing when driving at night. The dilator pupillae muscles become less efficient, so the pupils stay partly constricted. These two changes together decrease the amount of light reaching the retina, and visual acuity is dramatically lower in people over 70. In addition, the lacrimal glands are less active and the eyes tend to be dry and more susceptible to infection. Elderly persons are also at risk for certain conditions that cause blindness, such as macular degeneration, glaucoma, cataracts, arteriosclerosis, and diabetes mellitus.

Hearing and Balance

The ear begins to develop in the three-week embryo. The internal ears develop first, from thickenings of the surface ectoderm called the **otic placodes** (o′tik), which lie lateral to the hindbrain on each side. The otic placode invaginates, forming the **otic pit** and then the **otic vesicle**, which detaches from the surface epithelium. The otic vesicle develops into the membranous labyrinth. The surrounding mesenchyme forms the bony labyrinth.

The middle ear cavity and pharyngotympanic tube of the middle ear develop from **pharyngeal pouches**, lateral outpocketings of the endoderm lining the pharynx. The auditory ossicles develop from neural crest cells.

The external acoustic meatus and external face of the tympanic membrane of the external ear differentiate from the **branchial groove** (brang′ke-al), an indentation of the surface

15

ectoderm, and the auricle develops from swellings of the surrounding tissue.

Newborn infants can hear, but early responses to sound are mostly reflexive—for example, crying and clenching the eyelids in response to a startling noise. By the fourth month, infants will turn to the voices of family members. Critical listening begins as toddlers increase their vocabulary, and good language skills are closely tied to the ability to hear well.

HOMEOSTATIC IMBALANCE

Congenital abnormalities of the ears are fairly common. Examples include partly or completely missing pinnae and closed or absent external acoustic meatuses. Maternal rubella during the first trimester commonly results in sensorineural deafness. ■

Except for ear inflammations, mostly due to infections, few problems affect the ears during childhood and adult life. By the 60s, however, deterioration of the spiral organ becomes noticeable. We are born with approximately 40,000 hair cells, but their number decreases when they are damaged or destroyed by loud noises, disease, or drugs. The hair cells *are* replaced, but at such a slow rate that there really is no functional regeneration. It is estimated that if we were to live 140 years, we would have lost all of our hearing receptors.

The ability to hear high-pitched sounds leaves us first. This condition, called **presbycusis** (pres″bĭ-ku′sis), is a type of sensorineural deafness. Although presbycusis is considered a disability of old age, it is becoming much more common in younger people as our world grows noisier. Since noise is a stressor, one of its physiological consequences is vasoconstriction, and when delivery of blood to the ear is reduced, the ear becomes even more sensitive to the damaging effects of noise.

CHECK YOUR UNDERSTANDING

17. What age-related changes make it more difficult for the elderly to see at night?

For answers, see Appendix G.

Our abilities to see, hear, taste, and smell—and some of our responses to the effects of gravity—are largely the work of our brain. However, as we have discovered in this final nervous system chapter, the large and often elaborate sensory receptor organs that serve the special senses are works of art in and of themselves.

The concluding chapter of this unit describes how the body's functions are controlled by chemicals called hormones in a manner quite different from what we have described for neural control.

RELATED CLINICAL TERMS

15

Ageusia (ah-gu′ze-ah) Loss or impairment of the taste sense.

Age-related macular degeneration (ARMD) Progressive deterioration of the retina that affects the macula lutea and leads to loss of central vision; the main cause of vision loss in those over age 65. Early stages and mild forms involve the buildup of pigments in the macula and impaired functioning of the pigmented epithelium. Continued accumulation of pigment leads to the "dry" form of ARMD, in which many pigment epithelial cells and macular photoreceptors die. The dry form is largely untreatable, although a specific cocktail of vitamins and zinc has been shown to slow its progression. Less common is the "wet" form in which an overgrowth of new blood vessels invades the retina from the choroid. Leakage of blood and fluids from these vessels causes scarring and detachment of the retina. The cause of wet ARMD is unknown, but several treatment options can slow its progression—laser treatments that destroy some of the growing vessels and drugs that prevent blood vessel growth.

Blepharitis (blef″ah-ri′tis; *blephar* = eyelash; *itis* = inflammation) Inflammation of the margins of the eyelids.

Enucleation (e-nu″kle-a′shun) Surgical removal of an eyeball.

Exophthalmos (ek″sof-thal′mos; *exo* = out; *phthalmo* = the eye) Anteriorly bulging eyeballs; this condition is seen in some cases of hyperthyroidism.

Labyrinthitis Inflammation of the labyrinth.

Ophthalmology (of″thal-mol′o-je) The science that studies the eye and eye diseases. An ophthalmologist is a medical doctor who specializes in treating eye disorders.

Optometrist A licensed nonphysician who measures vision and prescribes corrective lenses.

Otalgia (o-tal′je-ah; *algia* = pain) Earache.

Otitis externa Inflammation and infection of the external acoustic meatus, caused by bacteria or fungi that enter the canal from outside, especially when the canal is moist (e.g., after swimming).

Papilledema (pap″il-ĕ-de′mah; *papill* = nipple; *edema* = swelling) Protrusion of the optic disc into the eyeball, which can be observed by ophthalmoscopic examination; caused by conditions that increase intracranial pressure.

Scotoma (sko-to′mah; *scoto* = darkness) A blind spot other than the normal (optic disc) blind spot; many causes, including the presence of a brain tumor pressing on fibers of the visual pathway, and stroke.

Trachoma (trah-ko′mah; *trach* = rough) A highly contagious bacterial (chlamydial) infection of the conjunctiva and cornea. Common worldwide, it blinds millions of people in poor countries of Africa and Asia; treated with eye ointments containing antibiotic drugs.

Weber's test Hearing test during which a sounding tuning fork is held to the forehead. In those with normal hearing, the tone is heard equally in both ears. The tone will be heard best in the "good" ear if sensorineural deafness is present, and in the "bad" ear if conduction deafness is present.

CHAPTER SUMMARY

The Eye and Vision   (pp. 548–569)

1. The eye is enclosed in the bony orbit and cushioned by fat.

Accessory Structures of the Eye   (pp. 548–551)

2. Eyebrows help to shade and protect the eyes.

3. Eyelids protect and lubricate the eyes by reflex blinking. Within the eyelids are the orbicularis oculi and levator palpebrae muscles, and modified sebaceous and sweat glands.

4. The conjunctiva is a mucosa that lines the eyelids and covers the anterior eyeball surface. Its mucus lubricates the eyeball surface.

5. The lacrimal apparatus consists of the lacrimal gland (which produces a saline solution containing mucus, lysozyme, and antibodies), the lacrimal canaliculi, the lacrimal sac, and the nasolacrimal duct.

6. The extrinsic eye muscles (superior, inferior, lateral, and medial rectus and superior and inferior oblique) move the eyeballs.

Structure of the Eyeball   (pp. 551–556)

7. The wall of the eyeball is made up of three layers. The outermost fibrous layer consists of the sclera and the cornea. The sclera protects the eye and gives it shape; the cornea allows light to enter the eye.

8. The middle, pigmented vascular layer (uvea) consists of the choroid, the ciliary body, and the iris. The choroid provides nutrients to the eye and prevents light scattering within the eye. The ciliary muscles of the ciliary body control lens shape; the iris controls the size of the pupil.

9. The sensory layer, or retina, consists of an outer pigmented layer and an inner neural layer. The neural layer contains photoreceptors (rods and cones), bipolar cells, and ganglion cells. Ganglion cell axons form the optic nerve, which exits via the optic disc ("blind spot").

10. Rods respond to low-intensity light and provide night and peripheral vision. Cones are bright-light, high-discrimination receptors that provide for color vision. Anything that must be viewed precisely is focused on the cone-rich fovea centralis.

11. The posterior segment of the eyeball, behind the lens, contains vitreous humor, which helps support the eyeball and keep the retina in place. The anterior segment, anterior to the lens, is filled with aqueous humor, formed by capillaries in the ciliary processes and drained into the scleral venous sinus. Aqueous humor is a major factor in maintaining intraocular pressure.

12. The biconvex lens is suspended within the eye by the ciliary zonule attached to the ciliary body. It is the only adjustable refractory structure of the eye.

Physiology of Vision   (pp. 556–569)

13. Light is made up of those wavelengths of the electromagnetic spectrum that excite the photoreceptors.

14. Light is refracted (bent) when passing from one transparent medium to another of different density. Concave lenses disperse light; convex lenses converge light and bring its rays to a focal point. The greater the lens curvature, the more light bends.

15. As light passes through the eye, it is bent by the cornea and the lens and focused on the retina. The cornea accounts for most of the refraction, but the lens allows active focusing for different distances.

16. Focusing for distance vision requires no special movements of the eye structures. Focusing for close-up vision requires accommodation (bulging of the lens), pupillary constriction, and convergence of the eyeballs. All three reflexes are controlled by cranial nerve III.

17. Refractory problems include presbyopia, myopia, hyperopia, and astigmatism.

18. The outer segments of the photoreceptors contain light-absorbing visual pigment in membrane-bounded discs.

19. The light-absorbing molecule retinal is combined with various opsins to form the visual pigments. When struck by light, retinal changes shape (11-*cis* to all-*trans*) and activates opsin. Activated opsin activates transducin (a G protein) which in turn activates PDE, an enzyme that breaks down cGMP, allowing the cation channels to close. This results in hyperpolarization of the receptor cells and inhibits their release of neurotransmitter.

20. Rod visual pigment, rhodopsin, is a combination of retinal and opsin. The light-triggered changes in retinal cause hyperpolarization of the rods. Photoreceptors and bipolar cells generate graded potentials only; action potentials are generated by the ganglion cells.

21. The three types of cones all contain retinal, but each has a different type of opsin. Each cone type responds maximally to one color of light: red, blue, or green. The chemistry of cone function is similar to that of rods.

22. During light adaptation, photopigments are bleached and rods are inactivated; then, as cones decrease their light sensitivity, high-acuity vision ensues. In dark adaptation, cones cease functioning, and visual acuity decreases; rod function begins when sufficient rhodopsin has accumulated.

23. The visual pathway to the brain begins with the optic nerve fibers (ganglion cell axons) from the retina. At the optic chiasma, fibers from the medial half of each retina cross over and continue on in the optic tracts to the thalamus. Thalamic neurons project to the visual cortex via the optic radiation. Fibers also project from the retina to the midbrain pretectal nuclei and the superior colliculi, and to the suprachiasmatic nucleus of the hypothalamus.

24. Each eye receives a slightly different view of the visual field. These views are fused by the visual cortices to provide for depth perception.

25. Retinal processing involves the selective destruction of inputs so as to emphasize bright/dark or color contrasts (edges). (The horizontal cells and amacrine cells are local integrator cells of the retina that modify and process inputs to the ganglion cells.) Thalamic processing subserves high-acuity color vision and depth perception. Cortical processing involves neurons of the striate (primary) cortex, which receive inputs from the retinal ganglion cells, and neurons of the prestriate (association) cortices, which receive inputs from striate cortical cells and mostly integrate inputs concerned with color, form, and movement. Visual processing also proceeds anteriorly in the "what" and "where" processing streams via the temporal and parietal lobes, respectively.

The Chemical Senses: Taste and Smell   (pp. 569–574)
The Olfactory Epithelium and the Sense of Smell (pp. 569–571)

1. The olfactory epithelium is located in the roof of the nasal cavity. The receptor cells are ciliated bipolar neurons. Their axons are the filaments of the olfactory nerve (cranial nerve I).

2. Individual olfactory neurons show a range of responsiveness to different chemicals. Olfactory cells bearing the same odorant receptors synapse in the same glomerulus type.

3. Olfactory neurons are excited by volatile chemicals that bind to receptors in the olfactory cilia.

4. Action potentials of the olfactory nerve filaments are transmitted to the olfactory bulb where the filaments synapse with mitral cells. The mitral cells send impulses via the olfactory tract to the olfactory cortex. Fibers carrying impulses from the olfactory receptors also project to the limbic system.

Taste Buds and the Sense of Taste   (pp. 571–573)

5. The taste buds are scattered in the oral cavity and pharynx but are most abundant on the tongue papillae.

6. Gustatory cells, the epithelial receptor cells of the taste buds, have gustatory hairs (microvilli) that serve as the receptor regions. The gustatory cells are excited by the binding of tastants (food chemicals) to receptors on their microvilli.

7. The five basic taste qualities are sweet, sour, salty, bitter, and umami.

8. The taste sense is served by cranial nerves VII, IX, and X, which send impulses to the solitary nucleus of the medulla. From there, impulses are sent to the thalamus and the gustatory cortex.

Homeostatic Imbalances of the Chemical Senses (pp. 573–574)

9. Most chemical sense dysfunctions are olfactory disorders (anosmias). Common causes are nasal damage or obstruction.

The Ear: Hearing and Balance   (pp. 574–588)
Structure of the Ear   (pp. 574–577)

1. The auricle and external acoustic meatus compose the external ear. The tympanic membrane, the boundary between the outer and middle ears, transmits sound waves to the middle ear.

2. The middle ear is a small chamber within the temporal bone, connected by the pharyngotympanic tube to the nasopharynx. The ossicles, which help to amplify sound, span the middle ear cavity and transmit sound vibrations from the tympanic membrane to the oval window.

3. The internal ear consists of the bony labyrinth, within which the membranous labyrinth is suspended. The bony labyrinth chambers contain perilymph; the membranous labyrinth ducts and sacs contain endolymph.

4. The vestibule contains the saccule and utricle. The semicircular canals extend posteriorly from the vestibule in three planes. They contain the semicircular ducts.

5. The cochlea houses the cochlear duct (scala media), containing the spiral organ (of Corti), the receptor organ for hearing. Within the cochlear duct, the hair (receptor) cells rest on the basilar membrane, and their hairs project into the gelatinous tectorial membrane.

Physiology of Hearing   (pp. 577–583)

6. Sound originates from a vibrating object and travels in waves consisting of alternating areas of compression and rarefaction of the medium.

7. The distance from crest to crest on a sine wave is the sound's wavelength; the shorter the wavelength, the higher the frequency (measured in hertz). Frequency is perceived as pitch.

8. The amplitude of sound is the height of the peaks of the sine wave, which reflect the sound's intensity. Sound intensity is measured in decibels. Intensity is perceived as loudness.

9. Sound passing through the external acoustic meatus sets the tympanic membrane into vibration at the same frequency. The ossicles amplify and deliver the vibrations to the oval window.

10. Pressure waves in cochlear fluids set specific locations on the basilar membrane into resonance. At points of maximal membrane vibration, the hair cells of the spiral organ are alternately depolarized and hyperpolarized by the vibratory motion. Movements of the stereocilia toward the kinocilium depolarize the hair cells and increase the rate of impulse generation in the auditory nerve fibers. Movements away from the kinocilium have the opposite effect. High-frequency sounds stimulate hair cells near the oval window; low-frequency sounds stimulate hair cells near the apex. Most auditory inputs are sent to the brain by inner hair cells. Outer hair cells amplify responsiveness of the inner hair cells.

11. Impulses generated along the cochlear nerve travel to the cochlear nuclei of the medulla and from there through several brain stem nuclei to the medial geniculate nucleus of the thalamus and then the auditory cortex. Each auditory cortex receives impulses from both ears.

12. Auditory processing is analytic; each tone is perceived separately. Perception of pitch is related to the position of the excited hair cells along the basilar membrane. Intensity perception reflects the fact that as sound intensity increases, basilar membrane motion is increased and the frequency of impulse transmission to the cortex is enhanced. Cues for sound localization include the intensity and timing of sound arriving at each ear.

Homeostatic Imbalances of Hearing   (p. 583)

13. Conduction deafness results from interference with conduction of sound vibrations to the fluids of the internal ear. Sensorineural deafness reflects damage to neural structures.

14. Tinnitus is an early sign of sensorineural deafness; it may also result from the use of certain drugs.

15. Ménière's syndrome is a disorder of the membranous labyrinth. Symptoms include tinnitus, deafness, and vertigo. Excessive endolymph accumulation is the suspected cause.

Equilibrium and Orientation   (pp. 584–588)

16. The equilibrium receptor regions of the internal ear are called the vestibular apparatus.

17. The receptors for static equilibrium are the maculae of the saccule and utricle. A macula consists of hair cells with stereocilia and a kinocilium embedded in an overlying otolithic membrane. Linear movements cause the otolithic membrane to move, pulling on the hair cells and changing the rate of impulse generation in the vestibular nerve fibers.

18. The dynamic equilibrium receptor, the crista ampullaris within each semicircular duct, responds to angular or rotatory movements in one plane. It consists of a tuft of hair cells whose microvilli are embedded in the gelatinous cupula. Rotatory movements cause the endolymph to flow in the opposite direction, bending the cupula and either exciting or inhibiting the hair cells.

19. Impulses from the vestibular apparatus are sent via vestibular nerve fibers mainly to the vestibular nuclei of the brain stem and the cerebellum. These centers initiate responses that fix the eyes on objects and activate muscles to maintain balance.

Developmental Aspects of the Special Senses (pp. 588–589)
Taste and Smell   (p. 588)

1. The chemical senses are sharpest at birth and gradually decline with age as replacement of the receptor cells becomes more sluggish.

15

Vision　(p. 588)

2. Congenital eye problems are uncommon, but maternal rubella can cause blindness.
3. The eye starts as an optic vesicle, an outpocketing of the diencephalon that invaginates to form the optic cup, which becomes the retina. Overlying ectoderm folds to form the lens vesicle, which gives rise to the lens. The remaining eye tissues and the accessory structures are formed by mesenchyme.
4. The eye is foreshortened at birth and reaches adult size at the age of 8–9 years. Depth perception and color vision develop during early childhood.
5. With age, the lens loses its elasticity and clarity, there is a decline in the ability of the iris to dilate, and visual acuity decreases. The elderly are at risk for eye problems resulting from dry eyes and disease.

Hearing and Balance　(pp. 588–589)

6. The membranous labyrinth develops from the otic placode, an ectodermal thickening lateral to the hindbrain. Mesenchyme forms the surrounding bony structures. Pharyngeal pouch endoderm, in conjunction with mesenchyme, forms most middle ear structures; the external ear is formed largely by ectoderm.
7. Congenital ear problems are fairly common. Maternal rubella can cause deafness.
8. Response to sound in infants is reflexive. By the fourth month, an infant can locate sound. Critical listening develops in toddlers.
9. Deterioration of the spiral organ (of Corti) occurs throughout life as noise, disease, and drugs destroy cochlear hair cells. Age-related loss of hearing (presbycusis) occurs in the 60s and 70s.

REVIEW QUESTIONS

Multiple Choice/Matching

(Some questions have more than one correct answer. Select the best answer or answers from the choices given.)

1. The accessory glands that produce an oily secretion are the (a) conjunctiva, (b) lacrimal glands, (c) tarsal glands.
2. The portion of the fibrous layer that is white and opaque is the (a) choroid, (b) cornea, (c) retina, (d) sclera.
3. Which sequence best describes a normal route for the flow of tears from the eyes into the nasal cavity? (a) lacrimal canaliculi, nasolacrimal ducts, nasal cavity; (b) lacrimal ducts, lacrimal canaliculi, nasolacrimal ducts; (c) nasolacrimal ducts, lacrimal canaliculi, lacrimal sacs.
4. Activation of the sympathetic nervous system causes (a) contraction of the sphincter pupillae muscles, (b) contraction of the dilator pupillae muscles, (c) contraction of the ciliary muscles, (d) a decrease in ciliary zonule tension.
5. Damage to the medial recti muscles would probably affect (a) accommodation, (b) refraction, (c) convergence, (d) pupil constriction.
6. The phenomenon of dark adaptation is best explained by the fact that (a) rhodopsin does not function in dim light, (b) rhodopsin breakdown occurs slowly, (c) rods exposed to intense light need time to generate rhodopsin, (d) cones are stimulated to function by bright light.
7. Blockage of the scleral venous sinus might result in (a) a sty, (b) glaucoma, (c) conjunctivitis, (d) a cataract.
8. Nearsightedness is more properly called (a) myopia, (b) hyperopia, (c) presbyopia, (d) emmetropia.
9. Of the neurons in the retina, the axons of which of these form the optic nerve? (a) bipolar cells, (b) ganglion cells, (c) cone cells, (d) horizontal cells.
10. Which sequence of reactions occurs when a person looks at a distant object? (a) pupils constrict, ciliary zonule (suspensory ligament) relaxes, lenses become less convex; (b) pupils dilate, ciliary zonule becomes taut, lenses become less convex; (c) pupils dilate, ciliary zonule becomes taut, lenses become more convex; (d) pupils constrict, ciliary zonule relaxes, lenses become more convex.
11. During embryonic development, the lens of the eye forms (a) as part of the choroid coat, (b) from the surface ectoderm overlying the optic cup, (c) as part of the sclera, (d) from mesodermal tissue.
12. The blind spot of the eye is (a) where more rods than cones are found, (b) where the macula lutea is located, (c) where only cones occur, (d) where the optic nerve leaves the eye.
13. Olfactory tract damage would probably affect your ability to (a) see, (b) hear, (c) feel pain, (d) smell.
14. Sensory impulses transmitted over the facial, glossopharyngeal, and vagus nerves are involved in the sensation of (a) taste, (b) touch, (c) equilibrium, (d) smell.
15. Taste buds are found on the (a) anterior part of the tongue, (b) posterior part of the tongue, (c) palate, (d) all of these.
16. Gustatory cells are stimulated by (a) movement of otoliths, (b) stretch, (c) substances in solution, (d) photons of light.
17. Cells in the olfactory bulb that act as local "integrators" of olfactory inputs are the (a) hair cells, (b) granule cells, (c) basal cells, (d) mitral cells, (e) supporting cells.
18. Olfactory nerve filaments are found (a) in the optic bulbs, (b) passing through the cribriform plate of the ethmoid bone, (c) in the optic tracts, (d) in the olfactory cortex.
19. Conduction of sound from the middle ear to the internal ear occurs via vibration of the (a) malleus against the tympanic membrane, (b) stapes in the oval window, (c) incus in the round window, (d) stapes against the tympanic membrane.
20. The transmission of sound vibrations through the internal ear occurs chiefly through (a) nerve fibers, (b) air, (c) fluid, (d) bone.
21. Which of the following statements does not correctly describe the spiral organ (of Corti)? (a) Sounds of high frequency stimulate hair cells at the basal end, (b) the "hairs" of the receptor cells are embedded in the tectorial membrane, (c) the basilar membrane acts as a resonator, (d) the more numerous outer hair cells are largely responsible for our perception of sound.
22. Pitch is to frequency of sound as loudness is to (a) quality, (b) intensity, (c) overtones, (d) all of these.
23. The structure that allows pressure in the middle ear to be equalized with atmospheric pressure is the (a) pinna, (b) pharyngotympanic tube, (c) tympanic membrane, (d) oval window.
24. Which of the following is important in maintaining the balance of the body? (a) visual cues, (b) semicircular canals, (c) the saccule, (d) proprioceptors, (e) all of these.
25. Static equilibrium receptors that report the position of the head in space relative to the pull of gravity are (a) spiral organs, (b) maculae, (c) cristae ampullares, (d) otoliths.

26. Which of the following is *not* a possible cause of conduction deafness? (**a**) impacted cerumen, (**b**) middle ear infection, (**c**) cochlear nerve degeneration, (**d**) otosclerosis.

27. Which of the following are intrinsic eye muscles? (**a**) superior rectus, (**b**) orbicularis oculi, (**c**) smooth muscles of the iris and ciliary body, (**d**) levator palpebrae superioris.

28. Which lies closest to the exact posterior pole of the eye? (**a**) optic nerve, (**b**) optic disc, (**c**) macula lutea, (**d**) point of entry of central artery into the eye.

29. Otoliths (ear stones) are (**a**) a cause of deafness, (**b**) a type of hearing aid, (**c**) important in equilibrium, (**d**) the rock-hard petrous temporal bones.

Short Answer Essay Questions

30. Why do you often have to blow your nose after crying?

31. How do rods and cones differ functionally?

32. Where is the fovea centralis, and why is it important?

33. Describe the response of rhodopsin to light stimuli. What is the outcome of this cascade of events?

34. Since there are only three types of cones, how can you explain the fact that we see many more colors?

35. Where are the olfactory receptors, and why is that site poorly suited for their job?

36. Each olfactory cell responds to a single odorant molecule. True or false? Explain your choice.

37. Name the five primary taste qualities and the cranial nerves that serve the sense of taste.

38. Describe the effect of aging on the special sense organs.

Critical Thinking and Clinical Application Questions

1. During an ophthalmoscopic examination, Mrs. James was found to have bilateral papilledema. Further investigation indicated that this condition resulted from a rapidly growing intracranial tumor. First, define papilledema. Then, explain its presence in terms of Mrs. James's diagnosis.

2. Sally, a 9-year-old girl, told the clinic physician that her "ear lump hurt" and she kept "getting dizzy and falling down." As she told her story, she pointed to her mastoid process. An otoscopic examination of the external acoustic meatus revealed a red, swollen eardrum, and her throat was inflamed. Her condition was described as mastoiditis with secondary labyrinthitis (inflammation of the labyrinth). Describe the most likely route of infection and the infected structures in Sally's case. Also explain the cause of her dizziness and falling.

3. Mr. Gaspe appeared at the eye clinic complaining of a chip of wood in his eye. No foreign body was found, but the conjunctiva was obviously inflamed. What name is given to this inflammatory condition, and where would you look for a foreign body that has been floating around on the eye surface for a while?

4. Mrs. Orlando has been noticing flashes of light and tiny specks in her right visual field. When she begins to see a "veil" floating before her right eye, she makes an appointment to see the eye doctor. What is your diagnosis? Is the condition serious? Explain.

5. David Norris, an engineering student, has been working in a disco to earn money to pay for his education. After about eight months, he notices that he is having problems hearing high-pitched tones. What is the cause-and-effect relationship here?

6. Assume that a tumor in the pituitary gland or hypothalamus is protruding inferiorly and compressing the optic chiasma. What could be the visual outcome?

7. Four-year-old Gary Zammer is brought to the ophthalmologist for a routine checkup on his vision. Gary is an albino. How do you think albinism affects vision?

8. Right before Jan, a senior citizen, had a large plug of earwax cleaned from her ear, she developed a constant howling sound in her ear that would not stop. It was very annoying and stressful, and she had to go to counseling to learn how to live with this awful noise. What was her condition called?

9. During an anatomy and physiology lab exercise designed to teach the use of the ophthalmoscope, you notice that your lab partner has difficulty seeing objects in the darkened room. Upon examining her retina through the ophthalmoscope, you observe streaks and patches of dark pigmentation at the back of the eye. What might this condition be?

10. Henri, a chef in a five-star French restaurant, has been diagnosed with leukemia. He is about to undergo chemotherapy, which will kill rapidly dividing cells in his body. He needs to continue working between bouts of chemotherapy. What consequences of chemotherapy would you predict that might affect his job as a chef?

15

PEARSON Access everything you need to practice, review, and self-assess for both your A&P lecture and lab courses at **myA&P** (www.myaandp.com). There, you'll find powerful online resources, including chapter quizzes and tests, games, A&P Flix animations with quizzes, *Interactive Physiology*® with quizzes, MP3 Tutor Sessions, Practice Anatomy Lab™, and more to help you get a better grade in your course.

16

The Endocrine System: An Overview (pp. 595–596)

Hormones (pp. 596–601)

The Chemistry of Hormones (p. 596)

Mechanisms of Hormone Action (pp. 596–598)

Target Cell Specificity (p. 598)

Half-Life, Onset, and Duration of Hormone Activity (p. 599)

Interaction of Hormones at Target Cells (p. 600)

Control of Hormone Release (pp. 600–601)

The Pituitary Gland and Hypothalamus (pp. 601–608)

Pituitary-Hypothalamic Relationships (p. 603)

Anterior Pituitary Hormones (pp. 603–605)

The Posterior Pituitary and Hypothalamic Hormones (pp. 605–608)

The Thyroid Gland (pp. 608–612)

Location and Structure (p. 608)

Thyroid Hormone (pp. 609–611)

Calcitonin (p. 611)

The Parathyroid Glands (pp. 612–614)

The Adrenal (Suprarenal) Glands (pp. 614–620)

The Adrenal Cortex (pp. 614–618)

The Adrenal Medulla (pp. 618–620)

The Pineal Gland (p. 620)

Other Endocrine Glands and Tissues (pp. 620–624)

The Pancreas (pp. 620–623)

The Gonads and Placenta (p. 623)

Hormone Secretion by Other Organs (p. 624)

Developmental Aspects of the Endocrine System (pp. 624, 626–627)

The Endocrine System

Y ou don't have to watch *CSI* to experience action-packed drama. Molecules and cells inside your body have dynamic adventures on microscopic levels all the time. For instance, when insulin molecules, carried passively along in the blood, attach to protein receptors of nearby cells, the response is dramatic: Glucose molecules begin to disappear from the blood into the cells, and cellular activity accelerates. Such is the power of the second great control system of the body, the **endocrine system**, which interacts with the nervous system to coordinate and integrate the activity of body cells.

APPENDIX A The Metric System

MEASUREMENT	UNIT AND ABBREVIATION	METRIC EQUIVALENT	METRIC TO ENGLISH CONVERSION FACTOR	ENGLISH TO METRIC CONVERSION FACTOR
Length	1 kilometer (km)	$= 1000 \ (10^3)$ meters	1 km = 0.62 mile	1 mile = 1.61 km
	1 meter (m)	$= 100 \ (10^2)$ centimeters = 1000 millimeters	1 m = 1.09 yards 1 m = 3.28 feet 1 m = 39.37 inches	1 yard = 0.914 m 1 foot = 0.305 m
	1 centimeter (cm)	$= 0.01 \ (10^{-2})$ meter	1 cm = 0.394 inch	1 foot = 30.5 cm 1 inch = 2.54 cm
	1 millimeter (mm)	$= 0.001 \ (10^{-3})$ meter	1 mm = 0.039 inch	
	1 micrometer (μm) [formerly micron (μ)]	$= 0.000001 \ (10^{-6})$ meter		
	1 nanometer (nm)	$= 0.000000001 \ (10^{-9})$ meter		
	1 angstrom (Å)	$= 0.0000000001 \ (10^{-10})$ meter		
Area	1 square meter (m^2)	= 10,000 square centimeters	1 m^2 = 1.1960 square yards 1 m^2 = 10.764 square feet	1 square yard = 0.8361 m^2 1 square foot = 0.0929 m^2
	1 square centimeter (cm^2)	= 100 square millimeters	1 cm^2 = 0.155 square inch	1 square inch = 6.4516 cm^2
Mass	1 metric ton (t)	= 1000 kilograms	1 t = 1.103 ton	1 ton = 0.907 t
	1 kilogram (kg)	= 1000 grams	1 kg = 2.205 pounds	1 pound = 0.4536 kg
	1 gram (g)	= 1000 milligrams	1 g = 0.0353 ounce 1 g = 15.432 grains	1 ounce = 28.35 g
	1 milligram (mg)	= 0.001 gram	1 mg = approx. 0.015 grain	
	1 microgram (μg)	= 0.000001 gram		
Volume (solids)	1 cubic meter (m^3)	= 1,000,000 cubic centimeters	1 m^3 = 1.3080 cubic yards 1 m^3 = 35.315 cubic feet	1 cubic yard = 0.7646 m^3 1 cubic foot = 0.0283 m^3
	1 cubic centimeter (cm^3 or cc)	= 0.000001 cubic meter = 1 milliliter	1 cm^3 = 0.0610 cubic inch	1 cubic inch = 16.387 cm^3
	1 cubic millimeter (mm^3)	= 0.000000001 cubic meter		
Volume (liquids and gases)	1 kiloliter (kl or kL)	= 1000 liters	1 kL = 264.17 gallons	1 gallon = 3.785 L
	1 liter (l or L)	= 1000 milliliters	1 L = 0.264 gallon 1 L = 1.057 quarts	1 quart = 0.946 L
	1 milliliter (ml or mL)	= 0.001 liter = 1 cubic centimeter	1 ml = 0.034 fluid ounce 1 ml = approx. $\frac{1}{5}$ teaspoon 1 ml = approx. 15–16 drops (gtt)	1 quart = 946 ml 1 pint = 473 ml 1 fluid ounce = 29.57 ml 1 teaspoon = approx. 5 ml
	1 microliter (μl or μL)	= 0.000001 liter		
Time	1 second (s)	$= \frac{1}{60}$ minute		
	1 millisecond (ms)	= 0.001 second		
Temperature	Degrees Celsius (°C)		$°F = \frac{9}{5}(°C) + 32$	$°C = \frac{5}{9}(°F - 32)$

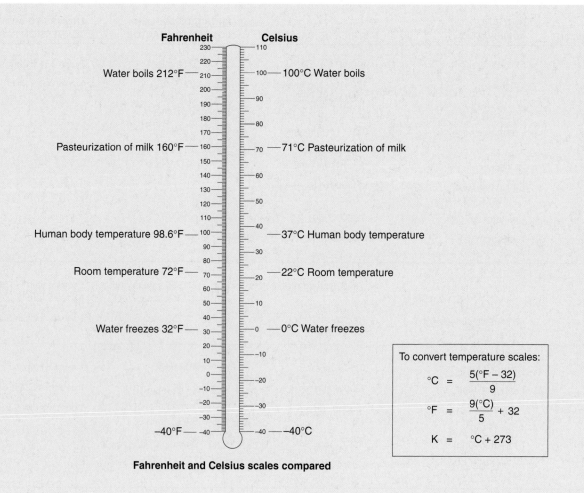

Fahrenheit and Celsius scales compared

To convert temperature scales:

$$°C = \frac{5(°F - 32)}{9}$$

$$°F = \frac{9(°C)}{5} + 32$$

$$K = °C + 273$$

APPENDIX B Functional Groups in Organic Molecules

Functional group	General formula	Name of compounds	Example	Where else found
Hydroxyl —OH (or HO—)	—O—H	Alcohols	Ethanol	Sugars; water-soluble vitamins
Carbonyl >CO	(—C=O with H)	Aldehydes	Propanal	Some sugars; formaldehyde (a preservative)
	(—C=O—)	Ketones	Acetone	Some sugars; "ketone bodies" in urine (from fat breakdown)
Carboxyl —COOH	—C(=O)OH	Carboxylic acids	Acetic acid	Amino acids; proteins; some vitamins; fatty acids
Amino —NH₂ (or H₂N—)	—N(H)(H)	Amines	Methylamine	Amino acids; proteins; urea in urine (from protein breakdown)

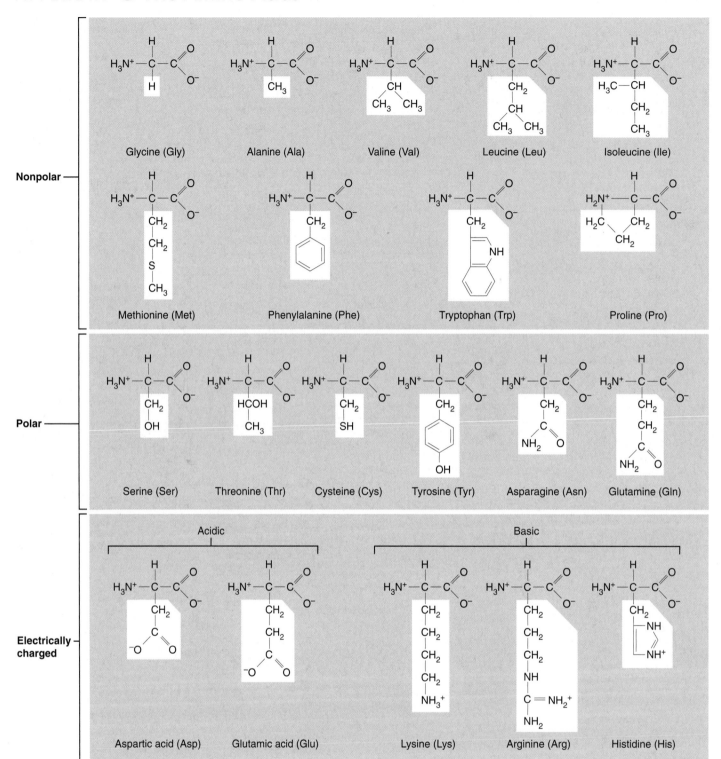

Nonpolar

Glycine (Gly)

Alanine (Ala)

Valine (Val)

Leucine (Leu)

Isoleucine (Ile)

Methionine (Met)

Phenylalanine (Phe)

Tryptophan (Trp)

Proline (Pro)

Polar

Serine (Ser)

Threonine (Thr)

Cysteine (Cys)

Tyrosine (Tyr)

Asparagine (Asn)

Glutamine (Gln)

Electrically charged

Acidic

Basic

Aspartic acid (Asp)

Glutamic acid (Glu)

Lysine (Lys)

Arginine (Arg)

Histidine (His)

(1) Glucose enters the cell and is phosphorylated by the enzyme hexokinase, which catalyzes the transfer of a phosphate group, indicated as ⓟ, from ATP to the number six carbon of the sugar, producing glucose-6-phosphate. The electrical charge of the phosphate group traps the sugar in the cell because the plasma membrane is impermeable to ions. Phosphorylation of glucose also makes the molecule more chemically reactive. Although glycolysis is supposed to *produce* ATP, ATP is actually consumed in step 1—an energy investment that will be repaid with dividends later in glycolysis.

(2) Glucose-6-phosphate is rearranged and converted to its isomer, fructose-6-phosphate. Isomers, remember, have the same number and types of atoms but in different structural arrangements.

(3) In this step, still another molecule of ATP is used to add a second phosphate group to the sugar, producing fructose-1,6-bisphosphate. So far, the ATP ledger shows a debit of −2. With phosphate groups on its opposite ends, the sugar is now ready to be split in half.

(4) This is the reaction from which glycolysis gets its name. An enzyme cleaves the sugar molecule into two different 3-carbon sugars: glyceraldehyde 3-phosphate and dihydroxyacetone phosphate. These two sugars are isomers of one another.

(5) An isomerase enzyme interconverts the 3-carbon sugars, and if left alone in a test tube, the reaction reaches equilibrium. This does not happen in the cell, however, because the next enzyme in glycolysis uses only glyceraldehyde phosphate as its substrate and not dihydroxyacetone phosphate. This pulls the equilibrium between the two 3-carbon sugars in the direction of glyceraldehyde phosphate, which is removed as fast as it forms. Thus, the net result of steps 4 and 5 is cleavage of a 6-carbon sugar into two molecules of glyceraldehyde phosphate; each will progress through the remaining steps of glycolysis.

(6) An enzyme now catalyzes two sequential reactions while it holds glyceraldehyde phosphate in its active site. First, the sugar is oxidized by the transfer of H from the number one carbon of the sugar to NAD, forming NADH + H$^+$. Here we see in metabolic context the oxidation-reduction reaction described in Chapter 24. This reaction releases substantial amounts of energy, and the enzyme capitalizes on this by coupling the reaction to the creation of a high-energy phosphate bond at the number one carbon of the oxidized substrate. The source of the phosphate is inorganic phosphate (P$_i$) always present in the cytosol. The enzyme releases NADH + H$^+$ and 1,3-bisphosphoglyceric acid as products. Notice in the figure that the new phosphate bond is symbolized with a squiggle (~), which indicates that the bond is at least as energetic as the high-energy phosphate bonds of ATP.

THE TEN STEPS OF GLYCOLYSIS Each of the ten steps of glycolysis is catalyzed by a specific enzyme found dissolved in the cytoplasm. All steps are reversible. An abbreviated version of the three major phases of glycolysis appears in the lower right-hand corner of the next page.

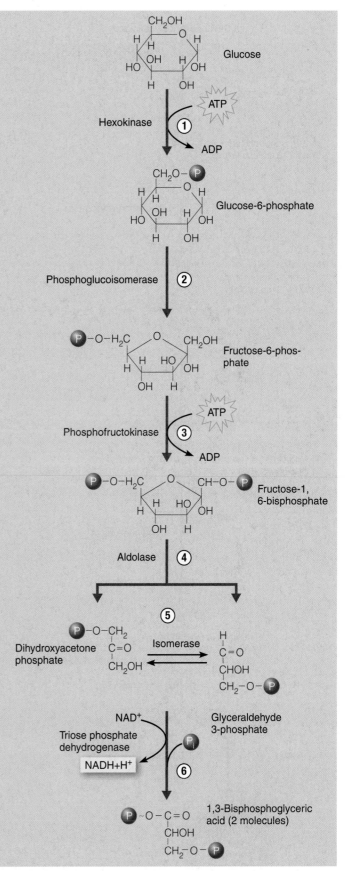

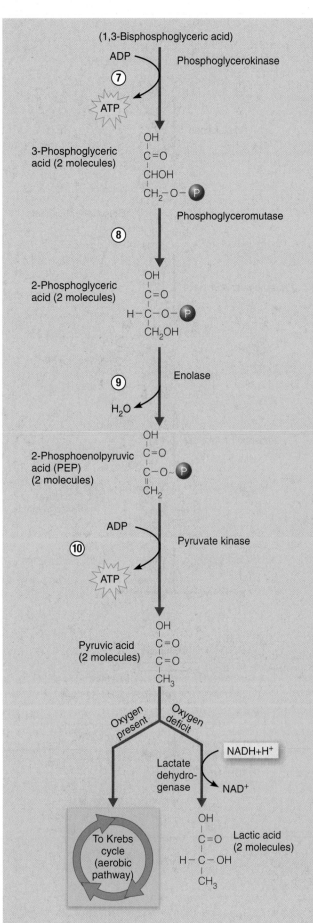

⑦ Finally, glycolysis produces ATP. The phosphate group, with its high-energy bond, is transferred from 1,3-bisphosphoglyceric acid to ADP. For each glucose molecule that began glycolysis, step 7 produces two molecules of ATP, because every product after the sugar-splitting step (step 4) is doubled. Of course, two ATPs were invested to get sugar ready for splitting. The ATP ledger now stands at zero. By the end of step 7, glucose has been converted to two molecules of 3-phosphoglyceric acid. This compound is not a sugar. The sugar was oxidized to an organic acid back in step 6, and now the energy made available by that oxidation has been used to make ATP.

⑧ Next, an enzyme relocates the remaining phosphate group of 3-phosphoglyceric acid to form 2-phosphoglyceric acid. This prepares the substrate for the next reaction.

⑨ An enzyme forms a double bond in the substrate by removing a water molecule from 2-phosphoglyceric acid to form phosphoenolpyruvic acid, or PEP. This results in the electrons of the substrate being rearranged in such a way that the remaining phosphate bond becomes very unstable; it has been upgraded to high-energy status.

⑩ The last reaction of glycolysis produces another molecule of ATP by transferring the phosphate group from PEP to ADP. Because this step occurs twice for each glucose molecule, the ATP ledger now shows a net gain of two ATPs. Steps 7 and 10 each produce two ATPs for a total credit of four, but a debt of two ATPs was incurred from steps 1 and 3. Glycolysis has repaid the ATP investment with 100% interest. In the meantime, glucose has been broken down and oxidized to two molecules of pyruvic acid, the compound produced from PEP in step 10.

Summary

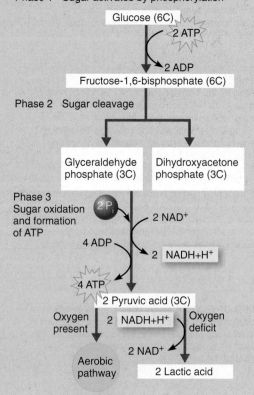

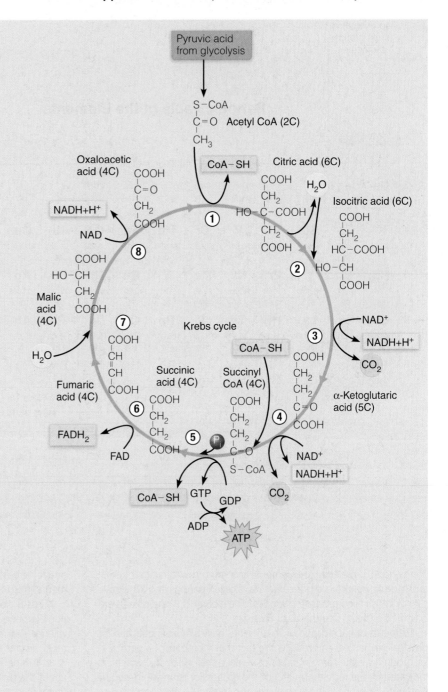

① Two-carbon acetyl CoA is combined with oxaloacetic acid, a 4-carbon compound. The unstable bond between the acetyl group and CoA is broken as oxaloacetic acid binds and CoA is freed to prime another 2-carbon fragment derived from pyruvic acid. The product is the 6-carbon citric acid, for which the cycle is named.

② A molecule of water is removed, and another is added back. The net result is the conversion of citric acid to its isomer, isocitric acid.

③ The substrate loses a CO_2 molecule, and the remaining 5-carbon compound is oxidized, forming an α-ketoglutaric acid and reducing NAD^+.

④ This step is catalyzed by a multienzyme complex very similar to the one that converts pyruvic acid to acetyl CoA. CO_2 is lost; the remaining 4-carbon compound is oxidized by the transfer of electrons to NAD^+ to form $NADH+H^+$ and is then attached to CoA by an unstable bond. The product is succinyl CoA.

⑤ Substrate-level phosphorylation occurs in this step. CoA is displaced by a phosphate group, which is then transferred to GDP to form guanosine triphosphate (GTP). GTP is similar to ATP, which is formed when GTP donates a phosphate group to ADP. The products of this step are succinic acid and ATP.

⑥ In another oxidative step, two hydrogens are removed from succinic acid (forming fumaric acid) and transferred to FAD to form $FADH_2$. The function of this coenzyme is similar to that of $NADH+H^+$, but $FADH_2$ stores less energy. The enzyme that catalyzes this oxidation-reduction reaction is the only enzyme of the cycle that is embedded in the mitochondrial membrane. All other enzymes of the citric acid cycle are dissolved in the mitochondrial matrix.

⑦ Bonds in the substrate are rearranged in this step by the addition of a water molecule. The product is malic acid.

⑧ The last oxidative step reduces another NAD^+ and regenerates oxaloacetic acid, which accepts a 2-carbon fragment from acetyl CoA for another turn of the cycle.

Krebs Cycle (Citric Acid Cycle) All but one of the steps (step 6) occur in the mitochondrial matrix. The preparation of pyruvic acid (by oxidation, decarboxylation, and reaction with coenzyme A) to enter the cycle as acetyl CoA is shown above the cycle. Acetyl CoA is picked up by oxaloacetic acid to form citric acid; and as it passes through the cycle, it is oxidized four more times [forming three molecules of reduced NAD ($NADH + H^+$) and one of reduced FAD ($FADH_2$)] and decarboxylated twice (releasing 2 CO_2). Energy is captured in the bonds of GTP, which then acts in a coupled reaction with ADP to generate one molecule of ATP by substrate-level phosphorylation.

Periodic Table of the Elements

Representative (main group) elements

Representative (main group) elements

Transition metals

	IA	IIA	IIIB	IVB	VB	VIB	VIIB	VIIIB			IB	IIB	IIIA	IVA	VA	VIA	VIIA	VIIIA
1	1 **H** 1.0079																	2 **He** 4.003
2	3 **Li** 6.941	4 **Be** 9.012											5 **B** 10.811	6 **C** 12.011	7 **N** 14.007	8 **O** 15.999	9 **F** 18.998	10 **Ne** 20.180
3	11 **Na** 22.990	12 **Mg** 24.305											13 **Al** 26.982	14 **Si** 28.086	15 **P** 30.974	16 **S** 32.065	17 **Cl** 35.453	18 **Ar** 39.948
4	19 **K** 39.098	20 **Ca** 40.078	21 **Sc** 44.956	22 **Ti** 47.867	23 **V** 50.942	24 **Cr** 51.996	25 **Mn** 54.938	26 **Fe** 55.845	27 **Co** 58.933	28 **Ni** 58.69	29 **Cu** 63.546	30 **Zn** 65.38	31 **Ga** 69.723	32 **Ge** 72.64	33 **As** 74.922	34 **Se** 78.96	35 **Br** 79.904	36 **Kr** 83.8
5	37 **Rb** 85.468	38 **Sr** 87.62	39 **Y** 88.906	40 **Zr** 91.224	41 **Nb** 92.906	42 **Mo** 95.96	43 **Tc** 98	44 **Ru** 101.07	45 **Rh** 102.906	46 **Pd** 106.42	47 **Ag** 107.868	48 **Cd** 112.411	49 **In** 114.82	50 **Sn** 118.71	51 **Sb** 121.76	52 **Te** 127.60	53 **I** 126.905	54 **Xe** 131.29
6	55 **Cs** 132.905	56 **Ba** 137.327	57 **La** 138.906	72 **Hf** 178.49	73 **Ta** 180.948	74 **W** 183.84	75 **Re** 186.207	76 **Os** 190.23	77 **Ir** 192.22	78 **Pt** 195.08	79 **Au** 196.967	80 **Hg** 200.59	81 **Tl** 204.383	82 **Pb** 207.2	83 **Bi** 208.980	84 **Po** 209	85 **At** 210	86 **Rn** 222
7	87 **Fr** 223	88 **Ra** 226	89 **Ac** 227	104 **Rf** 267	105 **Db** 268	106 **Sg** 271	107 **Bh** 272	108 **Hs** 270	109 **Mt** 276	110 **Ds** 281	111 **Rg** 280	112 **Uub** 285	113 **Uut** 284	114 **Uuq** 289	115 **Uup** 288	116 **Uuh** 293		118 **Uuo** 294

Rare earth elements

	58	59	60	61	62	63	64	65	66	67	68	69	70	71
Lanthanides	**Ce** 140.116	**Pr** 140.908	**Nd** 144.24	**Pm** 145	**Sm** 150.36	**Eu** 151.964	**Gd** 157.25	**Tb** 158.925	**Dy** 162.5	**Ho** 164.93	**Er** 167.26	**Tm** 168.934	**Yb** 173.054	**Lu** 174.967

	90	91	92	93	94	95	96	97	98	99	100	101	102	103
Actinides	**Th** 232.038	**Pa** 231.036	**U** 238.029	**Np** 237.048	**Pu** 244	**Am** 243	**Cm** 247	**Bk** 247	**Cf** 251	**Es** 252	**Fm** 257	**Md** 258	**No** 259	**Lr** 262

The periodic table arranges elements according to atomic number and atomic weight into horizontal rows called periods and 18 vertical columns called groups or families. The elements in the groups are classified as being in either A or B classes.

Elements of each group of the A series have similar chemical and physical properties. This reflects the fact that members of a particular group have the same number of valence shell electrons, which is indicated by the roman numeral of the group. For example, group IA elements have one valence shell electron, group IIA elements have two, and group VA elements have five. In contrast, as you progress across a period from left to right, the properties of the elements change in discrete steps, varying gradually from the very metallic properties of groups IA and IIA elements to the nonmetallic properties seen in group VIIA (chlorine and others), and finally to the inert elements (noble gases) in group VIIIA. This change reflects the continual increase in the number of valence shell electrons seen in elements (from left to right) within a period.

Class B elements are referred to as transition elements. All transition elements are metals, and in most cases they have one or two valence shell electrons. (In these elements, some electrons occupy more distant electron shells before the deeper shells are filled.)

In this periodic table, the colors are used to convey information about the phase (solid, liquid, or gas) in which a pure element exists under standard conditions (25 degrees centigrade and 1 atmosphere of pressure). If the element's symbol is solid black, then the element exists as a solid. If its symbol is red, then it exists as a gas. If its symbol is dark blue, then it is a liquid. If the element's symbol is green, the element does not exist in nature and must be created by some type of nuclear reaction.

*Atomic weights of the elements per IUPAC Commission on Isotopic Abundances and Atomic Weights, 2007.

The reference values listed for the selected blood and urine studies are common ranges for adults, but specific "normals" are established by the laboratory performing the analysis. The values may be affected by a wide range of circumstances, including testing methods and equipment used, client age, body mass, sex, diet, activity level, medications, and extent of disease processes.

Reference values are identified in both standard or conventional units and in the system of international (SI) units. SI units (given in parentheses) are measurements of amount per volume and are used in most countries and scientific journals. SI units are often given as moles or millimoles per liter. Most clinical laboratories and textbooks in the United States use conventional or standard units, which measure mass per volume. These values are given as grams, milligrams, or milliequivalents per deciliter or liter. It is anticipated that the United States will eventually use SI units exclusively.

For enzymes, 1 international unit (IU) represents an arbitrary but defined amount of activity, whereas 1 katal (kat) is the amount of enzyme required to consume 1 mol of substrate per second.

Sample types in column 1 are serum (S), plasma (P), arterial whole blood (A), and whole blood (WB).

TEST (SAMPLE)	REFERENCE VALUES: CONVENTIONAL (SI)	PHYSIOLOGICAL INDICATION AND CLINICAL IMPLICATIONS
Blood Chemistry Studies		
Ammonia (P)	15–120 μg/dl (9–70 μmol/L)	Liver and renal function. Increased values in liver disease, renal failure, newborn hemolytic disease, heart failure, cor pulmonale. Decreased values in hypertension.
Amylase (S)	56–190 IU/L (0.4–2.1 μkat/L)	Pancreatic function. Increased values in pancreatitis, mumps, obstruction of pancreatic duct, ketoacidosis. Decreased values in kidney disease, pancreatic damage or cancer, toxemia of pregnancy.
Aspartate aminotransferase (AST, or SGOT) (S)	≤40 U/ml (≤0.7 μkat/L)	Cellular damage. Increased after myocardial infarction, acute liver disease, drug toxicity, muscle trauma. Decreased in pyridoxine (vitamin B_6) deficiency.
Bilirubin (S)	Total: 0.1–1.0 mg/dl (1.7–17.1 μmol/L) Direct: <0.4 mg/dl (<6.8 μmol/L) Indirect: 0.1–1.0 mg/dl (1.7–17.1 μmol/L) Newborn: <13.0 mg/dl (<222 μmol/L)	Liver function and red cell breakdown. Increased levels of direct in liver disease and biliary obstruction. Increased levels of indirect in hemolysis of red blood cells.
Blood urea nitrogen (S)	7–26 mg/dl (2.5–9.3 mmol/L)	Kidney function. Increased values in renal disease, dehydration, urinary obstruction, congestive heart failure, myocardial infarction, burns. Decreased values in liver failure, overhydration, impaired protein absorption, pregnancy.
Cholesterol	<200 mg/dl (<5.2 mmol/L)	Metabolism—fat utilization. Increased values in diabetes mellitus, pregnancy, use of oral contraceptives or anabolic steroids.
High-density lipoprotein (HDL) cholesterol (S)	20–30% of total >40 mg/dl (>1.0 mmol/L)	Increased levels in liver disease, aerobic exercise. Decreased levels in atherosclerotic heart disease, malnutrition.
Low-density lipoprotein (LDL) cholesterol (S)	60–70% of total <130 mg/dl (<3.4 mmol/L)	Increased values in hyperlipidemia, atherosclerotic heart disease. Decreased values in fat malabsorption and malnutrition.
Very low density lipoprotein cholesterol (VLDL) (S)	10–15% of total	Same as LDL.
Creatine kinase (CK) (S)	Female: ≤190 U/L (≤3.2 μkat/L) Male: ≤235 U/L (≤3.9 μkat/L)	Cellular damage. Increased values in myocardial infarction, muscular dystrophy, hypothyroidism, pulmonary infarction, cerebrovascular accident (CVA), shock, tissue damage, and trauma.
Creatinine (S)	0.5–1.2 mg/dl (44–106 μmol/L)	Renal function. Increased values in renal disease and acromegaly. Decreased in muscular dystrophy.

TEST (SAMPLE)	REFERENCE VALUES: CONVENTIONAL (SI)	PHYSIOLOGICAL INDICATION AND CLINICAL IMPLICATIONS
Blood Chemistry Studies (continued)		
Gases (A)		
Bicarbonate	22–26 mEq/L (22–26 mmol/L)	Acid-base balance. Increased values in metabolic alkalosis and respiratory acidosis. Decreased values in metabolic acidosis and respiratory alkalosis.
Carbon dioxide content	Arterial: 19–24 mEq/L (19–24 mmol/L) Venous: 22–30 mEq/L (22–30 mmol/L)	
Carbon dioxide partial pressure (P_{CO_2})	Arterial: 35–45 mm Hg Venous: 45 mm Hg	
Oxygen (O_2) saturation	95–98% (same)	Values increased slightly in hyperventilation. Decreased values (hypoxia) in pulmonary disease, hypoventilation, high altitude.
Oxygen partial pressure (P_{O_2})	80–105 mm Hg	
pH	7.35–7.45 (same)	Increased values in metabolic and respiratory alkalosis. Decreased values in metabolic and respiratory acidosis.
Glucose (S)	70–120 mg/dl (3.9–6.7 mmol/L)	Metabolic function. Increased values in diabetes mellitus, Cushing's syndrome, liver disease, acute stress, and acromegaly. Decreased levels in Addison's disease, insulinomas.
Immunoglobulins (S)		
IgG	560–1800 mg/dl (5.6–18 g/L)	Immune response. Increased levels in chronic infections, rheumatic fever, liver disease, rheumatoid arthritis. Decreased levels in amyloidosis, leukemia, and preeclampsia.
IgE	<43.2 µg/dl (<432 µg/L)	Allergic responses. Increased values in allergic responses. Decreased values in agammaglobulinemia.
IgA	85–563 mg/dl (0.85–5.6 g/L)	Immune integrity. Increased values in liver disease, rheumatic fever, chronic infection, inflammatory bowel disease. Decreased values in immunodeficiency disorders and immunosuppression.
IgM	55–375 mg/dl (0.5–3.8 g/L)	Immune integrity. Increased in autoimmune disease (e.g., rheumatoid arthritis), acute infections. Decreased in amyloidosis and leukemia.
IgD	0.5–14 mg/dl (5–140 mg/L)	Immune integrity. Increased values in myelomas.
Ketone bodies (S or P)	Negative Toxic level >20 mg/dl (0.2 g/L)	Fatty acid catabolism. Increased values (ketosis, ketoacidosis) in starvation, low-carbohydrate diet, uncontrolled diabetes mellitus, aspirin overdose.
Lactate dehydrogenase (LDH) (S)	105–333 U/L (1.7–5.6 µkat/L)	Tissue damage of organs or striated muscle. Increased in myocardial infarction, pulmonary infarction, liver disease, cerebrovascular accident, infectious mononucleosis, muscular dystrophy, fractures.
Lactic acid (lactate) (P)	9–16 mg/dl (1.0–1.8 mmol/L)	Anaerobic tissue metabolism. Increased values in congestive heart failure, shock, hemorrhage, strenuous exercise.
Osmolality (S)	280–300 mOsm/kg H_2O (280–300 mmol/kg H_2O)	Fluid and electrolyte balance. Increased levels in hypernatremia, dehydration, kidney disease, alcohol ingestion. Decreased levels in hyponatremia, overhydration, and syndrome of inappropriate ADH secretion (SIADH).
Phosphate (S) (phosphorus)	2.5–4.5 mg/dl (0.8–1.5 mmol/L)	Parathyroid function; bone disease. Increased levels in hypoparathyroidism, renal failure, bone metastasis, hypocalcemia. Decreased values in hyperparathyroidism, hypercalcemia, alcoholism, vitamin D deficiency, ketoacidosis, osteomalacia.
Potassium (S)	3.5–5.5 mEq/L (3.5–5.5 mmol/L)	Fluid and electrolyte balance. Increased levels in renal disease, Addison's disease, ketoacidosis, burns, and crush injuries. Decreased levels in vomiting, diarrhea, Cushing's syndrome, alkalosis, diuretics.

TEST (SAMPLE)	REFERENCE VALUES: CONVENTIONAL (SI)	PHYSIOLOGICAL INDICATION AND CLINICAL IMPLICATIONS
Blood Chemistry Studies *(continued)*		
Protein (S) Total	6.0–8.5 g/dl (60–85 g/L)	Osmotic pressure; immune system integrity. Increased values in multiple myeloma, dehydration, myxedema. Decreased values in protein malnutrition, burns, diarrhea, renal failure, liver failure.
Albumin	3.2–5.0 g/dl (32–50 g/L)	Osmotic pressure. Increased levels in dehydration. Decreased levels in liver disease, malnutrition, Crohn's disease, nephrotic syndrome, systemic lupus erythematosus.
Sodium (S)	135–145 mEq/L (135–145 mmol/L)	Fluid and electrolyte balance. Increased values in dehydration, diabetes insipidus, Cushing's syndrome. Decreased values in vomiting, diarrhea, burns, Addison's disease, myxedema, congestive heart failure, overhydration, syndrome of inappropriate ADH secretion (SIADH).
Triglycerides	10–150 mg/dl (0.1–1.5 g/L)	Increased values in diabetes mellitus, liver disease, nephrotic syndrome, pregnancy.
Uric acid (S)	Female: 2.0–7.3 mg/dl (119–434 μmol/L) Male: 2.1–8.5 mg/dl (125–506 μmol/L)	Renal function. Increased in lead poisoning, impaired renal function, gout, alcoholism, hematologic cancers. Decreased in Wilson's disease.
Hematology Studies		
Hemoglobin (S)	Female: 12–16 g/dl (120–160 g/L) Male: 13–18 g/dl (130–180 g/L)	Oxygenation status. Increased values in dehydration, polycythemia, congestive heart failure, chronic obstructive pulmonary disease, high altitudes. Decreased levels in anemia, hemorrhage, bone marrow cancer, renal disease, systemic lupus erythematosus, nutritional deficiency.
Hematocrit (WB)	Female: 37–47% (same) Male: 42–52% (same)	Oxygenation status. Increased levels in polycythemia, dehydration, congestive heart failure, shock, surgery. Decreased levels in anemia, hemorrhage, bone marrow disease, malnutrition, cirrhosis, rheumatoid arthritis.
Partial thromboplastin time (activated) (PTT or aPTT)	20–36 s (same)	Clotting mechanisms. Increased values in clotting factor deficiencies, cirrhosis, vitamin K deficiency, disseminated intravascular coagulation (DIC). Decreased values in early DIC, extensive cancer.
Platelet count (WB)	150,000–400,000/μl (150–400 $\times$ 10^9/L)	Clotting mechanisms. Increased values in polycythemia, cancers, rheumatoid arthritis, trauma. Decreased values in liver disease, hemolytic uremic syndrome, disseminated intravascular coagulation (DIC), idiopathic thrombocytopenic purpura (ITP), systemic lupus erythematosus (SLE).
Prothrombin time (PT) (WB)	11–12.5 s (same) 1.5–2 $\times$ control (evaluating anticoagulant treatment)	Clotting mechanisms. Increased values in liver disease, vitamin K deficiency, salicylate intoxication. Decreased values in disseminated intravascular coagulation (DIC).
Red blood cell count (RBC) (WB)	Female: 4.2–5.4 million/μl (4.2–5.4 $\times$ 10^{12}/L) Male: 4.7–6.1 million/μl (4.7–6.1 $\times$ 10^{12}/L)	Oxygenation status. Increased values in high altitudes, polycythemia, hemoconcentration, cor pulmonale. Decreased values in hemorrhage, hemolysis, anemias, chronic illness, nutritional deficiencies, leukemia, overhydration.
Reticulocyte count (WB)	0.5–2.0% (same)	Bone marrow function. Increased values in hemolytic anemia, sickle-cell anemia, leukemia, pregnancy. Decreased values in pernicious anemia, folic acid deficiency, cirrhosis, chronic infection, bone marrow depression or failure.
White blood cell count (WBC) (WB) Total (males)	 4800–10,800/μl (4.8–10.8 $\times$ 10^9/L)	Immune system integrity. Increased values in infection, trauma, stress, tissue necrosis, inflammation. Decreased values in bone marrow depression or failure, drug toxicity, overwhelming infection, malnutrition.

TEST (SAMPLE)	REFERENCE VALUES: CONVENTIONAL (SI)	PHYSIOLOGICAL INDICATION AND CLINICAL IMPLICATIONS
Hematology Studies (continued)		
White blood cell count, differential (WB)		
Neutrophils	50–70% (same)	Immune system integrity. Increased values in acute bacterial infections, stress, Cushing's syndrome, inflammatory disorders, ketoacidosis, gout. Decreased levels in aplastic anemia, bone marrow suppression, and overwhelming bacterial infections.
Lymphocytes	25–40% (same)	Immune system integrity. Increased values in viral infections (e.g., mumps, rubella, infectious mononucleosis, hepatitis), lymphocytic leukemia, certain bacterial infections. Decreased levels in leukemia, immunodeficiency, lupus erythematosus, bone marrow depressive drugs.
Eosinophils	1–4% (same)	Immune system integrity. Increased levels in allergic reactions, parasitic infections, leukemia. Decreased levels in excess adrenosteroid production.
Monocytes	3–8% (same)	Immune system integrity. Increased levels in certain infections (e.g., tuberculosis, malaria), inflammatory disorders.
Basophils	0.5–1.0% (same)	Immune system integrity. Increased levels in myeloproliferative disorders, leukemia. Decreased levels in allergic reactions, hyperthyroidism, stress.
Urine Tests		
Amylase (24 h)	<6000 Somogyi units/24 h 0–500 U/24 h (0–8.3 μkat/24h)	Pancreatic function. Increased values in pancreatic disease or obstruction, inflammation of the salivary glands, and cholecystitis.
Bilirubin (random)	Negative (same)	Liver function. Increased values in liver disease, extrahepatic obstruction (gallstones, tumor, inflammation).
Blood (hemoglobin) (random)	Negative (same)	Urinary system function. Increased values in cystitis, renal disease, hemolytic anemia, transfusion reaction, prostatitis, burns.
Osmolality (random or fasting)	Random: 50–1200 mOsm/kg H_2O (50–1200 mmol/kg H_2O) Fluid restriction: ≥850 mOsm/kg H_2O (≥850 mmol/kg H_2O)	Fluid and electrolyte balance, renal function, and endocrine function. Increased levels in hypernatremia, syndrome of inappropriate ADH secretion (SIADH), congestive heart failure, metabolic acidosis. Decreased levels in diabetes insipidus, water intoxication, pyelonephritis, renal tubular necrosis, aldosteronism.
Phosphate (24 h)	0.9–1.3g/24 hr (same)	Parathyroid function. Increased levels in hyperparathyroidism, osteomalacia, certain renal diseases, vitamin D deficiency. Decreased levels in hypoparathyroidism.
Potassium (24 h)	25–120 mEq/24 h (25–120 mmol/24 h)	Fluid and electrolyte balance. Increased values in renal tubular necrosis, metabolic acidosis, dehydration, aldosteronism, Cushing's syndrome. Decreased values in Addison's disease, malabsorption, acute renal failure.
Protein (random)	<8 mg/dl (<80 mg/L)	Renal function. Increased levels in nephrotic syndrome, renal trauma, hyperthyroidism, diabetic nephropathy, lupus erythematosus.
Sodium (24 h)	40–220 mEq/24 h (40–220 mmol/24 h)	Fluid and electrolyte balance. Increased values in dehydration, ketoacidosis, syndrome of inappropriate ADH secretion (SIADH), adrenocortical insufficiency. Decreased levels in congestive heart failure, renal failure, diarrhea, aldosteronism.
Uric acid (24 h)	250–750 mg/24 h (1.5–4.5 mmol/24 h)	Renal function and metabolism. Increased in gout, leukemia, liver disease, ulcerative colitis. Decreased in renal disease, alcoholism, lead toxicity, folic acid deficiency.

TEST (SAMPLE)	REFERENCE VALUES: CONVENTIONAL (SI)	PHYSIOLOGICAL INDICATION AND CLINICAL IMPLICATIONS
Urine Tests (continued)		
Urinalysis (random)		
Color	Straw, yellow, amber	Fluid balance and renal function. Darker in dehydration. Lighter in overhydration, diabetes insipidus. Color varies with disease states, diet, and medications.
Odor	Aromatic	Metabolic function, infection. Abnormal odors in infection, ketonuria, rectal fistula, hepatic failure, phenylketonuria.
Specific gravity	1.001–1.035	An indirect measurement of urine concentration (osmolality). Same physiological indications and clinical implications as osmolality.
pH	4.5–8.0	A crude indicator of acid-base balance. Decreased by acidic diet (proteins). Increased by a vegetarian diet, prolonged vomiting, and bacterial infection of the urinary tract.
Urobilinogen (24 h)	0.2–1.0 mg/dl (2–10 mg/L)	Liver function. Increased in hemolytic anemias, hepatitis, cirrhosis, biliary disease. Decreased in common bile duct obstruction.
Volume (24 h)	800–2000 ml/24 h (0.8–2.0 L/24 h)	Fluid and electrolyte balance, renal function. Increased values in diabetes insipidus, diabetes mellitus, renal disease. Decreased values in dehydration, syndrome of inappropriate ADH secretion (SIADH), renal disease.

APPENDIX G Answers to Check Your Understanding, Clinical Connections, Multiple Choice, and Matching Questions

Chapter 1

Check Your Understanding 1. The operation or function of a structure is dictated (promoted or prevented) by its anatomy. For example, oxygen and carbon dioxide are exchanged across the very thin membranes of the lungs but not across the skin. **2.** Muscle shortening is a topic of physiology. The body location of the lungs is an anatomy topic. **3.** Cytologists study the cellular level of organization. **4.** The order in the structural hierarchy is cell, tissue, organ, and organism. **5.** Bones and cartilages are part of the skeletal system. The nasal cavity, lungs, and trachea are organs of the respiratory system. **6.** Living organisms are able to maintain their boundaries, move, respond to environmental changes, digest nutrients, carry out metabolism, dispose of wastes, reproduce, and grow. While inanimate objects may exhibit some of these properties, they do not exhibit all of them. **7.** Metabolism is the term that encompasses all the chemical reactions that occur in body cells. **8.** In flight, the cabin must be pressurized because the atmosphere is thinner at high altitudes and the amount of oxygen entering the blood under such conditions may be insufficient to maintain life. **9.** Negative feedback mechanisms allow us to adjust to conditions outside the normal temperature range by causing heat to be lost from the body (in hot conditions) and retained or generated by the body (in cold conditions). **10.** Thirst is part of a negative feedback control system because it prods us to drink, which ends the thirst stimulus and returns body fluid volume to the normal range. **11.** This is a positive feedback mechanism because it enhances the change (formation of a platelet plug) set into motion by the stimulus (damage to the blood vessel). The response ends when the platelet plug has plugged the hole in the blood vessel. **12.** The position in which a person is standing erect with feet slightly separated and palms facing anteriorly. Knowing the anatomical position is important because directional terms refer to the body as if it is in this position. **13.** Axillary region is the armpit. Acromial area is the tip of the shoulder. **14.** A frontal (coronal) section would separate the brain into anterior and posterior parts. **15.** He may have appendicitis if the pain is in the lower right quadrant of his abdomen. **16.** Of these organs, only the spinal cord is in the dorsal body cavity. **17.** As mobile organs (heart, lungs, digestive organs) work, friction is greatly reduced by the presence of serous fluid. Serous fluid allows the surrounding serous membranes to glide easily over one another.

Review Questions 1. c; **2.** a; **3.** e; **4.** a, d; **5.** (a) wrist (b) hip bone (c) nose (d) toes (e) scalp; **6.** neither c nor d would be visible in the median section; **7.** (a) dorsal (b) ventral (c) dorsal (d) ventral; **8.** b; **9.** b; **10.** c

Chapter 2

Check Your Understanding 1. Foods contain chemical energy. **2.** Electrical energy is the energy used by nerve cells to transmit messages in the body. **3.** Potential energy (PE) is available when we are still. PE is converted to kinetic (working) energy when we exercise. **4.** Besides hydrogen and nitrogen, carbon and oxygen help to make up the bulk of living matter. **5.** This element has 82 protons in its nucleus and 82 electrons in its orbitals (electron cloud). **6.** Atomic mass indicates the sum of the protons and neutrons in a given atom's nucleus. Atomic weight indicates the average mass of all the isotopes of a given element. **7.** A molecule is 2 or more atoms held together by chemical bonds. **8.** A compound is formed when two or more different kinds of atoms chemically bond together, as in NaCl. Oxygen gas is 2 oxygen atoms (the same kind of atom) bonded together. **9.** Blood is a mixture because its components are not changed by their combination and they can be separated by physical means. **10.** Hydrogen bonds (linking H of one water molecule to O of another) form between water molecules. **11.** Argon's valence shell is full:)2e)8e)8e. Hence it is nonreactive. **12.** Electrons would spend more time in the

vicinity of the more electronegative atom in XY, whereas electrons in XX would orbit both X atoms to an equal extent. **13.** Fats are digested in the small intestine by decomposition reactions. **14.** Biochemical reactions in the body tend to be irreversible because (a) one or more of the products is removed from the reaction site or (b) the product is needed more than the reactants, so the cell would not provide energy to reverse the reaction. **15.** Decomposition reactions in which foods are broken down for energy are oxidation-reduction (O-R) reactions. **16.** Water is an excellent solvent because of its polarity. As a dipole, it can orient itself to the end of other molecules, causing them to dissociate or go into solution. **17.** Electrolytes are substances like salts that will conduct an electrical current in aqueous solution. **18.** H^+ is responsible for acidity. **19.** It is better to add a weak base, which will act to buffer the strong acid. **20.** Monomers of carbohydrates are called monosaccharides or simple sugars. Glucose is blood sugar. **21.** The animal form of stored carbohydrate is glycogen. **22.** Triglycerides, the major source of stored energy in the body, are composed of three fatty acid chains and a glycerol molecule and are found in fat tissue. Phospholipids consist of two fatty acid chains and a charged P-containing group. They are found in all cell membranes where they form the basis of those membranes. **23.** Hydrolysis reactions break down polymers or macromolecules to their monomers by adding water to each bond joining monomers. **24.** An "amino acid" has an amine group (NH_2) and a COOH group that has acidic properties. **25.** The primary structure of proteins is the stringlike chain of amino acids. **26.** The secondary structures of proteins are the alpha helix and the beta-pleated sheet. **27.** Molecular chaperones prevent inaccurate or inappropriate folding in the 3-D structure of a protein. **28.** Enzymes hold the substrate(s) in a desirable position to interact. **29.** DNA contains deoxyribose sugar and the bases A, T, G, C. RNA contains ribose sugar and the bases A, U, G, C. **30.** DNA dictates protein structure by its base sequence and reproduces itself before a cell divides to ensure that the genetic information in the daughter cells is identical. **31.** ATP stores energy in smaller packets that are more readily released and transferred (during ATP hydrolysis) than the energy stored in glucose. Hence the use of ATP as an energy source keeps energy waste to a minimum. **32.** When ATP releases energy, it loses a phosphate group and becomes ADP (also energy rich).

Review Questions 1. d; **2.** d; **3.** b; **4.** a; **5.** b; **6.** a; **7.** a; **8.** b; **9.** d; **10.** a; **11.** b; **12.** a, c; **13.** (1)a, (2)c; **14.** c; **15.** d; **16.** e; **17.** d; **18.** d; **19.** a; **20.** b; **21.** b; **22.** c

Chapter 3

Check Your Understanding 1. The three basic parts of a cell are the plasma membrane (the outer boundary of the cell), the nucleus (control center of the cell), and the cytoplasm (the fluid material between the nucleus and plasma membrane), which contains the organelles. **2.** It is the cell concept that includes structures and functions common to all cells. **3.** All cellular membranes consist of a double layer of phospholipids in which proteins are embedded. **4.** Hydrophobic regions (tails of phospholipid molecules) orient toward each other while the hydrophilic regions (phospholipid heads) orient to the aqueous fluid inside and outside the cell. **5.** The sugar residues of the glycocalyx provide recognizable biological markers for cells to recognize each other. **6.** The heart has desmosomes (anchoring junctions) that secure cardiac cells together as the heart works and gap junctions (communicating junctions) that allow ions to flow from cardiac cell to cardiac cell. **7.** Diffusion is driven by kinetic energy of the molecules. **8.** The relative concentration of the substance in different areas determines the direction of diffusion. Diffusion occurs from regions of high concentration to regions of low concentration. **9.** In channel-mediated diffusion, the diffusing substance moves through a membrane channel. In carrier-mediated diffusion, the diffusing substance attaches to a membrane (protein) carrier which moves it across the membrane. **10.** Phosphorylation of the Na$^+$-K$^+$ pump causes the pump protein to change shape so that it "pumps" Na$^+$ across the membrane. K$^+$ binding to the pump protein triggers the release of phosphate and the pump protein returns to its original shape. **11.** The plasma membrane expands as a result of exocytosis. **12.** Phagocytic cells engulf debris and a smoker's lungs would be laden with carbon particles and other debris from smoke inhalation. **13.** Cholesterol is taken in by receptor-mediated endocytosis. **14.** Diffusion of ions, mainly the diffusion of K$^+$ from the cell through leakage channels, establishes the resting membrane potential. **15.** In a polarized membrane, the inside is negative relative to its outside. **16.** Signaling chemicals that bind to membrane receptors are called ligands. G protein–linked receptors direct intracellular events by promoting formation of second messengers. **17.** Mitochondria are the major sites of ATP synthesis. **18.** Ribosomes are the sites of protein synthesis. The rough ER provides a site for ribosome attachment and its cisternae package in vesicles the proteins made on the ribosomes for transport to the Golgi apparatus. The Golgi apparatus modifies and packages the proteins it receives for various destinations within or outside the cell. **19.** The lysosomal enzymes digest foreign substances engulfed by the cell, nonuseful or deteriorating organelles, or even the cell itself to prevent the buildup of cellular debris. The enzymes in peroxisomes detoxify harmful chemicals and neutralize free radicals. **20.** Both microfilaments and microtubules are involved in organelle movements within the cell and/or movements of the cell as a whole. **21.** Intermediate filaments are the most important cytoskeletal elements in maintaining cell shape. **22.** The major function of microvilli is to increase the cell's surface area for absorption or filtration of substances. **23.** If a cell loses its nucleus, it is doomed to die because it will be unable to make proteins, which include the enzymes needed for all metabolic reactions. **24.** Nucleoli are the site of synthesis of ribosomal subunits. **25.** Histone proteins provide the means to pack DNA in a compact, orderly way and play a role in gene regulation. **26.** The base sequence of the corresponding strand will be GCTTAC. **27.** DNA is synthesized during the S phase. **28.** Nuclear envelope breaks up, spindle forms, nucleoli disappear, and the chromosomes coil and condense. **29.** Codons are three base sequences in mRNA, each of which specifies an amino acid. Anticodons are three-base sequences in tRNA that are complementary to the codons specifying the amino acid they transport to the ribosome during protein synthesis. **30.** A site = entry site for tRNA at the ribosome. P site = site where peptide bonds form between delivered amino acids. E site = the tRNA exit site from the ribosome. **31.** DNA provides the coded instructions (is the template) for protein synthesis via the mRNA synthesized on it. **32.** Ubiquitin attaches to misfolded, damaged, or unneeded proteins, tagging them for destruction by proteasomes. **33.** Blood plasma is extracellular fluid that transports nutrients, gases, hormones, and other substances throughout the body. Interstitial fluid is an important transport and dissolving medium. **34.** Apoptosis is a process of programmed cell death which rids the body of cells that are stressed, damaged, old, or no longer needed. **35.** The wear-and-tear theory of aging attributes aging to little chemical insults and free radicals which have cumulative detrimental effects.

Review Questions 1. d; **2.** a, c; **3.** b; **4.** b; **5.** e; **6.** c; **7.** d; **8.** a; **9.** d; **10.** a; **11.** b; **12.** d; **13.** c; **14.** b; **15.** d; **16.** a; **17.** b; **18.** d; **19.** c

Chapter 4

Check Your Understanding 1. Fixing tissue preserves it and prevents it from deteriorating. **2.** Organic dyes are used to stain tissues viewed by a light microscope. Heavy metal salts are used to stain tissues viewed by electron microscopes. **3.** Epithelial tissue lines body cavities and covers the body's external surface; thus polarity with one free (apical) surface is a requirement. **4.** Epithelial tissue can regenerate and its cells are joined by lateral contacts. **5.** Simple epithelia are "built" to provide for efficient absorption and filtration across their thin epithelial barriers. **6.** Pseudostratified epithelia appear to be stratified because their cells' nuclei lie at different distances from the basement membrane. However, all cells rest on the basement membrane. **7.** Transitional epithelium is found in the urinary bladder and other hollow urinary organs. The ability of this epithelium to thin allows the urinary organs to handle (store or transport) a larger urine volume when necessary. **8.** All unicellular exocrine glands secrete the protein mucin (which becomes mucus on mixing with water). **9.** These exocrine glands are classified by duct and secretory unit types. **10.** Holocrine glands have the highest rate of cell division. The secretory cells fragment and are lost in the secretion; thus the secretory cells must be continuously replaced. **11.** Connective tissue functions to bind, support, protect, and insulate body organs. In addition, blood acts to transport substances throughout the body. **12.** Reticular, collagen, and elastic fibers are found in the various connective tissues. **13.** Areolar connective tissue, because of its loose weblike nature, is capable of serving as a fluid reservoir. **14.** Dense regular connective tissue is damaged when you lacerate a tendon. **15.** Hyaline cartilage forms the growth plates. **16.** With extended processes, a neuron can conduct electrical signals a greater distance within the body. **17.** Cardiac muscle cells have striations and are branching cells. **18.** Skeletal muscle tissue is voluntary and is the muscle tissue injured when you "pull a muscle" while exercising. **19.** A mucous membrane consists of both connective tissue and epithelium. It lines body cavities open to the exterior. **20.** The serous membranes called pleurae line the thorax walls and cover the lungs. **21.** The three main steps of tissue repair are inflammation, organization, and regeneration and fibrosis (which is a permanent repair). **22.** More severe injuries damage and destroy more tissue, requiring greater replacement with scar tissue. **23.** The three embryonic germ layers are the ectoderm, mesoderm, and endoderm. **24.** Ectoderm gives rise to the nervous system. **25.** Epithelium and some connective tissues (areolar, dense irregular, and blood-forming tissue) remain highly mitotic all through life.

Review Questions 1. a, c, d, b; **2.** c, e; **3.** b, f, a, d, g, d; **4.** b; **5.** c; **6.** b

Chapter 5

Check Your Understanding 1. Since the sole of the foot has thick skin, the layers from most superficial to deepest would be the stratum corneum, stratum lucidum, stratum granulosum, stratum spinosum, and stratum basale. **2.** The stratum basale undergoes almost continuous mitosis to replace cells lost by abrasion. **3.** The skin is subjected to a lot of abrasion and physical trauma. The desmosomes, which are connecting junctions, help to hold the cells together during such stress. **4.** The stratum basale, which abuts the dermis where the blood supply is, has the best nourished cells. **5.** The papillary layer of the dermis gives rise to fingerprint patterns. **6.** Fatty tissue in the hypodermis gives it insulating and shock-absorbing properties. **7.** Because there is no bleeding, the cut has penetrated into the avascular epidermis only. **8.** The third pigment contributing to skin color is hemoglobin, the pigment found in red blood cells found in blood vessels of the dermis. **9.** Cyanosis is a bluish cast of the skin that indicates that hemoglobin in the red blood cells in the dermal capillaries is poorly oxygenated. **10.** Jaundice or a yellow cast to the skin due to the deposit of yellow bile pigments in body tissues may indicate a liver disorder. **11.** Sebaceous (oil) glands and apocrine glands are associated with the hair follicles. **12.** His sympathetic nervous system activated his eccrine sweat glands and caused heat-induced sweating in order to cool the body. **13.** Heat-induced sweating occurs all over the body when we are overheated. A cold sweat is emotionally induced sweating that begins on the palms, soles, and armpits and then spreads to other body areas. Both types of sweating are produced by the eccrine sweat glands, but activity of apocrine sweat glands is also likely during a cold sweat. **14.** The palms of the hands and soles of the feet are thick skin areas. It would be dangerous to have oily soles, and oily palms would decrease the ability of the hands to hang onto things. **15.** The regions of a hair from outside in are the cuticle, cortex, and medulla. **16.** There are no nerves in a hair, so cutting hair is painless. **17.** The arrector pili muscles pull the hair (normally slanted) to the upright position (when cold or scared). **18.** The hair papilla contains a knot of capillaries that supplies nutrients to cells of the hair bulb. **19.** The lunule of the nail is white because the thick nail matrix that underlies it blocks the rosy color of the dermal blood supply from showing through. **20.** Nails are hard because the keratin they contain is the hard keratin variety. **21.** The low pH of skin secretions (acid mantle) inhibits division of bacteria, and many bacteria are killed by bactericidal substances in sebum or by natural antibiotics called defensins. Damaged skin secretes cathelicidins that are effective against a certain strain of strep bacteria. **22.** The epidermal dendritic cells play a role in body immunity. **23.** Sunlight causes the skin to produce a precursor of vitamin D from cholesterol. **24.** The skin carries out chemical conversions that supplement some of the protective conversions carried out by the liver, convert some chemicals into carcinogens, activate some steroid hormones, and synthesize the vitamin D precursor. **25.** Basal cell carcinoma develops from the youngest epidermal cells. **26.** The ABCD rule helps one to recognize signs of melanoma. **27.** First- and second-degree burns can heal uneventfully by regeneration of epidermal cells as long as infection does not occur. Third-degree burns destroy the entire epidermis and regeneration is not possible. Infection and loss of body fluid and proteins are problematic. **28.** Burns to the face are serious because damage to the lungs can occur in such burns. **29.** Vernix caseosa is a product of the sebaceous glands. **30.** Loss of subcutaneous fat, common in the elderly, leads to cold intolerance seen in this group of people. **31.** UV radiation degrades collagen and leads to loss of skin elasticity and water-holding capacity.

Clinical Connections 1. The skin separates and protects the internal environment of the body from potentially dangerous elements in the external environment. Mrs. DeStephano's chart indicates epidermal abrasions, which represent the loss of this barrier. Epidermal loss will also cost Mrs. DeStephano the acid mantle of her skin, protection against UV radiation, and epidermal dendritic (Langerhans) cells, which protect against invasion by microorganisms. **2.** Macrophages found in the dermis can act as a backup system against bacterial and viral invasion when the epidermis is damaged. **3.** Suturing brings the edges of wounds close together and promotes faster healing because smaller amounts of granulation tissue need to be formed. This is termed *healing by first intention.* **4.** Cyanosis signals a decrease in the amount of oxygen carried by hemoglobin in the blood. Respiratory system and/or cardiovascular system impairments can lead to cyanosis.

Review Questions 1. a; **2.** c; **3.** d; **4.** d; **5.** b; **6.** b; **7.** c; **8.** c; **9.** b; **10.** a; **11.** d; **12.** b

Chapter 6

Check Your Understanding 1. Hyaline cartilage is the most plentiful in the adult body. **2.** The epiglottis and external ear cartilages are flexible elastic cartilage. **3.** Interstitial growth is growth from within. **4.** The components of the axial skeleton are the skull, the vertebral column, and the thoracic cage. **5.** The major function of the axial skeleton is to establish the long axis of the body and to protect structures that it encloses. The general function of the appendicular skeleton is to allow us mobility for propulsion and manipulation of our environment. **6.** The ribs and skull bones are flat bones. **7.** Skeletal muscles use bones as levers to cause movement of the body and its parts. **8.** Bone matrix stores minerals and growth factors. **9.** Bone marrow cavities serve as sites for blood cell formation and fat storage. **10.** Crests, tubercles, and spines are bony projections.

11. Compact bone looks fairly solid and homogeneous whereas spongy bones have an open network of bone spicules. **12.** Endosteum lines the internal canals and covers the trabeculae. **13.** Bone's inorganic component (bone salts) makes it hard. **14.** The osteoclast fits this description. **15.** Bones begin as fibrous membranes or hyaline cartilages. **16.** The cartilage model grows, then breaks down and is replaced by bone. **17.** The primary ossification center in a long bone is in the center of the shaft. The secondary ossification centers are in the epiphyses (bone ends). **18.** The chondrocytes are enlarging and their lacunae are breaking down and leaving holes in the cartilage matrix. **19.** If bone-destroying cells (osteoclasts) are more active than bone-forming cells (osteoblasts), bone mass will decrease. **20.** The hormonal stimulus maintains homeostatic blood calcium levels. **21.** In an open fracture, the bone ends are exposed to the external environment. In a closed fracture, the bone ends do not penetrate the external boundary of the skin. **22.** Bone growth increases bone mass, as during childhood or when exceptional stress is placed on the bones. Bone remodeling follows bone growth to maintain the proper proportions of the bone considering stresses placed upon it. **23.** Paget's disease is characterized by excessive deposit of weak, poorly mineralized bone. **24.** Sufficient vitamin D, calcium, and weight-bearing exercise all help to maintain healthy bone density. **25.** Adult rickets is called osteomalacia. **26.** At birth, most bones are well formed and ossified. Two areas of hyaline cartilage remain—in the epiphyseal plates and covering the bone ends (articular cartilage). **27.** The skull bones do not appear to lose mass with aging.

Clinical Connections 1. Mrs. DeStephano's broken leg has a transverse fracture of the open variety because the broken ends of the bone are protruding through the skin. **2.** The laceration of the skin caused by the broken end of the bone creates a breach in the protective barrier created by the skin, providing an entry point for bacteria and other microorganisms. In addition, the protruding ends of the bone have now been exposed to the nonsterile external environment. This could result in the development of osteomyelitis, a bacterial infection, which can be treated with antibiotics. **3.** Reduction of a fracture is the clinical term for "setting the bone." Mrs. DeStephano's physician chose internal reduction, in which surgery is performed and the broken ends of the bone are secured together by pins or wires. A cast was applied to keep the aligned ends of the bone immobile until healing of the fracture has occurred. **4.** Healing of Mrs. DeStephano's fracture will begin as bony callus formation fills the break in the bone with bony tissue. This process begins 3–4 weeks after the break occurs and is completed within 2–3 months. **5.** Nutrient arteries supply blood to the bone tissue. In order for Mrs. DeStephano's break to heal normally, the bony tissue must be supplied with oxygen (to generate ATP for energy) and nutrients in order to rebuild the bone. Damage to a nutrient artery will decrease the delivery of these building materials and could slow the process of healing. **6.** For a fracture that is slow to heal, new techniques that promote healing include electrical stimulation, which promotes the deposition of new bone tissue; ultrasound treatments, known to speed healing; and possibly the addition of bone substitutes to the fractured area. **7.** At age 45, Mrs. DeStephano will most likely not regenerate her knee cartilage. (Cartilage growth typically ends during adolescence.) Cartilage damage that occurs during adulthood is slow to heal, due to the avascular nature of cartilage, and is usually irreparable. Surgical removal of cartilage fragments to allow improved movement of the joint is the usual treatment for this type of damage.

Review Questions 1. e; **2.** b; **3.** c; **4.** d; **5.** e; **6.** b; **7.** c; **8.** b; **9.** d, e; **10.** c; **11.** b; **12.** c; **13.** a; **14.** b

Chapter 7

Check Your Understanding 1. The three main parts of the axial skeleton are the skull, vertebral column, and thoracic cage. **2.** The axial skeleton is more important in protecting internal organs. **3.** The frontal, parietal, temporal, sphenoid, and ethmoid bones are all cranial bones. **4.** The ethmoid bone forms the crista galli. **5.** The temporal bones house the external ear canals. **6.** The parietal bones abut each other at the sagittal suture. The occipital bone abuts the parietal bones at the lambdoid suture. **7.** The zygomatic bone are the cheekbones. **8.** Eating or talking, because the only freely movable joints of the skull are the temporomandibular joints of the jaw. **9.** The maxillae are the keystone bones of the facial skeleton. **10.** The sphenoid, ethmoid, frontal, and maxillary bones contain paranasal sinuses. **11.** The cribriform plates of the ethmoid bone form the roof of the nasal cavity. **12.** The maxillae form the bulk of the orbit floor. The eye is housed in the orbit. **13.** The five major regions of the vertebral column are the cervical, thoracic, lumbar, sacral, and coccygeal regions. **14.** The cervical and lumbar regions are concave posteriorly. **15.** The fibrocartilage discs contribute to the flexibility of the vertebral column. **16.** There are 7 cervical and 12 thoracic vertebrae. **17.** The dens is the axis on which the atlas rotates. If it's broken, movements of the atlas would be less controllable. **18.** A lumbar vertebra is heavier and its massive body is kidney shaped. Its spinous processes are short and project directly back. A thoracic vertebral body is generally heart shaped, its spinous process is long, sharp, and points downward, and its transverse processes have facets for articulating with the ribs. **19.** A true rib connects to the sternum by its own costal cartilage. A false rib connects to the sternum via costal cartilages of other ribs or not at all. **20.** The sternal angle is a ridge across the front of the sternum where the manubrium joins the sternal body. It acts as a hinge allowing the sternum to swing anteriorly when we inhale. Because it is aligned with the second rib, it is a handy cue for finding that rib and then counting the ribs during a physical exam. **21.** The thoracic vertebrae also contribute to the thoracic cage. **22.** Each pectoral girdle is formed by a scapula and a clavicle. **23.** The pectoral girdle attaches to the sternal manubrium of the axial skeleton via the medial end of its clavicle. **24.** A consequence of its flexibility is that it is easily dislocated. **25.** Together the ulna and humerus form the elbow joint. **26.** The ulna and the radius each have a styloid process distally. **27.** Carpals are found in the proximal region of the palm. They are short bones. **28.** The third bone of the os coxae is the ischium. **29.** The pelvic girdle (along with the sacrum) receives the weight of the upper body (trunk, head, and upper limbs) and transmits that weight to the lower limbs. **30.** The female pelvis is wider and has a shorter sacrum and a more movable coccyx. **31.** The tibia is the second largest bone in the body. **32.** The medial malleolus is located on the distalmost medial aspect of the tibia. **33.** The lateral condyles are not sites of muscle attachment, they are articular surfaces. **34.** Because of their springiness, the foot arches save energy during locomotion. **35.** The two largest tarsals are the talus, and the calcaneus which forms the heel. **36.** The enlargement of the facial skeleton between ages 6 and 13 is due to the enlargement of the nose and paranasal sinuses and the development of the permanent teeth. **37.** The lumbar curvature develops when the baby begins to walk.

Review Questions 1. (1)b, g; (2)h; (3)d; (4)d, f; (5)e; (6)c; (7)a, b, d, h; (8)i; **2.** (1)g, (2)f, (3)b, (4)a, (5)b, (6)c, (7)d, (8)e; **3.** (1)b, (2)c, (3)e, (4)a, (5)h, (6)e, (7)f

Chapter 8

Check Your Understanding 1. Joint and articulation are synonyms. **2.** The synarthroses are the least mobile of the joint types. **3.** Symphyses and synchondroses are cartilaginous joints. **4.** In general, the more stable a joint, the less mobile it is. **5.** The fibrous capsule and the synovial membrane make up the wall of the articular capsule. **6.** Bursae and tendon sheaths help to reduce friction during joint movement. **7.** The muscle tendons that cross the joint are typically the most important factor in stabilizing synovial joints. **8.** Weeping lubrication helps keep the joint

cartilages nourished and "lubricates" the joint surfaces. **9.** John's hip joint was flexed and his knees extended and his thumb was in opposition (to his index finger). **10.** The hinge and pivot joints are uniaxial joints. **11.** The knee and temporomandibular joints have menisci. The elbow and knee act mainly as a uniaxial hinge. The shoulder depends largely on muscle tendons for stability. **12.** Arthritis means inflammation of the joint. **13.** RA typically produces pain, swelling, and joint deformations that tend to be bilateral and crippling. OA patients tend to have pain, particularly on arising, which is relieved by gentle exercise, and enlarged bone ends (due to spurs) in affected joints. Affected joints may exhibit crepitus. **14.** Lyme disease is caused by spirochete bacteria and transmitted by a tick bite. **15.** Regular exercise strengthens joints and keeps them well nourished.

Review Questions 1. (1)c, (2)a, (3)a, (4)b, (5)c, (6)b, (7)b, (8)a, (9)c; **2.** b; **3.** d; **4.** d; **5.** b; **6.** d; **7.** d

Chapter 9

Check Your Understanding 1. Striated means "with stripes." **2.** He should have responded "smooth muscle," which fits the description. **3.** "Epimysium" literally translates to "outside the muscle" and this connective tissue sheath is the outermost muscle sheath which encloses the entire muscle. **4.** The thin myofilaments have binding sites for calcium on the troponin molecules forming part of those filaments. **5.** In a resting muscle fiber, the SR would have the highest concentration of calcium ions. The mitochondrion provides the ATP needed for muscle activity. **6.** The components of the neuromuscular junction are the axon terminal, the synaptic cleft and the junctional folds of the sarcolemma. **7.** The final trigger for contraction is a certain concentration of calcium ions in the cytosol. The initial trigger is depolarization of the sarcolemma. **8.** There are always some myosin cross bridges bound to the actin myofilament during the contraction phase. Thus, backward sliding of the actin filaments is prevented. **9.** Without ATP, rigor would occur because the myosin heads could not detach. **10.** A motor unit is an axon of a motor neuron and all the muscle fibers it innervates. **11.** During the latent period, events of excitation-contraction coupling are occurring. **12.** Immediately after Jay grabs the bar, his biceps muscles are contracting isometrically. As his body moves upward toward the bar, they are contracting isotonically and concentrically. As he lowers his body, the biceps are contracting isotonically and eccentrically. **13.** Eric was breathing heavily because it takes some time for his heart rate and overall metabolism to return to the resting state after exercise. Moreover, he had likely incurred an oxygen deficit. Although jogging is primarily an aerobic exercise, there is always some anaerobic respiration that occurs as well—the amount depends on exercise intensity. As fatigue occurs, potassium ions accumulate in the T tubules, and lactic acid and phosphate ions accumulate in the muscle cells. **14.** Factors that influence muscle contractile force include muscle fiber size, the number of muscle fibers stimulated, the frequency of stimulation, and the degree of muscle stretch. Factors that influence velocity of contraction include muscle fiber type, load, and the number of motor units contracting. **15.** Fast glycolytic fibers would provide for short periods of intense strength needed to lift and move furniture. **16.** To increase muscle size and strength, anaerobic exercise is best. Muscle endurance is enhanced by aerobic exercise. **17.** Both skeletal and smooth muscle fibers are elongated cells, but unlike smooth muscle cells, which are spindle shaped, uninucleate, and nonstriated, skeletal muscle cells are very large cigar-shaped, multinucleate, striated cells. **18.** Calcium binds to troponin on the actin filaments in skeletal muscle cells. In smooth muscle cells, it binds to a cytoplasmic protein called calmodulin. **19.** Hollow organs that have smooth muscle cells helping to form their walls often must temporarily store the organ's contents (urine, food residues, etc.), an ability ensured by the stress-relaxation response. **20.** During development of skeletal muscle fibers, the myoblast cells join together, forming multinucleate myotubes. **21.** The connective tissue in muscles increases with age, causing the muscles to get stringier. **22.** Regular exercise and strength training help to defer the loss in strength and muscle wasting that tends to occur with age, and improve neuromuscular function.

Clinical Connections 1. The first reaction to tissue injury is the initiation of the inflammatory response. The inflammatory chemicals increase the permeability of the capillaries in the injured area, allowing white blood cells, fluid, and other substances to reach the injured area. The next step in healing involves the formation of granulation tissue, in which the vascular supply for the injured area is regenerated and collagen fibers to knit the torn edges of the tissue together are formed. Skeletal muscle does not regenerate well, so the damaged areas of Mrs. DeStephano's muscle tissue will probably be repaired primarily by the formation of fibrous tissue, creating scar tissue. **2.** Healing is aided by good circulation of blood within the injured area. Vascular damage compromises healing because the supply of oxygen and nutrients to the tissue is reduced. **3.** Under normal circumstances, skeletal muscles receive electrical signals from the nervous system continuously. These signals help to maintain muscle tone and readiness. Severing of the sciatic nerve removes this continuous nervous input to the muscles and will lead to muscle atrophy. Immobility of muscles will lead to a replacement of contractile muscle tissue with noncontractile fibrous connective tissue. Distal to the point of transection, the muscle will begin to decrease in size within 3–7 days of becoming immobile. This process can be delayed by electrically stimulating the tissues. Passive range-of-motion exercises also help prevent loss of muscle tone and joint range, and improve circulation in the injured areas. **4.** Mrs. DeStephano's physician wants to supply her damaged tissues with the necessary building materials to encourage healing. A high-protein diet will provide plenty of amino acids to rebuild or replace damaged proteins, carbohydrates will provide the fuel molecules needed to generate the required ATP, and vitamin C is important for the regeneration of connective tissue.

Review Questions 1. c; **2.** b; **3.** (1)b, (2)a, (3)b, (4)a, (5)b, (6)a; **4.** c; **5.** a; **6.** a; **7.** d; **8.** a; **9.** (1)a, (2)a, c, (3)b, (4)c, (5)b, (6)b; **10.** a; **11.** c; **12.** c; **13.** c; **14.** b

Chapter 10

Check Your Understanding 1. The term "prime mover" refers to the muscle that bears the most responsibility for causing a particular movement. **2.** The iliacus overlies the iliac bone; the adductor brevis is a small (size) muscle that adducts (movement caused) the thigh; and the quadriceps (4 heads) femoris muscle follows the course of the femur. **3.** Of the muscles illustrated in Figure 10.1, the one with the parallel arrangement (sartorius) could shorten to the greatest degree. The stocky bipennate (rectus femoris) and multipennate (deltoid) muscles would be most powerful because they pack in the most fibers. **4.** Third-class levers are the fastest levers. **5.** A lever that operates at a mechanical advantage allows the muscle to exert less force than the load being moved. **6.** John was using the frontal belly of his epicranius to raise his eyebrows and the orbicularis oculi muscles to wink at Sarah. **7.** To make a sad clown's face you would contract your platysma, depressor anguli oris, and depressor labii inferioris muscles. **8.** The deltoid has a broad origin. When only its anterior fibers contract, it flexes and medially rotates the humerus. When only its posterior fibers contract, it extends and laterally rotates the humerus. **9.** The opponens pollicis does not have an insertion on the bones of the thumb.

Review Questions 1. c; **2.** c; **3.** (1)e, (2)c, (3)g, (4)f, (5)d; **4.** a; **5.** c; **6.** d; **7.** c; **8.** c; **9.** b; **10.** d; **11.** b; **12.** a; **13.** c; **14.** d; **15.** a, b; **16.** a

Chapter 11

Check Your Understanding 1. Integration involves processing and interpreting sensory information, and making a decision about motor output.

Integration occurs primarily in the CNS. **2.** (a) This "full stomach" feeling would be relayed by the sensory (afferent) division of the PNS (via its visceral afferent fibers). (b) The somatic nervous system, which is part of the motor (efferent) division of the PNS, controls movement of skeletal muscle. (c) The autonomic nervous system, which is part of the motor (efferent) division of the PNS, controls the heart rate. **3.** Astrocytes control the extracellular environment around neuron cell bodies in the CNS, whereas satellite cells perform this function in the PNS. **4.** Oligodendrocytes and Schwann cells form myelin sheaths in the CNS and PNS, respectively. **5.** A nerve fiber is a long *axon*, an extension of the cell. In connective tissue, fibers are extracellular *proteins* that provide support. In muscle tissue, a muscle fiber is a muscle *cell*. **6.** A nucleus within the brain is a cluster of cell bodies, whereas the nucleus within each neuron is a large organelle that acts as the control center of the cell. **7.** In the CNS, a myelin sheath is formed by oligodendrocytes that wrap their plasma membranes around the axon. The myelin sheath protects and electrically insulates fibers and increases the speed of transmission of nerve impulses. **8.** Burning a finger will first activate unipolar (pseudounipolar) neurons that are sensory (afferent) neurons. The impulse to move your finger away from the heat will be carried by multipolar neurons that are motor (efferent) neurons. **9.** The concentration gradient and the electrical gradient—together called the electrochemical gradient—determine the direction in which ions flow through an open membrane channel. **10.** There is more leakage of K^+ than of any other cations. **11.** Action potentials are larger than graded potentials and travel further. Graded potentials generally initiate action potentials. **12.** An action potential is regenerated anew at each membrane patch. **13.** Conduction of action potentials is faster in myelinated axons because myelin allows the axon membrane between nodes to change its voltage rapidly, and allows current to flow only at the widely spaced nodes. **14.** If a second stimulus occurs before the end of the absolute refractory period, no AP can occur because sodium channels are still inactivated. **15.** At an electrical synapse, neurons are joined by gap junctions. **16.** Voltage-gated ion (Ca^{2+}) channels are found in the presynaptic axon terminal and open when an action potential reaches the axon terminal. Chemically gated ion channels are found in the postsynaptic membrane and open when neurotransmitter binds to the receptor protein. **17.** IPSPs result from the flow of either K^+ or Cl^- through chemically gated channels. EPSPs result from the flow of both Na^+ and K^+ through chemically gated channels. **18.** Temporal summation is summation in *time* of graded potentials occurring in quick succession at the postsynaptic membrane. It can result from EPSPs arising from just one synapse. Spatial summation is summation in *space*—a postsynaptic neuron is stimulated by a large number of terminals at the same time. **19.** ACh interacts with more than one specific receptor type, and this explains how it can excite at some synapses and inhibit at others. **20.** cAMP is called a second messenger because it relays the message between the *first messenger* (the original chemical messenger) outside of the cell and effector molecules that will ultimately bring about the desired response within the cell. **21.** Reverberating circuits and parallel after-discharge circuits both result in prolonged output. **22.** The pattern of neural processing is serial processing. The response is a reflex arc. **23.** The pattern of neural processing is parallel processing. **24.** The growing tip of an axon is called a growth cone. Neurotropins are chemicals that signal the growth cone.

Review Questions 1. b; **2.** (1)d, (2)b, (3)f, (4)c, (5)a; **3.** b; **4.** c; **5.** a; **6.** c; **7.** b; **8.** d; **9.** c; **10.** c; **11.** a; **12.** (1)d, (2)b, (3)a, (4)c

Chapter 12

Check Your Understanding 1. The third ventricle is surrounded by the diencephalon. **2.** The cerebral hemispheres and the cerebellum have an outside layer of gray matter in addition to central gray matter and its surrounding white matter. **3.** Convolutions increase surface area of the cortex, which allows more neurons to occupy the limited space within the skull. **4.** The central sulcus separates primary motor areas from somatosensory areas. **5.** Motor functions on the left side of the body are controlled by the right hemisphere of the brain because motor tracts from the right hemisphere cross over (in the medulla oblongata) to the left side of the spinal cord to go to the left side of the body. **6.** Commissural fibers (which form commissures) allow the cerebral hemispheres to "talk to each other." **7.** The caudate nucleus, putamen, and globus pallidus together form the basal nuclei. **8.** Virtually all inputs ascending to the cerebral cortex synapse in the thalamus en route. **9.** The hypothalamus oversees the autonomic nervous system. **10.** The pyramids of the medulla are the corticospinal (pyramidal) tracts, the large voluntary motor tracts descending from the motor cortex. The result of decussation (crossing over) is that each side of the motor cortex controls the opposite side of the body. **11.** The cerebral peduncles and the colliculi are associated with the midbrain. **12.** There are many possible answers to this question— here are a few: Structurally, the cerebellum and cerebrum are similar in that they both have a thin outer cortex of gray matter, internal white matter, and deep gray matter nuclei. Also, both have body maps (homunculi) and large fiber tracts connecting them to the brain stem. Both receive sensory input and influence motor output. A major difference is that the cerebellum is almost entirely concerned with motor output, whereas the cerebrum has much broader responsibilities. Also, while a cerebral hemisphere controls the opposite side of the body, a cerebellar hemisphere controls the same side of the body. **13.** The hypothalamus is part of the limbic system and also an autonomic (visceral) control center. **14.** Taylor is increasing the amount of sensory stimuli she receives, which will be relayed to the reticular activating system, which, in turn, will increase activation of the cerebral cortex. **15.** Delta waves are typically seen in deep sleep in normal adults. **16.** Drowsiness (or lethargy) and stupor are stages of consciousness between alertness and coma. **17.** Most skeletal muscles are actively inhibited during REM sleep. **18.** Transfer of memory from STM to LTM is enhanced by (1) rehearsal, (2) association (tying "new" information to "old" information), and (3) a heightened emotional state (for example, alert, motivated, surprised, or aroused). **19.** The basal nuclei and premotor cortex are involved in procedural (skills) memory, but not in declarative memory. **20.** CSF, formed by the choroid plexuses as a filtrate of blood plasma, is a watery "broth" similar in composition to plasma. It protects the brain and spinal cord from blows and other trauma, helps nourish the brain, and carries chemical signals from one part of the brain to another. **21.** A TIA is a temporary loss of blood supply to brain tissue, and it differs from a stroke in that the resultant impairment is fully reversible. **22.** Mrs. Lee might have Parkinson's disease. **23.** Alar plate neuroblasts become interneurons, whereas basal plate neuroblasts become motor (efferent) neurons. **24.** The nerves serving the limbs arise in the cervical and lumbar enlargements of the spinal cord. **25.** In the spinothalamic pathway, the cell bodies of first-order sensory neurons are outside the spinal cord in a ganglion, cell bodies of second-order sensory neurons are in the dorsal horn of the spinal cord, and cell bodies of third-order sensory neurons are in the thalamus. (See also Figure 12.34b.) **26.** Roy had lower limb paralysis. This could be caused by a spinal cord injury in the thoracic region (between T_1 and L_1). If the spinal cord is transected, the result is paraplegia. If the cord is only bruised, he may regain function in the limbs. An MRI scan (or CT scan) of the spinal cord would be helpful. **27.** Premature babies have trouble regulating body temperature because the hypothalamus is immature. **28.** Reversible causes of dementia include prescription drug effects, low blood pressure, poor nutrition, hormone imbalances, depression, and dehydration.

Review Questions 1. a; **2.** d; **3.** c; **4.** a; **5.** (1)d, (2)f, (3)e, (4)g, (5)b, (6)f, (7)i, (8)a; **6.** b; **7.** c; **8.** a; **9.** (1)a, (2)b, (3)a, (4)a, (5)b, (6)a, (7)b, (8)b, (9)a; **10.** d; **11.** (1)d, (2)e, (3)c and d, (4)a; **12.** (c)

Chapter 13

Check Your Understanding 1. In addition to nerves, the PNS also consists of sensory receptors, motor endings, and ganglia. **2.** Nociceptors respond to painful stimuli. They are exteroceptors that are simple and unencapsulated (free nerve endings). **3.** The three levels of sensory integration are receptor level, circuit level, and perceptual level. **4.** Phasic receptors adapt, whereas tonic receptors exhibit little or no adaptation. Pain receptors are tonic so that we are reminded to protect the injured body part. **5.** Hot and cold are conveyed by different sensory receptors that are parts of separate "labeled lines." Cool and cold are two different intensities of the same stimulus, detected by frequency coding—the frequency of APs would be higher for a cold than a cool stimulus. Action potentials arising in the fingers and foot arrive at different locations in the somatosensory cortex via their own "labeled lines" and in this way the cortex can determine their origin. **6.** Ganglia are collections of neuron cell bodies in the PNS. **7.** Nerves also contain connective tissue, blood vessels, lymphatic vessels, and the myelin surrounding the axons. **8.** Schwann cells, macrophages, and the neurons themselves were all important in healing the nerve. **9.** The oculomotor (III), trochlear (IV), and abducens (VI) nerves control eye movements. Sticking out your tongue involves the hypoglossal nerve (XII). The vagus nerve (X) influences heart rate and digestive activity. The accessory nerve (XI) innervates the trapezius muscle, which is involved in shoulder shrugging. **10.** Roots lie medial to spinal nerves, whereas rami lie lateral to spinal nerves. Dorsal roots are purely sensory, whereas dorsal rami carry both motor and sensory fibers. **11.** The spinal nerve roots were C_3–C_5, the spinal nerve was the phrenic nerve, the plexus was the cervical plexus. The phrenic nerve is the sole motor nerve supply to the diaphragm, the primary muscle for respiration. **12.** Varicosities are the series of knoblike swellings that are the axon endings of autonomic motor neurons. You would find them on axon endings serving smooth muscle or glands. **13.** The cerebellum and basal nuclei, which form the precommand level of motor control, plan and coordinate complex motor activities. **14.** The five components of a reflex arc are receptor, sensory neuron, integration center, motor neuron, and effector. **15.** The stretch reflex is important for maintaining muscle tone and adjusting it reflexively by causing muscle contraction in response to increased muscle length (stretch). It maintains posture. The flexor or withdrawal reflex is initiated by a painful stimulus and causes automatic withdrawal of the painful body part from the stimulus. It is protective. **16.** This response is called Babinski's sign and it indicates damage to the corticospinal tract or primary motor cortex. **17.** The vertebral column, spinal nerves, and dermatomes are all examples of segmentation in the adult.

Review Questions 1. b; **2.** c; **3.** d; **4.** c; **5.** e; **6.** c; **7.** (1)d, (2)c, (3)f, (4)b, (5)e, (6)a; **8.** (1)f, (2)i, (3)b, (4)g, h, (5)e, (6)i, (7)c, (8)k, (9)l, (10)c, d, f, k; **9.** (1)b 6; (2)d 8; (3)c 2; (4)c 5; (5)a 4; (6)a 3, 9; (7)a 7; (8)a 7; (9)d 1; (10)a 3, 4, 7, 9; **10.** (1)a, 1 and 5; (2)a, 3 and 5; (3)a, 4; (4)a, 2; (5)c, 2; (6)b, 2; **11.** c

Chapter 14

Check Your Understanding 1. The effectors of the autonomic nervous system are cardiac muscle, smooth muscle, and glands. **2.** The somatic motor system relays instructions to muscles more quickly because it involves only one motor neuron, whereas the ANS uses a two-neuron chain. Moreover, axons of somatic motor neurons are typically heavily myelinated, whereas preganglionic autonomic axons are lightly myelinated and postganglionic axons are unmyelinated. **3.** While you relax in the sun on the beach, the parasympathetic branch of the ANS would probably predominate. When you perceive danger (as in a shark), the sympathetic branch of the ANS predominates. **4.** "Short preganglionic fibers," "origin from thoracolumbar region of spinal cord," "collateral ganglia," and "innervates adrenal medulla" are all characteristic of the sympathetic nervous system. Terminal ganglia are found in the parasympathetic nervous system. **5.** The major differences are (1) the ANS has visceral afferents rather than somatic afferents, (2) the ANS has a two-neuron efferent chain, whereas the somatic nervous system (SNS) has one, and (3) the effectors of the ANS are smooth muscles, cardiac muscles, and glands, whereas the effectors of the SNS are skeletal muscles. **6.** The parasympathetic nervous system increases digestive activity and decreases heart rate. The sympathetic nervous system increases blood pressure, dilates bronchioles, stimulates the adrenal medulla to release its hormones, and causes ejaculation. **7.** You would find nicotinic receptors on skeletal muscle and the hormone-producing cells of the adrenal medulla, but not on smooth muscle or glands. Virtually all types of receptors (including nicotinic receptors) are also found in the CNS (see Table 11.3 on p. 416). **8.** The main integration center of the ANS is the hypothalamus, although the most direct influence is through the brain stem reticular formation and the reflex centers in the pons and medulla oblongata. **9.** Jackson's doctor may have prescribed a beta-blocker because Jackson has hypertension. (Chronic stress is a factor in causing hypertension.) The beta-blocker will decrease blood pressure by blocking beta-adrenergic receptors in the heart and blood vessels, thereby decreasing heart rate and dilating blood vessels. **10.** The neural crest gives rise to both autonomic ganglia and the adrenal medulla.

Clinical Connections 1. The location of Jimmy's lacerations and bruises and his inability to rise led the paramedics to suspect a head, neck, or back injury. They immobilized his head and torso to prevent any further damage to the brain and spinal cord. **2.** The worsening neurological signs indicate a probable intracranial hemorrhage. The blood escaping from the ruptured blood vessel(s) will begin to compress Jimmy's brain and increase his intracranial pressure. Jimmy's surgery will involve repair of the damaged vessel(s) and removal of the mass of clotted blood pressing on his brain. **3.** Loss of motor and sensory function below the level of the nipples indicates a lesion at T_4. See Figure 13.12. **4.** Jimmy is suffering from spinal shock, which occurs as a result of injury to the spinal cord. Spinal shock is a temporary condition in which all reflex and motor activities caudal to the level of spinal cord injury are lost, so Jimmy's muscles are paralyzed. His blood pressure is low due to the loss of sympathetic tone in his vasculature. **5.** Jimmy's exaggerated reflexes are caused by damaged upper motor neuron axons in the spinal cord. These upper motor neurons normally inhibit spinal reflexes. He is incontinent because there are no longer pathways to support voluntary control of bowel and bladder emptying. **6.** This condition is called *autonomic dysreflexia* (or *autonomic hyperreflexia*). This is a condition in which a normal stimulus triggers a massive activation of autonomic neurons. **7.** Extremely high arterial blood pressure can cause a rupture of the cerebral blood vessels (as well as other blood vessels in the body) and put Jimmy's life at risk.

Review Questions 1. d; **2.** (1)S, (2)P, (3)P, (4)S, (5)S, (6)P, (7)P, (8)S, (9)P, (10)S, (11)P, (12)S; **3.** b; **4.** c; **5.** a

Chapter 15

Check Your Understanding 1. Tears (lacrimal fluid) are a dilute saline secretion that contains mucus, antibodies, and lysozyme. They are secreted by the lacrimal glands. **2.** The blind spot of the eye is the optic disc. It is the part of the retina where the optic nerve exits the eye and it is "blind" because it is a region of the retina that lacks photoreceptors. **3.** An increase in intraocular pressure is called glaucoma and is due to an accumulation of aqueous humor, usually because of impaired drainage of the fluid. **4.** Light passes through the cornea, aqueous humor, lens, vitreous humor, ganglion cells and bipolar cells before it reaches the photoreceptors. **5.** The ciliary muscles and sphincter pupillae relax for distant vision. (If you said the medial rectus muscles also relax, this is true, but remem-

ber that the rectus muscles are *extrinsic* eye muscles, not intrinsic.) **6.** The near point moves farther away as you age because the lens becomes less flexible (presbyopia), so that it is unable to assume the more rounded shape required for near vision. **7.** The following are characteristics of cones: "vision in bright light," "color vision," and "higher acuity." The following are characteristics of rods: "only one type of visual pigment," "most abundant in the periphery of the retina," "many feed into one ganglion cell," and "higher sensitivity." **8.** Breakdown of the retinal-opsin combination is called bleaching of the pigment. It occurs with exposure to light. **9.** A tumor in the right visual cortex would affect the left visual field. A tumor compressing the right optic nerve would affect both the left and right visual fields from the right eye only. **10.** The five taste modalities are sweet, sour, bitter, salty, and umami. The fungiform, circumvallate, and foliate papillae contain taste buds. **11.** The cilia and hairs of these receptor cells greatly increase the surface area for sensory receptors. **12.** The tympanic membrane separates the external from the middle ear. The oval and round windows separate the middle from the inner ear. **13.** The basilar membrane allows us to differentiate sounds of different pitch. **14.** You would not be able to locate the origin of a sound if the brain stem did not receive input from both ears. **15.** The "fullness" in Mohammed's ears is likely due to an accumulation of fluid in the middle ear as a result of his upper respiratory infection ("cold") spreading into his ear. He has a form of conduction deafness. **16.** The following apply to a macula: "contains otoliths," "responds to linear acceleration or deceleration," and "inside a saccule." The following apply to a crista ampullaris: "inside a semicircular canal," "has a cupula," "responds to rotational acceleration and deceleration." **17.** With age, the lens discolors and loses its clarity and the dilator pupillae muscles become less efficient, decreasing the amount of light that reaches the retinas at night.

Review Questions 1. c; **2.** d; **3.** a; **4.** b; **5.** c; **6.** c; **7.** b; **8.** a; **9.** b; **10.** b; **11.** b; **12.** d; **13.** d; **14.** a; **15.** d; **16.** c; **17.** d; **18.** b; **19.** b; **20.** c; **21.** d; **22.** b; **23.** b; **24.** e; **25.** b; **26.** c; **27.** c; **28.** c; **29.** c

Chapter 16

Check Your Understanding 1. The endocrine system is more closely associated with growth and development, and its responses tend to be long-lasting, whereas nervous system responses tend to be rapid and discrete. **2.** The thyroid and parathyroid glands are found in the neck. **3.** Hormones are released into the blood and transported throughout the body, whereas paracrines act locally, generally within the same tissue. **4.** The two major chemical classes of hormones are amino acid–based hormones and steroids. Steroids are all lipid soluble. Thyroid hormones are the only amino acid–based hormones that are lipid soluble. **5.** Water-soluble hormones act on receptors in the plasma membrane coupled most often via regulatory molecules called G proteins to intracellular second messengers. Lipid-soluble hormones act on intracellular receptors, directly activating genes and stimulating synthesis of specific proteins. **6.** Hormone release can be triggered by humoral, neural, or hormonal stimuli. **7.** The hypothalamus communicates with the anterior pituitary via *hormones* released into a special portal system of blood vessels. In contrast, it communicates with the posterior pituitary via *action potentials traveling down axons* that connect the hypothalamus to the posterior pituitary. **8.** LH and FSH are tropic hormones that act on the gonads, TSH is a tropic hormone that acts on the thyroid, and ACTH is a tropic hormone that acts on the adrenal cortex. (If you said growth hormone, that's also a good answer, as GH causing the liver to release IGFs might also be considered a tropic effect.) **9.** Drinking alcoholic beverages inhibits ADH secretion from the posterior pituitary and causes copious urine output and dehydration. The dehydration causes the hangover effects. **10.** Thyroid hormone increases basal metabolic rate (and heat production) in the body. Parathyroid hormone increases blood Ca^{2+} levels in a variety of ways.

Calcitonin at high (pharmacological) levels has a Ca^{2+}-lowering, bone-sparing effect. (At normal blood levels its effects in humans are negligible.) **11.** Thyroid follicle cells release thyroid hormone, chief cells in the parathyroid gland release parathyroid hormone, and parafollicular (C) cells in the thyroid gland release calcitonin. **12.** Glucocorticoids are stress hormones that, among many effects, increase blood glucose. Mineralocorticoids increase blood Na^+ (and blood pressure) and decrease blood K^+. Gonadocorticoids are male and female sex hormones that are thought to have a variety of effects (for example, onset of puberty, sex drive in women, pubic and axillary hair development in women). **13.** Melatonin is used by some individuals as a sleep aid, particularly to counter jet lag. **14.** When we say Sharon is diabetic, this means that she has insufficient insulin action in her body. The most likely explanation for Sharon's behavior is that she has taken too much insulin and is experiencing hypoglycemia. Ingesting some sugar will likely help her. **15.** Diabetes mellitus is due to a lack of insulin production or action, whereas diabetes insipidus is due to a lack of ADH. Both conditions are characterized by production of copious amounts of urine. You would find glucose in the urine of a patient with diabetes mellitus, but not in the urine of a patient with diabetes insipidus. **16.** The gonadal hormones are steroid hormones. A major endocrine gland that also secretes steroid hormones is the adrenal cortex. **17.** The heart produces atrial natriuretic peptide (ANP). ANP decreases blood volume and blood pressure by increasing the kidneys' production of salty urine. **18.** Vitamin D_3, produced in inactive form by the skin, increases intestinal absorption of calcium. **19.** The decline in growth hormone with age contributes to muscle atrophy. The decline in estrogen contributes to osteoporosis in women.

Clinical Connections 1. Rationale for orders: As Mr. Gutteman is unconscious, the level of damage to his brain is unclear. Monitoring his responses and vital signs every hour will provide information for his care providers about the extent of his injuries. Turning him every 4 hours and providing careful skin care will prevent decubitus ulcers (bedsores) as well as stimulating his proprioceptive pathways. **2.** Mr. Gutteman's condition is termed *diabetes insipidus*, a condition in which insufficient quantities of antidiuretic hormone (ADH) are produced or released. Diabetes insipidus patients excrete large volumes of urine but do not have glucose or ketones present in the urine. The head trauma could have damaged Mr. Gutteman's hypothalamus, which produces the hormone, or injured his posterior pituitary gland, which releases ADH into the bloodstream. **3.** Diabetes insipidus is not life threatening for most individuals with normal thirst mechanisms, as they will be thirsty and drink to replenish the lost fluid. However, Mr. Gutteman is comatose, so his fluid output must be monitored closely so that the volume lost can be replaced by IV line. His subsequent recovery may be complicated if he has suffered damage to his hypothalamus, which houses the thirst center neurons.

Review Questions 1. b; **2.** a; **3.** c; **4.** d; **5.** (1)c, (2)a and b, (3)f, (4)d, (5)e, (6)g, (7)a, (8)h, (9)b and e, (10)a; **6.** d; **7.** c; **8.** b; **9.** d; **10.** b; **11.** d; **12.** b; **13.** c; **14.** d

Chapter 17

Check Your Understanding 1. The hematocrit is the percentage of blood that is occupied by erythrocytes. It is normally about 45%. **2.** Blood can prevent blood loss by forming clots when a blood vessel is damaged. Blood can prevent infection because it contains antimicrobial proteins and white blood cells. **3.** Plasma proteins are not used as fuel for body cells because their presence in blood is required to perform many key functions. **4.** Each hemoglobin molecule can transport four O_2. The heme portion of the hemoglobin binds the O_2. **5.** The kidneys' synthesis of erythropoietin is compromised in advanced kidney disease, so RBC production decreases, causing anemia. **6.** Monocytes become macrophages in tissues. Neutrophils are also voracious phagocytes. **7.** "Thrombopoietin"

is derived from the same word as "thrombocyte." It is the hormone that promotes platelet formation. **8.** Amos's red bone marrow is spewing out many abnormal white blood cells, which are crowding out the production of normal bone marrow elements. The lack of normal white blood cells allows the infections, the lack of platelets fails to stop bleeding, and the lack of erythrocytes is anemia. **9.** The three steps of hemostasis are vascular spasm, platelet plug formation, and coagulation. **10.** Fibrinogen is water soluble, whereas fibrin is not. Prothrombin is an inactive precursor, whereas thrombin acts as an enzyme. Most factors are inactive in blood before activation and become enzymes upon activation. (There are exceptions, such as fibrinogen and calcium.) **11.** Thrombocytopenia (platelet deficiency) results in failure to plug the countless small tears in blood vessels, and so manifests as small purple spots. Hemophilia A results from the absence of clotting factor VIII. **12.** Nigel has anti-A antibodies in his blood and type B agglutinogens on his RBCs. He can donate blood to an AB recipient, but he should not receive blood from an AB donor because his anti-A antibodies will cause a transfusion reaction. **13.** If Emily has a bacterial meningitis, a differential WBC count would likely reveal an increase in neutrophils because neutrophils are a major body defense against bacteria. **14.** Hemoglobin F has a higher affinity (binding strength) for oxygen than adult hemoglobin does.

Review Questions 1. c; **2.** c; **3.** d; **4.** b; **5.** d; **6.** a; **7.** a; **8.** b; **9.** c; **10.** d

Chapter 18

Check Your Understanding 1. The mediastinum is the medial cavity of the thorax within which the heart, great vessels, and trachea are found. **2.** The layers of the heart wall are the endocardium, the myocardium, and the epicardium. The epicardium is also called the visceral layer of the serous pericardium. This is surrounded by the parietal layer of the serous pericardium and the fibrous pericardium. **3.** The serous fluid decreases friction caused by movement of the layers against one another. **4.** The right side of the heart acts as the pulmonary pump, whereas the left acts as the systemic pump. **5.** (a) True. The left ventricle wall is thicker than the right. (b) True. The left ventricle pumps blood at much higher pressure than the right ventricle because the left ventricle supplies the whole body, whereas the right ventricle supplies only the lungs. (c) False. Each ventricle pumps the *same amount* of blood with each beat. If this were not true, blood would back up in either the systemic or pulmonary circulation (because the two ventricles are in series). **6.** The branches of the right coronary artery are the right marginal artery and the posterior interventricular artery. **7.** The papillary muscles and chordae tendineae keep the AV valve flaps from everting into the atria as the ventricles contract. **8.** (a) The refractory period is almost as long as the contraction in cardiac muscle. (b) The source of Ca^{2+} for the contraction is *only* SR in skeletal muscle. (c) The AP exhibits a plateau phase in cardiac muscle. (d) Both skeletal muscle and cardiac muscle have troponin. (e) Only skeletal muscle has triads. **9.** Cardiac muscle cannot go into tetany because the absolute refractory period is almost as long as the contraction. **10.** The Purkinje fibers excite ventricular muscle fibers. The depolarization wave travels upward from the apex toward the atria **11.** (a) The QRS wave occurs during ventricular depolarization. (b) The T wave of the ECG occurs during ventricular repolarization. (c) The P-Q interval of the ECG occurs during atrial depolarization and the conduction of the action potential through the rest of the intrinsic conduction system. **12.** The second heart sound is associated with the closing of the semilunar valves. **13.** The murmur of mitral insufficiency occurs during ventricular systole (because this is when the valve should be closed, and the murmur is due to blood leaking through the incompletely closed valve into the atrium). **14.** The periods when all four valves are closed are the isovolumetric contraction phase and the isovolumetric relaxation phase. **15.** Exercise activates the sympathetic nervous system. Sympathetic nervous system activity increases heart rate. It also directly increases ventricular contractility, thereby increasing Josh's stroke volume. **16.** If the heart is beating very rapidly, the amount of time for ventricular filling between contractions is decreased. This decreases the end diastolic volume, decreases the stroke volume, and therefore decreases the cardiac output. **17.** The foramen ovale and the ductus arteriosus both allow blood to bypass the fetal lungs. **18.** Elderly athletes may be hampered by sclerosis and thickening of heart valve flaps, a decline in cardiac reserve, fibrosis of cardiac muscle, and atherosclerosis.

Review Questions 1. a; **2.** c; **3.** b; **4.** c; **5.** b; **6.** b; **7.** c; **8.** d; **9.** b

Chapter 19

Check Your Understanding 1. The sympathetic nervous system innervates blood vessels. The sympathetic nerves innervate the tunica media. The effector cells in the tunica media are smooth muscle cells. **2.** When vascular smooth muscle contracts, the diameter of the blood vessel becomes smaller. This is called vasoconstriction. **3.** *Elastic arteries* play a major role in dampening the pulsatile pressure of heart contractions. Dilation or constriction of *arterioles* determines blood flow to individual capillary beds. *Muscular arteries* have the thickest tunica media relative to their lumen size. **4.** If you were doing calf raises, your capillary bed would be in the condition depicted in part (a). The true capillaries would be flushed with blood to ensure that the working calf muscles could receive the needed nutrients and dispose of their metabolic wastes. **5.** Valves prevent blood from flowing backwards in veins. They are formed from folds of the tunica intima. **6.** In the systemic circuit, veins contain more blood than arteries (see Figure 19.5). **7.** The three factors that determine resistance are blood viscosity, vessel length, and vessel diameter. Vessel diameter is physiologically most important. **8.** The rate of flow will decrease 81-fold from its original flow ($3 \times 3 \times 3 \times 3 = 81$). **9.** When you first stand up, mean arterial pressure (MAP) temporarily decreases and this is sensed by aortic and carotid baroreceptors. Medullary cardiac and vasomotor center reflexes increase sympathetic and decrease parasympathetic outflow to the heart. Heart rate and contractility increase, increasing cardiac output, and therefore MAP. Further, sympathetic constriction of arterioles increases peripheral resistance, also increasing MAP. (In addition, increased constriction of veins increases venous return, which increases end diastolic volume, increasing stroke volume, and therefore cardiac output and MAP.) See also Figure 19.9 (bottom). **10.** The kidneys help maintain MAP by influencing blood volume. In renal artery obstruction, the blood pressure in the kidney is lower than in the rest of the body (because it is downstream of the obstruction). Low renal blood pressure triggers both direct and indirect renal mechanisms to increase blood pressure by increasing blood volume. This can cause hypertension (called "secondary hypertension" because it is secondary to a defined cause—in this case the renal artery obstruction). **11.** In a bicycle race, autoregulation by intrinsic metabolic controls causes arteriolar smooth muscle in your legs to relax, dilating the vessels and supplying more O_2 and nutrients to the exercising muscles. **12.** Extrinsic mechanisms, primarily the sympathetic nervous system, prevent blood pressure from plummeting by constricting arterioles elsewhere (such as gut, kidneys). In addition, cardiac output increases, which also helps maintain MAP. **13.** (a) An increase in interstitial fluid osmotic pressure (OP_{if}) would tend to pull more fluid out of capillaries (causing localized swelling, or edema). (b) An increase of OP_{if} to 10 mm Hg would decrease the net osmotic pressure on both the arteriole and venule ends of the capillary to 16 mm Hg (26 mm Hg − 10 mm Hg). The NFP at the venous end would become 1 mm Hg (17 mm Hg − 16 mm Hg). (c) Fluid would flow *out of* the venous end of the capillary rather than in. **14.** Bob is in vascular shock due to anaphylaxis, a systemic allergic reaction to his medication. His blood pressure is low because of widespread vasodilation triggered by the

massive release of histamine. Bob's rapid heart rate is a result of the baroreceptor reflex triggered by his low blood pressure. This activates the sympathetic nervous system, increasing heart rate, in an attempt to restore blood pressure. **15.** The external carotid arteries supply most of the tissues of the head except for the brain and orbits. **16.** The cerebral arterial circle (circle of Willis) is the arterial anastomosis at the base of the brain. **17.** The four unpaired arteries that emerge from the abdominal aorta are the celiac trunk, the superior and inferior mesenteric arteries, and the median sacral artery. **18.** You would palpate the popliteal artery behind the knee, the posterior tibial artery behind the medial malleolus of the tibia, and the dorsalis pedis artery on the foot. (See also Figure 19.12.) **19.** The vertebral arteries help supply the brain, but the vertebral veins do *not* drain much blood from the brain. **20.** The internal jugular veins drain the dural venous sinuses. Each internal jugular vein joins a subclavian vein to form a brachiocephalic vein. **21.** A portal system is a system where two capillary beds occur in series. In other words, in a portal system, a capillary bed is drained by a vein that leads into a second capillary bed. The function of the hepatic portal system is to transport venous blood from the digestive organs to the liver for processing before it enters the rest of the systemic circulation. This plays an important role in defense against absorbed toxins or microorganisms and also allows direct delivery of absorbed nutrients to the liver for processing. **22.** The leg veins that often become varicosed are the great and small saphenous veins. **23.** Three differences between arteries and veins are (1) arteries run deep while veins are both deep and superficial, (2) venous pathways are more interconnected than arterial pathways, and (3) the brain and digestive systems have unique venous drainage systems, whereas their arterial supply patterns are not substantially different from those of other organs. **24.** The foramen ovale and the ductus arteriosus both bypass the fetal lungs. The ductus venosus bypasses the fetal liver. **25.** Varicose veins, atherosclerosis, and hypertension are associated with aging.

Clinical Connections 1. The tissues in Mr. Hutchinson's right leg were deprived of oxygen and nutrients for at least one-half hour. When tissues are deprived of oxygen, tissue metabolism decreases and eventually ceases, so these tissues may have died due to anoxia. **2.** Mr. Hutchinson's vital signs (low BP; rapid, thready pulse) indicate that he is facing a life-threatening problem that must be stabilized before other, less vital problems can be addressed. As for surgery, he may be scheduled for open reduction of his crushed bone, depending upon the condition of the tissues in his crushed right leg. If tissue death has occurred in his leg, he may undergo amputation of that limb. **3.** Mr. Hutchinson's rapid, thready pulse and falling blood pressure are indications of hypovolemic shock, a type of shock resulting from decreased blood volume. Because his blood volume is low, his heart rate is elevated to increase cardiac output in an effort to maintain the blood supply to his vital organs. Mr. Hutchinson's blood volume must be increased as quickly as possible with blood transfusions or intravenous saline. This will stabilize his condition and allow his physicians to continue with his surgery.

Review Questions 1. d; **2.** b; **3.** d; **4.** c; **5.** e; **6.** d; **7.** c; **8.** b; **9.** b; **10.** a; **11.** b; **12.** c; **13.** b; **14.** d; **15.** (1)b, e, g; (2)c; (3)i; (4) f, h; (5) d

Chapter 20

Check Your Understanding 1. Lymph is the fluid inside lymphatic vessels. It enters lymphatic vessels from interstitial fluid. Interstitial fluid, in turn, is a filtrate of blood plasma. **2.** The right lymphatic duct receives lymph from the right upper limb and the right side of the head and thorax. The thoracic duct drains lymph from the rest of the body. **3.** Lymph movement is driven by the contraction of adjacent skeletal muscles, pressure changes in the thorax during breathing, and the pulsations of nearby arteries. (Valves in lymphatic vessels prevent backflow of lymph.) **4.** Lymphoid follicles are solid, spherical bodies consisting of tightly packed reticular elements and cells, often with a lighter-staining central region. They are regions where B cells predominate. **5.** Having fewer efferents causes lymph to accumulate in lymph nodes, allowing more time for its cleansing. **6.** MALT (mucosa-associated lymphatic tissue) is lymphoid tissue found in the mucosa of the digestive, respiratory, and genitourinary tracts. **7.** The spleen cleanses the blood, stores breakdown products of RBCs, stores platelets, and is thought to be a site of erythrocyte production in the fetus. **8.** The thymus develops first.

Clinical Connections 1. The red streaks radiating from Mr. Hutchinson's finger indicate that his lymphatic vessels are inflamed. This inflammation may be caused by a bacterial infection. If Mr. Hutchinson's arm had exhibited edema without any accompanying red streaks, the problem would likely have been impaired lymph transport from his arm back to his trunk, due to injury or blockage of his lymphatic vessels. **2.** Mr. Hutchinson's arm was placed in a sling to immobilize it, slowing the drainage of lymph from the infected area in an attempt to limit the spread of the infection. **3.** Mr. Hutchinson's low lymphocyte count indicates that his body's ability to fight infection by bacteria or viruses is impaired. The antibiotics and additional staff protection will protect Mr. Hutchinson until his lymphocyte count increases again. Gloving and gowning also protect the staff caring for Mr. Hutchinson from any body infection he might have. **4.** Mr. Hutchinson's recovery may be problematic, as he probably already has an ongoing bacterial infection and his ability to raise a defense to this infection is impaired.

Review Questions 1. c; **2.** c; **3.** a, d; **4.** c; **5.** a; **6.** b; **7.** a; **8.** b; **9.** d

Chapter 21

Check Your Understanding 1. The innate defense system is always ready to respond immediately, whereas it takes considerable time to mount the adaptive defense system. The innate defenses consist of surface barriers and internal defenses, whereas the adaptive defenses consist of humoral and cellular immunity, which rely on B and T lymphocytes. **2.** Surface barriers (the skin and mucous membranes) constitute the first line of defense. **3.** Opsonization is the process of making pathogens more susceptible to phagocytosis by decorating their surface with molecules that phagocytes can bind. Antibodies and complement proteins are examples of molecules that act as opsonins. **4.** Our own cells are killed by NK cells when they have been infected by viruses or when they have become cancerous. **5.** Redness, heat, swelling, and pain are the cardinal signs of inflammation. Redness and local heat are both caused by vasodilation of arterioles, which increases the flow of blood (warmed by the body core) to the affected area. The swelling (edema) is due to the release of histamine and other chemical mediators of inflammation, which increase capillary permeability. This increased permeability allows proteins to leak into the interstitial fluid (IF), increasing the IF osmotic pressure and drawing more fluid out of blood vessels and into the tissues, thereby causing swelling. The pain is due to two things: (1) the actions of certain chemical mediators (kinins and prostaglandins) on nerve endings, and (2) the swelling, which can compress free nerve endings. **6.** Three key characteristics of adaptive immunity are that it is specific, it is systemic, and it has memory. **7.** A complete antigen has both immunogenicity and reactivity, whereas a hapten has reactivity but not immunogenicity. **8.** Self-antigens, particularly MHC proteins, mark a cell as self. **9.** Development of immunocompetence of a B or T cell is signaled by the appearance on its surface of specific and unique receptors for an antigen. In the case of a B cell, this receptor is a membrane-bound antibody. (In T cells, it is simply called the T cell receptor.) **10.** The T cell that would survive is (c), one that recognizes MHC but not self-antigen. **11.** Dendritic cells, macrophages, and B cells can all act as APCs. Dendritic cells are most important for T cell activation. **12.** In clonal selection, the antigen does the selecting. What is being selected is a particular clone of B or T cells that

has antigen receptors corresponding to that antigen. **13.** The secondary response to an antigen is faster than the primary response because the immune system has already been "primed" and has memory cells that are specific for that particular antigen. **14.** Vaccinations protect by providing the initial encounter to an antigen—the primary response to that antigen. As a result, when the pathogen for that illness is encountered again, the pathogen elicits the much faster, more powerful secondary response, which is generally effective enough to prevent clinical illness. **15.** IgG antibody is most abundant in blood. IgM is secreted first in a primary immune response. IgA is most abundant in secretions. **16.** Antibodies can bring about destruction of pathogen via "PLAN"—**p**hagocytosis, **l**ysis (via complement), **a**gglutination, or **n**eutralization. **17.** Class II MHC proteins display exogenous antigens. Class II MHC proteins are recognized by CD4 T cells (which usually become helper T cells). APCs display class II MHC proteins. **18.** When antigens are bound in the absence of co-stimulators this causes the lymphocyte to develop *anergy*—a state of permanent unresponsiveness to that antigen. **19.** Helper T cells are central to both humoral and cell-mediated immunity because they are required for activation of both cytotoxic T cells and most B cells. **20.** The cytotoxic T cell releases perforins and granzymes onto the identified target cell. Perforins form a pore in the target cell membrane, and granzymes enter through this pore, triggering apoptosis (cell suicide). **21.** MHC proteins and blood type antigens (ABO, etc.) are carefully matched before an organ transplant. **22.** HIV is particularly hard for the immune system to defeat because (1) it destroys helper T cells, which are key players in adaptive immunity and (2) it has a high mutation rate and so it rapidly becomes resistant to drugs. **23.** Binding of an allergen onto specific IgE antibodies attached to mast cells triggers the mast cells to release histamine.

Review Questions 1. c; **2.** a; **3.** d; **4.** d, e; **5.** a; **6.** d; **7.** b; **8.** c; **9.** d; **10.** d; **11.** d; **12.** (1)b, g; (2)d, i; (3)a, e; (4)a, e, f, h; (5)e, h; (6)c, f, g

Chapter 22

Check Your Understanding 1. The structures that air passes by are the nasal cavity (nares, nasal vestibule, nasal conchae), nasopharynx (with pharyngeal tonsil), oropharynx (with palatine tonsil), laryngopharynx, and larynx (with epiglottis, vestibular fold, and vocal fold). **2.** The epiglottis seals the larynx when we swallow. **3.** The incomplete, C-shaped cartilage rings of the trachea allow it to expand and contract and yet keep it from collapsing. **4.** The many tiny alveoli together have a large surface area. This and the thinness of their respiratory membranes make them ideal for gas exchange. **5.** The peanut was most likely in the right main bronchus because it is wider and more vertical than the left. **6.** The two circulations of the lungs are the pulmonary circulation, which delivers deoxygenated blood to the lungs for oxygenation and returns oxygenated blood to the heart, and the bronchial circulation, which provides systemic (oxygenated) blood to lung tissue. **7.** The driving force for pulmonary ventilation is a pressure gradient created by changes in the thoracic volume. **8.** The intrapulmonary pressure decreases during inspiration because of the increase in thoracic cavity volume brought about by the muscles of inspiration. **9.** The partial vacuum (negative pressure) inside the pleural cavity is caused by the opposing forces acting on the visceral and parietal pleurae. The visceral pleurae are pulled inward by the lungs' natural tendency to recoil and the surface tension of the alveolar fluid. The parietal pleurae are pulled outward by the elasticity of the chest wall. If air enters the pleural cavity, the lung on that side will collapse. This condition is called pneumothorax. **10.** Airway resistance is low because (1) the diameters of most airways are relatively large, (2) for smaller airways there are many in parallel, making their combined diameter large, and (3) air has a low viscosity. **11.** A lack of surfactant increases surface tension in the alveoli and causes them to collapse between breaths. (In other words, it markedly decreases lung compliance.) **12.** Slow, deep breaths ventilate the alveoli more effectively because a smaller fraction of the tidal volume of each breath is spent moving air into and out of the dead space. **13.** In a sealed container, the air and water would be at equilibrium. Therefore, the partial pressures of CO_2 and O_2 (P_{CO_2} and P_{O_2}) will be the same in the water as in the air: 100 mm Hg each. More CO_2 than O_2 molecules will be dissolved in the water (even though they are at the same partial pressure) because CO_2 is much more soluble than O_2 in water. **14.** The difference in P_{O_2} between inspired air and alveolar air can be explained by (1) the gas exchange occurring in the lungs (O_2 continuously diffuses out of the alveoli into the blood), (2) the humidification of inspired air (which adds water molecules that dilute the O_2 molecules), and (3) the mixing of newly inspired air with gases already present in the alveoli. **15.** The arterioles leading into the O_2-enriched alveoli would be dilated. This response allows matching of blood flow to availability of oxygen. **16.** Both CO_2 and H^+ increase O_2 unloading by binding to Hb. This is called the Bohr effect. **17.** About 70% of CO_2 is transported as bicarbonate ion (HCO_3^-) in plasma. Just over 20% is transported bound to hemoglobin in the RBCs, and 7–10% is dissolved in plasma. **18.** As blood CO_2 increases, blood pH decreases. This is because CO_2 combines with water to form carbonic acid. (However, the change in pH in blood for a given increase in CO_2 is minimized by other buffer systems.) **19.** The ventral respiratory group of the medulla (VRG) is thought to be the rhythm-generating area. **20.** CO_2 in blood normally provides the most powerful stimulus to breathe. Central chemoreceptors are most important in this response (see Figure 22.25). **21.** The injured soccer player's P_{CO_2} is low. (Recall that normal P_{CO_2} = 40 mm Hg.) The low P_{CO_2} reveals that this is hyperventilation and not hyperpnea (which is not accompanied by changes in blood CO_2 levels). **22.** Long-term adjustments to altitude include an increase in erythropoiesis, resulting in a higher hematocrit; an increase in BPG, which decreases Hb affinity for oxygen; and an increase in minute respiratory volume. **23.** The obstruction in asthma is *reversible*, and acute exacerbations are typically followed by symptom-free periods. In contrast, the obstruction in chronic bronchitis is generally not reversible. **24.** The underlying defect in cystic fibrosis is an abnormality in a protein (CFTR protein) that acts as a membrane channel for chloride ions. **25.** Vital capacity declines with age because the thoracic wall becomes more rigid and the lungs lose their elasticity.

Clinical Connections 1. Spinal cord injury from a fracture at the level of the C_2 vertebra would interrupt the normal transmission of signals from the brain stem down the phrenic nerve to the diaphragm, and Barbara would be unable to breathe due to paralysis of the diaphragm. **2.** Barbara's head, neck, and torso should have been immobilized to prevent further damage to the spinal cord. In addition, she required assistance to breathe, so her airway was probably intubated to permit ventilation of her lungs. **3.** Cyanosis is a decrease in the degree of oxygen saturation of hemoglobin. As Barbara's respiratory efforts cease, her alveolar P_{O_2} will fall, so there is less oxygen to load onto hemoglobin. In her peripheral tissues, what little oxygen hemoglobin carries will be consumed leaving these tissues with a bluish tinge. **4.** Injury to the spinal cord at the level of the C_2 vertebra will cause quadriplegia (paralysis of all four limbs). **5.** Atelectasis is the collapse of a lung. Because it is the right thorax that is compressed, only her right lung is affected. Because the lungs are in separate pleural cavities, only the right lung collapsed. **6.** Barbara's fractured ribs probably punctured her lung tissue and allowed air within the lung to enter the pleural cavity. **7.** The atelectasis will be reversed by inserting a chest tube and removing the air from the pleural cavity. This will allow her lung to heal and reinflate.

Review Questions 1. b; **2.** a and c; **3.** c; **4.** c; **5.** b; **6.** d; **7.** d; **8.** b; **9.** c, d; **10.** c; **11.** b; **12.** b; **13.** b; **14.** c; **15.** b; **16.** b

Chapter 23

Check Your Understanding 1. The esophagus is found in the thorax. Three alimentary canal organs found in the abdominal cavity include the stomach, small intestine, and large intestine. **2.** The usual site of ingestion in a healthy person is the mouth. **3.** The process of absorption moves nutrients into the body. **4.** Reflexes associated with the GI tract promote muscle contraction and secretion of digestive juices or hormones. **5.** The term "gut brain" refers to the enteric nervous system or web of neurons closely associated with the digestive organs. **6.** The visceral peritoneum is the outermost layer of the digestive organ; the parietal peritoneum is the serous membrane covering the wall of the abdominal cavity. **7.** The pancreas is retroperitoneal. **8.** The hepatic portal circulation is the venous portion of the splanchnic circulation. **9.** From deep to superficial the layers of the alimentary canal are the mucosa, submucosa, muscularis externa, and serosa. **10.** He should temporarily refrain from eating because the parasympathetic nervous system oversees digestive activities. **11.** The vestibule is the region between the cheek and the teeth. The oral cavity proper is the area enclosed by the teeth. **12.** The palate forms the roof of the mouth. The hard palate supported by bone is anterior to the soft palate (no bony support). **13.** The tongue is important for speech, particularly for uttering consonants, and taste. **14.** The serous portion of saliva is rich in salivary amylase, an enzyme that chemically breaks down starch. Additionally, the serous portion of saliva helps to hydrate the foodstuffs and helps provide protection against microorganisms. **15.** Antimicrobial substances found in saliva include lysozyme, defensins, a cyanide compound, and IgA antibodies. **16.** Tina's "show and tell" tooth is a primary tooth, also called a deciduous tooth. **17.** Enamel is harder than bone. Pulp consists of nervous tissue and blood vessels. **18.** The molars are grinding teeth. **19.** The pharynx is part of the digestive and respiratory systems. **20.** The esophageal mucularis externa undergoes a transformation along its length from skeletal muscle superiorly to smooth muscle near the stomach. **21.** The esophagus is merely a chute for food passage and is subjected to a good deal of abrasion, which a stratified squamous epithelium can withstand. The stomach mucosa is a secretory mucosa served well by a simple columnar epithelium. **22.** The tongue mixes the chewed food with saliva and compacts the food into a bolus. **23.** During swallowing the larynx rises and the epiglottis covers its lumen so that foodstuffs are diverted into the esophagus posteriorly. **24.** The stomach has three layers of smooth muscle—longitudinal, circular, and oblique. Addition of the oblique layer allows the stomach to pummel food in addition to its peristaltic movements. **25.** The chief cells produce pepsinogen, which is the inactive pepsin enzyme, and the parietal cells secrete HCl needed to activate pepsinogen. **26.** The mucosal barrier consists of the thick alkaline mucus secreted by the mucous cells, the fact that the epithelial cells of the mucosa are joined by tight junctions, and the quick replacement of dead or dying cells by stem cells. **27.** The three phases of gastric secretion are the cephalic, gastric, and intestinal phases. **28.** The presence of food in the duodenum inhibits gastric activity by triggering the enterogastric reflex and the secretion of certain enterogastrones (hormones). **29.** Venous blood leaving the stomach during a meal becomes more alkaline due to the alkaline tide occurring during HCl secretion. **30.** All of these modifications increase the surface area of the small intestine. The circular folds force the chyme to spiral through the lumen. **31.** Brush border enzymes are enzymes associated with the microvilli of the small intestine mucosal cells. **32.** A lacteal is a blind-ended lymphatic capillary that picks up lymph (fluid and proteins leaked from the bloodstream), which is then returned to the blood. **33.** IgA, HCl, defensins, and lysozyme protect the intestinal cells from bacterial damage. **34.** A portal triad is a region at the corner of a hepatic lobule that contains a branch of the hepatic portal vein, a branch of the hepatic artery, and a bile duct. **35.** The enterohepatic circulation is an important recycling mechanism for retaining bile salts needed for fat absorption. **36.** Kupffer cells are macrophages that rid the blood of bacteria and dead cells. **37.** Zymogen granules contain digestive enzymes. **38.** The pancreas is the only important source of lipases, so fats will probably not be digested or absorbed during her illness. **39.** Pancreatic acini produce the exocrine products of the pancreas (digestive enzymes and bicarbonate-rich juice). The islets produce pancreatic hormones, most importantly insulin and glucagon. **40.** Fluid in the pancreatic duct is bicarbonate-rich, enzyme-rich pancreatic juice. Fluid in the cystic and bile ducts is bile. **41.** CCK is secreted in response to the entry of chyme rich in protein and fat into the duodenum. It causes the pancreatic acini to secrete digestive enzymes and stimulates the gallbladder to contract. **42.** Distension of stomach walls enhances stomach secretory activity. Distension of the walls of the small intestine reduces stomach secretory activity (to give the small intestine time to carry out its digestive and absorptive activities). **43.** Segmentation is more important for moving food along the small intestine. **44.** MMC is the migrating motility complex, a pattern of peristalsis seen in the small intestine that moves the last remnants of a meal plus bacteria and other debris into the large intestine. MMC is important to prevent the overgrowth of bacteria in the small intestine. **45.** Mass movements are unique to the large intestine. They are long, slow, powerful contractions that move over large areas of the colon three or four times a day, forcing the contents toward the rectum. **46.** Activation of stretch receptors in the rectal wall initiates the defecation reflex. **47.** Enteric bacteria synthesize B vitamins and most of the vitamin K the liver needs to synthesize clotting proteins. **48.** All food digestion depends on hydrolysis reactions. **49.** Amylase is to starch as lipase is to fats. **50.** Bile salts emulsify fats so that they can be acted on efficiently by lipase enzymes, and form micelles that aid fat absorption. **51.** The digestive system mucosa develops from the endoderm. **52.** The thick viscous mucus produced in cystic fibrosis patients clogs pancreatic ducts and prevents the delivery of pancreatic fluid to the duodenum, thus inhibiting fat digestion and absorption. **53.** Colon and stomach cancers are dangerous because they have few early signs and symptoms.

Clinical Connections 1. Mr. Gutteman's statement about the effects of milk on his digestive tract suggests that he may be deficient in lactase, a brush border enzyme that breaks down lactose (milk sugar). **2.** His responses to the questions reduced the possibility that he has gastric ulcers. Mr. Gutteman's diarrhea may be due to gluten enteropathy. To verify this diagnosis, Mr. Gutteman should be screened for specific IgA antibodies in his blood. If these tests are positive, a biopsy of the intestinal mucosa would be performed to verify or negate the diagnosis. A positive diagnosis of gluten enteropathy would lead to dietary restriction of all grains but rice and corn. In the meantime, grains should not be restricted.

Review Questions 1. c; **2.** d; **3.** d; **4.** b; **5.** b; **6.** a; **7.** d; **8.** d; **9.** b; **10.** c; **11.** c; **12.** a; **13.** d; **14.** d; **15.** b; **16.** c; **17.** a

Chapter 24

Check Your Understanding 1. The six major nutrients are carbohydrates, proteins, fats, water, minerals, and vitamins. **2.** Cellulose provides fiber, which helps in elimination. **3.** Triglycerides are used for ATP synthesis, body insulation and protective padding, and to help the body absorb fat-soluble vitamins. Cholesterol is the basis of our steroid hormones and bile salts, and stabilizes cellular membranes. **4.** Beans (legumes) and grains (rice) are good sources of protein, but neither is a complete one. Together they should provide all the essential amino acids. Like beans, the bread supplies carbohydrates. **5.** Vitamins serve as the basis for coenzymes, which work with enzymes to accomplish metabolic reactions. **6.** Vitamin B_{12} needs intrinsic factor to be absorbed by the intestine. **7.** Iodine is essential for thyroxine synthesis. Calcium in the form of bone salts is needed to make bones hard. Iron is needed to make functional hemoglobin.

8. A redox reaction is a combination of an oxidation and a reduction reaction. As one substance is oxidized, another is reduced. **9.** Some of the energy released during catabolism is captured in the bonds of ATP, which provides the energy needed to carry out the constructive activities of anabolism. **10.** The energy released during the oxidation of food fuels is used to pump protons across the inner mitochondrial membrane. **11.** In substrate-level phosphorylation, high-energy phosphate groups are transferred directly from phosphorylated intermediates to ADP to form ATP. In oxidative phosphorylation, electron transport proteins forming part of the mitochondrial cristae use energy released during oxidation of glucose to create a steep gradient for protons across the crista membrane. Then as protons flow back through the membrane, gradient energy is captured to attach phosphate to ADP. **12.** If oxygen and pyruvic acid are not available, glycolysis will stop because the supply of NAD^+ is limited and glycolysis can continue only if the reduced coenzymes ($NADH + H^+$) formed during glycolysis are relieved of their extra hydrogen. **13.** Oxidation (via removal of H) is common in the Krebs cycle; it is indicated by the reduction of a coenzyme (either NAD^+ or FAD). Decarboxylations are also common, and are indicated by the removal of CO_2 from the cycle. **14.** Glycogenolysis is the reaction in which glycogen is broken down to its glucose units. **15.** Carbo loading forces the skeletal muscles to store more glycogen than they ordinarily would. **16.** Glycerol, a breakdown product of fat metabolism, directly enters the glycolysis pathway. **17.** Acetyl CoA is the central molecule of fat metabolism. **18.** The products of beta oxidation are acetyl CoA (acetic acid + coenzyme A), $NADH^+ + H^+$, and $FADH_2$. **19.** The liver uses keto acids drained off the Krebs cycle and amino groups (from other nonessential amino acids) as substrates to make the nonessential amino acids that the body needs. **20.** The ammonia removed from amino acids is combined with carbon dioxide to form urea, which is then eliminated by the kidneys. **21.** The three organs or tissues that regulate the directions of interconversions in the nutrient pools are the liver, skeletal muscles, and adipose tissues. **22.** Anabolic reactions and energy storage typify the absorptive state. Catabolic reactions (to increase blood sugar levels) such as lipolysis and glycogenolysis, and glucose sparing occur in the postabsorptive state. **23.** The main antagonist of glucagon is insulin. **24.** A rise in amino acid levels in blood increases both insulin and glucagon release. **25.** High HDLs would be preferable because the cholesterol these particles transport is destined for the liver and elimination from the body. **26.** A total cholesterol level of 200 mg/dl of blood or lower is recommended. **27.** Trans fats are oils that have been hydrogenated (with H atoms). They are unhealthy because they cause LDLs to increase and HDLs to decrease, exactly the opposite of what is desirable. **28.** Among short-term stimuli influencing feeding behavior are neural signals from the digestive tract, nutrient signals related to energy stores, and GI tract hormones (CCK, insulin, glucagon, and ghrelin). **29.** Leptin is the most important long-term regulator of feeding behavior. **30.** Of the factors listed, breathing and kidney function contribute to BMR. **31.** Samantha has a larger relative body surface area and well-toned muscles, both of which promote a higher BMR. **32.** The body's core is the organs within the skull, and the thoracic and abdominal cavities. **33.** Cindy's body temperature is rising as heat-promoting mechanisms (shivering, chills) are activated. Something (an infection?) has caused the hypothalamic thermostat to be set to a higher level (fever) temporarily. **34.** In conduction, heat is transferred directly from one object to another (a hot surface to your palm). In convection, air warmed by body heat is continually removed (warm air rises) and replaced by cooler air (cool air falls), which in turn will absorb heat radiating from the body. **35.** Metabolic rate falls in old age because muscle mass declines and physical activity tends to be reduced. **36.** Elderly nutrition can be influenced and impaired by alcoholism, certain antibiotics that interfere with food absorption, other drugs that may cause electrolyte imbalances, and use of mineral oil.

Review Questions 1. a; **2.** c; **3.** b; **4.** d; **5.** b; **6.** c; **7.** a; **8.** d; **9.** d; **10.** a; **11.** b; **12.** d; **13.** c; **14.** d; **15.** a

Chapter 25

Check Your Understanding 1. The lower part of his rib cage and the perirenal fat capsule protect his kidneys from blows. **2.** The layers of supportive tissue around each kidney are the fibrous capsule, the perirenal fat capsule, and the renal fascia. The parietal peritoneum overlies the anterior renal fascia. **3.** The renal pelvis, which has extensions called calyces, is continuous with the ureter. **4.** Filtrate is formed in the glomerular capsule and then passes through the proximal convoluted tubule (PCT), the descending and ascending limbs of the loop of Henle, and the distal convoluted tubule (DCT). **5.** The structural differences are (1) juxtamedullary nephrons have long loops of Henle (with long thin segments) and renal corpuscles that are near the cortex-medulla junction, whereas cortical nephrons have short loops of Henle and renal corpuscles that lie more superficially in the cortex; (2) efferent arterioles of juxtamedullary nephrons supply vasa recta, while efferent arterioles of cortical nephrons supply peritubular capillaries. **6.** The glomerular capillaries are fenestrated capillaries. (See Figure 19.3 on p. 699 to refresh your memory of capillary types.) Their function is to filter large amounts of plasma into the glomerular capsule. **7.** Intrinsic controls serve to maintain a nearly constant GFR in spite of changes in systemic blood pressure. Extrinsic controls serve to maintain systemic blood pressure. **8.** Net filtration pressure is 5 mm Hg [50 mm Hg − (25 mm Hg + 20 mm Hg)]. **9.** The two main ways in which angiotensin II increases blood pressure and blood volume are by causing vasoconstriction and by causing aldosterone release. (In addition, angiotensin II causes ADH release, activates the thirst mechanism, increases tubular reabsorption, and contracts mesangial cells, which decreases the GFR.) **10.** The majority of reabsorption occurs in the proximal convoluted tubule. **11.** In primary active transport, the energy for the process is provided directly by the cleavage of ATP. In secondary active transport, the energy for the process is provided by the Na^+ concentration gradient. As Na^+ moves down its own concentration gradient established by the active pumping of Na^+ occurring elsewhere in the cell, it drives the movement of another substance (e.g., glucose) against its concentration gradient. **12.** The reabsorption of Na^+ by primary active transport, in turn, drives reabsorption of amino acids and glucose by secondary active transport. It also drives passive reabsorption of chloride, and reabsorption of water by osmosis. The reabsorption of water leaves behind other solutes, which become more concentrated and can therefore be reabsorbed by diffusion. **13.** H^+, K^+, NH_4^+, creatinine, urea, and uric acid are all substances that are secreted into the kidney tubules. **14.** The descending limb of the loop of Henle is permeable to water and impermeable to NaCl. The ascending limb is impermeable to water and permeable to NaCl. **15.** ADH is released from the posterior pituitary in response to hyperosmotic extracellular fluid (as sensed by hypothalamic osmoreceptors). ADH causes insertion of aquaporins into the luminal membrane of the principal cells of the collecting ducts. **16.** The normal renal clearance value for amino acids is zero. You would expect this because amino acids are valuable as nutrients and as the building blocks for protein synthesis, so it would not be good to lose them in the urine. **17.** The three major nitrogenous wastes excreted in urine are urea, creatinine, and uric acid. **18.** A kidney stone blocking the ureter would interfere with urine flow to the bladder. The pain would occur in waves that coincide with the peristaltic contractions of the smooth muscle of the ureter. **19.** The trigone is a smooth triangular region at the base of the bladder. Its borders are defined by the openings for the ureters and the urethra. **20.** The prostatic urethra, membranous urethra, and spongy urethra are the three regions of the male urethra. **21.** The detrusor muscle contracts in response to increased firing of parasympathetic nerves. Contraction of the detrusor muscle opens the internal urethral sphincter.

22. The three sets of embryonic kidneys in the order that they develop are the pronephros, mesonephros, and metanephros. **23.** Both loss of bladder tone with age and an increase in size of the prostate can contribute to urinary retention in elderly men.

Review Questions 1. d; **2.** b; **3.** c; **4.** d; **5.** c; **6.** b; **7.** a; **8.** c; **9.** a; **10.** b

Chapter 26

Check Your Understanding 1. You have more intracellular than extracellular fluid and more interstitial fluid than plasma. **2.** Na^+ is the major cation in the ECF and K^+ is the major cation in the ICF. The intracellular counterparts to extracellular Cl^- are HPO_4^{2-} and protein anions. **3.** If you eat salty pretzels, your extracellular fluid volume will expand even if you don't ingest fluids. This is because water will flow by osmosis from the intracellular fluid to the extracellular fluid. **4.** An increases in osmolality of the plasma is most important for triggering thirst. This change is sensed by osmoreceptors in the hypothalamus. **5.** ADH cannot add water—it can only conserve what is already there. In order to reduce an increase in osmolality of body fluids, the thirst mechanism is required. **6.** (a) A loss of plasma proteins causes edema. (b) Copious sweating causes dehydration. (c) Using ecstasy (together with drinking lots of fluids) could cause hypotonic hydration because it promotes ADH secretion, which interferes with the body's ability to get rid of extra water. **7.** Insufficient aldosterone would cause Jacob's plasma Na^+ to be decreased and his plasma K^+ to be elevated. The decrease in plasma Na^+ would cause a decrease in blood pressure, because plasma Na^+ is directly related to blood volume, which is a major determinant of blood pressure. **8.** The kidneys' handling of K^+ can be summed up as "The kidneys reabsorb most of the filtered K^+ in the proximal parts of the kidney's tubules and then secrete just the right amount in the distal parts (cortical collecting duct)." **9.** The major regulator of calcium in the blood is parathyroid hormone. Hypercalcemia decreases excitability of neurons and muscle cells and may cause life-threatening cardiac arrhythmias. Hypocalcemia increases excitability and causes muscle tetany. **10.** Acidemia is an arterial pH below 7.35 and alkalemia is a pH above 7.45. **11.** A weak base would be better at minimizing the shift in pH caused by adding a strong acid to a solution because its ability to loosely tie up H^+ allows it to act as a buffer. **12.** The three major chemical buffer systems of the body are the bicarbonate buffer system, the phosphate buffer system, and the protein buffer system. The most important intracellular buffer is the protein buffer system. **13.** Joanne's ventilation would be increased. The acidosis caused by the accumulated ketone bodies will stimulate the peripheral chemoreceptors, and this will cause more CO_2 to be "blown off" in an attempt to restore pH to normal. **14.** Reabsorption of HCO_3^- is always linked with secretion of H^+. **15.** The most important urine buffer of H^+ is the phosphate buffer system. **16.** The tubule and collecting duct cells generate new HCO_3^- either by excreting ammonium ion (NH_4^+) or by excreting buffered H^+ ions. **17.** Key features of an uncompensated metabolic alkalosis are an increase in blood pH and an increase in blood HCO_3^-. Key features of an uncompensated respiratory acidosis are a decrease in blood pH and an increase in blood P_{CO_2}. **18.** The kidneys compensate for respiratory acidosis by excreting more H^+ and generating new HCO_3^- to buffer the acidosis. **19.** Infants' immature kidneys are not as proficient at concentrating urine. In addition, they have a high metabolic rate, so they produce more metabolic water and also have larger amounts of metabolic wastes and acids that need to be excreted with water.

Clinical Connections 1. Mr. Heyden's vital signs suggest that he is in hypovolemic shock, which is probably due to an internal hemorrhage. **2.** The spleen is a highly vascular organ due to its role as a blood-filtering organ. The macrophages in Mr. Heyden's liver and bone marrow will help compensate for the loss of his spleen. **3.** Elevation of renin, aldosterone, and antidiuretic hormone indicate that Mr. Heyden's body is trying to compensate for his falling blood pressure and blood loss. *Renin*: released when renal blood flow is diminished and blood pressure falls. The angiotensin-aldosterone response is initiated by renin. The formation of angiotensin II leads to vasoconstriction, which will increase blood pressure, and to the release of aldosterone. *Aldosterone*: increases Na^+ reabsorption by the kidney. The movement of this reabsorbed Na^+ into the bloodstream will promote the movement of water from the interstitial fluid, resulting in an increase in blood volume. *Antidiuretic hormone (ADH)*: released when the hypothalamic osmoreceptors sense an increase in osmolality. ADH has two consequences: It is a potent vasoconstrictor and will increase blood pressure, and it promotes water retention by the kidney, increasing blood volume. **4.** Mr. Heyden's urine production may be decreased for several reasons. The severe drop in his blood pressure would reduce renal blood flow, thus reducing glomerular blood pressure and decreasing his glomerular filtration rate. The elevation in his ADH levels can reduce urine output due to increased water reabsorption by the kidney. He may also have damage to the kidney due to his crush injury in the left lumbar region. The presence of casts and a brownish-red color in his urine are probably damaged cells and blood. If he has suffered kidney damage due to being crushed, he may have nephron damage that would include disruption of the filtration membrane, allowing red blood cells to pass into the filtrate and therefore the urine. He may also have damaged renal tubules and peritubular capillaries, allowing entry of blood and damaged renal tubule epithelial cells into the filtrate.

Review Questions 1. a; **2.** c; **3.** b; **4.** a and b; **5.** h, i, j; **6.** c, g; **7.** a, e; **8.** b; **9.** a, b; **10.** j; **11.** b, d; **12.** a; **13.** c

Chapter 27

Check Your Understanding 1. The testes produce the male gametes (sperm) and testosterone. **2.** The sperm factories are the seminiferous tubules. **3.** When the ambient temperature is cold, the muscles contract, bringing the testes close to the warm body wall. When body temperature is high, the muscles relax, allowing the testes to hang away from the body wall. The pampiniform venous plexus absorbs heat from the arterial blood before it enters the testes. **4.** The erectile tissue of the penis allows the penis to become stiff so that it may more efficiently enter the female vagina to deliver sperm. **5.** The organs of the male duct system in order from the epididymis to the body exterior are the ductus deferens, ejaculatory duct, prostatic urethra, membranous urethra, and spongy urethra. **6.** These stereocilia pass nutrients to the sperm and absorb excess testicular fluid. **7.** The ductus deferens runs from the scrotum into the abdominal cavity. **8.** Adolph probably has a hypertrophied prostate, a condition which can be felt through the anterior wall of the rectum. **9.** The seminal vesicles produce the bulk of seminal fluid. **10.** Semen is sperm plus the secretions of the male accessory glands. **11.** Erection is the stiffening of the penis that occurs when blood in the cavernous tissue is prevented from leaving the penis. It is caused by the parasympathetic division of the autonomic nervous system. **12.** Resolution is a period of muscular and psychological relaxation that follows orgasm. It results as the sympathetic nervous system constricts the internal pudendal arteries, reducing blood flow to the penis, and activates small muscles that force blood out of the penis. **13.** Meiosis reduces the chromosomal count from *2n* to *n* and introduces variability. **14.** The sperm head is the compacted DNA-containing nucleus. The acrosome that caps the head is a lysosome-like sac of enzymes. The midpiece contains the energy-producing mitochondria. The tail fashioned by a centriole is the propulsive structure. **15.** Sustentacular cells provide nutrients and essential development signals to the developing sperm and form the blood-testis barrier that prevents sperm antigens from escaping into the blood. Interstitial cells secrete testosterone. **16.** The HPG axis is the hormonal interrelationship between the hypothalamus, anterior pituitary, and gonads that regulates the production of gametes and sex hormones (e.g., sperm production and testosterone in the male). **17.** Follicle-stimulating hormone indirectly stimulates spermatogenesis by prompting the sustentacular cells to secrete androgen-binding protein. Androgen-binding protein keeps the concentration of testosterone high in the vicinity of the spermatogenic cells, which directly stimulates spermatogenesis. **18.** Secondary sex characteristics of males include appearance of pubic, axillary, and facial hair, deepening of the voice, increased oiliness of the skin, and increased size (length and mass) of the bones and skeletal muscles. **19.** The female's internal genitalia include the ovaries and duct system (uterine tubes, uterus, and vagina). **20.** The ovaries produce the female gametes and secrete female sex hormones (estrogens and progesterone). **21.** A primary follicle has one layer of cuboidal follicle cells surrounding the oocyte; a secondary follicle has more than one layer of follicle cells, and small fluid-filled spaces form between the follicle cells. A vesicular follicle has several layers of follicle cells surrounding a fluid-filled cavity (antrum) that pushes the oocyte to one side. **22.** Women are more at risk for PID than men because the duct system of women is incomplete—there is no physical connection between the ovary and the uterine tubes, which are open to the pelvic cavity. In men, the duct system is continuous from the testes to the body exterior. **23.** The waving action of the fimbriae helps to direct the ovulated oocytes into the uterine tube. **24.** The usual site of fertilization is the uterine tube. The uterus serves as the incubator for fetal development. **25.** The greater vestibular glands are the female homologue of the male bulbourethral glands. **26.** Both the penis and clitoris are hooded by a skin fold and are largely erectile tissue. However, the clitoris lacks a corpus spongiosum containing a urethra, so the urinary and reproductive systems are completely separate in females. **27.** Developmentally, the mammary glands are modified sweat glands. **28.** Breast cancer usually arises from the epithelial cells of the small ducts. **29.** The products of meiosis in females are 3 polar bodies (tiny haploid cells with essentially no cytoplasm) and 1 haploid ovum (functional gamete). Meiosis in males yields 4 functional gametes, the haploid sperm. **30.** Identical twins develop from separation of a very young embryo (the result of fertilization by a single sperm) into two parts. Fraternal twins develop when different oocytes are fertilized by different sperm. **31.** In the luteal phase, the ovulated follicle develops into a corpus luteum, which then secretes progesterone (and some estrogen). **32.** Leptin is important in advising the brain of the girl's readiness (relative to energy stores) for puberty. **33.** FSH prompts follicle growth and LH prompts ovulation. **34.** Estrogen exerts positive feedback on the anterior pituitary that leads to a burstlike release of LH. **35.** Estrogen is responsible for the secondary sex characteristics of females. **36.** Estrogen promotes epiphyseal closure in both males and females. **37.** The human papillomavirus (HPV) is most associated with cervical cancer. **38.** Chlamydia is the most common bacterial sexually transmitted infection in the U.S. **39.** No. If the sex chromosomes are XY, a male baby will develop. **40.** The sexually indifferent stage of development is the early period when the presumptive reproductive structures can produce either male or female organs. **41.** The gubernaculum guides the descent of the testis into the scrotum. **42.** Early signs of puberty's onset in boys are enlargement of the testes and scrotum. **43.** Menopause has happened when ovulation and menstruation have not occurred for a year.

Clinical Connections 1. *Carcinoma* is the term for cancer originating from epithelial tissue. The primary source of Mr. Heyden's cancer is likely to be the prostate. **2.** Elevation of serum acid phosphatase levels is diagnostic for carcinoma of the prostate. (In addition, Mr. Heyden's age places him in a group that is at relatively higher risk for this type of cancer.) **3.** Digital examination of Mr. Heyden's prostate should detect the presence of carcinoma in this tissue. In addition, serum levels of prostate-specific antigen (PSA) should be checked, as an increase in this antigen is often indicative of prostate cancer. **4.** Mr. Heyden's carcinoma has advanced to the point of metastasis. He will probably undergo a treatment that reduces the levels of androgens in his body, as androgens promote growth of the prostate-derived tissue. These treatments could include castration or administration of drugs that block the production and/or effects of androgens.

Review Questions 1. a and b; **2.** d; **3.** a; **4.** d; **5.** b; **6.** d; **7.** d; **8.** c; **9.** a, c, e, f; **10.** (1)c, f; (2)e, h; (3)g; (4)a; (5)b, g, and e; (6)f; **11.** a; **12.** c; **13.** d; **14.** b; **15.** a; **16.** b; **17.** c

Chapter 28

Check Your Understanding 1. Sperm must be capacitated before they can penetrate an oocyte. **2.** The cortical reaction involves the release of enzymes from cortical granules to the oocyte exterior, which accomplishes the slow block to polyspermy. **3.** The blastocyst is only slightly larger than the zygote because, although cell division has been going on (cleavage divisions), there is essentially no time for growth between divisions, so the resulting cells get smaller and smaller. **4.** The trophoblast cells adhere to and secrete digestive enzymes onto the uterine endometrium, accomplishing implantation, and they contribute to the formation of the placenta. **5.** The syncytiotrophoblast actually accomplishes implantation. **6.** The blastocyst secretes the hormone human chorionic gonadotropin, which is detectable in the urine. **7.** The chorion develops from the trophoblast and a layer of extraembryonic mesoderm. **8.** The decidua basalis cooperates with the chorionic villi to form the placenta. **9.** The placenta is usually fully functional by the end of the third month of pregnancy. **10.** The amnion helps to maintain a constant temperature for the developing fetus and protects it from physical trauma. **11.** The allantois provides the basis of the umbilical cord, which provides a pathway for the embryonic blood vessels to reach the placenta. **12.** Before organogenesis can occur in earnest, the embryonic body must fold and undercut to form a tubular embryo. **13.** The mesoderm gives rise to essentially all body tissues except neural and epidermal tissue and mucosae. **14.** The fetal period begins at the end of 8 weeks. **15.** Difficult breathing during late pregnancy is due to the fact that the uterus is pressing against and crowding the diaphragm (and hence the lungs). The waddling gait is due to the relaxing effect of relaxin on the pelvic ligaments and the pubic symphysis. **16.** While the exact cause of morning sickness is unknown, it is thought to be due to the rising levels of female sex hormones in the mother's blood, which sometimes takes awhile to get used to. **17.** The hormone hCT increases the pregnant woman's metabolic rate. **18.** Breech presentation is a buttock-first presentation of the baby during labor. **19.** Prostaglandins are most responsible for triggering true labor. **20.** The descent of the baby's head (the largest part of its body) follows the widest dimensions of the bony pelvis.

21. The foramen ovale and ductus arteriosus allow most of the blood to bypass the heart. **22.** For the most part, the special fetal circulatory modifications are occluded at birth or shortly thereafter. **23.** Oxytocin causes the let-down reflex.

Review Questions 1. (1)a, (2)b, (3)b, (4)a; **2.** b; **3.** c; **4.** b; **5.** a; **6.** d; **7.** d; **8.** c; **9.** b; **10.** c; **11.** a; **12.** c; **13.** a; **14.** (1)e, (2)g, (3)a, (4)f, (5)i, (6)b, (7)h, (8)d, (9)c

Chapter 29

Check Your Understanding 1. Chromosomes are not visible during interphase. The DNA-containing material is in the form of dispersed strands of chromatin. As mitosis begins, the chromatin coils and condenses, becoming visible. Chromosomes continue to condense throughout prophase and are most visible during metaphase. **2.** Chromosomes other than sex chromosomes are called autosomes. **3.** An allele represented by a capital letter is presumed to be a dominant allele. **4.** Descriptions of his phenotype are blond, blue-eyed, and hairy chest. **5.** The alleles pertaining to the same trait are segregated independently of each other to different gametes. **6.** It causes separations of linked genes on the same chromosome, producing gametes with variable genomes. **7.** Dominant genes are expressed. Thus if the dominant gene is detrimental (lethal), the carrier will probably not live very long or will die during development. **8.** In incomplete dominance, the heterozygote has a phenotype intermediate between that of the dominant and recessive alleles [for example, for the sickling gene, the dominant homozygote (*SS*) has no evidence of sickling; the heterozygote (*Ss*) has sickle-cell trait; and the homozygote for the recessive gene (*ss*) has sickle-cell anemia]. In codominance, both dominant alleles are expressed (as in ABO blood types). **9.** A male always expresses an X-linked recessive allele because, unlike a female, he does not have a second X containing homologous alleles to blunt or counteract the effect. The Y chromosome lacks most of the genes carried on the X chromosome. **10.** Height is an example of a trait conferred by polygene inheritance in which several genes on different chromosomes contribute to the trait. Such traits show a distribution of phenotypes that yields a bell-shaped curve. **11.** Other genes, measles in a pregnant woman, and lack of key dietary nutrients all may alter gene expression. **12.** Genomic imprinting labels genes as maternal or paternal. **13.** Maternal mitochondrial DNA confers extranuclear inheritance. **14.** Amniocentesis analyzes chemicals and cells in amniotic fluid. **15.** Ultrasound imaging is used to determine some aspects of fetal development (fetal age for example) and is noninvasive.

Review Questions 1. (1)d, (2)g, (3)b, (4)a, (5)f, (6)c, (7)e, (8)h; **2.** (1)e, (2)a, (3)b, (4)d, (5)c, (6)d, (7)f

Glossary

Pronunciation Key

′ = Primary accent

″ = Secondary accent

Pronounce:

a, fa, āt	as in	fate	o, no, ōt	as in	note
ă, hă, at		hat	ŏ, frŏ, og		frog
ah		father	oo		soon
ar		tar	or		for
e, stre, ēt		street	ow		plow
ĕ, hĕ, en		hen	oy		boy
er		her	sh		she
ew		new	u, mu, ūt		mute
g		go	ŭ, sŭ, un		sun
i, bi, īt		bite	z		zebra
ĭ, hĭ, im		him	zh		measure
ng		ring			

Abduct (ab-dukt′) To move away from the midline of the body.

Absolute refractory period Period following stimulation during which no additional action potential can be evoked.

Absorption Process by which the products of digestion pass through the alimentary tube mucosa into the blood or lymph.

Accessory digestive organs Organs that contribute to the digestive process but are not part of the alimentary canal; include the tongue, teeth, salivary glands, pancreas, liver.

Accommodation The process of increasing the refractive power of the lens of the eye; focusing.

Acetabulum (as″ĕ-tab′u-lum) Cuplike cavity on lateral surface of the hip bone that receives the femur.

Acetylcholine (ACh) (as″ĕ-til-ko′lēn) Chemical transmitter substance released by some nerve endings.

Acetylcholinesterase (AChE) (as″ĕ-til-ko″lin-es′ter-ās) Enzyme present at the neuromuscular junction and synapses that degrades acetylcholine and terminates its action.

Achilles tendon *See* Calcaneal tendon.

Acid A substance that releases hydrogen ions when in solution (compare with Base); a proton donor.

Acid-base balance Situation in which the pH of the blood is maintained between 7.35 and 7.45.

Acidosis (as″ĭ-do′sis) State of abnormally high hydrogen ion concentration in the extracellular fluid.

Actin (ak′tin) A contractile protein of muscle.

Action potential A large transient depolarization event, including polarity reversal, that is conducted along the membrane of a muscle cell or a nerve fiber.

Activation energy The amount of energy required to push a reactant to the level necessary for action.

Active immunity Immunity produced by an encounter with an antigen; provides immunological memory.

Active site Region on the surface of a functional (globular) protein where it binds and interacts chemically with other molecules of complementary shape and charge.

Active (transport) processes (1) Membrane transport processes for which ATP is required, e.g., solute pumping and endocytosis. (2) "Active transport" also refers specifically to solute pumping.

Adaptation (1) Any change in structure or response to suit a new environment; (2) decline in the transmission of a sensory nerve when a receptor is stimulated continuously and without change in stimulus strength.

Adduct (a-dukt′) To move toward the midline of the body.

Adenine (A) (ad′ĕ-nēn) One of the two major purines found in both RNA and DNA; also found in various free nucleotides of importance to the body, such as ATP.

Adenohypophysis (ad″ĕ-no-hi-pof′ĭ-sis) Anterior pituitary; the glandular part of the pituitary gland.

Adenoids (ad′en-noids) Pharyngeal tonsil.

Adenosine triphosphate (ATP) (ah-den′o-sēn tri″fos′fāt) Organic molecule that stores and releases chemical energy for use in body cells.

Adipocyte (ad′ĭ-po-sīt) An adipose, or fat, cell.

Adipose tissue (ad′ĭ-pōs) Areolar connective tissue modified to store nutrients; a connective tissue consisting chiefly of fat cells.

Adrenal glands (uh-drē′nul) Hormone-producing glands located superior to the kidneys; each consists of medulla and cortex areas.

Adrenergic fibers (ad″ren-er′jik) Nerve fibers that release norepinephrine.

Adrenocorticotropic hormone (ACTH) (ah-dre′no-kor″tĭ-ko-trō′pik) Anterior pituitary hormone that influences the activity of the adrenal cortex.

Adventitia (ad″ven-tish′e-ah) Outermost layer or covering of some organs.

Aerobic (a′er-ōb″ik) Oxygen-requiring.

Aerobic endurance The length of time a muscle can continue to contract using aerobic pathways.

Aerobic respiration Respiration in which oxygen is consumed and glucose is broken down entirely; water, carbon dioxide, and large amounts of ATP are the final products.

Afferent (af′er-ent) Carrying to or toward a center.

Afferent (sensory) nerve Nerve that contains processes of sensory neurons and carries nerve impulses to the central nervous system.

Agglutination (ah-gloo″tĭ-na′shun) Clumping of (foreign) cells; induced by cross-linking of antigen-antibody complexes.

Agonist (ag′o-nist) Muscle that bears the major responsibility for effecting a particular movement; a prime mover.

AIDS Acquired immune deficiency syndrome; caused by human immunodeficiency virus (HIV); symptoms include severe weight loss, night sweats, swollen lymph nodes, opportunistic infections.

Albumin (al-bu′min) The most abundant plasma protein.

Aldosterone (al-dos′ter-ōn) Hormone produced by the adrenal cortex that regulates Na^+ reabsorption and K^+ secretion by the kidneys.

Alimentary canal (al″ĭ-men′tar-e) The continuous hollow tube extending from the mouth to the anus; its walls are constructed by the oral cavity, pharynx, esophagus, stomach, and small and large intestines.

Alkalosis (al″kah-lo′sis) State of abnormally low hydrogen ion concentration in the extracellular fluid.

Allantois (ah″lan′to-is) Embryonic membrane; its blood vessels develop into blood vessels of the umbilical cord.

Alleles Genes coding for the same trait and found at the same locus on homologous chromosomes.

Allergy A type of hypersensitivity (overzealous immune response to an otherwise harmless antigen) that involves IgE antibodies and histamine release.

Alopecia (al″o-pe′she-ah) Baldness.

Alpha (α)-helix The most common type of secondary structure of the amino acid chain in proteins; resembles the coils of a telephone cord.

Alveolar (acinar) gland (al-ve′o-lar) A gland whose secretory cells form small, flasklike sacs.

Alveolar ventilation rate (AVR) An index of respiratory efficiency; measures volume of fresh air that flows in and out of alveoli.

Alveolus (al-ve′o-lus) (1) One of the microscopic air sacs of the lungs; (2) tiny milk-producing glandular sac in the breast; (3) tooth socket.

Alzheimer's disease (AD) (altz′hi-merz) Degenerative brain disease resulting in progressive loss of memory and motor control, and increasing dementia.

Amino acid (ah-me′no) Organic compound containing nitrogen, carbon, hydrogen, and oxygen; building block of protein.

Ammonia (NH_3) Common waste product of protein breakdown in the body; a colorless volatile gas, very soluble in water and capable of forming a weak base; a proton acceptor.

Amniocentesis A common form of fetal testing in which a small sample of fluid is removed from the amniotic cavity.

Amnion (am′ne-on) Fetal membrane that forms a fluid-filled sac around the embryo.

Amoeboid motion (ah-me′boyd) The flowing movement of the cytoplasm of a phagocyte.

Amphiarthrosis (am″fe-ar-thro′sis) A slightly movable joint.

Ampulla (am-pul′lah) A localized dilation of a canal or duct.

Amylase Digestive system enzyme that breaks down starchy foods.

Anabolism (ah-nab′o-lizm) Energy-requiring building phase of metabolism in which simpler substances are combined to form more complex substances.

Anaerobic (an-a′er-ōb-ik) Not requiring oxygen.

Anaerobic glycolysis (gli-kol′ĭ-sis) Energy-yielding conversion of glucose to lactic acid in various tissues, notably muscle, when sufficient oxygen is not available.

Anaerobic threshold The point at which muscle metabolism converts to anaerobic glycolysis.

Anaphase Third stage of mitosis, meiosis I, and meiosis II in which daughter chromosomes move toward each pole of a cell.

Anastomosis (ah-nas″to-mo′sis) A union or joining of nerves, blood vessels, or lymphatics.

Anatomy Study of the structure of living organisms.

Androgen (an′dro-jen) A hormone such as testosterone that controls male secondary sex characteristics.

Anemia (ah-ne′me-ah) Reduced oxygen-carrying ability of blood resulting from too few erythrocytes or abnormal hemoglobin.

Aneurysm (an′u-rizm) Blood-filled sac in an artery wall caused by dilation or weakening of the wall.

Angina pectoris (an′jĭ-nah pek′tor-is) Severe suffocating chest pain caused by brief lack of oxygen supply to heart muscle.

Angiotensin II (an″je-o-ten′sin) A potent vasoconstrictor activated by renin; also triggers release of aldosterone.

Anion (an′i-on) An ion carrying one or more negative charges and therefore attracted to a positive pole.

Anoxia (ah-nŏk′se-ah) Deficiency of oxygen.

Antagonist (an-tag′o-nist) (1) Muscle that reverses, or opposes, the action of another muscle. (2) Hormone that opposes the action of another hormone.

Anterior pituitary *See* Adenohypophysis.

Antibody A protein molecule that is released by a plasma cell (a daughter cell of an activated B lymphocyte) and that binds specifically to an antigen; an immunoglobulin.

Anticodon (an″ti-ko′don) The three-base sequence complementary to the messenger RNA (mRNA) codon.

Antidiuretic hormone (ADH, also called vasopressin) (an″ti-di″yer-eh′tik) Hormone produced by the hypothalamus and released by the posterior pituitary; stimulates the kidneys to reabsorb more water, reducing urine volume.

Antigen (Ag) (an′tĭ-jen) A substance or part of a substance (living or nonliving) that is recognized as foreign by the immune system, activates the immune system, and reacts with immune cells or their products.

Antigen-presenting cell (APC) A specialized cell (dendritic cell, macrophage, or B cell) that captures, processes, and presents antigens on its surface to T lymphocytes.

Anucleate cell (a-nu′kle-āt) A cell without a nucleus.

Anus (a′nus) Distal end of digestive tract; outlet of rectum.

Aorta (a-or′tah) Major systemic artery; arises from the left ventricle of the heart.

Aortic body Receptor in the aortic arch sensitive to changing oxygen, carbon dioxide, and pH levels of the blood.

Apgar score Evaluation of an infant's physical status at 1 and 5 minutes after birth by assessing five criteria: heart rate, respiration, color, muscle tone, and reflexes.

Apnea Breathing cessation.

Apocrine sweat gland (ap′o-krin) The less numerous type of sweat gland; produces a secretion containing water, salts, proteins, and fatty acids.

Apoenzyme (ap′ō-en-zīm) The protein portion of an enzyme.

Aponeurosis (ap″o-nu-ro′sis) Fibrous or membranous sheet connecting a muscle and the part it moves.

Apoptosis A process of controlled cellular suicide; eliminates cells that are unneeded, stressed, or aged.

Appendicitis (ă-pen′dĭ-sī′tis) Inflammation of the appendix (wormlike sac attached to the cecum of the large intestine).

Appendicular Relating to the limbs; one of the two major divisions of the body.

Appositional growth Growth accomplished by the addition of new layers onto those previously formed.

Aquaporins (ă″kwă-por′ins) Transmembrane proteins that form water channels.

Aqueous humor (a′kwe-us) Watery fluid in the anterior segment of the eye.

Arachnoid (ah-rak′noid) Weblike; specifically, the weblike arachnoid mater, the middle layer of the three meninges.

Areola (ah-re′o-lah) Circular, pigmented area surrounding the nipple; any small space in a tissue.

Areolar connective tissue A type of loose connective tissue.

Arrector pili (ah-rek′tor pi′li) Tiny, smooth muscles attached to hair follicles; contraction causes the hair to stand upright.

Arrhythmia (a-rith′me-ah) Irregular heart rhythm, often caused by defects in the intrinsic conduction system.

Arteries Blood vessels that conduct blood away from the heart and into the circulation.

Arteriole (ar-tēr′e-ōl) A minute artery.

Arteriosclerosis (ar-tēr′e-o-skler-o′sis) Any of a number of proliferative and degenerative changes in the arteries leading to their decreased elasticity.

Arthritis Inflammation of the joints.

Arthroscopic surgery (ar-thro-skop′ik) Procedure enabling a surgeon to repair the interior of a joint through a small incision.

Articular capsule Double-layered capsule composed of an outer fibrous capsule lined by synovial membrane; encloses the joint cavity of a synovial joint.

Articular cartilage Hyaline cartilage covering bone ends at movable joints.

Articulation (joint) The junction of two or more bones.

Association areas Functional areas of the cerebral cortex that act mainly to integrate diverse information for purposeful action.

Astigmatism (ah-stig′mah-tizm) A condition in which unequal curvatures in different parts of the cornea or lens of the eye lead to blurred vision.

Astrocyte (as′tro-sīt) A type of CNS supporting cell; assists in exchanges between blood capillaries and neurons.

Atelectasis (at″ĕ-lik′tah-sis) Lung collapse.

Atherosclerosis (a″ther-o″skler-o′sis) Changes in the walls of large arteries consisting of lipid deposits on the artery walls; one form of arteriosclerosis.

Atmospheric pressure Force that air exerts on the surface of the body (760 mm Hg at sea level).

Atom Smallest particle of an elemental substance that exhibits the properties of that element; composed of protons, neutrons, and electrons.

Atomic number The number of protons in an atom.

Atomic symbol The one- or two-letter symbol used to indicate an element; usually the first letter(s) of the element's name.

Atomic weight The average of the mass numbers of all the isotopes of an element.

ATP (adenosine triphosphate) (ah-den′o-sēn tri″fos′fāt) Organic molecule that stores and releases chemical energy for use in body cells.

Atria (a′tre-ah) The two superior receiving chambers of the heart.

Atrial natriuretic peptide (ANP) (a′tre-al na″tre-u-ret′ik) A hormone released by certain cells of the heart atria that reduces blood pressure and blood volume by inhibiting nearly all events that promote vasoconstriction and Na$^+$ and water retention.

Atrioventricular (AV) bundle (a″tre-o-ven-trĭ′kyoo-ler) Bundle of specialized fibers that conduct impulses from the AV node to the right and left ventricles; also called bundle of His.

Atrioventricular (AV) node Specialized mass of conducting cells located at the atrioventricular junction in the heart.

Atrioventricular (AV) valve Valve that prevents backflow into the atrium when the connected ventricle is contracting.

Atrophy (at′ro-fe) Reduction in size or wasting away of an organ or cell resulting from disease or lack of use.

Auditory ossicles (ah′sih-kulz) The three tiny bones serving as transmitters of vibrations and located within the middle ear: the malleus, incus, and stapes.

Auditory tube See Pharyngotympanic tube.

Autoimmunity Production of antibodies or effector T cells that attack a person's own tissue.

Autolysis (aw″tol′ĭ-sis) Process of autodigestion (self-digestion) of cells, especially dead or degenerate cells.

Autonomic ganglion Collection of sympathetic or parasympathetic ganglionic neuronal cell bodies.

Autonomic nervous system (ANS) Efferent division of the peripheral nervous system that innervates cardiac and smooth muscles and glands; also called the involuntary or visceral motor system.

Autonomic (visceral) reflexes Reflexes that activate smooth or cardiac muscle and/or glands.

Autoregulation The automatic local adjustment of blood flow to a particular body area in response to its current requirements.

Autosomes Chromosomes number 1 to 22; do not include the sex chromosomes.

Avogadro's number (av″o-gad′rōz) The number of molecules in one mole of any substance, 6.02×10^{23}.

Axial Relating to the head, neck, and trunk; one of the two major divisions of the body.

Axolemma (ak″so-lem′ah) The plasma membrane of an axon.

Axon Neuron process that carries impulses away from the nerve cell body; efferent process; the conducting portion of a nerve cell.

Axon terminals (synaptic knobs, boutons) The bulbous distal endings of the terminal branches of an axon.

B cells Also called B lymphocytes; oversee humoral immunity; their descendants differentiate into antibody-producing plasma cells.

Baroreceptor (bayr″o-re-sep′tor) A sensory nerve ending in the wall of the carotid sinus or aortic arch sensitive to vessel stretching.

Basal body (ba′sal) An organelle structurally identical to a centriole and forming the base of a cilium or flagellum.

Basal ganglia See Basal nuclei.

Basal lamina (lam′ĭ-nah) Noncellular, adhesive supporting sheet consisting largely of glycoproteins secreted by epithelial cells.

Basal metabolic rate (BMR) Rate at which energy is expended (heat produced) by the body per unit time under controlled (basal) conditions: 12 hours after a meal, at rest.

Basal nuclei (basal ganglia) Specific gray matter areas located deep within the white matter of the cerebral hemispheres.

Basal surface The surface near the base or interior of a structure; nearest the lower side or bottom of a structure.

Base A substance capable of binding with hydrogen ions; a proton acceptor.

Basement membrane Extracellular material consisting of a basal lamina secreted by epithelial cells and a reticular lamina secreted by underlying connective tissue cells.

Basophil (ba′zo-fil) White blood cell whose granules stain purplish-black and nucleus purple with basic dye.

Benign (be-nīn′) Not malignant.

Bile Greenish-yellow or brownish fluid produced in and secreted by the liver, stored in the gallbladder, and released into the small intestine.

Bilirubin (bil″ĭ-roo′bin) Yellow pigment of bile.

Bipolar neuron Neuron with axon and dendrite that extend from opposite sides of the cell body.

Blastocyst (blas′to-sist) Stage of early embryonic development; the product of cleavage.

Blood pressure (BP) Force exerted by blood against a unit area of the blood vessel walls; differences in blood pressure between different areas of the circulation provide the driving force for blood circulation.

Blood-brain barrier Mechanism that inhibits passage of materials from the blood into brain tissues; reflects relative impermeability of brain capillaries.

Bolus (bo′lus) A rounded mass of food prepared by the mouth for swallowing; any soft round mass.

Bone marrow Fat- or blood-forming tissue found within bone cavities; called yellow and red bone marrow, respectively.

Bone (osseous tissue) (os′e-us) A connective tissue that forms the bony skeleton.

Bone remodeling Process involving bone formation and destruction in response to hormonal and mechanical factors.

Bone resorption The removal of osseous tissue; part of the continuous bone remodeling process.

Bowman's capsule (bo-manz) *See* Glomerular capsule.

Boyle's law States that when the temperature is constant, the pressure of a gas varies inversely with its volume.

Bradycardia (brad″e-kar′de-ah) A heart rate below 60 beats per minute.

Brain death State of irreversible coma, even though life-support measures may have restored other body organs.

Brain stem Collectively the midbrain, pons, and medulla of the brain.

Brain ventricle Fluid-filled cavity of the brain.

Branchial groove (brang′ke-al) An indentation of the surface ectoderm in the embryo; the external acoustic meatus develops from it.

Bronchioles Smaller (<1 mm in diameter) branching air passageways inside the lungs.

Bronchus (brong′kus) One of the two large branches of the trachea that leads to the lungs.

Buffer Chemical substance or system that minimizes changes in pH by releasing or binding hydrogen ions.

Burn Tissue damage inflicted by intense heat, electricity, radiation, or certain chemicals, all of which denature cell proteins and cause cell death in the affected areas.

Bursa (ber′sa) A fibrous sac lined with synovial membrane and containing synovial fluid; occurs between bones and muscle tendons (or other structures), where it acts to decrease friction during movement.

Bursitis Inflammation of a bursa.

Calcaneal tendon (kal-ka′ne-al) Tendon that attaches the calf muscles to the heelbone (calcaneus); also called the Achilles tendon.

Calcitonin (kal″sih-to′nin) Hormone released by the thyroid. Lowers blood calcium levels only when present at high (therapeutic). levels.

Calculus (kal′ku-lus) A stone formed within various body parts.

Callus (kal′lus) (1) Localized thickening of skin epidermis resulting from physical trauma; (2) repair tissue (fibrous or bony) formed at a fracture site.

Calorie (cal) Amount of energy needed to raise the temperature of 1 gram of water 1° Celsius. Energy exchanges associated with biochemical reactions are usually reported in kilocalories (1 kcal = 1000 cal), also called large calories (Cal).

Calyx (ka′liks) A cuplike extension of the pelvis of the kidney.

Canaliculus (kan″ah-lik′u-lus) Extremely small tubular passage or channel.

Cancer A malignant, invasive cellular neoplasm that has the capability of spreading throughout the body or body parts.

Capillaries (kap′il-layr″ēs) The smallest of the blood vessels and the sites of exchange between the blood and tissue cells.

Carbohydrate (kar″bo-hi′drāt) Organic compound composed of carbon, hydrogen, and oxygen; includes starches, sugars, cellulose.

Carbonic acid–bicarbonate buffer system Chemical system that helps maintain pH homeostasis of the blood.

Carbonic anhydrase (kar-bon′ik an-hi′drās) Enzyme that facilitates the combination of carbon dioxide with water to form carbonic acid.

Carcinogen (kar″sĭ′no-jin) Cancer-causing agent.

Cardiac cycle Sequence of events encompassing one complete contraction and relaxation of the atria and ventricles of the heart.

Cardiac muscle Specialized muscle of the heart.

Cardiac output (CO) Amount of blood pumped out of a ventricle in one minute.

Cardiac reserve The difference between resting and maximal cardiac output.

Cardiogenic shock Pump failure; the heart is so inefficient that it cannot sustain adequate circulation.

Cardiovascular system Organ system that distributes the blood to deliver nutrients and remove wastes.

Carotene (kar′o-tēn) Yellow to orange pigment that accumulates in the stratum corneum epidermal layer and in fatty tissue of the hypodermis.

Carotid body (kar-rot′id) A receptor in the common carotid artery sensitive to changing oxygen, carbon dioxide, and pH levels of the blood.

Carotid sinus (si′nus) A dilation of a common carotid artery; involved in regulation of systemic blood pressure.

Carrier A transmembrane protein that changes shape to envelop and transport a polar substance across the cell membrane.

Cartilage (kar′tĭ-lij) White, semiopaque connective tissue.

Cartilage bone (endochondral bone) Bone formed by using hyaline cartilage structures as models for ossification.

Cartilaginous joints (kar″ti-laj′ĭ-nus) Bones united by cartilage; no joint cavity is present.

Catabolism (kat-tab′o-lizm) Process in which living cells break down substances into simpler substances.

Catalyst (kat′ah-list) Substance that increases the rate of a chemical reaction without itself becoming chemically changed or part of the product.

Cataract Clouding of the eye's lens; often congenital or age-related.

Catecholamines (kat″ĕ-kol′ah-mēnz) Epinephrine, norepinephrine, and dopamine; a class of amines that act as chemical transmitters.

Cation (kat′i-on) An ion with a positive charge.

Caudal (kaw′dul) Literally, toward the tail; in humans, the inferior portion of the anatomy.

Cecum (se′kum) The blind-end pouch at the beginning of the large intestine.

Cell Structural unit of all living things.

Cell differentiation The development of specific and distinctive features in cells, from a single cell (the fertilized egg) to all the specialized cells of adulthood.

Cell life cycle Series of changes a cell goes through from the time it is formed until it reproduces itself.

Cell-mediated immunity Immunity conferred by activated T cells, which directly kill infected or cancerous body cells or cells of foreign grafts and release chemicals that regulate the immune response.

Cell membrane *See* Plasma membrane.

Cellular respiration Metabolic processes in which ATP is produced.

Cellulose (sel′u-lōs) A fibrous carbohydrate that is the main structural component of plant tissues.

Central (Haversian) canal (hah-ver′zhan) The canal in the center of each osteon that contains minute blood vessels and nerve fibers that serve the needs of the osteocytes.

Central nervous system (CNS) Brain and spinal cord.

Centriole (sen′tre-ol) Minute body found near the nucleus of the cell; active in cell division.

Centrosome (cell center) A region near the nucleus which contains paired organelles called centrioles.

Cerebellum (ser″ĕ-bel′um) Brain region most involved in producing smooth, coordinated skeletal muscle activity.

Cerebral aqueduct (ser′ĕ-bral, sĕ-re′bral) The slender cavity of the midbrain that connects the third and fourth ventricles.

Cerebral arterial circle (circle of Willis) An arterial anastomosis at the base of the brain.

Cerebral cortex The outer gray matter region of the cerebral hemispheres.

Cerebral dominance Designates the hemisphere that is dominant for language.

Cerebral palsy Neuromuscular disability in which voluntary muscles are poorly controlled or paralyzed as a result of brain damage.

Cerebral white matter Consists largely of myelinated fibers bundled into large tracts; provides for communication between cerebral areas and lower CNS centers.

Cerebrospinal fluid (CSF) (ser′ĕ-bro-spi′nal) Plasmalike fluid that fills the cavities of the CNS and surrounds the CNS externally; protects the brain and spinal cord.

Cerebrovascular accident (CVA) (ser″ĕ-bro-vas′ku-lar) Condition in which brain tissue is deprived of a blood supply, as in blockage of a cerebral blood vessel; a stroke.

Cerebrum (ser′ĕ-brum) The cerebral hemispheres and the structures of the diencephalon.

Cervical vertebrae The seven vertebrae of the vertebral column located in the neck.

Cervix Lower outlet of the uterus extending into the vagina.

Channel A transmembrane protein that forms an aqueous pore, allowing substances to move from one side of the membrane to the other.

Chemical bond An energy relationship holding atoms together; involves the interaction of electrons.

Chemical digestion A series of catabolic steps in which complex food molecules are broken down to their building blocks by enzymes.

Chemical energy Energy stored in the bonds of chemical substances.

Chemical equilibrium A state of apparent repose created by two reactions proceeding in opposite directions at equal speed.

Chemical reaction Process in which molecules are formed, changed, or broken down.

Chemoreceptor (ke″mo-re-sep′ter) Receptor sensitive to various chemicals in solution.

Chemotaxis (ke″mo-tak′sis) Movement of a cell, organism, or part of an organism toward or away from a chemical substance.

Cholecystokinin (CCK) (ko″le-sis″to-ki′nin) An intestinal hormone that stimulates gallbladder contraction and pancreatic juice release.

Cholesterol (ko-les′ter-ol″) Steroid found in animal fats as well as in most body tissues; made by the liver.

Cholinergic fibers (ko″lin-er′jik) Nerve endings that, upon stimulation, release acetylcholine.

Chondroblast (kon′dro-blast) Actively mitotic cell of cartilage.

Chondrocyte (kon′dro-sīt) Mature cell of cartilage.

Chorion (kor′e-on) Outermost fetal membrane; helps form the placenta.

Chorionic villi sampling (ko″re-on′ik vil′i) Fetal testing procedure in which bits of the chorionic villi from the placenta are snipped off and the cells karyotyped. This procedure can be done as early as 8 weeks into the pregnancy.

Choroid (ko′roid) The vascular middle layer of the eye.

Choroid plexus (ko′roid plex′sus) A capillary knot that protrudes into a brain ventricle; involved in forming cerebrospinal fluid.

Chromatin (kro′mah-tin) Structures in the nucleus that carry the hereditary factors (genes).

Chromosomes (kro′mo-somz) Barlike bodies of tightly coiled chromatin; visible during cell division.

Chronic obstructive pulmonary disease (COPD) Collective term for progressive, obstructive respiratory disorders; includes emphysema, chronic bronchitis.

Chyme (kīm) Semifluid, creamy mass consisting of partially digested food and gastric juice.

Cilia (sil′e-ah) Tiny, hairlike projections on cell surfaces that move in a wavelike manner.

Circumduction (ser″kum-duk′shun) Movement of a body part so that it outlines a cone in space.

Cirrhosis (sĭ-ro′sis) Chronic disease of the liver, characterized by an overgrowth of connective tissue or fibrosis.

Cisterna chyli (sis-ter′nah ki′li) An enlarged sac at the base of the thoracic duct; the origin of the thoracic duct.

Cisternae (sis-ter′ne) Any cavity or enclosed space serving as a reservoir.

Cleavage An early embryonic phase consisting of rapid mitotic cell divisions without intervening growth periods; product is a blastocyst.

Clonal selection (klo′nul) Process during which a B cell or T cell becomes activated by binding contact with an antigen.

Clone Descendants of a single cell.

Coagulation Process in which blood is transformed from a liquid to a gel; blood clotting.

Cochlea (kok′le-ah) Snail-shaped chamber of the bony labyrinth that houses the receptor for hearing [the spiral organ (of Corti)].

Codon (ko′don) The three-base sequence on a messenger RNA molecule that provides the genetic information used in protein synthesis; code for a given amino acid.

Coenzyme (ko-en′zīm) Nonprotein substance associated with and activating an enzyme, typically a vitamin.

Cofactor Metal ion or organic molecule that is required for enzyme activity.

Collagen fiber The most abundant of the three fibers found in the matrix of connective tissue.

Colloid (kol′oid) (1) A mixture in which the solute particles (usually proteins) do not settle out readily. (2) Substance in the thyroid gland containing thyroglobulin protein.

Colloid osmotic pressure (kol′oid ahz-mah′tik) Pressure created in a fluid by large nondiffusible molecules, such as plasma proteins that are prevented from moving through a (capillary) membrane. Such substances tend to draw water to them.

Colon Regions of the large intestine; includes ascending, transverse, descending, and sigmoid portions.

Combination (synthesis) reaction Chemical reaction in which larger, more complex atoms or molecules are formed from simpler ones.

Complement A group of bloodborne proteins, which, when activated, enhance the inflammatory and immune responses and may lead to cell lysis.

Complementarity of structure and function The relationship between a structure and its function; i.e., structure determines function.

Complementary base Refers to how a given nitrogenous base of DNA or RNA bonds to another nitrogenous base. For example, adenine (A) is the complementary base of thymine (T). The result is base pairing.

Complete blood count (CBC) Clinical test that includes counts of all formed elements, a hematocrit, and measurements of erythrocyte size and hemoglobin content.

Compound Substance composed of two or more different elements, the atoms of which are chemically united.

Concentration gradient The difference in the concentration of a particular substance between two different areas.

Conducting zone Includes all respiratory passageways that provide conduits for air to reach the sites of gas exchange (the respiratory zone).

Conductivity Ability to transmit an electrical impulse.

Cones One of the two types of photoreceptor cells in the retina of the eye; provide for color vision.

Congenital (kun-jeh′nih-tul) Existing at birth.

Congestive heart failure (CHF) Condition in which the pumping efficiency of the heart is depressed so that circulation is inadequate to meet tissue needs.

Conjunctiva (kon″junk-ti′vah) Thin, protective mucous membrane lining the eyelids and covering the anterior surface of the eye itself.

Connective tissue A primary tissue; form and function vary extensively. Functions include support, storage, and protection.

Consciousness The ability to perceive, communicate, remember, understand, appreciate, and initiate voluntary movements.

Contraception The prevention of conception; birth control.

Contractility Muscle cell's ability to move by shortening.

Contraction To shorten or develop tension, an ability highly developed in muscle cells.

Contralateral Relating to the opposite side.

Cornea (kor′ne-ah) Transparent anterior portion of the eyeball; part of the fibrous layer.

Corona radiata (kor-o′nah ra-de-ah′tah) (1) Arrangement of elongated follicle cells around a mature ovum; (2) crownlike arrangement of nerve fibers radiating from the internal capsule of the brain to every part of the cerebral cortex.

Coronary circulation The functional blood supply of the heart; shortest circulation in the body.

Cortex (kor′teks) Outer surface layer of an organ.

Corticosteroids (kor″tĭ-ko-stě′roidz) Steroid hormones released by the adrenal cortex.

Cortisol (hydrocortisone) (kor′tih-sol) Glucocorticoid produced by the adrenal cortex.

Covalent bond (ko-va′lent) Chemical bond created by electron sharing between atoms.

Cranial nerves The 12 nerve pairs that arise from the brain.

Craniosacral division Another name for the parasympathetic division of the autonomic nervous system.

Cranium (cranial bones) (kra′ne-um) Bony protective encasement of the brain and organs of hearing and equilibrium; also called the skull.

Creatine kinase (kre′ah-tin) Enzyme that catalyzes the transfer of phosphate from creatine phosphate to ADP, forming creatine and ATP; important in muscle contraction.

Creatine phosphate (CP) (fos-fāt) Compound that serves as an alternative energy source for muscle tissue.

Creatinine (kre-at′ĭ-nin) A nitrogenous waste molecule which is not reabsorbed by the kidney; this characteristic makes it useful for measurement of the GFR and glomerular function.

Crista ampullaris Sensory receptor organ within the ampulla of each semicircular canal of the inner ear; dynamic equilibrium receptor.

Cross section A cut running horizontally from right to left, dividing the body or an organ into superior and inferior parts.

Cutaneous (ku-ta′ne-us) Pertaining to the skin.

Cutaneous sensory receptors Receptors located throughout the skin that respond to stimuli arising outside the body; part of the nervous system.

Cyclic AMP Intracellular second messenger that mediates the effects of the first (extracellular) messenger (hormone or neurotransmitter); formed from ATP by a plasma membrane enzyme (adenylate cyclase).

Cystic fibrosis (CF) Genetic disorder in which secretion of overly viscous mucus clogs the respiratory passages, predisposes to fatal respiratory infections.

Cytochromes (si′to-krōmz) Brightly colored iron-containing proteins that form part of the inner mitochondrial membrane and function as electron carriers in oxidative phosphorylation.

Cytokines Small proteins that act as chemical messengers between various parts of the immune system.

Cytokinesis (si″to-kĭ-ne′sis) The division of cytoplasm that occurs after the cell nucleus has divided.

Cytoplasm (si′to-plazm) The cellular material surrounding the nucleus and enclosed by the plasma membrane.

Cytosine (C) (si′to-sēn) Nitrogen-containing base that is part of a nucleotide structure.

Cytoskeleton Literally, cell skeleton. An elaborate series of rods running through the cystol, supporting cellular structures and providing the machinery to generate various cell movements.

Cytosol Viscous, semitransparent fluid substance of cytoplasm in which other elements are suspended.

Cytotoxic T cell (T$_C$ cell) Effector T cell that directly kills foreign cells, cancer cells, or virus-infected body cells by inducing apoptosis (cell suicide).

Deamination (de′am″ih-na′shun) Removal of an amine group from an organic compound.

Decomposition reaction Chemical reaction in which a molecule is broken down into smaller molecules or its constituent atoms.

Defecation (def″ih-ka′shun) Elimination of the contents of the bowels (feces).

Deglutition (deg″loo-tish′un) Swallowing.

Dehydration (de″hi-dra′shun) Condition of excessive water loss.

Dehydration synthesis Process by which a large molecule is synthesized by removing water and covalently bonding smaller molecules together.

Dendrite (den′drīt) Branching neuron process that serves as a receptive, or input, region; transmits an electrical signal toward the cell body.

Dendritic cells Protective cells that phagocytize antigens, migrate to lymph nodes, and present the antigen to T cells, causing them to activate and mount an immune response; called epidermal dendritic cells or Langerhans cells in the skin.

Depolarization (de-po″ler-ah-za′shun) Loss of a state of polarity; loss or reduction of negative membrane potential.

Dermatome (der′mah-tōm) Portion of somite mesoderm that forms the dermis of the skin; also the area of skin innervated by the cutaneous branches of a single spinal nerve.

Dermis Layer of skin deep to the epidermis; composed mostly of dense irregular connective tissue.

Desmosome (dez′muh-sōm) Cell junction composed of thickened plasma membranes joined by filaments.

Diabetes insipidus (di″ah-be′tēz in-sih′pih-dus) Disease characterized by passage of a large quantity of dilute urine plus intense thirst and dehydration caused by inadequate release of antidiuretic hormone (ADH).

Diabetes mellitus (DM) (meh-li′tus) Disease caused by deficient insulin release or by insulin resistance, leading to inability of the body cells to use carbohydrates.

Dialysis (di-al′ah-sis) Diffusion of solute(s) through a semipermeable membrane.

Diapedesis (di″ah-pĕ-de′sis) Passage of white blood cells through intact vessel walls into tissue.

Diaphragm (di′ah-fram) (1) Any partition or wall separating one area from another; (2) a muscle that separates the thoracic cavity from the lower abdominopelvic cavity.

Diaphysis (di-af′ĭ-sis) Elongated shaft of a long bone.

Diarthrosis (di″ar-thro′sis) Freely movable joint.

Diastole (di-as′to-le) Period of the cardiac cycle when either the ventricles or the atria are relaxing.

Diastolic pressure (di-as-tah′lik) Arterial blood pressure reached during or as a result of diastole; lowest level of any given cardiac cycle.

Diencephalon (interbrain) (di″en-seh′fuh-lon) That part of the forebrain between the cerebral hemispheres and the midbrain including the thalamus, the epithalamus, and the hypothalamus.

Differential white blood cell count Diagnostic test to determine relative proportion of individual leukocyte types.

Diffusion (dĭ-fu′zhun) The spreading of particles in a gas or solution with a movement toward uniform distribution of particles; driven by kinetic energy.

Digestion Chemical or mechanical process of breaking down foodstuffs to substances that can be absorbed.

Digestive system System that processes food into absorbable units and eliminates indigestible wastes.

Dipeptide A combination of two amino acids united by means of a peptide bond.

Diploë (dip′lo-e) The internal layer of spongy bone in flat bones.

Diploid chromosomal number The chromosomal number characteristic of an organism, symbolized as $2n$; twice the chromosomal number (n) of the gamete; in humans, $2n = 46$.

Diplopia (dĭ-plo′pe-ah) Double vision.

Dipole (polar molecule) Nonsymmetrical molecules that contain electrically unbalanced atoms.

Disaccharide (di-sak′ah-rīd″, di-sak′ah-rid) Literally, double sugar; e.g., sucrose, lactose.

Dislocation (luxation) Occurs when bones are forced out of their normal alignment at a joint.

Displacement (exchange) reaction Chemical reaction in which bonds are both made and broken; atoms become combined with different atoms.

Distal (dis′tul) Away from the attached end of a limb or the origin of a structure.

Diuretics (di″u-ret′iks) Chemicals that enhance urinary output.

Diverticulum (di″ver-tik′u-lum) A pouch or sac in the walls of a hollow organ or structure.

DNA (deoxyribonucleic acid) (de-ok″sĭ-ri″bo-nu-kla′ik) A nucleic acid found in all living cells; it carries the organism's hereditary information.

DNA replication Process that occurs before cell division; ensures that all daughter cells have identical genes.

Dominant traits Occurs when one allele masks or suppresses the expression of its partner.

Dominant-recessive inheritance Reflects the interaction of dominant and recessive alleles.

Dorsal (dor′sul) Pertaining to the back; posterior.

Dorsal root ganglion Peripheral collection of cell bodies of first-order afferent neurons whose central axons enter the spinal cord.

Double helix The secondary structure assumed by two strands of DNA, held together throughout their length by hydrogen bonds between bases on opposite strands.

Duct (dukt) A canal or passageway; a tubular structure that provides an exit for the secretions of a gland, or for conducting any fluid.

Ductus (vas) deferens Extends from the epididymis to the urethra; propels sperm into the urethra by peristalsis during ejaculation.

Duodenum (du″o-de′num) First part of the small intestine.

Dura mater (du′rah ma′ter) Outermost and toughest of the three membranes (meninges) covering the brain and spinal cord.

Dynamic equilibrium Sense that reports on angular (rotatory) acceleration or deceleration of the head in space.

Dyskinesia (dis-kĭ-ne′ze-ah) Disorders of muscle tone, posture, or involuntary movements.

Dyspnea (disp-ne′ah) Difficult or labored breathing; air hunger.

Eccrine glands (ek′rin) Sweat glands abundant on the palms, soles of feet, and the forehead.

Ectoderm (ek′to-derm) Embryonic germ layer; forms the epidermis of the skin and its derivatives, and nervous tissues.

Edema (ĕ-de′mah) Abnormal increase in the amount of interstitial fluid; causes swelling.

Effector (ef-ek′ter) Organ, gland, or muscle capable of being activated by nerve endings.

Efferent (ef′er-ent) Carrying away or away from, especially a nerve fiber that carries impulses away from the central nervous system.

Elastic cartilage Cartilage with abundant elastic fibers; more flexible than hyaline cartilage.

Elastic fiber Fiber formed from the protein elastin, which gives a rubbery and resilient quality to the matrix of connective tissue.

Electrical energy Energy formed by the movement of charged particles across cell membranes.

Electrocardiogram (ECG or EKG) (e-lek″tro-car′de-o-gram″) Graphic record of the electrical activity of the heart.

Electrochemical gradient The combined difference in concentration and charge; influences the distribution and direction of diffusion of ions.

Electroencephalogram (EEG) (e-lek″tro-en-sef′ah-lo-gram″) Graphic record of the electrical activity of nerve cells in the brain.

Electrolyte (e-lek′tro-līt) Chemical substances, such as salts, acids, and bases, that ionize and dissociate in water and are capable of conducting an electrical current.

Electrolyte balance Refers to the balance between input and output of salts (sodium, potassium, calcium, magnesium) in the body.

Electromagnetic radiation Emitted photons (wave packets) of energy, e.g., light, X ray, infrared.

Electron Negatively charged subatomic particle; orbits the atom's nucleus.

Electron shells (energy levels) Regions of space that consecutively surround the nucleus of an atom.

Element One of a limited number of unique varieties of matter that composes substances of all kinds; e.g., carbon, hydrogen, oxygen.

Embolism (em′bo-lizm) Obstruction of a blood vessel by an embolus (blood clot, fatty mass, bubble of air, or other debris) floating in the blood.

Embryo (em′bre-o) Developmental stage extending from fertilization to the end of the eighth week.

Emesis Reflexive emptying of the stomach through the esophagus and pharynx; also known as vomiting.

Encephalitis (en″seh-fuh-lī′tis) Inflammation of the brain.

Endergonic reaction Chemical reaction that absorbs energy, e.g., an anabolic reaction.

Endocardium (en″do-kar′de-um) Endothelial membrane that lines the interior of the heart.

Endochondral ossification (en″do-kon′dral) Embryonic formation of bone by the replacement of calcified cartilage; most skeletal bones are formed by this process.

Endocrine glands (en′do-krin) Ductless glands that empty their hormonal products directly into the blood.

Endocrine system Body system that includes internal organs that secrete hormones.

Endocytosis (en″do-si-to′sis) Means by which fairly large extracellular molecules or particles enter cells, e.g., phagocytosis, pinocytosis, receptor-mediated endocytosis.

Endoderm (en′do-derm) Embryonic germ layer; forms the lining of the digestive tube and its associated structures.

Endogenous (en-doj′ĕ-nŭs) Originating or produced within the organism or one of its parts.

Endometrium (en″do-me′tre-um) Mucous membrane lining of the uterus.

Endomysium (en″do-mis′e-um) Thin connective tissue surrounding each muscle cell.

Endoplasmic reticulum (ER) (en″do-plaz′mik rĕ-tik′u-lum) Membranous network of tubular or saclike channels in the cytoplasm of a cell.

Endosteum (en-dos′te-um) Connective tissue membrane covering internal bone surfaces.

Endothelium (en″do-the′le-um) Single layer of simple squamous cells that line the walls of the heart, blood vessels, and lymphatic vessels.

Energy The capacity to do work; may be stored (potential energy) or in action (kinetic energy).

Energy intake Energy liberated during food oxidation.

Energy output Sum of energy lost as heat, as work, and as fat or glycogen storage.

Enzyme (en′zīm) A protein that acts as a biological catalyst to speed up a chemical reaction.

Eosinophil (e″o-sin′o-fil) Granular white blood cell whose granules readily take up an acid stain called eosin.

Ependymal cell (ĕ-pen′dĭ-mul) A type of CNS supporting cell; lines the central cavities of the brain and spinal cord.

Epidermis (ep″ĭ-der′mis) Superficial layer of the skin; composed of keratinized stratified squamous epithelium.

Epididymis (ep″ĭ-dĭ′dĭ-mis) That portion of the male duct system in which sperm mature. Empties into the ductus (or vas) deferens.

Epidural space Area between the bony vertebrae and the dura mater of the spinal cord.

Epiglottis (eh″puh-glah′tis) Elastic cartilage at the back of the throat; covers the opening of the larynx during swallowing.

Epileptic seizures Abnormal electrical discharges of groups of brain neurons, during which no other messages can get through.

Epimysium (ep″ĭ-mis′e-um) Sheath of fibrous connective tissue surrounding a muscle.

Epinephrine (ep″ĭ-nef′rin) Chief hormone produced by the adrenal medulla. Also called adrenaline.

Epiphyseal plate (e″pĭ-fis′e-ul) Plate of hyaline cartilage at the junction of the diaphysis and epiphysis that provides for growth in length of a long bone.

Epiphysis (e-pif′ĭ-sis) The end of a long bone, attached to the shaft.

Epithalamus Most dorsal portion of the diencephalon; forms the roof of the third ventricle with the pineal gland extending from its posterior border.

Epithelium (epithelial tissue) (ep″ĭ-the′le-ul) Pertaining to a primary tissue that covers the body surface, lines its internal cavities, and forms glands.

Erythrocytes (e-rith′ro-sīts) Red blood cells.

Erythropoiesis (ĕ-rith″ro-poi-e′sis) Process of erythrocyte formation.

Erythropoietin (EPO) (ĕ-rith″ro-poi′ĕ-tin) Hormone that stimulates production of red blood cells.

Esophagus (ĕ-sof′ah-gus) Muscular tube extending from the laryngopharynx through the diaphragm to join the stomach; collapses when not involved in food propulsion.

Estrogens (es′tro-jenz) Hormones that stimulate female secondary sex characteristics; female sex hormones.

Eupnea (ūp-ne′ah) Normal respiratory rate and rhythm.

Exchange (displacement) reaction Chemical reaction in which bonds are both made and broken; atoms become combined with different atoms.

Excitability (irritability) Ability to respond to stimuli.

Excitation-contraction (E-C) coupling Sequence of events by which transmission of an action potential along the sarcolemma leads to the sliding of myofilaments.

Excitatory postsynaptic potential (EPSP) Depolarizing graded potential in a postsynaptic neuron.

Excretion (ek-skre′shun) Elimination of waste products from the body.

Exergonic reaction Chemical reaction that releases energy, e.g., a catabolic or oxidative reaction.

Exocrine glands (ek′so-krin) Glands that have ducts through which their secretions are carried to a particular site.

Exocytosis (ek″so-si-to′sis) Mechanism by which substances are moved from the cell interior to the extracellular space as a secretory vesicle fuses with the plasma membrane.

Exons Amino acid–specifying informational sequences (separated by introns) in the genes of higher organisms.

Extension Movement that increases the angle of a joint, e.g., straightening a flexed knee.

Exteroceptor (ek″ster-o-sep′tor) Sensory end organ that responds to stimuli from the external world.

Extracellular fluid (ECF) Internal fluid located outside cells; includes interstitial fluid, blood plasma, and cerebrospinal fluid.

Extracellular matrix Nonliving material in connective tissue consisting of ground substance and fibers that separates the living cells.

Extrasystole (ek″strah-sis′to-le) Premature heart contraction.

Extrinsic (ek-strin′sik) Of external origin.

Extrinsic eye muscles The six skeletal muscles which attach to and move each eye.

Facilitated diffusion Passive transport process used by certain molecules, e.g., glucose and other simple sugars too large to pass through plasma membrane pores. Involves movement through channels or movement facilitated by a membrane carrier.

Fallopian tube (fah-lo′pe-un) *See* Uterine tube.

Fascia (fash′e-ah) Layers of fibrous tissue covering and separating muscle.

Fascicle (fas′ĭ-kl) Bundle of nerve or muscle fibers bound together by connective tissue.

Fatty acids Linear chains of carbon and hydrogen atoms (hydrocarbon chains) with an organic acid group at one end. A constituent of fat.

Feces (fe′sēz) Material discharged from the bowel; composed of food residue, secretions, bacteria.

Fenestrated (fen′es-tra-tid) Pierced with one or more small openings.

Fertilization Fusion of the sperm and egg nuclei.

Fetus Developmental stage extending from the ninth week of development to birth.

Fiber A slender threadlike structure or filament. *See also* Nerve fiber, Muscle fiber.

Fibrillation Condition of rapid and irregular or out-of-phase heart contractions.

Fibrin (fi′brin) Fibrous insoluble protein formed during blood clotting.

Fibrinogen (fi-brin′o-jin) A soluble blood protein that is converted to insoluble fibrin during blood clotting.

Fibrinolysis Process that removes unneeded blood clots when healing has occurred.

Fibroblast (fi′bro-blast) Young, actively mitotic cell that forms the fibers of connective tissue.

Fibrocartilage The most compressible type of cartilage; resistant to stretch. Forms vertebral discs and knee joint cartilages.

Fibrocyte (fi′bro-sīt) Mature fibroblast; maintains the matrix of fibrous types of connective tissue.

Fibrosis Proliferation of fibrous connective tissue called scar tissue.

Fibrous joints Bones joined by fibrous tissue; no joint cavity is present.

Filtrate A plasma-derived fluid that is processed by the renal tubules to form urine.

Filtration Passage of a solvent and dissolved substances through a membrane or filter.

First-degree burn A burn in which only the epidermis is damaged.

Fissure (fih′sher) (1) A groove or cleft; (2) the deepest depressions or inward folds on the brain.

Fixator (fix′a-ter) Muscle that immobilizes one or more bones, allowing other muscles to act from a stable base.

Flagellum (flah-jel′lum) Long, whiplike cellular extension containing microtubules; propels sperm and some single-celled eukaryotes.

Flexion (flek′shun) Movement that decreases the angle of the joint, e.g., bending the knee from a straight to an angled position.

Flexor (withdrawal) reflex Reflex initiated by a painful stimulus (actual or perceived); causes automatic withdrawal of the threatened body part from the stimulus.

Fluid mosaic model A depiction of the structure of the membranes of a cell as phospholipid bilayers in which proteins are dispersed.

Follicle (fah′lih-kul) (1) Ovarian structure consisting of a developing egg surrounded by one or more layers of follicle cells; (2) colloid-containing structure of the thyroid gland; (3) B cell–rich region in lymphoid tissue.

Follicle-stimulating hormone (FSH) Hormone produced by the anterior pituitary that stimulates ovarian follicle production in females and sperm production in males.

Fontanelles (fon″tah-nelz′) Fibrous membranes at the angles of cranial bones that accommodate brain growth in the fetus and infant.

Foramen (fo-ra′men) Hole or opening in a bone or between body cavities.

Forebrain (prosencephalon) Anterior portion of the brain consisting of the telencephalon and the diencephalon.

Formed elements Cellular portion of blood.

Fossa (fos′ah) A depression, often an articular surface.

Fovea (fo′ve-ah) A pit.

Fracture A break in a bone.

Free radicals Highly reactive chemicals with unpaired electrons that can scramble the structure of proteins, lipids, and nucleic acids.

Frontal (coronal) plane Longitudinal (vertical) plane that divides the body or an organ into anterior and posterior parts.

Fulcrum The fixed point on which a lever moves when a force is applied.

Fundus (fun′dus) Base of an organ; part farthest from the opening of the organ. For example, the posterior wall of the eye.

G protein Protein that relays signals between extracellular first messengers (hormones or neurotransmitters) and intracellular second messengers (such as cyclic AMP) via an effector enzyme.

Gallbladder Sac beneath the right lobe of the liver used for bile storage.

Gallstones (biliary calculi) Crystallized cholesterol that obstructs the flow of bile from the gallbladder.

Gamete (gam′ēt) Sex or germ cell.

Gametogenesis (gam″eh-to-jen′eh-sis) Formation of gametes.

Ganglion (gang′gle-on) Collection of nerve cell bodies outside the CNS.

Ganglionic neuron (gan″gle-ah′nik) Autonomic motor neuron that has its cell body in a peripheral ganglion and projects its (postganglionic) axon to an effector.

Gap junction A passageway between two adjacent cells; formed by transmembrane proteins called connexons.

Gastrin Hormone secreted in the stomach; regulates gastric juice secretion by stimulating HCl production.

Gastroenteritis Inflammation of the gastrointestinal tract.

Gastrulation (gas″troo-la′shun) Developmental process that produces the three primary germ layers (ectoderm, mesoderm, and endoderm).

Gene One of the biological units of heredity located in chromatin; transmits hereditary information.

Genetic code Refers to the rules by which the base sequence of a DNA gene is translated into protein structures (amino acid sequences).

Genitalia (jen″i-ta′le-ă) The internal and external reproductive organs.

Genome The complete set of chromosomes derived from one parent (the haploid genome); or the two sets of chromosomes, i.e., one set from the egg, the other from the sperm (the diploid genome).

Genotype (jen′o-tīp) One's genetic makeup or genes.

Germ layers Three cellular layers (ectoderm, mesoderm, and endoderm) that represent the initial specialization of cells in the embryonic body and from which all body tissues arise.

Gestation period (jes-ta′shun) The period of pregnancy; about 280 days for humans.

Gland Organ specialized to secrete or excrete substances for further use in the body or for elimination.

Glaucoma (glaw-ko′mah) Condition in which intraocular pressure increases to levels that cause compression of the retina and optic nerve; results in blindness unless detected early.

Glial cells (gle′al) *See* Neuroglia.

Glomerular capsule (glo-mer′yoo-ler) Double-walled cup at end of a renal tubule; encloses a glomerulus. Also called Bowman's capsule.

Glomerular filtration rate (GFR) Rate of filtrate formation by the kidneys.

Glomerulus (glo-mer′u-lus) (1) Cluster of capillaries forming part of the nephron; forms filtrate; (2) odor-specific processing unit in olfactory bulb.

Glottis (glah′tis) Opening between the vocal cords in the larynx.

Glucagon (gloo′kah-gon) Hormone formed by alpha cells of pancreatic islets; raises the glucose level of blood.

Glucocorticoids (gloo″ko-kor′tĭ-koidz) Adrenal cortex hormones that increase blood glucose levels and aid the body in resisting long-term stressors.

Gluconeogenesis (gloo″ko-ne″o-jen′ĕ-sis) Formation of glucose from noncarbohydrate molecules.

Glucose (gloo′kōs) Principal blood sugar; a hexose.

Glycerol (glis′er-ol) A modified simple sugar (a sugar alcohol); a building block of fats.

Glycocalyx (cell coat) (gli″ko-kal′iks) A layer of externally facing glycoproteins on a cell's plasma membrane that determines blood type; involved in the cellular interactions of fertilization, embryonic development, and immunity, and acts as an adhesive between cells.

Glycogen (gli′ko-jin) Main carbohydrate stored in animal cells; a polysaccharide.

Glycogenesis (gli″ko-jen′ĕ-sis) Formation of glycogen from glucose.

Glycogenolysis (gli″ko-jĕ-nol′ĭ-sis) Breakdown of glycogen to glucose.

Glycolipid (gli″ko-lip′id) A lipid with one or more covalently attached sugars.

Glycolysis (gli-kol′ĭ-sis) Breakdown of glucose to pyruvic acid—an anaerobic process.

Goblet cells Individual cells (unicellular glands) that produce mucus.

Golgi apparatus (gol′je) Membranous system close to the cell nucleus that packages protein secretions for export, packages enzymes into lysosomes for cellular use, and modifies proteins destined to become part of cellular membranes.

Golgi tendon organs Proprioceptors located in tendons; monitor muscle tension to prevent tearing and help smooth onset and termination of muscle contraction.

Gonad (go′nad) Primary reproductive organ; i.e., the testis of the male or the ovary of the female.

Gonadocorticoids (gon″ah-do-kor′tĭ-koidz) Sex hormones, primarily androgens, secreted by the adrenal cortex.

Gonadotropins (gon″ah-do-trōp′inz) Gonad-stimulating hormones produced by the anterior pituitary.

Graafian follicle (graf′e-an) *See* Vesicular follicle.

Graded muscle responses Variations in the degree of muscle contraction by changing either the frequency or strength of the stimulus.

Graded potential A local change in membrane potential that varies directly with the strength of the stimulus, declines with distance.

Graves' disease Disorder resulting from hyperactive thyroid gland.

Gray matter Gray area of the central nervous system; contains neuronal cell bodies and their dendrites.

Growth hormone (GH) Hormone that stimulates growth in general; produced in the anterior pituitary; also called somatotropin (STH).

Guanine (G) (gwan′ēn) One of two major purines occurring in all nucleic acids.

Gustation (gus-ta′shun) Taste.

Gyrus (ji′rus) An outward fold of the surface of the cerebral cortex.

Hair follicle Structure with outer and inner root sheaths extending from the epidermal surface into the dermis and from which new hair develops.

Hapten (hap′ten) An incomplete antigen; has reactivity but not immunogenicity.

Haversian system (hah-ver′zhen) *See* Osteon.

Heart attack (coronary) *See* Myocardial infarction.

Heart block Impaired transmission of impulses from atrium to ventricle resulting in abnormally slow heart rhythms.

Heart murmur Abnormal heart sound (usually resulting from valve problems).

Heimlich maneuver Procedure in which the air in a person's own lungs is used to expel an obstructing piece of food.

Helper T cell Type of T lymphocyte that orchestrates cellular immunity by direct contact with other immune cells and by releasing chemicals called cytokines; also helps to mediate the humoral response by interacting with B cells.

Hematocrit (he-mat′o-krit) The percentage of total blood volume occupied by erythrocytes.

Hematoma (he″mah-to′mah) Mass of clotted blood that forms at an injured site.

Hematopoiesis (hem″ah-to-poi-e′sis) Blood cell formation; hemopoiesis.

Heme (hēm) Iron-containing pigment that is essential to oxygen transport by hemoglobin.

Hemocytoblast (he″mo-si′to-blast) Bone marrow cell that gives rise to all the formed elements of blood; hematopoietic stem cell.

Hemoglobin (he′muh-glo-bin) Oxygen-transporting protein of erythrocytes.

Hemolysis (he-mah′lĕ-sis) Rupture of erythrocytes.

Hemophilia (he″mo-fil′e-ah) A term loosely applied to several different hereditary bleeding disorders that exhibit similar signs and symptoms.

Hemopoiesis (he″mo-poi-e′sis) *See* Hematopoiesis.

Hemorrhage (hem′or-ij) Loss of blood from the vessels by flow through ruptured walls; bleeding.

Hemostasis (he″mo-sta′sis) Stoppage of bleeding.

Heparin Natural anticoagulant secreted into blood plasma.

Hepatic portal system (hĕ-pat′ik) Circulation in which the hepatic portal vein carries dissolved nutrients to the liver tissues for processing.

Hepatitis (hep″ah-ti′tis) Inflammation of the liver.

Hernia (her′ne-ah) Abnormal protrusion of an organ or a body part through the containing wall of its cavity.

Heterozygous (het″er-o-zi′gus) Having different allelic genes at a given locus or (by extension) many loci.

Hilton's law Any nerve serving a muscle that produces movement at a joint also innervates the joint and the skin over the joint.

Hilum (hi′lum) The indented region of an organ from which blood and/or lymphatic vessels and nerves enter and exit.

Hippocampus Limbic system structure that plays a role in converting new information into long-term memories.

Histamine (his′tuh-mēn) A chemical messenger (neurotransmitter or paracrine); causes vasodilation and increased capillary permeability; in stomach causes acid secretion.

Histology (his-tol′o-je) Branch of anatomy dealing with the microscopic structure of tissues.

HIV (human immunodeficiency virus) Virus that destroys helper T cells, thus depressing adaptive immunity; symptomatic AIDS gradually appears when lymph nodes can no longer contain the virus.

Holocrine glands (hol′o-krin) Glands that accumulate their secretions within their cells; secretions are discharged only upon rupture and death of the cell.

Homeostasis (ho″me-o-sta′sis) A state of body equilibrium or stable internal environment of the body.

Homologous (ho-mol′ŏ-gus) Parts or organs corresponding in structure but not necessarily in function.

Homozygous (ho-mo-zi′gus) Having identical genes at one or more loci.

Hormones Steroidal or amino acid–based molecules released to the blood that act as chemical messengers to regulate specific body functions.

Humoral immunity (hu′mer-ul) Immunity conferred by antibodies present in blood plasma and other body fluids.

Huntington's disease Hereditary disorder leading to degeneration of the basal nuclei and the cerebral cortex.

Hyaline cartilage (hi′ah-līn) The most abundant cartilage type in the body; provides firm support with some pliability.

Hydrochloric acid (HCl) (hi″dro-klor′ik) Acid that aids protein digestion in the stomach; produced by parietal cells.

Hydrogen bond Weak bond in which a hydrogen atom forms a bridge between two electron-hungry atoms. An important intramolecular bond.

Hydrogen ion (H⁺) A hydrogen atom minus its electron and therefore carrying a positive charge (i.e., a proton).

Hydrolysis (hi″drah′lă-sis) Process in which water is used to split a substance into smaller particles.

Hydrophilic (hi″dro-fil′ik) Refers to molecules, or portions of molecules, that interact with water and charged particles.

Hydrophobic (hi″dro-fo′bik) Refers to molecules, or portions of molecules, that interact only with nonpolar molecules.

Hydrostatic pressure (hi″dro-stă′tic) Pressure of fluid in a system.

Hydroxyl ion (OH⁻) (hi-drok′sil) An ion liberated when a hydroxide (a common inorganic base) is dissolved in water.

Hyperalgesia Pain amplification.

Hypercapnia (hi″per-kap′ne-ah) High carbon dioxide levels in the blood.

Hyperemia An increase in blood flow into a tissue or organ; congested with blood.

Hyperglycemic (hi″per-gli-se′mik) Term used to describe hormones such as glucagon that elevate blood glucose level.

Hyperopia (hi″per-o′pe-ah) A condition in which visual images are routinely focused behind rather than on the retina; commonly known as farsightedness.

Hyperplasia (hi″per-pla′ze-ah) Accelerated growth, e.g., in anemia, the bone marrow produces red blood cells at a faster rate.

Hyperpnea (hi″perp-ne′ah) An increase in ventilation in response to metabolic need (e.g., during exercise).

Hyperpolarization An increase in membrane potential in which the membrane becomes more negative than resting membrane potential.

Hypersensitivity Overzealous immune response to an otherwise harmless antigen.

Hypertension (hi″per-ten′shun) High blood pressure.

Hypertonic (hi″per-ton′ik) Excessive, above normal, tone or tension.

Hypertonic solution A solution that has a higher concentration of non-penetrating solutes than the reference cell; having greater osmotic pressure than the reference solution (blood plasma or interstitial fluid).

Hypertrophy (hi-per′trah-fe) Increase in size of a tissue or organ independent of the body's general growth.

Hyperventilation An increase in the depth and rate of breathing that is in excess of the body's need for removal of carbon dioxide.

Hypocapnia Low carbon dioxide levels in the blood.

Hypodermis (superficial fascia) Subcutaneous tissue just deep to the skin; consists of adipose plus some areolar connective tissue.

Hypoglycemic (hi″po-gli-se′mik) Term used to describe hormones such as insulin that decrease blood glucose level.

Hyponatremia Abnormally low concentrations of sodium ions in extracellular fluid.

Hypoproteinemia (hi″po-pro″te-ĭ-ne′me-ah) A condition of unusually low levels of plasma proteins causing a reduction in colloid osmotic pressure; results in tissue edema.

Hypotension Low blood pressure.

Hypothalamic-hypophyseal tract (hi″po-thah-lam′ik–hi″po-fiz′-e-al) Nerve bundles that run through the infundibulum and connect the neurohypophysis and the hypothalamus.

Hypothalamus (hi″po-thal′ah-mus) Region of the diencephalon forming the floor of the third ventricle of the brain.

Hypotonic (hi″po-ton′ik) Below normal tone or tension.

Hypotonic solution A solution that is more dilute (containing fewer nonpenetrating solutes) than the reference cell. Cells placed in hypotonic solutions plump up rapidly as water rushes into them.

Hypoventilation A decrease in the depth and rate of breathing; characterized by an increase in blood carbon dioxide.

Hypovolemic shock (hi″po-vo-le′mik) Most common form of shock; results from extreme blood loss.

Hypoxia (hi-pok′se-ah) Condition in which inadequate oxygen is available to tissues.

Ileocecal valve (il″e-o-se′kal) Site where the small intestine joins the large intestine.

Ileum (il′e-um) Terminal part of the small intestine; between the jejunum and the cecum of the large intestine.

Immune system A functional system whose components attack foreign substances or prevent their entry into the body.

Immunity (im″ūn′ĭ-te) Ability of the body to resist many agents (both living and nonliving) that can cause disease; resistance to disease.

Immunocompetence Ability of the body's immune cells to recognize (by binding) specific antigens; reflects the presence of plasma membrane–bound receptors.

Immunodeficiency Any congenital or acquired condition causing a deficiency in the production or function of immune cells or certain molecules (complement, antibodies, etc.) required for normal immunity.

In vitro (in ve′tro) In a test tube, glass, or artificial environment.

In vivo (in ve′vo) In the living body.

Incompetent valve Valve which does not close properly.

Incontinence Inability to control micturition or defecation voluntarily.

Infarct (in′farkt) Region of dead, deteriorating tissue resulting from a lack of blood supply.

Infectious mononucleosis Highly contagious viral disease; marked by excessive agranulocytes.

Inferior (caudal) Pertaining to a position toward the lower or tail end of the long axis of the body.

Inferior vena cava Vein that returns blood from body areas below the diaphragm.

Inflammation (in″flah-ma′shun) An innate (nonspecific) defensive response of the body to tissue injury; includes dilation of blood vessels and an increase in vessel permeability; indicated by redness, heat, swelling, and pain.

Infundibulum (in″fun-dib′u-lum) (1) A stalk of tissue that connects the pituitary gland to the hypothalamus; (2) the distal end of the uterine (fallopian) tube.

Inguinal (ing′wĭ-nal) Pertaining to the groin region.

Inhibitory postsynaptic potential (IPSP) A graded potential in a postsynaptic neuron that inhibits action potential generation; usually hyperpolarizing.

Inner cell mass Accumulation of cells in the blastocyst from which the embryo develops.

Innervation (in″er-va′shun) Supply of nerves to a body part.

Inorganic compound Chemical substances that do not contain carbon, including water, salts, and many acids and bases.

Insertion Movable attachment of a muscle.

Insula Lobe of the cerebral cortex that is buried in the lateral sulcus beneath portions of the parietal, frontal, and temporal lobes.

Insulin A hormone that enhances the carrier-mediated diffusion of glucose into tissue cells, thus lowering blood glucose levels.

Insulin resistance State in which a greater than normal amount of insulin is required to maintain normal glucose blood levels.

Integration The process by which the nervous system processes and interprets sensory input and makes decisions about what should be done at each moment.

Integumentary system (in-teg″u-men′tar-e) Skin and its derivatives; provides the external protective covering of the body.

Intercalated discs (in-ter′kah-la″ted) Specialized connections between myocardial cells containing gap junctions and desmosomes.

Interferons (IFNs) (in-ter-fēr′ons) Proteins released from virus-infected (and other) cells that protect uninfected cells from viral takeover. Also inhibit some cancers.

Internal capsule Band of projection fibers that runs between the basal nuclei and the thalamus.

Internal respiration Exchange of gases between blood and tissue fluid and between tissue fluid and cells.

Interneuron (association neuron) Nerve cell located between motor and sensory neurons that shuttles signals through CNS pathways where integration occurs.

Interoceptor (in″ter-o-sep′tor) Sensory receptor nerve ending in the viscera, which is sensitive to changes and stimuli within the body's internal environment; also called visceroceptor.

Interphase One of two major periods in the cell life cycle; includes the period from cell formation to cell division.

Interstitial cells Cells located in the loose connective tissue surrounding the seminiferous tubules; they produce androgens (most importantly testosterone), which are secreted into the surrounding interstitial fluid.

Interstitial fluid (IF) (in″ter-stish′al) Fluid between the cells.

Interstitial lamellae Incomplete lamellae that lie between intact osteons, filling the gaps between forming osteons, or representing the remnants of an osteon that has been cut through by bone remodeling.

Intervertebral discs (in″ter-ver′teh-brul) Discs of fibrocartilage between vertebrae.

Intracapsular ligament Ligament located within and separate from the articular capsule of a synovial joint.

Intracellular fluid (ICF) (in″trah-sel′u-ler) Fluid within a cell.

Intrinsic factor Substance produced by the stomach that is required for vitamin B_{12} absorption.

Intron Noncoding segment or portion of DNA that ranges from 60 to 100,000 nucleotides long.

Involuntary muscle Muscle that cannot ordinarily be controlled voluntarily (e.g., smooth and cardiac muscle).

Involuntary nervous system The autonomic nervous system.

Ion (ī′on) Atom with a positive or negative electric charge.

Ionic bond (ī-ah′nik) Chemical bond formed by electron transfer between atoms.

Ipsilateral (ip″sih-lă′ter-ul) Situated on the same side.

Ischemia (is-ke′me-ah) Local decrease in blood supply.

Isograft Tissue graft donated by an identical twin.

Isomer (i′so-mer) One of two or more substances that has the same molecular formula but with its atoms arranged differently.

Isometric contraction (i″so-mě′trik) Contraction in which the muscle does not shorten (the load is too heavy) but its internal tension increases.

Isotonic contraction (i″so-tah′nik) Contraction in which muscle tension remains constant at a given joint angle and load, and the muscle shortens.

Isotonic solution A solution with a concentration of nonpenetrating solutes equal to that found in the reference cell.

Isotopes (i′so-tōps) Different atomic forms of the same element, vary only in the number of neutrons they contain; the heavier species tend to be radioactive.

Jejunum (jĕ-joo′num) The part of the small intestine between the duodenum and the ileum.

Joint (articulation) The junction of two or more bones.

Joint kinesthetic receptor (kin″es-thet′ik) Receptor that provides information on joint position and motion.

Juxtaglomerular apparatus (JGA) (juks″tah-glo-mer′u-lar) Cells of the distal part of the ascending limb of the loop of Henle and afferent arteriole located close to the glomerulus; involved in blood pressure regulation (via release of the hormone renin) and autoregulation of GFR.

Karyotype (kar′e-o-tīp) The diploid chromosomal complement, typically shown as homologous chromosome pairs arranged from longest to shortest (X and Y are arranged by size rather than paired).

Keratin (ker′ah-tin) Fibrous protein found in the epidermis, hair, and nails that makes those structures hard and water resistant; precursor is keratohyaline.

Ketones (ketone bodies) (ke′tōnz) Fatty acid metabolites; strong organic acids.

Ketosis (kē-tō′sis) Excess levels of ketone bodies in blood. Called ketoacidosis if blood pH is low.

Killer T cell *See* Cytotoxic T cell.

Kilocalories (kcal) *See* Calorie.

Kinetic energy (ki-net′ik) The energy of motion or movement, e.g., the constant movement of atoms, or the push given to a swinging door that sets it into motion.

Krebs cycle Aerobic metabolic pathway occurring within mitochondria, in which food metabolites are oxidized and CO_2 is liberated, and coenzymes are reduced. Also called the citric acid cycle.

Labia (la′be-ah) Lips; singular: labium.

Labor Collective term for the series of events that expel the infant from the uterus.

Labyrinth (lab′ĭ-rinth″) Bony cavities and membranes of the inner ear.

Lacrimal (lak′ri-mal) Pertaining to tears.

Lactation (lak-ta′shun) Production and secretion of milk.

Lacteal (lak′te-al) Special lymphatic capillaries of the small intestine that take up lipids.

Lactic acid (lak′tik) Product of anaerobic metabolism, especially in muscle.

Lacuna (lah-ku′nah) A small space, cavity, or depression; lacunae in bone or cartilage are occupied by cells.

Lamella (lah-mel′ah) A layer, such as of bone matrix in an osteon of compact bone.

Lamina (lam′ĭ-nah) (1) A thin layer or flat plate; (2) the portion of a vertebra between the transverse process and the spinous process.

Large intestine Portion of the digestive tract extending from the ileocecal valve to the anus; includes the cecum, appendix, colon, rectum, and anal canal.

Larynx (lar′ingks) Cartilaginous organ located between the trachea and the pharynx; voice box.

Latent period Period of time between stimulation and the onset of muscle contraction.

Lateral Away from the midline of the body.

Leptin Hormone released by fat cells that signals satiety.

Leukemia Refers to a group of cancerous conditions of white blood cells.

Leukocytes (loo′ko-sīts) White blood cells; formed elements involved in body protection that take part in inflammatory and immune responses.

Leukocytosis An increase in the number of leukocytes (white blood cells); usually the result of a microbiological attack on the body.

Leukopenia (loo″ko-pe′ne-ah) Abnormally low white blood cell count.

Leukopoiesis The production of white blood cells.

Lever system Consists of a lever (bone), effort (muscle action), resistance (weight of object to be moved), and fulcrum (joint).

Ligament (lig′ah-ment) Band of regular fibrous tissue that connects bones.

Ligands Signaling chemicals that bind specifically to membrane receptors.

Limbic system (lim′bik) Functional brain system involved in emotional response and memory formation.

Lipid (lih′pid) Organic compound formed of carbon, hydrogen, and oxygen; examples are fats and cholesterol.

Lipolysis (lĭ-pol′ĭ-sis) The breakdown of stored fats into glycerol and fatty acids.

Liver Lobed accessory organ that overlies the stomach; produces bile to help digest fat, and serves other metabolic and regulatory functions.

Lumbar (lum′bar) Portion of the back between the thorax and the pelvis.

Lumbar vertebrae The five vertebrae of the lumbar region of the vertebral column, commonly called the small of the back.

Lumen (loo′min) Cavity inside a tube, blood vessel, or hollow organ.

Luteinizing hormone (LH) (lu′te-in-īz″ing) Anterior pituitary hormone that aids maturation of cells in the ovary and triggers ovulation in females. In males, causes the interstitial cells of the testis to produce testosterone.

Lymph (limf) Protein-containing fluid transported by lymphatic vessels.

Lymph node Small lymphoid organ that filters lymph; contains macrophages and lymphocytes.

Lymphatic system (lim-fat′ik) System consisting of lymphatic vessels, lymph nodes, and lymph; drains excess tissue fluid from the extracellular space. The nodes provide sites for immune surveillance.

Lymphatics General term used to designate the lymphatic vessels that collect and transport lymph.

Lymphocyte Agranular white blood cell that arises from bone marrow and becomes functionally mature in the lymphoid organs of the body.

Lysosomes (li′so-sōmz) Organelles that originate from the Golgi apparatus and contain strong digestive enzymes.

Lysozyme (li′so-zīm) Enzyme in sweat, saliva, and tears that is capable of destroying certain kinds of bacteria.

Macromolecules Large, complex molecules containing from 100 to over 10,000 subunits.

Macrophage (mak′ro-fāj″) Protective cell type common in connective tissue, lymphoid tissue, and many body organs; phagocytizes tissue cells, bacteria, and other foreign debris; presents antigens to T cells in the immune response.

Macula (mak′u-lah) (1) Static equilibrium receptor within the vestibule of the inner ear; (2) a colored area or spot.

Malignant (muh-lig′nent) Life threatening; pertains to neoplasms that spread and lead to death, such as cancer.

Malignant melanoma (mel″ah-no′mah) Cancer of the melanocytes; can begin wherever there is pigment.

Mammary glands (mam′mer-e) Milk-producing glands of the breast.

Mandible (man′dĭ-bl) Lower jawbone; U shaped, largest bone of the face.

Mass number Sum of the number of protons and neutrons in the nucleus of an atom.

Mast cells Immune cells that function to detect foreign substances in the tissue spaces and initiate local inflammatory responses against them; typically found clustered deep to an epithelium or along blood vessels.

Mastication (mas″tĭ-ka′shun) Chewing.

Meatus (me-a′tus) External opening of a canal.

Mechanical advantage (power lever) Condition that occurs when the load is close to the fulcrum and the effort is applied far from the fulcrum; allows a small effort exerted over a relatively large distance to move a large load over a small distance.

Mechanical disadvantage (speed lever) Condition that occurs when the load is far from the fulcrum and the effort is applied near the fulcrum; the effort applied must be greater than the load to be moved.

Mechanical energy The energy directly involved in moving matter; e.g., in bicycle riding, the legs provide the mechanical energy that moves the pedals.

Mechanoreceptor (meh″kĕ-no-re-sep′tor) Receptor sensitive to mechanical pressure such as touch, sound, or exerted by muscle contraction.

Medial (me′de-ahl) Toward the midline of the body.

Median (midsagittal) plane Specific sagittal plane that lies exactly in the midline.

Mediastinum (me″de-ah-sti′num) The medial cavity of the thorax containing the heart, great vessels, and trachea.

Medulla (mĕ-dul′ah) Central portion of certain organs.

Medulla oblongata (mĕ-dul′ah ob″long-gah′tah) Inferiormost part of the brain stem.

Medullary cavity Central cavity of a long bone. Contains yellow or red (bone) marrow.

Meiosis (mi-o′sis) Nuclear division process that reduces the chromosomal number by half and results in the formation of four haploid (*n*) cells; occurs only in certain reproductive organs.

Melanin (mel′ah-nin) Dark pigment formed by cells called melanocytes; imparts color to skin and hair.

Melatonin (mel′ah-to′nin) A hormone secreted by the pineal gland; secretion peaks at night and helps set sleep-wake cycles; also a powerful antioxidant.

Membrane potential Voltage across the plasma membrane.

Membrane receptors A large, diverse group of integral proteins and glycoproteins that serve as binding sites for signaling molecules.

Memory cells Members of T cell and B cell clones that provide for immunological memory.

Menarche (mĕ-nar′ke) Establishment of menstrual function; the first menstrual period.

Meninges (mĕ-nin′jēz) Protective coverings of the central nervous system; from the most external to the most internal, the dura mater, arachnoid mater, and pia mater.

Meningitis (mĕ-nin-ji′tis) Inflammation of the meninges.

Menopause Period of life when, prompted by hormonal changes, ovulation and menstruation cease.

Menstruation (men″stroo-a′shun) The periodic, cyclic discharge of blood, secretions, tissue, and mucus from the mature female uterus in the absence of pregnancy.

Merocrine glands (mer′o-krin) Glands that produce secretions intermittently; secretions do not accumulate in the gland.

Mesencephalon (mes″en-sef′ah-lon) One of the three primary vesicles of the developing brain; becomes the midbrain.

Mesenchyme (meh′zin-kīm) Common embryonic tissue from which all connective tissues arise.

Mesenteries (mes″en-ter′ēz) Double-layered extensions of the peritoneum that support most organs in the abdominal cavity.

Mesoderm (mez′o-derm) Primary germ layer that forms the skeleton and muscles of the body.

Mesothelium (mez″o-the′le-um) The epithelium found in serous membranes lining the ventral body cavity and covering its organs.

Messenger RNA (mRNA) Long nucleotide strands that reflect the exact nucleotide sequences of the genetically active DNA and carry the message of the latter.

Metabolic (fixed) acid Acid generated by cellular metabolism that must be eliminated by the kidneys.

Metabolic rate (mĕt″ah-bol′ik) Energy expended by the body per unit time.

Metabolic water (water of oxidation) Water produced from cellular metabolism (about 10% of our body's water).

Metabolism (mĕ-tab′o-lizm) Sum total of the chemical reactions occurring in the body cells.

Metaphase Second stage of mitosis.

Metastasis (mĕ-tas′tah-sis) The spread of cancer from one body part or organ into another not directly connected to it.

Metencephalon (afterbrain) A secondary brain vesicle; anterior portion of the rhombencephalon of the developing brain; becomes the pons and the cerebellum.

MHC (major histocompatibility complex) proteins Molecules on the outer plasma membrane of all cells; help the immune system distinguish self from nonself. T cells recognize antigens only when combined with these proteins.

Microfilaments (mi″kro-fil′ah-ments) Thin strands of the contractile protein actin.

Microglia (mi-kro′gle-ah) A type of CNS supporting cell; can transform into phagocytes in areas of neural damage or inflammation.

Microtubules (mi″kro-tu′būlz) One of three types of rods in the cytoskeleton of a cell; hollow tubes made of spherical protein that determine the cell shape as well as the distribution of cellular organelles.

Microvilli (mi″kro-vil′i) Tiny projections on the free surfaces of some epithelial cells; increase surface area for absorption.

Micturition (mik″tu-rish′un) Urination, or voiding; emptying the bladder.

Midbrain (mesencephalon) Region of the brain stem between the diencephalon and the pons.

Midsagittal (median) plane Specific sagittal plane that lies exactly in the midline.

Milliequivalents per liter (mEq/L) The units used to measure electrolyte concentrations of body fluids; a measure of the number of electrical charges in 1 liter of solution.

Mineralocorticoid (min″er-al″ō-kor′tih-koyd) Steroid hormone of the adrenal cortex that regulates Na^+ and K^+ metabolism and fluid balance.

Minerals Inorganic chemical compounds found in nature; salts.

Mitochondria (mi″to-kon′dre-ah) Cytoplasmic organelles responsible for ATP generation for cellular activities.

Mitosis Process during which the chromosomes are redistributed to two daughter nuclei; nuclear division. Consists of prophase, metaphase, anaphase, and telophase.

Mitotic (M) phase One of two major periods in the cell life cycle; involves the division of the nucleus (mitosis) and the division of the cytoplasm (cytokinesis).

Mitral (bicuspid) valve (mi′tral) The left atrioventricular valve.

Mixed nerves Nerves containing the processes of motor and sensory neurons; their impulses travel to and from the central nervous system.

Molar (mo′lar) (1) A solution concentration determined by mass of solute—1 liter of solution contains an amount of solute equal to its molecular weight in grams. (2) Broad back teeth that grind and crush.

Molarity (mo-lar′ĭ-te) A way to express the concentration of a solution; moles per liter of solution.

Mole (mōl) A mole of any element or compound is equal to its atomic weight or its molecular weight (sum of atomic weights) measured in grams.

Molecule Particle consisting of two or more atoms joined together by chemical bonds.

Monoclonal antibodies (mon″o-klo′nal) Pure preparations of identical antibodies that exhibit specificity for a single antigen.

Monocyte (mon′o-sīt) Large single-nucleus white blood cell; agranular leukocyte.

Monosaccharide (mon″o-sak′ah-rīd) Literally, one sugar; building block of carbohydrates; e.g., glucose.

Morula (mor′u-lah) The mulberry-like solid mass of blastomeres resulting from cleavage in the early conceptus.

Motor areas Functional areas in the cerebral cortex that control voluntary motor functions.

Motor (efferent) nerves Nerves that carry impulses leaving the brain and spinal cord, and destined for effectors.

Motor unit A motor neuron and all the muscle cells it stimulates.

Mucous membranes (mucosae) Membranes that form the linings of body cavities open to the exterior (digestive, respiratory, urinary, and reproductive tracts).

Mucus (myoo′kus) A sticky, thick fluid secreted by mucous glands and mucous membranes; keeps the free surface of membranes moist.

Multinucleate cell (mul″tĭ-nu′kle-āt) Cell with more than one nucleus, e.g., skeletal muscle cells, osteoclasts.

Multiple sclerosis (MS) Demyelinating disorder of the CNS; causes hardened patches (sclerosis) in the brain and spinal cord.

Multipolar neurons Neurons with three or more processes; most common neuron type in the CNS.

Muscarinic receptors (mus″kah-rin′ik) Acetylcholine-binding receptors of the autonomic nervous system's target organs; named for activation by the mushroom poison muscarine.

Muscle fiber A muscle cell.

Muscle spindle (neuromuscular spindle) Encapsulated receptor found in skeletal muscle that is sensitive to stretch.

Muscle tension The force exerted by a contracting muscle on some object.

Muscle tone Low levels of contractile activity in relaxed muscle; keeps the muscle healthy and ready to act.

Muscle twitch The response of a muscle to a single brief threshold stimulus.

Muscular dystrophy A group of inherited muscle-destroying diseases.

Muscular system The organ system consisting of the skeletal muscles of the body and their connective tissue attachments.

Myelencephalon (spinal brain) A secondary brain vesicle; lower part of the developing hindbrain, especially the medulla oblongata.

Myelin sheath (mi′ĕ-lin) Fatty insulating sheath that surrounds all but the smallest nerve fibers.

Myoblasts Embryonic mesoderm cells from which all muscle fibers develop.

Myocardial infarction (MI) (mi″o-kar′de-al in-fark′shun) Condition characterized by dead tissue areas in the myocardium; caused by interruption of blood supply to the area. Commonly called heart attack.

Myocardium (mi″o-kar′de-um) Layer of the heart wall composed of cardiac muscle.

Myofibril (mi″o-fi′bril) Rodlike bundle of contractile filaments (myofilaments) found in muscle fibers (cells).

Myofilament (mi″o-fil′ah-ment) Filament that constitutes myofibrils. Of two types: actin and myosin.

Myoglobin (mi″o-glo′bin) Oxygen-binding pigment in muscle.

Myogram A graphic recording of mechanical contractile activity produced by an apparatus that measures muscle contraction.

Myometrium (mi″o-me′tre-um) Thick uterine musculature.

Myopia (mi-o′pe-ah) A condition in which visual images are focused in front of rather than on the retina; nearsightedness.

Myosin (mi′o-sin) One of the principal contractile proteins found in muscle.

Myxedema (mik″sĕ-de′mah) Condition resulting from underactive thyroid gland.

Nares (na′rez) Nostrils.

Natural killer (NK) cell Defensive cell (a type of lymphocyte) that can kill cancer cells and virus-infected body cells before the adaptive immune system is activated.

Necrosis (nĕ-kro′sis) Death or disintegration of a cell or tissues caused by disease or injury.

Negative feedback mechanisms The most common homeostatic control mechanism. The net effect is that the output of the system shuts off the original stimulus or reduces its intensity.

Neonatal period The four-week period immediately after birth.

Neoplasm (ne′o-plazm) An abnormal mass of proliferating cells. Benign neoplasms remain localized; malignant neoplasms are cancers, which can spread to other organs.

Nephron (nef′ron) Structural and functional unit of the kidney; consists of the glomerulus and renal tubule.

Nerve A bundle of axons in the peripheral nervous system.

Nerve fiber Axon of a neuron.

Nerve growth factor (NGF) Protein that promotes survival and development of neurons; secreted by their target cells and many other cell types.

Nerve impulse A self-propagating wave of depolarization; also called an action potential.

Nerve plexuses Interlacing nerve networks that occur in the cervical, brachial, lumbar, and sacral regions and primarily serve the limbs.

Nervous system Fast-acting control system that triggers muscle contraction or gland secretion.

Neural tube Fetal structure which gives rise to the brain, spinal cord, and associated neural structures; formed from ectoderm by day 23 of embryonic development.

Neuroglia (nu-rog′le-ah) Nonexcitable cells of neural tissue that support, protect, and insulate the neurons; glial cells.

Neurohypophysis (nu″ro-hi-pof′ĭ-sis) Posterior pituitary plus infundibulum; portion of the pituitary gland derived from the brain.

Neuromuscular junction Region where a motor neuron comes into close contact with a skeletal muscle cell.

Neuron (nerve cell) (nu′ron) Cell of the nervous system specialized to generate and transmit electrical signals (action potentials and graded potentials).

Neuron cell body The biosynthetic center of a neuron; also called the perikaryon, or soma.

Neuronal pools Functional groups of neurons that process and integrate information.

Neuropeptides (nu″ro-pep′tīds) A class of neurotransmitters including beta endorphins and enkephalins (which act as euphorics and reduce perception of pain) and gut-brain peptides.

Neurotransmitter Chemical messenger released by neurons that may, upon binding to receptors of neurons or effector cells, stimulate or inhibit those neurons or effector cells.

Neutral fats Consist of fatty acid chains and glycerol; also called triglycerides or triacylglycerols. Commonly known as oils when liquid.

Neutralization reaction Displacement reaction in which mixing an acid and a base forms water and a salt.

Neutron (nu′tron) Uncharged subatomic particle; found in the atomic nucleus.

Neutrophil (nu′tro-fil) Most abundant type of white blood cell.

Nicotinic receptors (nik″o-tin′ik) Acetylcholine-binding receptors of all autonomic ganglionic neurons and skeletal muscle neuromuscular junctions; named for activation by nicotine.

Nitric oxide (NO) A gaseous chemical messenger; diverse functions include participation in memory formation in the brain, and causing vasodilation throughout the body.

Nociceptor (no″se-sep′tor) Receptor sensitive to potentially damaging stimuli that result in pain.

Nondisjunction Failure of sister chromatids to separate during mitosis or failure of homologous pairs to separate during meiosis; results in abnormal numbers of chromosomes in the resulting daughter cells.

Nonpolar molecules Electrically balanced molecules.

Norepinephrine (NE) (nor″ep-ĭ-nef′rin) A catecholamine neurotransmitter and adrenal medullary hormone, associated with sympathetic nervous system activation.

Nuclear envelope The double membrane barrier of a cell nucleus.

Nucleic acid (nu-kle′ik) Class of organic molecules that includes DNA and RNA.

Nucleoli (nu-kle′o-li) Dense spherical bodies in the cell nucleus involved with ribosomal RNA (rRNA) synthesis and ribosomal subunit assembly.

Nucleosome (nu′kle-o-sōm) Fundamental unit of chromatin; consists of a strand of DNA wound around a cluster of eight histone proteins.

Nucleotide (nu′kle-o-tīd) Building block of nucleic acids; consists of a sugar, a nitrogen-containing base, and a phosphate group.

Nucleus (nu′kle-is) (1) Control center of a cell; contains genetic material; (2) clusters of nerve cell bodies in the CNS.

Nutrients Chemical substances taken in via the diet that are used for energy and cell building.

Oblique section A cut made diagonally between the horizontal and vertical plane of the body or an organ.

Occlusion (ah-kloo′zhun) Closure or obstruction.

Octet rule (rule of eights) (ok-tet′) The tendency of atoms to interact in such a way that they have eight electrons in their valence shell.

Olfaction (ol-fak′shun) Smell.

Oligodendrocyte (ol″ĭ-go-den′dro-sīt) A type of CNS supporting cell that composes myelin sheaths.

Oocyte (o′o-sīt) Immature female gamete.

Oogenesis (o″o-jen′ĕ-sis) Process of ovum (female gamete) formation.

Ophthalmic (of-thal′mik) Pertaining to the eye.

Optic (op′tik) Pertaining to the eye or vision.

Optic chiasma (op′tik ki-az′muh) The partial crossover of fibers of the optic nerves.

Organ A part of the body formed of two or more tissues and adapted to carry out a specific function; e.g., the stomach.

Organ system A group of organs that work together to perform a vital body function; e.g., the nervous system.

Organelles (or″gah-nelz′) Small cellular structures (ribosomes, mitochondria, and others) that perform specific metabolic functions for the cell as a whole.

Organic compound Any compound composed of atoms (some of which are carbon) held together by covalent (shared electron) bonds.

Organic Pertaining to carbon-containing molecules, such as proteins, fats, and carbohydrates.

Organism The living animal (or plant), which represents the sum total of all its organ systems working together to maintain life.

Origin Attachment of a muscle that remains relatively fixed during muscular contraction.

Osmolality The number of solute particles dissolved in 1 kilogram (1000 g) of water; reflects the solution's ability to cause osmosis.

Osmolarity (oz″mo-lar′ĭ-te) The number of solute particles present in 1 liter of a solution.

Osmoreceptor (oz″mo-re-sep′tor) Structure sensitive to osmotic pressure or concentration of a solution.

Osmosis (oz-mo′sis) Diffusion of a solvent through a membrane from a dilute solution into a more concentrated one.

Osmotic pressure A measure of the tendency of water to move into a more concentrated solution.

Ossicles *See* Auditory ossicles.

Ossification (os″ĭ-fi-ka′shun) *See* Osteogenesis.

Osteoblasts (os′te-o-blasts) Bone-forming cells.

Osteoclasts (os′te-o-klasts) Large cells that resorb or break down bone matrix.

Osteocyte (os′te-o-sīt) Mature bone cell.

Osteogenesis (os″te-o-jen′e-sis) The process of bone formation; also called ossification.

Osteoid (os′te-oid) Unmineralized bone matrix.

Osteomalacia (os″te-o-mah-la′she-ah) Disorder in which bones are inadequately mineralized; soft bones.

Osteon (os′te-on) System of interconnecting canals in the microscopic structure of adult compact bone; unit of bone; also called Haversian system.

Osteoporosis (os″te-o-po-ro′sis) Decreased density and strength of bone resulting from a gradual decrease in rate of bone formation.

Ovarian cycle (o-vayr′e-an) Monthly cycle of follicle development, ovulation, and corpus luteum formation in an ovary.

Ovary (o′var-e) Female reproductive organ in which ova (eggs) are produced; female gonad.

Ovulation (ov″u-la′shun) Ejection of an immature egg (oocyte) from the ovary.

Ovum (o′vum) Female gamete; egg.

Oxidases Enzymes that catalyze the transfer of oxygen in oxidation-reduction reactions.

Oxidation (oks′ĭ-da″shun) Process of substances combining with oxygen or the removal of hydrogen.

Oxidation-reduction (redox) reaction A reaction that couples the oxidation (loss of electrons) of one substance with the reduction (gain of electrons) of another substance.

Oxidative phosphorylation (ok″sĭ-da″tiv fos″for-ĭ-la′shun) Process of ATP synthesis during which an inorganic phosphate group is attached to ADP; occurs via the electron transport chain within the mitochondria.

Oxygen deficit The volume of oxygen required after exercise to replenish stores of O_2, ATP, creatine phosphate, and glycogen and oxidize the lactic acid formed during exercise.

Oxyhemoglobin (ok″sĭ-he″mo-glo′bin) Oxygen-bound form of hemoglobin.

Oxytocin (ok″sĭ-to′sin) Hormone synthesized in the hypothalamus and secreted by the posterior pituitary; stimulates contraction of the uterus during childbirth and the ejection of milk during nursing.

Paget's disease (paj′ets) Disorder characterized by excessive bone breakdown and abnormal bone formation.

Palate (pal′at) Roof of the mouth.

Pancreas (pan′kre-us) Gland located behind the stomach, between the spleen and the duodenum; produces both endocrine and exocrine secretions.

Pancreatic juice (pan″kre-at′ik) Bicarbonate-rich secretion of the pancreas containing enzymes for digestion of all food categories.

Papilla (pah-pil′ah) Small, nipple-like projection; e.g., dermal papillae are projections of dermal tissue into the epidermis.

Paracrine (par′ah-krin) A chemical messenger that acts locally within the same tissue and is rapidly destroyed. Examples are prostaglandins and nitric oxide.

Parasagittal planes All sagittal planes offset from the midline.

Parasympathetic division The division of the autonomic nervous system that oversees digestion, elimination, and glandular function; the resting and digesting subdivision.

Parasympathetic tone Normal (background) level of parasympathetic output; sustains normal gastrointestinal and urinary tract activity, lowers heart rate.

Parathyroid glands (par″ah-thi′roid) Small endocrine glands located on the posterior aspect of the thyroid gland.

Parathyroid hormone (PTH) Hormone released by the parathyroid glands that regulates blood calcium level.

Parietal (pah-ri′ĕ-tal) Pertaining to the walls of a cavity.

Parietal serosa The part of the double-layered membrane that lines the walls of the ventral body cavity.

Parkinson's disease Neurodegenerative disorder of the basal nuclei due to insufficient secretion of the neurotransmitter dopamine; symptoms include tremor and rigid movement.

Partial pressure The pressure exerted by a single component of a mixture of gases.

Parturition (par″tu-rish′un) Culmination of pregnancy; giving birth.

Passive immunity Short-lived immunity resulting from the introduction of "borrowed antibodies" obtained from an immune animal or human donor; immunological memory is not established.

Passive (transport) processes Membrane transport processes that do not require cellular energy (ATP), e.g., diffusion, which is driven by kinetic energy.

Pathogen (path′o-jen) Disease-causing organism.

Pectoral (pek′tor-al) Pertaining to the chest.

Pectoral (shoulder) girdle Bones that attach the upper limbs to the axial skeleton; includes the clavicle and scapula.

Pedigree Traces a particular genetic trait through several generations and helps predict the genotype of future offspring.

Pelvic girdle (hip girdle) Consists of the paired coxal bones that attach the lower limbs to the axial skeleton.

Pelvis (pel′vis) (1) Basin-shaped bony structure composed of the pelvic girdle, sacrum, and coccyx; (2) funnel-shaped tube within the kidney continuous with the ureter.

Penis (pe′nis) Male organ of copulation and urination.

Pepsin Enzyme capable of digesting proteins in an acid pH.

Peptide bond (pep′tīd) Bond joining the amine group of one amino acid to the acid carboxyl group of a second amino acid with the loss of a water molecule.

Perforating canals Canals that run at right angles to the long axis of the bone, connecting the vascular and nerve supplies of the periosteum to those of the central canals and medullary cavity; also called Volkmann's canals.

Pericardium (per″ĭ-kar′de-um) Double-layered sac enclosing the heart and forming its superficial layer; has fibrous and serous layers.

Perichondrium (per″ĭ-kon′dre-um) Fibrous, connective-tissue membrane covering the external surface of cartilaginous structures.

Perimysium (per″ĭ-mis′e-um) Connective tissue enveloping bundles of muscle fibers.

Perineum (per″ĭ-ne′um) That region of the body spanning the region between the ischial tuberosities and extending from the pubic arch to the coccyx.

Periosteum (per″e-os′te-um) Double-layered connective tissue that covers and nourishes the bone.

Peripheral congestion Condition caused by failure of the right side of the heart; results in edema in the extremities.

Peripheral nervous system (PNS) Portion of the nervous system consisting of nerves and ganglia that lie outside of the brain and spinal cord.

Peripheral resistance A measure of the amount of friction encountered by blood as it flows through the blood vessels.

Peristalsis (per″i-stal′sis) Progressive, wavelike contractions that move foodstuffs through the alimentary tube organs (or that move other substances through other hollow body organs).

Peritoneum (per″ĭ-to-ne′um) Serous membrane lining the interior of the abdominal cavity and covering the surfaces of abdominal organs.

Peritonitis (per″ĭ-to-ni′tis) Inflammation of the peritoneum.

Permeability That property of membranes that permits passage of molecules and ions.

Peroxisomes (pĕ-roks′ĭ-sōmz) Membranous sacs in cytoplasm containing powerful oxidase enzymes that use molecular oxygen to detoxify harmful or toxic substances, such as free radicals.

Peyer's patches (pi′erz) Lymphoid organs located in the small intestine; also called aggregated lymphoid nodules.

pH unit (pe-āch) The measure of the relative acidity or alkalinity of a solution.

Phagocytosis (fag″o-si-to′sis) Engulfing of foreign solids by (phagocytic) cells.

Phagosome (fag′o-sōm) Vesicle formed as a result of phagocytosis.

Pharmacological dose A drug dose that is dramatically higher than normal levels of that substance (e.g., hormone) in the body.

Pharyngotympanic tube Tube that connects the middle ear and the pharynx. Also called auditory tube, eustachian tube.

Pharynx (fayr′inks) Muscular tube extending from the region posterior to the nasal cavities to the esophagus.

Phenotype (fe′no-tīp) Observable expression of the genotype.

Phospholipid (fos″fo-lip′id) Modified lipid, contains phosphorus.

Phosphorylation A chemical reaction in which a phosphate molecule is added to a molecule; for example, phosphorylation of ADP yields ATP.

Photoreceptor (fo″to-re-sep′tor) Specialized receptor cells that respond to light energy; rods and cones.

Physiological acidosis (as″ĭ-do′sis) Arterial pH lower than 7.35 resulting from any cause.

Physiological dose A drug dose that replicates normal levels of that substance (e.g., hormone) in the body.

Physiology (fiz″e-ol′o-je) Study of the function of living organisms.

Pineal gland (body) (pin′e-al) A hormone-secreting part of the diencephalon of the brain thought to be involved in setting the biological clock and influencing reproductive function.

Pinocytosis (pe″no-si-to′sis) Engulfing of extracellular fluid by cells.

Pituitary gland (pĭ-tu′ih-tayr″e) Neuroendocrine gland located beneath the brain that serves a variety of functions including regulation of gonads, thyroid, adrenal cortex, lactation, and water balance.

Placenta (plah-sen′tah) Temporary organ formed from both fetal and maternal tissues that provides nutrients and oxygen to the developing fetus, carries away fetal metabolic wastes, and produces the hormones of pregnancy.

Plasma (plaz′mah) The nonliving fluid component of blood within which formed elements and various solutes are suspended and circulated.

Plasma cells Members of a B cell clone; specialized to produce and release antibodies.

Plasma membrane Membrane, composed of phospholipids, cholesterol, and proteins, that encloses cell contents; outer limiting cell membrane.

Platelet (plāt′let) Cell fragment found in blood; involved in clotting.

Pleurae (ploo′re) Two layers of serous membrane that line the thoracic cavity and cover the external surface of the lung.

Pleural cavity (ploo′ral) A potential space between the two layers of pleura; contains a thin film of serous fluid.

Plexus (plek′sus) A network of converging and diverging nerve fibers, blood vessels, or lymphatics.

Polar molecules Nonsymmetrical molecules that contain electrically unbalanced atoms.

Polarized State of a plasma membrane of an unstimulated neuron or muscle cell in which the inside of the cell is relatively negative in comparison to the outside; the resting state.

Polycythemia (pol″e-si-the′me-ah) An abnormally high number of erythrocytes.

Polymer A substance of high molecular weight with long, chainlike molecules consisting of many similar (repeated) units.

Polypeptide (pol″e-pep′tīd) A chain of amino acids.

Polyps Benign mucosal tumors.

Polysaccharide (pol″e-sak′ah-rīd) Literally, many sugars, a polymer of linked monosaccharides; e.g., starch, glycogen.

Pons (1) Any bridgelike structure or part; (2) the part of the brain stem connecting the medulla with the midbrain, providing linkage between upper and lower levels of the central nervous system.

Pore The surface opening of the duct of a sweat gland.

Positive feedback mechanisms Feedback that tends to cause the level of a variable to change in the same direction as an initial change.

Posterior pituitary *See* Neurohypophysis.

Postganglionic axon (fiber) (post″gang-gle-ah′nik) Axon of a ganglionic neuron, an autonomic motor neuron that has its cell body in a peripheral ganglion; the axon projects to an effector.

Potential energy Stored or inactive energy.

Preganglionic neuron Autonomic motor neuron that has its cell body in the central nervous system and projects its axon to a peripheral ganglion.

Presbyopia (pres″be-o′pe-ah) A condition that results in the loss of near focusing ability; typical onset is around age 40.

Pressure gradient Difference in pressure (hydrostatic or osmotic) that drives movement of fluid.

Primary active transport A type of active transport in which the energy needed to drive the transport process is provided directly by hydrolysis of ATP.

Prime mover Muscle that bears the major responsibility for effecting a particular movement; an agonist.

Process (1) Prominence or projection; (2) series of actions for a specific purpose.

Progesterone (pro-jes′ter-ōn) Hormone partly responsible for preparing the uterus for the fertilized ovum.

Prolactin (PRL) (pro-lak′tin) Adenohypophyseal hormone that stimulates the breasts to produce milk.

Pronation (pro-na′shun) Inward rotation of the forearm causing the radius to cross diagonally over the ulna—palms face posteriorly.

Prophase The first stage of mitosis, consisting of coiling of the chromosomes accompanied by migration of the two daughter centrioles toward the poles of the cell, and nuclear membrane breakdown.

Proprioceptor (pro″pre-o-sep′tor) Receptor located in a joint, muscle, or tendon; concerned with locomotion, posture, and muscle tone.

Prostaglandin (PG) (pros″tah-glan′din) A lipid-based chemical messenger synthesized by most tissue cells that acts locally as a paracrine.

Prostate Accessory reproductive gland; produces one-third of semen volume, including fluids that activate sperm.

Protein (pro′tēn) Complex substance containing carbon, oxygen, hydrogen, and nitrogen; composes 10–30% of cell mass.

Prothrombin time Diagnostic test to determine status of hemostasis system.

Proton (pro′ton) Subatomic particle that bears a positive charge; located in the atomic nucleus.

Proton acceptor A substance that takes up hydrogen ions in detectable amounts. Commonly referred to as a base.

Proton donor A substance that releases hydrogen ions in detectable amounts; an acid.

Proximal (prok′si-mul) Toward the attached end of a limb or the origin of a structure.

Pseudounipolar neuron (soo″do-u″nĭ-po′lar) Another term for unipolar neuron.

Puberty Period of life when reproductive maturity is achieved.

Pulmonary (pul′muh-nayr-e) Pertaining to the lungs.

Pulmonary arteries Vessels that deliver blood to the lungs to be oxygenated.

Pulmonary circuit System of blood vessels that serves gas exchange in the lungs; i.e., pulmonary arteries, capillaries, and veins.

Pulmonary edema (ĕ-de′muh) Leakage of fluid into the air sacs and tissue of the lungs.

Pulmonary veins Vessels that deliver freshly oxygenated blood from the respiratory zones of the lungs to the heart.

Pulmonary ventilation Breathing; consists of inspiration and expiration.

Pulse Rhythmic expansion and recoil of arteries resulting from heart contraction; can be felt from outside the body.

Pupil Opening in the center of the iris through which light enters the eye.

Purkinje fibers (pur-kin′je) Modified ventricular muscle fibers of the conduction system of the heart.

Pus Fluid product of inflammation composed of white blood cells, the debris of dead cells, and a thin fluid.

Pyloric sphincter (pi-lor′ik sfink′ter) Valve of the distal end of the stomach that controls food entry into the duodenum.

Pyramidal (corticospinal) tracts Major motor pathways concerned with voluntary movement; descend from pyramidal cells in the frontal lobes of each cerebral hemisphere.

Pyruvic acid An intermediate compound in the metabolism of carbohydrates.

Radioactivity The process of spontaneous decay seen in some of the heavier isotopes, during which particles or energy is emitted from the atomic nucleus; results in the atom becoming more stable.

Radioisotope (ra″de-o-i′so-tōp) Isotope that exhibits radioactive behavior.

Ramus (ra′mus) Branch of a nerve, artery, vein, or bone.

Rapid eye movement (REM) sleep Stage of sleep in which rapid eye movements, an alert EEG pattern, and dreaming occur.

Reactant A substance taking part in a chemical reaction.

Receptor (re-sep′tor) (1) A cell or nerve ending of a sensory neuron specialized to respond to particular types of stimuli; (2) protein that binds specifically with other molecules, e.g., neurotransmitters, hormones, paracrines, antigens.

Receptor-mediated endocytosis One of three types of endocytosis in which engulfed particles attach to receptors before endocytosis occurs.

Receptor potential A graded potential that occurs at a sensory receptor membrane.

Recessive traits A trait due to a particular allele that does not manifest itself in the presence of other alleles that generate traits dominant to it; must be present in double dose to be expressed.

Reduction Chemical reaction in which electrons and energy are gained by a molecule (often accompanied by gain of hydrogen ions) or oxygen is lost.

Referred pain Pain felt at a site other than the area of origin.

Reflex Automatic reaction to stimuli.

Refraction The bending of a light ray when it meets a different surface at an oblique rather than right angle.

Regeneration Replacement of destroyed tissue with the same kind of tissue.

Regulatory T cells (T_Reg cells) Population of T cells (usually expressing CD4) that suppress the immune response.

Relative refractory period Follows the absolute refractory period; interval when a threshold for action potential stimulation is markedly elevated.

Renal (re′nal) Pertaining to the kidney.

Renal autoregulation Process the kidney uses to maintain a nearly constant glomerular filtration rate despite fluctuations in systemic blood pressure.

Renal clearance The volume of plasma from which a particular substance is completely removed in a given time, usually 1 minute; provides information about renal function.

Renin (re′nin) Hormone released by the kidneys that is involved with raising blood pressure.

Rennin Stomach-secreted enzyme that acts on milk protein; not produced in adults.

Repolarization Movement of the membrane potential to the initial resting (polarized) state.

Reproductive system Organ system that functions to produce offspring.

Resistance exercise High-intensity exercise in which the muscles are pitted against high resistance or immovable forces and, as a result, muscle cells increase in size.

Respiration The processes involved in supplying the body with oxygen and disposing of carbon dioxide.

Respiratory system Organ system that carries out gas exchange; includes the nose, pharynx, larynx, trachea, bronchi, lungs.

Resting membrane potential The voltage that exists across the plasma membrane during the resting state of an excitable cell; ranges from −90 to −20 millivolts depending on cell type.

Reticular activating system (RAS) (re-tik′u-lar) Diffuse brain stem neural network that receives a wide variety of sensory input and maintains wakefulness of the cerebral cortex.

Reticular connective tissue Connective tissue with a fine network of reticular fibers that form the internal supporting framework of lymphoid organs.

Reticular formation Functional system that spans the brain stem; involved in regulating sensory input to the cerebral cortex, cortical arousal, and control of motor behavior.

Reticular lamina A layer of extracellular material containing a fine network of collagen protein fibers; together with the basal lamina it is a major component of the basement membrane.

Reticulocyte (rĕ-tik′u-lo-sīt) Immature erythrocyte.

Retina (ret′ĭ-nah) Neural layer of the eyeball; contains photoreceptors (rods, cones).

Rhombencephalon (hindbrain) (romb″en-sef′ah-lon) Caudal portion of the developing brain; constricts to form the metencephalon and myelencephalon; includes the pons, cerebellum, and medulla oblongata.

Ribosomal RNA (rRNA) A constituent of ribosome; exists within the ribosomes of cytoplasm and assists in protein synthesis.

Ribosomes (ri′bo-sōmz) Cytoplasmic organelles at which proteins are synthesized.

RNA (ribonucleic acid) (ri′bo-nu-kle′ik) Nucleic acid that contains ribose and the bases A, G, C, and U. Carries out DNA's instructions for protein synthesis.

Rods One of the two types of photosensitive cells in the retina.

Rotation The turning of a bone around its own long axis.

Rugae (ru′ge) Elevations or ridges, as in stomach mucosa.

Rule of nines Method of computing the extent of burns by dividing the body into a number of areas, each accounting for 9% (or a multiple thereof) of the total body area.

S (synthetic) phase The part of the interphase period of the cell life cycle in which DNA replicates itself, ensuring that the two future cells will receive identical copies of genetic material.

Sagittal plane (saj′ĭ-tal) A longitudinal (vertical) plane that divides the body or any of its parts into right and left portions.

Saliva Secretion of the salivary glands; cleanses and moistens the mouth and begins chemical digestion of starchy foods.

Saltatory conduction Transmission of an action potential along a myelinated fiber in which the nerve impulse appears to leap from node to node.

Sarcolemma The plasma membrane surface of a muscle fiber.

Sarcomere (sar′ko-mēr) The smallest contractile unit of muscle; extends from one Z disc to the next.

Sarcoplasm The nonfibrillar cytoplasm of a muscle fiber.

Sarcoplasmic reticulum (SR) (sar″ko-plaz′mik rĕ-tik′u-lum) Specialized endoplasmic reticulum of muscle cells.

Schwann cell A type of supporting cell in the PNS; forms myelin sheaths and is vital to peripheral nerve fiber regeneration.

Sclera (skle′rah) White opaque portion of the fibrous layer of the eyeball.

Scrotum (skro′tum) External sac enclosing the testes.

Sebaceous glands (oil glands) (se-ba′shus) Epidermal glands that produce an oily secretion called sebum.

Sebum (se′bum) Oily secretion of sebaceous glands.

Second-degree burn A burn in which the epidermis and the upper region of the dermis are damaged.

Second messenger Intracellular molecule generated by the binding of a chemical (hormone or neurotransmitter) to a plasma membrane receptor; mediates intracellular responses to the chemical messenger.

Secondary sex characteristics Anatomic features, not directly involved in the reproductive process, that develop under the influence of sex hormones, e.g., male or female pattern of muscle development, bone growth, body hair distribution.

Secretion (se-kre′shun) (1) The passage of material formed by a cell to its exterior; (2) cell product that is transported to the exterior of a cell.

Secretory vesicles (granules) Vesicles that migrate to the plasma membrane of a cell and discharge their contents from the cell by exocytosis.

Section A cut through the body (or an organ) that is made along a particular plane; a thin slice of tissue prepared for microscopic study.

Segregation During meiosis, the distribution of the members of the allele pair to different gametes.

Selectively permeable membrane A membrane that allows certain substances to pass while restricting the movement of others; also called differentially permeable membrane.

Semen (se′men) Fluid mixture containing sperm and secretions of the male accessory reproductive glands.

Semilunar valves (sĕ″me-loo′ner) Valves that prevent blood return to the ventricles after contraction; aortic and pulmonary valves.

Seminiferous tubules (sem″ĭ-nif′er-us) Highly convoluted tubes within the testes; form sperm.

Sense organs Localized collections of many types of cells working together to accomplish a specific receptive process.

Sensory (afferent) nerves Nerves that contain processes of sensory neurons and carry impulses to the central nervous system.

Sensory areas Functional areas of the cerebral cortex that provide for conscious awareness of sensation.

Sensory receptor Dendritic end organs, or parts of other cell types, specialized to respond to a stimulus.

Serosa (serous membrane) (se-ro′sah) The moist membrane found in closed ventral body cavities.

Serous fluid (sēr′us) Clear, watery fluid secreted by cells of a serous membrane.

Serum (sēr′um) Amber-colored fluid that exudes from clotted blood as the clot shrinks; plasma without clotting factors.

Sesamoid bones (ses′ah-moid) Short bones embedded in tendons, variable in size and number, many of which influence the action of muscles; largest is the patella (kneecap).

Severe combined immunodeficiency syndromes (SCIDs) Congenital conditions resulting in little or no protection against disease-causing organisms of any type.

Sex chromosomes The chromosomes, X and Y, that determine genetic sex (XX = female; XY = male); the 23rd pair of chromosomes.

Sex-linked inheritance Inherited traits determined by genes on the sex chromosomes, e.g., X-linked genes are passed from mother to son, Y-linked genes are passed from father to son.

Sexually transmitted infection (STI) Infectious disease spread through sexual contact.

Signal sequence A short peptide segment present in a protein being synthesized that causes the associated ribosome to attach to the membrane of rough ER.

Simple diffusion The unassisted transport across a plasma membrane of a lipid-soluble or very small particle.

Sinoatrial (SA) node (si″no-a′tre-al) Specialized myocardial cells in the wall of the right atrium; pacemaker of the heart.

Sinus (si′nus) (1) Mucous-membrane-lined, air-filled cavity in certain cranial bones; (2) dilated channel for the passage of blood or lymph.

Skeletal muscle Muscle composed of cylindrical multinucleate cells with obvious striations; the muscle(s) attached to the body's skeleton; voluntary muscle.

Skeletal system System of protection and support composed primarily of bone and cartilage.

Skull Bony protective encasement of the brain and the organs of hearing and equilibrium; includes the facial bones. Also called the cranium.

Small intestine Convoluted tube extending from the pyloric sphincter to the ileocecal valve where it joins the large intestine; the site where digestion is completed and virtually all absorption occurs.

Smooth muscle Spindle-shaped cells with one centrally located nucleus and no externally visible striations (bands). Found mainly in the walls of hollow organs.

Sodium-potassium (Na$^+$-K$^+$) pump A primary active transport system that simultaneously drives Na$^+$ out of the cell against a steep gradient and pumps K$^+$ back in.

Sol-gel transformation Reversible change of a colloid from a fluid (sol) to a more solid (gel) state.

Solute (sol′yoot) The substance that is dissolved in a solution.

Solute pump Enzyme-like protein carrier that mediates active transport of solutes such as amino acids and ions uphill against their concentration gradients.

Somatic nervous system (so-mă′tik) Division of the peripheral nervous system that provides the motor innervation of skeletal muscles; also called the voluntary nervous system.

Somatic reflexes Reflexes that activate skeletal muscle.

Somatosensory system That part of the sensory system dealing with reception in the body wall and limbs; receives inputs from exteroceptors, proprioceptors, and interoceptors.

Somite (so′mīt) A mesodermal segment of the body of an embryo that contributes to the formation of skeletal muscles, vertebrae, and dermis of skin.

Spatial discrimination The ability of neurons to identify the site or pattern of stimulation.

Special senses The senses of taste, smell, vision, hearing, and equilibrium.

Specific gravity Term used to compare the weight of a substance to the weight of an equal volume of distilled water.

Sperm (spermatozoon) Male gamete.

Spermatogenesis (sper″mah-to-jen′ĕ-sis) The process of sperm (male gamete) formation; involves meiosis.

Sphincter (sfink′ter) A circular muscle surrounding an opening; acts as a valve.

Spinal cord The bundle of nervous tissue that runs from the brain to the first to third lumbar vertebrae and provides a conduction pathway to and from the brain.

Spinal nerves The 31 nerve pairs that arise from the spinal cord.

Splanchnic circulation (splangk′nik) The blood vessels serving the digestive system.

Spleen Largest lymphoid organ; provides for lymphocyte proliferation, immune surveillance and response, and blood-cleansing functions.

Spongy bone Internal layer of skeletal bone. Also called cancellous bone.

Sprain Ligaments reinforcing a joint are stretched or torn.

Static equilibrium Sense of head position in space with respect to gravity.

Stenosis (stĕ-no′sis) Abnormal constriction or narrowing.

Steroids (stĕ′roidz) Group of chemical substances including certain hormones and cholesterol; they are fat soluble and contain little oxygen.

Stimulus (stim′u-lus) An excitant or irritant; a change in the environment that evokes a response.

Stomach Temporary reservoir in the gastrointestinal tract where chemical breakdown of proteins begins and food is converted into chyme.

Stressor Any stimulus that directly or indirectly causes the hypothalamus to initiate stress-reducing responses, such as the fight-or-flight response.

Stroke *See* Cerebrovascular accident.

Stroke volume (SV) Amount of blood pumped out of a ventricle during one contraction.

Stroma (stro′mah) The basic internal structural framework of an organ.

Structural (fibrous) proteins Consist of extended, strandlike polypeptide chains forming a strong, ropelike structure that is linear, insoluble in water, and very stable; e.g., collagen.

Subcutaneous (sub″kyu-ta′ne-us) Beneath the skin.

Substrate A reactant on which an enzyme acts to cause a chemical action to proceed.

Sudoriferous gland (su″do-rif′er-us) Epidermal gland that produces sweat.

Sulcus (sul′kus) A furrow on the brain, less deep than a fissure.

Summation Accumulation of effects, especially those of muscular, sensory, or mental stimuli.

Superficial Located close to or on the body surface.

Superior Toward the head or upper body regions.

Superior vena cava Vein that returns blood from body regions superior to the diaphragm.

Supination (soo″pĭ-na′shun) The outward rotation of the forearm causing palms to face anteriorly.

Surfactant (ser-fak′tant) Secretion produced by certain cells of the alveoli that reduces the surface tension of water molecules, thus preventing the collapse of the alveoli after each expiration.

Suspension Heterogeneous mixtures with large, often visible solutes that tend to settle out.

Suture (soo′cher) An immovable fibrous joint; with one exception, all bones of the skull are united by sutures.

Sweat gland *See* Sudoriferous gland.

Sympathetic division The division of the autonomic nervous system that prepares the body for activity or to cope with some stressor (danger, excitement, etc.); the fight, fright, and flight subdivision.

Sympathetic (vasomotor) tone State of partial vasoconstriction of the blood vessels maintained by sympathetic fibers.

Symphysis (sim′fih-sis) A joint in which the bones are connected by fibrocartilage.

Synapse (sin′aps) Functional junction or point of close contact between two neurons or between a neuron and an effector cell.

Synapsis (sĭ-nap′sis) Pairing of homologous chromosomes during the first meiotic division.

Synaptic cleft (si-nap′tik) Fluid-filled space at a synapse.

Synaptic delay Time required for an impulse to cross a synapse between two neurons.

Synaptic vesicles Small membranous sacs containing neurotransmitter.

Synarthrosis (sin″ar-thro′sis) Immovable joint.

Synchondrosis (sin″kon-dro′sis) A joint in which the bones are united by hyaline cartilage.

Syndesmosis (sin″des-mo′sis) A joint in which the bones are united by a ligament or a sheet of fibrous tissue.

Synergist (sin′er-jist) (1) Muscle that aids the action of a prime mover by effecting the same movement or by stabilizing joints across which the prime mover acts, preventing undesirable movements. (2) Hormone that amplifies the effect of another hormone at a target cell.

Synostosis (sin″os-to′sis) A completely ossified joint; a fused joint.

Synovial fluid Fluid secreted by the synovial membrane; lubricates joint surfaces and nourishes articular cartilages.

Synovial joint Freely movable joint exhibiting a joint cavity; also called a diarthrosis.

Synthesis (combination) reaction A chemical reaction in which larger, more complex atoms or molecules are formed from simpler ones.

Systemic (sis-tem′ik) Pertaining to the whole body.

Systemic circuit System of blood vessels that serves gas exchange in the body tissues.

Systole (sis′to-le) Period when either the ventricles or the atria are contracting.

Systolic pressure (sis-tah′lik) Pressure exerted by blood on the blood vessel walls during ventricular contractions.

T cells Lymphocytes that mediate cellular immunity; include helper, cytotoxic, regulatory, and memory cells. Also called T lymphocytes.

T tubule (transverse tubule) Extension of the muscle cell plasma membrane (sarcolemma) that protrudes deeply into the muscle cell.

Tachycardia (tak″e-kar′de-ah) A heart rate over 100 beats per minute.

Taste buds Sensory receptor organs that house gustatory cells, which respond to dissolved food chemicals.

Telencephalon (endbrain) (tel″en-seh′fuh-lon) Anterior subdivision of the primary forebrain that develops into olfactory lobes, cerebral cortex, and basal nuclei.

Telophase The final phase of mitosis; begins when migration of chromosomes to the poles of the cell has been completed and ends with the formation of two daughter nuclei.

Tendon (ten′dun) Cord of dense fibrous tissue attaching muscle to bone.

Tendonitis Inflammation of tendon sheaths, typically caused by overuse.

Terminal branches Branching ends of an axon that allow it to form many axon terminals; telodendria.

Testis (tes′tis) Male primary reproductive organ that produces sperm; male gonad.

Testosterone (tes-tos′tĕ-rōn) Male sex hormone produced by the testes; during puberty promotes virilization, and is necessary for normal sperm production.

Tetanus (tet′ah-nus) (1) A smooth, sustained muscle contraction resulting from high-frequency stimulation; (2) an infectious disease caused by an anaerobic bacterium.

Thalamus (thal′ah-mus) A mass of gray matter in the diencephalon of the brain.

Thermogenesis (ther″mo-jen′ĕ-sis) Heat production.

Thermoreceptor (ther″mo-re-sep′ter) Receptor sensitive to temperature changes.

Third-degree burn A burn that involves the entire thickness of the skin; also called a full-thickness burn. Usually requires skin grafting.

Thoracic cage (bony thorax) Bones that form the framework of the thorax; includes sternum, ribs, and thoracic vertebrae.

Thoracic duct Large duct that receives lymph drained from the entire lower body, the left upper extremity, and the left side of the head and thorax.

Thorax (tho′raks) That portion of the body trunk above the diaphragm and below the neck.

Threshold stimulus Weakest stimulus capable of producing a response in an irritable tissue.

Thrombin (throm′bin) Enzyme that induces clotting by converting fibrinogen to fibrin.

Thrombocyte (throm′bo-sīt) Platelet; cell fragment that participates in blood coagulation.

Thrombocytopenia (throm″bo-si″to-pe′ne-ah) A reduction in the number of platelets circulating in the blood.

Thrombus (throm′bus) A clot that develops and persists in an unbroken blood vessel.

Thymine (T) (thi′mēn) Single-ring base (a pyrimidine) in DNA.

Thymus (thi′mus) Lymphoid organ and endocrine gland active in immune response; site of maturation of T lymphocytes.

Thyroid gland (thi′roid) One of the largest of the body's endocrine glands; straddles the anterior trachea.

Thyroid hormone (TH) The major hormone secreted by thyroid follicles; stimulates enzymes concerned with glucose oxidation.

Thyroid-stimulating hormone (TSH) Adenohypophyseal hormone that regulates secretion of thyroid hormones.

Thyroxine (T₄) (thi-rok′sin) Iodine-containing hormone secreted by the thyroid gland; accelerates cellular metabolic rate in most body tissues.

Tight junction Area where plasma membranes of adjacent cells are fused.

Tissue A group of similar cells and their intercellular substance specialized to perform a specific function; primary tissue types of the body are epithelial, connective, muscle, and nervous tissue.

Tissue perfusion Blood flow through body tissues or organs.

Tonicity (to-nis′ĭ-te) A measure of the ability of a solution to cause a change in cell shape or tone by promoting osmotic flows of water.

Tonsils A ring of lymphoid tissue around the entrance to the pharynx. *See also* Adenoids.

Trabecula (trah-bek′u-lah) (1) Any of the fibrous bands extending from the capsule into the interior of an organ; (2) strut or thin plate of bone in spongy bone.

Trachea (tra′ke-ah) Windpipe; cartilage-reinforced tube extending from larynx to bronchi.

Tract A collection of axons in the central nervous system having the same origin, termination, and function.

Transcription One of the two major steps in the transfer of genetic code information from a DNA base sequence to the complementary base sequence of an mRNA molecule.

Transduction (trans-duk′shun) The conversion of the energy of a stimulus into an electrical event.

Transepithelial transport (trans-ep″ĭ-the′le-al) Movement of substances through, rather than between, adjacent epithelial cells connected by tight junctions, such as absorption of nutrients in the small intestine.

Transfer RNA (tRNA) Short-chain RNA molecules that transfer amino acids to the ribosome.

Transfusion reaction Agglutination and destruction of red blood cells following transfusion of incompatible blood.

Translation One of the two major steps in the transfer of genetic code information, in which the information carried by mRNA is decoded and used to assemble polypeptides.

Transverse (horizontal) plane A plane running from right to left, dividing the body or an organ into superior and inferior parts.

Tricuspid valve (tri-kus′pid) The right atrioventricular valve.

Triglycerides (tri-glis′er-īdz) Fats and oils composed of fatty acids and glycerol; are the body's most concentrated source of energy fuel; also known as neutral fats.

Triiodothyronine (T₃) (tri″i-o″do-thi′ro-nēn) Thyroid hormone; secretion and function similar to those of thyroxine (T₄).

Trophoblast (tro′fo-blast) Outer sphere of cells of the blastocyst.

Tropic hormone (trōp′ik) A hormone that regulates the secretory action of another endocrine organ.

Trypsin Proteolytic enzyme secreted by the pancreas.

Tubular reabsorption The movement of filtrate components from the renal tubules into the blood.

Tubular secretion The movement of substances (such as drugs, urea, excess ions) from blood into filtrate.

Tumor An abnormal growth of cells; a swelling; may be cancerous.

Tunica (too′nĭ-kah) A covering or tissue coat; membrane layer.

Tympanic membrane (tim-pan′ik) Eardrum.

Ulcer (ul′ser) Lesion or erosion of the mucous membrane, such as gastric ulcer of stomach.

Umbilical cord (um-bĭ′lĭ-kul) Structure bearing arteries and veins connecting the placenta and the fetus.

Umbilicus (um-bĭ′lĭ-kus) Navel; marks site where umbilical cord was attached in fetal stage.

Unipolar neuron Neuron in which embryological fusion of the two processes leaves only one process extending from the cell body.

Unmyelinated fibers (un-mi′ĕ-lĭ-nāt″ed) Axons lacking a myelin sheath and therefore conducting impulses quite slowly.

Uracil (U) (u′rah-sil) A smaller, single-ring base (a pyrimidine) found in RNA.

Urea (u-re′ah) Main nitrogen-containing waste excreted in urine.

Ureter (u-re′ter) Tube that carries urine from kidney to bladder.

Urethra (u-re′thrah) Canal through which urine passes from the bladder to outside the body.

Uric acid The nitrogenous waste product of nucleic acid metabolism; component of urine.

Urinary bladder A smooth, collapsible, muscular sac that stores urine temporarily.

Urinary system System primarily responsible for water, electrolyte, and acid-base balance and removal of nitrogenous wastes.

Uterine tube (u′ter-in) Tube through which the ovum is transported to the uterus. Also called fallopian tube.

Uterus (u′ter-us) Hollow, thick-walled organ that receives, retains, and nourishes fertilized egg; site where embryo/fetus develops.

Uvula (u′vu-lah) Tissue tag hanging from soft palate.

Vaccine Preparation that provides artificially acquired active immunity.

Vagina Thin-walled tube extending from the cervix to the body exterior; often called the birth canal.

Valence shell (va′lens) Outermost electron shell (energy level) of an atom that contains electrons.

Varicosities Knoblike swellings of certain autonomic axons containing mitochondria and synaptic vesicles.

Vas (vaz′) A duct; vessel.

Vasa recta (va′sah rek′tah) Capillary branches that supply loops of Henle in the medulla region of the kidney.

Vascular Pertaining to blood vessels or richly supplied with blood vessels.

Vascular spasm Immediate response to blood vessel injury; results in constriction.

Vasoconstriction (vas″o-kon-strik′shun) Narrowing of blood vessels.

Vasodilation (vas″o-di-la′shun) Relaxation of the smooth muscles of the blood vessels, producing dilation.

Vasomotion (vas″o-mo′shun) Intermittent contraction or relaxation of the precapillary sphincters, resulting in a staggered blood flow when tissue needs are not extreme.

Vasomotor center (vas″o-mo′ter) Brain area concerned with regulation of blood vessel resistance.

Vasomotor fibers Sympathetic nerve fibers that cause the contraction of smooth muscle in the walls of blood vessels, thereby regulating blood vessel diameter.

Veins (vānz″) Blood vessels that return blood toward the heart from the circulation.

Ventral Pertaining to the front; anterior.

Ventricles (1) Paired, inferiorly located heart chambers that function as the major blood pumps; (2) cavities in the brain.

Venule (ven′ūl) A small vein.

Vertebral column (spine) (ver′tĕ-brul) Formed of a number of individual bones called vertebrae and two composite bones (sacrum and coccyx).

Vesicle (vĕ′sĭ-kul) A small liquid-filled sac or bladder.

Vesicular (bulk) transport The movement of large particles and macromolecules across a plasma membrane.

Vesicular follicle Mature ovarian follicle.

Vestibule An enlarged area at the beginning of a canal, i.e., inner ear, nose, larynx.

Villus (vil′us) Fingerlike projections of the small intestinal mucosa that tremendously increase its surface area for absorption.

Visceral (vis′er-al) Pertaining to an internal organ of the body or the inner part of a structure.

Visceral muscle Type of smooth muscle; its cells contract as a unit and rhythmically, are electrically coupled by gap junctions, and often exhibit spontaneous action potentials.

Visceral organs (viscera) A group of internal organs housed in the ventral body cavity.

Visceral serosa (se-ro′sah) The part of the double-layered membrane that lines the outer surfaces of organs within the ventral body cavity.

Viscosity (vis′kos′ĭ-te) State of being sticky or thick.

Visual field The field of view seen when the head is still.

Vital capacity (VC) The volume of air that can be expelled from the lungs by forcible expiration after the deepest inspiration; total exchangeable air.

Vital signs Includes pulse, blood pressure, respiratory rate, and body temperature measurements.

Vitamins Organic compounds required by the body in minute amounts.

Vocal folds Mucosal folds that function in voice production (speech); also called the true vocal cords.

Volatile acid An acid that can be eliminated by the lungs; carbonic acid is converted to CO_2, which diffuses into the alveoli.

Volkmann's canals *See* Perforating canals.

Voluntary muscle Muscle under strict nervous control; skeletal muscle.

Voluntary nervous system The somatic nervous system.

Vulva (vul′vuh) Female external genitalia.

Wallerian degeneration (wal-er′ē-an) A process of disintegration of an axon that occurs when it is crushed or severed and cannot receive nutrients from the cell body.

White matter White substance of the central nervous system; myelinated nerve fibers.

Xenograft Tissue graft taken from another animal species.

Yolk sac (yōk) One of the extraembryonic membranes; involved in early blood cell formation.

Zygote (zi′gōt) Fertilized egg.

Photo and Illustration Credits

Photo Credits

Chapter 1
Chapter Opener: Jorge Silva/Corbis.
1.1: GoGo Images/Jupiter Images.
1.3: Pearson Science.
1.8.1: Jenny Thomas/Addison Wesley Longman.
1.8.2: Howard Sochurek.
1.8.3: James Cavallini/Photo Researchers.
1.8.4: CNRI/Science Photo Library/Photo Researchers.
1.12a: Custom Medical Stock Photo, Inc.
A Closer Look: a: Clinique Ste Catherine/CNRI/
Science Photo Library/Photo Researchers.
b: Willaim Klunk, Chet Mathis, University of
Pittsburgh, PET Amyloid Imaging Group.
c: Custom Medical Stock Photography.

Chapter 2
Chapter Opener: Chuck Haney Outdoor Photography/
Danita Delimont.
2.4.1: Stockbyte/Getty Images.
2.4.2: Marc O. Finley, Stock Food Creative/Getty Images.
2.4.3: Cristina Pedrazzini/Photo Researchers.
2.10b: Bernard Photo Productions/Animals
Animals/Earth Sciences.
2.22c: Computer Graphics Laboratory, University of
California, San Francisco.

Chapter 3
Chapter Opener: Paul Burns/Getty Images.
3.9a–c: David M. Philips/Photo Researchers.
3.14b: Birgit H. Satir, Dept. of Anatomy and Structural Biology, Albert Einstein College of Medicine.
3.17c: Professors P. Motta & T. Naguro/SPL/Photo
Researchers.
3.18b: R. Bolender and Donald Fawcett/Visuals
Unlimited.
3.19b: P. Motta & T. Naguro/SPL/Photo Researchers.
3.21: K. G. Murti/Visuals Unlimited.
3.23a: Mary Osborn, Max Planck Institute.
3.23b: Frank Solomon and J. Dinsmore, Massachusetts Institute of Technology.
3.23c: Mark S. Ladinsky and J. Richard McIntosh,
University of Colorado.
3.25b: David M. Philips/Visuals Unlimited.
3.26.1: OMIKRON/Science Source/Photo Researchers.
3.26.2 and 3: W. L. Dentler/Biological Photo Service.
3.28: Don W. Fawcett/Photo Researchers.
3.29b.1: From L. Orci and A. Perrelet, *Freeze-Etch Histology.* (Heidelberg: Springer-Verlag, 1975) © 1975
Springer-Verlag.
3.29b.2: From A. C. Faberge, *Cell Tiss. Res.* 151
(1974):403. © 1974 Springer-Verlag.
3.29b.3: U. Aebi et al. *Nature* 323 (1996):560–564,
Figure 1a. Used by permission.

3.30.1: Dr. Victoria E. Foe.
3.30.2: GF Bahr, Armed Forces Institute of Pathology.
3.33.1–6: Conly Rieder.
3.38b: Barbara Hamkalo.

Chapter 4
Chapter Opener: Mark Karrass/Corbis.
4.3a: G. W. Willis/Visuals Unlimited.
4.3b, f: Allen Bell, University of New England;
Pearson Science.
4.3c: Cabisco/Visuals Unlimited.
4.3d: Ed Reschke.
4.3e: Nina Zanetti, Pearson Science.
4.4a: SPL/Photo Researchers.
4.8a, e, g, k: Ed Reschke.
4.8b, f, h: Nina Zanetti, Pearson Science.
4.8c, i, j: Allen Bell, University of New England;
Pearson Science.
4.8d: Ed Reschke/Peter Arnold.
4.9: Biophoto Associates/Photo Researchers.
4.10a: Eric Graves/Photo Researchers.
4.10b: Ed Reschke.
4.10c: SPL/Photo Researchers.

Chapter 5
Chapter Opener: Creasource/Corbis.
5.2a: Ed Reschke/Peter Arnold.
5.3a: Ed Reschke/Peter Arnold.
5.3b, c: Kessel and Kardon/Visuals Unlimited.
5.4a: Kessel and Kardon/Visuals Unlimited.
5.5a: Cabisco/Visuals Unlimited.
5.5b: John D. Cunningham/Visuals Unlimited.
5.6b: Carolina Biological Supply/Phototake.
5.6d: Manfred Kage/Peter Arnold.
5.8a: Bart's Medical Library/Phototake.
5.8b: P. Marazzi/SPL/Photo Researchers.
5.8c: Zeva Oelbaum/Peter Arnold.
5.10a: Scott Camazine/Photo Researchers.
5.10b: Dr. M.A. Ansary/Photo Researchers.

Chapter 6
Chapter Opener: Luciana Ellington/age fotostock.
6.5.1: seelevel.com.
6.5.2: Steve Gschmeissner/Photo Researchers.
6.7c.1: Kessel and Kardon/Visuals Unlimited.
6.7c.2: Ed Reschke/Peter Arnold.
6.10: Ed Reschke.
6.14a: Martin Rose/Bongarts/Getty Images.
6.16a, b: P. Motta, Department of Anatomy, University
"La Sapienza," Rome/Science Photo Library/Photo
Researchers.
6.17: Carolina Biological Supply.
Table 6.2.1: Lester Bergman/Corbis.
Table 6.2.2: ISM/Phototake.
Table 6.2.3: SIU/Peter Arnold.

Table 6.2.4: SIU/Visuals Unlimited.
Table 6.2.5: William T. C. Yuh.
Table 6.2.6: Charles Stewart MD.

Chapter 7
Chapter Opener: George Shelley/Masterfile.
7.5c: Ralph T. Hutchings.
7.6b: Ralph T. Hutchings.
7.7b: Ralph T. Hutchings.
7.8: Ralph T. Hutchings.
7.9a, b: Ralph T. Hutchings.
7.10: Ralph T. Hutchings.
7.11c: Ralph T. Hutchings/Pearson Science.
7.13a: Ralph T. Hutchings.
7.17d: Neil Borden/Photo Researchers.
7.22b: Dissection by Shawn Miller, photography by
Mark Nielsen and Alexa Doig.
7.23c: Pearson Science.
7.30c, d: Ralph T. Hutchings.
7.32c, d: Ralph T. Hutchings.
7.32.e: Biophoto Associates/Science Source/Photo
Researchers.
7.34b: Elaine N. Marieb.
7.36: Center For Cranialfacial Anomalies, University
of California, San Francisco.
7.37: Reik/age fotostock.
Table 7.4.2–5: From *A Stereoscopic Atlas of Human
Anatomy* by David L. Bassett.

Chapter 8
Chapter Opener: ANP/AFP/Getty Images.
8.5a–f: John Wilson White, Pearson Science.
8.6a–f: John Wilson White, Pearson Science.
8.8f: L. Bassett/Visuals Unlimited.
8.10b: Mark Neilsen, University of Utah; Pearson Science.
8.10e: VideoSurgery/Photo Researchers.
8.12b: From *A Stereoscopic Atlas of Human Anatomy*
by David L. Bassett.
8.14: Elaine Marieb.
8.15: CNRI/Science Photo Library/Photo Researchers.
A Closer Look: 1: Lawrence Livermore National
Laboratory/Photo Researchers. 2: Elaine Marieb.

Chapter 9
Chapter Opener: Robert Michael/Corbis.
9.1b: John D. Cunningham/Visuals Unlimited.
9.2a: Marian Rice.
9.4: John Heuser.
9.6.1, 3: James Dennis/Phototake.
9.13b: Eric Graves/Photo Researchers.
9.24: National Library of Medicine.
A Closer Look: Moritz Steiger/Riser/Getty Images.
Table 9.3.4: Eric Graves/Photo Researchers.
Table 9.3.5: Marian Rice.
Table 9.3.6: SPL/Photo Researchers.

Chapter 10
Chapter Opener: Goodshoot/Jupiter Images.
10.8b: Creative Digital Visions, Pearson Science.
10.9c: Dissection by Shawn Miller, photography by Mark Nielsen and Alexa Doig.
10.10c: From *A Stereoscopic Atlas of Human Anatomy* by David L. Bassett.
10.13b: Ralph T. Hutchings.
10.13d, e: Dissection by Shawn Miller, photography by Mark Nielsen and Alexa Doig.
10.14d: Dissection by Shawn Miller, photography by Mark Nielsen and Alexa Doig.
10.20b: Ralph T. Hutchings.

Chapter 11
Chapter Opener: Hulton Archive Photos/Getty Images.
11.4a: Manfred Kage/Peter Arnold.
11.5d: Don W. Fawcett/Photo Researchers.
11.17b: Oliver Meckes/Ottawa/Photo Researchers.
11.24: Tibor Harkany, Science Magazine.
A Closer Look: Brookhaven National Laboratory/PictureQuest.

Chapter 12
Chapter Opener: Getty Images.
12.6c: Robert A. Chase.
12.6d: A. Glauberman/Photo Researchers.
12.7: Volker Steger/Peter Arnold.
12.10b: Ralph T. Hutchings.
12.11b: Pat Lynch/Photo Researchers.
12.14: Ralph T. Hutchings/Visuals Unlimited.
12.17a: Ralph T. Hutchings.
12.17c: L. Bassett/Visuals Unlimited.
12.20a: Hank Morgan/Photo Researchers.
12.25b: From *A Stereoscopic Atlas of Human Anatomy* by David L. Bassett.
12.27: Carroll H. Weiss.
12.29b–d: L. Bassett/Visuals Unlimited.
12.36: Biophoto Associates/Science Source/Photo Researchers.

Chapter 13
Chapter Opener: AP Photo/Andy Wong.
13.3a: Kessel and Kardon/Visuals Unlimited.
13.9b: Ralph T. Hutchings.
13.11c: Ralph T. Hutchings.
Table 13.2.8: William Thompson, Pearson Science.

Chapter 14
Chapter Opener: Dorling Kindersley.

Chapter 15
Chapter Opener: LWA/Dann Tardif/Jupiter Images.
15.1a: Richard Tauber, Pearson Science.
15.4b: From *A Stereoscopic Atlas of Human Anatomy* by David L Bassett.
15.6c: Ed Reschke/Peter Arnold.
15.7: A. L. Blum/Visuals Unlimited.
15.9: NMSB/Custom Medical Stock Photography.
15.11: Charles D. Wintrer/Photo Researchers.
15.19b: Stephen Spector/Benjamin Cummings.
15.23d: Carolina Biological Supply Company/Phototake, NYC.
15.28d: P. Motta/Department of Anatomy/University "La Sapienza," Rome/Science Photo Library/Photo Researchers.
15.32: *Science* Vol.279 March 1998, p. 1870.
15.36b: I. M. Hunter-Duvar, Department of Oto-laryngology, The Hospital for Sick Children, Toronto.

Chapter 16
Chapter Opener: Creasource/Corbis.
16.8b: Ed Reschke.
16.10a: John Paul Kay/Peter Arnold.
16.10b: Photo Researchers.

16.11b: From *Color Atlas of Histology* by Leslie P. Garner and James L. Hiatt, © Williams and Wilkins, 1990.
16.13b: Ed Reschke.
16.15a, b: Charles B. Wilson, Neurological Surgery, University of California Medical Center, San Francisco.
16.17: Carolina Biological Supply/Phototake NYC.
A Closer Look: Saturn Stills/Science Photo Library/Photo Researchers.

Chapter 17
Chapter Opener: Mark Scoggins/Jupiter Images.
17.2: Ed Reshke/Peter Arnold.
17.8a, b: Stan Flegler/Visuals Unlimited.
17.10a–e: Nina Zanetti, Pearson Science.
17.15: Meckes/Ottawa/Photo Researchers.
17.16.1–4: Jack Scanlon, Holyoke Community College.

Chapter 18
Chapter Opener: Brian Bahr/Getty Images.
18.4a: A. & F. Michler/Peter Arnold.
18.4c: L. Bassett/Visuals Unlimited.
18.4f: *Color Atlas of Anatomy: A Photographic Study of the Human Body*. Germany: © Schattauer Publishing.
18.8b: From *A Stereoscopic Atlas of Human Anatomy* by David L. Bassett.
18.8c: Lennart Nilsson, *The Body Victorious*, New York: Dell, © Boehringer Ingelheim International GmbH.
18.8d: L. Bassett/Visuals Unlimited.
18.11a: Manfred Kage/Peter Arnold.
18.19: Phil Jude/Science Photo Library/Photo Researchers.
18.22: Chris Cole/Getty Images.

Chapter 19
Chapter Opener: Jim Cummins/Getty Images.
19.1a: Gladden Willis/Visuals Unlimited.
19.13: Asia Images Group/Getty Images.
19.22c: Science Photo Library/Photo Researchers.
A Closer Look: 1: Sheila Terry/Science Photo Library/Photo Researchers. 2: ISM/Phototake.

Chapter 20
Chapter Opener: Stockbyte/Getty Images.
20.3: Francis Leroy, Biocosmos/Science Photo Library/Photo Researchers.
20.4b: Biophoto Associates/Photo Researchers.
20.6c: Mark Neilsen/Benjamin Cummings.
20.6d: LUMEN Histology, Loyola University Medical Education Network, http://www.lumen.luc.edu/lumen/MedEd/Histo/frames/histo_frames.html.
20.7: Astrid and Hanss-Freider Michler/Science Photo Library/Photo Researchers.
20.8: John Cunningham/Visuals Unlimited.
20.9: Biophoto Associates/Science Source/Photo Researchers.

Chapter 21
Chapter Opener: Jim Cummins/Getty Images.
21.2a: Dr. David M. Phillips/Visuals Unlimited/Getty Images.
21.10: David Scharf/Photo Researchers, Inc.
21.14b: Eduardo A. Padlan, National Institutes of Health.
21.20b: Andrejs Liepins/Science Photo Library/Photo Researchers.

Chapter 22
Chapter Opener: AP World Wide Photos.
22.2a: Jenny Thomas/Benjamin Cummings.
22.3a: From *A Stereoscopic Atlas of Human Anatomy* by David L. Bassett.
22.4c, d: From *A Stereoscopic Atlas of Human Anatomy* by David L. Bassett.
22.6b: Nina Zanetti, Pearson Science.

22.6c: Science Photo Library/Photo Researchers.
22.8b: Carolina Biological Supply/Phototake.
22.9b: Kessel and Kardon/Visuals Unlimited.
22.10a: Richard Tauber/Benjamin Cummings.
22.10b: From *A Stereoscopic Atlas of Human Anatomy* by David L. Bassett.

Chapter 23
Chapter Opener: Al Bello/Allsport/Getty Images.
23.9b: Science Photo Library/Photo Researchers.
23.10.b: Elaine N. Marieb.
23.12a: Biophoto Associates/Photo Researchers.
23.12b: From *Color Atlas of Histology* by Leslie P. Garner and James L. Hiatt, © Williams and Wilkins, 1990.
23.14.b: From *A Stereoscopic Atlas of Human Anatomy* by David L. Bassett.
23.16.a: Javer Domingo/Phototake NYC.
23.16.b: Oliver Meckes/Ottawa/Photo Researchers.
23.22d: Steve Gschmeissner/Photo Researchers, Inc.
23.23a: P. Motta/Department of Anatomy/University "La Sapienza," Rome/Science Photo Library/Photo Researchers.
23.23b: Secchi-Lecaque-Roussel-UCLAF/CNRI/Science Photo Library/Photo Researchers.
23.24a, b: From *A Stereoscopic Atlas of Human Anatomy* by David L. Bassett.
23.25b: From *A Stereoscopic Atlas of Human Anatomy* by David L. Bassett.
23.26b: Victor Eroschenko, University of Idaho; Benjamin Cummings.
23.30a: From *A Stereoscopic Atlas of Human Anatomy* by David L. Bassett.

Chapter 24
Chapter Opener: Stewart Cohen/Getty Images.
24.10: Andreas Engel and Daniel J. Müller.
24.CL: Bartomeu Amengual/age footstock.
24.26: Jeff Greenberg/Omni-Photo.

Chapter 25
Chapter Opener: Zefa RF/age fotostock.
25.2b: Richard Tauber, Benjamin Cummings.
25.3a: Ralph T. Hutchings.
25.6a: Biophoto Associates/Photo Researchers.
25.6b: Dennis Kunkel/PhotoTake.
25.7b: Kessel and Kardon/Visuals Unlimited.
25.9b: P. Motta and M. Castellucci/Science Photo Library/Photo Researchers.
25.19: National Institute of Health.
25.20: Biophoto Associates/Photo Researchers.

Chapter 26
Chapter Opener: Jim Cummins/Getty Images.
26.5: Spencer Grant/Stock Boston.

Chapter 27
Chapter Opener: Lisette Le Bon/SuperStock.
27.3b: From *A Stereoscopic Atlas of Human Anatomy* by David L. Bassett.
27.3c: Ed Reschke.
27.8a: Kessel and Kardon/Visuals Unlimited.
27.8b: Juergen Berger/Photo Researchers, Inc.
27.9b: Manfred Kage/Peter Arnold.
27.11b: Biophoto Associates/Photo Researchers, Inc.
27.12b: From *A Stereoscopic Atlas of Human Anatomy* by David L. Bassett.
27.13a: Carolina Biological Supply Company/Phototake.
27.16a: Mark Thomas/Photo Researchers, Inc.
27.16b, c: Leonard Lessin/Peter Arnold.
27.18.1–3: Science Pictures Ltd./Photo Researchers, Inc.
27.18.4: ISM/Phototake.
27.18.5: Ed Reschke/Peter Arnold.
27.18.6: C. Edelman/La Vilette/Photo Researchers.
27.18.7: Lester V. Bergman/Corbis.

Chapter 28

Chapter Opener: John Lund/Drew Kelly/Blend Images/Jupiter Images.
28.2b: Lennart Nilsson, *A Child Is Born*, New York: Dell, © Boehringer Ingelheim International GmbH.
28.3b: CC Studio/Science Photo Library/Photo Researchers, Inc.
28.5b: R. O'Rahilly and R. Muller, *Human Embryology and Teratology*. This material is reproduced with permission of Wiley-Liss, Inc., a subsidiary of John Wiley & Sons, Inc.
28.5d: Allen C. Enders, University of California, Davis/Carnegie Collection.
28.15a: From *A Stereoscopic Atlas of Human Anatomy* by David L. Bassett.
28.15b, c: From Lennart Nilsson/Albert Bonniers Forlag.

Chapter 29

Chapter Opener: Ariel Skelley/Corbis.
29.1b: Lester Lefkowitz/Corbis.
29.1c: L.Williatt, East Anglian Regional Genetics/SPL/Photo Researchers.
29.5: Andrew Syred/Photo Researchers.
29.7.1, 2: PhotoDisc/Getty Images.

Illustration Credits

All illustrations by Imagineering STA Media Services unless otherwise noted.

Chapter 1

1.3: Vincent Perez/Wendy Hiller Gee.
1.7: Imagineering STA Media Services/Precision Graphics
1.10a: Adapted from Seeley, Stephens, and Tate, *Anatomy & Physiology*, 4e, F1.15a, New York: WCB/McGraw-Hill, © McGraw-Hill, 1998.

Chapter 3

3.2: Imagineering STA Media Services/Precision Graphics
3.3: Imagineering STA Media Services/Precision Graphics
3.19: Tomo Narashima.
3.20: Imagineering STA Media Services/Precision Graphics
3.24: Adapted from Campbell, *Biology*, 4e, F7.21, © Benjamin Cummings, 1996.
3.27: Imagineering STA Media Services/Precision Graphics
3.29: Tomo Narashima.

Chapter 4

4.6: From Mathews, Van Holde, and Ahern, *Biochemistry*, 3e, F9.24, © Benjamin Cummings, 2000.

Chapter 5

5.1, 5.2, 5.5: Electronic Publishing Services, Inc.
Making Connections: Vincent Perez/Wendy Hiller Gee.

Chapter 6

6.9: Imagineering STA Media Services/Precision Graphics
Making Connections: Vincent Perez/Wendy Hiller Gee.

Chapter 7

7.3, 7.5, 7.6, 7.7, 7.8: Nadine Sokol.

Chapter 9

9.1: Imagineering STA Media Services/Precision Graphics
9.2: Imagineering STA Media Services/Precision Graphics
9.8, 9.9, 9.11, 9.12, 9.13, 9.26, 9.27, 9.28: Electronic Publishing Services, Inc.
Making Connections: Vincent Perez/Imagineering STA Media Services.

Chapter 11

11.2, 11.17, 11.23: Electronic Publishing Services, Inc.
11.3: Imagineering STA Media Services/Precision Graphics
11.5: Imagineering STA Media Services/Precision Graphics

Chapter 12

12.1–12.6, 12.8–12.11, 12.13, 12.15–12.19, 12.23–12.26: Electronic Publishing Services, Inc.
12.12: Electronic Publishing Services, Inc./Precision Graphics
12.31: Imagineering STA Media Services/Electronic Publishing Services, Inc.
12.32–12.35: Electronic Publishing Services, Inc.

Chapter 13

13.1, 13.3–13.5, 13.13, 13.14, 13.17, 13.18, 13.19: Electronic Publishing Services, Inc.
13.T02.06: Imagineering STA Media Services/Precision Graphics
13.15: Imagineering STA Media Services/Precision Graphics

Chapter 14

14.1–14.4, 14.6, 14.7, 14.9: Electronic Publishing Services, Inc.
Making Connections: Vincent Perez/Wendy Hiller Gee.

Chapter 15

15.1–15.6, 15.8, 15.15, 15.16, 15.18, 15.20, 15.21, 15.23–15.24, 15.26, 15.27, 15.28, 15.31, 15.33–15.36 : Electronic Publishing Services, Inc.
15.25: Electronic Publishing Services, Inc./Precision Graphics

Chapter 16

16.1: Electronic Publishing Services, Inc.
Making Connections: Vincent Perez/Wendy Hiller Gee.
16.8: Imagineering STA Media Services/Precision Graphics

Chapter 18

18.1: Electronic Publishing Services, Inc./Precision Graphics
18.4, 18.8, 18.11, 18.14: Electronic Publishing Services, Inc.
18.9: Imagineering STA Media Services/Precision Graphics

Chapter 19

19.1, 19.4, 19.21–19.30: Electronic Publishing Services, Inc.
Making Connections: Vincent Perez/Wendy Hiller Gee.

Chapter 20

Making Connections: Vincent Perez/Wendy Hiller Gee.

Chapter 21

21.16: Adapted from Johnson, *Human Biology*, 2e, F9.13, © Benjamin Cummings, 2003.

Chapter 22

22.1: Electronic Publishing Services, Inc./Precision Graphics
22.3, 22.4, 22.7–22.10, 22.26: Electronic Publishing Services, Inc.
Making Connections: Vincent Perez/Wendy Hiller Gee.

Chapter 23

23.1, 23.6–23.9, 23.14, 23.15, 23.21, 23.22, 23.29–23.31: Electronic Publishing Services, Inc.
Making Connections: Vincent Perez/Wendy Hiller Gee.
23.25: Electronic Publishing Services, Inc./Precision Graphics
23.28: Imagineering STA Media Services/Precision Graphics

Chapter 24

24.1b: Willett, W.C., Eat, Drink, and Be Healthy. Nutrition Source, Simon & Schuster, Harvard School of Public Health, Food Pyramids, 2001. www.hsph.harvard.edu/nutritionsource/pyramids.html.

Chapter 25

25.1, 25.5, 25.7–25.9, 25.21: Electronic Publishing Services, Inc.
25.12: Imagineering STA Media Services/Precision Graphics

Chapter 26

Making Connections: Vincent Perez/Wendy Hiller Gee.
26.09: Imagineering STA Media Services/Precision Graphics

Chapter 27

27.1–27.4, 27.10–27.12: Electronic Publishing Services, Inc.
Making Connections: Vincent Perez/Wendy Hiller Gee.

Chapter 28

28.4, 28.13: Electronic Publishing Services, Inc.

Index

NOTE: Page numbers in **boldface** indicate a definition. A *t* following a page number indicates tabular material, an *f* indicates an illustration, and a *b* indicates boxed material.

A agglutinins, 655, 655*t*
A bands, **281**
  in cardiac muscle, 673, 674*f*
  in skeletal muscle, 280*f*, **281**
  in sliding filament model of contraction, 284, 284*f*
ABCD/ABCD(E) rule, for melanoma recognition, **163**
Abdomen
  arteries of, 730–733*f*, 730–733*t*
  muscles of, 326*f*, 342*t*, 343*f*
  sympathetic pathways to, 532, 533*f*
  veins of, 742–743*f*, 742*t*
Abdominal aorta, **724***t*, 725*f*, 730*f*, 730–733*f*, 730*t*
  branches of, 724*f*, 730–733*f*, 730–733*t*
Abdominal aortic plexus, **530**, 532
Abdominal cavity, **16**, 16*f*
Abdominal organs, perfusion (blood flow) of, 713*f*
Abdominal reflexes, **519**
Abdominal wall
  innervation of, 504
  muscles of, 342*t*, 343*f*
Abdominopelvic cavity, **16**, 16*f*
  regions/quadrants of, 17–20, 17*f*, 20*f*
Abdominopelvic organs, muscles supporting, 344*t*, 345*f*
Abducens nerve (cranial nerve VI), 446*f*, 447, **493**, 494*f*, **498***t*
  extrinsic eye muscles supplied by, 498*t*, 551
  paralysis of, 498*t*
Abduction (body movement), **256**, 257*f*
  of lower limb, 380*t*, 381*f*
  of upper limb, 358*t*, 359*f*
Abductor digiti minimi muscle
  of foot, **376***t*, 377*f*
  of hand, **360***t*, 361*f*
Abductor hallucis muscle, **376***t*, 377*f*
Abductor muscles, of thigh, 363*t*
Abductor pollicis brevis muscle, **360***t*, 361*f*
Abductor pollicis longus muscle, **356***t*, 357*f*, 358*t*, 359*f*
ABO blood groups, **654–655**, 655*t*
  multiple-allele inheritance and, 1106, 1106*t*
  transplantation and, 792

Abortion, 1096*b*, **1097**
Abortion pill (RU-486), 1096*b*
Abscess, 773
Absence (petit mal) seizures, 454
Absolute refractory period, **404**, 404*f*
  in cardiac muscle, 673, 675*f*
Absorption (food/nutrient), **852**, 853*f*, **854**, 898–901
  deficiencies of (malabsorption), **901**
  in large intestine, 888*t*, 898
  in small intestine, 878, 888*t*, 896*f*, 898–899
Absorptive cells, of small intestine, 878, 879*f*, 880*f*
Absorptive (fed) state, **936**, 936–938, 937*f*, 938*f*
Abstinence methods, of contraception, 1095*b*
Acceleration
  crista ampullaris response to, 585, 586*f*
  macular response to, 584, 585, 585*f*
Accessory digestive organs, **852–853**, 852*f*. *See also specific structure*
Accessory hemiazygos vein, 740*f*, 741*f*, **741***t*
Accessory nerve (cranial nerve XI), 446–447*f*, **493**, 494*f*, **501***t*, 504*f*
Accessory oculomotor (Edinger-Westphal) nuclei, 529
Accessory pancreatic duct, 878*f*, 885
Accessory reproductive ducts, **1028**. *See also* Reproductive duct system
Accessory reproductive organs/glands, **1024**
  in male, 1025*f*, 1029*f*, **1030–1031**
Acclimatization, **840**
Accommodation, **558–559**
Accommodation pupillary reflex, **559**
ACE. *See* Angiotensin converting enzyme
Acetabular labrum, **267**, 267*f*
Acetabulum, 233*f*, 234*f*, **235**, 236*t*, 267
Acetic acid, 39, 931, 931*f*
Acetylcholine (ACh), **285**, 415, 416*t*, **527**, 535, 536*t*

in autonomic versus somatic nervous system, **527**, 527*f*, 535
in hydrochloric acid secretion control, 873
memory circuits affected by, 458, 459*f*
in muscle contraction, 285, 286*f*, 288, 512
  excitation-contraction coupling and, 290*f*
in neuromuscular junction, 285, 286*f*, 512
Acetylcholine (ACh) receptors, **285**, 535, 535*t*
Acetylcholinesterase (AChE), **285**, 286*f*, 415, 512
Acetylcholinesterase (AChE) inhibitors, autonomic activity and, 537*t*
Acetyl coenzyme A (acetyl CoA), 919, 920*f*, **924**
  in glucose metabolism, **924**, 925*f*
  in lipid metabolism, 931, 931*f*
ACh. *See* Acetylcholine
AChE. *See* Acetylcholinesterase
Achilles (calcaneal) tendon, 240, 327*f*
  rupture of, **382**
Achondroplasia, **195**
Acid(s), **39**, 1009
  metabolic (fixed), **1011**
  pH of, 40, 40*f*
  strong, **41**, 1009, 1009*f*
  volatile, **1011**
  weak, **41**, 1009, 1009*f*
Acid-base balance, 41, 834, 1008–1014, 1009*f*, 1012*f*, 1013*f*
  abnormalities of, 1014–1015, 1016*t*. *See also* Acidosis; Alkalosis
    respiratory and renal compensations and, **1014**, 1014–1015
  chemical buffer systems in, 41, **1009**–1010, 1009*f*
  developmental aspects of, 1015
  potassium and, 1006
  renal regulation of, 978, 983*f*, 1011–1014, 1012*f*, 1013*f*
    compensations for abnormalities and, 1014, 1015

    respiratory regulation of, 41, 834, 837*f*, 838, 1010–1011
    compensations for abnormalities and, 1014, 1014–1015
Acidemia, **1008**. *See also* Acidosis
Acid group, amino acid, 47, 48*f*
Acid hydrolases, 86
Acidic solution, 40
Acid mantle, **160**
Acidosis, 56, **1008**
  blood values in evaluation of, 1017*b*
  in diabetes, 622, 623*t*, 938
  effects of, 1014
  metabolic, 932, **1014**, 1016*t*, 1017*b*
  newborn's first breath and, 1093
  physiologic, 1009
  renal compensations and, 1014, 1015
  renal tubular, **1020**
  respiratory (hypoventilation), **840**, 1011, **1014**, 1016*t*, 1017*b*
  respiratory compensations and, 1014, 1014–1015
Acinar (alveolar) glands, **122**, 123*f*
Acini/acinar cells, pancreatic, 620, 620*f*, **885–886**, 885*f*
Acinus (secretory unit), of multicellular exocrine gland, 121, 122, 123*f*
Acne, 157, 165
Acoustic meatus
  external (external auditory/ear canal), 204, 205*f*, 207*f*, **214***t*, **574**, 575*f*
  internal, 207, 214*t*
Acoustic nerve. *See* Vestibulocochlear nerve
Acquired immune deficiency syndrome (AIDS), **796–797**, 1058
Acquired (learned) reflex, 514
Acromegaly, **604**
Acromial end of clavicle, 226, 226*f*
Acromioclavicular joint, 228, 254*t*
Acromion, 227*f*, **228**
Acrosomal process, 1073, 1074*f*
Acrosomal reaction, **1073**, 1074*f*
Acrosome, **1037**, 1037*f*
ACTH. *See* Adrenocorticotropic hormone
Actin, 51*t*, 88, 279*t*, 280*f*, **281**, 282*f*, 310*t*

Actin (contd.)
   clot retraction and, 652
   cross bridge activity and,
      288–289, 292f
   in excitation-contraction
      coupling, 291f
   in sliding filament model, 284,
      288–289
Actin (thin) filaments, 88, 136, **281**
   in cardiac muscle, 310t, 673
   in cytokinesis, 97, 99f
   in microvilli, 91
   in skeletal muscle, 279t, 280f,
      281, 282f, 310t
   in sliding filament model, 284,
      284f, 307, 307f
   in smooth muscle, 306, 307, 307f
Action potential, **285**, **399**, **400–401f**
   in muscle fiber contraction, **285**,
      285f, 286f, 288, 290–291f, 308
      cardiac muscle, 675, 675f,
         676, 676f
         sequence of excitation
            and, 676–678, 677f
      excitation-contraction cou-
         pling and, **288**, 290–291f
      generation/propagation of,
         285–288, 287f, 288f
   in neuron, 24, 395, **399–406**,
      400–401f, 410–411t
      conduction velocity of,
         404–406, 405f
      generation of, 399–402,
         400–401f
      graded potential compared
         with, 410–411t
      information transfer at chem-
         ical synapse and, 408, 409f
      propagation of, **402–403**, 403f
      refractory periods and,
         404, 404f
      stimulus intensity and,
         404, 404f
      threshold/all-or-none phe-
         nomenon and, 403–**404**
Activation energy, 52, 52f, 923
Activation gate, action potential and,
   401f, 402
Active (exercise) hyperemia, **716**
Active immunity, 781–782, 782f
Active sites, 50, 52–53, 53f
Active processes/transport, **68**,
   72–79, **73**, 77t
   in absorption, 898
   primary, **73**, 74f, 77t
      in sodium reabsorption, 974,
         976f, 983f
   secondary, **73**, 75f, 77t, **975**
      in tubular reabsorption, 975,
         976f, 983f
      of sodium, 974, 976f, 983f
   vesicular, **73–79**, 76f, 77t, 78f
Acute (immediate/type I) hypersen-
   sitivity, **798**, 798f
Acute glomerulonephritis, **991**. See
   also Glomerulonephritis
Acute leukemia, 648
Acute mountain sickness, 839
Acyclovir, 1059
AD. See Alzheimer's disease
Adam's apple (laryngeal promi-
   nence), **810**, 810f

Adaptation, **489**
   dark and light, 564–566
   olfactory, 570
Adaptive immune system, **767**, 767f,
   775–795, 794f, 795t
Addison's disease, 616, **618**,
   1002, 1004
   skin color in, 155
Adduction (body movement), **256**
   of lower limb, 380t, 381f
   of upper limb, 358t, 359f
Adductor(s)/adductor muscles, of
   thigh, 363t, 365t, 381f
Adductor brevis muscle, 364f,
   365t, 380t
Adductor hallucis muscle,
   378t, 379f
Adductor hiatus, 734f, 734t, 735f
Adductor longus muscle, 326f, 364f,
   365t, 380t
Adductor magnus muscle, 327f, 364f,
   365t, 380t
Adductor pollicis muscle,
   360t, 361f
Adductor tubercle, **237**, 238f
A delta fibers, 490
Adenine (A), **53**, 54f
Adenocarcinoma, of lung, **842**
Adenohypophysis, 601. See also
   Anterior pituitary gland
Adenoidectomy (adenotonsillec-
   tomy), **846**
Adenoids, 760, 809. See also Pharyn-
   geal tonsils
Adenoma, **144**
Adenosine, 418t, **419**
   glomerular filtration rate regula-
      tion and, 974
Adenosine diphosphate. See ADP
Adenosine monophosphate.
   See AMP
Adenosine triphosphate. See ATP
Adenotonsillectomy (adenoidec-
   tomy), **846**
Adenylate cyclase, in hormone
   mechanism of action,
   597, 597f
ADH. See Antidiuretic hormone
Adherence, in phagocytosis,
   768, 769f
Adhesions, 141
Adipocytes (adipose/fat cells), 125f,
   126, **127**, 128f, 134t. See also
   Adipose (fat) tissue
Adiponectin, 624, 625t, 948b
Adipose (fat) tissue, **127–129**,
   128f, 134t
   autonomic innervation/effects
      and, 538t
   hormones produced by, 624, 625t
   lipid transport to, 943
   lipolysis in, 939–940, 939f
   metabolic fuel used by, 935t
Adluminal compartment, of seminiferous tubule, 1036f, **1038**
ADP (adenosine diphosphate),
   55–56, 55f, **650**, 928
   phosphorylation of,
      921–922, 921f
   ATP for muscle activity and,
      298, 298f
   platelet aggregation and, **650**

Adrenal cortex, **614**, 614–618,
   615f, 617t
Adrenal (suprarenal) gland(s), 595f,
   614–620, 615f. See also
   Adrenal cortex; Adrenal
   medulla
   arteries of, 732t
   autonomic innervation/effects
      and, 528f
   developmental aspects of, 626
   in stress response, 617, 619, 619f
Adrenaline. See Epinephrine
Adrenal insufficiency, 616, 618
Adrenal medulla, **614**, 615f, 617t,
   618–620
   autonomic pathways with
      synapses in/autonomic inner-
      vation and, 532, 533f
   blood pressure control and, 709
Adrenergic fibers, **535**
Adrenergic receptors, 536, **536t**
Adrenocortical hormones, 45t, 47,
   614–618, 617t
Adrenocorticotropic hormone
   (ACTH), 602f, **605**, **606t**
   aldosterone regulation and,
      615, 616f
   cortisol regulation and, 616–617
   in stress response, 617, 619f
Adrenogenital syndrome, 618
Adult respiratory distress syndrome
   (ARDS), **846**
Adventitia
   in alimentary canal, **857**
   of bladder, 986, 987f
   of esophagus, 857, 865, 865f
   tracheal, 812, 812f, **813**
   of ureter, 986, 986f
   vaginal, 1044
Aerobic cellular respiration, 83, 924.
   See also Krebs cycle
   ATP for muscle activity and,
      298f, 299, 299f, 300, 310t
Aerobic endurance, 299
Aerobic exercise, **304**. See also Exercise
Aerobic pathways, **924**
Aerobic respiration, 299
Afferent arteriole, glomerular, **966**,
   967f, 968
Afferent (sensory) division of pe-
   ripheral nervous system, 386,
   387f, 485f
Afferent lymphatic vessels, 757, 757f
Afferent nerves/neurons/tracts. See
   Sensory (afferent) nerves;
   Sensory (afferent) neurons;
   Sensory (ascending)
   pathways/tracts
Afferent pathways. See also Sensory
   (ascending) pathways/tracts
   in homeostasis, 9, 9f, 10f
Affinity, hemoglobin, for
   oxygen, 831
Afterbirth, **1092**
After-discharge circuit, parallel,
   422, 422f
After-hyperpolarization (under-
   shoot), **402**
Afterload, **684–685**
Ag. See Antigen(s)
Age-related macular degeneration
   (ARMD), **589**

Ageusia, **589**
Agglutination, 656, **785**
   by antibodies, **785**, 785f
Agglutinins, **655**, 655t
Agglutinogens, **654**
Aggregated lymphoid nodules
   (Peyer's patches), 758f,
   760–761, 761f, 880
   in small intestine, **880**
Aging
   bladder affected by, 991
   blood vessels affected by, 745
   bone loss/osteoporosis and, 191,
      194, 244
   cardiovascular system and, 316
   cellular, 108
   central nervous system and, 478
   chemical senses and, 588
   digestive system and, 904
   endocrine system and, 624,
      626–627
   gonadal changes and, 626
   heart affected by, 689
   hypertension and, 713, 745
   immune system affected by, 799
   joints affected by, 272
   kidney function/kidneys affected
      by, 991
   metabolism and, 947, 954–955
   muscles and, 312–316
   osteoarthritis and, 270
   skeletal system and, 244
   skin changes and, 165
   sleep and, 456
   thymus affected by, 759
   tissue changes and, 144
   urinary system and, 991
Aging pigment (lipofuscin), 389–390
Agouti-related peptides, in food
   intake regulation, 945, 946f
Agonist (muscle), **321**
Agranulocytes, 643, 644f, 645t, **646**
Agrin, 311
Ags. See Antigen(s)
AIDS (acquired immune deficiency
   syndrome), **796–797**, 1058
Air–blood barrier (respiratory membrane), **815**, 816f
   gas exchange at, 805, 815, 816f,
      828–830, 828f, 829f
   thickness/surface area of, 830
Air cells, mastoid, 574
Air flow, resistance to, 822–823, 823f
   asthma and, 823
Air movements, nonrespiratory,
   826, 826t
Airway resistance, 822–823, 823f
   asthma and, 823
Ala(e), **223**, **235**
   of ilium, 234f, **235**
   of nose, 806, 806f
   of sacrum, **223**
Alar plate, **466**, 466f
Albinism, **168**, 1106
Albumin, 51t, **636**, 636t
Albuminuria, 985t
Alcohol
   antidiuretic hormone and, 608
   teratogenic effects of (fetal alco-
      hol syndrome), 1085
Aldosterone, **614–615**, 615f, 616f,
   617t, **710**, **1004**, 1004f

blood pressure and, 615, 616*f*, 709*t*, **710**, 710*f*, 1004, 1007*f*
electrolyte balance and, 615, 616*f*, 1004, 1004*f*
potassium regulation and, 1004*f*, 1006
sodium regulation and, **1004**, 1004*f*
tubular reabsorption and, 978, 983*f*, 1004, 1004*f*
Aldosteronism (hyperaldosteronism/ Conn's disease), 616, **1020**
Alendronate, for osteoporosis, 191
Alertness, 455
Alimentary canal (gastrointestinal tract), **852**, 852*f*. *See also specific structure and* Digestive system
development of, 901–904, 901*f*
endocrine (enteroendocrine) cells in, 624, 869*f*, **870**
enteric nervous system of, 534, 854, 855*f*, **857–858**, 857*f*
histology of, 856–857, 857*f*
hormones produced by, 624, 625*t*
neural signals from, food intake regulation and, 945–946, 946*f*
pregnancy and, 1090
thyroid hormone affecting, 612*t*
Alkalemia, **1008**. *See also* Alkalosis
Alkaline phosphatase, in bone remodeling, 186
Alkaline reserve, 834, **1009**, 1011
Alkaline solution, 40
Alkaline tide, **873**, 874*f*
Alkalosis, 56, **1008**
blood values in evaluation of, 1017*b*
effects of, 1014
metabolic, **1014**, 1016*t*, 1017*b*
renal compensations and, 1014, 1015
respiratory (hyperventilation), **837**, 1011, **1014**, 1016*t*, 1017*b*
respiratory compensations and, 1014, 1015
Allantois, 1079*f*, **1080**
Allele(s), **1102–1103**
multiple-allele inheritance and, **1106**, 1106*t*
segregation and, 1103–**1104**, 1103*f*
Allergen, **798**, 798*f*
Allergic contact dermatitis, **799**
Allergies, **798**, 798*f*
protein absorption and, 899
Allografts, **792**
All-or-none phenomenon, **404**
All-*trans*-retinal, **562**, 563*f*, 564*f*
Alopecia, **159**
Alopecia areata, 159
Alpha-blocking drugs, 537
Alpha (α) cells, pancreatic, 620*f*, **621**
Alpha (α) efferent fibers, **515**, 515*f*
α-γ coactivation, **515**, 516*f*
Alpha (α) globin chains, 638, 638*f*
Alpha globulin, 636*t*
Alpha (α)-helix, **48**, 49*f*
Alpha (α) interferon, 774, 790*t*
Alpha (α) motor neurons, 515
Alpha (α) particles, 28

Alpha (α) receptors, **536**, 536*t*
Alpha waves, **454**, 454*f*
ALS. *See* Amyotrophic lateral sclerosis
Alternative pathway, of complement activation, 774*f*, **775**
Altitude
partial pressure affected by, 827
respiratory adjustments and, 839–840
Alveolar dead space, **824**
Alveolar ducts, 814*f*, **815**
Alveolar gas, composition of, 828
Alveolar (acinar) glands, **122**, 123*f*
Alveolar macrophages, **815**, 816*f*
Alveolar margins, 203*f*, **209**, **210**, 210*f*
Alveolar pores, 814*f*, **815**
Alveolar sacs, 814*f*, **815**
Alveolar surface tension, 823
Alveolar ventilation rate, **826**, 826*t*
blood pH and, 1010–1011
Alveoli
of breast, 1047*f*, **1048**
dental (tooth sockets), 209, **215***t*
articulation of tooth with (gomphosis), 249*f*, **250**, 863
respiratory/lung, 807*t*, 814*f*, **815**, 816*f*
developmental aspects of, 843
gas partial pressures in, 827*t*, 828
Alzheimer's disease, **465**
Amacrine cells, in retina, 554*f*
Ameboid motion, white blood cell, **643**
Amenorrhea, 1056
Amine group, amino acid, 47, 48*f*
Amines, biogenic, **415–418**, 416*t*
Amino acid(s), **47–48**, 48*f*, **417***t*, 418, 896*f*, **897**, 898*f*
in absorptive state, 937–938, 937*f*
deamination of, **933**–934, 933*f*, 934*t*
essential, 914, 915*f*
in food intake regulation, 946, 946*f*
as neurotransmitters, **417***t*, 418
in protein metabolism, 933–934, 933*f*
in protein synthesis/metabolism, 47–48, 48*f*, 920*f*
supply of (amino acid pool), **935**–936, 935*f*
transamination of, **933**, 933*f*, 934*t*
translation in synthesis of, **103**–105, 104*f*
transport of, 899
Amino acid–based hormones, **596**
Amino acid pool, **935**–936, 935*f*
Aminoacyl-tRNA, 104, 104*f*, 105
γ-Aminobutyric acid (GABA), 417*t*, **418**
Aminopeptidase, 896*f*, **897**, 898*f*
Amitotic cells, neurons as, 389
Ammonia, **40**, 933, 933*f*
odor of in urine, 985
Ammonium ion, 40
excretion of in acid-base balance, 1012, 1013*f*

Amnesia, 458–459
Amniocentesis, **1110**, 1111*f*
Amnion, 1079*f*, **1080**, 1080*f*, 1081*f*, 1082*f*, 1083*f*
Amniotic cavity, 1079*f*, 1082*f*
Amniotic fluid, **1080**
testing (amniocentesis), **1110**, 1111*f*
Amoeboid motion, **75**, 88
AMP (adenosine monophosphate), 55*f*, 56
cyclic. *See* Cyclic AMP
Amphiarthroses, **249**
Amphoteric molecules, **1010**
Amplitude, sound wave, 579*f*, **580**
Ampulla, **576**, **1029**, **1042**
of ductus deferens, 1025*f*, **1029**, 1029*f*
hepatopancreatic, **877**
of semicircular duct, **576**
of uterine tube, **1042**, 1043*f*
AMS. *See* Acute mountain sickness
Amygdala, **452**, 452*f*
Amylase, **886**
pancreatic, **886**, 896*f*, **897**
salivary, **895**, 896*f*
Amyloid precursor protein (APP), in Alzheimer's disease, 465
Amyotrophic lateral sclerosis (ALS/Lou Gehrig's disease), **476–477**
Anabolic hormones/steroids, 312, 313*b*, 914–915
Anabolism, 5, **36**, 918–920, 920*f*
absorptive state and, 936, 936–938, 937*f*, 938*f*
synthesis reactions and, **36**
Anaerobic glycolysis, **298**, 919, 920*f*, 922, 922*f*, 923–924, 923*f*
muscle activity and, **298**–299, 298*f*, 299, 299*f*, 310*t*
Anaerobic threshold, **299**
Anal canal, 852*f*, **891**, 891*f*
Anal columns, 891*f*, **893**
Analgesia, **520**
Anal sinuses, 891*f*, **893**
Anal sphincters, 891, 891*f*
external, 345*f*, **891**, 891*f*
internal, **891**, 891*f*
Anal veins, varices of (hemorrhoids), 701, 893
Anandamide, 418*t*
Anaphase
in meiosis, 1033, 1034*f*, **1035***f*
in mitosis, 96*f*, **97**, 99*f*
Anaphylactic shock, 719–720, 720*f*, **798**
Anaplasia, **109**
Anastomoses (vascular), **701**
portal-caval, 884
Anatomical dead space, **824**
Anatomical direction/directional terms, 12*t*, **13**, 13*f*
Anatomical neck, of humerus, **228**, 229*f*
Anatomical position, 12*t*, **13**, 13*f*
Anatomy, **2**
complementarity principle and, **3**
developmental, **2**
gross (macroscopic), **2**
microscopic, **2**

pathological, 2
radiographic, 2
regional, **2**
surface, **2**
systemic, **2**
terminology used in, 2, 11–20
anatomical position/ directional terms and, 12*t*, **13**, 13*f*
for body cavities/membranes, 14–20, 16*f*, 17*f*, 20*f*
for body planes/sections, 14, 15*f*, 18–19*b*
regional terms and, 13*f*, **14**
variability/variations in, 14
Anchoring junctions, 66–67, 67*f*. *See also* Desmosomes
Anconeus muscle, 351*f*, **353***t*, 357*f*, 358*t*
Androgen(s), **618**. *See also* Testosterone
adrenal, 615*f*, 617*t*, **618**
apocrine glands and, 156
interstitial (Leydig) cell production of, 1026, 1039, 1039*f*
sebum secretion affected by, 156
terminal hair growth affected by, 159
Androgen-binding protein, **1038**, 1039*f*
Andropause, 1066
Androstenedione, 618
Anemias, **641–643**, 642*f*. *See also specific type*
Anemic hypoxia, **832**
Anencephaly, **477**
Anergy, 778, **790**
Aneurysm, **748**
Angelman syndrome, 1109
Angina pectoris, **670**
Angiogenesis, 715
Angiogram/angiography, **748**
cerebral, 477
digital subtraction (DSA), **18***b*, 19*f*
Angioplasty, balloon, 703*b*
Angiotensin I, **972**
Angiotensin II, **615**, 616*f*, **709**, **972**, 1004
blood pressure/glomerular filtration and, **709**, 709*t*, 710, 710*f*, 711*f*, 972–974, 973*f*, 1007*f*
intrarenal, 974
Angiotensin converting enzyme, 818, **972**
Angiotensinogen, **615**, **972**
Angular body movements, **255–256**, 256–257*f*
Anion(s), **32**
balance of, regulation of, 1008
protein, in plasma/interstitial fluid/intracellular fluid, 997*f*
resting membrane potential and, 396
Ankle joint, 255*t*
muscles controlling movements of, 370–373*t*, 371*f*, 372*f*, 374–375*f*, 380*t*, 381*f*
Ankyloglossia, 859
Ankylosing spondylitis, **272**
Ankylosis, in rheumatoid arthritis, 271

Annular (common tendinous) ring, **550**
Anopsias, 495*t*
Anosmias, 495*t*, 573
ANP. *See* Atrial natriuretic peptide
ANS. *See* Autonomic nervous system
Ansa cervicalis, 504*f*, 504*t*
Antacid, **1020**
Antagonism, hormone, **600**
Antagonist (muscle), **321**
Antebrachial vein, median, 740*f*, **740***t*, 741*f*
Antebrachium. *See* Forearm
Anterior (term), 12*t*. *See also under Ventral*
Anterior arch, 219
Anterior association area (prefrontal cortex), 436*f*, **439**
    homeostatic imbalance and, 439
    in memory, 458, 459*f*
Anterior border, of tibia, 238, 239*f*
Anterior cardiac veins, 665*f*, 669*f*, **670**
Anterior cerebral artery, 726*f*, 726*t*
Anterior chamber, **555**, 555*f*
Anterior circumflex humeral artery, 728*f*, **728***t*, 729*f*
Anterior commissure, **441**, 443*f*
Anterior communicating artery, 726*f*, **726***t*, 727*f*
Anterior cranial fossa, **200**, 201*f*, 206*f*
Anterior cruciate ligament, 262–263*f*, **263**
Anterior cutaneous branch of intercostal nerve, 503*f*
Anterior division, brachial plexus, **505**, 506*f*
Anterior extensor compartment, of leg, muscles of, 370*t*
Anterior flexor compartment, of forearm, 351–352*f*, 353*t*, 354*t*, 358*t*
Anterior fontanelle, 242, 243*f*
Anterior forearm muscles, 354–356*t*, 355*f*, 358*t*
Anterior fornix, 1040*f*, 1045
Anterior (ventral) funiculi, 469*f*, **470**
Anterior gluteal line, 234*f*, **235**
Anterior (ventral) horns, 433*f*, **468**, 470*f*
Anterior inferior iliac spine, 233*f*, 234*f*, 235
Anterior intercostal arteries, 728*f*, 729*f*, **729***t*
Anterior interventricular artery (left anterior descending artery), 665*f*, **669**, 669*f*
Anterior interventricular sulcus, **664**, 666*f*
Anterior lobe, of cerebellum, **450**, 451*f*
Anterior longitudinal ligament, **217**, 218*f*
Anterior (ventral) median fissure, **468**, 469*f*
Anterior muscles/muscle compartment of hip and thigh, 363*t*, 364*f*, 365–366*t*, 380*t*, 381*f*
    of leg, 370*t*, 371*f*, 372*f*, 380*t*, 381*f*
Anterior nasal spine, **210**, 210*f*

Anterior pituitary gland (adenohypophysis), **601**, 602*f*
    hormones of, 603–605
    hypothalamus relationship and, 602*f*, 603, 603–605, 606–607*t*
Anterior pole of eye, **551**, 552*f*
Anterior sacral foramina, 221*f*, **223**
Anterior scalene muscle, 336*t*, 337*f*
Anterior segment of eye, 551, 552*f*, **555**, 555*f*
Anterior semicircular canal, 576, 577*f*
Anterior (ventral) spinocerebellar tract, **471–472**, 471*f*, 473*t*
Anterior (ventral) spinothalamic tracts, **471**, 471*f*, 473*t*
Anterior superior iliac spine, 233*f*, 234*f*, **235**
Anterior thalamic nuclei, limbic system and, 452, 452*f*
Anterior tibial artery, 725*f*, 734*f*, **734***t*, 735*f*
Anterior tibial vein, 744*f*, **744***t*
Anterior vagal trunk, **530**
Anterograde amnesia, 459
Anterograde movement, 391
Anterolateral pathways, **471**, 472*f*, 473*t*
Anteverted uterus, 1043
Anti-A antibodies, 655, 655*t*
Anti-B antibodies, 655, 655*t*
Antibodies, 51*t*, **646**, 775, **783–786**, 794*f*, 795*t*. *See also* Humoral (antibody-mediated) immunity
    in breast milk/colostrum, 1093
    classes of, 784, 784*t*
    in complement activation, 774*f*, 775, 785, 785*f*
    diversity and, 779, 784
    in humoral immune response, 780–781, 781*f*, 794*f*
    maternal, passive immunity and, 782, 782*f*
    monoclonal, **786**
    self (autoantibodies), 797
    structure of, 783–784, 783*f*
    targets/functions of, 784–786, 785*f*, 794*f*
Antibody diversity, generation of, 779, 784
Antibody-mediated (humoral) immunity. *See* Humoral (antibody-mediated) immunity
Antibody monomer, **783**, 783*f*
Antibody titer, 781
Anticancer drugs (chemotherapy), 143*b*
Anticoagulants, **652**
Anticodon(s), **103**
Antidiuretic hormone (ADH/vasopressin), 602*f*, **607***t*, **608**, **709**, **981**, 1000–1001, 1000*f*
    blood pressure and, **709**, 709*t*, 710*f*, 711*f*, 1001, 1007*f*
    in blood volume control, 10
    syndrome of inappropriate secretion of (SIADH), 608, **1020**
    tubular reabsorption and, 978, **981**, 983*f*, 1000, 1000*f*

urea recycling and, 981
    in water balance regulation, 1000–1001, 1000*f*
Antigen(s), 756, **776–777**, 776*f*, 794*f*, 795*t*. *See also* Immunity/immune response
    autoimmune disease and, 797
    endogenous, **787**, 788*f*
    exogenous, 788*f*, **789**
    presentation of, 161, 779–780, 780*f*, 794*f*
        MHC proteins and, 786–789, 787*f*, 788*f*
        T cell activation and, 789–790, 789*f*, 794*f*
    receptors for, diversity and, 779, 784
    red blood cell, blood groups and, 654
    self, **777**, 797
    T cell-dependent, **791**
    T cell-independent, **791**
    transplantation and, 793–794
Antigen-antibody (immune) complexes, **784–785**, 785*f*
    in complement activation, 774*f*, 775, 785, 785*f*
Antigen binding, T cell activation and, 789, 789*f*
Antigen-binding site, **783**, 783*f*
Antigen challenge, 780
Antigenic determinants, **776–777**, 776*f*
Antigen-presenting cells, 161, **779–780**, 780*f*, 794*f*, 795*t*
    MHC proteins and, 786–789, 787*f*, 788*f*
Antihemophilic factor (AHF/factor VIII), 651*t*, **654**
Anti-insulin effect, of growth hormone, 603
Antimicrobial proteins, 772*t*, **773–775**, 773*f*, 774*f*
Antioncogenes (tumor suppressor genes), 142*b*, 143*f*
Antioxidants, 916
Antiport system, **73**
Antirachitic factor. *See* Vitamin D
Antisense RNAs, **105**
Antithrombin III, **652**
Antitoxin, passive immunity and, 782
Antivenom, passive immunity and, 782
Antrum, **1052**
    mastoid, **574**
    ovarian follicle, 1041*f*, 1042, 1051*f*, **1052**
    pyloric, **867**, 868*f*
Anuclate cells, **91**
Anular ligament, **266**, 266*f*
Anulus fibrosus, **218**, 218*f*
Anuria, **974**
Anus, 852*f*, **891**, 891*f*. *See also under Anal*
    development of, 901*f*, 904, 1062*f*
Anvil (incus), 215*t*, 575*f*, **576**, 576*f*
Aorta, 665–667*f*, **668**, 724*t*, 725*f*
    abdominal, **724***t*, 725*f*, 730*f*, 730–733*f*, 730*t*

branches of, 724*f*, 730–733*f*, 730–733*t*
    ascending, 665*f*, **724***t*, 725*f*
    blood flow velocity and, 714, 714*f*
    blood pressure in, 705*f*
    branches of, 724–725*f*, 724*t*
    coarctation of, 689, 689*f*
    thoracic (descending), **724***t*
Aortic arch, 665*f*, 667*f*, **724***t*, 725*f*
    baroreceptors in, **707**
Aortic bodies, **709**, 837, 838*f*
Aortic reflex, **708**
Aortic sinus, 724*t*
Aortic valve (aortic semilunar valve), 667*f*, **670**, 671*f*
APCs. *See* Antigen-presenting cells
Apex, **663**
    of heart, 662*f*, **663**, 665*f*, 666*f*
    of lung, **815**, 817*f*
    of nose, **806**, 806*f*
Apgar score, **1093**
Aphasia, 457
Apical-basal polarity, epithelial, 115
Apical foramen, of root canal, **863**, 863*f*
Apical impulse, **663**
Apical surface, epithelial, **115**, 116, 116*f*
Aplastic anemia, 642
Apnea, **837**
    sleep, **457**, 846
Apneustic breathing, 835
Apocrine glands, 122–124
Apocrine sweat glands, **156**
Apoenzyme, **52**
Aponeuroses, 129, **278**
Apoptosis, **108**, **424**
    B cell development and, 778
    T cell development and, 778, 779*f*
APP. *See* Amyloid precursor protein
Appendages
    body. *See* Lower limbs; Upper limbs
    epiploic, **890**, 891*f*
    skin, 149*f*, **155–160**. *See also specific structure*
Appendicitis, **890**
Appendicular region, 13*f*, **14**
Appendicular skeleton, **173**, 174*f*, 199*f*, **225–241**. *See also specific region and specific bone*
    homeostatic imbalances and, 244
    lower limbs, 199*f*, **237–241**, 238*f*, 239*f*, 240*f*, 241*f*, 242*t*
    pectoral (shoulder) girdle, **225–228**, 226*f*, 232*t*
    pelvic (hip) girdle, 199*f*, **233–237**, 233*f*, 234*f*, 236*t*, 242*t*
    upper limbs, **228–233**, 229*f*, 230*f*, 231*f*, 232*t*
Appendix, 758*f*, **760**, 852*f*, **890**, 891*f*
Appetite, **955**
Appetite stimulants, food intake regulation and, 946, 946*f*
Appositional growth, **173**
    of bone, 185, 185*f*
    of cartilage, **173**
AQPs. *See* Aquaporin(s)
Aquaporin(s), 69*f*, **70**, **975**, 976*f*
Aqueous humor, 552*f*, **555**, 555*f*
    in glaucoma, 556
Arachidonic acid, 47
2-Arachidonoylglycerol, 418*t*

Arachnoid mater, **461**
of brain, 460*f*, **461**
spinal, 466–468, 467*f*, 468*f*, 469*f*
Arachnoid villi, 460*f*, **461**
Arbor vitae, **450**, 451*f*
ARC. *See* Arcuate nucleus
Arches of foot, 241, 241*f*
muscles supporting, 376–378*t*, 377*f*, 379*f*
Arcuate arteries, **963**, **1044**
of foot, 734*f*, 735*f*
of kidney, **963**, 964*f*
of uterus, **1044**, 1045*f*
Arcuate line, 234*f*, **235**
Arcuate nucleus, food intake regulation and, 945, 946*f*
Arcuate popliteal ligament, 262*f*, **263**
Arcuate veins, **964**, 964*f*
ARDS (adult respiratory distress syndrome), **846**
Areola, **1047**, 1047*f*
Areolar connective tissue, 124, 125*f*, **126**–127, 127*f*, 134*t*. *See also* Connective tissue
Arm
bones of, 228, 229*f*, 232*t*
deep artery of, 728*f*, **728***t*, 729*f*
muscles of/muscles controlling movement of, 326*f*, 327*f*, 350–352*t*, 351–352*f*, 358*t*, 359*f*
ARMD. *See* Age-related macular degeneration
Arrector pili muscle(s), 149*f*, 156, **158**, 158*f*
autonomic innervation/effects and, 533*f*, 538*t*
Arrhythmias, **678**–679, 680, 681*f*
ART. *See* Assisted reproductive technology
Arterial anastomoses, **701**
Arterial blood pressure, **705**, 705*f*. *See also* Blood pressure
Arterial pulse, 705, **711**
monitoring, 711, 712*f*
pregnancy and, 1090
Arteries, **695**, 695–698, 696*f*, 697*f*. *See also specific structure supplied or specific named artery*
blood flow velocity and, 714, 714*f*
blood pressure in, 705, 705*f*. *See also* Blood pressure
blood volume in, 701*f*
of brain and circle of Willis, 726*f*, 727*f*, **727***t*
pulmonary, 665–667*f*, 722*f*, **722**–723*t*, 817*f*, **818**
structure of, 696*f*, 697, 698, 698*t*
systemic, 721
Arterioles, 697*f*, **698**, 698*t*
blood flow velocity and, 714*f*
blood pressure in, 705*f*
glomerular, 966–968, 967*f*
terminal, 697*f*, **700**, 700*f*
Arteriosclerosis, 702*b*. *See also* Atherosclerosis
Arteriovenous anastomoses, **701**
Arthritis, **270**–271
gouty, **271**
Lyme, **271**
osteoarthritis, **270**
rheumatoid (RA), **270**–271, 271*f*

Arthrology, **272**
Arthroplasty, **272**
Arthroscopic surgery, for cartilage tear, **269**, 269*f*
Articular (joint) capsule, **251**, 251*f*
of elbow joint, 266, 266*f*
of knee joint, 262*f*, 263
of shoulder joint, 264, 265*f*
Articular cartilage, 131, 173, 174*f*, 176*f*, **251**
after endochondral ossification, 183*f*, 184
in symphyses, 250*f*, 251
in synovial joints, 174*f*, 251, 251*f*
Articular discs (menisci), **252**, **262**
of knee, **262**–263, 262–263*f*
injury of, 269, 269*f*
of temporomandibular joint, 268*f*, 269
Articular processes, vertebral, 218*f*, **219**, 219*f*, 222*t*
Articular surfaces, synovial joint stability and, 252
Articular tubercle, **268**, 268*f*
Articulations, **248**. *See also* Joint(s)
Artifacts, in microscopy, **115**
Artificial joints, 261*b*
Artificially acquired immunity
active, **781**–782, 782*f*
passive, **782**, 782*f*
Artificial skin, for burn injury, 164
Arytenoid cartilage, 810*f*, **811**
Ascending aorta, 665*f*, **724***t*, 725*f*
branches of, 724*f*
Ascending colon, 852*f*, **890**, 891*f*
Ascending limb of loop of Henle, 965*f*, 966, 967*f*, **983***f*
absorptive capability of, 977*t*, 978
as countercurrent multiplier, 979–980, 980*f*
Ascending lumbar veins, **740***t*, 741*f*, **741***t*, 742*f*, 743*f*
Ascending (sensory) pathways/tracts, 470, 471–473, 471*f*, 472*f*, 473*t*
Ascites, **905**
Ascorbic acid (vitamin C), 917*t*
deficiency of (scurvy), **144**, 917*t*
A site, 104*f*, 105
Aspartate, **418**
Aspartic acid, 48*f*
Aspiration, **846**
Aspiration pneumonia, cleft lip/palate and, 243
Aspirin, **653**
in atherosclerosis prevention, 703*b*
Assisted reproductive technology, 1095
Association areas, 435, 436*f*, **439**
anterior, 436*f*, **439**. *See also* Prefrontal cortex
auditory, 436*f*, **438**
limbic, **439**
multimodal, **439**
posterior, **439**
somatosensory, 436*f*, 437
visual, 436*f*, **438**, 568
homeostatic imbalance and, 439
Association cortex
language and, 457
memory and, 458, 459*f*
somatosensory, 436*f*, **437**
Association fibers, 440, 440*f*, **441**

Association neurons (interneurons). *See* Interneurons
Asters, 98*f*
Asthma, 798, 823, **841**
Astigmatism, **559**
Astrocytes, **388**–389, 388*f*
Asystole, **690**
Atelectasis, **820**
Atheroma(s), 702*b*
Atherosclerosis, **687**, 689, **702**–703*b*, 745
cholesterol levels and, 702*b*, 943, 944
coronary artery disease and, 702–703*b*
cardiac output and, **687**
Atherosclerotic (fibrous) plaques, **702***b*
Athlete(s), carbohydrate needs and, 930
Athlete's anemia, **642**
Atlantoaxial joint, 254*t*
Atlanto-occipital joint, 254*t*
Atlas, 219, 220*f*, 221*f*
Atmospheric pressure, **819**
appropriate, as survival need, 8
respiratory pressures and, 819, 821, 821*f*
Atom(s), 3, 4*f*, **25**–28, 25*f*
structure of, 25–27, 25*f*, 27*f*
Atomic mass number, 27, 28*f*
Atomic mass unit, **25**
Atomic number, **27**
Atomic structure, 25–27, 25*f*, 27*f*
Atomic symbols, **25**
Atomic weight, **27**–28
Atonic bladder, **544**
Atopic dermatitis, 800
ATP (adenosine triphosphate), 24, **55**–56, 55*f*, 56*f*, **419**, 911
in active transport, 56*f*, 73–74, 74*f*, 75*f*, 77*t*
chemical energy in form of, 24, 55
in exchange reactions, 36, 36*f*
mitochondrial supply of, 83
for muscle contraction, 56*f*, 289, 297–300, 298*f*, 307, 307*f*, 308
muscle fiber classification and, 302
as neurotransmitter, 418*t*, **419**
synthesis of, 919, 920*f*, 921–922, 921*f*, 922*f*, 928–929, 929*f*
fat metabolism in, 920*f*, 930–932, 931*f*, 932*f*
glucose metabolism in, 37, 43, 920, 923–929, 923*f*, 925*f*, 926*f*, 927*f*, 928*f*, 929*f*
ATPase, myosin, 307, 307*f*, 308
ATP synthases, **927**–928, 928*f*
Atria, of heart, **664**, 664–668, 665–667*f*, **688**
development of, 688, 688*f*
Atrial natriuretic peptide (ANP), 615, 616*f*, **624**, 625*t*, **709**, **1004**–1005, 1005*f*
blood pressure and, **709**, 709*t*, 711*f*, 1005, 1005*f*
in sodium regulation, **1004**–1005, 1005*f*
tubular reabsorption and, 978, 1005, 1005*f*

Atrial (Bainbridge) reflex, **686**
Atrial systole, **682**, 683*f*
Atrial tachycardia, paroxysmal, **690**
Atrioventricular (AV) bundle (bundle of His), **677**, 677*f*
Atrioventricular groove (coronary sulcus), **664**, 665*f*, 666*f*
Atrioventricular (AV) node, **677**, 677*f*, 678
Atrioventricular (AV) valves, **670**, 671*f*, 672*f*. *See also* Mitral (bicuspid) valve; Tricuspid valve
Atrium. *See* Atria
Atrophy, **108**
disuse, 305
Atropine, autonomic activity and, 536
Attenuated pathogens, for vaccines, 782, 782*f*
Auditory areas, 436*f*, 438
Auditory association area, 436*f*, **438**
Auditory cortex, primary, 436*f*, **438**, **582**, 582*f*
Auditory (acoustic) canal/meatus, external, 204, 205*f*, 207*f*, **214***t*, **574**, 575*f*
Auditory ossicles, **215***t*, 575*f*, **576**, 576*f*
Auditory pathway, **582**, 582*f*
Auditory processing, **582**–583
Auditory (pharyngotympanic) tube, **574**, 575*f*, 808*f*, 809
Aura, **454**
epileptic seizure and, **454**
olfactory, 573
Auricle (atrial), **664**, 665–667*f*
Auricle (pinna), **574**, 575*f*
Auricular nerve, greater, 504*f*, 504*t*
Auricular surface, **220**, 235
of ilium, 234*f*, **235**
of sacrum, **220**, 221*f*
Auricular vein, 738*f*, 739*f*
Auscultation, 2
Auscultatory method, for blood pressure measurement, **711**
Autism, **479**
Autoantibodies, 797
Autocrines, **595**
Autografts, **792**
for burn injury, 164
Autoimmune diseases, **797**
rheumatoid arthritis as, 271
Autoimmunity, **797**
Autologous chondrocyte implantation, 261*b*
Autologous transfusions, **656**
Autolysis, **87**
Automaticity (autorhythmicity), of cardiac muscle, **673**, 676
action potential initiation and, 676, 676*f*
defects in, 678–679
sequence of excitation and, 676–678, 677*f*
Autonomic dysreflexia, 541
Autonomic ganglion, **526**
Autonomic nervous system, **386**–387, 387*f*, 485*f*, **525**–546, 526*f*. *See also specific division*
anatomy of, 528–535, 529*f*, 531*f*, 533*f*, 534*f*, 534*t*, 535*f*
biofeedback in regulation of, **540**

Autonomic nervous system (*contd.*)
blood pressure and, 537, 1007*f*
control of, 539–540, 539*f*
developmental aspects of, 541
digestion and, 538*t*, 854, 855*f*, 858
divisions of, 526*f*, 527–528
comparison of, 534*t*
interactions of, 536–539, 538*t*
parasympathetic (craniosacral), 387, 387*f*, 485*f*, 526*f*, **527–528**, 528*f*
sympathetic (thoracolumbar), 387, 387*f*, 485*f*, 526*f*, **528**, 528*f*
drug effects and, 536, 537*t*
dual innervation and, **527**, 536–537, 538*t*
heart regulation and, 528*f*, 529*f*, 533*f*, 537, 538*t*, 678*f*, 679, 685, 686*f*, 707*f*
homeostatic imbalances of, 540–541
homeostatic relationships of, 542*b*, 543*b*
hypothalamus in control of, 443
physiology of, 535–540, 536*t*, 537*t*, 538*t*, 539*f*
smooth muscle innervated by, 306, 306*f*, 308, 310*t*
somatic nervous system compared with, 526–527, 527*f*
Autonomic neuropathy, **538**
Autonomic (visceral) reflex, **514**, 534–535, 534*f*, 535*f*
Autonomic reflex arc, **534**
Autonomic (visceral) sensory (VS) neurons, **470**, 470*f*, **534**
Autopsy, **144**
Autoregulation, **714**
blood flow, **714–715**, 715*f*
renal, **972**
in ventilation-perfusion coupling, 829–830, 829*f*
Autorhythmicity (automaticity), of cardiac muscle, **673**, 676
action potential initiation and, 676, 676*f*
defects in, 678–679
sequence of excitation and, 676–678, 677*f*
Authrhythmic cells, **676**
Autosome(s), **1059**, **1102**
Avascularity, of epithelial tissue, 116
AV node. *See* Atrioventricular (AV) node
Avogadro's number, **30**
AVR. *See* Alveolar ventilation rate
AV valves. *See* Atrioventricular (AV) valves
Axial region, 13*f*, **14**
Axial skeleton, **173**, 174*f*, **199–225**, 199*f*. *See also specific region and specific bone*
skull, 199*f*, **200–216**, 201*f*, 202*f*, 203–204*f*, 205*f*, 206*f*, 214–215*t*
thoracic cage, 199*f*, 223–225, 224*f*, 225*f*
vertebral column (spine), 199*f*, **216–223**, 217*f*, 218*f*, 219*f*, 220*f*, 221*f*, 222*t*

Axial tomography. *See* Computed tomography
Axillary artery, 725*f*, 727*f*, 728*f*, **728***t*, 729*f*
Axillary (lateral) border of scapula, 228
Axillary lymph nodes, 755*f*
Axillary nerve, **505**, 506*f*, 507*t*
Axillary vein, 736*f*, 737*f*, 740*f*, **740***t*, 741*f*
Axis (C$_2$), 219, **220**, 220*f*, 221*f*
Axoaxonic synapses, 406, 407*f*
Axodendritic synapses, **406**, 407*f*
Axolemma, **391**
Axon(s), 134–136, 135*f*, **390–391**, 390*f*, 393*t*
action potential generated in, 399
conduction velocity of action potential and, 404
of motor neurons, 285, 289, 293*t*
in motor unit, 289, 293*f*
myelinated, 134–136. *See also* Myelin sheath(s)
regeneration of, 491–492, 493*f*
unmyelinated. *See* Unmyelinated fibers
Axon collaterals, **391**
Axon hillock, **390–391**, 390*f*
Axon terminals, 390*f*, 391, 512
in chemical synapses, 407
in motor unit, 289, 293*f*
Axosomatic synapses, **406**, 407*f*
Azygos system, 736*f*, 740*f*, **740***t*, 740–741*t*, 741*f*
Azygos vein, 740*f*, **740***t*, 741*f*

B7 proteins, in co-stimulation, 789
Babinski's sign, **519**
Baby teeth (deciduous/primary dentition), **862**, 862*f*
Back
innervation of, 504
intrinsic (deep) muscles of, 336–338*t*, 339*f*
Bacterial flora, in digestion, **893**
Bactericidal action, of sebum, 156
B agglutinins, 655, 655*t*
Bainbridge (atrial) reflex, **686**
Balance. *See* Equilibrium/orientation
Baldness (true/frank), 159, 165
male pattern, 159
Ball-and-socket joints, **259**, 260*f*
Balloon angioplasty, 703*b*
Band cells, **646**, 647*f*
Bare area of liver, 881, 882*f*
Baroreceptors, **707**
blood pressure and, **707**, 707–709, 708*f*, 710*f*, 1006, 1007*f*
sodium regulation and, 1006, 1007*f*
Barrett's esophagus, **905**
Barrier methods, for contraception, 1095–1096*b*
Bartholin's (greater vestibular) glands, 1040*f*, **1046**, 1046*f*
Basal bodies, **90**, 90*f*. *See also* Centrioles
Basal cell(s), **570**, 571
olfactory receptor, 569*f*, **570**
taste bud, 571, 572*f*
Basal cell carcinoma, of skin, 162*f*, **163**

Basal compartment, of seminiferous tubule, 1036*f*, **1038**
Basal forebrain, brain dysfunction and, 465
Basal ganglia. *See* Basal nuclei
Basal lamina, **115**
Basal layer (stratum basalis) of endometrium, **1044**, 1045*f*
Basal metabolic rate, **947**
heat production and, 947–950, 953
thyroid hormone/thyroxine affecting, 612*t*, **948**
Basal nuclei (basal ganglia), 435, **441**, 442*f*, **449***t*, 513
in memory, 459, 459*f*
in motor control, **513**
in Parkinson's disease, 465
Basal plate, **466**, 466*f*
Basal surface, epithelial, **115**, 116*f*
Base, **663**
of bone, of metacarpals, 231*f*, **233**
of heart, **663**
of lung, 815, 817*f*
Base(s) (chemical), **39–40**, 1009
pH of, 40–41, 40*f*
strong, **41**
weak, **41**
Base(s) (DNA), 53, 54*f*
Basement membrane, **116**
glomerular, 969, 970*f*
Basic electrical rhythm, of stomach, **876**
Basilar artery, 726*f*, **726***t*, 727*f*
Basilar membrane, **577**, 578*f*
resonance of, 580, 581*f*
Basilic vein, 737*f*, 740*f*, **740***t*, 741*f*
Basolateral membrane, renal tubule, in transcellular route of tubular reabsorption, 974
Basophilic (early) erythroblasts, **639**, 639*f*
Basophils, 644*f*, 645*t*, **646**, 647*f*
in immediate hypersensitivity, 798, 798*f*
B cells. *See* B lymphocytes
BDNF (brain-derived neurotrophic factor), in memory, 460
Beau's lines, 160
Bedsores (decubitus ulcers), **168**
Bell's palsy, **498**
Benign neoplasm, 142*b*
Benign prostatic hyperplasia (BPH), 1030
BER. *See* Basic electrical rhythm
Beriberi, 916*t*
Bernard, Claude, 996
Beta amyloid peptide, in Alzheimer's disease, 465
Beta-carotene, 915–916
Beta (β) cells, pancreatic, 620*f*, **621**
destruction of in diabetes, 626*b*
Beta (β)-defensins, 771. *See also* Defensins
Beta endorphin, **418–419**
Beta (β) globin chains, 638*f*, 638*f*
Beta globulin, 636*t*
Beta (β) interferon, 774, 790*t*
Beta oxidation, **931**, 931*f*, 934*t*
Beta (β) particles, 28
Beta (β)-pleated sheet, 49*f*, **50**

Beta (β) receptors, **536**, 536*t*
Beta waves, **454**, 454*f*
Biaxial movement, **253**
Bicarbonate/bicarbonate ion, **40**, **834**
in acid-base balance/bicarbonate buffer system, 41, **834**, **1009**–1010, 1017*b*
bicarbonate reabsorption and, 1011, 1012*f*
bicarbonate regeneration and, 1011–1014, 1013*f*
renal compensations and, 1015
tubular secretion and, 1014
in acidosis/alkalosis, 1017*b*
carbon dioxide transport as, 833*f*, **834**
normal levels of, 1017*b*
in pancreatic juice, 886
in plasma/interstitial fluid/intracellular fluid, 997*f*
Bicarbonate buffer system, 41, 834, **1009**–1010
bicarbonate reabsorption and, 1011, 1012*f*
bicarbonate regeneration and, 1011–1014, 1013*f*
Biceps brachii muscle, 326*f*, 351*f*, 352*f*, **353***t*, 358*t*, 359*f*
tendon of long head of, 264
Biceps femoris muscle, 327*f*, 367*f*, **369***t*, 380*t*
Bicipital groove (intertubercular sulcus), **228**, 229*f*
Bicuspid (mitral) valve, 667*f*, **670**, 671*f*
Bicuspids (premolars), **862**, 862*f*
Bilayer, plasma membrane, 64, 65*f*
Bile/bile salts, 45*t*, **884**, 896*f*, 897, 899, 899*f*
homeostatic imbalances and, 885
regulation of secretion of, 886–887, 887*f*
in urine, 985*t*
Bile canaliculi, **881–884**, 883*f*
Bile duct, 877, 878*f*, **881**, 882*f*, 883*f*
blockage of, 885
Biliary calculi (gallstones), **885**
Biliopancreatic diversion (BPD), for obesity, 949*b*
Bilirubin, 641, 641*f*, **884**
Bilirubinuria, 985*t*
Binucleate cells, 99*f*
Biochemistry, **38–56**
inorganic compounds in, **38**, 38–41
organic compounds in, **38**, 42–56
Bioenergetics, cancer cell, drugs targeting, 143*b*
Biofeedback/biofeedback training, 540
Biogenic amines, **415–418**, 416*t*
Biologic response modifiers, for rheumatoid arthritis, 271
Biology, molecular, 2
Biopsy, in cancer diagnosis, 142*b*
Biotin, 917*t*
Biotransformation, liver in, 942*t*
Bipennate fascicle pattern/muscles, 322*f*, 323

Bipolar cells, retinal, **553**, 554*f*, 561*f*, 568
Bipolar neurons, **392**, 393–394*t*
Birth (parturition), **1090**–1092, 1091*f*, 1092*f*
  adjustment to extrauterine life after, 1092–1093
  cardiovascular system changes at, 1086*f*, 1093
  oxytocin in labor and, 606, 607, **1091**, 1091*f*
  pelvic structure and, 235–237, 236*t*
Birth canal, 1044. *See also* Vagina
Birth control (contraception), **1095**–1096*b*
Birth control pill, 1096*b*
2,3-Bisphosphoglycerate (BPG), hemoglobin saturation affected by, 831–832
Bitter taste, 572
Black-and-blue marks, 155
Blackhead, 157
Black patients, sickle-cell anemia in, **642**–643
Bladder, 961, 961*f*, 985*f*, **986**–988, 987*f*
  atonic, **544**
  autonomic innervation/effects and, 528*f*, 529*f*, 533*f*, 538*t*
  cancer of, **991**
  developmental aspects/ embryologic/fetal development of, 990–991, 990*f*, 1061*f*
  emptying (micturition), **988**, 989*f*
  infection of (cystitis), 988
  urinary retention and, **988**
Bladder trigone, **986**, 987*f*
Blanching, 155
Blast cells, 125–126, 134*t. See also specific type*
Blastocyst, **1075**, 1076*f*
  formation of, 1075–1076, 1076*f*
  implantation of, **1076**–1078, 1076*f*, 1077*f*
Blastomeres, 1075
Bleaching of the pigment, **562**, 563*f*
Bleeding disorders, **653**, 653–654
  anemia and, 641
  liver and, 653–654
Blepharitis, **589**
Blindness, 566
  functional, 439
  night, 566
  optic nerve damage causing, 495*t*
  trachoma causing, **589**
Blind spot (optic disc), 552*f*, **553**, 554*f*
Blinking, 549
Blister(s), 153
Blood, **133**, 134*t*, 135*f*, 634–660. *See also* Blood plasma
  components of, 635, 635*f*
  developmental aspects of, 657
  distribution functions of, 635
  formed elements of, 635, 635*f*, **637**–649, 637*f*, 644*f*, 645*t. See also* Blood cells
  gas transport by, 637, 638, 830–834, 831*f*, 832*f*, 833*f*
  hemostasis and, **649**–654, 649*f*

pH of, 40*f*, 1008–1009. *See also* Acid-base balance
  carbon dioxide affecting, 834, 837*f*, 838
  hemoglobin saturation affected by, 831–832, 832*f*
  renal control and, 978, 983*f*, 1011–1014, 1012*f*, 1013*f*
    compensations for abnormalities and, 1014, 1015
  respiratory control and, 838, 1010–1011
    compensations for abnormalities and, 1014, 1014–1015
  physical characteristics of, 635
  protective functions of, 636
  regulatory functions of, 636
  transfusion/replacement of, 654–657
    blood groups and, 654–655, 655*t*, 656*f*
Blood–air barrier (respiratory membrane), **815**, 816*f*
  gas exchange at, 805, 815, 816*f*, 828–830, 828*f*, 829*f*
  thickness/surface area of, 830
Blood–brain barrier, **463**–464, 699
Blood buffers, acid-base balance and, 41, 834. *See also* Buffers
Blood cells, 133, 635, 635*f*, 637–649, 637*f*, 644*f*, 645*t. See also specific type*
  formation of (hematopoiesis/ hemopoiesis), **638**–639, 639*f. See also* Hematopoiesis
Blood chemistry tests, 657, **658**
  for genetic screening, 1110
Blood clot (fibrin mesh), 636*t*, 650, 650*f*, 651, 651*t. See also* Clotting
  factors limiting growth of, 652–653
  factors preventing undesirable formation of, 653
Blood doping, **643**
Blood flow (blood circulation), **703**. *See also specific organ*
  autoregulation of, **714**–715, 715*f*
  pressure/resistance relationship and, 704
  through body tissues (tissue perfusion), **713**–721, 714*f*, 715*f*, 718*f*, 719*f*, 720*f*
  velocity of, 713–714, 714*f*
Blood fraction, **658**
Blood glucose. *See* Glucose
Blood groups, 654–655, 655*t*
  multiple-allele inheritance and, 1106, 1106*t*
  transplantation and, 792
  typing and, 656, 656*f*
Blood islands, 657, **745**
Blood plasma, 133, 135*f*, 635, 635*f*, **636**, 636*t*
Blood pressure, **703**, 704–713, 1007*f*
  age affecting, 745
  aldosterone regulation and, 615, 616*f*, 1004, 1007*f*
  alterations in, 712–713. *See also* Hypertension; Hypotension

arterial, **705**, 705*f*
  autonomic nervous system in regulation of, 537, 1007*f*
  capillary, 705, 705*f*
  flow/resistance relationship and, 704
  glomerular filtration rate and, 972–974, 973*f*
  hormonal control of, 709–710, 709*t*, 710*f*
  maintenance of, 706–713, 707*f*, 708*f*, 709*t*, 710*f*, 711*f*
  measuring, 711–712
  neural control of, 706–709, 708*f*, 1007*f*
  normal, 745
  pregnancy and, 1090
  renal regulation of, 710, 710*f*, 711*f*, 972–974, 973*f*, 1007*f*
  systemic, 704–706, 705*f*, 706*f*
  venous, 705–706, 705*f*, 706*f*
Blood pressure cuff, 711
Blood reservoir
  skin as, 161–162
  veins as, **701**, 701*f*
Blood sinusoids/sinusoidal capillaries, 638, 697*f*, **699**, 699*f*
  in liver, 881, 883*f*
  in splenic pulp, 758, 759*f*
Blood sugar. *See* Glucose
Blood supply. *See specific organ or system and* Blood vessels; Circulation
Blood–testis barrier, **1038**
Blood tests, diagnostic, 657
Blood–thymus barrier, 759
Blood typing, 656, 656*f*
Blood vessels, 694–751, 696*f*, 697*f*, 698*t. See also specific type and* Circulation
  anatomy of, 695, 696*f*, 697*f*, 698*t*
  atherosclerosis affecting, 702–703*b*, 745
  autonomic innervation/effects and, 533*f*, 537, 538*t*
  circulation physiology and, 703–721
  circulatory pathways and, 721–744
  clot in (thrombus), **653**
  congenital disorders of, 745
  constriction of, heat promotion and, 952*f*, 952*f*
  developmental aspects of, 745
  diameter of, resistance and, 704
  dilation of, 695
    heat loss and, 952*f*, 953
    in inflammation, 769–771
  embolus/embolism in, **653**
  interconnections (anastomoses) of, **701**
  length of, resistance and, 704
  structure of walls of, 695, 696*f*
  tunics of, 695, 696*f*
Blood viscosity, 704
Blood volume, 635, 684
  aldosterone regulation and, 615, 616*f*, 1004
  blood pressure and, 706, 710, 710*f*, 711*f*, 972–974, 973*f*, 1007*f*

homeostatic control of, 10
  pregnancy and, 1090
  restoration of, 656–657
Blue cones, 562
B lymphocytes (B cells), **646**, **756**, **777**, **779**, 794*f*, 795*t*
  clonal selection/activation of, 778, **780**, 781*f*, 794*f*
  in humoral (antibody-mediated) immune response, 776, 780–786, 781*f*, 782*f*, 794*f*, 795*t*. *See also* Humoral (antibody-mediated) immunity
  memory, **780**, 781*f*, 794*f*
  receptors on, 777
  T cell interaction and, 791, 791*f*, 794*f*
BMI. *See* Body mass index
BMR. *See* Basal metabolic rate
Body
  of bone
    of ilium, **235**
    of ischium, 234*f*, **235**
    of mandible, **209**, 210*f*
    of pubis, 234*f*, **235**
    of sphenoid bone, **207**, 208*f*
    of sternum, 223, 224*f*
    of vertebra, **219**, 219*f*, 222*t*
  of clitoris, **1046**–1047, 1046*f*
  of epididymis, 1028
  of nail, 160, 160*f*
  of penis, 1028, 1029*f*
  of stomach, **867**, 868*f*
  of uterus, **1043**, 1043*f*
Body cavities, 14–20, 16*f*, 17*f*, 20*f*
Body defenses. *See also* Immune system
  adaptive, **767**, 767*f*, **775**–795, 794*f*, 795*t*
  innate, **767**, 767*f*, 767*f*, 772*t*, 794*f*
Body energy balance, 944–945. *See also under* Energy
Body fluids, 107, 996–998, 996*f*, 997*f*, 998*f*
  electrolytes/nonelectrolytes in, **996**–997, 997*f*
  extracellular versus intracellular, 997–998
  movement of among compartments, 998
Body mass index (BMI), **945**
Body movements, 5, 6*f*, 253–259, 256–258*f*
Body planes/sections, 14, 15*f*, 18–19*b*
Body position, muscles in maintenance of, 276
Body proportions, skeletal growth and, 244, 244*f*
Body regions, anatomical terms describing, 13*f*, 14
Body stalk, 1079*f*
Body temperature
  metabolic rate and, 947–948
  normal, 950, **8**
  as survival need, **8**
  regulation of, 10, 10*f*, 950–954, 950*f*, 951*f*, 952*f*
    energy conversions and, 25
    heat generation by muscles and, 276–277, 300, 952*f*, 953

Body temperature (*contd.*)
    hypothalamus in, 10, 10*f*, 444, 951–952
    skin in, 161, 952–953, 952*f*
    sympathetic nervous system and, 539
    thyroid hormone/thyroxine in, 612*t*, 948
Body tissues. *See* Tissue(s)
Body water, 996, 997*f*. *See also* Water balance
    developmental changes in, 1015
Body weight, regulation of, 945–947, 946*f*
Bohr effect, **832**
Boils, 168
Bolus (food), **859**, 866, 867*f*
Bonds. *See* Chemical bonds
Bone(s)/skeletal tissue, **133**, 133*f*, 134*t*, 172–197. *See also specific named bone and* Skeletal system; Skeleton
    aging affecting, 194. *See also* Osteoporosis
    appositional growth of, 185, 185*f*
    in calcium regulation, 1008
    chemical composition of, 180
    classification of, 173–175, 174*f*, 175*f*
    compact, 134*t*, 176*f*, **177**, 179–180, 179*f*, 180*f*, 181*f*
    developmental aspects of, 194, 194*f*
    flat, **175**, 175*f*, 179, 179*f*
    formation of, 182–185
    fracture of, **188**, 190*t*
        in osteoporosis, 190*t*, 191
        pathologic, 195
        repair and, 188–189, 189*f*
    functions of, 175–176
    growth of
        hormonal regulation of, 185
        postnatal, 184–185, 184*f*, 185*f*
    homeostasis (remodeling/repair) of, **185–189**. *See also* Bone remodeling; Bone repair
    homeostatic imbalances of, 189–194
    hormones produced by, 624, 625*t*
    irregular, **175**, 175*f*, 179
    long, **174**, 175*f*, 176*f*, 177–178
        endochondral ossification in, **183–184**, 183*f*
        postnatal growth of, 184–185, 184*f*, 185*f*
        longitudinal growth of, 184–185, 184*f*, 185*f*
    mechanical stress affecting, 187–188, 187*f*, 188*f*
    membrane, **182**
    muscle relationships and (lever systems), **323–324**, 323–324*f*, 325*f*
    osteoporotic, 191, 191*f*
    Pagetic, 191
    parathyroid hormone affecting, **186**, 187*f*, 613, 614*f*
    sesamoid, **174–175**
    short, **174–175**, 175*f*, 179
    spongy, 134*t*, 176*f*, **177**, 179*f*

structure of, 176–179
    gross anatomy, 176*f*, 177–179, 177*f*, 178*t*, 179*f*
    microscopic anatomy, 179–180, 180*f*, 181*f*
    surface markings of, 177, 178*t*
    woven
        in intramembranous ossification, 182*f*
        in longitudinal bone growth, 184
Bone cells, 177, 177*f*. *See also* Osteoblasts; Osteoclasts; Osteocytes
Bone collar, 177
    in endochondral ossification, 183, 183*f*
Bone deposit, **186**
Bone markings, **177**, 178*t*
Bone marrow
    cancer of (leukemia), 648
    hematopoiesis in, 176, 179, **638–639**, 657
    red, **179**, 182*f*, **638–639**
    yellow, 177
Bone marrow biopsy, **658**
Bone mass, aging/osteoporosis affecting, 191, 194, 244
Bone matrix (osteoid), **180**
    in intramembranous ossification, 182*f*
Bone remodeling, **185–188**, 185*f*
    in fracture repair, 189, 189*f*
    hormonal control of, 186, 187*f*
    in longitudinal bone growth, 185, 185*f*
    mechanical stress and, 187–188, 187*f*, 188*f*
Bone repair, 188–189, 189*f*
Bone resorption, **186**
    in osteoporosis, 191
Bone (osseous) tissue, **133**, 133*f*, 134*t*, 172–197. *See also* Bone(s)
Bony callus, in bone repair, **189**, 189*f*
Bony (osseous) labyrinth, **576**
Bony pelvis, **233**, 233*f*
Bony skeleton, formation of, 182–184, 182*f*, 183*f*
Bony spur, **195**
Bony thorax, 199*f*, **223–225**, 224*f*, 225*f*
Booster shots, vaccine, 782
Boundary maintenance, **5**
    plasma membrane in, 5
    skin in, 5, 5*f*, 6*f*, 149, 160–161
Boutons (axon terminals), 390*f*, **391**
    in motor unit, 289, 293*f*
Bowman's (glomerular) capsule, **964**, 965*f*, 967*f*
Boyle's law, **820**
BP. *See* Blood pressure
BPD. *See* Biliopancreatic diversion
BPG, hemoglobin saturation affected by, 831–832
BPH. *See* Benign prostatic hyperplasia
Brachial artery, 725*f*, 728*f*, **728***t*, 729*f*
    pulse at, 712*f*, 728*t*
Brachialis muscle, 326*f*, 327*f*, 351*f*, 352*f*, **353***t*, 358*t*, 359*f*

Brachial plexus, 502*f*, **505–507**, 506*f*, 507*t*
    injuries to, 505
Brachial vein, 737*f*, 740*f*, **740***t*, 741*f*
Brachiocephalic trunk (artery), 665*f*, **724***t*, 725*f*, 726*f*, 728*f*, 729*f*
Brachiocephalic veins, 736*f*, **736***t*, 737*f*, 738*f*, 739*f*, 740*f*, **740***t*, 741*f*
Brachioradialis muscle, 326*f*, 327*f*, 351*f*, **353***t*, 355*f*, 358*t*, 359*f*
Brachium. *See* Arm
Brachytherapy, for atherosclerosis, 703*b*
Bradycardia, **687**
Bradykinin, 716, 772*t*
Brain, 386, 387*f*, **430–453**. *See also specific part*
    arterial supply of, 726–727*f*, 726–**727***t*
    capillaries in, 699
    degenerative disease of, 465–466
    developmental aspects/embryology of, 430–431, 430*f*, 431*f*, 432*f*, 478, 1082*f*, 1083
    functional systems of, 449*t*, 451–453, 452*f*
    gray and white matter of, 431, 432*f*
        brain stem gray matter, 432*f*, 445
        cerebellar gray matter, 431, 432*f*, 450, 451*f*. *See also* Cerebellar cortex
        cerebellar white matter, 450
        cerebral gray matter, 431, 432*f*, 434*f*, 435–440, 435*f*, 436*f*, 438*f*, 449*t*. *See also* Cerebral cortex
        cerebral white matter, 434*f*, 435, **440–441**, 440*f*
    homeostatic imbalances/dysfunction of, 464–466
    diagnosis of, 477
    functional, 479
    inflammation of (encephalitis), 463
    metabolic fuel used by, 935*t*, 940
    perfusion (blood flow) of, 713, 713*f*, 716
    protection of, 460–464
        blood–brain barrier and, **463–464**
        cerebrospinal fluid and, 462*f*, 463
        meninges and, 460*f*, **461–463**
    regions/organization of, 431, 431*f*
    swelling of (cerebral edema), **464**
    traumatic injury of, 464
    veins of, 721, 738–739*f*, 738*t*
    ventricles of, 431, **431–433**, 431*f*, 433*f*
Brain death, **455**
    flat EEG and, 454
Brain-derived neurotrophic factor (BDNF), in memory, 460
Brain stem, **431**, 443*f*, 445–450, 445*f*, 446–447*f*, 448*f*, **449***t*
    autonomic regulation by, 539*f*, 540
    development of, 431, 431*f*, 432*f*

Brain vesicles, 1083
    primary, **430**, 431*f*
    secondary, **430**, 431*f*
Brain waves, **453–455**, 454*f*
Branchial groove, ear development from, **588–589**
Braxton Hicks contractions, 1091
BRCA1/BRCA2 genes, in breast cancer, 1048
Breast(s) (mammary glands), 156, **1047–1049**, 1047*f*
    cancer of, 1048, 1048*f*
    pregnancy affecting, 1089
    prolactin affecting, 605
Breast cancer, 1048, 1048*f*
Breast feeding/lactation, **1093–1094**, 1094*f*
    oxytocin and, 607, 1093–1094, 1094*f*
Breast milk, benefits of, 1094
Breathing, 805. *See also* Respiration
    age affecting, 843
    altitude affecting, 839–840
    apneustic, 835
    cessation of. *See* Apnea
    Cheyne-Stokes, **846**
    exercise affecting, 839
    expiration and, 821*f*, 822, 822*f*
    immediately after birth, 1093
    inspiration and, 820–822, 821*f*, 822*f*
    mechanics of, 819–826, 819*f*, 821*f*, 822*f*, 823*f*, 825*f*, 826*t*
    muscles of, 340*t*, 341*f*, 820, 821*f*
    neural control of, 835–836, 835*f*, 836*f*
    physical factors influencing, 822–824, 823*f*
    rate and depth of, factors affecting, 836–839, 836*f*, 837*f*, 838*f*
Breech presentation, 1092
Bridge of nose, 806, 806*f*
Broad ligament, **1041**, 1043*f*
Broca's area, 436*f*, **437**, 457
    language and, **457**
Brodmann, K., 435
Brodmann areas, **435**
Bronchi/bronchial tree, 805*f*, 807*t*, **813–815**, 813*f*, 814*f*, 818*f*
    lobar (secondary), 813*f*, **814**
    main (primary), 805*f*, 813*f*, **814**
    segmental (tertiary), 813*f*, **814**
Bronchial arteries, 729*t*, 818
Bronchial circulation, 818
Bronchial tree. *See* Bronchi/bronchial tree
Bronchial veins, 741*t*, 818
Bronchioles, **814**, 814*f*
    respiratory, 814*f*, **815**
    terminal, 814, 814*f*
Bronchitis, chronic, **840**, 841*f*
Bronchomediastinal trunks, **754**, 755*f*
Bronchopulmonary dysplasia, 823
Bronchopulmonary segments, **815–816**, 818*f*
Bronchoscopy, **846**
Bronchus. *See* Bronchi
Bronzing of skin, 155
Brown fat (brown adipose tissue), **127–129**
Browning reactions, 955
Brows (eyebrows), **548**, 548*f*
Bruises, 155

Brunner's (duodenal) glands, 879f, **880**
Brush border, 115, **878**, 879f. *See also* Microvilli
  of proximal convoluted tubule, 966
Brush border enzymes, **878**, 896f, 897, 898f
Bruxism, **905**
Buboes, 757
Buccal branch of facial nerve, 498t, 499t
Buccal cavity, 858. *See also* Mouth
Buccal glands (intrinsic salivary glands), **860**
Buccal phase of swallowing, 866, 867f, 888t
Buccinator muscle, 330t, 331f, 332t, 333f, 858
Buffers, in acid-base balance, **41**
  chemical, 41, **1009**–1010, 1009f
    bicarbonate buffer system, 41, 834, **1009**–1010
      bicarbonate reabsorption and, 1011, 1012f
      bicarbonate regeneration and, 1011–1014, 1013f
    phosphate buffer system, **1010**, 1012, 1013f
    protein buffer system, **1010**
  physiological
    renal, 978, 983f, 1011–1014, 1012f, 1013f
    respiratory, 41, 834, 837f, 838, 1010–1011
Buffy coat, **635**, 635f
Bulb(s)
  of hair, **157**, 158f
  of penis, 1025f, **1028**
  of vestibule, 1046f, **1047**
Bulbar conjunctiva, 548f, 549
Bulbospongiosus muscle, **344**t, 345f
Bulbourethral glands, 1025f, 1029f, **1031**
  embryologic/fetal development of, 1061f
Bulbus cordis, **688**, 688f
Bulimia, **905**
Bulk flow, 717–719, 719f
Bundle branches, right and left, **677**, 677f
Bundle of His (atrioventricular bundle), **677**, 677f
Bundles, cardiac muscle, 663–664, 664f
Burns, **163**–165, 163f, 164f
Bursae, **252**, 253f
Bursitis, **270**

C. *See* Carbon
Ca. *See* Calcium
Cadherins, 66, 67f, 80–81
Café coronary, 813
Cajal, interstitial cells of, 876
Calcaneal nerve, 510t
Calcaneal (Achilles) tendon, 240, 327f
  rupture of, **382**
Calcaneal tuberosity, **240**, 240f
Calcaneus, **240**, 240f, 242t
Calcarine sulcus, 436f, **437**
Calcification
  cartilage, 173
  metastatic, 613
  trigger for, 186

Calcification front, 186
Calcification zone (epiphyseal plate), 184, 184f
Calcitonin, **186**, 608, **611**–612
  in calcium regulation, 186, 611–612
Calcitriol, **624**
  parathyroid hormone and, 613
Calcium, 26t, **421**, 918t
  absorption of, 900
  balance of
    abnormalities of, 1003t. *See also* Hypercalcemia; Hypocalcemia
    developmental aspects of, 1015
    regulation of, 1008
  in blood clotting, 651t
  in bone remodeling, 186
  calcitonin in regulation of, 186, 611–612
  cardiac function affected by, 684, 685f, 686
  cross bridge activity and, 288–289
  deficiency of, 918t
    osteomalacia and rickets and, **189**
  dietary, 918t
  homeostatic imbalances and, 186
  information transfer at chemical synapse and, 408, 409f
  in muscle contraction, 286f, 288–289, 291f, 307, 307f, 310t
    cardiac muscle, 673, 674–675, 676, 676f
    excitation-contraction coupling and, 288, 291f
  for osteoporosis, 191
  parathyroid hormone relationship and, 186, 187f, 613, 614f, **1008**
  in plasma/interstitial fluid/intracellular fluid, 997f
  as second messenger, **421**
  in taste transduction, 573
  vitamin D in regulation of, 186, 900
Calcium channels, **676**
  in cardiac muscle contraction, **675**, 676, 676f
  information transfer at chemical synapse and, 408, 409f
  male infertility and, 1038
  in skeletal muscle contraction, 286f, 288
  slow, **675**
  in smooth muscle contraction, 306, 307, 307f
Calcium phosphate, in bone tissue, 180
Calculus (dental), **864**
Callus, 150
  in bone repair
    bony, **189**, 189f
    fibrocartilaginous, 188–**189**, 189f
Calmodulin, 306, **307**, 307f, 310t, **598**
Calories, 911
Calorigenic effect, of thyroid hormone, **609**
Calorimeter, **947**

Calyces (calyx), renal, major and minor, **962**, 963f
cAMP. *See* Cyclic AMP
cAMP response-element binding protein (CREB), in memory, 460
CAMs. *See* Cell adhesion molecules
Canaliculi, **180**
  bile, **881**–884, 883f
  bone, **180**, 181f
  lacrimal, 549, 549f
Canal of Schlemm (scleral venous sinus), 552f, **555**, 555f
Cancellous bone. *See* Spongy bone
Cancer, 142–143b. *See also specific type or organ affected*
  aging and, 799
  apoptosis absent in, 108
  basement membrane ignored in, 116
  sentinel nodes in, **764**
  T cell attacks on, 793f
Cancer chemotherapy, 143b
Cancer vaccine, 143b
Canines (eyeteeth), **862**, 862f
Cannabinoid receptors, 419
Canthi (commissures), medial and lateral, **548**, 548f
Capacitance vessels, veins as, 697f, **701**
Capacitation, **1072**–1073
Capillaries. *See also specific organ or structure supplied*
  blood, 695, 696f, 697f, **698**–700, 698t
    blood flow through/capillary dynamics, 717–719, 718f, 719f
    blood flow velocity and, 714f
    blood pressure in, 705, 705f
    blood volume in, 701f
    structure of, 696f, 698–699, 698t, 699f
    in tissue repair, 139–140
    true, **700**, 700f
  lymphatic, 697f, **753**–754, 753f
Capillary beds, **699**–700, 700f
  nephron, 964–969, 967f
Capillary blood pressure, 705, 705f, 718
Capillary colloid osmotic pressure (OP$_c$/oncotic pressure), **718**, 719f
  of glomerular blood, **971**, 971f
Capillary dynamics, 717–719, 718f, 719f
Capillary gas exchange, 717, 828f, 830
Capillary hydrostatic pressure (HP$_c$), **718**, 719f
Capillary plexus, primary, 602f, **603**
Capillary pores (fenestrations), 699, 699f
  glomerular, 964, 965f, 969, 969–970f
Capitate, **231**, 231f, 232t
Capitulum, **228**, 229f
Capsular hydrostatic pressure, **971**, 971f
Capsular (intrinsic) ligaments, of synovial joints, **252**
Capsular space, 966

Capsule
  lymph node, **756**–757, 757f
  splenic, 758, 759f
Caput medusae, 884
Carbaminohemoglobin, **638**, 833
  carbon dioxide transport and, **833**–834
  oxygen association and, 831–832, 831f, 832f
Carbohydrate(s), 8, **43**, 44f, 912, 913t
  absorption of, 896f, 899
  in absorptive state, 936, 937f
  athletes and, 930
  digestion of, 895–897, 896f
  interconversion of, 936f
  metabolism of, 920f, 922–930, 934t
    gluconeogenesis in, 930, 934t, 939
    glucose oxidation in, 923–929, 923f, 925f, 926f, 927f, 928f, 929f, 934t
    glycogenesis and glycogenolysis in, 929–930, 930f, 934t, 938–939, 939f
    liver in, 938, 939–940, 939f, 942t
    thyroid hormone affecting, 612t
  supply of (carbohydrate pool), 935f, **936**, 936f
Carbohydrate pool, 935f, **936**, 936f
Carbon, 25, 26t
  as chemically reactive element, 31f
  electroneutrality of, 42
  isotopes of, 27
  in organic compounds, 42
Carbon dioxide, 34, 34f
  acid-base balance/blood pH and, 834, 837f, 838, 1010
    respiratory compensations and, 1014–1015
    tubular secretion of hydrogen and, 1011, 1012f
  in blood, erythrocytes carrying, 638
  partial pressure of (P_{CO_2}), 827, 827t
    in acidosis/alkalosis, 1017b
    alveolar, 828
    external respiration (pulmonary gas exchange) and, 828–829, 828f, 829f
    hemoglobin saturation affected by, 831–832, 832f
    internal respiration and, 830
    normal, 1017b
    respiration affected by, 836–837, 837f, 838
  solubility of, 827
  transport of, 638, 805, 832–834, 833f
Carbonic acid, 39
  in acid-base balance, 41, 834, 1009–1010, 1011
Carbonic acid-bicarbonate buffer system, **41**, 834, 1009–1010
  bicarbonate reabsorption and, 1011, 1012f
Carbonic anhydrase, 834, 1011
Carbon monoxide (CO), 832, **419**
  as neurotransmitter, 418t, **419**

Carbon monoxide poisoning, **832**
Carboxypeptidase, **886**, 886*f*, 896*f*, **897**, 898*f*
Carbuncles, **168**
Carcinoembryonic antigen, in cancer vaccine, 143*b*
Carcinogens, **142***b*
Carcinogenesis, 142*b*, 143*f*
Carcinoma, **144**
Cardia (cardiac region of stomach), **867**, 868*f*
Cardiac catheterization, **690**
Cardiac center, medullary, 449, 540
Cardiac conduction system. *See* Conduction system of heart
Cardiac cycle, **682**, 683*f*
Cardiac muscle/cardiac muscle tissue, **136**, 137*f*, **276**, 309–310*t*, **672–676**, 673*f*, 674*f*, 675*f*. *See also* Heart
   contraction of, 276, 673–675, 675*f*
      electrical events and, 676–681, 676*f*, 677*f*, 678*f*, 679*f*, 680*f*, 681*f*
   development of, 311–312, 311*f*
   fibrosis of, aging and, **689**
   length-tension relationship in, stroke volume and, 684
   metabolic fuel used by, 935*t*
   microscopic anatomy of, 672–673, 674*f*
Cardiac muscle bundles, 663–664, 664*f*
Cardiac muscle cells/fibers, 136, 137*f*, 276, 309*t*, 672–676, 673*f*, 674*f*, 675*f*. *See also* Cardiac muscle/cardiac muscle tissue
Cardiac notch, **815**
Cardiac orifice, **864**
Cardiac output, **682–685**, 685*f*, 686*f*, 707*f*
   blood pressure and, 706, 707*f*, 710, 711*f*
   pregnancy and, 1090
Cardiac plexus, 529*f*, **530**, 533*f*
Cardiac region of stomach (cardia), **867**, 868*f*
Cardiac reserve, **684**, **689**
   aging affecting, 689
Cardiac (gastroesophageal) sphincter, **864**
Cardiac tamponade, 663
Cardiac veins, 665*f*, 666*f*, 669*f*, **670**, 737*f*
Cardinal (cervical) ligaments, lateral, 1043*f*, **1044**
Cardioacceleratory center, 678*f*, **679**, 706
Cardiogenic shock, **720**
Cardioinhibitory center, 678*f*, **679**, 706
Cardiomyopathy
   dilated, cardiac output and, 687
   hypertrophic, **690**
Cardiovascular center, 449, **707**
   blood pressure and, **707**
Cardiovascular system, 6*f*. *See also* Blood; Blood vessels; Circulation; Heart
   autonomic nervous system and, 542*b*

blood vessels, 694–751, 696*f*, 697*f*, 698*t*
   developmental aspects of, 316
   digestive system and, 902*b*, 903*b*
   endocrine system and, 628*b*
   fetal (fetal circulation), 1084–1085, 1086*f*
      changes in at birth, 1086*f*, 1093
   heart, 661–693, **662**, 665–667*f*
   homeostatic relationships of, 5*f*, 746*b*, 747*b*
   integumentary system and, 166*b*, 167*b*
   lymphatic system and, 762*b*, 763*b*
   muscular system and, 314*b*, 315*b*
   physiology/functions of, 3, 6*f*
   pregnancy and, 1090
   reproductive system and, 1064*b*
   respiratory system and, 746*b*, 805, 844*b*, 845*b*
   skeletal system and, 192*b*
   thyroid hormone affecting, 612*t*
   urinary system and, 1018*b*, 1019*b*
Caries, dental (cavities), 861, **864**
Carina, 805*f*, **813**
Carotene, **154–155**
   skin color and, 155
Carotid arteries, 724*t*, 726*t*, 727*f*
   common, **724***t*, 725*f*, 726*f*, **726***t*, 727*f*, 728*f*, 729*f*
      pulse at, 712*f*
   external, 725*f*, 726*f*, **726***t*, 727*f*
   internal, 725*f*, 726*f*, **726***t*, 727*f*
Carotid bodies, 709, **726***t*, **837**, 838*f*
Carotid canal, 205*f*, **207**, 214*t*
Carotid sinuses, 707, **726***t*
Carotid sinus reflex, **708**
Carpal bones/carpus (wrist), 199*f*, **231**, 231*f*, 232*t*
Carpal tunnel, 231
Carpal tunnel syndrome, 231, 505
Carpometacarpal joint
   of digits, 254*t*
   of thumb, 254*t*
Carpus (wrist)
   bones of (carpals), 199*f*, **231**, 231*f*, 232*t*
   muscles of, 199*f*, 231, 231*f*, 232*t*
Carriers (genetic), 1106
   identification of, 1109–1110, 1110*f*
Carriers (protein), 64, 69, 899
   in active transport, 73
   in diffusion, **69**, 69*f*, 72*t*
CART. *See* Cocaine-and amphetamine-regulated transcript
Cartilage(s), **131–133**, 131–132*f*, 134*t*. *See also specific type*
   elastic, 132*f*, **133**, 134*t*
   fibrocartilage, 132*f*, **133**, 134*t*
   growth of, 173
   hyaline, **131–133**, 131*f*, 134*t*, **173**, 174*f*
   skeletal, **173**, 174*f*
   torn, 269, 269*f*
Cartilage (endochondral) bones, **182**, 183, 183*f*
Cartilage plates, bronchial, 814
Cartilage tears, 269, 269*f*
Cartilaginous joints, 249, **250–251**, 250*f*, 252*t*

Caruncle, lacrimal, **548**, 548*f*
Cascades, positive feedback mechanisms as, 11
Caspases, in apoptosis, 108
CAT (computerized axial tomography). *See* Computed tomography
Catabolic-anabolic steady state, 935–936, 935*f*, 936*f*
Catabolism, 5, **36**, 895, 918, **919**, **920**, 920*f*. *See also* Digestion
   decomposition reactions and, **36**
   postabsorptive state and, 936, 938–941, 939*f*, 940*f*
Catalase(s), 87
Catalysts, **38**, 51–52, 81. *See also* Enzymes
Cataplexy, 456–457
Cataract, **556**, 556*f*
Catecholamines, **415**, 619
   hypersecretion of, 620
   stress response/sympathetic stimulation and, 619, 619*f*
Cathelicidins, 160
Catheter, urinary, 988
Catheterization, cardiac, **690**
Cation(s), **32**
   resting membrane potential and, 396
Cauda equina, 467*f*, **468**, 502*f*
Caudal (term), 12*t*. *See also under* Inferior
Caudate lobe, of liver, 881, 882*f*
Caudate nucleus, **441**, 442*f*
Caveolae, **76–77**, 77*t*, **306**
   in smooth muscle, 306, 306*f*
Caveolin, **77**, 77*t*
Cavernous sinuses, 738*f*, **738***t*, 739*f*
Cavities (body), 14–20, 16*f*, 17*f*, 20*f*
Cavities (dental), 861, **864**
CBC. *See* Complete blood count
C (parafollicular) cells, 608, 609*f*, **611**
CCK. *See* Cholecystokinin
CD4 cells, **786**, 787*f*. *See also* Helper T cells
   HIV infection and, 796
   MHC restriction and, 789
CD8 cells, **786**, 787*f*. *See also* Cytotoxic T cells
   MHC restriction and, 789
Cdks (cyclin-dependent kinases), **100**
Cecum, 852*f*, **890**, 891*f*
Celiac disease (gluten-sensitive enteropathy), 901
Celiac ganglion, **532**, 533*f*
Celiac plexus, 529*f*
Celiac trunk, 725*f*, 730*f*, 731*f*, **731***t*, 733*f*
   branches of, 730*f*, 731*f*, 731*t*
Cell(s), 3, 4*f*, **61–112**, 94*t*. *See also under Cellular*
   aging of, 108
   in connective tissue, 125–126, 125*f*
   cytoplasm of, 62, 63*f*, **81–95**, 94*t*
   developmental aspects of, 108–109
   differentiation of, **108**
   diversity/specialization of, 62, 62*f*, 108

division of. *See* Cell division
   environmental interactions with, 80–81, 82*f*
   extracellular materials and, **107**
   generalized/composite, **62**, 63*f*
   growth/reproduction of, 95–107
      cell division and, 95, 96*f*, 97–100, 98–99*f*
      protein synthesis and, 100–105, 101*f*, 102*f*, 103*f*, 104*f*, 105*f*
   membrane of, 62, **63–81**, 63*f*, **94**t. *See also* Plasma membrane
   nucleus of, 63*f*, **91–95**, 92*f*, 93*f*, **95**t
   polarity of, resting membrane potential and, 79
Cell adhesion molecules (CAMs), **80–81**
   in ground substance, 124
   nerve cell, 424
   in phagocyte mobilization, 771
Cell body
   neuron, 135*f*, **389–390**, 390*f*, 393*t*
   rod and cone, 560, 561*f*
Cell–cell recognition, glycocalyx in, 64, 65*f*
Cell center. *See* Centrosome
Cell death, programmed (apoptosis), **108**, 424
   B cell development and, 778
   T cell development and, 778, 779*f*
Cell differentiation glycoproteins, 786, 787*f*
Cell division, 95, 96*f*, 97–100, 98–99*f*. *See also* Cytokinesis; Mitosis
   in cancer, 100
   control of, 100
   development and, 108
Cell (membrane) junctions, 66–67, 67*f*
Cell life cycle, **95–100**, 96*f*, 97*f*, 98–99*f*
   cancer and, 100
   cell division, 97–100, 98–99*f*
   cytokinesis, 96*f*, **97**, 97–100, **99***f*, 1035*f*
   DNA replication, 96–97, 97*f*
   interphase, **95–97**, 96*f*
   mitosis, **97**, 98–99*f*
Cell lysis, in antibody mechanism of action, 785, 785*f*
Cell-mediated (cellular) immunity, **776**, **786–795**, 787*f*, 794*f*
   clonal selection/differentiation of T lymphocytes and, 786–791, 787*f*, 788*f*, 789*f*
   organ transplants and, 792–795, 795*t*
Cell membrane. *See* Plasma membrane
Cell theory, **62**
Cellular extensions, 90–91, 90*f*, 91*f*, **95**t
Cellular (cell-mediated) immunity. *See* Cell-mediated (cellular) immunity
Cellular level, structural organization at, 3, 4*f*
Cellular metabolism. *See also* Metabolism
   autonomic effects and, 538*t*

Cellular organelles. *See* Organelles
Cellular respiration, 5, 83, 805, **919**, 920, 922*f*, 928, 934*t*
 ATP for muscle activity and, 298*f*, 299, 299*f*, 300, 310*t*
 redox reactions in, 37
Cellular secretions, 107
Cellular trophoblast (cytotrophoblast), **1077**, 1077*f*, 1079*f*
Cellulose, 43, 912
Cementum, **863**, 863*f*
Central artery
 of retina, 552*f*, **553**, 554*f*
 of spleen, 758, 759*f*
Central (Haversian) canal, **179**, 181*f*
Central canal of spinal cord, 431*f*, 433*f*, 469*f*
Central chemoreceptors, respiratory rate/rhythm affected by, **836**, 836*f*, 837*f*
Central deafness, vestibulocochlear damage causing, 499*t*
Central nervous system, **386**, 387*f*, **429–483**. *See also* Brain; Spinal cord
 autonomic nervous system regulated by, 539–540, 539*f*
 brain, **430–466**
 congenital disorders and, 477–478, 478*f*
 developmental aspects of, 477–478
 dysfunction of, diagnostic procedures for assessment of, 477
 gender-specific differences in, 477
 gray and white matter of, 431, 432*f*
 higher mental functions and, 453–460
 neuroglia (supporting cells) of, 388–389, 388*f*
 neuronal circuit types and, 422, 422*f*
 protection of, 460–464
  blood–brain barrier and, **463–464**
  cerebrospinal fluid and, 462*f*, **463**
  meninges and, 460*f*, **461–463**
 spinal cord, **466–477**
Central pattern generators, **512**
Central process, 393*t*, **394**
Central sulcus, **433**, 434*f*, 436*f*
Central tendon of perineum, **344***t*
Central thermoreceptors, **951–952**
Central vein, **881**
 of liver lobule, **881**, 883*f*
 of retina, 552*f*, **553**, 554*f*
Centrioles, 63*f*, **89**, 89*f*, 94*t*
 in cell division, 98*f*
 in cilia, 90, 90*f*
Centromere, 98*f*
Centrosome/centrosome matrix, 63*f*, 88, **89**, 89*f*
Centrum (body) of vertebra, **219**, 219*f*, 222*t*
Cephalic (reflex) phase, of gastric secretion, **872–873**, 872*f*
Cephalic vein, 737*f*, 740*f*, **740***t*, 741*f*
Cephalin, 45*t*
Cephalization, **429–430**
Cerebellar cortex, 431, 432*f*, 450, 451*f*

Cerebellar gray matter, 431, 432*f*, 450, 451*f*
Cerebellar hemispheres, **450**, 451*f*
Cerebellar peduncles, 446–447*f*, 450, 451*f*
 inferior, 446–447*f*, 447, 448*f*, **450**, 451*f*
 middle, 446–447*f*, 447, 448*f*, **450**, 451*f*
 superior, 445, 446–447*f*, 448*f*, **450**, 451*f*
Cerebellar white matter, 450
Cerebellum, **449***t*, **450–451**, 451*f*, 452*f*, 453*f*, **513**, **587**
 development of, 431, 431*f*, 432*f*
 in equilibrium pathway, **587**, 587*f*
 in motor control, **513**
Cerebral angiography, 477
Cerebral aqueduct, 431*f*, **432**, 433*f*, 443*f*, 446, 448*f*
Cerebral arterial circle (circle of Willis), 726*f*, 727*f*, **727***t*
Cerebral arteries
 anterior, **726***t*
 middle, **726***t*, 727*f*
 posterior, 726*f*, **726***t*, 727*f*
Cerebral blood flow, 716
Cerebral cortex, 431, 432*f*, 434*f*, **435–440**, 435*f*, 436*f*, 438*f*, 449*t*
 association areas of, 435, 436*f*, 439. *See also* Association areas
 autonomic regulation by, 539*f*, 540
 blood pressure regulation and, 709
 functional regions of, 435, 435*f*
 lateralization and, 439–**440**
 motor areas of, **435–437**, 436*f*, 438*f*
 respiratory control and, 838–839
 sensory areas of, **437–439**, 438*f*
 sensory integration in, 489*f*, 490
Cerebral dominance, **440**
Cerebral edema, **464**
Cerebral fissures, **433**, 434*f*
Cerebral gray matter, 431, 432*f*, 434*f*, 435–440, 435*f*, 436*f*, 438*f*, 449*t*. *See also* Cerebral cortex
Cerebral hemispheres (cerebrum), 431, **433–441**, 434*f*, 449*t*
 development of, 431, 431*f*, 432*f*, 478
Cerebral palsy, **477**
Cerebral peduncles, **445**, 446*f*
Cerebral white matter, 434*f*, 435, **440–441**, 440*f*
Cerebrospinal fluid (CSF), 462*f*, **463**, 466
Cerebrovascular accidents (strokes), **464–465**
 diagnosis of, 477
Cerebrum (cerebral hemispheres), **431**, **433–441**, 434*f*, 449*t*
 development of, 431, 431*f*, 432*f*, 478
Cerumen (earwax), 156, **574**
Ceruminous glands, **156**, **574**
Cervical branch of facial nerve, 498*t*, 499*t*
Cervical canal, **1043–1044**, 1043*f*
Cervical cancer, 1044

Cervical cap, for contraception, 1095–1096*b*
Cervical curvature of spine, 217, 217*f*
 developmental aspects of, 243
Cervical enlargement, 467*f*, **468**, 502*f*
Cervical flexure, 431, 432*f*
Cervical ganglia, superior/middle/inferior, **532**, 533*f*
Cervical glands, 1044
Cervical lymph nodes, 755*f*
Cervical mucus, 1044
Cervical nerves, 502*f*, 504–505, 504*f*, 504*t*
Cervical plexus, 502*f*, **504–505**, 504*f*, 504*t*
Cervical plug, 1056
Cervical vertebrae, **216**, 217*f*, 219–220, 220*f*, 221*f*, 222*t*
Cervix, 1040*f*, **1043–1044**, 1043*f*
 cancer of, 1044
 dilation of in labor, **1091–1092**, 1092*f*
Cesarean section (C-section), 1092
CF. *See* Cystic fibrosis
C fibers, 486, 490
CFTR (cystic fibrosis transmembrane conductance regulator) protein, 843
cGMP. *See* Cyclic GMP
Chadwick's sign, 1089
Chain ganglia (sympathetic trunk/paravertebral ganglia), 503*f*, **530**, 531*f*
 pathways with synapses in, 531*f*, 532, 533*f*
Chalazion, 549
Chancre, syphilitic, 1058
Channel-linked (inotropic) receptors, **420–421**, 420*f*
Channels (protein), 64, **69–70**, 69*f*, 395, 396*f*. *See also specific type*
 action potential and, 401*f*, 402
 gated, 69, 81, **395**, 396*f*
 information transfer at chemical synapse and, 408, 409*f*
 muscle contraction and, 286*f*, 287, 288, 288*f*
Charley horse, 382
Charnley, John, 261*b*
Cheekbones. *See* Zygomatic bones
Cheeks, **858**
Chemical barriers, skin, 160
Chemical bonds, **31–35**, 31*f*, 34*f*. *See also specific type*
 chemical reactions and, 35, 36
 energy stored in, 24
Chemical buffer systems, in acid-base balance, 41, **1009–1010**, 1009*f*
 bicarbonate buffer system, 41, 834, **1009–1010**
  bicarbonate reabsorption and, 1011, 1012*f*
  bicarbonate regeneration and, 1011–1014, 1013*f*
 phosphate buffer system, **1010**, 1012, 1013*f*
 protein buffer system, **1010**
Chemical digestion, 853*f*, **854**, 888*t*, **895–897**, 896*f*, 898*f*, 899*f*. *See also* Digestion

Chemical energy, **24**
Chemical equations, 35–36
Chemical equilibrium, **37**
Chemical level, structural organization at, 3, 4*f*
Chemically-gated (ligand-gated) channel(s), **395**, 396*f*
 muscle fiber action potential and, 287, 287*f*
Chemically gated channel-linked receptors, 81
Chemical mediators, inflammatory, 772*t*
Chemical reactions, **35–38**, 36*f*
 energy flow in, 37
 factors influencing rate of, 37–38
 patterns of, 36–37, 36*f*
 reversibility of, 37
Chemical senses, **569–574**, 588. *See also* Smell; Taste
 development of, 588
 homeostatic imbalances of, 573
Chemical signaling, 81
 cell division control and, 100
Chemical synapses, **407–408**, **409***f*
Chemical (nonshivering) thermogenesis, **953**
Chemiosmotic processes/chemiosmosis, **922**, 926*f*
 metabolic poisons and, 928
Chemistry, 24–38
 bonds and, **31–35**, 31*f*, 34*f*
 chemical reactions and, 35–38, 36*f*
 energy and, **24–25**
 matter and, **24**
  in combination (molecules/mixtures), 28–30, 29*f*
  composition of, 25–28, 25*f*, 26*t*, 27*f*, 28*f*
  living matter. *See* Biochemistry
Chemoreceptors, **485**, 487*t*, **569**, **709**, **835**
 in blood pressure control, 707, **709**
 in digestion, 854, 855*f*
 respiratory rate/rhythm affected by, **836–838**, 836*f*, 837*f*, 838*f*
 for taste and smell, 569
Chemotactic agents, 773
Chemotaxis, **773**
 positive, 643, 773
Chemotherapy, in cancer treatment, 143*b*
Chewing (mastication), **866**, 888*t*
 muscles of, 332*t*, 333*f*
Cheyne-Stokes breathing, **846**
CHF. *See* Congestive heart failure
Chiasmata (crossovers), **1033**, 1035*f*, **1104**
 genetic variation and, **1104**, 1104*f*
Chief cells, **612**, **870**
 gastric, 869*f*, 870
 parathyroid, **612**, 613*f*
Childbirth, **1090–1092**, 1091*f*, 1092*f*. *See also* Birth
Chimeric immune system, **795**
Chiropractic, **244**

Chlamydia, **1058**
 STIs caused by, **1058**–1059
 trachoma caused by, 589, 1059
Chlamydia trachomatis, 1059
Chlamydophila pneumoniae,
 atherosclerosis and, 702*b*
Chloride
 balance of
  abnormalities of, 1003*t*
  regulation of, 1008
 in plasma/interstitial fluid/
  intracellular fluid, 997, 997*f*
Chloride shift, **834**
Chlorine, 26*t*, 918*t*
 dietary, 918*t*
 sodium chloride formation and,
  32, 32*f*
Choanae, nasal (posterior nasal
 apertures), **806**
Chocolate cysts, 1066
Choking (tracheal obstruction), 813
Cholecalciferol, **624**, 625*t*
Cholecystitis, **904**
Cholecystokinin, 417*t*, 419, 625*t*,
 873, 875*t*, 886–887, 887*f*
 in food intake regulation,
  946, 946*f*
Cholesterol, 45*t*, 46*f*, 47, 912, 913*t*,
 914, **943**
 blood levels of
  atherosclerosis and, **702***b*,
   943, 944
  drugs lowering, 703*b*, 944
  factors regulating, 944
  recommended, 943
 in membranes, 47, 64, 65*f*
 metabolism of, 943–944, 943*f*
 transport of, 943, 943*f*
Cholesterol-lowering drugs,
 703*b*, 944
Choline acetyltransferase, 415
Cholinergic fibers, **535**
Cholinergic receptors, 535, **536***t*
Chondroblasts, **125**, 131, 134*t*
Chondrocytes, **131**, 131*f*, 134*t*, 173
 in fibrocartilage, 132*f*, 133
Chondroitin sulfate, in ground
 substance, 124
Chondromalacia patellae, **272**
Chordae tendinae, 667*f*, **670**, 671*f*
Chorda tympani, in gustatory
 pathway, 573
Chorea, in Huntington's disease, 466
Chorion, **1078**, 1079*f*, 1080
Chorionic gonadotropin, human
 (hCG), **1077**, 1078*f*
Chorionic somatomammotropin,
 human (hCS/human placental
 lactogen), 1078, **1090**
Chorionic thyrotropin, human
 (hCT), 1078, **1090**
Chorionic villi, **1078**, 1079*f*, 1080*f*
Chorionic villus sampling,
 1110, 1111*f*
Choroid, 551, 552*f*, 554*f*
Choroid plexuses, 462*f*, **463**
Chromaffin cells, **618**–619
Chromatids, sister, 98*f*, 1033,
 1034*f*, 1035*f*
Chromatin, 63*f*, 91, 92*f*, **93**–95,
 93*f*, 95*t*
 in cell division, 93–94, 93*f*, 98*f*

Chromatophilic substance (Nissl
 bodies), **389**, 390*f*
Chromium, 919*t*
Chromosomal number
 diploid (*2n*), **1032**
 haploid (*n*), **1032**, 1033
Chromosome(s), 93*f*, **95**. *See also*
 Heredity
 during cell division, 98*f*, 99*f*
 homologous (homologues),
  1032, 1033, 1102
 maternal, 1032
 paternal, 1032
 recombinant, **1104**, 1104*f*
 segregation of, independent assortment and, 1103–**1104**, 1103*f*
 sex, **1059**, 1102
  genetic sex determination
   and, 1059–1060
Chromosome territories, 93
Chronic bronchitis, **840**, 841*f*
Chronic leukemia, 648
Chronic obstructive pulmonary diseases (COPD), **840**–841, 841*f*
Chronic renal disease, **984**
Chronotropic factors, positive and
 negative, 685
Chyle, **754**
Chylomicrons, 899*f*, **900**, 943, 943*f*
Chyme, **866**
 entry of into small intestine, 875,
  887–889
Chymotrypsin, **886**, 886*f*, 896*f*,
 897, 898*f*
Chymotrypsinogen, 886, 886*f*
Cigarette smoking. *See* Smoking
Cilia, **90**–91, 90*f*, 91*f*, 95*t*, **115**
 in body defense, 772*t*
 epithelial, **115**
 olfactory, 569*f*, **570**
 in trachea, 812, 812*f*
 smoking affecting, 813
Ciliary body, 551, 552*f*, 555*f*
Ciliary ganglia, **529**, 529*f*
Ciliary glands, 549
Ciliary muscles, **551**
 autonomic innervation/effects
  and, 538*t*
 in light focusing, 558, 558*f*
Ciliary processes, 551, 552*f*, 555*f*
Ciliary zonule (suspensory liga-
 ment), **551**, 552*f*, 555*f*
Ciliated pseudostratified columnar
 epithelium, 119, 119*f*
Cingulate gyrus, 436*f*, 439, **452**, 452*f*
Circadian rhythm, sleep-wake cycle
 as, 455
Circle of Willis (cerebral arterial
 circle), 726*f*, 727*f*, **727***t*
Circuit(s), **422**, 422*f*
 sensory integration at level of,
  489*f*, 490
Circular fascicle pattern/muscles,
 322, 322*f. See also*
  Sphincter(s)
Circular folds (plicae circulares),
 878, 879*f*
Circular layer of smooth muscle,
 305, 305*f*
 in alimentary canal muscularis,
  857, 857*f*
 in stomach muscularis, 868*f*, 869*f*

Circulation. *See also specific type and*
 Blood vessels; Cardiovascular
 system; Lymphatic system
 fetal, 1084–1085, 1086*f*
  changes in at birth, 1086*f*,
   1093
 monitoring, 710–712, 712*f*
 pulmonary, **668**, 668*f*, 717, 721,
  722*f*, **722**–723*t*, 818
 systemic, **668**, 668*f*, 721, 723*f*, **723***t*
  arteries of, 721, 724–725*f*, 724*t*
  veins of, 721, 736–737*f*, 736*t*
 tissue perfusion and, **713**–721,
  714*f*, 715*f*, 718*f*, 719*f*, 720*f*
Circulatory shock, **719**–721, 720*f*
 autonomic effects and, 537
 hypotension and, 712
Circumcision, 1028
Circumduction (body movement),
 256, 257*f*
Circumferential lamellae, **180**, 181*f*
Circumflex artery (coronary), 665*f*,
 669, 669*f*
Circumflex femoral arteries, lateral
 and medial, 734*f*, **734***t*
Circumflex humeral artery, anterior
 and posterior, 728*f*, **728***t*, 729*f*
Circumvallate (vallate) papillae, **571**,
 572*f*, **859**, 860*f*
Cirrhosis, **884**
Cis face, of Golgi apparatus, 85, 85*f*
11-*Cis*-retinal, **562**, 563*f*, 564*f*
Cisterna(e), **84**
 Golgi apparatus, 85*f*
 rough endoplasmic reticulum,
  84, 86*f*, 92*f*
 terminal, of sarcoplasmic reticu-
  lum, **283**, 283*f*
Cisterna chyli, **754**, 755*f*
Citric acid, **924**, 925*f*
Citric acid cycle (Krebs cycle), 919,
 920*f*, 922, 922*f*, **924**–925, 925*f*,
 929*f*, 934*t*
Cl. *See* Chlorine
C_L. *See* Lung compliance
Class I MHC proteins, 777, **786**–789,
 787*f*, 788*f*
Class II MHC proteins, 787*f*,
 788*f*, **789**
Classical pathway, of complement
 activation, 774*f*, **775**
Clathrin/clathrin-coated vesicles, **75**,
 76*f*, 77*t*
Claudication, intermittent, 316
Claudins, 66
Clavicles (collarbones), 199*f*, 225,
 226, 226*f*, 232*t*
Clavicular notches, **223**, 224*f*
Clawhand, 505
Cleavage, **1075**–1076, 1076*f*
Cleavage furrow, **97**, 99*f*
Cleavage (tension) lines, **152**–153,
 154*f*
Cleft lip/palate, 243, 243*f*, **904**
Climax (sexual), **1032**
 in female, 1058
 in male, **1032**
Clitoris, 1040*f*, **1046**, 1046*f*
 autonomic innervation/effects
  and, 538*t*
 embryologic/fetal development
  of, 1062*f*

Cloaca, 989, 990*f*, 1060, 1061*f*
Cloacal membrane, 901*f*, **904**
Clonal deletion, 778
Clonal selection
 B lymphocyte, **780**, 781*f*
 T lymphocyte, **786**–791, 787*f*,
  788*f*, 789*f*
Clone, **780**, 781*f*
Cloning, reproductive, 1096–1097
Closed (simple) fracture, 188
Closed (external) reduction of
 fracture, 188
Close vision, focusing for, 558–559,
 558*f*
Clot (fibrin mesh), 636*t*, 650, 650*f*,
 651, 651*t*
 factors limiting growth of,
  652–653
 factors preventing undesirable
  formation of, 653
Clot retraction, **652**
Clotting (blood clotting/coagulation),
 649*f*, **650**–652, 650*f*
 autonomic effects and, 538*t*
 disorders of, 653–654
 homeostatic control in, 11, 11*f*
 platelets in, 11, 11*f*, 648, 649–650,
  649*f*
 undesirable, prevention of, 653
Clotting cascade, 651
Clotting factors, 649, **650**, 650*f*, 651*t*
Clubfoot, **244**
CNS. *See* Central nervous system
CO. *See* Carbon monoxide; Cardiac
 output
Coagulation, 649*f*, **650**–652, 650*f*
 autonomic effects and, 538*t*
 disorders of, 653–654
 homeostatic control in, 11, 11*f*
 platelets in, 11, 11*f*, 648, 649–650,
  649*f*
 undesirable, prevention of, 653
Coagulation cascade, 651
Coagulation factors, 649, **650**,
 650*f*, 651*t*
Coarctation of aorta, 689, 689*f*
Coated pits, 75, 76*f*
Coatomer proteins, 77, 77*t*
Cobalt, 919*t*
Cocaine abuse, 414–415*b*
Cocaine-and amphetamine-
 regulated transcript (CART),
 in food intake regulation,
 945, 946*f*
Coccygeal nerve, 502*f*
Coccygeus muscle, 344*t*, 345*f*
Coccyx, 217, 217*f*, 221*f*, 223
 in male versus female, 236*t*
Cochlea, 575*f*, 576, **577**, 578*f*
Cochlear duct, **577**, 578*f*
Cochlear hair cells, 580. *See also* Hair
 cells
Cochlear nerve, 499*t*, 575*f*, 577, 577*f*,
 578*f*, **580**, 582*f*
Cochlear nuclei, **448**, 582, 582*f*
Cochlear (round) window,
 574, 575*f*
Coding strand, in transcription,
 102, 102*f*
Codominant alleles, 1106
Codon(s), **103**
Coelom, 1079*f*, 1082*f*, **1084**

Coenzyme(s), **52, 915**
  in redox reactions, 921
  vitamins as, **915**
Cofactor(s), **52**, 926, 926*f*
Cognition/cognitive function, 453–460
  brain wave patterns/EEG and, **453–455**, 454*f*
  cerebellum in, 450–451
  consciousness and, **455**
  language and, 457
  memory and, **457–460**, 458*f*, 459*f*
  prefrontal cortex and, 436*f*, 439
  sleep and sleep-wake cycles and, 455–457, 456*f*
Cohesin, 96
Coiled (spiral) arteries of uterus, **1044**, 1045*f*
Coitus interruptus, 1095*b*
Cold exposure, hypothermia and, **953**
Cold sores (fever blisters), **168**
Colic arteries, left, 730*f*, 732*t*, 733*f*
Colitis, ulcerative, 905
Collagen, 50, 51*t*, 124–125
Collagen fibers, **124**–125
  in bone lamellae, 179, 180*f*
  in dense irregular connective tissue, 129, 130*f*
  in dense regular connective tissue, 129, 129*f*
  in dermis, 129, 130*f*, 153
  in fibrocartilage, 132*f*, 133
Collarbones. *See* Clavicles
Collateral blood supply, cardiac, 669
Collateral channels, **701**
Collateral (prevertebral) ganglia, **530**
  pathways with synapses in, 532, 533*f*
Collateral ligaments
  fibular and tibial, 262–263*f*, **263**
  radial and ulnar, of elbow, **266**, 266*f*
Collecting ducts, 964, 965*f*, **966**, 967*f*, **983***f*
  absorptive capability of, 977*t*, 978
  cortical, in potassium balance, 1006
  hydrogen secretion in, in acid base balance, 1011
Collecting vessels, lymphatic, 753*f*, **754**, 755*f*
Colle's fracture, 231
Colliculi
  inferior, **446**, 446–447*f*, **582**, 582*f*
  superior, **446**, 446–447*f*, 476, **566**, 567*f*
Colloid(s), 29*f*, **30**, **608**
  biological, 38
  thyroid gland storage of, **608**, 609*f*
Colloidal (endemic) goiter, **611**, 611*f*
Colloid osmotic pressure, **718**, 719*f*
  of glomerular blood, **971**, 971*f*
Colon, 852*f*, **890**, 891*f*. *See also* Large intestine
Colon cancer, 904
  genetic mutations and, 142*b*, 143*f*, 904
Colony-stimulating factors, in leukopoiesis, **646**
Color blindness, 562–563

Colorectal cancer, 904
  genetic mutations and, 142*b*, 143*f*, 904
Color of light, 556–557, 557*f*
Color vision, 562
Colostrum, **1093**
Columnar cells/epithelium, 116, 116*f*
  pseudostratified, **119**, 119*f*
  simple, **117**–119, 118*f*
  stratified, **121**
Coma, **455**
  reticular activating system injury causing, 453
Combination reactions. *See* Synthesis reactions
Comminuted fracture, 190*t*
Commissural fibers, 440, 440*f*, **441**, 470
Commissures, **441**
Commissures (canthi), medial and lateral, **548**, 548*f*
Common carotid arteries, 724*t*, 725*f*, 726*f*, **726***t*, 727*f*, 728*f*, 729*f*
  pulse at, 712*f*
Common fibular (peroneal) nerve, 509, 509*f*, **510**, 510*t*
Common hepatic artery, 730*f*, 731*f*, **731***t*. *See also* Hepatic artery
Common hepatic duct, 878*f*, **881**
Common iliac arteries, 724*t*, 725*f*, 730*f*, **732***t*, 733*f*, 734–735*f*, **734***t*
Common iliac veins, 736*f*, **736***t*, 737*f*, 742*f*, 743*f*, **744***t*
Common interosseous artery, 728*f*, **728***t*, 729*f*
Common tendinous (annular) ring, **550**
Commotio cordis, **690**
Communicating arteries
  anterior, 726*f*, **726***t*, 727*f*
  posterior, 726*f*, 727*f*, **727***t*
Compact bone, 134*t*, 176*f*, **177**, 179*f*
  microscopic anatomy of, 179–180, 179*f*, 180*f*, 181*f*
Complement/complement system, 51*t*, **770**, 772*t*, **774–775**, 774*f*, 795*f*
  antibodies in fixation/activation of, 774*f*, 775, **785**, 785*f*
Complementarity of structure and function, **3**
  cell theory and, 62
Complementary bases, **54**
Complement fixation, 774*f*, 775, **785**, 785*f*
Complete antigens, **776**
Complete blood count (CBC), **657**
Complete fracture, 188
Complete proteins, 913*t*, **914**
Complete (fused) tetanus, 294*f*, **295**
Complex carbohydrates, 913*t*. *See also* Starch
Complex receptors, **486**
Compliance
  blood pressure and, 705
  lung, **824**
Complicated plaque, **702***b*
Compound(s), **28–29**. *See also* specific type
  inorganic, **38**, 38–41
  mixtures differentiated from, 30
  organic, **38**, 42–56

Compound (open) fracture, 188
Compound glands, **122**, 123*f*
Compression fracture, 190*t*
  in osteoporosis, 190*t*, 191
Computed tomography (CT), 18*b*
  in diagnosis of CNS dysfunction, 477
Computerized axial tomography (CAT). *See* Computed tomography
Concave lens, 557, 560*f*
Concentration, 29–30
  chemical reaction rate affected by, 38
Concentration gradient, **68**, 395
  active transport and, 73, 77*t*
  diffusion and, **68**, 68*f*
  osmosis and, 70–71, 70*f*, 71*f*
  resting membrane potential and, 79–80, 396, 397*f*
Concentric contractions, **296**, 297*f*
Conception. *See* Fertilization
Conceptus, **1072**, 1072*f*
Concha(e), nasal, 202*f*, **209**, 212–216, 807–809, 808*f*
  inferior, 202*f*, **211**, 213*f*, 807–809, 808*f*
  middle, 202*f*, **209**, 209*f*, **215***t*, 807–809, 808*f*
  superior, **209**, **215***t*, 807–809, 808*f*
Concussion, **464**
Condensed chromatin, 93
Condoms
  for birth control, 1095–1096*b*
  STI prevention and, 1058
Conducting (elastic) arteries, **697**, 697*f*, 698*t*
Conducting region of neuron, **391**
Conducting zone, **806**, 813*f*, 814–815
Conduction, heat loss by, 950*f*, **951**, 951*f*
Conduction deafness, **583**
Conduction system of heart
  autonomic nervous system affecting, 678*f*, 679
  defects in, 678–679
    ECG in, 680, 681*f*
  extrinsic, 678*f*, 679
  intrinsic, **676–679**, 677*f*, 678*f*
Conduction velocity of action potential, 404–405, 405*f*
Conductivity, 276
Condyle (bone marking), 178*t*
  of femur, 237, 238*f*
  mandibular, 203*f*, **209**, 210*f*, **215***t*, 268, 268*f*
  occipital, **201–204**, 202*f*, 205*f*, **214***t*
  of tibia, 238, 239*f*
Condyloid (ellipsoidal) joints, **259**, 260*f*
Cone(s), **553**, 554*f*, 560–566, 561*f*. *See also* Photoreceptors
  electromagnetic spectrum and sensitivities of, 557*f*
  excitation of, 562
Cone inner segments, 560
Cone outer segments, 554*f*, 560, 561*f*
Congenital thymic aplasia, **800**
Congestive heart failure, **687**
Conjunctiva, 548*f*, **549**
Conjunctival sac, 548*f*, **549**

Conjunctivitis, 549
Connective tissue, 114*f*, **124–134**, 125*f*, 127–135*f*, 134*t*. *See also* specific type
  blood, **133**, 134*t*, 135, 135*f*, 634–660. *See also* Blood
  in cardiac muscle, 309*t*
  common characteristics of, 124
  dense (fibrous), **126**, **129–131**, 129–130*f*, 134*t*
  elastic, 130*f*, **131**, 134*t*
  epithelia supported by, 115–116
  exocrine glands supported by, 121–122
  loose, **126**–129, 127–128*f*, 134*t*
  reticular, 128*f*, **129**, 134*t*, 756
    lymph node/lymphoid organ, **756**, 756*f*, 758
  skeletal muscle sheath of, 277, 278*f*, 279*t*, 309*t*
  in smooth muscle, 305, 309*t*
  structural elements of, 124–126, 125*f*, 134*t*
Connective tissue proper, **126–131**, 127–130*f*, 134*t*
Connective tissue root sheath, **157**, 158*f*
Connexons, 67, 67*f*
Conn's disease (aldosteronism/hyperaldosteronism), 616, **1020**
Conoid tubercle, 226, 226*f*
Consciousness, **455**
Consensual light reflex, 566
Constant (C) region, **783**, 783*f*
Constipation, 895
  pregnancy and, 1090
Constrictor muscles, pharyngeal, **334***t*, 335*f*, **335***t*, 864
Contact dermatitis, 168
  allergic, **799**
Contact inhibition, 100
Contact signaling, 81
Continuous capillaries, **699**, 699*f*
Continuous conduction, **404**, 405*f*
Contraception, 1095–1096*b*
Contractile proteins, 50, 51*t*
Contractile ring, in cytokinesis, 97, 99*f*
Contractility, muscle, **5**, 276, 684. *See also* Muscle contraction
  cardiac muscle, cardiac output and, **684**, 685*f*, 686*f*, 707*f*
  movement and, 5
Contraction
  muscle, **284**, 310*t*. *See also* Muscle contraction
    sliding filament model of, **284**, 284*f*, 307, 307*f*
  uterine
    Braxton Hicks, 1091
    in labor, 1091, 1092
Contracture(s), muscle fatigue and, **300**
Contrecoup injury, 464
Control center, in homeostasis, **9**, 9*f*, 10*f*
Contusion, brain, **464**
Conus medullaris, 467*f*, **468**
Convection, heat loss by, 950*f*, **951**, 951*f*
Convergence, **559**

Convergent fascicle pattern/muscles, **322**, 322f
Converging circuits, **422**, 422f
Convex lens, 557, 558f, 560f
COP1/COP2 (coatomer) proteins, 77, 77t
COPD. See Chronic obstructive pulmonary diseases
CO poisoning. See Carbon monoxide poisoning
Copper, 919t
Coracobrachialis muscle, 350t, 351f, 352f, **352t**, 358t
Coracohumeral ligament, **264**, 265f
Coracoid process, 227f, **228**
Cord(s), brachial plexus, 505, 506f
Cordotomy, **479**
Core temperature, **950**
  in hyperthermia, 953
  in hypothermia, 953
Cornea, 548f, **551**, 552f
Corneal endothelium, 551
Corneal epithelium, 551
Corniculate cartilage, 810f, **811**
Cornified (horny) cells, 152
Cornua, hyoid bone, 211, 211f
Coronal (frontal) plane/section, **14**, 15f
Coronal suture, 200, **201**, 201f, 203f
Corona radiata (cerebral projection fibers), **440f**, 441, 442f
Corona radiata (oocyte), 1041f, 1051f, **1052**
Coronary arteries, 665f, 666f, **669**–670, 669f, **724t**, 725f
Coronary blood vessels, autonomic innervation/effects and, 538t
Coronary bypass surgery, 703b
Coronary circulation, 669–670, 669f
Coronary sinus, **664**, 666f, 669f, **670**, 701
Coronary sulcus, **664**, 665f, 666f
Coronoid fossa, **228**, 229f
Coronoid process, **209**, 215t, **229**
  of mandible, **209**, 210f, **215t**
  of ulna, **229**, 230f
Corpora cavernosa, **1028**
  of clitoris, 1046f, 1047
  of penis, 1025f, **1028**, 1029f
Corpora quadrigemina, 443f, **446**, 447f
Cor pulmonale, **690**
Corpus albicans, 1041f, 1051f, 1052
Corpus callosum, 436f, 440f, **441**
Corpus hemorrhagicum, 1052
Corpus luteum, 1041f, **1042**, 1051f, 1052, 1054
Corpus spongiosum, 1025f, **1028**, 1029f
Corpus striatum, **441**, 442f
Corrugator supercilii muscle, **329t**, 331f
Cortex
  adrenal. See Adrenal cortex
  cerebellar, 431, 450, 451f
  cerebral. See Cerebral cortex
  hair, 157, 158f
  lymph node, **757**, 757f
  ovarian, 1041f, 1042
  renal, **962**, 963f, 965f, 966f

Corti, spiral organ of, 577, 577f, 578f, 582f
  excitation of hair cells in, 580–582, 582f
Cortical nephrons, **966**, 967f
Cortical processing, visual, 568–569
Cortical radiate arteries, 963, 964f, 967f, 968
Cortical radiate veins, 964, 964f, 967f
Cortical reaction, **1073**, 1074f
Corticomedullary junction, 967f
Corticospinal (pyramidal) tracts, 435, 471f, **474**, 474t, 475f
Corticosteroids, 45t, 47, **614**
Corticosterone, **616**
Corticotrophs, 605
Corticotropin, 605. See also Adrenocorticotropic hormone
Corticotropin-releasing hormone (CRH), 605
  in food intake regulation, 945, 946f
Cortisol, 615f, **616**–617, 617t
  blood pressure and, 709t
  excess levels of, 617, 617–618
  metabolism and, 941t
  sodium regulation and, 1005–1006
Cortisone, **616**
Costal cartilages, 173, 174f, 224f, 225, 225f
Costal facets
  superior and inferior, 220, 225f
  transverse, 220, 225f
Costal groove, 224, 225f
Costal margin, **224**, 224f, 225f
Costal surface, of lung, 815
Co-stimulatory signals, T cell activation and, **789**–790, 794f
  autoimmunity and, 797
Costocervical trunk, 727t, 728f, 729f, 729t
Cough/cough reflex, 811, 826t
Coumadin. See Warfarin
Countercurrent mechanisms, **979**
  countercurrent exchanger, 979, 980f, **981**
  countercurrent multiplier, 979, **979**–981, 980f
Coup injury, 464
Coupled systems, in secondary active transport, 73
Covalent bonds, **32**–34, 33f, 34f
Covering and lining epithelium/membranes, 115, 138–139, 138f
Coxal bones (hip bones/os coxae), **233**, 234–235, 233f, 234f, 242t
Coxal (hip) joint, 235, 255t, 266–267, 267f
  artificial/replacement, 261b
  muscles crossing/acting on, 327f, 363–369t, 364f, 367–368f, 380t, 381f
COX inhibitors, prostaglandins and, 47
CP. See Creatine phosphate
CPGs. See Central pattern generators
C proteins, 282
Cramps (muscle), heat, 951
Cranial (term), 12t. See also under Superior

Cranial bones, 199f, 200, 200–209, 201f, 202f, 203–204f, 206f. See also specific bone
Cranial cavity, 14, 16f, 201f
Cranial fossae, 201f
  anterior, 200, 201f, 206f
  middle, 201f, 206f, **207**
  posterior, 201, 201f, 206f
Cranial nerves, 386, 387f, **493**–501, 494f, 495–501t. See also specific nerve
Cranial outflow, parasympathetic, 529–530
Cranial root, accessory nerve and, 501f
Cranial sensory ganglia, **494**
Cranial sutures, 200, 200–201, 201f, **249**, 249f
Craniosacral division of autonomic nervous system. See Parasympathetic (craniosacral) division of autonomic nervous system
Cranium, **200**. See also under Cranial bones of, 199f, **200**, 200–209, 201f, 202f, 203–204f, 206f. See also specific bone
  growth and development of, 243
Creatine kinase, in CP-ADP reaction, **298**, 298f
Creatine phosphate (CP), ADP phosphorylation by, **298**, 298f
Creatinine, 985
  glomerular filtration rate estimated by clearance rate of, 984
CREB (cAMP response-element binding protein), in memory, 460
C (constant) region, **783**, 783f
Cremaster muscle, **1026**, 1026f
Crenation, in hypertonic solution, 71f, 72
Crepitus, 270
Crest (bone marking), 178t
Cretinism, **611**
CRH. See Corticotropin-releasing hormone
Cribriform plates, 206f, **208**, 209f, **215t**
Cricoid cartilage, 808f, 810f, **811**
Cricothyroid ligament, 810f
Cricotracheal ligament, 810f
Crista(e), **83**, 83f
Crista ampullaris, 576, 577f, **585**, 586f
Crista galli, 203f, 204f, 206f, **208**, 209f, **215t**
Crista terminalis, 664, 666f
Crohn's disease, 905
Cross bridges, **281**, 283f, 288–289, 292f
  in excitation-contraction coupling, 291f
  in sliding filament model, 284, 307, 307f
Crossed-extensor reflex, **519**, 519f
Cross matching, blood, 656
Crossovers (chiasmata), **1033**, 1035f, **1104**
  genetic variation and, **1104**, 1104f

Cross section (transverse section), **14**, 15f
Crowning, in labor, 1091
Crown-rump measurement, 1083, 1087
Crown of tooth, **863**, 863f
Cruciate ligaments, 262–263f, 263–264
Crura
  of clitoris, 1046f
  of penis, **1028**
Crus cerebri, 445, 446f, 448f
Crying, 826t
Cryogens, 954
Cryptorchidism, 1028, 1063
Crypts, tonsillar, **760**, 760f
Crypts of Lieberkühn (intestinal crypts), **879**, 879f
Crystal, ionic bonds forming, **32**, 32f
Crystallins, lens, 556
C-section (cesarean section), 1092
CSF. See Cerebrospinal fluid
CSFs. See Colony-stimulating factors
CT. See Computed tomography
Cubital vein, median, 737f, 740f, **740t**, 741f
Cuboidal cells/epithelium, **116**, 116f
  simple, **117**, 118f
  stratified, **119**
Cuboid bone, 240, 240f, 242t
Cuneiform bones, 240, 240f, 242t
Cuneiform cartilage, 810f, **811**
Cupula, **585**, 586f
Current, 395
Curvatures
  spinal, 217, 217f
    developmental aspects of, 243, 243f
    primary and secondary, **243**
    vertebral collapse/osteoporosis and, 190t, 244
  of stomach, greater and lesser, **868**, 868f
Cushingoid signs, 618, 618f
Cushing's disease/Cushing's syndrome, **617**–618, 618f
Cushioning function, of water, 39
Cutaneous branches of intercostal nerve, lateral and anterior, 503f, 504
Cutaneous glands, 155–157, 156f
Cutaneous membrane, 138f **139**. See also Skin
Cutaneous nerves, **504**
  cervical, 504, 504t
  development of, 520
  lateral femoral, 508f, 508t
  posterior femoral, 509f, 510t
Cutaneous plexus, 149f, 152
Cutaneous sensation (receptors/sense organs), 149f, 150, 151f, **161**
Cuticle
  hair, 157, 158f
  nail, **160**, 160f
CVAs. See Cerebrovascular accidents
CVS. See Chorionic villus sampling
Cyanide, mechanism of poisoning by, 928
Cyanocobalamin (vitamin B$_{12}$), 900, 916t
  intrinsic factor and, 872, 900

Cyanosis, 155
Cyclic AMP, **81**, 420*f*, **421**, **596**
  cardiac contractility affected by, 684, 685*f*
  in hormone mechanism of action, **596**–597, 597*f*
Cyclic GMP, 419, **421**, **563**, 564*f*
  in hormone mechanism of action, 598
Cyclic slow waves, of stomach, 876
Cyclin-dependent kinases (Cdks), **100**
Cyclins, **100**
Cysteine, 48*f*
Cystic duct, 878*f*, **881**
Cystic fibrosis, 843, 954, 1106
  pancreas affected in, 904
Cystic fibrosis transmembrane conductance regulator (CFTR) protein, 843
Cystic veins, 742*f*, **742***t*
Cystitis, 988
Cystocele, **991**
Cystoscopy, **991**
Cytochromes, **926**, 926*f*
Cytokines, 769, 772*t*, **790**–791, 790*t*, 794*f*, 795*t*
Cytokinesis, 96*f*, **97**, 97–100, 99*f*, 1035*f*
Cytology, 2
Cytoplasm, 62, 63*f*, **81**–95, 94*t*. *See also specific structure*
  division of. *See* Cytokinesis
Cytoplasmic inclusions, **83**, 94*t*
Cytoplasmic organelles, 3, 4*f*, **83**, 83–89, 94*t*. *See also specific type*
Cytosine (C), **53**, 54*f*
Cytoskeleton, 63*f*, 64, 65*f*, **87**–89, 88*f*, 89*f*
Cytosol, 63*f*, **83**, 94*t*
  as colloid, 30
Cytosolic protein, degradation of, 106–107
Cytotoxic (type II) hypersensitivity, **799**
Cytotoxic T cells, **786**, 787*f*, **792**, 793*f*, 794*f*, 795*t*
  CD8 cell activation in, 786, 787*f*, 789, 791, 791*f*, 794*f*
Cytotrophoblast (cellular trophoblast), **1077**, 1077*f*, 1079*f*

DAG. *See* Diacylglycerol
Dalton's law of partial pressures, **827**, 827*t*
Dark adaptation, **564**–565
Dark potential, 563
Dartos muscle, **1026**, 1026*f*
Daughter cells
  of meiosis, **1033**, 1034*f*, 1035*f*
  of mitosis, 99*f*, **1034***f*
  in spermatogenesis, 1033, 1036*f*, 1037
Daughter chromosomes, 99*f*
DCT. *See* Distal convoluted tubule
Dead space, 824
Deafness, **583**
  vestibulocochlear damage causing, 499*t*
Deamination, oxidative, **933**–934, 933*f*, 934*f*

Decarboxylation, **924**, 925*f*
Decibels (dB), **580**
Decidua basalis, **1078**, 1079*f*, 1080*f*
Decidua capsularis, **1078**, 1079*f*, 1080*f*
Deciduous teeth (primary dentition), **862**, 862*f*
Declarative (fact) memory, **458**, 459*f*
Decomposition reactions, **36**, 36*f*
Decubitus ulcers (bedsores), **168**
Decussation, 470
  of pyramids, 446*f*, **447**
Deep (term), 12*t*. *See also under Internal*
Deep artery
  of arm, 728*f*, **728***t*, 729*f*
  of thigh, **734***t*, 735*f*
Deep (intrinsic) back muscles, 336–338*t*, 339*f*
Deep brain stimulation, for Parkinson's disease, 465–466
Deep femoral artery (deep artery of thigh), **734***t*, 735*f*
Deep fibular (peroneal) nerve, 509*f*
Deep (forced) inspiration, 821–822
Deep palmar arch, 725*f*, 728*f*, **728***t*, 729*f*
Deep palmar venous arch, 740*f*, 740*t*, 741*f*
Deep plantar arch, 744*f*
Deep transverse perineal muscle, **344***t*, 345*f*
Deep veins
  of lower limbs, 744*t*
  of upper limbs, 740*t*
Defecation, 853*f*, **854**, 888*t*, 894–895, 894*f*
Defecation reflex, **894**–895, 894*f*
Defense system. *See* Body defenses
Defensins, 160, **644**, 768, 771, 807, 858, 860
Defibrillation (heart), 679
Degenerative brain diseases, 465–466
Degenerative joint disease (osteoarthritis), 270
Deglutition (swallowing), 853, 853*f*, **866**, 867*f*, 888*t*
  difficulty with (dysphagia), **905**
  epiglottis in, 811
  muscles controlling, 334–335*t*, 335*f*
Degradation, enzymatic, neurotransmitter, 408, 409*f*
Dehydration, **1001**, 1001*f*
Dehydration synthesis, 39, 42–43, 42*f*, 43
  in peptide bond formation, 47, 48*f*
Dehydroepiandrosterone (DHEA), 618, 1063
  in female sexual response, 1058
Dehydrogenases, 921
Delayed action gene, in Huntington's disease, 1106
Delayed (type IV) hypersensitivity, **799**
Deletion, **1112**
Delta waves, **454**, 454*f*
Deltoid muscle, 326*f*, 327*f*, 349*f*, **350***t*, 351*f*, 358*t*
Deltoid tuberosity, **228**, 229*f*

Dementia, 478
  in AIDS, 796
  Alzheimer's, 465
Demifacets, vertebral, 220
Demyelinating diseases, 405–406
Denaturation, protein, **50**
Dendrites, 134, 135*f*, **390**, 390*f*, 393*t*
Dendritic cells, **756**, 779, 780, 780*f*
  epidermal (Langerhans cells), **150**, 151*f*, 161, 779
  vaginal, HIV infection and, 1045
Dendritic spines, 390, 390*f*
Dendrodendritic synapses, 406
Dendrosomatic synapses, 406
Dens of axis, **220**, 221*f*
Dense bodies, in smooth muscle, 306–307, 306*f*
Dense (fibrous) connective tissue, **126**, **129**–131, 129–130*f*, 134*t*
Dental caries (cavities), 861, **864**
Dental formula, **862**–863
Dental plaque, **864**
Dentate gyrus, 452, 452*f*
Dentate nuclei, 450
Denticulate ligaments, 467*f*, **468**
Dentin, **863**, 863*f*
Dentinal tubules, 863, 863*f*
Dentition, 862–863, 862*f. See also Teeth*
Deoxyhemoglobin, **638**, 831
Deoxyribonucleic acid. *See* DNA
Deoxyribose, 43, 44*f*
  in DNA, 54, 54*f*
Depolarization, **287**, **398**
  of heart, ECG and, 679*f*, 680, 680*f*
  muscle contraction and, 285–287, 286*f*, **287**, 287*f*, 288, 288*f*
    in cardiac muscle, 674, 675*f*, 676, 676*f*
  neuron, **398**, 398*f*
    action potential and, 399, 400–401*f*, 402
    graded potential and, 398, 399*f*
Deprenyl, for Parkinson's disease, 465
Depressed fracture, 190*t*
Depression (body movement), 258*f*, **259**, 269
Depressor anguli oris muscle, **330***t*, 331*f*
Depressor labii inferioris muscle, **330***t*, 331*f*
Depth perception, **566**
Dermal papillae, 149*f*, **152**
Dermal ridges, 152
Dermatitis, 165
  atopic, 800
  contact, **168**
  allergic, 799
Dermatology, 168
Dermatome (somite), 1082*f*, **1084**, 1085*f*
Dermatomes, 510–511, 511*f*, 520
Dermicidin, 155, 767
Dermis, 129, 130*f*, 139, 149, 149*f*, **152**–153, 153*f*, 154*f*
Dermoid cysts, 1066
Descending (thoracic) aorta, **724***t*
  branches of, 724*f*

Descending colon, 852*f*, **890**, 891*f*
Descending limb of loop of Henle, 965*f*, 966, 967*f*, **983***f*
  absorptive capability of, 976–978, 977*t*
  as countercurrent multiplier, 979, 980*f*
Descending (motor) pathways/tracts, 470, 471*f*, 473–476, 474*f*, 475*f*
Desmin (intermediate) filaments, 281
Desmosomes (anchoring junctions), 66–67, 67*f*
  in cardiac muscle, 673, 674*f*
  in epidermis, 150, 151*f*
  epithelial, 115
Detached retina, 553
Detrusor muscle, **986**, 987*f*
Deuterium, 28*f*
Development. *See* Human development
Developmental anatomy, **2**
Deviated septum, 846
DHEA. *See* Dehydroepiandrosterone
DHT. *See* Dihydrotestosterone
Diabetes insipidus, **608**, 991
Diabetes mellitus, **622**, 623*t*, 626–627*b*, 797, 938, 954
  biliopancreatic diversion in obesity and, 949*b*
  obesity and, 954
  steroid administration and, 617–618
  type 1, **626**–627*b*, 797, 954
  type 2, **627***b*, 954
  urinary excretion of glucose and, 622, 623*t*, 975
Diacylglycerol, **421**, 598
Dialysis, 984
Diapedesis, **643**, 771*f*, 773
DiaPep277, 626*b*
Diaphragm (contraceptive), 1095–1096*b*
Diaphragm
  pelvic, **344***t*, 345*f*
  respiratory, **340***t*, 341*f*, 805*f*, **820**, 821*f*
  slit, renal, 969, 970*f*
  urogenital, **344***t*, 345*f*, 987, 987*f*
Diaphysis, 176*f*, **177**
  in endochondral ossification, 183*f*, 184
Diarrhea, **895**
Diarthroses, **249**
Diastole, **682**, 683*f*
Diastolic pressure, **705**, 705*f*
DIC. *See* Disseminated intravascular coagulation
Dicrotic notch, **682**, 683*f*
Diencephalon, **430**, 441–445, 443*f*, 444*f*, 446–447*f*, **449***t*
  development of, 430, 431*f*, 432*f*
Diet, 911–918. *See also* Nutrient(s); Nutrition
  cholesterol levels and, 944
  erythropoiesis and, 640
  hypertension and, 713
  pregnancy and, 954, 1090
  weight loss and, 948–949*b*
Diet drugs, for obesity, 949*b*

Differential permeability, **68**. *See also* Membrane transport
Differential white blood cell count, **657**
Differentiation, cell, **108**
Diffuse endocrine system, 121
Diffuse junctions, 306, 306*f*
Diffuse lymphatic tissue, **756**
Diffusion, 68–72, 68*f*, 69*f*, 70*f*, 71*f*, 72*t*, **717**
   in capillary exchange, **717**
   membrane polarity/resting membrane potential and, 79–80, 79*f*
   neurotransmitter, 408, 409*f*
Digastric muscle, 334*t*, 335*f*
Digestion, 5, 7*f*, 852, 853–854, 853*f*, 888*t*. *See also specific digestive organ and nutrient and Digestive system*
   autonomic nervous system affecting, 538*t*, 854, 855*f*, 858
   chemical, 853*f*, 854, 888*t*, **895**–897, 896*f*, 898*f*, 899*f*
   congenital defects of, 904
   hydrolysis in, 39, 43, **895**
   in large intestine, 888*t*, 893–895, 894*f*
   mechanical, 853–854, 853*f*, 888*t*
   in mouth/esophagus, 866, 888*t*, 895, 896*f*
   processes of, 853–854, 853*f*
   in small intestine, 887–890, 888*t*, 889*t*, 896*f*, 897
   in stomach, 871–877, 872*f*, 874*f*, 875*t*, 876*f*, 877*f*, 888*t*, 896*f*
Digestive cavity, 20
Digestive enzymes, 887, 888*t*. *See also Pancreatic juice*
   in chemical digestion, 895
Digestive system, 7*f*, 851–909, 852*f*. *See also specific organ or structure*
   accessory organs of, **852**–853, 852*f*
   autonomic innervation/effects and, 529*f*, 533*f*, 537, 538*t*, 542*b*, 543*b*, 854, 855*f*, 858
   cardiovascular system and, 746*b*
   developmental aspects of, 901–904, 901*f*
   endocrine system and, 628*b*
   functional anatomy of, 858–895. *See also specific organ or structure*
   functions/functional concepts and, 5, 6, 7*f*, 854, 855*f*, 888*t*
   homeostatic relationships of, 5*f*, 902*b*, 903*b*
   integumentary system and, 166*b*
   lymphatic system and, 762*b*
   muscular system and, 314*b*
   neural signals from, food intake regulation and, 945–946, 946*f*
   physiology of, 895–901. *See also Absorption; Digestion*
   pregnancy and, 1090
   relationships of organs of, 854–858, 855*f*, 857*f*
   reproductive system and, 1064*b*
   respiratory system and, 844*b*

   skeletal system and, 192*b*
   urinary system and, 1018*b*
   venous drainage of, 721, 856
Digital arteries
   of fingers, 725*f*, 728*f*, **728***t*, 729*f*
   of toes, **735***t*
Digital subtraction angiography (DSA), **18***b*, 19*f*
Digital veins, 737*f*, 740*f*, 741*f*, 744*f*
Digits (fingers), 199*f*, 231*f*, 232*t*, **233**
   carpometacarpal joint of, 254*t*
Dihydrotestosterone, 1039
Dihydroxyacetone phosphate, 923, 923*f*
Diiodotyrosine (DIT/T$_2$), **610**, 610*f*
Dilated cardiomyopathy, cardiac output and, **687**
Dilation, vascular, **695**
   heat loss and, 952*f*, 953
   in inflammation, 769–771
Dilation (first) stage of labor, **1091**, 1092*f*
Dilator pupillae, 551, 553*f*
Dimers, 162
Dipeptidase, 896*f*, **897**, 898*f*
Dipeptide, 47, 48*f*
Diploë, 179, **179***f*, 182*f*
Diploid chromosomal number (*2n*), **1032**, 1102
Diplopia (double vision), **551**
Dipoles (polar molecules), 34, 34*f*
Direct (fleshy) muscle attachments, **277**–278
Directional terms in anatomy, 12*t*, **13**, 13*f*
Direct (pyramidal) system, 474, 474*t*, 475*f*, 512–513
Disaccharides, **43**, 44*f*, 895, 896*f*, 912
Discharge zone, 421, 421*f*
Discs, intervertebral, **217**–218, 217*f*, 218*f*
   herniated (prolapsed/slipped), **218**, 218*f*
   aging and, 244
Dislocation(s)/luxation(s), **270**
Displaced fracture, 188
Displacement (exchange) reactions, 36, 36*f*
Disseminated intravascular coagulation (DIC), **653**
Dissociation
   strong and weak acids and, 41
   water polarity and, 38, 39*f*
Distal (term), 12*t*
Distal convoluted tubule, 965*f*, **966**, 967*f*, **983***f*
   absorptive capability of, 977*t*, 978
Distal phalanx
   finger, 231*f*, 232*t*, 233
   toe, 240*f*, 242*t*
Distal radioulnar joint, 230*f*, 254*t*
Distal tibiofibular joint, 238, 239*f*, 255*t*
Distant vision, focusing for, 558, 558*f*
Distributing (muscular) arteries, 697*f*, **698**, 698*t*
Distribution functions of blood, 635
Disuse atrophy, 305
DIT. *See Diiodotyrosine*
Diuretics, 608, **748**, **982**
   for heart failure, 687
   for weight loss, 948*b*

Diverging circuits, **422**, 422*f*
Diversity
   antigen receptor/antibody, 779, 784
   cellular, 62, 62*f*, 108
Diverticula, **894**
Diverticulitis, **894**
Diverticulosis, **894**
Division(s), brachial plexus, **505**, 506*f*
DM. *See Diabetes mellitus*
DMD. *See Duchenne muscular dystrophy*
DNA (deoxyribonucleic acid), **53**–54, 54*f*, 55*t*, 93. *See also Genome; Heredity*
   in chromatin/chromosomes, 93, 93*f*
   digestion of, 896*f*, 897
   linker, 93, 93*f*
   mitochondrial, 83, 1109
   mutations in in cancer, 142*b*, 143*f*
   packing, 93, 93*f*
   in protein synthesis, 53, 100–101, 107*f*. *See also Transduction; Translation*
   replication of, 53, 96–97, 97*f*
   structure of, 53, 54, 54*f*
   UV radiation protection and, 161
DNA fingerprinting, 53
DNA ligase, **96**
DNA polymerase, 96, 97*f*
DNA probe, 1110
DNA-RNA hybrid, **102**, 102*f*
Domains, cortical, 435
Dominant allele, **1103**
Dominant follicle, 1052
Dominant-recessive inheritance, **1105**–1106, 1105*f*, 1106*t*
   incomplete dominance and, **1106**
Dominant traits, 1105–1106, 1106*t*
L-Dopa, for Parkinson's disease, 465
Dopamine, 416*t*, 418
   cocaine abuse and, 414–415*b*
   deficiency of, in Parkinson's disease, 465
   as prolactin-inhibiting hormone, 605
Dorsal (term), 12*t*. *See also under Posterior*
Dorsal body cavity, **14**, 16*f*
Dorsal column–medial lemniscal pathways, **471**, 472*f*, 473*t*, 490
Dorsal (posterior) funiculi, 469*f*, **470**
Dorsal (posterior) horns, 433*f*, **468**, 469*f*, 470*f*
Dorsal interossei muscle
   of foot, 378*t*, 379*f*
   of hand, 361*f*, 362*t*
Dorsalis pedis artery, 734*f*, 735*f*
   pulse at, 712*f*
Dorsalis pedis vein, 744*f*, **744***t*
Dorsal (posterior) median sulcus, **468**, 469*f*
Dorsal mesentery, 855, 855*f*
Dorsal metatarsal arteries, 734*f*, 735*f*
Dorsal metatarsal veins, 737*f*, 744*f*
Dorsal motor nuclei, 530
Dorsal ramus/rami, **502**, 503*f*, 504

Dorsal respiratory group, 835, 835*f*. *See also Medullary respiratory centers*
Dorsal root(s), 467*f*, **468**–470, 469*f*, 470*f*, **502**, 503*f*
Dorsal root ganglion, 466, 469*f*, **470**, 470*f*
Dorsal rootlets, 469*f*, 470, 503*f*
Dorsal scapular nerve, 506*f*, 507*t*
Dorsal (posterior) spinocerebellar tract, **471**–473, 471*f*, 472*f*, 473*t*
Dorsal venous arch
   foot, 737*f*, 744*f*, **744***t*
   hand, **740***t*
Dorsal white column, **471**, 471*f*, 473*t*
Dorsiflexion (body movement), 258*f*, **259**
   of lower limb, 380*t*, 381*f*
Dorsum of foot, muscles on, 376*t*
Dorsum nasi, 806, 806*f*
Double covalent bond, 33*f*, 34
Double helix, DNA, **54**, 54*f*
Double sugars (disaccharides), **43**, 44*f*
Doublets (microtubule), 90
Double vision (diplopia), **551**
Double zipper, 284
Down-regulation, **598**
Down syndrome, **1112**
DRG. *See Dorsal respiratory group*
Drowsiness, 455
Drug abuse, 414–415*b*
Drug therapy, autonomic effects and, 536, 537*t*
Dry mouth (xerostomia), 861, **906**
DSA. *See Digital subtraction angiography*
DSR. *See Dynamic spatial reconstruction*
Duchenne muscular dystrophy, **312**
Duct(s)
   glandular, 121
      exocrine gland, 121, 122, 123*f*
   reproductive
      embryologic/fetal development of, 1061*f*
      in female, 1040–1041, 1040*f*, 1042–1046, 1043*f*, 1045*f*
      in male, 1025, 1025*f*, **1028**–1030
Duct of epididymis, 1028
Ductless glands, 121, 595. *See also Endocrine system/glands*
Ductules, efferent, 1026, 1027*f*
   embryologic/fetal development of, 1061*f*
Ductus arteriosus, **688**, 688*f*, **1085**, 1086*f*
   closure of, 1086*f*, 1093
Ductus (vas) deferens, 1025*f*, 1026*f*, 1027*f*, 1028, **1029**–1030, 1029*f*
   ampulla of, 1025*f*, **1029**, 1029*f*
   embryologic/fetal development of, 1061*f*
   resection of (vasectomy), **1030**, 1096*b*
Ductus venosus, 745, **1085**, 1086*f*
   closure of, 1086*f*, 1093
Duodenal (Brunner's) glands, 879*f*, **880**

Duodenal papilla, major, **877**, 878*f*
Duodenal ulcers, 880
Duodenum, 852*f*, **877**, 878*f*
  gastric emptying and, 876, 877*f*
  hormones produced by, 625*t*
Dural septa, **461**, 461*f*
Dural venous sinuses, **461**, 461*f*, 701, 721, 736*f*, 737*f*, **738***t*
Dura mater, **461**
  of brain, 460*f*, **461**, 461*f*
  spinal, **466**, 467*f*, 468*f*, 469*f*
Dwarfism, 185
  pituitary, **604**
  psychosocial, **627**
Dynamic equilibrium, 585, 586*f*
Dynamic spatial reconstruction (DSR), **18***b*
Dynein(s), 88, 90, 90*f*
Dynorphin, 417*t*, **418–419**
Dysarthria, **520**
Dysmenorrhea, **1066**
Dysphagia, **905**
Dysplasia, **109**
Dyspnea, **840**
  pregnancy and, 1090
Dysreflexia, autonomic, 541
Dystocia, 1092
Dystonia, **520**
Dystrophin, 51*t*, **282**
  defect/deficiency of in muscular dystrophy, 312
Dysuria, 988

e⁻. *See* Electron(s)
Ear, 574–577, 575*f*. *See also specific region and* Balance; Hearing
  developmental aspects of, 588–589
  external (outer), **574**, 575*f*
  inner (internal), 575*f*, **576**–577, 577*f*, 578*f*
    sound transmission to, 580, 581*f*
  middle, 20, **574**–576, 575*f*, 576*f*
  structure of, 574–577, 575*f*, 576*f*, 577*f*, 578*f*
Earache (otalgia), **589**
Ear canal, auditory/external (external acoustic meatus), **204**, 205*f*, 207*f*, **214***t*, **574**, 575*f*
Eardrum (tympanic membrane), **574**, 575*f*
  perforated/ruptured, 583
Earlobes (lobule), **574**, 575*f*
Early (basophilic) erythroblasts, **639**, 639*f*
Earwax (cerumen), **156**
Eating. *See* Ingestion
Eccentric contraction, **296**
E-C coupling. *See* Excitation-contraction coupling
Eccrine (merocrine) sweat glands, 149*f*, **155**–156, 156*f*
ECF. *See* Extracellular fluid
ECG. *See* Electrocardiogram
ECL cells. *See* Enterochromaffin-like cells
ECPs. *See* Emergency contraceptive pills
Ecstasy abuse, 415*b*

Ectoderm, **141**, 141*f*, 1079*f*, **1081**, 1082*f*
  differentiation of, 1082*f*, 1083, 1083*f*, 1085*f*
  neural plate and, 430, 430*f*, 1082*f*, **1083**
Ectopic focus, **679**
Ectopic pregnancy, 1042, **1097**
Eczema, **168**, **800**
ED. *See* Erectile dysfunction
Edema, **127**, **1001**–1002
  cerebral, **464**
  in heart failure, 687
  hypertonic solutions for, 72
  in inflammation, 770, 771
  lymphatic vessels and (lymphedema), 755
Edinger-Westphal (accessory oculomotor) nuclei, 529
EEG. *See* Electroencephalogram
Effacement, in labor, 1091
Effector, **9**
  in homeostasis, 9, 9*f*, 10*f*
  in reflex arc, 514, 514*f*
Effector organs, 386
  in autonomic versus somatic nervous system, 526, 527*f*
Effector regions (antibody), 783*f*, 784
Efferent arteriole, glomerular, **966**, 967*f*, 968
Efferent (motor) division of peripheral nervous system, **386**, 387*f*, 485*f*
Efferent ductules, **1026**, 1027*f*
  embryologic/fetal development of, 1061*f*
Efferent fibers
  α, **515**, 515*f*
  γ, **515**, 515*f*
Efferent lymphatic vessels, **757**, 757*f*
Efferent nerves/neurons/tracts. *See* Motor (efferent) nerves; Motor (efferent) neurons; Motor (descending) pathways/tracts
Efferent pathways. *See also* Motor (descending) pathways/tracts
  in autonomic versus somatic nervous system, 526–527, 527*f*
  in homeostasis, 9, 9*f*, 10*f*
Effort, in lever system, **323**, 323*f*, 324*f*, 325*f*
Eggs. *See* Ova
Eicosanoid(s), 45*t*, **47**, **596**
Eights, rule of (octet rule), **31**–32
Ejaculation, **1032**
  from epididymis, 1028, 1032
Ejaculatory duct, 1025*f*, **1029**, 1029*f*
EKG. *See* Electrocardiogram
Elastic (conducting) arteries, **697**, 697*f*, 698*t*
Elastic cartilage, 132*f*, **133**, 134*t*, **173**, 174*f*
  skeletal, **173**, 174*f*
Elastic connective tissue, 130*f*, **131**, 134*t*
Elastic fibers, **125**, 125*f*, 130*f*, 133
  bronchial, 814
  in dermis, 153

Elastic (titin) filaments, in skeletal muscle, 280*f*, **281**–282
Elasticity, muscle cell, **276**
Elastic lamina, of muscular arteries, 698
Elastin, 50, 51*t*, **125**
  in elastic arteries, 697
Elbow
  articulation at, 229*f*
  muscles of, 351–352*f*, 353*t*, 358*t*, 359*f*
Elbow joint, 254*t*, 266, 266*f*
  muscles crossing, 351–352*f*, 353*t*, 358*t*, 359*f*
Electrical energy, **24**
Electrical gradient, 395
Electrical signaling, 81
Electrical synapses, **406**
Electricity, basic principles of, 395
Electrocardiogram/electrocardiography (ECG/EKG), **679**–680, 679*f*, 680*f*, 681*f*, 683*f*
  sleep cycle and, 455, 456*f*
Electrochemical proton (H⁺) gradient, 80, **395**, **927**
Electroencephalogram/electroencephalography (EEG), **453**–455, 454*f*
Electrolysis, 159
Electrolyte(s), **39**, **996**
  absorption of, 900
  in body fluids, 996–997, 997*f*
  heart function and, 686
  in plasma, 636*t*, 997*f*
  salts as, **39**
Electrolyte balance, **1002**–1008, 1004*f*, 1005*f*, 1007*f*
  developmental aspects of, 1015
  sodium in, 1002–1004
    regulation and, 1004–1006, 1004*f*, 1005*f*, 1007*f*
Electrolyte imbalances, 39, 1002, 1003*t*
  heart rate and, 686
Electromagnetic (radiant) energy, **24**
Electromagnetic radiation, **556**–557, 557*f*
Electromagnetic spectrum, 24
Electromyography, **382**
Electron(s), 25*f*, **26**
  chemical bonds and, 31–32, 31*f*
Electron acceptor
  in ionic bond, 32
  in redox reaction, 37
Electron cloud, 26
Electron donor, in redox reaction, 37
Electronegativity, **34**
Electroneutrality, **42**
Electron microscopy
  scanning, 115
  transmission, 115
Electron sharing, in covalent bonds, 32
Electron shells (energy levels), **31**, 31*f*
Electron transport chain, **925**–926, 926*f*, 927*f*, 929*f*, 934*t*
Electropositive atoms, **34**
Elements, **25**–28, 26*t*
  atomic structure and, 25
  chemically inert, 31, 31*f*

  chemically reactive, 31–32, 31*f*
  identifying, 27–28
Elephantiasis, **761**
Elevation (body movement), 258*f*, **259**, 269
Ellipsoidal (condyloid) joints, **259**, 260*f*
Elongation, in transcription, **102**, 102*f*
EM. *See* Electron microscopy
Embolism, **653**
  pulmonary, 846–847
Embolus/emboli, **653**
Embryo, **1072**, 1072*f*, 1081
  blood supply for, 1084–1085, 1086*f*
  cleavage/blastocyst formation and, **1075**–1076, 1076*f*
  folding of, 1083–1084, 1083*f*
  implantation of, **1076**–1078, 1076*f*, 1077*f*
  sexually indifferent stage of, **1060**, 1061*f*, 1062*f*
Embryology, **2**. *See also* Embryonic period; Fetal period
Embryonic disc, 1076, **1079**, 1079*f*, 1081*f*, 1083*f*
Embryonic period, 1072
  cleavage/blastocyst formation, **1075**–1076, 1076*f*
  extraembryonic membrane formation, **1080**, 1080*f*
  gastrulation/germ layer formation, **1081**–1083, 1081*f*, 1082*f*
  implantation, **1076**–1078, 1076*f*, 1077*f*
  organogenesis (germ layer differentiation), **1083**–1087, 1083*f*, 1084*f*, 1086*f*
  placentation, **1078**, 1079*f*, 1080*f*
Embryonic stem cells, 108. *See also* Stem cell(s)
Emergency contraceptive pills, 1096*b*
Emesis (vomiting)/emetic center, **876**
Emmetropic eye, **558**, 560*f*
Emotional memory, **458**
Emotions
  hypothalamus and, 443–444
  limbic association area and, 439
  limbic system and, 452
Emphysema, 830, **840**, 841*f*
Emulsion(s), **30**
  in lipid digestion, 897, 899*f*
Enamel (tooth), **863**, 863*f*
Encapsulated dendritic endings, **486**–488, 487–488*t*. *See also specific type*
Encephalitis, 463
Encephalopathy, **479**
End diastolic volume, 682, 683*f*, **684**, 686*f*, 707*f*
Endemic (colloidal) goiter, **611**, 611*f*
Endergonic reactions, 37
Endocannabinoids, 418*t*, **419**
Endocarditis, **690**
Endocardium, 663*f*, **664**, 667*f*
Endochondral (cartilage) bones, **182**
Endochondral ossification, 182, **183**–184, 183*f*

Endocrine glands, **595**. *See also* Endocrine system/glands
Endocrine system/glands, 6f, **121**, **594**–**633**, **595**, 595f. *See also specific gland and* Hormone(s)
  aging affecting, 624
  autonomic nervous system and, 542b
  cardiovascular system and, 746b
  developmental aspects of, 624–627
  diffuse, 121
  digestive system and, 902b, 903b
  functions of, 6f
  homeostatic relationships of, 10, 628b, 629b
  hypothalamus in regulation of, 444
  integumentary system and, 166b
  lymphatic system and, 762b
  muscular system and, 314b, 315b
  reproductive system and, 1064b, 1065b
  respiratory system and, 844b
  skeletal system and, 192b, 193b
  stimuli activating, 600, 601f
  urinary system and, 1018b, 1019b
Endocrinology, **595**
Endocytosis, 75, 75f–77, 76f, 77t, 78f
  fluid-phase (pinocytosis), **76**, 77t, 78f
  receptor-mediated, **76**, 77t, 78f
Endoderm, 141, 141f, 1079f, **1081**, 1081f, 1082f
  differentiation of, 1083–1084, 1083f, 1084f, 1085f
Endogenous antigen, **787**, 788f
Endolymph, **576**, 578f
  equilibrium and, 585, 586f
Endomembrane system, 83, **87**, 87f
Endometrial cancer, **1066**
Endometriosis, **1066**
Endometrium, 1043f, **1044**, 1045f
Endomysium, **277**
  cardiac muscle, 309t, 673
  skeletal muscle, **277**, 278f, 279t, 309t
  smooth muscle, 305, 309t
Endoneurium, **491**, 492f
Endoplasmic reticulum, 63f, **84**–**85**, 84f, 87f
  rough, 63f, **84**, 84f, 86f, 87f, 94t
  smooth, **84**–**85**, 84f, 87f, 94t
Endoplasmic reticulum signal sequence, **105**, 106f
Endorphins, 417t, **418**–**419**, 490
Endoscopy, **905**
Endosome, 75, 76f
Endosteum, 176f, **178**, 181f
Endothelial tissue/endothelium, **117**, **695**
  blood vessel, **695**, 696f
  in atherosclerosis, 702b
  corneal, 551
Endothelins, blood flow regulation and, **714**, 715f
Endotracheal tube, **846**
End plate potential, 285–287, **287**, 287f, 288, 512
End systolic volume, 682, 683f, **684**, 686f, 707f

Endurance exercise, **304**
Energy, **24**–**25**
  activation, 52, 52f, 923
  from ATP, 24, 55
  chemical bonds and, 31, 31f
  in chemical reactions, 37
  diffusion and, 68
  enzyme action and, 52, 52f
  intake–output balance and, 944–945
  for muscle contraction, 297–300, 298f, 299f
  in cardiac muscle, 675
Energy balance, 944–945
Energy conversions, 24–25
Energy intake, **944**
Energy investment phase of glycolysis, 923, 923f
Energy levels (electron shells), 31, 31f
Energy output, **944**
Engagement, in labor, 1091
Enkephalins, 417t, **418**–**419**, 490
Enteric bacteria, 893
Enteric (intestinal) gastrin, 625t, **873**, 875t. *See also* Gastrin
Enteric nervous system/plexuses, 534, 854, 855f, **857**–**858**, 857f
Enteric neurons, 857
Enteritis, **905**
Enterochromaffin-like cells, 873
Enterocytes, 878
Enteroendocrine cells, 624, **870**
  in small intestine, 879, 879f
  in stomach, 869f, 870
Enterogastric reflex, **873**
Enterogastrones, **873**
Enterohepatic circulation, **884**
Enterokinase. *See* Enteropeptidase
Enteropathy, gluten-sensitive (celiac disease), 901
Enteropeptidase, **886**, 886f
Enucleation, **589**
Enuresis, nocturnal, **991**
Enzyme(s)/enzyme activity, 51–53, 51t, 52f, 53f
  chemical reactions regulated by, 38, 51–52
Enzyme-substrate complex, 52–53, 53f
Eosinophils, 126, 644f, **645**, 645t, 647f
Ependymal cells, 388f, **389**, 431
Epiblast, 1079, 1079f, 1081, 1081f
Epicanthic fold, 548
Epicardium (visceral layer of serous pericardium), 17, 17f, 138f, **663**, 663f, 667f
Epicondyle (bone marking), 178t
  of femur, 237, 238f
  of humerus, 228, 229f
Epicranius (occipitofrontalis) muscle, 326f, 327f, **329t**, 331f
Epidermal dendritic cells (Langerhans cells), **150**, 151f, 161, 779
Epidermal ridges, 152
Epidermis, 119, 139, 149, 149f, **150**–**152**, 151f
  in body defense, 160–161
  development of, 165
  hormones produced by, 624, 625t
  metabolic functions of, 161

Epidermolysis bullosa, **168**
Epididymis, 1025f, 1026, 1026f, 1027f, **1028**, 1029f
  embryologic/fetal development of, 1061f
Epidural space, **466**, 469f
Epigastric region, 17, 20f
Epigenetic marks, 1109
Epiglottis, 133, 808f, 810f, **811**
Epileptic seizures, **454**–**455**
Epimysium, **277**, 278f, 279t, 309t
Epinephrine, **619**, **709**
  adrenal secretion of, 532, 615f
  blood pressure and, 709, 709t, 711f
  in food intake regulation, 946, 946f
  heart rate affected by, 686, 707f
  metabolism and, 941, 941t
  stress response/sympathetic stimulation and, 619, 619f
Epineurium, **491**, 492f
Epiphyseal fracture, 190t
Epiphyseal line, 176f, **177**
Epiphyseal plates, 131–133, **177**, 183f, 184
  closure of, 185
  as synchondroses, 250–251, 250f
Epiphyses, 176f, **177**
  ossification of, 183f, 184
Epiploic appendages, **890**, 891f
Episiotomy, 1091
Epistaxis (nosebleed), 807, **846**
Epithalamus, **444**–**445**
  development of, 431, 431f
Epithelial cells. *See also* Epithelial tissue/epithelium
  taste bud, 571
Epithelial root sheath, **157**, 158f
Epithelial tissue/epithelium, 114f, **115**–**124**, 116f, 117f–120f, 122f, 123f. *See also specific type*
  of alimentary canal mucosa, **856**, 857f
  bronchial, 815
  classification of, 116–117, 116f
  columnar, **116**, 116f
  corneal, 551
  cuboidal, **116**, 116f
  ectoderm and endoderm as, 1083
  germinal, of ovary, 1041, 1041f
  glandular, 115, 121–124, 122f, 123f
  of mouth, 858
  olfactory, **569**–**571**, 569f, 571f, **806**–**807**, 808f
  regeneration of, 116, 140, 140f
  simple, **116**, 116f, 117–119, 117f–119f
  of small intestine, 878–880
  special characteristics of, 115–116
  squamous, **116**, 116f
  of stomach, 869f, 870
  stratified, **116**, 116f, 119–121, 120f
  transitional, 120f, **121**
    of bladder wall, 986
    in ureters, 986, 986f

Epithelium. *See* Epithelial tissue/ epithelium
Epitympanic recess, **574**
EPO. *See* Erythropoietin
Eponychium (nail cuticle), 160, 160f
EPSPs. *See* Excitatory postsynaptic potentials
Epstein-Barr virus, mononucleosis caused by, 648, 764
Equational division (meiosis II), **1033**, 1034f, 1035f
Equator, of mitotic spindle, 99f
Equilibrium (chemical), **37**
Equilibrium/orientation, 584–588. *See also* Ear
  cerebral cortex in, 439
  crista ampullaris in, **585**, 586f
  developmental aspects of, 588–589
  dynamic, 585, 586f
  maculae in, **584**–**585**, 584f, 585f
  static, 584–585, 584f, 585f
Equilibrium (vestibular) cortex, 439
Equilibrium pathway, 586–588, 587f
ER. *See* Endoplasmic reticulum
Erectile dysfunction (ED), **1032**
Erectile tissue/bodies
  in clitoris, 1046–1047
  of penis, 1028, 1031
Erection, 1028, **1031**–**1032**
Erector spinae (sacrospinalis) muscles, 336t, 338t, 339f, 367f
ERV. *See* Expiratory reserve volume
Erythema, 155
Erythroblastosis fetalis, **655**
Erythroblasts
  early (basophilic), **639**, 639f
  late, **639**, 639f
Erythrocytes (red blood cells), 133, 134t, 135f, 635, 635f, 637, **637**–**643**, 637f, **645**t
  antigens of, blood groups and, 654
    transplantation and, 792
  disorders of, 641–643, 642f
  hemoglobin in, 637, **638**
  life cycle of, 641, 641f, 645t
  production of, 638–640, 639f, 640f, 641f
  sickled, 642, 642f, 1106
  transfusion of, 654–656, 655t, 656f
  in urine, 985t
Erythropoiesis, 639, 639f, 641f
  regulation/requirements for, 639–640, 640f
Erythropoietin, 624, 625t, **639**, 640f, 641f, 961
  homeostatic imbalances and, 640
Eschar, 164
E site, 104f, 105
Esophageal arteries, **729**t
Esophageal glands, 865
Esophageal hiatus, **864**
Esophageal plexuses, **530**
Esophageal ulcers, 865
Esophagitis, 865
Esophagus, 852f, **864**–**866**, 865f, 888t
  Barrett's, **905**
  digestive processes occurring in, 866, 888t

Essential amino acids, 914, 915*f*
Essential fatty acids, 912, 913*t*
Essential (primary) hypertension, **713**
Essential nutrients, **912**
Estradiol, 1040
testosterone converted to, 1039
Estriol, 1040
Estrogen(s), **623**, **1005**, **1040**, 1056–1057, 1057*t*
adrenal, 618
labor initiation and, 1091, 1091*f*
in menopause, 1063
osteoporosis and, 191
in ovarian cycle, 1053*f*, 1054, 1057*t*
placental/during pregnancy, 1078, 1078*f*
in sodium regulation, **1005**
in uterine (menstrual) cycle, 1055*f*, 1056, 1056–1057, 1057*t*
Estrogen (hormone) replacement therapy, 1063
for osteoporosis, 191
Estrone, 1040
Ethmoid bone, 202*f*, 203*f*, 204*f*, 206*f*, **208**–209, 209*f*, 213*f*, 215*t*
Ethmoid sinuses (ethmoid air cells), 201*f*, **209**, 209*f*, 216*f*
Eupnea, **835**
Eustachian tube. *See* Pharyngotympanic (auditory) tube
Evaporation, heat loss by, 950*f*, **951**, 951*f*, 953
Eversion (body movement), 258*f*, **259**
of lower limb, 380*t*, 381*f*
Exchange (displacement) reactions, **36**, 36*f*
Exchange transfusions, **658**
for hemolytic disease of newborn, 655
Excitability, **276**
muscle cell, **276**
neuron, 395
Excitation-contraction coupling, 285, **288**, 290–291*f*
action potential generation/propagation and, 287–288, 290–291*f*
in cardiac muscle, 674
repolarization and, 288
Excitatory postsynaptic potentials (EPSPs), **411**–412, 411*t*, 412*f*
in phototransduction, 564, 565*f*
summation by, **412**, 413*f*
Excitatory synapses, 411–412
Excitotoxin, in cerebrovascular accident, 465
Excreta, 6
Excretion, **6**–7
skin in, 162
Excretory system. *See* Urinary system
Executive area, in prefrontal cortex, 436*f*, 439
Exercise
blood flow affected by, 716
bone remodeling/strength affected by, 187–188, 187*f*, 188*f*
energy systems used during, 299–300, 299*f*

heart affected by, 686*f*, 687
muscles affected by, 304–305, 316
for osteoporosis prevention/treatment, 191
respiratory adjustments during, 839
Exercise (active) hyperemia, **716**
Exergonic reactions, **37**
Exertion-induced heat exhaustion, 953
Exhalation. *See* Expiration
Exocrine glands, **121**–124, 122*f*, 123*f*
multicellular, **121**–124, 123*f*
unicellular (mucous/goblet cells), **121**, 122*f*
Exocytosis, **73**, 77*t*, 78, 78*f*
Exogenous antigens, 788*f*, **789**
Exons, **101**
mRNA processing and, 103
Exophthalmos, **589**, 611, 611*f*
Expiration, **819**, 821*f*, 822, 822*f*
muscles used in, 340*t*, 341*f*, 822
Expiratory reserve volume, **824**, 825*f*
Expulsion (second), stage of labor, **1091**–1092, 1092*f*
Extended chromatin, 93
Extensibility, muscle cell, **276**
Extension (body movement), **255**, 256*f*, 257*f*
of lower limb, 380*t*, 381*f*
of upper limb, 358*t*, 359*f*
Extensor carpi radialis brevis muscle, **356***t*, 357*f*, 358*t*
Extensor carpi radialis longus muscle, 327*f*, **356***t*, 357*f*, 358*t*
Extensor carpi ulnaris muscle, 327*f*, **356***t*, 357*f*, 358*t*
Extensor digitorum muscles, 327*f*, **356***t*, 357*f*, 358*t*
brevis, 371*f*, 372*f*, **376***t*
longus, 326*f*, **370***t*, 372*f*, 380*t*
Extensor hallucis longus muscle, **370***t*, 371*f*, 372*f*, 380*t*
Extensor indicis muscle, 357*f*, **357***t*, 358*t*
Extensor muscles
of back, 336–338, 339*f*
of forearm, 351–352*f*, 353*t*, 358*t*, 359*f*
of hand. *See also specific muscle*
of knee, 363*t*
of leg, anterior, 370*t*
of thigh, 363*t*
Extensor pollicis brevis muscle, **356***t*, 357*f*, 358*t*
Extensor pollicis longus muscle, **356***t*, 357*f*, 358*t*
Extensor retinacula, 354*t*, **370***t*
of forearm, 354*t*, 356*t*
of leg, **370***t*
External (term), 12*t*. *See also under Superficial*
External acoustic meatus (external ear/auditory canal), 204, 205*f*, 207*f*, **214***t*, 574, 575*f*
External anal sphincter, 345*f*, **891**, 891*f*
External carotid artery, 725*f*, 726*f*, **726***t*, 727*f*
External (outer) ear, 204, **574**, 575*f*

External genitalia, **1028**
embryologic/fetal development of, 1060, 1062*f*
in female, **1041**, 1046–1047, 1046*f*
in male, 1025–1026, 1025*f*, 1026*f*, **1028**, 1029*f*
External iliac artery, 725*f*, 734*f*, **734***t*, 735*f*
External iliac vein, 737*f*, 742*f*, 743*f*, **744***t*
External intercostal muscles, **340***t*, 341*f*, 820, 821*f*
External jugular vein, 736*f*, 737*f*, 738*f*, **738***t*, 739*f*, 741*f*
External oblique muscle, **342***t*, 343*f*, 367*f*
External occipital crest, 202*f*, 204, 205*f*, **214***t*
External occipital protuberance, 202*f*, 203*f*, **204**, 204*f*, 205*f*, **214***t*
External os, 1043, 1043*f*
External (closed) reduction of fracture, 188
External respiration, 805, 828–830, 828*f*, 829*f*
External spermatic fascia, 1026*f*
External strabismus, 496*t*
External tension, muscle contraction force and, **301**
External urethral orifice, **987**, 987*f*, 1025*f*, 1029*f*, 1030, 1040*f*, 1046*f*, 1060
External urethral sphincter, **344***t*, 345*f*, **987**, 987*f*
Exteroceptors, 161, **486**, 487*t*
Extracapsular ligaments, of synovial joints, **252**
Extracellular fluid, 63, 996, 996*f*
developmental changes in, 1015
electrolytes in, 997*f*
gas/nutrient/water/waste exchanges and, 998, 998*f*
intracellular fluid compared with, 997–998, 997*f*
resting membrane potential and, 396, 397*f*
Extracellular fluid compartment, **996**, 996*f*
Extracellular fluid osmolality, 998–1002, 999*f*, 1000*f*, 1001*f*. *See also* Water balance
Extracellular materials, **107**
Extracellular matrix, 107, **124**. *See also* Matrix
cartilage, 173
connective tissue, 107, **124**, 125*f*, 134*t*
Extraembryonic membranes, **1080**, 1080*f*
Extraembryonic mesoderm, 1079*f*
Extrafusal muscle fibers, **515**, 515*f*, 516*f*
Extraglomerular mesangial cells, 968*f*, 969
Extranuclear (mitochondrial) inheritance, 1108, 1109
Extrapyramidal (indirect) system, 474*t*, **476**, 512–513
Extrasystole (premature contraction), **679**

Extrauterine life, infant adjustment to, 1092–1093
Extremities. *See* Lower limbs; Upper limbs
Extrinsic conduction system of heart, 678*f*, 679
Extrinsic eye muscles, **550**–551, 550*f*
abducens nerve supplying, 498*t*, 551
oculomotor nerve supplying, 496*t*, 551
trochlear nerve supplying, 496*t*, 551
Extrinsic pathway, **650**–651, 650*f*
Extrinsic salivary glands, **860**, 861*f*
Extrinsic tongue muscles, 332*t*, 333*f*, **859**
Exudate, **770**
Eye, **548**–556, 548*f*. *See also under Visual and Vision*
accessory structures of, **548**–551. *See also specific structure*
autonomic innervation/effects and, 528*f*, 529*f*, 533*f*, 538*t*
developmental aspects of, 588
eyeball structure and, **551**–556, 552*f*, 553*f*, 554*f*, 555*f*, 556*f*
internal chambers/fluids of, 553–556, 555*f*
layers of, 551–553, 552*f*
muscles controlling movement of, **550**–551, 550*f*
Eyeballs, **551**. *See also* Eye
convergence of, in close vision, **559**
structure of, 551–556, 552*f*, 553*f*, 554*f*, 555*f*, 556*f*
Eyebrows, 548, 548*f*
Eyelashes, 548*f*, **549**
Eyelids, **548**–549, 548*f*
Eye muscles, extrinsic, **550**–551, 550*f*
abducens nerve supplying, 498*t*, 551
oculomotor nerve supplying, 496*t*, 551
trochlear nerve supplying, 496*t*, 551
Eyeteeth (canines), **862**, 862*f*

Face. *See also under Facial*
bones of, 199*f*, 200, 201*f*, 202*f*, 203*f*, 209–211, 215*t*
muscles of, 326*f*, 329–330*f*, 331*f*
Facet (bone marking), 178*t*
vertebral, 219, 220
Facial artery, 726*f*, **726***t*, 727*f*
pulse at, 712*f*
Facial bones, 199*f*, 200, 201*f*, 202*f*, 203*f*, 209–211, 215*t*
Facial expression, muscles controlling, 329–331*t*, 331*f*
Facial muscles, 326*f*, 329–330*f*, 331*f*
Facial nerve (cranial nerve VII), 446–447*f*, 447, **493**, 494*f*, **498**–499*t*, **573**
facial muscles supplied by, 329–330*t*, 498–499*t*
in gustatory pathway, **573**, 573*f*
parasympathetic fibers of, 529, 529*f*
scalp muscles supplied by, 329*t*

Facial paralysis, in Bell's palsy, 498*t*
Facial vein, 738*f*, **738***t*, 739*f*
Facilitated diffusion, 69, **69**–70, 69*f*, 72*t*
Facilitated neuron, **412**
Facilitated zone, 421, 421*f*
Fact (declarative) memory, **458**, 459*f*
F (fibrous) actin, 281
Factor III (tissue factor), 650*f*, **651**, 651*t*
Factor VIII (antihemophilic factor), 651*t*, **654**
Factor XIII (fibrin stabilizing factor), 651*t*, **652**
Facultative water reabsorption, **981**
FAD. *See* Flavin adenine dinucleotide
Failure to thrive, 444
Fainting, **455**, 716. *See also* Syncope
Falciform ligament, **881**, 882*f*, 892*f*
Fallopian (uterine) tubes, 1040*f*, **1042**, 1043*f*
   embryologic/fetal development of, 1061*f*
   fertilization in, 1042, 1076*f*
   inflammation of (salpingitis), **1066**
   resection of (tubal ligation), 1096*b*
Fallot, tetralogy of, 689, 689*f*
False labor, **1091**
False pelvis, **235**
False (vertebrochondral) ribs, **224**, 224*f*
False vocal cords (vestibular folds), 808*f*, 810*f*, **811**
Falx cerebelli, **461**, 461*f*
Falx cerebri, 460*f*, **461**, 461*f*
Familial hypercholesterolemia, **955**
Far point of vision, **558**
Farsightedness (hyperopia), **559**
   development/aging and, 588
FAS. *See* Fetal alcohol syndrome
Fascia(e), 129
   lata, 363*t*
   lumbar, 367*f*
   renal, **961**, 962*f*
   spermatic, external and internal, 1026*f*
   superficial (hypodermis), **149**–150, 149*f*
      development of, 165
Fascicle(s), **277**, 279*t*, **491**
   muscle, **277**, 278*f*, 279*t*
      arrangement of, 322–323, 322*f*
      naming muscles and, 321
   nerve, **491**, 492*f*
Fasciculus cuneatus, **471**, 471*f*, 472*f*, 473*t*
Fasciculus gracilis, **471**, 471*f*, 472*f*, 473*t*
Fas protein, sunburn and, 162
Fas receptor, **792**
Fast fibers, **302**, 302*t*
Fast glycolytic fibers, **302**, 302*f*, 302*t*, 303, 303*f*
Fasting (postabsorptive) state, **936**, 938–941, 939*f*, 940*f*
Fast motility, 581
Fast Na⁺ channels, in cardiac muscle contraction, **674**

Fast oxidative fibers, **302**, 302*t*, 303, 303*f*
Fat(s)/lipid(s), 8, **43**–47, 45*t*, 46*f*, 912–914, 913*t*
   absorption of, 896*f*, 899–900, 899*f*
   in atherosclerosis, 702*b*
   dietary, 912–914, 913*t*
      substitutes for, 914
   digestion of, 896*f*, 897, 899*f*
      bile salts in, 884, 896*f*, 897, 899*f*
   interconversion of, 936*f*
   metabolism of, 920*f*, 930–932, 931*f*, 932*f*, 934*t*
      glycerol/fatty acid oxidation in, 931, 931*f*, 934*t*
      lipogenesis and lipolysis, 931–932, 932*f*, 934*t*, 939–940, 939*f*
      liver in, 942*f*
      thyroid hormone affecting, 612*t*
   as neurotransmitters, **418***t*, 419
   neutral (triglycerides), **45**–47, 45*t*, 46*f*, 897, 912
   obesity and, 948*b*
   saturated and unsaturated, 46–47, 912
   storage of in bone, 176
   supply of (fat pool), 935*f*, **936**, 936*f*
   transport of, 943, 943*f*
Fat (adipose) cells, 125*f*, 126, 127, 128*f*, 134*t*. *See also* Fat (adipose) tissue
Fat pool, 935*f*, **936**, 936*f*
Fat-soluble vitamins, 45*t*, 897, 900, **916**, 917*t*
Fat substitutes, 914
Fat (adipose) tissue, **127**–129, 128*f*, 134*t*
   autonomic innervation/effects and, 538*t*
   hormones produced by, 624, 625*t*
   lipid transport to, 943
   lipolysis in, 939–940, 939*f*
   metabolic fuel used by, 935*t*
Fatty acids, 45, 46*f*, **897**, 899*f*, 920*f*
   essential, 912, 913*t*
   in food intake regulation, 946, 946*f*
   omega-3, **47**, 912, 944
   oxidation of, 931, 931*f*, 934*t*
Fatty pads, **252**
Fatty streak, 702*b*
Fauces, **858**
   isthmus of, 808*f*, **809**
Fe. *See* Iron
Feature abstraction, **490**
Feces, 890, 894
   expulsion of in defecation, 853*f*, **854**, 888*t*, 894–895, 894*f*
Fed (absorptive) state, **936**, 936–938, 937*f*, 938*f*
Feedback. *See also* Negative feedback; Positive feedback
   in homeostasis, 9–11, 9*f*, 10*f*, 11*f*
Feet. *See* Foot
Female(s)
   pelvis in, 235–237, 236*t*
   puberty in, 1063
   urethra in, 987, 987*f*, 988
Female pronucleus, **1073**, 1075*f*

Female reproductive system, 7*f*. *See also specific organ or structure*
   anatomy of, 1040–1049, 1040*f*
   embryologic/fetal development of, 1061*f*
   functions/physiology of, 7*f*, 1049–1058, 1050*f*, 1051*f*, 1053*f*, 1055*f*, 1057*f*
   lactation and, **1093**–1094, 1094*f*
   mammary glands (breasts) and, **156**, 1047–1049, 1047*f*
   parturition (birth) and, **1090**–1092, 1091*f*, 1092*f*
   pregnancy and, **1072**, 1089–1090, 1089*f*
Female sex hormones. *See also* Estrogen(s); Progesterone
   in sodium regulation, 1005
Female sexual response, **1058**
Femoral artery, 725*f*, 734*f*, **734***t*, 735*f*
   deep (deep artery of thigh), **734***t*, 735*f*
   medial and lateral circumflex, 734*f*, **734***t*, 735*f*
   pulse at, 712*f*
Femoral cutaneous nerve
   lateral, 508*f*, 508*t*
   posterior, 509*f*, 510*t*
Femoral nerve, **507**, 508*f*, 508*t*
Femoral vein, 737*f*, 744*f*, **744***t*
Femoropatellar joint, 255*t*, **262**, 263. *See also* Knee joint
Femur, 199*f*, **237**, 238*f*, 242*t*
   in hip fracture, 191
   in hip joint, 267, 267*f*
   in knee joint, 262, 262*f*
   ligament of head of (ligamentum teres), 237, **267**, 267*f*
Fenestrated capillaries, **699**, 699*f*
Fenestrations (capillary pores), 699, 699*f*
   glomerular, 964, 965*f*, 969, 969–970*f*
Fen-phen, for weight loss, 949*b*
Ferritin, **640**, **900**
   erythropoiesis and, **640**, 641*f*
Fertilization (conception), 1025, **1072**–1073, 1072*f*, 1074*f*, 1075*f*, 1076*f*. *See also* Zygote
   in vitro, 1095
   random, 1105
   in uterine tube, 1042, 1076*f*
Fetal alcohol syndrome (FAS), 1085
Fetal circulation, 1084–1085, 1086*f*
   changes in at birth, 1086*f*, 1093
Fetal fibronectin, 1091
Fetal heart rate, 686–687
Fetal hemoglobin (hemoglobin F), 643, **657**
Fetal period, 1072, 1087–1089, 1087*f*, 1088*t*
Fetal respiration, 843
Fetal testing, 1110, 1111*f*
Fetus, **1072**, 1072*f*
   development of, 1072, 1087–1089, 1087*f*, 1088*t*
FEV. *See* Forced expiratory volume
Fever, **775**, 954
   in body defense, 772*t*, **775**
   heart rate and, 687
   metabolic rate and, 947

Fever blisters (cold sores), 168
Fiber (dietary), 912, 913*t*
Fibers
   connective tissue, 124–125
   muscle. *See* Muscle cells/fibers
Fibrillation, cardiac, **679**
Fibrils (myofibrils), **278**, 279*t*
   cardiac muscle, 309*t*, 673
   skeletal muscle, **278**–282, 279*t*, 280*f*, 309*t*
Fibrin, 650*f*, **651**
Fibrin mesh (blood clot), 139, 140*f*, 650, 650*f*, 651–652, 652*f*. *See also* Clotting
   factors limiting growth of, 652–653
   factors preventing undesirable formation of, 653
Fibrinogen, 636*t*, 650, 650*f*, **651**, 651*t*
Fibrinolysis, **652**
Fibrin stabilizing factor (FSF), 651*t*, **652**
Fibroblasts, **125**, 125*f*, 126, 134*t*
   in tissue repair, 140, 140*f*
Fibrocartilage, 132*f*, **133**, 134*t*, **173**, 174*f*, 251
   skeletal, **173**, 174*f*
   in symphyses, 250*f*, 251
Fibrocartilaginous callus, in bone repair, **188**–189, 189*f*
Fibrocytes, 134*t*
Fibromyositis (fibromyalgia), **316**
Fibronectin
   fetal, 1091
   in ground substance, 124
Fibrosis, 139, 140, 140*f*, 141
   pulmonary, 824
Fibrous (F) actin, 281
Fibrous capsule, **251**, **961**
   of joint, **251**, 251*f*
   of kidney, **961**, 962*f*
   of multicellular exocrine gland, 122
Fibrous (dense) connective tissue, **126**, **129**–131, 129–130*f*, 134*t*
Fibrous joints, 249, **249**–250, 249*f*, 252*t*
Fibrous layer, **551**
   of eye, 551
   of periosteum, 177
Fibrous pericardium, **663**, 663*f*
Fibrous (atherosclerotic) plaques, 702*b*
Fibrous (structural) proteins, **50**, 51*t*
Fibrous skeleton, of heart, **664**, 671*f*
Fibula, 199*f*, **238**–240, 239*f*, 242*t*
   in knee joint, 262–263*f*
   Pott's fracture of, 239*f*, 240
Fibular (peroneal) artery, 734*f*, 735*f*
Fibular collateral ligament, 262–263*f*, **263**
Fibularis (peroneus) brevis muscle, 372*f*, **373***t*, 374–375*f*, 380*t*
Fibularis (peroneus) longus muscle, 326*f*, 327*f*, 372*f*, **373***t*, 374–375*f*, 380*t*
Fibularis (peroneus) tertius muscle, **370***t*, 371*f*, 372*f*, 380*t*
Fibular (peroneal) muscles, **370***t*. *See also specific muscle*

Fibular (peroneal) nerve
common, 509, 509f, **510**, 510t
injuries of, 510
deep, 509f
superficial, 509f
leg muscles supplied by, 373t
Fibular notch, **238**
Fibular (peroneal) retinacula, **370**t
Fibular (peroneal) vein, 744f, **744**t
"Fight-or-flight" response
adrenal medulla in, 619
autonomic nervous system in, 528, 537
Filaments (muscle cell/myofilaments), **136**, 279t, **281**
in skeletal muscle, 279t, 280f, **281**–282, 282f
Filaments (olfactory nerve), 494f, **495**t, 569f, **570**
Filiform papillae, **859**, 860f
Filling in, 553
Filopodia, 424
Filtrate, **964**, 970
Filtration, 68
in capillaries, 718
glomerular, **970**–974, 971f, 973f
aging affecting, 991
Filtration membrane, **969**, 970, 969–970f
Filtration slits, **966**, 969–970f
Filum terminale, 467f, **468**
Fimbriae, 1040f, **1042**, 1043f
Finger(s), **233**
bones of (phalanges), 199f, 231f, 232t, **233**
carpometacarpal joint of, 254t
joints of (interphalangeal joints), 254t
muscles controlling movement of, 354t, 356t, 357f, 358t, 359f, 360–362t, 361f
Fingerprints, 152, 154f
First breath, after birth, 1093
First-class lever, **324**, 325f
First-degree burns, **164**, 164f
First intention, healing by, **144**
First law of thermodynamics, 944
First messenger, in hormone mechanism of action, **597**, 597f
First-order neurons, in ascending pathways, **471**, 472f
First polar body, **1049**, 1050f
First (dilation) stage of labor, **1091**, 1092f
Fission, mitochondrial, 83
Fissure (bone marking), 178t
Fissure(s), **433**
cerebral, **433**, 434f
oblique and horizontal, of lung, 815, 817f
Fixation, tissue, for microscopy, **115**
Fixator (muscle), **321**
Fixed (metabolic) acids, **1011**
Fixed macrophages, 768
Flaccid paralysis, spinal cord damage causing, **476**
Flagella, **90**, 95t
Flat bones, **175**, 175f, 179, 179f
"Flat feet," 241
Flavin adenine dinucleotide (FAD), **921**

Flavins, **926**
Fleshy (direct) muscle attachments, **277**–278
Flexion (body movement), **255**, 256f, 257f
of upper limb, 358t, 359f
of lower limb, 380t, 381f
Flexor accessorius (quadratus plantae) muscle, 376t, 377f
Flexor carpi radialis muscle, 326f, **354**t, 355f, 358t
Flexor carpi ulnaris muscle, 327f, **354**t, 355f, 358t
Flexor digiti minimi brevis muscle
of foot, 378t, 379f
of hand, 360t, 361f
Flexor digitorum brevis muscle, **376**t, 377f
Flexor digitorum longus muscle, **373**t, 375f, 380t
Flexor digitorum profundus muscle, 355f, **355**t, 358t
Flexor digitorum superficialis muscle, 355f, **355**t, 358t
Flexor hallucis brevis muscle, **378**t, 379f
Flexor hallucis longus muscle, 372f, **373**t, 375f, 380t
Flexor muscles
of forearm, 351–352f, 353t, 359f
of thigh, 363t
Flexor pollicis brevis muscle, **360**t, 361f
Flexor pollicis longus muscle, 355f, **355**t, 358t
Flexor (withdrawal) reflex, 5, 10, **518**–519, 519f
Flexor retinacula, **354**t, **370**t
of forearm, **354**t, 355f
of leg, **370**t
Flexure lines, **153**
Flexures, midbrain and cervical, 431, 432f
Floating (vertebral) ribs, 224, 224f
Flocculonodular lobe, **450**, 451f
Floor
of nasal cavity, 212
of orbit, 212f
Flora (bacterial), intestinal, **893**
Fluid(s), body. See Body fluids
Fluid balance, 998–1002, 999f, 1000f, 1001f. See also Water balance
developmental aspects of, 1015
sodium in, 1002–1004
regulation and, 1004–1006, 1004f, 1005f, 1007f
Fluid compartments, **996**, 996f
fluid movement among, 998, 998f
Fluid mosaic model, **63**–66, 65f, 66f
Fluid movements, capillary, 717–719, 719f
Fluid-phase endocytosis (pinocytosis), **76**, 77t, 78f
Fluorine, 919t
fMRI. See Functional MRI
Foam cells, in atherosclerosis, 702b
Focal point, **557**, 558f
Focusing (light on retina), 557–559, 558f, 560f
Folacin. See Folic acid/folacin

Folding, embryo, 1083–1084, 1083f
Folia, cerebellar, **450**, 451f
Foliate papillae, **571**, 572f, **859**, 860f
Folic acid/folacin (vitamin B₉), 916t
during pregnancy, 1090
ultraviolet radiation affecting, 154
Follicle(s), **608**
hair, 149f, **157**–158, 158f
lymphoid, **756**, 757f
aggregated (Peyer's patches), 758f, **760**–761, 761f, **880**
in small intestine, **880**
ovarian, 1041f, **1042**, 1050f
development of in ovary, 1050f, 1051f
dominant, 1052
primary, 1041f, **1042**, 1050f, 1051f, 1052
primordial, **1042**, 1049, 1050f, 1051f
secondary, **1042**, 1050f, 1051f, 1052
late, 1041f, **1042**, 1051f, 1052
vesicular (Graafian/tertiary), 1041f, **1042**, 1050f, 1051f, 1052
thyroid, **608**, 609f
Follicle cells, **1042**
ovarian, **1042**, 1050f
thyroid, 608, 609f
Follicle retention cysts, 1066
Follicle-stimulating hormone (FSH), 602f, **605**, 606t, **1038**
in female reproductive function
ovarian cycle, 1053f, 1054, 1055f
uterine (menstrual) cycle, 1055f
in male reproductive function, **1038**, 1039, 1039f
Follicular phase of ovarian cycle, 1050, **1050**–1052, 1051f, 1055f
Fontanelles, **242**, 243f
Food. See also Nutrient(s); Nutrition
absorption of in digestive system, **852**, 853f, 854, 898–901. See also Absorption
digestion/breakdown of, 5, 7f, **852**, 853–854, 853f, 888t. See also Digestion
ingestion/intake of, **853**, 853f, 888t
regulation of, 444, 945–947, 946f
propulsion of through digestive system, **853**, 853f, 888t. See also Peristalsis
Food guide pyramids, 911, 911f
Food-induced thermogenesis, **949**
Foot
arches of, 241, 241f
muscles supporting, 376–378t, 377f, 379f
bones of, 240–241, 240f, 241f, 242t
dorsal venous arch of, 737f, 744f, **744**t
intrinsic muscles of/muscles acting on, 376–378t, 377f, 379f, 380t, 381f

Footdrop, 510
Foot processes, **966**, 969–970f
Foot proteins, 284
Foramen (bone marking), 178t
Foramen lacerum, 205f, 206f, **207**
Foramen magnum, **201**, 205f, 206f, **214**t
Foramen of Monro (interventricular foramen), **432**, 433f
Foramen ovale (heart), 664, **688**, 688f, **1085**, 1086f
closure of, 1086f, 1093
Foramen ovale (skull), 205f, 206f, **208**, 208f, **214**t
Foramen rotundum, 206f, **208**, 208f, **214**t
Foramen spinosum, 205f, 206f, **208**, 208f, **214**t
Forced convection, heat loss by, 951
Forced expiration, 822
Forced expiratory volume, **826**
Forced (deep) inspiration, 821–822
Forced vital capacity, **825**–826
Forearm
bones of, 228–231, 230f, 232t
muscles of/muscles controlling movement of, 326f, 327f, 351–352f, 353t, 354–357t, 355f, 357f, 358t, 359f
Forebrain (prosencephalon), **430**, 431f
Foregut, 1083f, 1084
Forehead, 200
Foreskin (prepuce), 1025f, **1028**, 1029f
Formed elements of blood, 635, 635f, **637**–649, 637f, 644f, 645t. See also Blood cells
Fornix, **452**
limbic system, 436f, **452**, 452f
vaginal, 1040f, **1045**
Fosamax. See Alendronate
Fossa(e) (bone marking), 178t
cranial, 200, 201f
Fossa ovalis, **664**, 666f, 667f, 1086f, **1093**
Fourchette, 1046, 1046f
Fourth ventricle, 431f, **432**–433, 433f
Fovea capitis, **237**, 238f
Fovea centralis, 552f, **553**
Foveal (hard) focus, 553
Fractures, **188**, 190t
in osteoporosis, 190t, 191
pathologic, **195**
repair of, 188–189, 189f
Frank-Starling law of heart, **684**
Fraternal twins, 1052
FRC. See Functional residual capacity
Freckles, 154
Free (naked) nerve endings, 152, 161, **486**, 487t
Free edge of nail, 160, 160f
Free fatty acids, 897, 899f
Free macrophages, 768
Free radicals, **87**
in aging, 108
Free ribosomes, 84
Frenulum
labial, **858**, 859f
lingual, **859**, 859f

Frequency (sound wave), **579–580**, 579f
Frequency (urinary), infection and, 988
Friction ridges, **152**, 154f
Friction rub, pericardial, 663
Frontal belly, of epicranius, 326f, **329t**, 331f
Frontal bone, **200**, 202f, 203–204f, 206f, 214t
in newborn, 243f
Frontal eye field, 436f, **437**
Frontal lobe, **433**, 434f, 435f
Frontal (coronal) plane/section, **14**, 15f
Frontal processes, **210**, 210f, 215t
Frontal sinuses, **200**, 201f, 203f, 204f, 216f
Frontonasal suture, 200, 202f
Frostbite, 953
Fructose, 43, 44f, 895, 896f
FSF. *See* Fibrin stabilizing factor
FSH. *See* Follicle-stimulating hormone
Fulcrum, in lever system, 323, 323f, 324f, 325f
Full-thickness burns, 164, 164f
Functional brain disorders, **479**
Functional brain systems, 449t, 451–453, 452f
Functional groups, 42
Functional layer (stratum functionalis) of endometrium, **1044**, 1045f
Functional MRI (fMRI), **19b**
Functional (globular) proteins, 49f, **50**, 51t
denaturation of, 50
Functional residual capacity, **824**, 825f
Functional syncytium, cardiac muscle as, **673**
Fundus
of eye, 553, 555f
of stomach, 867, 868f
of uterus, 1043, 1043f
Fungiform papillae, **571**, 572f, **859**, 860f
Funiculi (columns), white, 469f, **470**, 471f
Furosemide, 982
Fused (complete) tetanus, 294f, **295**
Fusiform muscles, **322**, 322f
Fusion inhibitors, for AIDS, 797
FVC. *See* Forced vital capacity

G₀ phase, **96**, 100
G₁ (gap 1), **95–96**, 96f, 98f
G₁ (gap 1) checkpoint (restriction point), 96f, 100
G₂ (gap 2), 96, 96f, 98f
GABA. *See* γ-Aminobutyric acid
G (globular) actin, 281
GAGs. *See* Glycosaminoglycans
Galactose, 43, 44f, 895, 896f
absorption of, 899
Galactosemia, 954
Gallbladder, 852f, 878f, 882f, **885**, 888t
autonomic innervation/effects and, 528f, 529f, 533f, 538t
homeostatic imbalance and, 904

Gallstones, **885**
Gamete intrafallopian transfer (GIFT), 1096
Gametes, **1024**, 1025. *See also* Ova; Sperm
meiosis in formation of, 1033, 1034f, 1035f, 1049, 1050f
Gamma (γ)-aminobutyric acid (GABA), 417t, **418**
Gamma (γ) efferent fibers, **515**, 515f
Gamma globulin, 636t, **783**. *See also* Antibodies
passive immunity and, 782, 782f
Gamma (γ) interferon, 773, 790t, 791
Gamma (γ) rays, 28
Ganglia, **390**, **491**. *See also specific type*
autonomic, 526–527, 527f
in parasympathetic versus sympathetic nervous system, 534t
cranial sensory, **494**
Ganglion cells, retinal, 553, 554f, 567
Ganglionic neuron, **526**
Gap 1 (G₁), **95–96**, 96f, 98f
Gap 1 (G₁) checkpoint (restriction point), 96f, 100
Gap 2 (G₂), 96, 96f, 98f
Gap junction(s), 67, 67f
in cardiac muscle, 310t, 673, 674f
in smooth muscle, 307, 310t
Gardasil vaccine, 1044
Gases, 24
basic properties of, 827–828
exchanges of among fluid compartments, 998, 998f
as neurotransmitters, **418t**, 419
partial pressures of, 827, 827t
Gas exchange, 827–830, 827t, 828f, 829f. *See also* Respiratory gases
internal respiration and, 805, 828f, 830
pulmonary (external respiration), 805, 815, 816f, 828–830, 828f, 829f
Gas flow. resistance to, 822–823, 823f
asthma and, 823
Gas (air) movements, nonrespiratory, 826, 826t
Gas transport, 637, 638, 717, 718f, **805**, 830–834, 831f, 832f, 833f
Gastric accommodation, **874**
Gastric arteries
left, 730f, 731f, **731t**
right, 730f, 731f, **731t**
Gastric contractile activity, 874–875
Gastric emptying, 876, 877f
Gastric glands, 869f, **870**
Gastric inhibitory peptide (GIP/glucose-dependent insulinotropic peptide), 625t, 875t
Gastric juice, **870**
in body defense, 772t
regulation of secretion of, 872–873, 872f, 874f
Gastric motility, 874–876, 876f
Gastric phase, of gastric secretion, 872f, **873**, 874f
Gastric pits, 869f, **870**

Gastric ulcers, 870–871, 871f
Gastric vein, 743f
Gastrin, 625t, **870**, 873, 875t, 889t, 890
intestinal (enteric), 625t, **873**, 875t
Gastritis, 870
Gastrocnemius muscle, 326f, 327f, 372f, **373t**, 374–375f, 380t
Gastrocolic reflex, **894**
Gastroduodenal artery, 730f, 731f, **731t**
Gastroenteritis, **904**
Gastroepiploic artery
left, 730f, 731f, **731t**
right, 730f, 731f, **731t**
Gastroepiploic vein, right, 743f
Gastroesophageal reflux disease (GERD), 864–865
Gastroesophageal (cardiac) sphincter, **864**
Gastroileal reflex, **890**
Gastrointestinal (GI) tract (alimentary canal), **852**, 852f. *See also specific structure and* Digestive system
development of, 901–904, 901f
endocrine (enteroendocrine) cells in, 624, 869f, **870**
enteric nervous system of, 534, 854, 855f, **857–858**, 857f
histology of, 856–857, 857f
hormones produced by, 624, 625t
neural signals from, food intake regulation and, 945–946, 946f
pregnancy and, 1090
thyroid hormone affecting, 612t
Gastrula, **1079**
Gastrulation, **1081–1083**, 1081f, 1082f
Gated channels, 69, 81, **395**, 396f. *See also specific type*
G cells, **873**
GDP (guanosine diphosphate), 597, 597f
Gemellus muscles, 368f, **368t**, 380t
Gender, genetic, determination of, 1059–1060
Gene(s), 53, **100**, 1101. *See also* Heredity
activation of, in hormone mechanism of action, 596, 599f
carcinogenesis and, 142b, 143f
expression of
environmental factors in, 1107–1108
regulation of, 1108–1109
linked, **1104**
obesity and, 948b
pairs of (alleles), **1102–1103**
recombination of, 1104, 1104f
Gene therapy, 1110
for muscular dystrophy, 312
Genetic code, **103**, 103f

Genetic counseling, 1109–1110, 1110f
Genetic disorders
dominant, 1106
recessive, 1106
Genetic recombination, 1104, 1104f
Genetics, **1101–1102**. *See also* Inheritance
vocabulary of, 1102–1103, 1102f
Genetic screening, 1109–1110, 1110f, 1111f
Genetic sex, determination of, 1059–1060
Genetic theory of aging, 108–109
Genetic variation, sexual sources of, 1103–1105, 1103f, 1104f
Geniculate ganglion, 498t
Geniculate nuclei
lateral, 442, 444f, **566**
in visual pathway/processing, 442, **566**, 567f, 568
medial, 442, 444f, **582**
in auditory pathway, 442, **582**, 582f
Genioglossus muscle, 332t, 333f
Geniohyoid muscle, **334t**, 335f
Genital(s)/genitalia
autonomic innervation/effects and, 528f, 529f, 533f, 537–538, 538t
embryologic/fetal development of, 1060, 1062f
female
internal, **1040**, 1040f
external, **1041**, 1046–1047, 1046f
male, external, 1025–1026, 1025f, 1026f, **1028**, 1029f
Genital herpes, 1059
Genital tubercle, **1060**, 1062f
Genital warts, 1059
Genitofemoral nerve, 508f, 508t
Genome, 53, **1102**. *See also* DNA; Gene(s); Heredity
Genomic imprinting, **1109**
Genotype, **1103**
GERD. *See* Gastroesophageal reflux disease
Germ cells, primordial, **1060**
Germinal centers, **756**, 757f
Germinal epithelium, of ovary, 1041, 1041f
Germ layers
differentiation of, 1083–1087, 1083f, 1084f, 1086f
formation of, 1081–1083, 1081f, 1082f
primary, **141**, 141f, 1079, 1079f, **1081**
Gestation period, **1072**
GFR. *See* Glomerular filtration rate
GH. *See* Growth hormone
GHIH. *See* Growth hormone–inhibiting hormone
Ghr. *See* Ghrelin
Ghrelin, in food intake regulation, 946, 946f
GHRH. *See* Growth hormone–releasing hormone
GIFT. *See* Gamete intrafallopian transfer

Gigantism, 185, **604**
Gingiva (gum), 859f, **863**, 863f
Gingival disease, 864
Gingival sulcus, 863
Gingivitis, **864**
GIP. See Gastric inhibitory peptide; Glucose-dependent insulinotropic peptide
GI tract. See Gastrointestinal (GI) tract
Glabella, **200**, 202f
Gland(s)/glandular epithelia, 115, **121–124**, 122f, 123f. See also specific type
    autonomic innervation/effects and, 538t
    cutaneous, 155–157, 156f
    ductless (endocrine), 121. See also Endocrine system/glands
    exocrine, **121–124**, 122f, 123f. See also Exocrine glands
Glans clitoris (glans of clitoris), **1046**, 1046f
    embryologic/fetal development of, 1062f
Glans penis, 1025f, **1028**, 1029f
    embryologic/fetal development of, 1062f
Glassy membrane, 157, 158f
Glaucoma, **556**
Gleevec. See Imatinib
Glenohumeral (shoulder) joint, 254t, **264–266**, 265f
    muscles crossing/acting on, 326f, 327f, 350–352t, 351–352f, 358t, 359f
Glenohumeral ligaments, **264**, 265f
Glenoid cavity, 226, 227f, **228**
Glenoid labrum, **264**, 265f
Glial cells (neuroglia), **388–389**, 388f
Gliding body movements, **255**, 256f
    at temporomandibular joint, 269
Globin, **638**
Globular (G) actin, 281
Globular (functional) proteins, 49f, **50**, 51t
    denaturation of, 50
Globulin(s), 636t
Globus pallidus, **441**, 442f
Glomerular (Bowman's) capsule, **964**, 965f, 967f
Glomerular filtration, **970–974**, 971f, 973f
Glomerular filtration rate, **971–972**
    aging affecting, 991
    regulation of, 972–974, 973f
Glomerular hydrostatic pressure, **971**, 971f
Glomerular mesangial cells, 969
Glomeruli (olfactory bulb), 569f, **570**
Glomerulonephritis, 797, **991**, 1002
Glomerulus (glomerular capillaries), **964**, 965f, 966f, 967f
Glossopharyngeal nerve (cranial nerve IX), 446–447f, 448, **493**, 494f, **500t**, 573
    in gustatory pathway, **573**, 573t
    injury/inflammation of, 500t
    parasympathetic fibers of, 529–530, 529f
Glottis, 810f, **811**, 811f
    sphincter function of, 812

GLP-1. See Glucagon-like peptide 1
Glucagon, 621, **621–622**, 621f, 941t, **940**
    in food intake regulation, 946, 946f
    metabolism and, 621–622, 621f, 622, 938, 938f, **940**, 940f, 941t
    pancreatic islets producing, 620f, 621, 886
    in postabsorptive state regulation, 940, 940f
Glucagon-like peptide 1 (GLP-1), 625t
Glucoamylase, 896f, **897**
Glucocorticoids, **616–618**, 617t, **1005**
    protein synthesis/growth and, 915
    in sodium regulation, 1005–1006
Gluconeogenesis, 617, 621, **930**, 934t, 939
Glucose, 43, 44f, 895, 896f, **912**
    absorption of, 899
    in absorptive state, 936, 937f
    aging affecting levels of, 626
    in ATP formation, 37, 43, 56
    conservation of, 940
    in diabetes mellitus, 622, 623t, 626b, 938
    in food intake regulation, 946, 946f
    insulin/glucagon in regulation of, 621–622, 621f, 622, 938, 938f, 940, 940f, 941t
    metabolism of, 37, 43, 920f, 922–930, 922f, 934t, 941t
        aging and, 955
        gluconeogenesis in, 930, 934t, 939
        glycogenesis and glycogenolysis in, 929–930, 930f, 934t, 938–939, 939f
        liver in, 938, 939–940, 939f, 942t
        oxidation in, 923–929, 923f, 925f, 926f, 927f, 928f, 929f, 934t
    molecular weight of, 30
    in postabsorptive state, 938–941, 939f, 940f
    sources of, 938–940, 939f
    transport of, 938
    in urine, 622, 623t, 975, 985t
Glucose-1-phosphate, 923, 930f
Glucose-6-phosphatase, 930, 930f
Glucose-6-phosphate, 923, 930, 930f
Glucose-dependent insulinotropic peptide (gastric inhibitory peptide/GIP), 625t, 875t
Glucose sparing, **940**
Glucose transporters, 938
    saturation of, urinary excretion of glucose and, 975
Glutamate/glutamic acid, 417t, **418**, 933, 933f
    in cerebrovascular accident, 465
    cocaine abuse and, 415b
    as neurotransmitter, 417t, **418**
    in pain perception, 490
Glutamine, renal metabolism of, ammonium ion excretion and, 1012, 1013f

Gluteal arteries, superior and inferior, 734f, **734t**, 735f
Gluteal lines, posterior/anterior/inferior, 234f, **235**
Gluteal nerves, superior/inferior, 509f, **510**, 510t
Gluteal surface, of ilium, **235**
Gluteal tuberosity, **237**, 238f
Gluten-sensitive enteropathy (celiac disease), 901
Gluteus maximus muscle, 327f, **363t**, **366t**, 367–368f, 380t
Gluteus medius muscle, 327f, **363t**, **366t**, 367–368f, 380t
Gluteus minimus muscle, **363t**, **366t**, 368f, 380t
Glyceraldehyde phosphate, 923, 923f, 931, 931f
Glycerol, 45, 46f, 920f
    as glucose source, 939–940, 939f
    oxidation of, 931, 931f
Glycine, 48f, 417t, **418**
Glycocalyx, **64**, 65f
    in cell–cell recognition, 64, 66f
Glycogen, 43, 44f, 895, 920f
    as glucose source, 938–939, 939f
Glycogenesis, **929–930**, 930f, 934t
Glycogenolysis, 621, 621f, **930**, 930f, 934t, 938–939, 939f
Glycogen phosphorylase, 930, 930f
Glycogen storage disease, 954
Glycogen synthase, 930, 930f
Glycolipids, **64**
    in plasma membrane, **64**, 65f
    in Tay-Sachs disease, 87
Glycolysis/glycolytic pathway, **298**, 919, 920f, 922, 922f, **923–924**, 923f, 929f, 934t
    muscle activity and, **298–299**, 298f, 299, 299f, 310t
Glycolytic fibers, **302**, 302t
    fast, **302**, 302f, 302t, 303, 303f
Glycoproteins, 65f
Glycosaminoglycans, in ground substance, 124
Glycosomes, **278**
Glycosuria, 622, 623t, 975, 985t
GN. See Glomerulonephritis
GnRH. See Gonadotropin-releasing hormone
Goblet cells, **121**, 122f
    in respiratory mucosa of nose, 807
    in small intestine, 878, 879f
Goiter, **611**, 611f
G_{olf}, 570
Golgi apparatus, 63f, **85–86**, 85f, 86f, 87f, 94t
Golgi tendon organ, **488**, 488t, 515, 515f, 518
Golgi tendon reflexes, 515, **518**
Gomphoses, 249, 249f, **250**, 863
Gonad(s), **623**, **1024**
    aging affecting, 626
    arteries of, 725f, 730f, **732t**
    descent of, 1062–1063
    differentiation of, 1060, 1061f
    female, **1040**. See also Ovaries
    hormones produced by, 623
    male, **1025**. See also Testes
    veins of, 736f, 742f, **742t**, 743f

Gonadal arteries, 725f, 730f, **732t**
Gonadal ridges, **1060**, 1061f
Gonadal veins, 736f, 742f, **742t**, 743f
Gonadocorticoids, 617t, **618**. See also Sex hormones
Gonadotrophs, **605**
Gonadotropin(s), **605**. See also Follicle-stimulating hormone; Luteinizing hormone
    in female reproductive function, 1053
        ovarian cycle, 1053f, 1054, 1055f
    human chorionic (hCG), **1077**, 1078f
    in male reproductive function, 1038, 1039, 1039f
Gonadotropin-releasing hormone (GnRH), **605**, **1038**
    in female reproductive function, 1052–1053, 1053f, 1054
    in male reproductive function, **1038**, 1039, 1039f
Gonorrhea, **1058**
    pelvic inflammatory disease and, **1042**, 1058
Gout/gouty arthritis, **271**
gp120/gp41 glycoprotein, HIV infection and, 796
G protein(s), 81, 82f, 420f, 421, **597**
    in hormone mechanism of action, **597**, 597t
G protein–linked (metabotropic) receptors, 81, 82f, **420f**, **421**
Graafian (vesicular/tertiary) follicles, 1041f, **1042**, 1050f, 1051f, 1052
Gracilis muscle, 326f, 364f, **365t**, 380t
Graded muscle responses, 293–296, **294**, 294f, 295f, 296f
Graded potentials, **398–399**, 399f, 408, **410–411t**
    action potentials compared with, 410–411t
    on dendrites and cell body, 390
    information transfer at chemical synapse and, 408, 409f
    in phototransduction, 564, 565f
    postsynaptic potentials as, 408, 411t
    sensory integration at receptor level and, 489
Gram molecular weight, 30
Grand mal (tonic-clonic) seizures, 454
Granular (juxtaglomerular/JG) cells, **968**, 968f
    renin release/blood pressure and, 968, 973f, 974
Granulation tissue, **139–140**, 140f
    in bone repair, 188–189, 189f
Granule cells, olfactory bulb, 570
Granulocyte-colony-stimulating factor (G-CSF), 646
Granulocytes, 643, **644–646**, 644f, 645t. See also specific type
Granulomas, infectious, 773
Granulosa cells, 1041f, **1042**, 1052
Granzymes, **792**, 793t, 795t
Graves' disease, **611**, 611f, 797
Gray commissure, **468**, 469f

Gray matter, **392**
of brain
brain stem, 432*f*, 445
cerebellar (cerebellar cortex), 431, 432*f*, 450, 451*f*
cerebral (cerebral cortex), 431, 432*f*, 434*f*, **435**–440, 435*f*, 436*f*, 438*f*, 449*t*. See also Cerebral cortex
periaqueductal, 446
development of, 431
of spinal cord, 432*f*, 468–470, 469*f*, 470*f*
Gray ramus communicans/rami communicantes, 531*f*, **532**
Great cardiac vein, 665*f*, 666*f*, 669*f*, **670**, 737*f*
Greater auricular nerve, 504*f*, 504*t*
Greater curvature of stomach, **868**, 868*f*
Greater omentum, **868**, 892*f*
Greater sciatic notch, 234*f*, **235**, 236*t*
Greater sphenoid wing, 202*f*, 203*f*, 204*f*, 205*f*, 206*f*, **207**, 208*f*
Greater trochanter, **237**, 238*f*
Greater tubercle, **228**, 229*f*
Greater vestibular (Bartholin's) glands, 1040*f*, **1046**, 1046*f*
Great saphenous vein, 737*f*, 744*f*, **744***t*
Great toe (hallux), **241**
Green cones, 562
Greenstick fracture, 190*t*
Gristle, 131. See also Hyaline cartilage
Groove (bone marking), 178*t*
Gross (macroscopic) anatomy, **2**
Ground substance, **124**, 125*f*
Group A fibers, **406**
Group B fibers, **406**
Group C fibers, **406**
Growth, **8**
cell division and, 8
Growth cone, **423**–424, 424*f*
Growth cycle(s), hair, 159
Growth factor(s), bone storage of, 176
Growth hormone (GH/somatotropin), 51*t*, 602*f*, **603**–605, 604*f*, **606***t*
bone growth and, 185
hyper-/hyposecretion of, 604–605
metabolism and, 941*t*
protein synthesis/growth and, 915
Growth hormone–inhibiting hormone (GHIH/somatostatin), 417*t*, 419, **603**, 604*f*
digestion/gastric secretion and, 870, 875*t*
Growth hormone–releasing hormone (GHRH), **603**, 604*f*
Growth (proliferation) zone (epiphyseal plate), 184, 184*f*
GTP (guanosine triphosphate), 597, 597*f*
Guanine (G), **53**, 54*f*
Guanosine diphosphate (GDP), 597, 597*f*
Guanosine triphosphate, (GTP), 597, 597*f*

Guanylyl cyclase, 419
Gubernaculum, **1062**, 1063
Gum (gingiva), 859*f*, **863**, 863*f*
Gum disease, 864
Gummas, syphilitic, 1058
Gustatory (taste) cells, **571**, 572*f*
activation of, 571
Gustatory (taste) cortex, 436*f*, **439**, 573, 573*f*
Gustatory hairs, **571**, 572*f*
Gustatory pathway, 573, 573*f*
Gustducin, 573
Gut. See also Gastrointestinal (GI) tract
primitive, 901, 1083*f*, 1084
Gut brain, **854**, 855*f*
Gut-brain peptides, **419**
Gynecology, **1066**
Gynecomastia, **1066**
Gyri (gyrus), **433**, 434*f*

H. See Hydrogen
Hageman factor, 651*t*
Hair(s), **157**–159, 158*f*
aging affecting, 165
thinning/loss of, 159
types and growth of, 159
Hair bulb, **157**, 158*f*
Hair bulge, 157
Hair cells, 578*f*, 580–582, 582*f*, **584**
in equilibrium, **584**, 584*f*, 585, 586*f*
in hearing, excitation of, 580–582, 582*f*
inner and outer, 578*f*, **580**
in maculae, **584**, 584*f*
Hair follicle(s), 149*f*, **157**–158, 158*f*
Hair follicle receptor (root hair plexus), 149*f*, **157**, 161, **486**, 487*t*
Hair loss, 159, 165
Hair matrix, **157**, 158*f*
Hair papilla, **157**, 158*f*
Hair root, 149*f*, **157**, 158*f*
Hair shaft, 149*f*, **157**, 158*f*
Haldane effect, **834**
Half-life, **599**
hormone, **599**
radioisotope, 28
Halitosis, 861
Hallucinations, olfactory, 573
Hallux (great toe), **241**
Hamate, **231**, 231*f*, 232*t*
Hammer (malleus), 215*t*, 575*f*, **576**, 576*f*
Hamstring muscles, 327*f*, **363***t*, 367*f*, **369***t*, 381*f*
Hamstring strain, **382**
Hand
bones of, 199*f*, 231–233, 231*f*, 232*t*
intrinsic muscles of/muscles controlling movement of, 354*t*, 356*t*, 357*t*, 358*t*, 359*f*, 360–362*t*, 361*f*
Handedness, 440
Haploid chromosomal number (*n*), **1032**, 1033
Hapten(s), **776**
Haptoglobin, 641

Hard (bony) callus, in bone repair, **189**, 189*f*
Hard (foveal) focus, 553
Hard keratin, 157, 160. See also Keratin
Hard palate, 205*f*, **806**, 808*f*, **858**, 859*f*
Hashimoto's thyroiditis, **800**
Hassall's (thymic) corpuscles, **759**, 760*f*
Haustra (haustrum), **890**, 891*f*
Haustral contractions, **893**
Haversian (central) canal, **179**, 181*f*
Haversian system (osteon), 133, **179**, 180*f*, 181*f*
Hb. See Hemoglobin
HbF. See Fetal hemoglobin
HbO₂. See Oxyhemoglobin
HbS. See Hemoglobin S
hCG. See Human chorionic gonadotropin
HCM. See Hypertrophic cardiomyopathy
HCO₃. See Bicarbonate/bicarbonate ion
hCS. See Human chorionic somatomammotropin
hCT. See Human chorionic thyrotropin
HDLs. See High-density lipoproteins
He. See Helium
Head. See also Skull
arteries supplying, 725*f*, 726–727*f*, 726–727*t*
muscles of/muscles controlling movement of, 326*f*, 336*t*, 337*f*
facial expression and, 329–331*t*, 331*f*
mastication/tongue control and, 332–333*t*, 333*f*
sympathetic pathways to, 532, 533*f*
trauma to, brain injury and, 464
veins of, 736*f*, 737*f*, 738–739*f*, 738*t*
Headache, sinus, 809
Head (bone marking), 178*t*
of femur, **237**, 238*f*
ligament of (ligamentum teres), 237, **267**, 267*f*
of fibula, **238**, 239*f*
of humerus, **228**, 229*f*
of metacarpals, 231*f*, **233**
of radius, 229*f*, **230**, 230*f*
of rib, 224, 225*f*
of ulna, **229**, 230*f*
Head of epididymis, 1028
Head injury, traumatic brain injury and, 464
Head of sperm, **1037**, 1037*f*
Healing, 139–141, 140*f*
by first and second intention, **144**
fracture, 188–189, 189*f*. See also Hearing. See also Ear
auditory pathway and, 582, 582*f*
auditory processing and, 582–583
basilar membrane resonance and, 580, 581*f*
developmental aspects of, 588–589

hair cell excitation and, 580–582, 582*f*
homeostatic imbalances of, 583
physiology of, 577–584
sound properties and, **577**–580, 579*f*
sound transmission to internal ear and, 580, 581*f*
Hearing loss, 583
loudness and, 580
Heart, 661–693, **662**. See also under Cardiac
age-related changes affecting, 689
anatomy of, 662–672, 662*f*, 665–667*f*
apex of, 662*f*, 665*f*, 666*f*
autonomic innervation/effects and, 528*f*, 529*f*, 533*f*, 537, 538*t*, 678*f*, 679, 685, 686*f*
blood flow through (pulmonary and systemic circuits), 668–669, 668*f*, 669*f*
blood supply of (coronary circulation), 669–670, 669*f*
blood volume in, 701*f*
chambers of, 664–668, 665–667*f*
conduction system of, **676**–679, 677*f*, 678*f*
congenital defects of, 688–689, 689*f*
coverings of, 663, 663*f*
developmental aspects of, 688–690, 688*f*, 689*f*
fibrous skeleton of, **664**, 671*f*
Frank-Starling law of, **684**
great vessels and, 664–668, 665–667*f*
hormones produced by, 616*f*, 624, 625*t*
muscle tissue of. See Cardiac muscle
perfusion of, 713, 713*f*, 717
physiology of, 676–687
cardiac output and, 682–685, 685*f*, 686*f*
electrical events and, 676–681, 676*f*, 677*f*, 678*f*, 679*f*, 680*f*, 681*f*
heart sounds and, 681, 681*f*
mechanical events (cardiac cycle) and, 682, 683*f*
size/location/orientation of, 662*f*
valves of, 667*f*, 670–672, 671*f*, 672*f*, 673*f*
aging and, 689
heart murmurs and, 681
wall of, 663–664, 663*f*, 664*f*
Heart attack (myocardial infarction), **670**
cardiac output and, **687**
Heart block, **679**
Heartburn, 864–865
pregnancy and, 1090
Heart failure, **687**
Heart murmurs, **681**
Heart palpitation, **690**
Heart rate
cardiac output and, 685–687, 686*f*, 706, 707*f*
fetal, 686–687
homeostatic imbalances and, 687

normal, 687
regulation of, 685–687, 686f, 707f
resting, 706
Heart sounds, **681**, 681f, 683f
Heart tube, 688, 688f
Heart valves, 667f, 670–672, 671f,
672f, 673f
aging and, 689
heart murmurs and, **681**
homeostatic imbalances and, 672
Heat. *See also* Body temperature
energy balance and, 944–945
loss of, 950–951, 950f, 951f,
952f, 953
insensible, **951**
muscles in generation of,
276–277, 300, 952f, 953
production of, 950f, 952–953, 952f
metabolic rate and, 947–950
Heat capacity, of water, 38
Heat cramps, 951
Heat exchange
blood in, 950
mechanisms of, 950–951, 951f
Heat exhaustion, 953
Heat-loss center, **951**, 952f, 953
Heat-loss mechanisms, 950–951,
950f, 951f, 952f, 953
Heat-promoting center, **951**, 952f, 953
Heat-promoting mechanisms,
952–953, 952f
Heat shock proteins (hsp), 51
in diabetes, 626b
Heat stroke, **953**
Heat therapy, in cancer treatment,
143b
Heat of vaporization, of water,
38, **951**
Heavy (H) chains, **783**, 783f
Heavy metals, 56
Heavy metal salts, skin penetrated
by, 161
Hedgehog protein, 943
Heimlich maneuver, **813**
Helicase, in DNA replication, 96, 97f
Helicobacter pylori, peptic ulcers and,
870–871, 871f
Helicotrema, **577**, 578f
Helium
atomic number of, 27
atomic structure of, 27, 27f
as chemically inert element, 31f
mass number of, 27
Helix, of auricle, **574**, 575f
Helper T cells, **786**, 787f, **791**–792,
791f, 794f, 795t
CD4 cell activation into, 786,
787f, 789, 791, 791f, 794f
cytotoxic T cell activation and,
791, 791f
HIV infection and, 796
vaccines and, 782
Hematocrit, **635**
erythropoietin affecting, 640
Hematology, **658**
Hematoma, 155, **188**, 658
in bone repair, 188, 189f
Hematopoiesis (hemopoiesis),
638–639, 639f
bone marrow as site of, 176, 179,
638–639, 657

Hematopoietic stem cells, **125**–126,
639, 639f, 646, 647f, 648f
Hematuria, 985t
Heme, **638**, 638f
Hemiazygos vein, 740f, 741f, **741**t
Hemiplegia, 464
Hemochromatosis, **658**, 905
Hemocytoblast, **639**, 639f, 646,
647f, 648f
Hemodialysis, **984**
Hemoglobin, 51t, **155**, 637, **638**,
638f, 831
abnormal, 642–643, 643f
in sickle-cell anemia, **642**,
642f, **1106**
as buffer, 1010
carbon dioxide transport in,
833–834
erythrocyte destruction and, 641
fetal, 643
low content of, 642
oxygen transport in, 637, 638,
805, 830–832, 831f, 832f
reduced (deoxyhemoglobin),
638, 831
skin color affected by, **155**
in urine, 985t
Hemoglobin F (fetal hemoglobin),
643, **657**
Hemoglobin S (HbS), 642, 642f, 1106
Hemoglobin saturation, 831–832,
831f, 832f
altitude affecting, 840
Hemoglobinuria, 985t
Hemolysis, Rh incompatibility
and, 655
Hemolytic anemia, 641
Hemolytic disease of newborn, **655**
Hemophilias (hemophilia A/B and
C), **654**
Hemopoiesis (hematopoiesis),
638–639, 639f
bone marrow as site of, 176, 179,
638–639, 657
Hemorrhagic anemia, 641
Hemorrhoidal veins, 893
varices of (hemorrhoids),
701, 893
Hemorrhoids, 701, 893
Hemosiderin, erythropoiesis and,
640, 641f
Hemostasis, **649**–654, 649f
disorders of, 653–654
Henle's loop, 965f, **966**, 967f, **983**f
absorptive capability of,
976–978, 977t
as countercurrent multiplier,
979–981, 980f
Henry's law, **827**–828
Heparin, **653**
in mast cells, 126
Hepatic artery, **881**, 882f
common, 730f, 731f, **731**t
Hepatic artery proper, 730f, **731**t
Hepatic ducts, 878f, 881
Hepatic (right colic) flexure,
890, 891f
Hepatic macrophages (Kupffer cells),
699, 768, **881**, 883f
Hepatic portal system, 721, 742f,
742t, 743f, 856

Hepatic portal vein, 737f, 742f, **742**t,
743f, **881**, 882f
Hepatic veins, 736f, 737f, 742f, **742**t,
743f, **882**f
Hepatitis, **884**
Hepatocyte(s), **881**, 883f
metabolic functions of, 941–944,
942t, 943f
Hepatopancreatic ampulla, **877**, 878f
Hepatopancreatic sphincter, **877**, 878f
Herceptin. *See* Trastuzumab
Heredity, 1101–1114. *See also*
Chromosome(s); Gene(s)
environmental factors in gene
expression and, 1107–1108
genetic
screening/counseling/therapy
and, 1109–1111, 1110f, 1111f
genetics vocabulary and,
1102–1103, 1102f
inheritance patterns and,
1105–1107, 1105f, 1106t,
1107f, 1108f
nontraditional inheritance and,
1108–1109
sexual sources of genetic variation and, 1103–1105,
1103f, 1104f
Hering-Breuer (inflation) reflex, **839**
Hermaphrodites, 1062
Hernia, **316**, **382**
hiatal, **865**
inguinal, **1066**
Herniated (prolapsed/slipped) disc,
218, 218f
aging and, 244
Herpes virus
cold sores (fever blisters) caused
by, 168
genital herpes caused by, **1059**
Herpes zoster (shingles), **425**
Hertz (Hz), 579
Heterogeneous mixture, 30
Heterozygous, **1103**
HHB. *See* Reduced hemoglobin
Hiatal hernia, **865**
Hiatus, esophageal, **864**
Hiccups, 826t
phrenic nerve irritation causing,
505
High blood pressure. *See*
Hypertension
High-density lipoproteins (HDLs),
702b, **943**, 943f
recommended blood levels
of, 943
High-energy phosphate bonds,
55, 55f
Higher mental functions. *See*
Cognition/cognitive function
Hilton's law, **511**
Hilum
lymph node, **757**, 757f
pulmonary, **815**, 817f
renal, **961**, 961f
splenic, 758, 759f
Hindbrain (rhombencephalon),
430, 431f
Hindgut, 1083f
Hinge joints, **259**, 260f
Hinge region (antibody), 783, 783f

Hip bones (coxal bones/os coxae),
233, 233–235, 233f, 234f, 242t
Hip dysplasia (congenital dislocation
of hip), 244
Hip fracture, in osteoporosis, 191
Hip (pelvic) girdle, 199f, **233**–237,
233f, 234f, 236t, 242t
Hip (coxal) joint, 235, 255t, 266–267,
267f
artificial/replacement, 261b
muscles crossing/acting on, 327f,
363–369t, 364f, 367–368f,
380t, 381f
Hippocampus, **439**, **452**
brain dysfunction and, 465
in memory, 458, 459f
Hirsutism, **159**, **627**
His bundle (atrioventricular bundle), **677**, 677f
Histamine, 416t, 418, 646, 772t,
769, **870**
in basophils, 646, 798, 798f
digestion/gastric secretion and,
870, 875t
in hydrochloric acid secretion
control, 873
in immediate hypersensitivity,
798, 798f
in inflammatory response, **769**
in mast cells, 126, **769**, 798, 798f
Histology, **2**, **114**
artifacts and, **115**
light and electron microscopy
in, 115
tissue preparation for, 114–115
Histones/histone proteins, **93**, 93f
in DNA replication, 96
epigenetic marks and, 1109
Histotoxic hypoxia, **832**
HIV (human immunodeficiency
virus), **796**, 1058
vaginal dendritic cells and, 1045
Hoarseness, 812
Hodgkin's disease, **761**, 796
Holocrine glands, **122**, 123f, 156
Holoenzyme, **52**
Homeostasis, **8**–11, 9f, 10f, 11f
control mechanisms and, 9–11,
9f, 10f, 11f
disturbances in (homeostatic imbalances), 11. *See also specific
type or organ/system affected*
Homeostatic relationships
of autonomic nervous system,
542b, 543b
of cardiovascular system, 5f,
746b, 747b
of digestive system, 5f, 902b, 903b
of endocrine system, 10,
628b, 629b
of integumentary system, 5f, 165,
166b, 167b
of lymphatic system, 762b, 763b
of muscular system, 314b, 315b
of reproductive system,
1064b, 1065b
of respiratory system, 5f,
844b, 845f
of skeletal system, 192b, 193b
of urinary system, 5f, 1018b, 1019b
Homogeneous mixture, 29

Homologous chromosomes (homologues), **1032**, 1033, 1102
Homozygous, **1103**
Hooke, Robert, 62
Horizontal canal, 576
Horizontal cells, in retina, 554*f*
Horizontal fissure, 815, 817*f*
Horizontal (transverse) plane/ section, 14, 15*f*
Horizontal plates, 205*f*, **211**, 213*f*
Hormonal stimuli, for hormone release, 600, 601*f*. See also Hormone(s)
Hormone(s), 51*t*, 81, **121**, 595, **596**–601. See also specific type
    absorptive state regulated by, 938, 938*f*
    anabolic, 312, 313*b*, 914–915
    blood pressure control and, 709–710, 709*t*, 710*f*
    chemistry of, 596
    in contraception, 1096*b*
    control of release of, 600, 601*f*
        hypothalamus in, 444
    developmental aspects of, 624–627
    in digestion, 875*t*
    food intake regulation and, 946, 946*f*
    half-life of, 599
    heart rate affected by, 686, 707*f*
    hyperglycemic, glucagon as, **940**, 940*f*, 941*t*
    hypoglycemic, insulin as, **938**, 938*f*, 941*t*
    inhibiting, **603**
    interaction of at target cells, 600
    male reproductive function regulation and, 1038–1040, 1039*f*
    mechanisms of action of, 596–598, 597*f*, 599*f*
    metabolism affected by, 938, 938*f*, 940, 940*f*, 941*t*
    non-endocrine tissues/organs producing, 624
    onset/duration of action of, 599
    in plasma, 636
    postabsorptive state regulated by, 940, 940*f*
    protein synthesis regulated by, 914–915
    releasing, **603**
    smooth muscle contraction regulated by, 308, 310*t*
    in sodium regulation, 1005–1006
    target cell specificity and, 598
    tropic, **603**
Hormone (estrogen) replacement therapy, 1063
    for osteoporosis, 191
Hormone response element, 598, 599*f*
Horner's syndrome, **544**
Horns, hyoid bone, 211, 211*f*
Horny (cornified) cells, 152
Horseshoe kidney, 990
Housemaid's knee, 270
HP$_c$. See Capillary hydrostatic pressure; Capsular hydrostatic pressure
HPg. See Glomerular hydrostatic pressure

HPG axis. See Hypothalamic-pituitary-gonadal axis
HP$_{if}$. See Interstitial fluid hydrostatic pressure
hPL. See Human placental lactogen
HPV. See Human papillomavirus
HRT. See Hormone (estrogen) replacement therapy
hsp. See Heat shock proteins
5-HT. See Serotonin
Human body. See also under Body
    levels of structural organization of, 3, 4*f*
    maintenance of life and, 4–8, 5*f*
    orientation to, 1–22
Human chorionic gonadotropin (hCG), **1077**, 1078*f*
Human chorionic somatomammotropin (hCS/human placental lactogen), 1078, **1090**
Human chorionic thyrotropin (hCT), 1078, **1090**
Human development, 1071–1100, 1072*f*. See also specific aspect
    assisted reproductive technology/reproductive cloning and, 1094–1097
    embryonic, 1072
        cleavage/blastocyst formation, **1075**–1076, 1076*f*
        extraembryonic membrane formation, **1080**, 1080*f*
        gastrulation/germ layer formation, **1081**–1083, 1081*f*, 1082*f*
        implantation, **1076**–1078, 1076*f*, 1077*f*
        organogenesis (germ layer differentiation), **1083**–1087, 1083*f*, 1084*f*, 1086*f*
        placentation, **1078**, 1079*f*, 1080*f*
    fertilization (egg to zygote), **1072**–1073, 1074*f*, 1075*f*
    fetal, 1072, 1087–1089, 1087*f*, 1088*t*
    infant adjustment to extrauterine life and, 1092–1093
    lactation and, **1093**–1094, 1094*f*
    parturition (birth) and, **1090**–1092, 1091*f*, 1092*f*
    pregnancy and, **1072**, 1089–1090, 1089*f*
Human gene therapy, 1110
    for muscular dystrophy, 312
Human Genome Project, 1102
Human herpes virus type 2, 1059
Human immunodeficiency virus (HIV), **796**, 1058
    vaginal dendritic cells and, 1045
Human papillomavirus
    cervical cancer and, 1044, 1059
    genital warts caused by, **1059**
    vaccine against, 1044
Human placental lactogen, 1078, **1090**
Humeral artery
    anterior circumflex, 728*f*, **728***t*, 729*f*
    posterior circumflex, 728*f*, **728***t*, 729*f*

Humerus, 199*f*, **228**, 229*f*, 232*t*
    muscles controlling movement of, 350–352*t*, 351–352*f*, 358*t*, 359*f*
    structure of, 176*f*
Humoral (antibody-mediated) immunity, **776**, 780–786, 781*f*, 782*f*, 794*f*. See also Antibodies
    active, **781**–782, 782*f*
    passive, **782**, 782*f*
    primary response, **780**–781, 781*f*, 782*f*, 794*f*
    secondary response, **781**, 781*f*, 782*f*
Humoral stimuli, for hormone release, 600, 601*f*
Humors, of eye, 551
Hunger, food intake regulation and, 946, 946*f*
Huntingtin protein, 466
Huntington's disease, **466**, 1106
Hyaline cartilage, **131**–133, 131*f*, 134*t*, **173**, 174*f*
    skeletal, **173**, 174*f*
    in symphyses, 250*f*, 251
    in synchondroses, 250, 250*f*
    in synovial joints, 174*f*, 251, 251*f*
    tracheal, 812*f*, 813
Hyaluronic acid, in ground substance, 124
Hybridomas, **786**
Hydatid (hydatidiform) mole, **1097**
Hydration, hypotonic, **1001**, 1001*f*
Hydration layers, 38
Hydrocarbon chains, 45, 46*f*
Hydrocephalus, 463, 463*f*
Hydrochloric acid
    in bone resorption, 186
    parietal cell secretion of, 869*f*, 870
        control of, 873, 874*f*
    peptic ulcers and, 870
Hydrocortisone (cortisol), 615*f*, **616**–617, 617*t*
    blood pressure and, 709*t*
    excess levels of, 617, 617–618
    metabolism and, 941*t*
    sodium regulation and, 1005–1006
Hydrogen, 25, 26*t*. See also Hydrogen ions
    atomic number/mass number of, 27
    atomic structure of, 27, 27*f*
    atomic weight of, 28
    as chemically reactive element, 31*f*
    isotopes of, 27, 28*f*
    in taste transduction, 573
Hydrogen bonds, 35, 35*f*
Hydrogen gas, formation of, 33
Hydrogen ions, **39**. See also Hydrogen
    in acid-base balance/pH, 40, 1009, 1009*f*. See also Acid-base balance
    renal regulation of
        bicarbonate regeneration and, 1012, 1013*f*
        tubular secretion and, 1011, 1012, 1012*f*, 1013*f*
        respiratory regulation of, 1010–1011

    acids releasing, 39
    bases taking up, 39
Hydrogen phosphate, in plasma/ interstitial fluid/intracellular fluid, 997, 997*f*
Hydrolase(s), 52
Hydrolysis reactions, 39, 42*f*, 43, **895**
    ATP in, 55, 56
    in digestion, 39, 43, **895**
    peptide bonds affected by, 48*f*
Hydronephrosis, 962
Hydrophilic polar head, of phospholipid, **64**, 65*f*
Hydrophobic nonpolar tail, of phospholipid, **64**, 65*f*
Hydrostatic-osmotic pressure interactions, 718–719, 719*f*
Hydrostatic pressure, 71, **718**, 719*f*
    capsular, **971**, 971*f*
    fluid movement among compartments and, 998
    glomerular, **971**, 971*f*
Hydroxide(s), 39–40
Hydroxyapatites
    in bone remodeling, 186
    in bone tissue, 180
Hydroxyl ion(s), **40**
Hydroxyurea, 643
Hymen, 1040*f*, **1045**, 1046*f*
    embryologic/fetal development of, 1061*f*
Hyoglossus muscle, **332***t*, 333*f*
Hyoid bone, **211**, 211*f*, 810, 810*f*
Hyperaldosteronism (aldosteronism/Conn's disease), 616, **1020**
Hyperalgesia, **491**
Hyperbaric oxygen chambers, 828
Hypercalcemia, 1003*t*
    bone remodeling and, 186
    heart function and, 686
    hyperparathyroidism and, 613
Hypercapnia, **837**, 1010
Hyperchloremia, 1003*t*
Hypercholesterolemia, **955**
Hyperemia, **770**
    active/exercise, **716**
    in inflammation, 770
    reactive, 715
Hyperextension (body movement), **255**, 256*f*
Hyperglycemia, 622, 623*t*, 626*b*, 620
    catecholamine hypersecretion and, **620**
Hyperglycemic hormone, glucagon as, **940**, 940*f*, 941*t*
Hyperinsulinism, 622–623
Hyperkalemia, 1003*t*, 1006
    heart function and, 686
Hypermagnesemia, 1003*t*
Hypernatremia, 1003*t*
Hyperopia (farsightedness), **559**, 560*f*
    development/aging and, 588
Hyperparathyroidism, 613
Hyperphosphatemia, 1003*t*
Hyperplasia, **108**
    smooth muscle, 308–311
Hyperpnea, **839**

Hyperpolarization, neuron, **398**, 398*f*
  action potential and, 399,
    400–401*f*, 402
  graded potential and, 398, 399*f*
Hyperprolactinemia, 605
Hypersensitivities, 776, **797**–**799**,
  798*f*
Hypersomnia, **479**
Hypertension, **712**–713, 745
  cardiac output and, **687**
  portal, **884**
  sympathetic vasoconstriction
    and, 540
Hyperthermia, **953**. *See also* Fever
  metabolic rate and, 947
Hyperthyroidism, 611, 611*f*, 948
Hypertonic solutions, 71*f*, **72**
Hypertrophic cardiomyopathy, **690**
Hypertrophic zone (epiphyseal
  plate), 184, 184*f*
Hypertrophy, **109**
  muscle
    contraction force and,
      301, 301*f*
    resistance exercise and, 304
Hypervariable regions, 784
Hyperventilation (respiratory alkalo-
  sis), **837**, 1011, **1014**, 1016*t*
  blood values in, 1017*b*
  renal compensations and, 1015
Hypervitaminoses, 916
Hypoadrenalism, 616, 618
Hypoaldosteronism (Addison's dis-
  ease), 616, 618, 1002, 1004
  skin color in, 155
Hypoblast, 1079, 1079*f*, 1081*f*
Hypocalcemia, 1003*t*
  heart function and, 686
  hypoparathyroidism and,
    613, 614*f*
Hypocapnia, **837**
Hypochloremia, 1003*t*
Hypochondriac regions, **17**, 20*f*
Hypodermis (superficial fascia),
  149–**150**, 149*f*
  development of, 165
Hypogastric plexus, inferior (pelvic),
  529*f*, **530**
Hypogastric (pubic) region, **17**, 20*f*
Hypoglossal canal, **204**, 206*f*,
  214*t*, 501*t*
Hypoglossal nerve (cranial nerve
  XII), 446*f*, 448, 448*f*, **493**,
  494*f*, **501***t*, 504*f*
  damage to, 501*t*
  tongue muscles supplied by, 332*t*
Hypoglycemia, **622**–**623**, 930
Hypoglycemic hormone, insulin as,
  938, 938*f*, 941*t*
Hypokalemia, 1003*t*, 1006
  heart function and, 686
Hypomagnesemia, 1003*t*
Hyponatremia, **1001**, 1003*t*
Hyponychium (nail), **160**, 160*f*
Hypoparathyroidism, 613
Hypophosphatemia, 1003*t*
Hypophyseal artery, inferior, 602*f*
Hypophyseal fossa, 206*f*, **207**, 208*f*
Hypophyseal portal system,
  602*f*, **603**
Hypophyseal portal vein, 602*f*, **603**

Hypophysectomy, **627**
Hypophysis, **601**. *See also* Pituitary
  gland
Hypoproteinemia, **1002**
Hypospadias, 990
Hypotension, **712**
  orthostatic, **541**, 712
Hypothalamic-hypophyseal tract,
  602*f*, **603**
Hypothalamic nuclei, 444*f*
Hypothalamic-pituitary-gonadal
  axis, **1038**–**1039**, 1039*t*
Hypothalamus, **443**–**444**, 443*f*, 444*f*,
  449*t*, 595*f*
  autonomic regulation by, 443,
    539, 539*f*, 540
  blood pressure regulation and,
    709
  in body temperature regulation,
    10, 10*f*, 444, 478
  development of, 431, 431*f*
  food intake regulation and,
    945, 946*f*
  hormone secretion regulated
    by, 444
  in labor, 1091, 1091*f*
  limbic system and, **452**, 452*f*
  pituitary relationship and,
    602*f*, 603
  respiratory regulation and, 838
  sleep cycle timing and, 455–456
  in temperature regulation, 10,
    10*f*, 444, 951–952
  thirst regulated by, 444, 999, 999*f*
Hypothenar eminence, muscles of,
  360*t*, 361*f*
Hypothermia, **953**
Hypothyroidism, 611, 948
Hypotonic hydration, **1001**, 1001*f*
Hypotonic solutions, 71*f*, **72**
Hypoventilation (respiratory acidosis), **840**, 1011, **1014**, 1016*t*
  blood values in, 1017*b*
  renal compensations and, 1015
Hypovolemic shock, **719**, 720*f*, 1001
Hypoxemic hypoxia, **832**
Hypoxia, **832**
Hypoxic drive, 841
Hysterectomy, **1066**
H zones, in skeletal muscle, 280*f*, **281**
  in sliding filament model of con-
    traction, 284, 284*f*

I. *See* Iodine
I bands, **281**
  in cardiac muscle, 673, 674*f*
  in skeletal muscle, 280*f*, **281**
    in sliding filament model of
      contraction, 284, 284*f*
IBD. *See* Inflammatory bowel
  disease
IBS. *See* Irritable bowel syndrome
IC. *See* Inspiratory capacity
ICF. *See* Intracellular fluid
IDDM. *See* Insulin-dependent
  (type I) diabetes mellitus
Identical twins, 1052
IELs. *See* Intraepithelial lymphocytes
IF. *See* Interstitial (tissue) fluid
IFNs. *See* Interferons

Ig(s) (immunoglobulins), 51*t*,
  783–**786**. *See also* Antibodies
IgA, 784, 784*t*
  in breast milk/colostrum,
    1093, 1094
  secretory, **784**
IgA antibodies, in saliva, 860
IgD, 784, 784*t*
IgE, 784, 784*t*
  in immediate hypersensitivity,
    798, 798*f*
IGFs. *See* Insulin-like growth
  factor(s)
IgG, 784, 784*t*
IgM, 784, 784*t*
IL. *See under* Interleukin
Ileoanal juncture, 893
Ileocecal valve/sphincter, **877**, 890
Ileocolic artery, 730*f*, **732***t*, 733*f*
Ileostomy, 893
Ileum, 852*f*, **877**
Ileus, **905**
Iliac arteries
  common, **724***t*, 725*f*, 730*f*, **732***t*,
    733*f*, 734–735*f*, **734***t*
  external, 725*f*, 734*f*, **734***t*, 735*f*
  internal, 725*f*, 734*f*, **734***t*, 735*f*
Iliac crest, 233*f*, 234*f*, **235**, 367*f*
Iliac fossa, 234*f*, **235**
Iliac (inguinal) regions, **17**, 20*f*
Iliac spines, 233*f*, 234*f*, **235**
Iliac veins
  common, 736*f*, **736***t*, 737*f*, 742*f*,
    743*f*, **744***t*
  external, 737*f*, 742*f*, 743*f*, **744***t*
  internal, 737*f*, 742*f*, 743*f*, **744***t*
Iliocostalis cervicis/lumborum/
  thoracis muscles, **338***t*, 339*f*
Iliofemoral ligament, **267**, 267*f*
Iliohypogastric nerve, 508*f*, 508*t*
Ilioinguinal nerve, 508*f*, 508*t*
Iliopsoas muscle, 326*f*, **363***t*,
  364*f*, 380*t*
Iliotibial tract, 327*f*
Ilium, 233*f*, 234*f*, **235**
Imaging (medical), 18–19*b*
Imatinib, 143*b*
Immediate (acute/type I) hypersen-
  sitivity, **798**, 798*f*
Immune (antigen-antibody) com-
  plexes, **784**–**785**, 785*f*
  in complement activation, 774*f*,
    775, 785, 785*f*
Immune complex (type III) hyper-
  sensitivity, **799**
Immune response. *See*
  Immunity/immune response
Immune serum, passive immunity
  and, 782, 782*f*
Immune system, 766–803, **767**, 767*f*.
  See also Immunity
  adaptive defenses and, 767, 767*f*,
    775–**795**, 794*f*, 795*t*
  autonomic nervous system
    and, 542*b*
  cardiovascular system and, 746*b*
  cells of, 777–780, 795*t*. *See also*
    specific type
    genetically modified, in can-
      cer treatment, 143*b*

chimeric, **795**
developmental aspects of, 799
digestive system and, 902*b*
endocrine system and, 628*b*
homeostatic imbalances/
  disorders of, 795–799
  aging and, 108
  HIV infection/AIDS, **796**–**797**
innate defenses and, **767**,
  767–775, 767*f*, 772*t*, 794*f*
integumentary system and,
  166*b*, 167*b*
muscular system and, 314*b*, 315*b*
nervous system and, 799
reproductive system and, 1064*b*
respiratory system and,
  844*b*, 845*b*
skeletal system and, 192*b*
stem cells of, 799
urinary system and, 1018*b*
Immune tolerance. *See also* Self-
  tolerance
  transplantation and, 795
Immunity/immune response, 7*f*,
  139, **767**. *See also* Immune
  system
  active, **781**–**782**, 782*f*
  artificially acquired, 781–782,
    782*f*
  cell-mediated (cellular), **776**,
    786–795, 787*f*, 794*f*. *See also*
    Cell-mediated (cellular)
    immunity; T lymphocytes
  homeostatic imbalances of,
    795–799
  humoral (antibody-mediated),
    776, 780–786, 781*f*, 782*f*. *See*
    also Antibodies; Humoral
    (antibody-mediated) immu-
    nity
  naturally acquired, 781, 782, 782*f*
  passive, **782**, 782*f*
  primary, **780**–**781**, 781*f*,
    782*f*, 794*f*
  secondary, **781**, 781*f*, 782*f*
Immunization, **800**
Immunocompetence, **777**
  development of, 777–778, 779*f*
Immunodeficiencies, **796**–**797**
Immunogenicity, **776**
Immunoglobulin(s), 51*t*, **783**–**786**,
  795*t*. *See also specific type*
  under Ig and Antibodies
  classes of, 784, 784*t*
Immunological memory, 775,
  780–**781**
Immunology, **800**
Immunopathology, **800**
Immunosuppressive therapy
  for autoimmune disease, 797
  after transplant, 793–795
Impacted teeth, 862
Impetigo, **168**
Implantation, **1076**–**1078**,
  1076*f*, 1077*f*
Imprinting, genomic, **1109**
Inactivation gate, action potential
  and, 401*f*, 402
Inborn errors of metabolism, 954
Inborn (intrinsic) reflex, 514
Incisive fossa, 205*f*, **210**, **215***t*

Incisors, **862**, 862*f*
Inclusions, **83**, **94***t*
Incompetent heart valve, 672
   heart murmurs and, 681
Incomplete antigen, **776**
Incomplete dominance, **1106**
Incomplete fracture, 188
Incomplete proteins, 913*t*, 914
Incomplete (unfused) tetanus,
   294*f*, **295**
Incontinence, **988**
   aging and, 991
   fecal, 895
   urinary, **988**
      pregnancy and, 988, 1090
Incretins, 625*t*
   type 2 diabetes and, 627*b*
Incus (anvil), 215*t*, 575*f*, **576**, 576*f*
Independent assortment,
   1103–**1104**, 1103*f*
Indifferent stage, of gonadal devel-
   opment, **1060**, 1061*f*, 1062*f*
Indirect muscle attachments, **278**
Indirect (multineuronal) path-
   ways, **476**
Indirect (extrapyramidal) system,
   474*t*, **476**, 512–513
Indolamines, **415**–418
Infant, adjustment to extrauterine
   life by, 1092–1093
Infant respiratory distress syndrome
   (IRDS), **823**
Infarct
   myocardial, **670**
   renal, **992**
Infection
   burn injury and, 164
   tissue repair in, 140
Infectious granulomas, 773
Infectious mononucleosis, 648, **764**
Inferior (term), 12*t*
Inferior angle of scapula, 227*f*, 228
Inferior articular process, vertebral,
   218*f*, **219**, 222*t*
Inferior cerebellar peduncles,
   446–447*f*, 447, 448*f*, **450**, 451*f*
Inferior cervical ganglion, **532**, 533*f*
Inferior colliculus, **446**, 446–447*f*,
   582, 582*f*
Inferior costal facet, 220
Inferior ganglion, 500*t*
Inferior gemellus muscle, 368*f*, 368*t*
Inferior gluteal artery, 734*f*, **734***t*
Inferior gluteal line, 234*f*, **235**
Inferior gluteal nerve, 509*f*, **510**, 510*t*
Inferior horns, 433*f*
Inferior hypogastric (pelvic) plexus,
   529*f*, **530**
Inferior hypophyseal artery, 602*f*
Inferior iliac spines, 233*f*, 234*f*, 235
Inferior mesenteric artery, 725*f*, 730*f*,
   732*t*, 733*f*
Inferior mesenteric ganglion,
   532, 533*f*
Inferior mesenteric vein, 737*f*, 742*f*,
   742*t*, 743*f*
Inferior nasal conchae, 202*f*, **211**,
   213*f*, 807–809, 808*f*
Inferior nasal meatus, 808*f*
Inferior nuchal line, 202*f*, 204, 205*f*
Inferior oblique muscle, 550, 550*f*

Inferior olivary nuclei, **447**–448, 448*f*
Inferior orbital fissure, 202*f*,
   210, 215*t*
Inferior pharyngeal constrictor mus-
   cle, 335*f*, 335*t*
Inferior phrenic arteries, 730*f*,
   731*t*, 733*f*
Inferior phrenic veins, 742*f*,
   742*t*, 743*f*
Inferior pubic ramus, 234*f*, **235**
Inferior rectus muscle, **550**, 550*f*
Inferior sagittal sinus, 738*f*, **738***t*, 739*f*
Inferior salivatory nuclei, 529
Inferior suprarenal artery, 732*t*
Inferior thyroid artery, 608, 609*f*
Inferior vena cava, **664**, 665–667*f*,
   731*f*, 736–737*f*, **736***t*, **742***t*
   veins draining into, 736–737*f*,
      736*t*, 742–743*f*, 742*t*
Inferior vestibular ganglion,
   577*f*, **584**
Infertility, male, 1038
Inflammation/inflammatory
   response, 139, **769**–773,
   770*f*, 772*t*
   in antibody mechanism of
      action, 785, 785*f*
   in tissue repair, 139, 140*f*
Inflammatory bowel disease, 905
Inflammatory chemicals. *See* Chemi-
   cal mediators
Inflammatory joint disease,
   270–271, 271*f*
Inflation (Hering-Breuer) reflex, **839**
Infrahyoid muscles, 334*t*, 334–335*t*,
   335*f*
Infraorbital foramen, 202*f*, **210**, 210*f*
Infraspinatus muscle, 327*f*, **350***t*,
   351*f*, **352***t*, 358*t*
Infraspinous fossa, 227*f*, 228
Infratemporal fossa, 268*f*, 269
Infundibulum, **443**, **601**, **1042**
   hypothalamic-pituitary gland,
      443, 446*f*, **601**, 602*f*
   uterine tube, 1040*f*, **1042**, 1043*f*
Ingestion (food intake), **853**,
   853*f*, 888*t*
   regulation of, 444, 945–947, 946*f*
Inguinal hernia, **1066**
Inguinal ligament, 235
Inguinal lymph nodes, 755*f*
Inguinal (iliac) regions, **17**, 20*f*
Inhalation. *See* Inspiration
Inheritance, 1105–1107, 1105*f*,
   1106*t*, 1107*f*, 1108*f*
   dominant-recessive, **1105**–1106,
      1105*f*, 1106*t*
   extranuclear (mitochondrial),
      1108, 1109
   incomplete dominance and, **1106**
   multiple-allele, **1106**, 1106*t*
   nontraditional, 1108–1109
   polygene, **1107**, 1108*f*
   sex-linked, **1107**, 1107*f*
Inhibin, **1039**
   in female reproductive function,
      ovarian cycle, 1053*f*, 1054
   in male reproductive function,
      1039, 1039*f*
Inhibiting hormones, hypothalamic, **603**

Inhibition, presynaptic, **413**
Inhibitory postsynaptic potentials
   (IPSPs), 411*t*, **412**, 412*f*
   in phototransduction, 564, 565*f*
   summation by, **412**, 413*f*
Inhibitory synapses, 412
Initiation
   in transcription, **102**, 102*f*
   in translation, 105
Initiator tRNA, **105**
Inlet, pelvic, **235**–237, 236*t*
Innate defenses, **767**, 767–775, 767*f*,
   772*t*, 794*f*
   internal (cells/chemicals),
      768–775, 772*t*, 794*f*
   surface barriers (skin/mucosae),
      160–161, 767–768, 772*t*, 794*f*
Inner cell mass, **1075**, 1076*f*
Inner (internal) ear, 575*f*, **576**–577,
   577*f*, 578*f*
   sound transmission to, 580, 581*f*
Inner fiber, rod and cone, 560, 561*f*
Inner hair cells, 578*f*, **580**
Inner layer of eye, 552*f*, 553, 554*f*,
   555*f*. *See also* Retina
Inner mitochondrial membrane,
   83, 83*f*
Inner segments, rod and cone, **560**
Innervation, of epithelial tissue, 116
Inorganic components, of bone, 180
Inorganic compounds, **38**, 38–41.
   See also specific type
Inositol trisphosphate, **598**
Inotropic agents, positive and nega-
   tive, 684
Inotropic (channel-linked) recep-
   tors, **420**–421, **420***f*
Input regions, **390**
Insensible heat loss, **951**
Insensible water loss, **951**, 998, 999*f*
Insertion (muscle), **253**, **277**
Insoluble fiber, 912
Insomnia, **457**
Inspiration, **819**, 820–822, 821*f*, 822*f*
   first after birth, 1093
   muscles used in, 340*t*, 341*f*,
      820, 821*f*
Inspiratory capacity, **824**, 825*f*
Inspiratory muscles, 340*t*, 341*f*,
   820, 821*f*
Inspiratory reserve volume, **824**, 825*f*
Insufficiency, cardiac valve, 681
Insula, **433**, 434*f*
Insulin, 51*t*, 621, 621*f*, **622**–623, 938,
   938*f*, 941*t*
   absorptive state regulated by,
      938, 938*f*
   deficit of, 622, 623*t*
   in diabetes mellitus, 622, 626*b*,
      938, 941*t*
   discovery of, 626*b*
   excess (hyperinsulinism), 622–623
   in food intake regulation, 946, 946*f*
   mechanism of action of, 598
   metabolism and, 621–622, 621*f*,
      622, 938, 938*f*, 940, 940*f*, 941*t*
   pancreatic islets producing, 620*f*,
      621, 622, 886
Insulin-dependent (type 1) diabetes
   mellitus (IDDM), **626**–627*b*,
   797, 954

Insulin-like growth factor(s)
   (IGFs), **603**
Insulin resistance, **627***b*
Integral proteins, **64**, 65*f*
Integration, **386**, 386*f*, **421**–422,
   421*f*, 422*f*
   motor, 512–513, 513*f*
   pain perception and, 490–491
   sensory, 488–491, 489*f*
   somatosensory system organiza-
      tion and, 488–490, 489*f*
Integration center, in reflex arc,
   514, 514*f*
Integrins, 80–81
Integument. *See* Skin
Integumentary system, 6*f*, **148**–171.
   See also Skin
   autonomic nervous system
      and, 542*b*
   in body defense, 5, 5*f*, 6*f*
   boundary maintenance and, 5, 5*f*,
      6*f*, 160–161
   cardiovascular system and, 746*b*
   developmental aspects of, 165
   digestive system and, 902*b*
   endocrine system and, 628*b*
   functions of, 6*f*, 149, 160–162
   homeostatic relationships of, 5*f*,
      165, 166*b*, 167*b*
   lymphatic system and, 762*b*
   muscular system and, 166*b*, 314*b*
   reproductive system and, 1064*b*
   respiratory system and, 844*b*
   skeletal system and, 192*b*, 193*b*
   thyroid hormone affecting, 612*t*
   urinary system and, 1018*b*
Interatrial septum, **664**, 666*f*
Intercalated cells, 965*f*, 966
   type A
      hydrogen secretion by, in acid
         base balance, 1011
      in potassium regulation, 1006
Intercalated discs, **136**, 137*f*,
   673, 674*f*
Intercarpal joint, 254*t*
Intercellular clefts, **699**, 699*f*
Intercondylar eminence, **238**, 239*f*
Intercondylar fossa, **237**, 238*f*
Intercostal arteries
   anterior, 728*f*, 729*f*, **729***t*
   posterior, 728*f*, 729*f*, **729***t*
Intercostal muscles, 326*f*, 340*t*, 341*f*,
   820, 821*f*
   external, 340*t*, 341*f*, 820, 821*f*
   internal, 340*t*, 341*f*
Intercostal nerves, 502*f*, 503*f*,
   504, **835**
   muscles of respiration supplied
      by, 340*t*
   in respiration, 835
Intercostal spaces, 223, 224*f*
Intercostal veins, posterior, 740*f*,
   740*t*, 741*f*, **741***t*
Interferons (IFNs), 772*t*, **773**–774,
   773*f*, 790*t*
Interleukin(s), 646, 790*t*
   in fever, 954
   in leukopoiesis, **646**
Interleukin 1, **790**, 790*t*
Interleukin 2, **790**, 790*t*
Interleukin 4, 790*t*, 792

Interleukin 5, 790*t*
Interleukin 10, 790*t*, 792
Interleukin 12, 790*t*, 792
Interleukin 17, 790*t*, 792
Interlobar arteries, **963**, 964*f*
Interlobar veins, **964**, 964*f*
Interlobular veins, hepatic, 883*f*
Intermaxillary suture, 205*f*, 210
Intermediate (term), 12*t*
Intermediate cuneiform bone, **240**, 240*f*, 242*t*
Intermediate filaments, 63*f*, **88–89**, 88*f*, 94*t*
    in desmosomes, 66, 67*f*, 88–89
    in neurons (neurofibrils), 89, **389**
    in skeletal muscle (desmin filaments), 281
    in smooth muscle, 306–307, 306*f*
Intermediate mass (interthalamic adhesion), **441**, 443*f*
Intermediate mesoderm, **1084**, 1085*f*
Intermittent claudication, 316
Internal (term), 12*t*. See also under Deep
Internal acoustic meatus, **207**, 214*t*
Internal anal sphincter, **891**, 891*f*
Internal capsule, 440*f*, **441**
Internal carotid artery, 725*f*, 726*f*, **726***t*, 726*f*
Internal (inner) ear, 575*f*, **576–577**, 577*f*, 578*f*
    sound transmission to, 580, 581*f*
Internal iliac artery, 725*f*, 734*f*, **734***t*, 735*f*
    uterine arteries arising from, 1044
Internal iliac vein, 737*f*, 742*f*, 743*f*, **744***t*
Internal intercostal muscles, 340*t*, 341*f*
Internal jugular veins, 736*f*, **736***t*, 737*f*, 738*f*, **738***t*, 739*f*, 740*f*, 741*f*
Internal oblique muscles, 326*f*, **342***t*, 343*f*
Internal os, 1043*f*, 1044
Internal pudendal artery, 734*f*, **734***t*
    constriction of after orgasm, 1032
Internal (open) reduction of fracture, 188
Internal respiration, **805**, 828*f*, 830
Internal spermatic fascia, 1026*f*
Internal tension, muscle contraction force and, **301**
Internal thoracic (internal mammary) artery, 727*f*, 728*f*, **728–729***t*, 729*f*
Internal urethral sphincter, **987**, 987*f*
Interneurons (association neurons), **394***t*, **395**
    development of, 466
    in posterior horns, 468
Internodal pathway, of cardiac conduction system, 677, 677*f*
Interoceptors (visceroceptors), **486**, 487*t*
Interossei muscles
    of foot, 378*t*, 379*f*
    of hand, 360*t*, 361*f*, 362*t*
Interosseous artery, common, 728*f*, **728***t*, 729*f*

Interosseous membrane, **228**
    in forearm, **228**, 230*f*
    in leg, 237, 239*f*
Interphalangeal joints
    of fingers, 254*t*
    of toes, 255*t*
Interphase, **95**, 98*f*
    DNA replication during, 96–97, 97*f*, 1035*f*
    in meiosis, 1035*f*
    in mitosis, **95–97**, 96*f*, 97*f*, **98***f*
Interspinous ligament, 218*f*
Interstitial cells, **1026**
    of Cajal, 876
    of testis (Leydig cells), **1026**, 1027*f*
        testosterone produced by, 1026, 1039, 1039*f*
Interstitial (tissue) fluid, **68**, **996**
    electrolytes in, 997*f*
    gas/nutrient/water/waste exchanges and, 998, 998*f*
    in ground substance, 124
Interstitial fluid hydrostatic pressure (HP$_{if}$), **718**, 719*f*
Interstitial growth, of cartilage, **173**
Interstitial lamellae, **180**, 181*f*
Intertarsal joint, 255*t*
Interthalamic adhesion (intermediate mass), **441**, 443*f*
Intertrochanteric crest, **237**, 238*f*
Intertrochanteric line, **237**, 238*f*
Intertubercular sulcus (bicipital groove), **228**, 229*f*
Interventricular artery
    anterior, 665*f*, **669**, 669*f*
    posterior, 666*f*, **669**, 669*f*
Interventricular foramen (foramen of Monro), **432**, 433*f*
Interventricular septum, **664**, 667*f*
Interventricular sulcus
    anterior, **664**
    posterior, **664**
Intervertebral discs, **217–218**, 217*f*, 218*f*
    herniated (slipped), **218**, 218*f*
    aging and, 244
    as symphyses, 251
Intervertebral foramina, 217, 218*f*, **219**, 219*f*, 222*t*
Intervertebral joint, 254*t*
Intervillous spaces, in stratum functionalis, **1078**, 1079*f*, 1080*f*
Intestinal arteries, 730*f*, **732***t*, 733*f*
Intestinal crypts (crypts of Lieberkühn), **879**, 879*f*
Intestinal flora, 893
Intestinal (enteric) gastrin, 625*t*, **873**, 875*t*. See also Gastrin
Intestinal juice, 879, **880**
Intestinal motility
    large intestine, 893–895, 894*f*
    small intestine, 889–890, 889*f*
Intestinal phase, of gastric secretion, 872*f*, **873**
Intestinal pits, 878–879
Intestinal trunk, **754**, 755*f*
Intestine(s). See also Large intestine; Small intestine
    arteries supplying, 730*f*, **732***t*
    autonomic innervation/effects and, 529*f*, 533*f*, 537

mucosa-associated lymphoid tissue (MALT) in, **761**, **856**, 857*f*, 879*f*
    parathyroid hormone affecting, 614*f*
Intestino-intestinal reflex, 890
Intra-alveolar (intrapulmonary) pressure, **819**, 819*f*, 821, 821*f*, 822, 822*f*
Intracapsular ligaments, of synovial joints, **252**
Intracellular fluid, 63, **996**, 996*f*
    electrolytes in, 997*f*
    extracellular fluid compared with, **997–998**, 997*f*
    gas/nutrient/water/waste exchanges and, 998, 998*f*
    resting membrane potential and, 396, 397*f*
Intracellular fluid compartment, **996**, 996*f*
Intracellular receptors, in hormone mechanism of action, 596, 599*f*
Intracranial dural sinuses. See Dural venous sinuses
Intracranial hemorrhage, 464
Intraepithelial lymphocytes, 879
Intrafusal muscle fibers, 488, **515**, 515*f*, 516*f*
Intramembranous ossification, 182, **182–183**, 182*f*
Intramolecular bonds, hydrogen bonds as, 35
Intramural ganglia, 530
Intraocular pressure, in glaucoma, 556
Intraperitoneal (peritoneal) organs, **856**
Intrapleural pressure, **819–820**, 819*f*, 821, 822*f*
Intrapulmonary (intra-alveolar) pressure, **819**, 819*f*, 821, 821*f*, 822, 822*f*
Intrauterine device, 1096*b*
Intravenous pyelogram (IVP), 985*f*, **991**
Intrinsic (deep) back muscles, **336–338***t*, 339*f*
Intrinsic cardiac conduction system, **676–679**, 677*f*, 678*f*
    action potential initiation and, 676, 676*f*
    defects in, 678–679
    ECG in, 680, 681*f*
    sequence of excitation and, 676–678, 677*f*
Intrinsic factor, **642**, **871–872**, 900
    parietal cells secreting, 870, 871
Intrinsic foot muscles, **376–378***t*, 377*f*, 379*f*
Intrinsic (capsular) ligaments, of synovial joints, **252**
Intrinsic nerve plexuses, of alimentary canal, 854, 855*f*, 857–858, 857*f*
Intrinsic palm muscles, 354*t*, **360–362***t*, 361*f*
Intrinsic pathway, **650–651**, 650*f*
Intrinsic (inborn) reflex, 514
Intrinsic salivary glands, 860

Intrinsic tongue muscles, 332*t*, **859**
Introns, **101**
    mRNA processing and, 103
Inulin, glomerular filtration rate estimated by clearance rate of, 984
Invariant chain, 788*f*, 789
Inversion (body movement), 258*f*, **259**
    of lower limb, 380*t*, 381*f*
In vitro fertilization, 1095
Involuntary muscle, **136**, 276. See also Cardiac muscle; Smooth muscle
Involuntary nervous system, **386**, **526**. See also Autonomic nervous system
Iodide, in thyroid hormone synthesis, 609–610, 610*f*
Iodine, 26*t*, 919*t*
    in thyroid hormone synthesis, 610, 610*f*
Ion(s), **32**, 32*f*, 39
    tubular reabsorption of, 975–976, 976*f*, 983*f*
Ion channels, 64, **69–70**, 69*f*, 395, 396*f*. See also specific type
    action potential and, 401*f*, 402
    gated, 69, 81, **395**, 396*f*
    information transfer at chemical synapse and, 408, 409*f*
    muscle contraction, 286*f*, 287, 288, 288*f*
Ionic bonds, **32**, 32*f*, 34*f*
    redox reactions and, 37
Ionizing radiation, 28, **56**
IP$_3$ (inositol trisphosphate, **598**
Ipsilateral fibers, cerebellar, **450**
Ipsilateral reflex, **516**
IPSPs. See Inhibitory postsynaptic potentials
IRDS. See Infant respiratory distress syndrome
Iris, 548*f*, **551–553**, 552*f*, 553*f*
    autonomic innervation/effects and, 538*t*
Iron, 26*t*, 918*t*
    absorption of, 900
    dietary, 918*t*
    erythropoiesis and, 640, 641*f*
Iron-deficiency anemia, 642
Irregular bones, **175**, 175*f*, 179
Irregular dense connective tissue, **129**, 130*f*, 134*t*
Irritability (responsiveness), **5**, 6*f*, **276**
    muscle cell, **276**
    neuron, 5, 6*f*, 395. See also Nerve impulse(s)
Irritable bowel syndrome, 894
IRV. See Inspiratory reserve volume
Ischemia, **464**
    myocardial, 670, 675
    in stroke, 464
Ischemic (stagnant) hypoxia, **832**
Ischemic (luteolytic) phase, of ovarian cycle, 1052
Ischial ramus, 234*f*, **235**
Ischial spine, 234*f*, **235**
Ischial tuberosity, 234*f*, **235**
Ischiocavernosus muscle, 344*t*, 345*f*

Ischiofemoral ligament, 267, 267*f*
Ischium, 233*f*, 234*f*, 235
Islets of Langerhans (pancreatic islets), 620*f*, 621, 886
  transplantation of for diabetes, 626–627*b*
Isografts, 792
Isomer(s), 43
Isometric contraction, 289, 296, 297*f*
Isometric exercises, muscles affected by, 304
Isotonic contraction, 289, 296, 297*f*
Isotonic solutions, 71, 71*f*
Isotopes, 27, 28*f*
Isovolumetric contraction phase, 682, 683*f*
Isovolumetric relaxation phase, 682, 683*f*
Isthmus, 1042
  of fauces, 808*f*, 809
  of thyroid gland, 608, 609*f*
  of uterine tube, 1042, 1043*f*
  of uterus, 1043, 1043*f*
Itch receptor, 486
IUD. *See* Intrauterine device
IVF. *See* In vitro fertilization

Jaundice, 155, 885
  physiological, 1094, 1097
Jaw/jawbone. *See* Mandible; Maxillary bones/maxilla(e)
Jaw joint. *See* Temporomandibular joint
Jejunum, 852*f*, 877
JGA. *See* Juxtaglomerular apparatus
Joint(s), 248–274, 254–255*t*. *See also specific joint*
  artificial (prosthetic), 261*b*
  cartilaginous, 249, 250–251, 250*f*, 252*t*
  classification of, 249, 252*t*
  degenerative disease of (osteoarthritis), 270
  developmental aspects of, 272
  fibrous, 249, 249–250, 249*f*, 252*t*
  homeostatic imbalances and, 269–271
  inflammatory/degenerative conditions of, 270–271, 271*f*
  innervation of, 511
  muscles in stabilization of, 276
  synovial, 249, 251–269, 251*f*, 252*t*, 260*f*, 261*b*
    membranes of, 251, 251*f*
Joint (articular) capsule, 251, 251*f*
  of elbow joint, 266, 266*f*
  of knee joint, 262*f*, 263
  of shoulder joint, 264, 265*f*
Joint (synovial) cavities, 20, 251, 251*f*
Joint kinesthetic receptors, 488, 488*t*
Jugular foramen, 205*f*, 206*f*, 207, 214*t*, 738*t*, 739*f*
Jugular lymph sacs, 761
Jugular (suprasternal) notch, 223, 224*f*
Jugular trunks, 754, 755*f*
Jugular veins
  external, 736*f*, 737*f*, 738*f*, 738*t*, 739*f*, 741*f*
  internal, 736*f*, 736*t*, 737*f*, 738*f*, 738*t*, 739*f*, 740*f*, 741*f*

Junctional folds, 285
Junctional rhythm, 679
Juxtaglomerular apparatus (JGA), 615, 968–969, 968*f*
  sodium regulation and, 1004
  tubuloglomerular feedback and, 972, 973*f*, 974
Juxtaglomerular (JG/granular) cells, 968, 968*f*
  renin release/blood pressure and, 968, 973*f*, 974
Juxtamedullary nephrons, 966, 967*f*

K. *See* Potassium
Kaposi's sarcoma, in AIDS, 796
Karyotype, 1102, 1102*f*
  in genetic screening, 1110, 1111*f*
kcal. *See* Kilocalories
Keloid, 144
Keratin, 50, 51*t*, 150
  in desmosomes, 66, 67*f*
  in hair, 157, 160
  in skin, 119
Keratin filaments, 89
Keratinization, 119, 150
  of nail, 160
  of stratum granulosum, 150
Keratinocytes, 150, 151*f*
Keratohyaline granules, 150
Ketoacidosis, 622, 623*t*
Keto acids, 924, 925*f*
  modification of in protein metabolism, 933*f*, 934
Ketogenesis, 932, 932*f*
Ketone(s)/ketone bodies, 622, 932, 932*f*, 1009
  in urine, 622, 623*t*, 985*t*
Ketonuria, 622, 623*t*, 985*t*
Ketosis, 56, 932
Kidney(s), 960–961, 961*f*, 985*f*. *See also under* Renal
  in acid-base balance, 978, 983*f*, 1011–1014, 1012*f*, 1013*f*
    compensations for abnormalities and, 1014, 1015
  aging affecting, 991
  anatomy of, 961–969
    internal, 962–963, 963*f*
    location/external anatomy, 961–962, 962*f*
    nephrons, 964–969, 967*f*. *See also* Nephron(s)
  autonomic innervation/effects and, 533*f*, 538*t*, 972
  blood pressure regulation and, 710, 710*f*, 711*f*, 972–974, 973*f*, 1007*f*
  blood supply of, 963–964, 964*f*
  in calcium regulation, 1008
  developmental aspects of, 988–990, 990*f*
  in fluid balance, 1004–1006, 1004*f*, 1005*f*, 1007*f*
  homeostatic imbalances and, 984
  hormones produced by, 624, 625*t*
  infection of (pyelitis/pyelonephritis), 963, 988
  nerve supply of, 964
  osmotic gradient in, 979*f*, 981
  parathyroid hormone affecting, 614*f*

perfusion (blood flow) of, 713, 713*f*
physiology of, 969–984, 971*f*. *See also* Urine, formation of
  polycystic, 990
  potassium balance regulation and, 1006
  pregnancy and, 1090
  sodium balance regulation and, 1004–1006, 1004*f*, 1005*f*, 1007*f*
  urine formation by, 969–984, 971*f*
Kidney (renal) failure, 974, 984
Kidney stones (renal calculi), 986
Killer cells, natural (NK), 768–769, 772*t*, 792
Kilocalories, 911
Kinesins, 88
Kinesthetic receptors, joint, 488, 488*t*
Kinetic energy, 24
  in diffusion, 68
  enzyme action and, 52, 52*f*
Kinetochore(s), 98*f*
Kinetochore microtubules, 98*f*
Kinins, in inflammatory response, 769, 772*t*
Kinocilium, 581, 584, 584*f*
Klinefelter's syndrome, 1060
Kneecap (patella), 199*f*, 237, 238*f*, 242*t*
Knee-jerk reflex, 515, 516, 517*f*
Knee joint, 262–264, 262–263*f*
  artificial/replacement, 261*b*
  femoropatellar, 255*t*, 262, 263
  injuries of, 264, 264*f*, 269, 269*f*
  muscles crossing/acting on, 363–369, 364*f*, 367–368*f*, 380*t*, 381*f*
  tibiofemoral, 255*t*, 262, 263
Knob, ATP synthase, 927, 928*f*
Knuckle (metacarpophalangeal joint), 233, 254*t*
Korotkoff sounds, 711–712
K-ras oncogene, in colorectal cancer, 142*b*, 143*f*
Krebs, Hans, 924
Krebs cycle, 919, 920*f*, 922, 922*f*, 924–925, 925*f*, 929*f*, 934*t*
Kupffer cells (hepatic macrophages), 699, 768, 881, 883*f*
Kwashiorkor, 955
Kyphosis, 217, 244

Labia (lips) of mouth, 858, 859*f*
  cleft, 904
Labial frenulum, 858, 859*f*
Labia majora (labium majus), 1040*f*, 1046, 1046*f*
  embryologic/fetal development of, 1062*f*
Labia minora (labium minus), 1040*f*, 1046, 1046*f*
  embryologic/fetal development of, 1062*f*
Labioscrotal swellings, 1060, 1062*f*
Labor, 1090
  false, 1091
  initiation of, 1091
  oxytocin in, 606, 607, 1091, 1091*f*
  stages of, 1091–1092, 1092*f*

Labyrinth (inner/internal ear), 575*f*, 576–577, 577*f*, 578*f*
  bony, 576
  membranous, 576
  sound transmission to, 580, 581*f*
Labyrinthitis, 589
Lacrimal apparatus, 549–550, 549*f*
Lacrimal bones, 202*f*, 203*f*, 211, 215*t*
Lacrimal canaliculi, 549, 549*f*
Lacrimal caruncle, 548, 548*f*
Lacrimal fossa, 203*f*, 211, 215*t*
Lacrimal gland, 549, 549*f*
  autonomic innervation/effects and, 529*f*, 533*f*, 538*t*
Lacrimal nuclei, 529
Lacrimal puncta, 549, 549*f*
Lacrimal sac, 211, 549, 549*f*
Lacrimal secretion (tears), 549
  in body defense, 772*t*
Lactase, 896*f*, 897
Lactation, 1093–1094, 1094*f*
  oxytocin and, 607, 1093–1094, 1094*f*
Lacteals, 754, 878
  in small intestine, 878, 879*f*
Lactic acid, 298, 924, 1009
  cardiac ischemia and, 675
  formation of, 923*f*, 924
    ATP for muscle activity and, 298, 298*f*
Lactiferous ducts, 1047*f*, 1048
Lactiferous sinus, 1047*f*, 1048
Lactogen, human placental, 1078, 1090
Lactose, 43, 44*f*, 895, 896*f*
Lactose intolerance, 897
Lactotrophs, 605
Lacunae, 180, 1078
  bone, 133, 133*f*, 180, 181*f*
  cartilage, 131, 131*f*, 173
  in stratum functionalis (intervillous spaces), 1078, 1079*f*, 1080*f*
Lagging strand, in DNA replication, 96, 97*f*
Lambdoid suture, 200, 201, 201*f*, 202*f*, 203*f*
Lamellae (bone), 179, 180, 180*f*, 181*f*
Lamellar bone, 179, 182*f*. *See also* Compact bone
Lamellated (Pacinian) corpuscles, 149*f*, 486–487, 487*t*
Lamellated granules, 150–152
Lamina(e)
  basal. *See* Basal lamina
  elastic, of muscular arteries, 698
  nuclear, 92, 92*f*
  osseous spiral, 577, 578*f*
  propria. *See* Lamina propria
  reticular, 115–116
  vertebral, 219, 219*f*
Lamina propria, 139
  of alimentary canal mucosa, 856, 857*f*
Laminar flow (streamlining), 704
Laminectomy, 245
Laminin, in ground substance, 124
Lamins, 92, 92*f*
Langerhans, islets of (pancreatic islets), 620*f*, 621, 886
  transplantation of for diabetes, 626–627*b*

Langerhans cells (epidermal dendritic cells), 150, 151*f*, 161, 779
Language, 457
Lanugo coat, 165
Laparoscopy, **905, 1066**
Large cell (medial) nuclear group, 448*f*, **452**
Large granular lymphocytes, 768–769
Large intestine, 852*f*, 888*t*, **890–895**, 891*f*, 892*f*
autonomic innervation/effects and, 529*f*, 533*f*
bacterial flora of, **893**
digestive processes occurring in, 888*t*, 893–895, 894*f*
gross anatomy of, 890–893, 891*f*
microscopic anatomy of, 891–893
motility of, 893–895, 894*f*
Laryngeal cartilages, 173, 810–811, 810*f*
Laryngeal prominence (Adam's apple), **810**, 810*f*
Laryngitis, **812**
Laryngopharynx, 808*f*, **809, 864**
Laryngotracheal bud, **842**, 843*f*
Larynx (voice box), 805*f*, 807*t*, 808*f*, **810–812**, 810*f*, 811*f*
cartilages in, 173, 810–811, 810*f*
sphincter functions of, 812
voice production and, 811–812
Lasix. *See* Furosemide
Latch state, 308
Late erythroblasts, **639**, 639*f*
Latent period, **293**
excitation-contraction coupling during, 288, 293
after orgasm, 1032
aging affecting, 1066
Latent syphilis, 1058
Lateral (term), 12*t*
Lateral angle of scapula, 228
Lateral apertures, **433**, 433*f*
Lateral (axillary) border of scapula, 227*f*, 228
Lateral cervical (cardinal) ligaments, 1043*f*, **1044**
Lateral circumflex femoral artery, 734*f*, **734*t***, 735*f*
Lateral commissure, **548**, 548*f*
Lateral compartment of leg, muscles of, 370*t*, 372*f*, 373*t*, 374–375*f*, 380*t*, 381*f*
Lateral condyle, **237, 238**
of femur, **237**, 238*f*
of tibia, **238**, 239*f*
Lateral cords, brachial plexus, **505**, 506*f*
Lateral cuneiform bone, **240**, 240*f*, 242*t*
Lateral cutaneous branch of intercostal nerve, 503*f*
Lateral epicondyle, **228, 237**
of femur, **237**, 238*f*
of humerus, **228**, 229*f*
Lateral excursion, 268*f*, 269
Lateral femoral cutaneous nerve, 508*f*, 508*t*
Lateral fornix, 1043*f*, 1045

Lateral funiculi, 469*f*, **470**
Lateral geniculate bodies/nuclei, 442, 444*f*, **566**
in visual pathway/processing, 442, **566**, 567*f*, 568
Lateral horns, **468**, 469*f*, **530**, 531*f*
Lateral hypothalamic area, food intake regulation and, 945, 946*f*
Lateral inhibition, 568
Lateralization, 439–**440**
Lateral lemniscus, in auditory pathway, **582**, 582*f*
Lateral ligaments, of temporomandibular joint, **268**
Lateral longitudinal arch of foot, **241**, 241*f*
Lateral malleolus, **238**, 239*f*
Lateral mass, **209**
of atlas, 219
of ethmoid bone, **209**, 209*f*
Lateral meniscus of knee, 262–263*f*
Lateral (small cell) nuclear group, 448*f*, **452**
Lateral patellar retinaculum, 262*f*, **263**
Lateral plantar artery, 734*f*, 735*f*, **735*t***
Lateral plantar nerve, **510**, 510*t*
Lateral plantar vein, **744*t***
Lateral plate mesoderm, **1084**, 1085*f*
Lateral pterygoid muscle, 332*t*, 333*f*
Lateral rectus muscle, **550**, 550*f*
Lateral rotation, 256, 257*f*
of lower limb, 380*t*, 381*f*
of upper limb, 358*t*, 359*f*
Lateral sacral crest, 221*f*, **223**
Lateral semicircular canal, 576, 577*f*
Lateral spinothalamic tract, **471**, 471*f*, 472*f*, 473*t*
Lateral sulcus, **433**, 434*f*
Lateral supracondylar line, **237**, 238*f*
Lateral supracondylar ridge, **228**, 229*f*
Lateral thoracic artery, 728*f*, **728*t***, 729*f*
Lateral ventricles, **431–432**, 431*f*, 433*f*
Late secondary follicle, 1041*f*, **1042**, 1051*f*, 1052
Latissimus dorsi muscle, 327*f*, 346*t*, 349*f*, **350*t***, 351*f*, 351*t*, 358*t*, 367*f*
Laughing, 826*t*
LDLs. *See* Low-density lipoproteins
L-dopa, for Parkinson's disease, 465
Leader sequence, in translation, 105
Leading strand, in DNA replication, 96, 97*f*
Leakage channels, 69, **395**
Learned (acquired) reflex, 514
Lecithin, 899, 912
Left anterior descending artery (anterior interventricular artery), 665*f*, **669**, 669*f*
Left ascending lumbar vein, **741*t***, 742*f*, 743*f*
Left atrium, 664, 665–667*f*
Left brachiocephalic vein, 736*f*, **736*t***, 737*f*
Left bundle branch, **677**
Left colic artery, 730*f*, **732*t***, 733*f*

Left colic (splenic) flexure, **890**, 891*f*
Left common carotid artery, **724*t***, 726*f*, 728*f*
Left common iliac artery, **724*t***
Left coronary artery, 665*f*, **669**, 669*f*, **724*t***
Left gastric artery, 730*f*, 731*f*, **731*t***
Left gastroepiploic artery, 730*f*, 731*f*, **731*t***
Left hepatic duct, 878*f*
Left hypochondriac region, 17, 20*f*
Left iliac (inguinal) region, 17, 20*f*
Left lobe, of liver, **881**, 882*f*
Left lower quadrant (LLQ), **17**, 17*f*
Left lumbar region, 17, 20*f*
Left main (primary) bronchus, 813*f*, **814**
Left pulmonary artery, 665–667*f*, **722*f*, 722*t***, 817*f*
Left pulmonary vein, 665–667*f*, **722*f*, 722*t***, 817*f*
Left subclavian artery, **724*t***, 726*f*, 729*f*
Left suprarenal vein, 736*f*, **742*t***, 743*f*
Left upper quadrant (LUQ), **17**, 17*f*
Left ventricle, 665–667*f*, **669**, 669*f*
Leg
bones of, 237–240, 239*f*, 242*t*
muscles of/muscles controlling movement of, 326*f*, 327*f*, 363–369*t*, 364*f*, 367–368*t*, 370–373*t*, 371*f*, 372*f*, 374–375*f*, 380*t*, 381*f*
Length-tension relationship, **301**
cardiac muscle, preload and, 684
skeletal muscle contraction force and, **301**, 301*f*
smooth muscle contraction and, 308
Lens (of eye), 552*f*, 555*f*, **556**
accommodation of, in close vision, **558–559**
clouding of (cataract), **556**, 556*f*
in light focusing, 558, 558*f*
suspensory ligament of (ciliary zonule), **551**, 552*f*, 555*f*
Lens crystallins, **556**
Lens epithelium, 555*f*, **556**
Lenses, refraction and, **557**
Lens fibers, **556**
Lens vesicle, **588**
Lentiform nucleus, **441**, 442*f*
Leptin, 624, 625*t*, **946–947**, 946*f*
bones affected by, 186–187
in female reproductive function, 1053, 1056
Lesion, **144**
Lesser curvature of stomach, **868**, 868*f*
Lesser occipital nerve, 504*f*, 504*t*
Lesser omentum, **868**, 892*f*
Lesser sciatic notch, 234*f*, **235**
Lesser sphenoid wing, 203*f*, 204*f*, 206*f*, **207**, 208*f*
Lesser trochanter, **237**, 238*f*
Lesser tubercle, **228**, 229*f*
Letdown reflex, oxytocin and, 607, **1093–1094**, 1094*f*
Lethal dominant genes, 1106
Lethal hit, cytotoxic T cell, **792**
Lethargy, 455

Leukemias, 648
Leukocyte(s) (white blood cells), **126**, 133, 134*t*, 135*f*, 635, 635*f*, 637, **643–648**, 644*f*, 645*t*. *See also specific type*
disorders of, 646–648
granular (granulocytes), 643, **644–646**, 644*f*, 645*t*
nongranular (agranulocytes), 643, 644*f*, 645*t*, **646**
production/life span of, 645*t*, 646
in urine, 985*t*
Leukocyte count, 643, 644*f*, 657
differential, **657**
Leukocytosis, **643**, 771, 771*f*
Leukocytosis-inducing factors, 771
Leukopenia, **646–648**
Leukoplakia, 142*b*
Leukopoiesis, **646**, 647*f*
Leukotrienes, 45*t*, 596, **769**
in inflammation, **769**
Levator ani muscle, 344*t*, 345*f*, 987
Levator labii superioris muscle, **330*t***, 331*f*
Levator palpebrae superioris muscle, 548*f*, **549**
Levator scapulae muscle, 346*t*, 348*f*, **348*t***, 349*f*
Lever(s), **323–324**, 323–324*f*, 325*f*
Lever systems, **323–324**, 323*f*, 324*f*, 325*f*
Leydig (interstitial) cells, **1026**, 1027*f*
testosterone produced by, 1026, 1039, 1039*f*
LH. *See* Luteinizing hormone
LHA. *See* Lateral hypothalamic area
Li. *See* Lithium
Lids (eyelids), **548–549**, 548*f*
Lieberkühn, crypts of (intestinal crypts/glands), **879**, 879*f*
Life, necessary functions/maintenance of, 4–8, 5*f*
Life cycle, cell, **95–100**, 96*f*, 97*f*, 98–99*f*. *See also* Cell life cycle
Ligament(s), 129, 131, **252**. *See also specific named ligament*
syndesmoses connected by, 249
of synovial joints, 251*f*, **252**
joint stability and, 253
of vertebral column, 217
Ligamentum arteriosum, 665*f*, 667*f*, **688**, 1086*f*, **1093**
Ligamentum flavum, 131, **217**, 218*f*
Ligamentum nuchae, 131, 339*f*
Ligamentum teres (ligament of head of femur), 237, **267**, 267*f*
Ligamentum teres (round ligament), **881**, 882*f*, 1086*f*, **1093**
Ligamentum venosum, 1086*f*, **1093**
Ligand(s), **81**, 82*f*
Ligand-gated (chemically-gated) channel(s), **395**, 396*f*
muscle fiber action potential and, 287, 287*f*
Ligase, DNA, **96**
Light
focusing of on retina, 557–559, 558*f*, 560*f*
pupillary reflex and, 565–566
reflection of, **557**
refraction of, **557**, 557*f*

Light (contd.)
visual disorders related to, 559, 560f
wavelength/color of, 556–557, 557f
Light adaptation, **564**
Light (L) chains, **783**, 783f
Light chain kinase (myosin), **307**, 307f
Light energy, 24
Light microscopy, tissue stains for, **115**
Light transduction (phototransduction), 559, 563–564, 564f, 565f
Limb(s) (appendages/extremities). See Lower limbs; Upper limbs
Limb buds, 1082f, **1084**
Limbic association area, **439**
Limbic system, 449t, **452**, 452f
autonomic regulation and, 539f, 540
Line (bone marking), 178t
Linea alba, **342**t, 343f
Linea aspera, **237**, 238f
Linear fracture, 188
Lingual artery, 726f, **726**t, 727f
Lingual frenulum, **859**, 859f
Lingual tonsils, 760, 760f, 808f, **809**, 859f, 860, 860f
Linked genes, **1104**, 1104f
Linker DNA, 93, 93f
Linker proteins, 66, 67f
Linoleic acid, 912
Lip(s) (labia), **858**, 859f
cleft, **904**
Lipase(s), **886**, 896f, **897**, 899f
chief cell secretion of, 870
lipoprotein, **900**, 936
Lipid, **43–47**, 45t, 46f. See also Fat(s)/lipid(s)
in plasma membrane, 64, 65f
Lipid bilayer, plasma membrane, 64, 65f
Lipidemia, diabetic, 623t, 626b
Lipid rafts, **64**
caveolae associated with, 77
in plasma membrane, **64**
Lipid-soluble substances, skin penetrated by, 161
Lipofuscin (aging pigment), 389–390
Lipogenesis, **931**, 932f, 934t
Lipolysis, **931–932**, 932f, 934t, 939–940, 939f
Lipoprotein(s), 45t, 51t, **943**
in atherosclerosis, 702–703b
high-density, 702b, **943**, 943f
lipid transport and, 943, 943f
low-density, 702b, **943**, 943f
very low density (VLDLs), 935, **943**, 943f
Lipoprotein (a), 702b
Lipoprotein lipase, **900**, 936
in obesity, 948b
Liposomes, **109**
skin lotions containing, 162–163
Liposuction, 949b
Liquid(s), 24
Lithium, atomic structure of, 27, 27f
Lithotripsy, shock wave, for renal calculi, 986

Liver, 852f, 880–884, **881**, 882f, 883f, 888t. See also under Hepatic
autonomic innervation/effects and, 528f, 529f, 533f, 538t
bile composition and, 884
bleeding disorders and, 653–654
digestive function of, 881, 884, 888t
glycogenolysis in, 938, 939f
gross anatomy of, 881, 882f
homeostatic imbalances and, 84
lipid transport to, 943
lipolysis in, 939–940, 939f
metabolic fuel used by, 935t
metabolic functions of, 941–944, 942t, 943f
absorptive state and, 937f
cholesterol regulation and, 944
postabsorptive state and, 938, 939–940, 939f
microscopic anatomy of, 881–884, 883f
round ligament of (ligamentum teres), 881, 882f, 1086f, **1093**
Liver cells (hepatocytes), **881**, 883f
metabolic functions of, 941–944, 942t, 943f
Liver lobules, **881**, 883f
Liver sinusoids, **881**, 883f
LM. See Light microscopy
Load, **289**, **323**
contraction duration/velocity affected by, 303, 304f
in lever system, **323**, 323–324f, 325f
Lobar arteries, 722f, **722**t
Lobar (secondary) bronchi, 813f, **814**
Lobe(s), **815**, **962**, **1047**
of breast, 1047, 1047f
of cerebral hemispheres, 433, 434f
of kidney, **962**
of liver, 881, 882f
of lungs, **815**, 817f, 818f
of multicellular exocrine gland, 122
of thyroid gland, 608, 609f
Lobule(s), **816**, **574**, **1048**
of breast, 1047f, **1048**
of ear (earlobes), **574**, 575f
of liver, **881**, 883f
of lung, **816**, 817f
of testis, 1026, 1027f
thymic, 759, 760f
Lockjaw, 316
Locus (gene), 1102
Long bones, **174**, 175f
endochondral ossification in, **183–184**, 183f
postnatal growth of, 184–185, 184f, 185f
structure of, 176f, 177–178
Longissimus capitis/cervicis/thoracis muscles, **338**t, 339f
Longitudinal arches of foot, medial and lateral, **241**, 241f
Longitudinal fissure, **433**, 434f, 435f
Longitudinal layer of smooth muscle, 305, 305f
in alimentary canal muscularis, 857, 857f
in stomach muscularis, 868f, 869f

Longitudinal ligaments, **217**, 218f
Longitudinal muscle layer. See Longitudinal layer of smooth muscle
Long reflexes, 854, 855f
Long-term memory (LTM), **457**, 458f
Long-term potentiation (LTP), 413, **460**
in memory, **460**
Long thoracic nerve, 506f, 507t
Loop diuretics, 982
Loop of Henle, 965f, **966**, 967f, **983**f
absorptive capability of, 976–978, 977f
as countercurrent multiplier, **979**–981, 980f
Loose connective tissue, **126–129**, 127–128f, 134t
Lordosis, 217, 243–244
during pregnancy, 1089
Loudness, 579f, **580**
detection of, 583
Lou Gehrig's disease (amyotrophic lateral sclerosis/ALS), 476–477
Low-density lipoproteins (LDLs), 702b, **943**, 943f
recommended blood levels of, 943
Lower limbs. See also Foot; Leg; Thigh
arteries of, 725f, 734–735f, 734–735t
bones of, 199–233, 237–241, 238f, 239f, 240f, 241f, 242t
innervation of, 507–510, 508f, 508t, 509f, 510t
veins of, 737f, 744f, 744t
Lower motor neurons, 474
Lower trunk, brachial plexus, **505**, 506f
LTM. See Long-term memory
LTP. See Long-term potentiation
Lumbar arteries, 730f, **732**f, 733f
Lumbar curvature of spine, **217**, 217f
developmental aspects of, 243
Lumbar enlargement, 467f, **468**, 502f
Lumbar fascia, 367f
Lumbar nerves, 502f
Lumbar plexus, 502f, **507**, 508f, 508t
Lumbar puncture (spinal tap), **468**, 468f
Lumbar regions, 17, 20f
Lumbar splanchnic nerves, 532, 533f
Lumbar trunks, **754**, 755f
Lumbar veins, 736f, **740**f, 741f, **741**t, 742f, **742**t, 743f
Lumbar vertebrae, **216**, 217f, 220, 221f, 222t
Lumbosacral plexus, 507–510, 508f, 508t, 509f, 510t
Lumbosacral trunk, **507**, 508f, 509, 509f
Lumbrical muscles
of foot, **376**t, 377f
of hand, **360**t, 361f, **362**t
Lumen, **695**
blood vessel, **695**, 696f
circular layer of smooth muscle affecting, 305

Luminal membrane, renal tubule, in transcellular route of tubular reabsorption, 974
sodium reabsorption and, 974, 976f
Lumpectomy, **1048**
Lunate, 231, 231f, 232t
Lung(s), 805f, 807t, **815–818**, 817f, 818f. See also under Pulmonary and Respiratory
autonomic innervation/effects and, 528f, 529f, 533f, 537, 538t
blood supply/innervation of, 816f, 818
collapse of (atelectasis), **820**
developmental aspects of, 843
gross anatomy of, 815–818, 817f, 818f
perfusion (blood flow) of, 717
Lung (respiratory) alveoli, 807t, 814f, **815**, 816f
developmental aspects of, 843
gas partial pressures in, 827t, 828
Lung cancer, 842
Lung compliance, **824**
Lung recoil
in expiration, 822, 822f
intrapleural pressure and, 819
Lung volume reduction surgery, 841
Lunule, 160, 160f
Lupus erythematosus, systemic (SLE), 797, **800**
Luteal phase of ovarian cycle, 1050, 1051f, 1052, 1055f
Luteinizing hormone (LH), 602f, **605**, 607t, **1038**
in female reproductive function
ovarian cycle, 1053f, 1054, 1055f
ovulation, **1052**, 1053f, 1054, 1055f
uterine (menstrual) cycle, 1055f, 1056
in male reproductive function, 1038, 1039, 1039f
Luteolytic (ischemic) phase, of ovarian cycle, 1052
Luxation(s)/dislocation(s), **270**
Lyme disease, **271**
Lymph, **753**
transport of, 754–755
Lymphadenopathy, **761**
Lymphangiography, **761**
Lymphangitis, 754
Lymphatic(s). See Lymphatic vessels
Lymphatic capillaries, 697f, **753–754**, 753f
Lymphatic collecting vessels, 753f, **754**, 755f
edema and, 754–755
Lymphatic ducts, 753f, **754**, 755f
Lymphatic system, 7f, 697f, **752–765**, **753**, 753f, 755f
autonomic nervous system and, 542b
cardiovascular system and, 746b
cells and tissues of, 755–756, 756f
developmental aspects of, 761
digestive system and, 902b, 903b
endocrine system and, 628b

functions of, 7f
homeostatic relationships of, 762b, 763b
integumentary system and, 166b, 167b
lymph nodes in, 755f, 756–758, 757f
muscular system and, 314b, 315b
organs of, 758–761, 758f
reproductive system and, 1064b
respiratory system and, 844b, 845b
skeletal system and, 192b
urinary system and, 1018b
vessels of (lymphatics), 753–755, 753f, 755f
Lymphatic tissues. See Lymphoid tissues
Lymphatic trunks, 753f, 754
Lymphatic vessels (lymphatics), 753–755, 753f, 755f. See also specific type and Lymphatic system
afferent and efferent, 757, 757f
edema and, 754–755
Lymphedema, 755
Lymph node(s), 697f, 753f, 755f, 756–758, 757f. See also specific type
in cancer, 758, 764
in infection, 757
malignancy of (Hodgkin's disease), 761, 796
reticular tissue in, 756, 756f
sentinel, 764
Lymphoblast, 646, 647f
Lymphocytes, 125f, 126, 135f, 637f, 644f, 645t, 646, 756, 756f, 777–779, 778f. See also B lymphocytes; T lymphocytes
antigen receptor/antibody diversity and, 779, 784
differentiation/maturation of, 777–778, 778f, 779f
formation of, 647f
immune functions of, 756, 777–779, 778f
intraepithelial, 879
large granular, 768–769
recirculation of, 779
Lymphocytic leukemia, 648
Lymphoid cells, 755–756, 756f
Lymphoid follicles/nodules, 756, 757f
aggregated (Peyer's patches), 758f, 760–761, 761f, 880
in small intestine, 880
Lymphoid organs, 758–761, 758f. See also specific type and Lymph node(s)
developmental aspects of, 761
primary/secondary, 777
Lymphoid stem cells, 646, 647f
Lymphoid tissues, 756, 756f
cancer of
Hodgkin's disease, 761, 796
non-Hodgkin's lymphoma, 764
developmental aspects of, 761
mucosa-associated (MALT), 761, 856, 857f, 879f

Lymphoma, 761
non-Hodgkin's, 764
Lymph sacs, 761
Lymph sinuses, 757, 757f
Lysine, 48f
Lysis, cell, in antibody mechanism of action, 785, 785f
Lysosomal enzymes, in bone resorption, 186
Lysosomes, 63f, 75, 76f, 86–87, 86f, 87f, 94t, 768
in phagocytosis, 768, 769f
in Tay-Sachs disease, 87
Lysozyme, 549
intestinal secretion of, 879
in lacrimal fluid, 549
in mucus, 807
in saliva, 860

M. See Molarity
MAC. See Membrane attack complex
Macrocytes, 642
Macromolecules, 47
Macrophage(s), 75, 125f, 126, 646, 647f, 768, 769f. See also Phagocytosis/phagocytes
alveolar, 815
antigen presentation by, 779
hepatic (Kupffer cells), 699, 768, 881, 883f
lymphoid, 756
Macroscopic (gross) anatomy, 2
Macula(e), of utricle and saccule, 576, 577f, 584–585, 584f, 585f
activating receptors of, 584–585, 585f
anatomy of, 584, 584f
Macula densa, 968–969, 968f
tubuloglomerular feedback and, 972, 973f, 974
Macula lutea, 552f, 553
Macular degeneration, age-related (ARMD), 589
Magnesium, 26t, 918t
balance of, abnormalities of, 1003t
dietary, 918t
in plasma/interstitial fluid/intracellular fluid, 997f
Magnetic resonance imaging (MRI), 14, 15f, 19b
in diagnosis of CNS dysfunction, 477
functional (fMRI), 19b
Magnetic resonance spectroscopy (MRS), 19b
Magnitude estimation, 490
Main (primary) bronchi, 813f, 814
Main pancreatic duct, 878f, 885
Major calyces, 962, 963f
Major duodenal papilla, 877, 878f
Major histocompatibility complex (MHC)/MHC proteins, 777, 786–789, 787f, 788f
transplantation and, 792–793
Major nutrients, 911
Malabsorption, 901
Male(s)
pelvis in, 235, 236t
puberty in, 1063

urethra in, 987, 987f, 1025f, 1029f, 1030
Male infertility, 1038
Male pattern baldness, 159
Male pronucleus, 1073, 1075f
Male reproductive system, 7f. See also specific organ or structure
anatomy of, 1025–1031, 1025f
embryologic/fetal development of, 1061f
functions/physiology of, 7f, 1031–1040, 1034f, 1035f, 1036f, 1037f, 1039f
hormonal regulation of, 1038–1040, 1039f
Male sexual response, 1031–1032
Malignant neoplasm, 142b. See also Cancer
Malleoli, medial and lateral, 238, 239f
Malleus (hammer), 215t, 575f
MALT. See Mucosa-associated lymphatic tissue
Maltase, 896f, 897
Maltose (malt sugar), 43, 44f, 895, 896f
Mammary artery, internal (internal thoracic artery), 727f, 728f, 728–729t, 729f
Mammary glands (breasts), 156, 1047–1049, 1047f
cancer of, 1048, 1048f
pregnancy affecting, 1089
prolactin affecting, 605
Mammillary bodies, 443, 443f, 444f
Mammography, 142b, 1048, 1048f
Mandible, 202f, 203f, 209, 210f, 215t
Mandibular angle, 203f, 209, 210f
Mandibular branch of facial nerve, 498t, 499t
Mandibular condyle, 203f, 209, 210f, 215t, 268, 268f
Mandibular division of trigeminal nerve (cranial nerve V_3), 497t
muscles of mastication supplied by, 332t
Mandibular foramina, 203f, 209, 210f, 215t
Mandibular fossa, 204, 205f, 207f, 210f, 214t, 268, 268f
Mandibular notch, 203f, 209, 210f
Mandibular ramus/rami, 203f, 209, 210f
Mandibular symphysis, 202f, 209, 215t
Manganese, 919t
Mantoux test, 799
Manubrium, 223, 224f
MAP. See Mean arterial pressure
MAPs. See Morning-after pills
Marasmus, 955
Marfan's syndrome, 144
Marginal artery, 665f
right, 669, 669f
Margination, 771, 771f
Marrow (bone). See Bone marrow
Marrow (medullary) cavity, 176f, 177
formation of, 183f, 184
Masculinization, in adrenogenital syndrome, 618

Mass, 24
Masseter muscle, 326f, 332t, 333f
Mass movements/peristalsis, 888t, 893–894
Mass number, 27
Mast cells, 125f, 126, 646, 769
in immediate hypersensitivity, 798, 798f
Mastectomy
radical, 1048
simple, 1048
Mastication (chewing), 866, 888t
muscles of, 332t, 333f
Mastoid air cells, 574
Mastoid antrum, 574
Mastoiditis, 207
Mastoid process, 202f, 203f, 204, 205f, 207f, 214t
Mastoid region, temporal bone, 204, 207f
Mastoid sinuses (mastoid air cells), 207
Maternal antibodies, passive immunity and, 782, 782f
Maternal chromosome, 1032
Matrix
bone, 133, 133f
cartilage, 131, 131f, 173
centrosome, 89, 89f
connective tissue, 107, 124, 125f, 134t
extracellular, 107, 124, 125f, 134t, 173
hair, 157, 158f
mitochondrial, 83
nail, 160, 160f
Matrix metalloproteinases, 165
Matter, 24
in combination (molecules/mixtures), 28–30, 29f
composition of, 25–28, 25f, 26t, 27f, 28f
Maxillary artery, 726f, 726t, 727f
Maxillary bones/maxilla(e), 202f, 203f, 205f, 210, 210f, 213f, 215t
Maxillary division of trigeminal nerve (cranial nerve V_2), 497t
Maxillary sinuses, 201f, 210, 216t
Maximal stimulus, 295, 295f
M cells, 568
Mean arterial pressure, 705, 705f, 710, 711f
Meatus (bone marking), 178t
Mechanical advantage, in lever system, 323, 323f
Mechanical digestion, 853–854, 853f, 888t. See also Digestion
Mechanical disadvantage, in lever system, 323, 324f
Mechanical energy, 24
Mechanically-gated channel(s), 395
Mechanical stress, bone remodeling and, 187–188, 187f, 188f
Mechanoreceptors, 485, 487f
in digestion, 854, 855f
lactation and, 1093, 1094f
Meconium, 1094
Medial (term), 12t
Medial (vertebral) border of scapula, 227f, 228

Medial circumflex femoral artery, 734f, **734**t, 735f
Medial commissure, **548**, 548f
Medial condyle, **237**, **238**
  of femur, **237**, 238f
  of tibia, **238**, 239f
Medial cords, brachial plexus, **505**, 506f
Medial cuneiform bone, **240**, 240f, 242t
Medial epicondyle, **228**, **237**
  of femur, **237**, 238f
  of humerus, **228**, 229f
Medial geniculate nuclei/bodies, 442, 444f, **582**
  in auditory pathway, 442, **582**, 582f
Medial lemniscus tract, 448, 448f, **471**, 472f
Medial longitudinal arch of foot, **241**, 241f
Medial malleolus, **238**, 239f
Medial meniscus of knee, 262–263f
Medial muscles/muscle compartment, of hip and thigh, 363t, 364f, 365t, 380t, 381f
Medial (large cell) nuclear group, 448f, **452**
Medial patellar retinaculum, 262f, **263**
Medial plantar artery, 734f, 735f, **735**t
Medial plantar nerve, **510**, 510t
Medial plantar vein, **744**t
Medial pterygoid muscle, **332**t, 333f
Medial rectus muscle, **550**, 550f
Medial rotation, 256, 257f
  of lower limb, 380t, 381f
  of upper limb, 358t, 359f
Medial supracondylar line, **237**, 238f
Medial supracondylar ridge, **228**, 229f
Medial umbilical ligaments, 1086f, **1093**
Median antebrachial vein, 740f, **740**t, 741f
Median aperture, **433**, 433f
Median cubital vein, 737f, 740f, **740**t, 741f
Median nerve, **505**, 506f, 507t
  compression of in carpal tunnel (carpal tunnel syndrome), 231
  forearm muscles supplied by, 354t
  injuries of, 505
Median palatine suture, 211, **215**t
Median (midsagittal) plane/section, **14**, 15f
Median sacral artery, 730f, **732**t, 733f
Median sacral crest, 221f, **223**, 367f
Mediastinal arteries, **729**t
Mediastinum, **16**, 16f, **663**
  heart in, 662f, **663**
Mediators, chemical, inflammatory, **772**t
Medical imaging, 18–19b
Medulla, **447**. See also Medulla oblongata
  adrenal. See Adrenal medulla
  hair, 157, 158f

lymph node, **757**, 757f
  ovarian, 1041f, 1042
  renal, **962**, 963f, 965f
    osmotic gradient in, 979f, 981
Medulla oblongata, 443f, 445f, **447**–450, 447f, **449**t
  development of, 431, 431f, 432f
  respiratory centers in, 835, 835f
    respiratory rate/rhythm affected by, 836–838, 836f, 837f, 838f
Medullary (marrow) cavity, 176f, **177**
  formation of, 183f, 184
Medullary cords, lymph node, **757**, 757f
Medullary osmotic gradient, 979f, 981
Medullary (renal) pyramids, **962**, 963f
Medullary respiratory centers, 449, 835, 835f, 836f
  respiratory rate/rhythm affected by, 836–838, 836f, 837f, 838f
Medullary (lymph) sinuses, **757**, 757f
Megakaryoblasts, **648**, 648f
Megakaryocytes, **648**, 648f. See also Platelet(s)
Meibomian (tarsal) glands, 548f, **549**
Meiosis, **97**, **1033**, 1034f, 1035f, **1050**f
  chromosome segregation in, 1103–1104, 1103f
  crossover and genetic recombination and, 1104, 1104f
  equational division of (meiosis II), **1033**, 1034f, 1035f
  fertilization and, 1073, 1075f
  homeostatic imbalances and, 1060
  mitosis compared with, 1033, 1034f
  in oogenesis, 1049, 1050f
  reduction division of (meiosis I), **1033**, 1034f, 1035f
  in spermatogenesis, 1036f, 1037
Meiosis I, 1033, **1034**f, **1035**f, **1050**f
  chromosome segregation in, 1103–1104, 1103f
  crossover and genetic recombination and, 1104, 1104f
Meiosis II, 1033, **1034**f, **1035**f, **1050**f
  fertilization and, 1073, 1075f
Meissner's (tactile) corpuscles, 152, 161, **486**, 487t
Melanin, 150, 151f, **154**
  skin color and, **154**
Melanocytes, 150, 151f
  hair pigment made by, 157
Melanocyte-stimulating hormone (MSH), 603
Melanoma, 162f, **163**
Melanopsin, 566
Melanosomes, 150
Melatonin, 444–445, **620**
Membrane(s). See also specific type
  basement, 116
  body cavity, 16–17, 17f
  of bone, 176f, 177–178
  boundary maintenance and, 5
  cell. See Plasma membrane

covering and lining, 115, 138–139, 138f
  cutaneous, 138f, **139**. See also Skin
  mucous (mucosa), 138f, **139**. See also Mucous membranes
  nuclear, 63f, 91, **91**–93, 92f, 95t
  permeability of, **68**. See also Membrane transport
    action potential and, 399–402, 400–401f
    resting membrane potential and, 396, 397f
  plasma. See Plasma membrane
  serous (serosa), **16**, 17f, 138f, **139**. See also Serous membranes
  synovial, **251**, 251f
Membrane attack complex (MAC), **774**f, **775**
Membrane bones, **182**
Membrane-bound ribosomes, 84
Membrane (cell) junctions, 66–67, 67f
Membrane lipids, 64, 65f
Membrane potentials, **79**–80, 79f
  resting, **79**–80, 79f, **396**–398, **397**f
  as signals, 398–406. See also Action potential
Membrane proteins, 64–66, 65f, 66f
  in exocytosis, 78, 78f
  in receptor-mediated endocytosis, 76, 78f
  as receptors, 64, **81**, 82f
Membrane receptors, 64, **81**, 82f
  in hormone mechanism of action, 596, 596–598, 597f
Membrane transport, 68–79
  active, **68**, 72–79, **73**, 74f, 75f, 76f, 77t, 78f
  passive, **68**, 68–72, 68f, 69f, 70f, 71f, 72t
    facilitated diffusion, 69, **69**–70, 69f, 72t
    osmosis, 69, 69f, **70**–72, 70f, 72t
    simple diffusion, **69**, 69f, 72t
Membranous labyrinth, **576**, 586f
Membranous organelles, 83
Membranous urethra, **987**, 987f, 1025f, 1029f, 1030
Memory, **457**–460, 458f, 459f
  immunological, 775, 780–**781**
  prefrontal cortex and, 438f, 439
Memory cells, 795t
  B cells, **780**, 781, 781f, 794f
  T cells, 787f, 794f
Memory consolidation, **458**
Menarche, **1053**
Mendel, Gregor, 1102
Ménière's syndrome, **583**
Meningeal artery, middle, 208, 726t
Meningeal branch, **502**
Meningeal layer of dura mater, 460f, 461
Meninges (meninx), **461**
  brain, 460f, **461**–463
  inflammation of (meningitis), 463
  spinal, 466–468, 468f, 469f
Meningitis, 463
Meningocele, 478

Menisci (articular discs), **252**, **262**
  of knee, **262**–263, 262–263f
    injury of, 269, 269f
  of temporomandibular joint, 268f, 269
Menix. See Meninges
Menopause, **1063**–1066
Menses, **1054**, 1055f
  blood/iron loss and, 900
Menstrual (uterine) cycle, **1054**–1057, 1055f, 1057t
Menstrual phase of uterine (menstrual) cycle, 1054–1056, 1055f
Menstruation, **1054**, 1055f
  blood/iron loss and, 900
Mental activity. See Cognition/cognitive function
Mental foramina, 202f, 203f, **209**, 210f, **215**t
Mental functioning. See Cognition/cognitive function
Mentalis muscle, **330**t, 331f
mEq/L. See Milliequivalents per liter
Meridia. See Sibutramine
Merkel (tactile) cells, **150**, 151f, 486
Merkel (tactile) discs, 150, 151f, 161, **486**, 487f
Merocrine glands, **122**, 123f
  apocrine sweat glands, **156**
  eccrine sweat glands, 149f, **155**–156, 156f
Mesangial cells
  extraglomerular, 968f, 969
  glomerular, 969
Mesencephalon (midbrain), **430**, 443f, 445f, **445**–447, 445f, 446–447f, 448f, **449**t
  development of, 430, 431, 431f, 432f
Mesenchymal cells, 126, 182–183, 182f
Mesenchymal stem cell regeneration, in joint therapy, 261b
Mesenchyme, **126**
  mesoderm as, 1083
Mesenteric arteries
  inferior, 725f, 730f, **732**t, 733f
  superior, 725f, 730f, 731f, **732**t, 733f
Mesenteric ganglia, inferior and superior, 532, 533f
Mesenteric veins
  inferior, 737f, 742f, **742**t, 743f
  superior, 737f, 742f, **742**t, 743f
Mesentery (mesenteries), **855**, 855f, 877, 892f
Mesocolons, **890**, 891f, 892f
Mesoderm, 141, 141f, 1079f, **1081**, 1081f, 1082f
  differentiation of, 1082f, 1083f, 1084, 1085f
  muscle and, 311, 311f
  extraembryonic, 1079f
  intermediate, **1084**, 1085f
  lateral plate, **1084**, 1085f
  somatic, 1082f, **1084**, 1085f
  splanchnic, 1082f, **1084**, 1085f
Mesometrium, 1043f, **1044**
Mesonephric (Wolffian) ducts, **989**, **1060**
  in gonadal development, **1060**, 1061f
  in kidney development, **989**, 990f

Mesonephros, **989**, 990*f*
Mesosalpinx, **1042**, 1043*f*
Mesothelium, **117**
  in visceral peritoneum, 857
Mesovarium, **1041**, 1041*f*, 1043*f*
Messenger RNA (mRNA), 55, **101**, 102, 102*f*, 107*f*
  processing of, 103
  in translation, 103–105, 104*f*
Messenger RNA complex proteins, 103
Metabolic acidosis, 932, **1014**, 1016*t*
  blood values in, 1017*b*
  respiratory compensations and, 1014–1015
Metabolic (fixed) acids, **1011**
Metabolic alkalosis, **1014**, 1016*t*
  blood values in, 1017*b*
  respiratory compensations and, 1015
Metabolic controls, of blood flow, 714–715, 715*f*
Metabolic rate, **947**, 949
  aging and, 947, 954–955
  heat production and, 947–950, 953
  thyroid hormone/thyroxine affecting, 612*t*, **948**
  total, **949**
Metabolic syndrome, obesity and, 949*b*
Metabolic water (water of oxidation), **998**
Metabolism, 5, 6*f*, **918–944**. *See also specific aspect*
  absorptive state and, **936**, 936–938, 937*f*, 938*f*
  anabolism and catabolism, 5, 895, 918–920, 920*f*
  ATP synthesis, 921–922, 921*f*, 922*f*
  autonomic effects and, 538*t*
    sympathetic division and, 539
  developmental aspects of, 954–955
  energy balance and, 944–954
  homeostatic imbalance and, 954–955
  hormone influences and, 941*t*
  inborn errors of, 954
  liver in, 941–944, 942*t*, 943*f*
    absorptive state and, 937*f*
    postabsorptive state and, 938, 939–940, 939*f*
  muscle, 296–300, 298*f*, 299*f*
    glycogenolysis and, 938–939, 939*f*
  nutrient, 922–934, 935*t*. *See also specific nutrient*
  oxidation-reduction reactions, 37, 920–**921**
  postabsorptive state and, **936**, 938–941, 939*f*, 940*f*
  pregnancy affecting, 1090
  steady state and, 935–936, 935*f*, 936*f*
  thermoregulation and, 947–950, 953
  thyroid hormone/thyroxine affecting, 612*t*, 941*t*, **948**
Metabotropic (G protein–linked) receptors, **81**, 82*f*, **420***f*, **421**

Metacarpal(s), 199*f*, **231–233**, 231*f*, 232*t*
  muscles controlling movement of, 360–362*t*, 361*f*
Metacarpal arteries, 728*f*, **728***t*
Metacarpal veins, 740*f*
Metacarpophalangeal joint (knuckle), 233, 254*t*
Metacarpus (palm of hand), **231**
  bones of (metacarpals), 199*f*, **231–233**, 231*f*, 232*t*
  muscles of, 354*t*, 360–362*t*, 361*f*
Metalloproteinases, matrix, 165
Metanephros, **989**, 990*f*
Metaphase
  in meiosis, 1033, **1034***f*, **1035***f*
  in mitosis, 96*f*, **97**, 99*f*, **1034***f*
Metaphase plate, 99*f*
Metaphysis, 177
Metarteriole, 697*f*, **700**, 700*f*
Metastasis, **142***b*
Metastatic calcification, 613
Metatarsal arteries, dorsal and plantar, 734*f*, 735*f*, **735***t*
Metatarsals, 199*f*, 240, 240*f*, **241**, 242*t*
Metatarsal veins, dorsal, 737*f*, 744*f*
Metatarsophalangeal joint, 255*t*
Metatarsus, bones of (metatarsals), 199*f*, 240, 240*f*, **241**, 242*t*
Metencephalon, **430–431**, 431*f*, 432*f*
Methamphetamine abuse, 414*b*
Methane gas, formation of, 33*f*
Mg. *See* Magnesium
MHC proteins, **777**, 786–789, 787*f*, 788*f*
MHC restriction, **777–778**, 779*f*, 789
Micelles, **899**, 899*f*
Microcephaly, **479**
Microcirculation, **699**
Microcytes, **642**
Microfilaments, **88**, 88*f*, 89*f*, 94*t*
Microglia, 388*f*, **389**
MicroRNAs (miRNAs), 55, 103, **105**
  single stranded, 1108
Microscopic anatomy, **2**
Microscopy, preparing tissue for, 114–115. *See also* Histology
Microtubules, 63*f*, **88**, 88*f*, 89*f*, 94*t*
  in cilia, 90, 90*f*
  kinetochore, 98*f*
  polar, 98*f*
Microvilli, 67*f*, **91**, 91*f*, 95*t*, 115, **878**
  in proximal convoluted tubule, 965*f*, 966
  in small intestine, **878**, 879*f*, 880*f*
Micturition, **988**, 989*f*
  development of control of, 990–991
Micturition center, pontine, 988, 989*f*
Midbrain (mesencephalon), **430**, 443*f*, **445–447**, 445*f*, 446–447*f*, 448*f*, **449***t*
  development of, 430, 431, 431*f*, 432*f*
Midbrain flexure, 431, 432*f*
Middle cardiac vein, 666*f*, 669*f*, **670**
Middle cerebellar peduncles, 446–447*f*, 447, 448*f*, **450**, 451*f*
Middle cerebral arteries, 726*f*, **726***t*, 727*f*

Middle cervical ganglion, **532**, 533*f*
Middle colic artery, 730*f*, **732***t*, 733*f*
Middle cranial fossa, 201*f*, 206*f*, **207**
Middle ear (tympanic cavity), **20**, **574–576**, 575*f*, 576*f*
Middle meningeal artery, 208, 726*t*
Middle nasal conchae, 202*f*, **209**, 209*f*, **215***t*, 807–809, 808*f*
Middle nasal meatus, 808*f*
Middle phalanx
  finger, 231*f*, 232*t*, 233
  toe, 240*f*, 242*t*
Middle pharyngeal constrictor muscle, 335*f*, 335*t*
Middle scalene muscle, 336*t*, 337*f*
Middle suprarenal arteries, 730*f*, **732***t*, 733*f*
Middle thyroid vein, 738*f*, 739*f*
Middle trunk, brachial plexus, **505**, 506*f*
Midpalmar muscles, 360*t*, 361*f*, 362*t*
Midpiece of sperm, **1037**, 1037*f*
Midsagittal (median) plane/section, **14**, 15*f*
Mifepristone (RU-486), 1096*b*
MIF/MIS. *See* Müllerian inhibitory factor/substance
Migrating motility complex (MMC), **889**
Milia, 165
Milk ejection, oxytocin and, 607, 1093–1094, 1094*f*
Milk intolerance, 897
Milk production, prolactin and, 605
Milk teeth (deciduous/primary dentition), **862**, 862*f*
Milliequivalents per liter, electrolytes measured in, **996–997**
Milligrams per deciliter, 30
Milliosmol, **979**
  milliequivalent per liter and, 997
Millivolt(s), 395
Mineral(s), 8, **917–918**, 918–919*t*
  dietary, 917–918, 918–919*t*
  storage of in bone, 176
  storage of in liver, 942*t*
Mineralocorticoids, **614–616**, 617*t*
  in stress response, 619*f*
Mineral salts, in bone tissue, 180
Minipill, for contraception, 1096*b*
Minivalves, lymphatic capillary, 753*f*, 754
Minor calyces, **962**, 963*f*
Minute ventilation, **825**
MiRNAs. *See* MicroRNAs
MIT. *See* Monoiodotyrosine
Mitochondria, 63*f*, **83–84**, 83*f*, 94*t*
  in cardiac muscle, 673, 674*f*
  free radicals in, 108
Mitochondrial DNA/genes, 83, 1109
Mitochondrial (extranuclear) inheritance, 1108, 1109
Mitosis, 96*f*, **97**, 98–99*f*, **1034***f*
  meiosis compared with, 1033, 1034*f*
  in spermatogenesis, 1033, 1036*f*
Mitotic (M) phase of cell cycle, 95, 96*f*, **97–100**, 98–99*f*. *See also* Cell division
Mitotic spindle, 98*f*
Mitral cells, olfactory bulb, 569*f*, 570

Mitral (bicuspid) valve, 667*f*, **670**, 671*f*
Mitral valve prolapse, **690**
Mittelschmerz, 1052
Mixed nerves, **491**
Mixture(s), **29–30**, 29*f*
  compounds differentiated from, 30
M lines, in skeletal muscle, 280*f*, **281**
  in sliding filament model of contraction, 284
MMC. *See* Migrating motility complex
Modiolus, **577**, 578*f*
Molarity, **30**
Molars, **862**, 862*f*
Mole (concentration unit), **30**
Mole(s) (skin), 154
  melanoma arising in, 163
Molecular biology, 2
Molecular chaperones, **50–51**, 51*t*
Molecular formula, **36**
Molecular mimicry, in diabetes mellitus, 626*b*
Molecular weight, **30**
Molecule(s), 3, 4*f*, **28**
Molybdenum, 919*t*
Monoblast, **646**, 647*f*
Monoclonal antibodies, **786**
Monocytes, 637*f*, 644*f*, 645*t*, **646**, 647*f*, **768**
  macrophages derived from, 768
Monoglycerides, **897**, 899*f*
Monohydrogen phosphate, 1012, 1013*f*
Monoiodotyrosine (MIT/T_1), **610**, 610*f*
Monomer(s), **42**, 44*f*
  antibody, **783**, 783*f*
  in chemical digestion, 895
Mononucleosis, 648, **764**
Monosaccharides, **43**, 43*f*, 895, 912
Monospermy, **1073**
Monosynaptic reflex, **514**, 516
Monounsaturated fats, **46–47**
Monro, foramen of (interventricular foramen), **432**, 433*f*
Mons pubis, 1040*f*, **1046**, 1046*f*
Morbid obesity, 948*b*
Morning-after pills, 1096*b*
Morning sickness, 1090
Morula, **1075**, 1076*f*
mOsm. *See* Milliosmol
Motilin, 875*t*, 889, 889*t*
Motility, intestinal. *See* Intestinal motility
Motion sickness, 587
Motor areas, **435–437**, 436*f*, 438*f*
Motor control, levels of, 512–513, 513*f*
Motor cortex, primary (somatic), **435–437**, 436*f*, 438*f*
  homeostatic imbalances and, 437
Motor (efferent) division of peripheral nervous system, **386**, 387*f*, 485*f*
Motor endings, **512**
Motor homunculi, **435–437**, 438*f*
Motor integration, 512–513, 513*f*
Motor memory, **458**
Motor molecules/proteins, **88**, 89*f*

Motor (efferent) nerves, 289, **491**
Motor (efferent) neurons, 285, 289, 293f, **394**, **394**t
α, **515**, 515f
in autonomic versus somatic nervous system, 526–527, 527f
development of, 466
in muscle contraction, 285, 310t
stimulus frequency changes and, 294, 294f, 301, 301f
stimulus strength changes and, 295, 295f
in neuromuscular junction, 293f
in reflex arc, 514, 514f
somatic, 285
upper and lower, 474
Motor nuclei, dorsal, 530
Motor output, **386**, 386f
Motor (descending) pathways/tracts, 470, 471f, 473–476, 474t, 475f
Motor proteins/molecules, **88**, 89f
Motor speech area (Broca's area), 436f, **437**
Motor unit(s), **289**–293, 293f
force of contraction affected by number of, 300, 301f
Mountain sickness, acute, 839
Mouth (oral cavity), **20**, 852f, **858**–864, 859f, 888t. See also specific structure
development of, 901f, 904
digestive processes occurring in, 866, 888t, 895, 896f
Movement. See also specific type
cerebellar processing and, 450
muscular system and, 5, 6f, 276, 312
skeletal system/bones and, 5, 6f, 175
at synovial joints, 253–259, 256–258f
osteoarthritis and, 270
MPF (M-phase promoting factor), cell division control and, **100**
M (mitotic) phase of cell cycle, 95, 96f, **97**–100, 98–99f. See also Cell division
M-phase promoting factor (MPF), cell division control and, **100**
MRI. See Magnetic resonance imaging
mRNA. See Messenger RNA
MRS. See Magnetic resonance spectroscopy
MS. See Multiple sclerosis
MSH. See Melanocyte-stimulating hormone
mtDNA. See Mitochondrial DNA
Mucin, 121
in cystic fibrosis, 843
in saliva, 860
Mucosa. See Mucous membranes
Mucosa-associated lymphatic tissue (MALT), **761**, 856, 857f, 879f
Mucosal barrier, **870**
Mucosal iron barrier, 900
Mucous cells, **121**, **860**
in salivary glands, **860**
in stomach, 869f, 870
Mucous glands, in respiratory mucosa of nose, 807

Mucous membranes (mucosae), 138f, **139**
of alimentary canal, **856**, 857f
of anal canal, 893
in body defense, 767–768, 772t
of colon, 891–892
of esophagus, 865, 865f
nasal, 807, 809
autonomic innervation/effects and, 529f, 533f, 538t
homeostatic imbalance and, 809
of pharynx, 808f
respiratory, **807**, 808f
of stomach, 869, 869f, 870
tracheal, **812**, 812f
of ureters, 986, 986f
of urinary bladder, 986
vaginal, 1044–1045
Mucous neck cells, 869f, **870**
Mucus, 121, **860**
in body defense, 772t
cervical glands producing, 1044
duodenal (Brunner's) glands secreting, 880
gastric epithelium producing, 870
mucosa of alimentary canal producing, 856
mucous neck cells producing (acidic), 870
respiratory mucosa of nose producing, 807
salivary glands producing, **860**
small intestine epithelium producing, 878
submucosa of trachea producing, 813
Müllerian (paramesonephric) ducts, **1060**, 1061f
Müllerian inhibitory factor/substance, 1060
Multiaxial movement, **253**
Multicellular glands, 121
exocrine, **121**–124, 123f
Multimodal association areas, **439**
Multineuronal pathways, **476**
Multinucleate cells, **91**
Multipennate fascicle pattern/muscles, 322f, 323
Multiple-allele inheritance, **1106**, 1106t
Multiple motor unit summation (recruitment), **295**, 295f, 296f
contraction duration/velocity affected by, 303
Multiple sclerosis, **405**–406, 797
Multipolar neurons, **392**, 393–394t
Multiunit smooth muscle, 309–310t, **311**
Mumps, 860
Murmurs, heart, **681**
Muscarinic agents, autonomic activity and, 537t
Muscarinic receptors, 416t, **535**, 536t
Muscle(s)/muscle tissue, 114f, **136**–138, 136–137f, 275–319, 279t. See also specific type and Muscular system; Skeletal muscle(s)
cardiac, **136**, 137f, **276**, 309–310t, **672**–676, 673f, 674f, 675f

developmental aspects of, 311–316, 311f
functions of, 276–277
homeostatic imbalances and, 312
homeostatic relationships of, 314b, 315b
metabolic fuel used by, 935t
skeletal, **136**, 136f, **276**, **277**–305, 278f, 279t, 309–310t
smooth, **136**, 137f, **276**, 305–311, 305f, 309–310t
special characteristics of, 276–277
types of, 276
Muscle atrophy, disuse causing, 305
Muscle attachments, 277–278
naming muscles and, 321–322
Muscle-bound, 304
Muscle cells/fibers, **136**, 136f, 137f, 237f, **276**, 279t, 309t. See also Cardiac muscle cells; Skeletal muscle fibers/cells; Smooth muscle fibers/cells
contraction of. See Muscle contraction
development of, 311–312, 311f
types/classification of, 302–303, 302f, 302t, 303f
Muscle contraction, **284**, 310t
cardiac muscle, 276, 310t, 673–675, 675f
heat production during, 276–277, 300, 952f, 953
metabolic fuel used during, 935t
movement and, 5, 6f, 276
skeletal muscle, 276, **284**, 284–289, 284f, 285f, 286f, 287f, 288f, 289–296, 293f, 294f, 295f, 296f, 310t. See also Skeletal muscle(s)/skeletal muscle tissue, contraction of
sliding filament model of, **284**, 284f, 307, 307f
smooth muscle, 276, 307–311, 307f, 310t
Muscle cramps, heat loss and, 951
Muscle fascicles, **277**, 278f, **279**t
arrangement of, 322–323, 322f
naming muscles and, 321
Muscle fatigue, 295, **300**
Muscle fibers/cells. See Muscle cells/fibers
Muscle kinase, in muscle fiber formation, 311–312
Muscle metabolism, 296–300, 298f, 299f
glycogenolysis and, 938–939, 939f
Muscle spasm, 316
Muscle spindle, **488**, 488t, 515, 515f, 516f, 517f
adjusting sensitivity of, 518
Muscle strain, 316
Muscle stretch
cardiac muscle contraction and, 310t
skeletal muscle contraction and, 301–302, 301f, 310t
smooth muscle contraction and, 308, 310t
Muscle tension, **289**
skeletal muscle contraction and, **289**

smooth muscle contraction and, 308
Muscle tone, 295–**296**
joint stability and, 253
smooth muscle, 308
Muscle twitch, **293**, 294f
Muscular (distributing) arteries, 697f, **698**, 698t
Muscular dystrophy, **312**
Muscularis externa
of alimentary canal, **857**, 857f
of esophagus, 865, 865f
of small intestine, 880
of stomach, 868f, 869, 869f
of ureter, 986, 986f
of vagina, 1044
Muscularis mucosae, of alimentary canal mucosa, **856**, 857f
Muscular pump, venous return and, **706**, 706f, 707f
Muscular system, 6f, 320–384. See also Muscle(s)/muscle tissue; Skeletal muscle(s)
autonomic nervous system and, 542b, 543b
cardiovascular system and, 746b, 747b
digestive system and, 902b
endocrine system and, 628b
functions of, 6f
homeostatic imbalances and, 312
homeostatic relationships of, 314b, 315b
integumentary system and, 166b, 314b
interactions of muscles in body and, 321
lymphatic system and, 762b
metabolic fuel used by, 935t
movement and, 5, 6f, 276, 312
naming muscles and, 321–322
reproductive system and, 1064b, 1065b
respiratory system and, 844b, 845b
skeletal system and, 192b, 193b, 314b, 315b
lever systems and, 323–324, 323–324f, 325f
in thermoregulation, 276–277, 300, 952f, 953
thyroid hormone affecting, 612t
urinary system and, 1018b
Musculocutaneous nerve, **505**, 506f, 507t
MuSK. See Muscle kinase
Mutation(s), **109**, **1112**
in carcinogenesis, 142b, 143f
Myalgia, **316**
Myasthenia gravis, 285, 797
Myelencephalon, **431**, 431f, 432f
Myelinated fibers, **391**
action potential conduction velocity and, 404–405, 405f
Myelination, 391–392, 392f
in CNS maturation, 478
conduction velocity of action potential and, 404–405, 405f
homeostatic imbalances/multiple sclerosis and, 405–406

Myelin sheath(s), **391**–392, 392*f*, 491
  neuroglia forming, 388*f*, 389,
    391, 392*f*
Myelin sheath gaps (nodes of Ranvier), 390*f*, **391**
Myelitis, **479**
Myeloblasts, **646**, 647*f*
Myelocytes, **646**, 647*f*
Myelocytic leukemia, 648
Myelogram, **479**
Myeloid stem cells, **639**, 639*f*,
    646, 647*f*
Myelomeningocele, 478, 478*f*
Myeloproliferative disorder, **658**
Myenteric nerve plexus, **857**, 857*f*
Mylohyoid muscle, **334***t*, 335*f*
Myo (prefix), **276**
Myoblasts, **311**, 311*f*, 312
Myoblast transfer therapy, for muscular dystrophy, 312
Myocardial infarction (heart attack), **670**
  cardiac output and, **687**
Myocarditis, **690**
Myocardium, **663**–664, 663*f*, 667*f*
Myoclonus, **479**
Myofascial pain syndrome, **316**
Myofibrils, **278**, 279*t*
  cardiac muscle, 309*t*, 673
  skeletal muscle, **278**–282, 279*t*,
    280*f*, 309*t*
Myofilaments, 136, 279*t*, 281
  in skeletal muscle, 279*t*, 280*f*,
    281–282, 282*f*
  in smooth muscle, 306–307, 306*f*
Myogenic controls, of blood flow,
    715, 715*f*
  cerebral flow and, 716
  glomerular filtration rate and,
    972, 973*f*
Myogenic mechanism, **972**
Myoglobin, **278**
Myogram, **293**
Myoid cells, **1026**, 1027*f*
Myomesin, 282
Myometrium, 1043*f*, **1044**
Myopathy, **316**
Myopia (nearsightedness), **559**, 560*f*
Myosin, 51*t*, 280*f*, 281, 282*f*,
    283*f*, 310*t*
  clot retraction and, 652
  cross bridge activity and,
    288–289, 292*f*
  in excitation-contraction coupling, 291*f*
  in sliding filament model, 284
  unconventional, 88
Myosin (thick) filaments, 88,
    136, **281**
  in cardiac muscle, 673
  in skeletal muscle, 280*f*, **281**, 282*f*
  in sliding filament model, 284,
    284*f*, 307, 307*f*
  in smooth muscle, 306, 307,
    307*f*, 310*t*
Myosin heads, 281, 282*f*, 283*f*, 289
  in cross bridge cycle, 288–289,
    292*f*
  in sliding filament model,
    284, 289
  in smooth muscle, 306

Myosin kinase (myosin light chain
    kinase), **307**, 307*f*
Myosin tail, 281, 282*f*
Myotome, 1082*f*, **1084**, 1085*f*
Myotonic dystrophy, **316**
Myotubules, 311, 311*f*
Myringotomy, 57
Mys (prefix), **276**
Myxedema, **611**
Myxovirus, mumps caused by, 860

N. *See* Nitrogen
n°. *See* Neutron(s)
Na. *See* Sodium
Na⁺-K⁺ ATPase (sodium-potassium
    pump), 73, **396**, 397*f*
  action potential and, 402
  in primary active transport,
    73, 74*f*
    tubular reabsorption of
      sodium and, 974, 976*f*
  resting membrane potential and,
    80, **396**–398, **397***f*
  in secondary active transport,
    73, 75*f*
    tubular reabsorption and,
      975, 976*f*
    of sodium, 974, 976*f*
NaCl. *See* Sodium chloride
NAD⁺. *See* Nicotinamide adenine
    dinucleotide
Nail(s), **160**, 160*f*
Nail bed, **160**, 160*f*
Nail body, **160**, 160*f*
Nail folds, **160**, 160*f*
Nail matrix, **160**, 160*f*
Nail root, 160, 160*f*
Naive lymphocytes, 777
Naked (free) nerve endings, 152, 161,
    486, 487*t*
Narcolepsy, 456–457
Nares (nostrils), 805*f*, **806**, 806*f*, 808*f*
Nasal apertures, posterior (choanae),
    806
Nasal bones, 202*f*, 203*f*, **211**,
    213*f*, 215*t*
Nasal cartilages, 173, 174*f*, 806, 806*f*
Nasal cavity, 20, 201*f*, **212**–216, 213*f*,
    805*f*, **806**, 808*f*
Nasal conchae, 202*f*, 209, 212–216,
    807–809, 808*f*
  inferior, 202*f*, **211**, 213*f*, 807–809,
    808*f*
  middle, 202*f*, **209**, 209*f*, 215*t*,
    807–809, 808*f*
  superior, **209**, 215*t*, 807–809, 808*f*
Nasal meatus, 212, 213*f*, 807–809,
    808*f*
Nasal mucosa, 807, 809
  autonomic innervation/effects
    and, 529*f*, 533*f*, 538*t*
  homeostatic imbalance and, 809
Nasal polyps, 846
Nasal septum, 212, **806**
  deviated, 846
Nasal vestibule, 806, 808*f*
Nasolacrimal duct, **549**, 549*f*
Nasopharynx, 808*f*, **809**
Natriuretic peptide, atrial. *See* Atrial
    natriuretic peptide

Natural killer (NK) cells, **768**–769,
    772*t*, 792
Naturally acquired immunity
  active, 781, 782*f*
  passive, 782, 782*f*
Nausea and vomiting, pregnancy
    and, 1090
Navel (umbilicus), 17, 1086*f*
Navicular, 240, 240*f*, 242*t*
N-CAM. *See* Nerve cell adhesion
    molecule
Ne. *See* Neon
NE. *See* Nocturnal enuresis
Near point of vision, **559**
Nearsightedness (myopia), **559**
Nebulin, 282
Neck
  arteries supplying, 726–727*f*,
    726–727*t*
  innervation of, 504–505. *See also*
    Cervical nerves
  muscles of, 326*f*, 327*f*, 336*t*,
    337*f*, 339*f*
    head movement and, 336*t*, 337*f*
    swallowing control and,
      334–335*t*, 335*f*
  veins of, 738–739*f*, 738*t*
Neck of bone
  of femur, 237, 238*f*
  of humerus
    anatomical, 228, 229*f*
    surgical, 228, 229*f*
  of radius, 230*f*
  of rib, 224, 225*f*
Neck of tooth, **863**, 863*f*
Necrosis, 109
Negative chronotropic factors, 685
Negative feedback, **9**, **600**
  in homeostasis, 9–10, 10*f*
  hormone secretion and, **600**, 601*f*
  ovarian function and, 1053*f*, 1054
Negative inotropic agents, 684
Negative nitrogen balance, 914
Negative selection, **778**, 779*f*
Neisseria gonorrhoeae, 1058
Neon, as chemically inert element,
    31*f*
Neonatal period, **1092**–1093. *See also*
    Newborn
Neoplasm, **142***b*
  malignant. *See* Cancer
Neostigmine, autonomic activity
    and, 536
Nephron(s), **964**–969, 967*f*, 983*f*
  blood vessels/capillary beds of,
    966–968, 967*f*
  cortical, **966**, 967*f*
  juxtamedullary, **966**, 967*f*
Nephron loop (loop of Henle), 965*f*,
    966, 967*f*, **983***f*
  absorptive capability of,
    976–978, 977*t*
  as countercurrent multiplier,
    979–981, 980*f*
Nephrotoxin, **991**
Nerve(s), **390**, **491**–511, 492*f*
  cranial, **493**–501, 494*f*, 495–501*t*
  spinal, **502**–511, 502*f*, 503*f*
  structure/classification of,
    491–492, 492*f*
Nerve cell(s). *See* Neuron(s)

Nerve cell adhesion molecule
    (N-CAM), 424
Nerve conduction studies, **520**
Nerve deafness, vestibulocochlear
    damage causing, 499*t*
Nerve endings
  encapsulated, 486, **486**–488,
    487–488*t*. *See also* specific type
  free, 152, 161, **486**, 487*t*
  unencapsulated, 486, 487*t*
Nerve fascicles, 491, 492*f*
Nerve fibers, **391**, 492*f*. *See also* Axon
  classification of, 406
  regeneration of, 491–492, 493*f*
Nerve growth factor, 424, **541**
Nerve impulse(s), 24, 395, **399**–406,
    400–401*f*
  conduction velocity of,
    404–406, 405*f*
  generation of, 399–402, 400–401*f*
  in muscle/muscle fiber contraction, 285, 285*f*, 288, 308
  propagation of, **402**–403, 403*f*
  refractory periods and, 404, 404*f*
  stimulus intensity and, 404
  threshold/all-or-none phenomenon and, 403–**404**
Nerve plexuses, **502**. *See also* specific
    type
Nerve roots, spinal. *See* specific type
    and Spinal roots
Nervous system, 6*f*, **385**–428, **386**.
    See also specific division and
    Nerve cells; Nervous tissue
  autonomic, **386**–387, 387*f*, 485*f*,
    525–546, 526*f*. *See also* Autonomic nervous system
  cardiovascular system and,
    746*b*, 747*b*
  central, **386**, 387*f*, **429**–483. *See
    also* Central nervous system
  developmental aspects of,
    423–424, 424*f*
  digestive system and, 902*b*
  divisions of, 386–388, 387*f*
  endocrine system and, 628*b*, 629*b*
  functions/physiology of, 2–3, 6*f*,
    386, 386*f*
  hormone release controlled
    by, 600
  immune system and, 799
  integumentary system and,
    166*b*, 167*b*
  lymphatic system and, 762*b*
  muscular system and, 314*b*
  peripheral, **386**, 387*f*, **484**–513,
    485, 485*f*. *See also* Peripheral
    nervous system
  reproductive system and, 1064*b*
  respiratory system and, 844*b*
  responsiveness/irritability and, 5,
    6*f*, 395
  skeletal system and, 192*b*
  thyroid hormone affecting, 612*t*
  urinary system and, 1018*b*, 1019*b*
Nervous tissue, 114*f*, 134–136, 135*f*
  developmental aspects of,
    423–424, 424*f*
  histology of, 388–395, 388*f*
  membrane potentials and,
    395–406, 410–411*t*

Nervous tissue (*contd.*)
  neurons. *See* Neuron(s)
  neurotransmitters/receptors and, 413–421, 416–418t
  supporting cells (neuroglia), **388–389**, 388f
  synapses and, **406–413**, 407f
Net effective hydrostatic pressure, 718, 719f
Net filtration pressure (NFP), **718, 971**
  glomerular filtration and, 970, **971**, 971f
Net osmosis, in digestion, 901
Neural crest, 423, **430**, 430f, **541**, 1082f, **1083**
  autonomic nervous system derived from, **541**
Neural folds, **430**, 430f, 1082f, **1083**
Neuralgia, **520**
Neural groove, **430**, 430f, 1082f, **1083**
Neural integration, 386, 386f, **421–422**, 421f, 422f
  motor, 512–513, 513f
  pain perception and, 490–491
  sensory, 488–491, 489f
  somatosensory system organization and, 488–490, 489f
Neural integrators, axon hillock membranes as, 412
Neural layer of retina, 553, 554f
Neural plate, **430**, 430f, 1082f, **1083**
Neural processing, 422–423, 423f
Neural stimuli
  blood pressure and, 706–709, 708f, 1007f
  digestion control and, 538t, 854, 855f, 858
  food intake regulation and, 945–946, 946f
  glomerular filtration rate control and, 972, 973f
  for hormone release, 600, 601f
  respiratory control and, 835–836, 835f, 836f
Neural tube, 423, **430**, 430f, 431f, 1082f, **1083**, 1083f
  preganglionic neurons derived from, 541
Neurilemma, 390f, **391**, 392f
Neuritis, **520**
Neuroblastoma, **424**
Neuroblasts, **423**
Neurocardiogenic (vasovagal) syncope, **544**
Neuroendocrine organ, hypothalamus as, **595**
Neuroepithelial cells, 423
Neurofibrillary tangles, in Alzheimer's disease, 465
Neurofibrils/neurofilaments, **89, 389**
Neurogenic shock, 720
Neuroglia (glial cells), **388–389**, 388f
Neurohormones, **601**
Neurohypophysis, **601**. *See also* Posterior pituitary gland
Neuroimaging, functional MRI (fMRI), **19b**
Neurokinin A, 417t

Neurolemmocytes (Schwann cells), 388f, **389**, 390f
  myelin sheaths formed by, 388f, 389, 391, 392f
Neurologist, **424**
Neuromodulators, **420**
Neuromuscular junction(s), **285**, 286f, 310t, **512**
  homeostatic imbalances affecting, 285
  muscle fiber activation at, 285, 285f, 286f
Neuron(s) (nerve cells), **134**, 135f, **389–395**, 390f, 393–394t
  association (interneurons), 394t, 395
  cell body of, 135f, **389–390**, 390f
  circuit types and, **422**, 422f
  classification of, 392–395, 393–394t
    functional, 394–395, 394t
    structural, 392–394, 393–394t
  developmental aspects of, 423–424, 424f
  enteric, **857**. *See also* Enteric nervous system
  facilitated, **412**
  motor (efferent), 285, 289, 293f, **394, 394t**. *See also* Motor (efferent) neurons
    in reflex arc, 514, 514f
  organization of (neuronal pools), **421–422**, 421f
  postsynaptic, **406**, 407f, 409f
  presynaptic, **406**, 409f
  processes of, 134, 135f, **390–392**
  regeneration of, 141
  responsiveness/irritability and, 5, 6f, 395
  sensory (afferent), **394, 394t**
    in reflex arc, 514, 514f
  somatic motor, 285, 310t, **470**, 470f
  somatic sensory, **470**, 470f
  synaptic communication and, 406–413, 407f
  visceral motor, **470**, 470f
  visceral sensory, **470**, 470f
Neuronal circuits, **422**, 422f
  sensory integration at level of, 489f, 490
Neuronal pools, **421–422**, 421f
Neuropathy, **424**
  autonomic, **538**
Neuropeptide(s), 417t, **418–419**
  in food intake regulation, 945, 946–947, 946f
Neuropeptide Y, in food intake regulation, 945, 946f
Neuropharmaclogy, **424**
Neurophysiology, 2–3
Neuroses, **479**
Neurotoxin, **424**
Neurotransmitter(s), 81, 391, 413–420, 414–415b, 416–418t, 535–536, 536t
  in autonomic nervous system, 535–536, 536t
  in parasympathetic versus sympathetic divisions, 534t

somatic nervous system compared with, 527, 527f
  in axonal terminals, 407
  classification of
    by chemical structure, 414–419, 416–418t
    by function, 419–420
    direct versus indirect acting, 419–420
    excitatory versus inhibitory, 419
    information transfer at chemical synapse and, 408, 409f
    in neuromuscular junction, 285, 286f
  receptors for, 420–421, 420f
Neurotransmitter receptor region, 407
Neurotropins, 424
Neurulation, 1082f, **1083**
Neutral fats (triglycerides), 45–47, 45t, 46f, 897, 912
  in absorptive state, 936–937
  storage of in bone, 176
  transport of, 943, 943f
Neutralization, by antibodies, **785**, 785f
Neutralization reaction, **41**
Neutron(s), **25**, 25f
Neutrophils, 125f, 126, 135f, 637f, **644**, 644f, 645t, 647f, **768**. *See also* Phagocytosis/phagocytes
Newborn
  circulation in, 1086f, 1093
  first breath by, 1093
  genetic screening of, 1109
  hemolytic disease of, **655**
  hydrocephalus in, 463, 463f
  immune system in, 799
  physiological jaundice in, 1094, **1097**
  skull in, 243f
Nexus. *See* Gap junction(s)
NFP. *See* Net filtration pressure
NGF. *See* Nerve growth factor
NH_3. *See* Ammonia
NH_4^+. *See* Ammonium ion
Niacin (vitamin B_3), 916t, 921
Nicotinamide adenine dinucleotide (NAD^+), **921**, 923f, 924
Nicotine, blood pressure and, 709, 713
Nicotinic agents, autonomic activity and, 537t
Nicotinic receptors, 416t, **535**, 536t
NIDDM. *See* Non-insulin-dependent (type II) diabetes mellitus
Night blindness, 566
Nipple(s), **1047**, 1047f
Nissl bodies (chromatophilic substance), **389**, 390f
Nitric oxide (NO), 81, **419**, 714
  blood flow regulation and, **714**, 715f
  in erection/erectile dysfunction, 1031, 1032
  as neurotransmitter, 418t, **419**
  production of from saliva, 860–861
Nitric oxide synthase, 419
Nitrogen, 25, 26t
  partial pressure of (P_{N_2}), 827, 827t
  solubility of, 827

Nitrogen balance, **914**
Nitrogen gas, formation of, 33f
Nitrogenous wastes, **985**
  exchanges of among fluid compartments, 998, 998f
NKA. *See* Neurokinin A
NK cells. *See* Natural killer (NK) cells
NMDA (N-methyl-D-aspartate) receptors
  in memory, 460
  pain activating, 491
  synaptic potentiation and, 413
NO. *See* Nitric oxide
Noble gases, 31
Nociceptors (pain receptors), 152, 161, **485**, 487t, 490
  in cornea, 551
Nocturia, 991
Nocturnal enuresis (NE), **991**
Nodes of Ranvier (myelin sheath gaps), 390f, **391**
Nodule(s), lymphoid (lymphoid follicles), **756**, 757f
  aggregated (Peyer's patches), 758f, **760–761**, 761f, **880**
  in small intestine, **880**
Nonaxial movement, 253
Nondeclarative memory, 458, 459f
Nondisjunction, **1060, 1112**
Nondisplaced fracture, 188
Nonelectrolytes, **996**
Nongated (leakage) channels, 69, **395**
Nongranular leukocytes (agranulocytes), 643, 644f, 645t, **646**
Non-Hodgkin's lymphoma, **764**
Non-insulin-dependent (type 2) diabetes mellitus (NIDDM), 627b, 954
Nonmembranous organelles, 83
Nonpolar molecules, **34**, 34f
Nonpolar tails, of membrane phospholipids, 64, 65f
Non-rapid eye movement (NREM) sleep, **455**, 456f
Nonrespiratory air (gas) movements, **826**, 826t
Nonself antigens, 776
Nonshivering (chemical) thermogenesis, **953**
Nonspecific (innate) defenses, **767**, 767–775, 767f, 772t, 794f
  internal (cells/chemicals), 768–775, 772t, 794f
  surface barriers (skin/mucosae), 160–161, 767–768, 772t, 794f
Nonsteroidal antiinflammatory drugs (NSAIDs)
  peptic ulcers and, 871
  prostaglandins and, 47
Nonstriated muscle. *See* Smooth muscle
Nontraditional inheritance, 1108–1109
Noradrenaline. *See* Norepinephrine
Norepinephrine, 416t, 418, **527**, 535, 536t, **619**, 709
  adrenal secretion of, 532, 615f
  in autonomic versus somatic nervous system, **527**, 527f, 535, 536t

blood pressure and, **709,** 709*t,* 711*f*
cardiac contractility affected by, 684, 685*f*
glomerular filtration affected by, 972
heart rate affected by, 685
receptors for, 535, 536*t*
stress response/sympathetic stimulation and, 619, 619*f*
Normoblasts, **639,** 639*f*
NOS. *See* Nitric oxide synthase
Nose, 806–809, 806*f,* 807*t. See also under* Nasal
Nosebleed (epistaxis), 807, **846**
Nostrils (nares), 805*f,* **806,** 806*f,* 808*f*
Notch (bone marking), 178*t*
Notochord, **1081,** 1081*f,* 1082*f,* 1083, 1083*f,* 1084, 1085*f*
NPY. *See* Neuropeptide Y
NREM sleep. *See* Non-rapid eye movement (NREM) sleep
NSAIDs. *See* Nonsteroidal antiin-flammatory drugs
Nuchal lines, 202*f,* 204, 205*f,* **214***t*
Nuclear envelope/membrane, 63*f,* 91, **91,** **91–93,** 92*f,* 95*t*
Nuclear lamina, 92, 92*f*
Nuclear pores/nuclear pore complexes, **92,** 92*f*
Nucleases, **886, 897**
Nuclei (neural), **390**
    basal. *See* Basal nuclei
    cochlear, **448, 582,** 582*f*
    cuneatus, **448,** 472*f*
    gracilis, **448,** 472*f*
    hypothalamic, 444*f*
    raphe, **452**
    septal, 452
    thalamic, 441–443, 444*f,* **449***t*
    vestibular (vestibular nuclear complex), **448,** 448*f,* **587,** 587*f*
Nucleic acids, **53–55,** 54*f,* 55*t. See also* DNA; RNA
    absorption of, 896*f,* 900
    digestion of, 896*f,* 897
Nucleolar organizer regions, 93
Nucleoli (nucleolus), 63*f,* 91, 92*f,* **93,** 95*t*
Nucleoplasm, 92–93
Nucleosidases, 896*f,* **897**
Nucleoside, 53
Nucleosome(s), **93,** 93*f*
Nucleotides/nucleotide bases, **53,** 54*f,* 55, **897**
    nucleic acid digestion to, **897**
    in protein synthesis, 100
Nucleus (atomic), **25,** 25*f*
Nucleus (cell), 63*f,* **91–95,** 92*f,* 93*f,* **95***t*
    division of. *See* Mitosis
Nucleus pulposus, **217–218,** 218*f*
    formation of, 1084, 1085*f*
Nursing (breast feeding/lactation), **1093–1094,** 1094*f*
    oxytocin and, 607, 1093–1094, 1094*f*
Nutrient(s), **8, 911.** *See also specific type*
    absorption of. *See* Absorption
    essential, **912**

exchanges of among fluid compartments, 998, 998*f*
    major, **911**
        metabolism of, 922–934, 934*t*
        malabsorption of, **901**
        transport of, 717, 718*f*
        tubular reabsorption of, 975–976, 976*f,* 983*f*
Nutrient arteries, 176*f*
Nutrient foramina, **178**
Nutrient pools, **935,** 935*f*
Nutrient signals, food intake regulation and, 946, 946*f*
Nutrition, 911–918
    developmental aspects of, 954–955
    medications affecting, 954–955
    pregnancy and, 954, 1090
Nyctalopia (night blindness), 566
Nystagmus, vestibular, **585**

O. *See* Oxygen
OA. *See* Osteoarthritis
Obesity, 945, 948–949*b*
    diabetes and, 954
    leptin and, 947
Obligatory water losses, **1000**
Obligatory water reabsorption, **975**
Oblique fissure, 815, 817*f*
Oblique layer, of stomach muscularis, 868*f,* 869, 869*f*
Oblique muscles
    of abdominal wall
        external, 342*t,* 343*f*
        internal, 342*t,* 343*f*
    of eye, 550, 550*f*
Oblique popliteal ligament, 262*f,* **263**
Oblique sections, **14**
Obstructive jaundice, 885
Obstructive pulmonary diseases
    chronic (COPD), **840–841,** 841*f*
    pulmonary function testing in, 825
Obturator artery, 734*f,* **734***t,* 735*f*
Obturator externus muscle, 368*f,* **368***t,* 380*t*
Obturator foramen, 234*f,* **235**
Obturator internus muscle, 368*f,* **368***t,* 380*t*
Obturator nerve, **507,** 508*f,* 508*t*
Occipital artery, 726*f,* **726***t,* 727*f*
Occipital belly, of epicranius, 327*f,* **329***t,* 331*f*
Occipital bone, **201–204,** 202*f,* 203*f,* 206*f,* 214*t*
    in newborn, 243*f*
Occipital condyles, **201–204,** 202*f,* 205*f,* 214*t*
Occipital crest, external, 204, 205*f,* 214*t*
Occipital lobe, 433, 434*f,* 436*f*
Occipital nerve, lesser, 504*f,* 504*t*
Occipital protuberance, external, 202*f,* 203*f,* **204,** 204*f,* 205*f,* **214***t*
Occipital vein, 738*f,* 739*f*
Occipitofrontalis (epicranius) muscle, 326*f,* 327*f,* **329***t,* 331*f*
Occipitomastoid suture, 201, 202*f,* 203*f*

Occludins, 66
Octet rule (rule of eights), **31–32**
Ocular fundus, **553,** 555*f*
Oculomotor nerve (cranial nerve III), 446*f,* **493,** 494*f,* **496***t*
    extrinsic eye muscles supplied by, 496*t,* 551
    paralysis of, 496*t*
    parasympathetic fibers of, 529, 529*f*
Oculomotor nuclei, 446, 448*f,* 540
Odontoblast, **863**
Odorants, 569, 570
Odor sensation, 569–571, 569*f,* 571*f*
    developmental aspects of, 588
Off-center fields, **567,** 568, 568*f*
OH⁻. *See* Hydroxyl ion(s)
Ohm's law, **395**
Oil(s), triglycerides as, 45, 47
Oil (sebaceous) glands, 122, 149*f,* **156–157,** 156*f*
Olecranon bursitis, 270
Olecranon fossa, **228,** 229*f*
Olecranon process, **229,** 229*f,* 230*f*
Oleoresins, skin penetrated by, 161
Olfaction (sense of smell), 569–571, 569*f,* 571*f*
    cortical areas for, 436*f,* **438–439**
    development of sense of, 588
    physiology of, 570, 571*f*
    taste sensation and, 573
Olfactory adaptation, 570
Olfactory auras, 573
Olfactory bulbs, 436*f,* 569*f,* **570**
Olfactory cilia, 569*f,* **570**
Olfactory (smell) cortex, primary, 436*f,* **438–439**
Olfactory epithelium, **569–571,** 569*f,* 571*f,* **806–807,** 808*f*
    development of, 588
Olfactory filaments, 494*f,* 569*f,* **570**
Olfactory foramina, 206*f,* 208, 209*f*
Olfactory gland, 569*f*
Olfactory hallucinations, 573
Olfactory mucosa. *See* Olfactory epithelium
Olfactory nerve (cranial nerve I), **493,** 494*f,* **495***t*
    filaments of, 494*f,* 495*t,* 569*f,* 570
Olfactory pathway, 570–571
Olfactory pits, **842**
Olfactory placodes, **842,** 843*f*
Olfactory receptors/cells, 569–**570,** 569*f*
    activation of, 570
    specificity of, 570
    sperm, 1073
Olfactory tract, 436*f,* 569*f,* **570–571**
Oligodendrocytes, 388*f,* **389**
    myelin sheaths formed by, 388, 389*f,* 392
Oligosaccharides, 895, 896*f*
Oliguria, 1001
Olivary nuclei
    inferior, **447–448,** 448*f*
    superior, in auditory pathway, **582,** 582*f*
Olive(s), 446*f,* **447**
Omega-3 fatty acids, 47, 912, 944
Omentum (omenta), greater and lesser, **868,** 892*f*

Omohyoid muscle, **334***t,* 335*f,* 337*f*
On-center fields, **567–568,** 568*f*
Oncogenes, **142***b*
Oncotic pressure (capillary colloid osmotic pressure/OP_c), **718,** 719*f*
    of glomerular blood, **971,** 971*f*
One-molar solution, 30
Oocyte(s), 1041*f,* 1042. *See also* Ova
    primary, **1049,** 1050*f,* 1051*f*
    secondary, **1049,** 1050*f,* 1051*f*
        fertilization of, 1025, **1072–1073,** 1072*f,* 1074*f,* 1075*f,* 1076*f. See also* Fertilization
        sperm-binding receptors on, 1073, 1074*f*
Oogenesis, **1049,** 1050*f*
Oogonia, **1049,** 1050*f*
Oophorectomy, 1066
OP_c. *See* Capillary colloid osmotic pressure
Open (compound) fracture, 188
Open (internal) reduction of fracture, 188
OP_g. *See* Colloid osmotic pressure, of glomerular blood
Ophthalmic artery, 726*f,* **726***t,* 727*f*
Ophthalmic division of trigeminal nerve (cranial nerve V₁), **497***t*
Ophthalmic vein, 738*f,* **738***t,* 739*f*
Ophthalmology, **589**
Opponens digiti minimi muscle, **360***t,* 361*f*
Opponens pollicis muscle, **360***t,* 361*f*
Opposition (body movement), 258*f,* **259**
Opsins, **562,** 563*f*
Opsonization, 768, 774*f,* 775
Optic canals, 206*f,* **208,** 208*f,* **214***t*
Optic chiasma, **566,** 567*f*
Optic cups, **588**
Optic disc (blind spot), 552*f,* **553,** 554*f*
Optic nerve (cranial nerve II), 446*f,* **493,** 494*f,* **495***t,* 552*f,* 554*f,* **566,** 567*f*
Optic radiation, **566,** 567*f*
Optic tracts, **566,** 567*f*
Optic vesicles, **588**
Optometrist, **589**
Oral cavity (mouth), 20, 852*f,* **858–864,** 859*f,* 888*t. See also specific structure*
    development of, 901*f,* 904
    digestive processes occurring in, 866, 888*t,* 895, 896*f*
Oral cavity proper, **858**
Oral membrane, 901*f,* **904**
Oral orifice, **858**
Ora serrata, 552*f,* **553**
Orbicularis oculi muscle, 326*f,* **330***t,* 331*f,* 548*f,* 551
Orbicularis oris muscle, 326*f,* **330***t,* 331*f,* 858
Orbit(s), **20,** 200, 201*f,* **211–212,** 212*f*
Orbital fissure
    inferior, 202*f,* **210, 215***t*
    superior, 202*f,* **208,** 208*f,* **214***t*
Orbital model of atom/orbitals, 25*f,* **26,** 31

Orbital plates, **209**, 209*f*
Orbital process, 211
Orchiectomy, 1028
Orchitis, **1066**
Orexins, 456, 457
   in food intake regulation, 946*f*
Organ(s), 3, 4*f. See also specific organ*
Organ of Corti, **577**, 577*f*, 578*f*, 582*f*
   excitation of hair cells in, 580–582, 582*f*
Organelles, 3, 4*f*, **83**, 83–89, **94***t. See also specific type*
Organic acid (carboxyl) groups, 1010
Organic components, in bone, 180
Organic compounds, **38**, 42–56. *See also specific type*
Organic salts, skin penetrated by, 161
Organismal level, structural organization at, **3**, 4*f*
Organization, in tissue repair, **139**, 140*f*
Organ level, structural organization at, **3**, 4*f*
Organogenesis (germ layer differentiation), **1083**–1087, 1083*f*, 1084*f*, 1086*f*
Organ systems, **3**, 4*f. See also specific system*
   interrelationships among, 5*f*
   structural organization at level of, **3**, 4*f*
Organ transplants, 792–795, 795*t*
Orgasm, **1032**
   in female, 1058
   in male, **1032**
      aging affecting, 1066
Orientation. *See* Equilibrium/orientation
Origin (muscle), **253**, **277**
   naming muscles and, 321
Orlistat, 949*b*
Oropharynx, 808*f*, **809**, 858, 859*f*, **864**
Orthodontics, **905**
Orthopedist/orthopedic surgeon, **245**
Orthopnea, **846**
Orthostatic hypotension, **541**, 712
Oscillating (reverberating) circuits, **422**, 422*f*
Os coxae (hip bones/coxal bones), **233**, 233–235, 233*f*, 234*f*, 242*t*
Osmol, 979
Osmolality, **979**
   extracellular fluid, 998–1002, 999*f*, 1000*f*, 1001*f. See also* Water balance
Osmolarity, **71**, 72
Osmoreceptors, **444**, 608, 999, 999*f*
   in digestion, 854, 855*f*
Osmosis, **69**, 69*f*, **70**–72, 70*f*, 72*t*
   net, in digestion, 901
Osmotic activity, 979
Osmotic diuretics, 982
Osmotic gradient, renal medullary, 979*f*, 981
Osmotic pressure, **71**
   colloid, **718**, 719*f*
   fluid movement among compartments and, 998

Osseous (bony) labyrinth, **576**
Osseous spiral lamina, **577**, 578*f*
Osseous tissue. *See* Bone(s)/skeletal tissue
Ossicles, auditory, **215***t*, 575*f*, **576**, 576*f*
Ossification (osteogenesis), **182**–185, 194, 194*f*
   endochondral, 182, **183**–184, 183*f*
   intramembranous, 182, **182**–183, 182*f*
   of skull bones, 242
Ossification centers
   in endochondral ossification, 183, 183*f*, 184
   in intramembranous ossification, 182*f*
   primary, **183**, 183*f*, 194, 194*f*
   secondary, 183*f*, **184**, 194
   in skull, 242
Ossification (osteogenesis) zone (epiphyseal plate), 184, 184*f*
Ostealgia, **195**
Osteitis, **195**
Osteitis fibrosa cystica, 613
Osteoarthritis (degenerative joint disease), **270**
Osteoblasts, **125**, 133, 134*t*, **177**, 177*f*, **179**
   hormones produced by, 624
Osteocalcin, 624, 625*t*
Osteochondral grafting, 261*b*
Osteoclasts, **177**, 177*f*, **186**
   bone resorption by, **186**
   parathyroid hormone release and, 613, 614*f*
Osteocytes, **133**, 133*f*, 134*t*, 177*f*, **180**, 181*f*
   in bone remodeling, 186
Osteogenesis (ossification), **182**–185, 194, 194*f*
   endochondral, 182, **183**–184, 183*f*
   intramembranous, 182, **182**–183, 182*f*
   of skull bones, 242
Osteogenesis imperfecta, **195**
Osteogenesis (ossification) zone (epiphyseal plate), 184, 184*f*
Osteogenic cell(s), **177**, 177*f*, 179
Osteogenic layer, of periosteum, 177
Osteoid, **180**
   in intramembranous ossification, 182*f*
Osteoid seam, 186
Osteomalacia, **189**
Osteomyelitis, **195**
Osteon (Haversian system), 133, **179**, 180*f*, 181*f*
Osteoporosis, 189–**191**, 190*t*, 191*f*
   hip fracture and, 191
   of spine, 190*t*, 191, 244
Osteoprogenitor cells. *See* Osteogenic cell(s)
Osteosarcoma, **195**
Otalgia, **589**
Otic ganglia, 500*t*, **529**, 529*f*
Otic pit, **588**
Otic placode, **588**
Otic vesicle, **588**

Otitis externa, **589**
Otitis media, **574**
Otoacoustic emissions, 582
Otolithic membrane, **584**, 584*f*
Otoliths, **584**, 584*f*
Otorhinolaryngology, **846**
Otosclerosis, **583**
Outer (external) ear, 204, **574**, 575*f*
Outer fiber, rod, 560, 561*f*
Outer hair cells, 578*f*, **580**
Outer mitochondrial membrane, 83, 83*f*
Outer segments, rod and cone, 554*f*, **560**, 561*f*
Outlet, pelvic, 236*t*, **237**
Ova (ovum/eggs), 1025, **1049**
   fertilization of, 1025, **1072**–1073, 1072*f*, 1074*f*, 1075*f*, 1076*f. See also* Fertilization
   production of (oogenesis), **1049**, 1050*f*
Oval (vestibular) window, **574**, 575*f*
Ovarian arteries, 732*t*, **1041**
Ovarian branch, of uterine arteries, 1041
Ovarian cancer, **1066**
Ovarian cortex, 1041*f*, 1042
Ovarian cycle, **1049**–1054, 1051*f*, 1055*f*
   establishing, 1053
   follicular phase of, **1050**, 1050–1052, 1051*f*, 1055*f*
   hormonal regulation of, 1052–1054, 1053*f*, 1055*f*
   luteal phase of, **1050**, 1051*f*, 1052, 1055*f*
   luteolytic (ischemic) phase of, 1052
   ovulation stage of, 1050, 1051*f*, **1052**, 1054, 1055*f*
Ovarian cysts, **1066**
Ovarian follicles, 1041*f*, 1042, 1050*f*
   development of in ovary, 1050*f*, 1051*f*
   dominant, 1052
   primary, 1041*f*, **1042**, 1050*f*, 1051*f*, 1052
   primordial, **1042**, 1049, 1050*f*, 1051*f*
   secondary, **1042**, 1050*f*, 1051*f*, 1052
      late, 1041*f*, **1042**, 1051*f*, 1052
   vesicular (Graafian/tertiary), 1041*f*, **1042**, 1050*f*, 1051*f*, 1052
Ovarian ligament, **1041**, 1041*f*, 1043*f*
Ovarian medulla, 1041*f*, 1042
Ovarian vein, **742***t*
Ovaries, 595*f*, 623, 1024, **1040**, 1040*f*, 1041–1042, 1041*f*
   cancer of, **1066**
   descent of, 1063
   embryologic/fetal development of, 1061*f*
   hormones of, 623
   polycystic, **1066**
   surgical removal of (oophorectomy), **1066**
Overflow incontinence, 988
Overhydration, 1001

Overload principle, in exercise, 304
Overuse injuries, **304**
   tendonitis, 270
Oviducts (uterine tubes), 1040*f*, **1042**, 1043*f*
   embryologic/fetal development of, 1061*f*
   fertilization in, 1042, 1076*f*
   inflammation of (salpingitis), **1066**
   resection of (tubal ligation), 1096*b*
Ovulation, 1042, 1050, 1050*f*, **1052**, 1054, 1055*f*
   awareness of, contraceptive methods and, 1095*b*
Ovum. *See* Ova
Oxaloacetic acid, **924**, 925*f*
Oxidase(s), 52, 87, **921**
Oxidation, 37, **920**, 924
   beta, **931**, 931*f*, 934*t*
   in Krebs cycle, 924, 925*f*
   water of (metabolic water), 998
Oxidation-reduction (redox) reactions, 37, 920–**921**
Oxidative deamination, **933**–934, 933*f*, 934*t*
Oxidative fibers, **302**, 302*t*
   fast, **302**, 302*t*, 303, 303*f*
   slow, **302**, 302*f*, 302*t*, 303, 303*f*
Oxidative phosphorylation, 919, 920*f*, 921*f*, **922**, 925–926, 926*f*, 929*f*
   metabolic poisons and, 928
Oxidized reactant in redox reaction, 37
Oxycodone abuse, 415*b*
Oxygen, **8**, 25, 26*t*
   in blood, erythrocytes carrying, 637, 638
   as chemically reactive element, 31*f*
   hyperbaric, 828
   maximum amount used in exercise, aging affecting, 846
   partial pressure of (P_{O_2}), 827, 827*t*
      alveolar, 828
      external respiration (pulmonary gas exchange) and, 828–829, 828*f*, 829*f*
      hemoglobin saturation affected by, 831, 831*f*
      internal respiration and, 830
      respiration affected by, 837–838, 838, 838*f*
   solubility of, 827
   as survival requirement, **8**
   toxicity of, **828**
   transport of, 637, 638, 805, 830–832, 831*f*, 832*f*, 833*f*
Oxygen deficit, **300**
Oxygen gas, formation of, 33*f*
Oxygen-hemoglobin dissociation curve, **831**–832, 831*f*, 832*f*
Oxyhemoglobin, **638**, 831
Oxyphil cells, 612, 613*f*
Oxytocin, 602*f*, **606**–608, **607***t*, **1091**
   homeostatic control of, 11
   labor and, 606, 607, **1091**, 1091*f*
   lactation and, 607, 1093–1094, 1094*f*

P. *See* Phosphorus
p⁺. *See* Proton(s)
p16 gene, in cancer, 142*b*
p53 gene
  in cancer, 100, 142*b*, 143*f*, 904
  cell division control and, 100
  UV radiation affecting, 162
p277, in diabetes mellitus, 626*b*
Pacemaker, **677**
Pacemaker cells
  in cardiac muscle, 310*t*, 677
    action potential initiation
      and, 676, 676*f*
    defects in, 678–679
    sequence of excitation and,
      676–678, 677*f*
  peristalsis in stomach and, 876
  respiratory rhythm and,
    835–836
  in smooth muscle, 307, 310*t*
Pacemaker potentials (prepotentials), **676**, 676*f*
Pacinian (lamellated) corpuscles,
  149*f*, **486**–487, 487*t*
Packed red cell transfusions, **654**
Pagetic bone, 191
Paget's disease, 191–194
Pain
  perception of, 490–491
  referred, **535**, 535*f*
Pain receptors (nociceptors), 152,
  161, **485**, 487*t*, 490
  in cornea, 551
Palate, 806, **858**, 859*f*
  cleft, 243, 243*f*, **904**
  hard, 205*f*, **806**, 808*f*, **858**, 859*f*
  soft, **806**, 808*f*, **858**, 859*f*
Palatine bones, 203*f*, 204*f*, 205*f*, **211**,
  213*f*, 215*t*
Palatine processes, 203*f*, 205*f*,
  210, 215*t*
Palatine raphe, 859*f*
Palatine suture, median, 211, **215***t*
Palatine tonsils, **760**, 760*f*, 808*f*, **809**
Palatoglossal arches, **858**, 859*f*
Palatopharyngeal arches, **858**, 859*f*
Pallidectomy, **479**
Pallor, 155
Palmar arches, 725*f*, 728*f*, **728***t*, 729*f*
Palmar interossei muscle, 361*f*, **362***t*
Palmaris longus muscle, 326*f*, **354***t*,
  355*f*, 358*t*
Palmar venous arches, 740*f*, **740***t*, 741*f*
Palm of hand (metacarpus), **231**
  bones of (metacarpals), 199*f*,
    231–233, 231*f*, 232*t*
  muscles of, 354*t*, 360–362*t*, 361*f*
Palpation, 2
Palpebrae (eyelids), **548**–549, 548*f*
Palpebral conjunctiva, 548*f*, **549**
Palpebral fissure, **548**, 548*f*
Palpitation, heart, **690**
Pampiniform venous plexus,
  1026*f*, **1027**
Pancreas, 595*f*, **620**–623, 620*f*, 621*f*,
  623*t*, 852*f*, 878*f*, **885**–886,
  885*f*, 886*f*, 888*t*
  autonomic innervation/effects
    and, 528*f*, 529*f*, 538*t*
  in digestion, 852*f*, 878*f*, 885–886,
    885*f*, 886–887, 886*f*, 887*f*, 888*t*

endocrine, 595*f*, **620**–623, 620*f*,
  621*f*, 623*t*
transplantation of for diabetes,
  626–627*b*
Pancreatic amylase, **886**, 896*f*, **897**
Pancreatic ducts
  accessory, 878*f*, 885
  main, 877, **885**
Pancreatic enzymes. *See* Pancreatic
  juice
Pancreatic islets (islets of Langerhans), 620*f*, **621**, 886
  transplantation of for diabetes,
    626–627*b*
Pancreatic juice/pancreatic enzymes,
  885, 886, 886*f*, 896*f*
  regulation of secretion of,
    886–887, 887*f*
Pancreatic nucleases, **886**, **897**
Pancreatitis, **905**
Paneth cells, 879, 880
Pannus, in rheumatoid arthritis, **271**
Panoramic vision, 566
Pantothenic acid (vitamin B₅), 916*t*
Papanicolaou (Pap) smear, 1044
Papilla(e), **571**
  dermal, 149*f*, **152**
  hair, 157, 158*f*
  renal medullary, **962**, 963*f*
  of tongue, **571**, 859, 860*f*
Papillary layer of dermis, 149*f*,
  152, 153*f*
Papillary muscles, 667*f*, **668**
Papilledema, **589**
Papillomavirus, human
  cervical cancer and, 1044, 1059
  genital warts caused by, **1059**
  vaccine against, 1044
Pap smear, 1044
Paracellular route, of tubular reab-
  sorption, 974, 975*f*
Paracrines, 81, **595**
  in digestion, 875*t*
  in glomerular filtration rate regu-
    lation, 974
Parafollicular (C) cells, 608, 609*f*, **611**
Parahippocampal gyrus, 436*f*, 439,
  452, 452*f*
Parallel after-discharge circuits,
  422, 422*f*
Parallel fascicle pattern/muscles,
  322, 322*f*
Parallel processing, **423**
Paralysis, spinal cord damage causing, **476**
Paramesonephric (Müllerian) ducts,
  1060, 1061*f*
Paranasal sinuses, **216**, 216*f*, 807*t*, **809**
Paraneuron(s), 624
Paraplegia, **476**
Parasagittal plane/section, **14**
Parasitic infections, 786
Parasympathetic (craniosacral) division of autonomic nervous
  system, 387, 387*f*, 485*f*, 526*f*,
  527–528, 528*f*, 529*f*, 534*t*
  anatomy of, 529–530, 529*f*
  cranial outflow, 529–530
  heart regulation and, 678*f*, 679,
    685, 686*f*, 707*f*
  role of, 527–528, 528*f*, 534*t*

sacral outflow, 530
somatic nervous system compared with, 527*f*
sympathetic division differentiated from, 534*t*
Parasympathetic tone, **537**
Parasympathomimetic agents, autonomic activity and, 537*t*
Parathyroid glands, 595*f*, **612**–614,
  613*f*, 614*f*
  aging affecting, 626–627
Parathyroid hormone
  (PTH/parathormone), **186**,
  612–613, **1008**
  bone and, 186, 187*f*, 613, 614*f*
  calcium relationship and, 186,
    187*f*, 613, 614*f*, 900, **1008**
Paraventricular nuclei, 444, 444*f*, **603**
Paravertebral (sympathetic
  trunk/chain) ganglia, 503*f*,
  530, 531*f*
  pathways with synapses in, 531*f*,
    532, 533*f*
Paresthesia, **476**, **520**
  spinal cord damage causing, 476
Parietal bones, **200**–201, 202*f*, 203*f*,
  205*f*, 206*f*, 214*t*
  in newborn, 243*f*
Parietal cells, 869*f*, **870**
  control of acid secretion by,
    873, 874*f*
Parietal layer, **663**
  of glomerular capsule, 964, 965*f*,
    968*f*, 969*f*
  of serous pericardium, 663, 663*f*
Parietal lobe, 433, 434*f*, 436*f*
Parietal pericardium, 17, 17*f*, 138*f*
Parietal peritoneum, 17, 138*f*, **855**,
  855*f*, 892*f*
Parietal pleura, 17, 138*f*, 817*f*, **818**
Parietal serosa, 16, 17*f*
Parieto-occipital sulcus, **433**,
  434*f*, 436*f*
Parkinson's disease, 465–466
Parotid glands, 852*f*, **860**
  mumps affecting, 860
Paroxysmal atrial tachycardia, **690**
Partial pressures, **827**, 827*t*. *See also*
  specific gas
  external respiration (pulmonary
    gas exchange) and, 828–829,
    828*f*, 829*f*
  internal respiration and, 830
Partial-thickness burns, 164, 164*f*
Particle size, chemical reaction rate
  affected by, 38
Parturition, **1090**–1092, 1091*f*, 1092*f*.
  See also Birth
Passive immunity, **782**, 782*f*
Passive processes/transport, **68**,
  68–72, 68*f*, 69*f*, 70*f*, 71*f*, 72*t*
Passive tubular reabsorption, **975**,
  976*f*, 983*f*
PAT. *See* Paroxysmal atrial
  tachycardia
Patched (*ptc*) gene, UV radiation af-
  fecting, 162
Patella, 199*f*, **237**, 238*f*, 242*t*
Patellar ligament, 262–263*f*, **263**
Patellar (knee-jerk) reflex, **515**,
  516, **517***f*

Patellar retinacula, medial and lat-
  eral, 262*f*, **263**
Patellar surface, **237**, 238*f*
Paternal chromosome, 1032
Pathogens, attenuated, for vaccines,
  782, 782*f*
Pathological anatomy, 2
Pathologic fracture, **195**
Pathology, 144
*P*atm. *See* Atmospheric pressure
Pattern generators, central, **512**
Pattern recognition, **490**
P (processing) bodies, 105
P cells, 568
P_{CO_2} (partial pressure of carbon
  dioxide), 827, 827*t*
  in acidosis/alkalosis, 1017*b*
  alveolar, 828
  external respiration (pulmonary
    gas exchange) and, 828–829,
    828*f*, 829*f*
  hemoglobin saturation affected
    by, 831–832, 832*f*
  internal respiration and, 830
  normal, 1017*b*
  respiration affected by, 836–837,
    837*f*, 838
PCT. *See* Proximal convoluted tubule
PDE (phosphodiesterase), 563, 564*f*
PDGF. *See* Platelet-derived growth
  factor
Pectinate line, 891*f*, 893
Pectinate muscles, **664**, 666*f*, 667*f*
Pectineus muscle, 326*f*, 364*f*,
  365*t*, 380*t*
Pectoral (shoulder) girdle, **225**
  bones of, 199*f*, **225**–228,
    226*f*, 232*t*
  muscles of, 326*f*, 327*f*, 346–349*t*,
    347*f*, 348–349*t*, 358*t*, 359*f*
Pectoralis major muscle, 326*f*, **346***t*,
  347*f*, **350***t*, 351*f*, 358*t*
Pectoralis minor muscle, 326*f*,
  346*t*, 347*f*
Pectoral nerves, 506*f*, 507*t*
Pedicles, vertebral, **219**, 219*f*
Pedigree, **1109**–1110, 1110*f*
Pellagra, 916*t*
Pelvic brim, 233*f*, **235**, 236*t*
Pelvic cavity, **16**, 16*f*
Pelvic diaphragm, muscles of,
  344*t*, 345*f*
Pelvic floor, muscles of, 344*t*, 345*f*
  prolapse of uterus and, **1044**
Pelvic (hip) girdle, 199*f*, **233**–237,
  233*f*, 234*f*, 236*t*, 242*t*. *See also*
  under Hip
Pelvic inflammatory disease (PID),
  1042, 1058
Pelvic inlet, **235**–237, 236*t*
Pelvic (pelvic splanchnic) nerves,
  529*f*, **530**
Pelvic outlet, 236*t*, **237**
Pelvic (inferior hypogastric) plexus,
  529*f*, **530**
Pelvimetry, **245**
Pelvis, 235
  arteries of, 734–735*f*, 734–735*t*
  bony, **233**, 233*f*
  childbearing and, 235–237, 236*t*
  muscles of, 326*f*

Pelvis (*contd.*)
　sympathetic pathways to, 532, 533*f*
　true and false, **235**
　veins of, 744*f*, 744*t*
Pelvis (renal), **962**, 963*f*, 985*f*
Penetration enhancers (drug
　　agents), 161
Penile (spongy) urethra, **987**, 987*f*,
　1025*f*, 1029*f*, 1030
Penis, 1025*f*, 1026*f*, **1028**, 1029*f*
　autonomic innervation/effects
　　and, 533*f*, 538*t*
　bulb of, 1025*f*, **1028**
　embryologic/fetal development
　　of, 1061*f*, 1062*f*
Pennate fascicle pattern/muscles,
　322*f*, **323**
Pepsin, 870, 871, 896*f*, **897**
　gastric secretion of, 869*f*, **870**
Pepsinogen, chief cell secretion of,
　869*f*, 870
Peptic ulcers, **870**, **905**
Peptide(s)/peptide hormones, 51*t*
　as neurotransmitters, **417***t*,
　　418–419
Peptide bond, 47, 48*f*
Percent, solution concentration, 29
Perception, 485, **488**
Perceptual detection, **490**
Perforated eardrum, 583
Perforating (Volkmann's) canals,
　180, 181*f*
Perforating (Sharpey's) fibers, 176*f*,
　178, 181*f*
Perforins, **792**, 793*f*, 795*t*
Perfusion, 829
Periaqueductal gray matter, 446, 448*f*
Pericardial arteries, 729*t*
Pericardial cavity, **16**, 16*f*, **663**, 663*f*
Pericardial friction rub, 663
Pericarditis, 663
Pericardium, 138*f*, **139**, **663**, 663*f*
Perichondrium, 173
Perikaryon (cell body), of neurons,
　135*f*, **389–390**, 390*f*
Perilymph, **576**
Perimetrium, 1040*f*, 1043*f*, **1044**
Perimysium, **277**, 278*f*, 309*t*
Perineal muscle
　deep transverse, **344***t*, 345*f*
　superficial transverse, **344***t*, 345*f*
Perineum, **1028**, **1047**
　central tendon of, **344***t*
　female, **1047**
　male, **1028**
　muscles of, 344*t*, 345*f*
Perineurium, **491**, 492*f*
Periodic table, **25**
Periodontal disease/periodontitis, **864**
Periodontal ligament, 249*f*, **250**,
　863, 863*f*
Periosteal bone collar, 183, 183*f*
Periosteal bud, **183**, 183*f*
Periosteal layer of dura mater,
　460*f*, 461
Periosteum (bone), 176*f*, **177–178**,
　181*f*
　in intramembranous ossification,
　　182*f*
Peripheral chemoreceptors, respira-
　　tory rate/rhythm affected by,
　836, 836*f*, 837–838, 837*f*, 838*f*

Peripheral congestion, in heart fail-
　ure, **687**
Peripheral nervous system, **386**, 387*f*,
　484–513, **485**, 485*f*
　developmental aspects of, 520
　divisions of, 485, 485*f*
　motor endings/motor activity
　　and, **512–513**, 513*f*
　nerves/associated ganglia and,
　　491–511, 492*f*
　　cranial nerves, **493–501**, 494*f*,
　　　495–501*t*
　　spinal nerves, **502–511**,
　　　502*f*, 503*f*
　neuroglia (supporting cells) of,
　　388*f*, 389
　pain perception and, 490–491
　reflex activity and, 514–520, 514*f*
　regeneration and, 491–492, 493*f*
　sensory integration and,
　　488–491, 489*f*
　sensory receptors and, **485–488**,
　　487–488*t*
Peripheral process, 393*t*, **394**
Peripheral proteins, **64**, 65*f*
Peripheral (vascular) resistance, **704**
　blood pressure and, 706, 710*f*, 711*f*
　in renal circulation, 968
Peripheral thermoreceptors, **951**
Peripheral tissues, cholesterol trans-
　port to, 943
Perirenal fat capsule, **961**, 962*f*
Peristalsis, **306**, 853, 853*f*, 888*t*
　in large intestine, 888*t*, 893–894
　mass, 888*t*, 893–894
　in small intestine, 888*t*, 889
　in stomach, 874–876, 876*f*
Peritoneal cavity, 855, 855*f*
　serous membrane lining. *See*
　　Peritoneum
Peritoneal (intraperitoneal) organs,
　856
Peritoneum(s), 138*f*, **139**, **855**
　parietal, 17, 138*f*, **855**, 855*f*, 892*f*
　visceral, 17, 138*f*, **855**, 855*f*, 857,
　　857*f*, 892*f*
Peritonitis, 17, **856**, 890
Peritubular capillaries, 966, 967*f*, **968**
Permanent teeth/permanent denti-
　tion, **862–863**, 862*f*
Permeability
　of lymph capillaries, 754
　membrane, **68**. *See also* Mem-
　　brane transport
　　action potential and,
　　　399–402, 400–401*f*
　　resting membrane potential
　　　and, 396, 397*f*
　vascular, inflammation and,
　　769–771
Permissiveness, hormone, **600**
Pernicious anemia, 642, 871–872, 916*t*
Peroneal (fibular) artery, 734*f*, 735*f*
Peroneal (fibular) muscles, 370*t*. *See
　also specific muscle*
Peroneal (fibular) nerve
　common, 509, 509*f*, **510**, 510*t*
　　injuries of, 510
　deep, 509*f*
　superficial, 509*f*
　leg muscles supplied by, 373*t*
Peroneal (fibular) retinacula, **370***t*

Peroneal (fibular) vein, 744*f*, 744*t*
Peroneus (fibularis) brevis muscle,
　372*f*, **373***t*, 374–375*f*, 380*t*
Peroneus (fibularis) longus muscle,
　326*f*, 327*f*, 372*f*, **373***t*,
　374–375*f*, 380*t*
Peroneus (fibularis) tertius muscle,
　370*t*, 371*f*, 372*f*, 380*t*
Peroxisomes, 63*f*, **87**, 94*t*
Perpendicular plate, 202*f*, 203*f*, 204*f*,
　209, 209*f*, **211**, 213*f*
PET. *See* Positron emission
　tomography
Petechiae, 653
Petit mal (absence) seizures, 454
Petrous region, temporal bone, 204,
　204*f*, 205*f*, 206*f*, **207**
Peyer's patches, 758*f*, **760–761**,
　761*f*, **880**
　in small intestine, **880**
PF$_3$ (platelet factor 3/
　phosphatidylserine),
　650*f*, 651
PGs. *See* Prostaglandin(s)
pH, **40–41**, 40*f*
　of blood, 40*f*, 1008–1009. *See also*
　　Acid-base balance
　　in acidosis/alkalosis, 1017*b*
　　carbon dioxide affecting, 834,
　　　837*f*, 838
　　hemoglobin saturation af-
　　　fected by, 831–832, 832*f*
　　normal, 1017*b*
　　renal control and, 978, 983*f*,
　　　1011–1014, 1012*f*, 1013*f*
　　　compensations for abnor-
　　　　malities and, 1014, 1015
　　respiratory control and, 838,
　　　1010–1011
　　　compensations for abnor-
　　　　malities and, 1014,
　　　　1014–1015
　of pancreatic fluid, 886
　of semen, 1031
　of urine, 985
　of vagina, 1045
Phagocytosis/phagocytes, **75**, 77*t*,
　80*f*, 86, 768, 769*f*, 771–773,
　771*f*, 772*t*
　in antibody mechanism of
　　action, 785, 785*f*
Phagolysosome, 768, 769*f*
Phagosome, **75**, 78*f*, 86*f*, **768**, 769*f*
Phalanges, **233**
　of foot (toes), 199*f*, 240, 240*f*,
　　241, 242*t*
　of hand (fingers), 199*f*, 231*f*,
　　232*t*, **233**
Phantom limb pain, **491**
Pharyngeal constrictor muscles,
　334*t*, 335*f*, 335*t*, 864
Pharyngeal-esophageal phase of
　swallowing, 866, 867*f*, 888*t*
Pharyngeal pouches, 588
Pharyngeal tonsils, **760**, 760*f*, 808*f*, 809
Pharyngeal tubercle, 201, 205*f*
Pharyngotympanic (auditory) tube,
　574, 575*f*, 808*f*, 809
Pharynx, 805*f*, 807*t*, 808*f*, **809**, 888*t*
　in digestion, 852*f*, 864, 888*t*
　muscles of, swallowing control
　　and, 334–335*t*, 335*f*

Phasic receptors, **489**
Phenocopies, **1108**
Phenotype, **1103**
Phentermine, 949*b*
Phenylketonuria (PKU), 954
Pheochromocytoma, 620
Philtrum, 806, 806*f*
Phlebitis, **748**
Phlebotomy, **748**
Phosphatases, 896*f*, **897**
Phosphate
　balance of
　　abnormalities of, 1003*t*
　　regulation of, 1008
　in bone remodeling, 186
Phosphate bonds, high-energy, 55, 55*f*
Phosphate buffer system, **1010**,
　1012, 1013*f*
Phosphatidylcholine, 45*t*, 46*f*
Phosphadidyl inositol bisphosphate
　(PIP$_2$), 598
Phosphatidylserine (PF$_3$/platelet fac-
　tor 3), 650*f*, 651
Phosphodiesterase (PDE), 563,
　564*f*, **597**
　in hormone mechanism of
　　action, **597**
Phospholipase C, in PIP$_2$-calcium
　signaling mechanism, **598**
Phospholipids, 45*t*, 46*f*, **47**
　in membranes, 47, 64, 65*f*
Phosphoric acid, 1009
Phosphorus, 26*t*, 918*t*
　dietary, 918*t*
Phosphorylation, 55, 56*f*, **919**,
　921–922, 921*f*
　oxidative, 919, 920*f*, 921*f*, **922**,
　　925–926, 926*f*, 929*f*
　　metabolic poisons and, 928
　substrate level, **921–922**, 921*f*,
　　924, 929*f*
Photons, 556
Photopigments (visual pigments),
　560, 561*f*, 562, 564*f*
　bleaching of, **562**, 563*f*
Photoreceptors, **485**, 553, 554*f*,
　559–566, 561*f*, 563*f*, 564*f*, 565*f*
　electromagnetic spectrum and
　　sensitivities of, 557*f*
　functional anatomy of, 559–562,
　　561*f*
　stimulation of, 562–563, 563*f*
Photosensitivity, 154
Phototransduction, **559**, 563–564,
　564*f*, 565*f*
Phrenic arteries
　inferior, 730*f*, **731***t*, 733*f*
　superior, 729*t*
Phrenic nerve, 504*f*, 504*t*, **505**, 835
　diaphragm supplied by, 340*t*,
　　504*t*, 505
　in respiration, **835**
Phrenic veins, inferior, 742*f*, **742***t*, 743*f*
pH units, **40**. *See also* pH
Phylloquinone (vitamin K), 45*t*, 917*t*
Physiological acidosis, 1009
Physiological buffering systems, in
　acid-base balance
　renal, 978, 983*f*, 1011–1014,
　　1012*f*, 1013*f*
　respiratory, 41, 834, 837*f*, 838,
　　1010–1011

Physiological jaundice, 1094, **1097**
Physiology, **2**, 2–3
    cardiovascular, **3**
    complementarity principle and, **3**
    neurologic (neurophysiology), 2–3
    renal, **2**
Pia mater, **463**
    of brain, 460*f*, **463**
    spinal, 466, 469*f*
Pica, 955, 1002
Pickup molecule, oxaloacetic acid as, 924, 925*f*
PID. *See* Pelvic inflammatory disease
Pigment(s)
    skin, 154–155
    visual (photopigments), **560**, 561*f*, 562, 564*f*
        bleaching of, **562**, 563*f*
Pigmented layer of retina, **553**, 554*f*
Pigmented nevi (moles), 154
    melanoma arising in, 163
PIH. *See* Prolactin-inhibiting hormone
Pili, 157. *See also* Hair(s)
Pineal gland/body, 443*f*, **444**–445, 447*f*, 595*f*, **620**
Pinealocytes, **620**
Pinkeye, 549
Pinna (auricle), **574**, 575*f*
Pinocytosis (fluid-phase endocytosis), **76**, 77*t*, 78*f*
P$_{ip}$. *See* Intrapleural pressure
PIP$_2$ (phosphadidyl inositol bisphosphate), **598**
PIP$_2$-calcium signaling mechanism, 598
Piriformis muscle, 366*t*, 368*f*, 380*t*
Piriform lobe, 438
Pisiform, **231**, 231*f*, 232*t*
Pit(s)
    gastric, 869*f*, **870**
    small intestine, 878–879
Pitch, 579*f*, **580**
    perception of, 582
Pitocin. *See* Oxytocin
Pituicytes, 601
Pituitary dwarfism, **604**
Pituitary gland (hypophysis), **443**, 595*f*, **601**–608, 602*f*, 606–607*t*. *See also* Anterior pituitary gland; Posterior pituitary gland
    developmental aspects of, 626
    hypothalamus relationship and, 602*f*, 603
Pivot joints, **259**, 260*f*
PKD. *See* Polycystic kidney disease
PKU. *See* Phenylketonuria
Placenta, 623, **1078**, 1079*f*, 1080*f*
    delivery of (placental stage), **1092**, 1092*f*
    in fetal circulation, 1084–1085, 1086*f*
    formation of (placentation), **1078**, 1079*f*, 1080*f*
    hormones secreted by, 623, 1078, 1090
    substances crossing, 1085
Placenta abruptio, **1097**
Placental (third) stage of labor, **1092**, 1092*f*

Placenta previa, **1097**
Placentation, **1078**, 1079*f*, 1080*f*
Plane joints, **259**, 260*f*
Planes (body), 14, 15*f*, 18–19*b*
Planetary model of atom, 25*f*, **26**
Plantar arch, 734*f*, 735*f*, 744*f*
Plantar arteries, medial and lateral, 734*f*, 735*f*, **735*t***
Plantar flexion (body movement), 258*f*, **259**
    of lower limb, 380*t*, 381*f*
Plantar interossei muscles, **378*t***, 379*f*
Plantaris muscle, 373*t*, 374–375*f*, 380*t*
Plantar metatarsal arteries, 734*f*, **735*t***
Plantar nerves, medial and lateral, **510**, 510*t*
Plantar reflex, **519**
Plantar veins, 744*f*, **744*t***
Plaque (dental), **864**
Plaques (desmosome), 66, 67*f*
Plaques (fibrous/atherosclerotic), **702*b***
Plasma, 133, 135*f*, 635, 635*f*, **636**, 636*t*, **996**, 996*f*
    carbon dioxide transport in, 833, 833*f*, 834
    electrolytes in, 636*t*, 997*f*
    gas/nutrient/water/waste exchanges and, 998, 998*f*
    oxygen transport in, 830, 833*f*
Plasma cells, 646, 647*f*, **756**, 780, 781*f*, 794*f*, 795*t*
Plasma expanders, **656**
Plasmalemma. *See* Plasma membrane
Plasma membrane, 62, **63**–81, 63*f*, **94*t***
    boundary maintenance and, 5
    cell–environment interactions and, 80–81, 82*f*
    in endomembrane system, 87, 87*f*
    resting membrane potential and, **79**–80, 79*f*, 396, 397*f*
    selective/differential permeability of, **68**. *See also* Membrane(s), permeability of; Membrane transport
    structure of, 63–67, 65*f*
        fluid mosaic model of, **63**–66, 65*f*, 66*f*
        membrane junctions and, 66–68, 67*f*
        transport functions of, 68–79
Plasmapheresis, **658**
Plasma proteins, 636*t*
Plasma thromboplastin antecedent (PTA), 651*t*
Plasma thromboplastin component (PTC), 651*t*
Plasmin, **652**
Plasminogen, **652**
Plasminogen activators, 652, 703*b*
Plateau, in cardiac muscle contraction, 675*f*, **675**
Platelet(s), 134*t*, 635, 635*f*, 637, 637*f*, **645*t***, 648–649, 648*f*
    deficiency of (thrombocytopenia), **653**
    formation of, 648–649, 648*f*
    in hemostasis, 11, 11*f*, 648, 649–650, 649*f*

Platelet count, **657**
Platelet-derived growth factor (PDGF), **652**, 772*t*
Platelet factor 3 (PF$_3$/phosphatidylserine), 650*f*, **651**
Platelet plug, 649–650, 649*f*
    positive feedback in formation of, 11, 11*f*
Platysma muscle, 326*f*, **330*t***, 331*f*
Pleura(e), 17, 138*f*, **139**, 807*t*, 817*f*, **818**–819
Pleural cavity, 16, 16*f*, 817*f*, **818**
Pleural effusion, 819
Pleural fluid, **818**, 820
Pleurisy, 17, 819
Plexuses, nerve. *See specific type*
Plicae circulares (circular folds), **878**
Pluripotent (hematopoietic) stem cells, **125**–126, **639**, 639*f*, 646, 647*f*, 648*f*
P$_{N_2}$ (partial pressure of nitrogen), 827, 827*t*
Pneumocystis pneumonia, in AIDS, 796
Pneumonia, **846**
    aspiration, cleft lip/palate and, 243
Pneumotaxic center. *See* Pontine respiratory centers/group
Pneumothorax, **820**
PNS. *See* Peripheral nervous system
P$_{O_2}$ (partial pressure of oxygen), 827, 827*t*
    alveolar, 828
    external respiration (pulmonary gas exchange) and, 828–829, 828*f*, 829*f*
    hemoglobin saturation affected by, 831, 831*f*
    internal respiration and, 830
    respiration affected by, 837–838, 838, 838*f*
Podocytes, 965*f*, **966**, 969, 969–970*f*
Poisons, chemiosmotic model of oxidative phosphorylation and, 928
Polar bodies
    first, **1049**, 1050*f*
    second, **1049**, 1050*f*
Polar heads, of membrane phospholipids, 64, 65*f*
Polarity, **79**, **396**
    of epithelial tissue, **115**
    of membrane, **79**, **396**
    phospholipid, 64, 65*f*
    of sarcolemma, 285
    of water, 38
Polar microtubules, 98*f*
Polar molecule(s), **34**, 34*f*
    water as, 38
Poliomyelitis, 476
Pollex. *See* Thumb
Polyatomic ions, 39
Polycystic kidney disease, 990
Polycystic ovary syndrome (PCOS), **1066**
Polycythemia, **643**
Polycythemia vera, 643
Polydipsia, in diabetes, **622**, 623*t*
Polygene inheritance, **1107**, 1108*f*
Polymer(s), **42**–43, 44*f*

Polymerase
    DNA, **96**, 97*f*
    RNA, **102**, 102*f*
Polymorphonuclear leukocytes (PMNs/polys), **644**. *See also* Neutrophils
Polyp(s), nasal, **846**
Polypeptide(s), 47, 105, 105*f*, 107*f*
Polyphagia, in diabetes, **622**, 623*t*
Polyribosome, 105, 105*f*
Polys (polymorphonuclear leukocytes), **644**. *See also* Neutrophils
Polysaccharides, **43**, 44*f*, 912
Polyspermy, **1073**
    blocks to, 1073, 1074*f*
Polysynaptic reflexes, **514**, 514*f*
Polyunsaturated fats, 46–47
Polyuria, in diabetes, **622**, 623*t*
POMC. *See* Pro-opiomelanocortin
Pons, 443*f*, 445*f*, 446–447*f*, **447**, 449*t*. *See also under* Pontine
    development of, 431, 431*f*, 432*f*
Pontine micturition center, 988, 989*f*
Pontine nuclei, 447, 448*f*
Pontine respiratory centers/group, **835**, 835*f*
Pontine storage center, 988, 989*f*
Popliteal artery, 725*f*, 734*f*, **734*t***, 735*f*
    pulse at, 712*f*
Popliteal ligaments
    arcuate, 262*f*, **263**
    oblique, 262*f*, **263**
Popliteal vein, 744*f*, **744*t***
Popliteus muscle, 370*t*, 373*t*, 374–375*f*, 380*t*
Pores
    alveolar, 814*f*, **815**
    in fenestrated capillaries, 699, 699*f*
    nuclear, **92**, 92*f*
    in plasma membrane. *See* Protein channels
    skin, 149*f*
    sweat, 155
    taste, **571**, 572*f*
Porphyria, **168**
Porta hepatis, **881**, 882*f*
Portal-caval anastomoses, 884
Portal hypertension, **884**
Portal system
    hepatic, 721, 742*f*, **742*t***, 743*f*, 856
    hypophyseal, 602*f*, **603**
Portal triad (portal tract region), **881**, 883*f*
Portal veins
    hepatic portal vein, 737*f*, 742*f*, **742*t***, 743*f*, **881**, 882*f*
    hypophyseal portal vein, 602*f*, **603**
Positional terms/anatomical position, 12*t*, **13**, 13*f*
Positive chemotaxis, **643**, 773
Positive chronotropic factors, 685
Positive feedback, **10**
    in action potential generation, 402
    in homeostasis, **10**–11, 11*f*
    labor and, 1091, 1091*f*
    lactation and, 1093–1094, 1094*f*
    ovarian function and, 1053*f*, 1054

Positive inotropic agents, 684
Positive nitrogen balance, 914
Positive selection, 777–778, 779f
Positron emission tomography
    (PET), 18b, 19f
    in diagnosis of CNS dysfunc-
        tion, 477
Postabsorptive (fasting) state, 936,
    938–941, 939f, 940f
Postcapillary venules, 700, 700f
Postcentral gyrus, 433, 434f, 438f
Postcoital contraception, 1096b
Posterior (term), 12t
Posterior arch, 219
Posterior association area, 439
    homeostatic imbalance and, 439
Posterior auricular vein, 738f, 739f
Posterior cerebral arteries, 726f,
    726t, 727f
Posterior chamber, 555, 555f
Posterior circumflex humeral artery,
    728f, 728t, 729f
Posterior commissure, 441, 443f
Posterior communicating arteries,
    726f, 727f, 727t
Posterior cords, brachial plexus,
    505, 506f
Posterior cranial fossa, 201,
    201f, 206f
Posterior cruciate ligament,
    262–263f, 264
Posterior division, brachial plexus,
    505, 506f
Posterior extensor compartment, of
    forearm, 351–352f, 353t,
    354f, 358t
Posterior femoral cutaneous nerve,
    509f, 510t
Posterior flexor compartment, of leg,
    muscles of, 370t
Posterior fontanelle, 243f
Posterior forearm muscles, 356–357t,
    357f, 358t
Posterior fornix, 1040f, 1045
Posterior (dorsal) funiculi, 469f, 470
Posterior gluteal line, 234f, 235
Posterior (dorsal) horns, 433f, 468,
    469f, 470f
Posterior inferior iliac spine,
    234f, 235
Posterior intercostal arteries, 728f,
    729f, 729t
Posterior intercostal veins, 740f,
    740t, 741f, 741t
Posterior interventricular artery,
    666f, 669, 669f
Posterior interventricular sulcus, 664
Posterior lobe, of cerebellum,
    450, 451f
Posterior longitudinal ligament,
    217, 218f
Posterior (dorsal) median sulcus,
    468, 469f
Posterior muscles/muscle
    compartment
    of hip and thigh, 363t, 367–368f,
        369t, 380t, 381f
    of leg, 370t, 373t, 374–375f,
        380t, 381f
Posterior nasal apertures (choanae),
    806

Posterior pituitary gland (neurohy-
    pophysis), 601, 602f
    hormones of, 605–608, 607t
    hypothalamus relationship and,
        602f, 603, 605–608, 607t
Posterior pole of eye, 551, 552f
Posterior sacral foramina,
    221f, 223
Posterior scalene muscle, 336t, 337f
Posterior segment of eye, 551,
    552f, 555
Posterior semicircular canal,
    576, 577f
Posterior (dorsal) spinocerebellar
    tract, 471–473, 471f,
    472f, 473t
Posterior superior iliac spine,
    234f, 235
Posterior tibial artery, 725f, 734f,
    734–735t, 735f
    pulse at, 712f
Posterior tibial vein, 744f, 744t
Posterior vagal trunk, 530
Postganglionic axon, 526, 527f
Postganglionic fibers, 530, 534t
Postovulatory (secretory) phase of
    uterine (menstrual) cycle,
    1055f, 1056
Postpartum bleeding, 1092
Postpolio syndrome, 476
Postsynaptic neuron, 406, 407f, 409f
Postsynaptic potentials, 399,
    408–413, 411t, 412f
    in phototransduction, 564, 565f
Posture, skeletal muscles in mainte-
    nance of, 276
Potassium, 26t, 918t
    absorption of, 900
    acid-base balance and, 1006
    action potential and, 287f,
        400–401f
    aldosterone regulation and,
        615, 616f
    balance of
        abnormalities of, 1003t
        developmental aspects
            of, 1015
        regulation of, 1006–1007
    dietary, 918t
    heart function and, 686
    in plasma/interstitial fluid/
        intracellular fluid, 997, 997f
    resting membrane potential and,
        79–80, 79f, 396, 397f
    in salt substitutes, 1007
    serum levels of, renal secretion
        and, 1006
    tubular secretion of, 978, 1006
Potassium channels
    action potential and, 401f, 402
    muscle contraction and, 287f,
        288, 289f
Potential/potential difference, 395
Potential energy, 24, 31
Potentiation, synaptic, 412–413
    long-term (LTP), 413, 460
    in memory, 460
Potosis, 76–77
Pott's fracture, 239f, 240
Power lever, 323, 323f
Power stroke, of cilia, 90, 91f

P_{pul}. See Intrapulmonary (intra-
    alveolar) pressure
P-Q interval, 679f, 680
Prader-Willi syndrome, 1109
Prealbumin, 49f, 50
Precapillary sphincter, 697f,
    700, 700f
Precentral gyrus, 433, 434f, 438f
Precipitation, by antibodies,
    785, 785f
Precommand areas, 513
Precommand level of motor control,
    513, 513f
Preeclampsia, 1090
Prefrontal cortex (anterior associa-
    tion area), 436f, 439
    homeostatic imbalance and, 439
    in memory, 458, 459f
Preganglionic axon, 526, 527f,
    529, 530
Preganglionic fibers
    parasympathetic, 530, 534t
    sympathetic, 530, 534t
Preganglionic neurons, 526, 530
    development of, 541
Pregnancy, 1072, 1089–1090, 1089f
    anatomical changes during,
        1089–1090, 1089f
    ectopic, 1042, 1097
    hormonal changes during, 1078f
    nutrition during, 954
    physiologic changes during, 1090
    prevention of (contraception),
        1095–1096b
    Rh incompatibility and, 655
    urinary incontinence and,
        988, 1090
Pregnancy tests, hCG-based, 1078
Preload, 684, 686f
Premature birth, infant respiratory
    distress syndrome and, 823
Premature contraction (extrasys-
    tole), 679
Premolars (bicuspids), 862, 862f
Premotor cortex, 436f, 437
    homeostatic imbalances and, 437
    in memory, 459f
Pre-mRNA, 103
Prenatal testing, 1110
Preoptic nucleus, 456
    in temperature regulation, 951
Preovulatory (proliferative) phase of
    uterine (menstrual) cycle,
    1055f, 1056
Prepatellar bursa, subcutaneous,
    262f, 263
    inflammation of, 270
Prepotentials (pacemaker poten-
    tials), 676, 676f
Prepuce, 1028
    of clitoris, 1046, 1046f
    of penis (foreskin), 1025f,
        1028, 1029f
Presbycusis, 589
Presbyopia, 559
Pressure gradient, in breathing,
    822–823, 823f
Pressure points, 711, 712f
Pressure receptors
    Pacinian corpuscles, 149f,
        486–487, 487t

Ruffini endings, 487, 487t
Pressure–volume relationships, pul-
    monary ventilation and, 820,
    821f, 822f
Prestriate cortices, 568
Presynaptic inhibition, 413
Presynaptic neuron, 406, 409f
Pretectal nuclei, in visual pathway,
    566, 567f
Prevertebral (collateral) ganglia, 530
    pathways with synapses in,
        532, 533f
Prickle cells, 150
Primary active transport, 73, 74f, 77t
    in sodium reabsorption, 974,
        976f, 983f
Primary auditory cortex, 436f, 438,
    582, 582f
Primary brain vesicles, 430, 431f
Primary (main) bronchi, 813f, 814
Primary capillary plexus, 602f, 603
Primary curvatures, 243, 243f
Primary dentition (deciduous teeth),
    862, 862f
Primary follicle, 1041f, 1042, 1050f,
    1051f, 1052
Primary germ layers, 141, 141f, 1079,
    1079f, 1081
Primary humoral response, 780–781,
    781f, 782f, 794f
Primary (essential) hypertension,
    713
Primary immune response, 780–781,
    781f, 782f, 794f
Primary lymphoid organs, 777
Primary (somatic) motor cortex,
    435–437, 436f, 438f
    homeostatic imbalances and, 437
Primary olfactory (smell) cortex,
    436f, 438–439
Primary oocytes, 1049, 1050f, 1051f
Primary ossification centers, 183,
    183f, 194, 194f
Primary sensory endings, 515,
    515f, 516f
Primary sex organs, 1024. See also
    Gonad(s); Ovaries; Testes
Primary somatosensory cortex, 436f,
    437, 438f
Primary spermatocyte, 1033,
    1036f, 1037
Primary structure of protein,
    48, 49f
Primary transcript (pre-mRNA), 103
Primary visual (striate) cortex, 436f,
    437–438, 566, 567f, 568–569
    homeostatic imbalance and, 439
Primase, in DNA replication, 96
Prime mover, 321
Primitive gut, 901, 1083f, 1084
Primitive streak, 1081, 1081f
Primordial follicles, 1042, 1049,
    1050f, 1051f
Primordial germ cells, 1060
Principal cells, 965f, 966
Principle of complementarity of
    structure and function, 3
    cell theory and, 62
P-R interval, 680
PRL. See Prolactin
Procarboxypeptidase, 886, 886f

Procedural (skills) memory, **458**, 459f
Process (bone marking), 178t
Processes (neuron), 134, 135f,
    390–392
Processing (P) bodies, 105
Procoagulants (clotting factors), 649,
    650, 650f, 651t
Proconvertin, 651t
Proctodeum, 901f, **904**
Proctology, **905**
Product(s), in chemical reaction, **36**
Proerythroblasts, **639**, 639f
Progesterone, 623, **1005**, 1040,
    1057, 1057t
    in ovarian cycle, 1053f,
        1054, 1057t
    placental/during pregnancy,
        1057, 1078, 1078f
    in sodium regulation, **1005**
    in uterine (menstrual) cycle,
        1055f, 1056, 1057, 1057t
Progestins, for contraception, 1096b
Programmed cell death (apoptosis),
    108, 424
    B cell development and, 778
    T cell development and, 778, 779f
Proinsulin, **622**
Projection, **490**
Projection fibers, 440, 440f, **441**
Projection level of motor control,
    512–513, 513f
Prolactin (PRL), 602f, **605**,
    607t, **1093**
    lactation and, **1093**, 1094, 1094f
Prolactin-inhibiting hormone
    (PIH), **605**
Prolactinoma, **627**
Prolactin-releasing factor, 605
    lactation and, 1093
Prolapsed (herniated/slipped) disc,
    218, 218f
    aging and, 244
Prolapse of uterus, **1044**
Proliferation (growth) zone (epiphy-
    seal plate), 184, 184f
Proliferative (preovulatory) phase of
    uterine (menstrual) cycle,
    1055f, 1056
Prolymphocytes, 646, 647f
Promegakaryocyte, 648f
Promonocytes, 646, 647f
Promoter, in transcription, **102**, 102f
Promyelocytes, 646, 647f
Pronation (body movement),
    256, 258f
    of upper limb, 358t, 359f
Pronator quadratus muscle, **354t**,
    355f, **356t**, 358t
Pronator teres muscle, 326f, **354t**,
    355f, 358t, 359f
Pronephric duct, **989**, 990f
Pronephros, **989**, 990f
Pronuclei, male and female,
    1073, 1075f
Pro-opiomelanocortin (POMC), **603**
    in food intake regulation,
        945, 946f
Propagation of action potential, **402**
    in muscle fiber contraction,
        285–288, 287f, 288f
    in neuron, **402**–403, 403f

Prophase
    in meiosis, 1033, **1034f**, **1035f**
    in mitosis, 96f, **97**, **98f**, 1034f
Proprioception, conscious, 471
Proprioceptors, **486**, 487t
Propulsion (food), 853, 853f, 888t.
    See also Peristalsis
Prosencephalon (forebrain), **430**, 431f
Prostacyclin, 649
Prostaglandin(s), 45t, 47, 596, **769**,
    914, **1091**
    in inflammation, **769**, 772t
    labor and, **1091**, 1091f
Prostaglandin E$_2$, in glomerular fil-
    tration rate regulation, 974
Prostate gland, 1025f, 1029f,
    1030–1031
    cancer of, 1030–1031
    embryologic/fetal development
        of, 1061f
Prostate-specific antigen (PSA), 1031
Prostatic hyperplasia, benign
    (BPH), 1030
Prostatic secretion, 1030
Prostatic urethra, **987**, 987f, 1025f,
    1029f, 1030
Prostatitis, 1030
Protease(s)
    in mast cells, 126
    pancreatic, 886, 886f, 898f
Protease inhibitors, for AIDS, 797
Proteasomes, **106**–107
Protective function
    of blood, 636
    of bones, 175
    of skin, 5, 5f, 6f, 160–161,
        767–768, 772t
Protein(s), 8, **47**–53, 100, 913t,
    914–915, 915f. *See also specific
    type*
    absorption of, 896f, 898f, 899
    amino acids/peptide bonds and,
        47–48, 48f
    complete, 913t, **914**
    cytosolic, degradation of, 106–107
    denaturation of, **50**
    dietary, 913t, 914–915, 915f
    digestion of, 871, 896f, 897, 898f
    enzymes/enzyme activity and,
        51–53, 52f, 53f
    fibrous (structural), **50**, 51t
    globular (functional), 49f, **50**, 51t
    as glucose source, 939f, 940
    incomplete, 913t, 914
    interconversion of, 936f
    membrane, 64–66, 65f, 66f. *See
        also* Membrane proteins
    metabolism of, 920f, 932–934,
        933f, 934t
        liver in, 942t
        in postabsorptive state,
            939f, 940
        thyroid hormone affecting,
            612t
    molecular chaperones, **50**–51
    plasma, 636t
    stress, 51
    structural levels of, 48–50, 49f
    synthesis of, 100–105, 101f, 102f,
        103f, 104f, 105f, 934. *See also*
        Protein synthesis

transport, 51t, 899
    in urine, 985t
Protein anions, in plasma/interstitial
    fluid/intracellular fluid, 997f
Protein buffer system, **1010**
Protein C, **652**
Protein-calorie malnutrition, 955
Protein channels, 64, **69**–70, 69f, 395,
    396f. *See also specific type*
    action potential and, 401f, 402
    gated, 69, 81, **395**, 396f
    information transfer at chemical
        synapse and, 408, 409f
    muscle contraction and, 286f,
        287, 288, 288f
Protein-coated pits, 75, 76f
Protein kinases, 81, **597**
    in hormone mechanism of ac-
        tion, **597**, 597f
Protein synthesis, 100–105, 106f,
    107f, 934
    DNA in, 53, 100–101, 107f
    in ribosomes, 84, 86f
    RNA in, 55, 101, 101f, 107f
    transcription, 101, **101**–102, 101f,
        102f, 107f
    translation, 101, 101f, **103**–105,
        103f, 104f, 105f, 107f
Proteinuria, 985t
Proteoglycans, in ground substance,
    124
Proteolysis, 106–107
Prothrombin, 650, 650f, 651, 651t
Prothrombin activator, 650,
    650f, **651**
    pathways to, 650–651, 650f
Prothrombin time, **657**
Proton(s), **25**, 25f
    acids releasing, 39
    amino acid, 47
Proton acceptors, bases as, **39**, 1009
    amino acid, 47
Proton donors, acids as, **39**, 1009
    amino acid, 47
Proton (H$^+$) gradient, electrochemi-
    cal, **395**, **927**
Proton therapy, in cancer treat-
    ment, 143b
Proto-oncogenes, **142b**
Protraction (body movement),
    258f, **259**
Provirus, in HIV infection, 796
Provitamin D$_3$ (cholecalciferol),
    624, 625t
Provitamins, 916
Proximal (term), 12t
Proximal convoluted tubule, 965f,
    966, 967f, 983f
    absorptive capability of, 976, 977t
    glutamine metabolism in, am-
        monium ion excretion and,
        1012, 1013f
    hydrogen secretion in, in acid
        base balance, 1011
    reabsorption in, 975, 976f, 983f
Proximal phalanx
    finger, 231f, 232t, 233
    toe, 240f, 242t
Proximal radioulnar joint, 230f, 254t
Proximal tibiofibular joint, 238,
    239f, 255t
PSA. *See* Prostate-specific antigen

Pseudogenes, 101
Pseudohermaphrodites, 1060–1062
Pseudopods, 75, 78f
Pseudostratified columnar epithe-
    lium, **119**, 119f
Pseudounipolar neurons, **394**,
    393–394f
P site, 104f, 105
Psoas major muscle, 363t, 364f
Psoriasis, **168**
Psychoneuroimmunology, 799
Psychoses, **479**
Psychosocial dwarfism, **627**
Psychosomatic illnesses, **452**
PTA. *See* Plasma thromboplastin
    antecedent
PTC. *See* Plasma thromboplastin
    component
ptc (patched) gene, UV radiation
    affecting, 162
Pterygoid muscles, medial and
    lateral, 332t, 333f
Pterygoid processes, 203f,
    207–208, 208f
Pterygopalatine ganglia, 498t,
    529, 529f
PTH. *See* Parathyroid hormone
Ptosis, 496t
    renal, 961–962
Puberty, **1063**
    in females, 1063
        leptin and, 1053, 1056
        secondary sex characteristics
            and, 1057, 1057t
    in males, 1063
        secondary sex characteristics
            and, **1040**, 1057t
Pubic arch, 233f, 235, 236t
Pubic bone (pubis), 233f, **235**
Pubic crest, 233f, **235**
Pubic rami, superior and inferior,
    234f, 235
Pubic (hypogastric) region, 17, 20f
Pubic symphysis, 233f, 235,
    250f, 255t
Pubic tubercle, 233f, 234f, **235**
Pubis (pubic bone), 233f, **235**
Pubofemoral ligament, **267**, 267f
Pudendal artery, internal, 734f, **734t**
    constriction of after orgasm,
        1032
Pudendal nerve, 509f, 510, 510t
Pudendum (external genitalia),
    1041, **1046**–1047, 1046f
    embryologic/fetal development
        of, 1062f
Pulmonary arteries, 665–667f, 722f,
    722–723t, 817f, 818
Pulmonary capillaries, 722f, **722t**,
    816f, **818**
    in respiratory membrane,
        815, 816f
    oxygenation of blood in,
        828–830, 829f
Pulmonary circuit/circulation, **668**,
    668f, 717, 721, 722f,
    722–723t, 818
Pulmonary congestion, in heart
    failure, **687**
Pulmonary embolism, **846**–847
Pulmonary function tests, 824–826

Pulmonary gas exchange (external respiration), **805**, 828–830, 828*f*, 829*f*
Pulmonary irritant reflexes, 839
Pulmonary (visceral) pleura, 17, 138*f*, 817*f*, **818**
Pulmonary plexus, 529*f*, **530**, 533*f*, **818**
Pulmonary trunk, 665*f*, 667*f*, **668**, 722*f*, **722***t*
Pulmonary valve (pulmonary semilunar valve), 667*f*, **670**, 671*f*
Pulmonary veins, **664**, 665–667*f*, 722*f*, **722**–723*f*, 817*f*, **818**
Pulmonary ventilation (breathing), **805**. *See also* Respiration
    age affecting, 843
    altitude affecting, 839–840
    apneustic, 835
    cessation of. *See* Apnea
    Cheyne-Stokes, **846**
    exercise affecting, 839
    expiration and, 821*f*, 822, 822*f*
    inspiration and, 820–822, 821*f*, 822*f*
    mechanics of, 819–826, 819*f*, 821*f*, 822*f*, 823*f*, 825*f*, 826*t*
    muscles of, 340*t*, 341*f*, 820, 821*f*
    neural control of, 835–836, 835*f*, 836*f*
    physical factors influencing, 822–824, 823*f*
    rate and depth of, factors affecting, 836–839, 836*f*, 837*f*, 838*f*
Pulp
    dental, **863**
    splenic, **758**, 759*f*
Pulp cavity, **863**, 863*f*
Pulse (arterial), 705, **711**
    monitoring, 711, 712*f*
    pregnancy and, 1090
Pulse pressure, **705**
Puncta, lacrimal, **549**, 549*f*
Punnett square, **1105**, 1105*f*
Pupil, 548*f*, **551**, 552*f*
    constriction/dilation of, 552, 553*f*
        in close vision, 559
        light/dark adaptation and, 565–566
Pupillary light reflex, 566
Pupillary reflex, accommodation, **559**
Purines, 53, **418***t*, 419
Purkinje cells, **450**
Purkinje fibers, **677**, **677***f*
Pus, **144**, 773
    in urine, 985*t*
Putamen, **441**, 442*f*
P wave, 679*f*, **680**, 680*f*
Pyelitis, 963, 988
Pyelogram, 985*f*, **991**
Pyelonephritis, 963, 988
Pyloric antrum, **867**, 868*f*
Pyloric canal, **867**, 868*f*
Pyloric region of stomach, **867**
    gastric contractile activity and, 875–876
Pyloric stenosis, **905**
Pyloric valve/sphincter, **867**, 868*f*
Pylorus, **867**, 868*f*
Pyramidal cells, in primary motor cortex, **435**

Pyramidal process, 211
Pyramidal (direct) system, 474, 474*t*, 475*f*, 512–513
Pyramidal (corticospinal) tracts, 435, 471*f*, **474**, 474*t*, 475*f*
Pyramids, **447**
    medulla oblongata, 446*f*, **447**, 448*f*
    renal (medullary), **962**, 963*f*
Pyridoxine (vitamin B₆), 916*t*
Pyrimidines, 53
Pyrogens, 775, 954
Pyruvic acid, 298, 298*f*, 919, 920*f*, 922*f*, 923, 923*f*, **924**, 929*f*
Pyuria, 985*t*

QRS complex, 679*f*, **680**, 680*f*
Q-T interval, **680**
Quadrants, abdominopelvic, 17, 17*f*
Quadrate lobe, of liver, 881, 882*f*
Quadratus femoris muscle, 368*f*, **368***t*, 380*t*
Quadratus lumborum muscle, **338***t*, 339*f*
Quadratus plantae (flexor accessorius) muscle, 376*t*, 377*f*
Quadriceps femoris muscle, **363***t*, 364*f*, **365***t*
Quadriceps strain, **382**
Quadriplegia, **476**
Qualities, **490**
    sound, **580**
Quality discrimination, **490**
Quanta, **556**
Quaternary structure of protein, 49*f*, 50
Quick of nail, 160
Quiescent period, cardiac cycle, **682**
Quiescent (resting) zone (epiphyseal plate), 184, 184*f*

RA. *See* Rheumatoid arthritis
Rabies, **425**
Radial artery, 728*f*, **728***t*, 729*f*
    pulse at, 711, 712*f*, 728*t*
    of uterus, **1044**, 1045*f*
Radial collateral ligament, of elbow, **266**, 266*f*
Radial fossa, **228**, 229*f*
Radial groove, **228**, 229*f*
Radial nerve, **505**–507, 506*f*, 507*t*
    injuries of, 507
Radial notch, **229**, 229*f*, 230*f*
Radial pulse, 711, 712*f*
Radial tuberosity, 229*f*, **230**, 230*f*
Radiant (electromagnetic) energy, 24
Radiate arteries, cortical, **963**, 964*f*, 967*f*, 968
Radiate veins, cortical, **964**, 964*f*, 967*f*
Radiation
    electromagnetic, 556–557, 557*f*
    heat loss by, 950*f*, 951, 951*f*
    ionizing, 28, **56**
    ultraviolet. *See* Ultraviolet radiation
Radiation sickness, **56**
Radiation therapy, for cancer, 143*b*

Radical mastectomy, **1048**
Radioactivity, 28
Radiocarpal (wrist) joint, 254*t*
Radiographic anatomy, 2
Radiographs, 18*b*
Radioisotopes, **28**
    in positron-emission tomography, 18*b*
Radioulnar joints, **228**
    distal, 230*f*, 254*t*
    proximal, 230*f*, 254*t*
Radius, 199*f*, 228, 229*f*, **230**–231, 230*f*, 232*t*
Ramus/rami (bone marking), 178*t*
    of ischium, 234*f*, **235**
    of mandible, 203*f*, 209, 210*f*
    of pubis, 234*f*, **235**, 1046*f*
Ramus/rami (nerve)
    communicantes, 502, 503*f*, 534*t*
        gray, 531*f*, **532**
        white, **530**, 531*f*, 533*f*
    development of, 502–504, 503*f*
    dorsal, **502**, 503*f*, 504
    ventral, **502**, 503*f*, 504, 504*f*
Random fertilization, 1105
Ranvier, nodes of (myelin sheath gaps), 390*f*, **391**
Raphe nuclei, 448*f*, **452**
Rapid eye movement (REM) sleep, **455**, 456*f*
RAS. *See* Reticular activating system
Rathke's pouch, 603
Raynaud's disease, 540–541
RBCs. *See* Red blood cells
Reabsorption, 718
    tubular, 971*f*, **974**–978, 975*f*, 976*f*, 977*t*, **983***f*
        absorptive capabilities of tubules/collecting ducts and, 976–978, 977*t*
        acid-base balance and, 1011, 1012*f*
        aldosterone affecting, 978, 983*f*, 1004, 1004*f*
        of bicarbonate, 1011, 1012*f*
        fluid balance and, 1000, 1000*f*
        of nutrients/water/ions, 975–976, 976*f*, 981–982, 982*f*, 983*f*
        passive, **975**, 976*f*, 983*f*
        of potassium, 1006
        of sodium, 974–975, 976*f*, 983*f*, 1004, 1004*f*
Reactant(s), in chemical reaction, **36**, 37
    water as, 39
Reactive hyperemia, **715**
Reactivity, of antigens, **776**
Real image, on retina, 557, 558*f*
Receptive endings, 393*f*, 394
Receptive field, 489, **567**
    ganglion cell, **567**
Receptive regions, **390**, 393*t*
Receptive relaxation, of stomach muscles, **874**
Receptor(s), 9. *See also specific type*
    complex and simple, **486**
    in homeostasis, 9, 9*f*, 10*f*
    in hormone mechanism of action, 596
    membrane, 64, **81**, 82*f*

    phasic, **489**
    in reflex arc, 514, 514*f*
    special sensory, **547**–548. *See also specific type*
    tonic, **489**
    up- and down-regulation of, **598**
Receptor binding, in chemical signaling, 81
Receptor cells, in special senses, 547–548
Receptor editing, 778
Receptor-mediated endocytosis, **76**, 77*t*, 78*f*
Receptor membrane, gustatory cell, 571
Receptor potential, 398, **489**
Receptor region, neurotransmitter, 407
Recessive allele, **1103**
Recessive traits, 1106, 1106*t*
Reciprocal activation, **518**, 518*f*
Reciprocal inhibition, **516**
Recoil (lung)
    in expiration, 822, 822*f*
    intrapleural pressure and, 819
Recombinant chromosomes, **1104**, 1104*f*
Recombination
    gene, 1104, 1104*f*
    somatic, antigen receptor diversity and, 779, 784
Recovery stroke, of cilia, 90, 91*f*
Recruitment (multiple motor unit summation), **295**, 295*f*, 296*f*
    contraction duration/velocity affected by, 303
Rectal arteries, superior, 730*f*, **732***t*, 733*f*
Rectal examination, **890**
Rectal valves, **890**–891, 891*f*
Rectouterine pouch, 1040*f*, 1044
Rectum, 852*f*, **890**–891, 891*f*. *See also under Rectal*
    autonomic innervation/effects and, 529*f*, 533*f*
Rectus abdominis muscles, 326*f*, **342***t*, 343*f*
Rectus femoris muscle, 326*f*, **363***t*, 364*f*, **365***t*, 380*t*, 381*f*
Rectus muscles, of eye, 550, 550*f*
Red blood cells (erythrocytes), 133, 134*t*, 135*f*, 635, 635*f*, 637, **637**–643, 637*f*, **645***t*
    antigens of, blood groups and, 654
        transplantation and, 792
    disorders of, 641–643, 642*f*
    hemoglobin in, 637, **638**
    life cycle of, 641, 641*f*, 645*t*
    production of, 638–640, 639*f*, 640*f*, 641*f*
    sickled, 642, 642*f*, 1106
    transfusion of, 654–656, 655*t*, 656*f*
    in urine, 985*t*
Red cones, 562
Red margin, 858
Red marrow, 179, 182*f*, **638**–639
    hematopoiesis in, 176, 179, **638**–639, 657
Red marrow cavities, **179**

Red nucleus, **446**–447, 448*f*

Redox (oxidation-reduction) reactions, 37, 920–**921**

Red pulp, **758**, 759*f*

Reduced hemoglobin (deoxyhemoglobin), **638**, 831

Reduced reactant, in redox reaction, **37**

Reduction, fracture, 188

Reduction division (meiosis I), **1033**, 1034*f*, **1035***f*

Reference man/woman, 2

Referred pain, **535**, 535*f*

Reflection (light), **557**

Reflex(es), **423**, 423*f*, 514–520, 514*f*
  spinal, 466, **514**–520
  testing, 477

Reflex arcs, **423**, 423*f*, 512, **514**, 514*f*
  visceral, **534**, 534*f*

Reflex (cephalic) phase, of gastric secretion, **872**–873, 872*f*

Refraction (light), **557**, 557*f*
  visual disorders related to, 559, 560*f*

Refractory periods, **288**
  muscle fiber, **288**
    in cardiac muscle, 673, 675*f*
  neuron, 404, 404*f*
    after orgasm, 1032
    aging affecting, 1066

Regeneration, **139**, 140, 140*f*, 141
  cardiac tissue, 141, 312
  epithelial tissue, 116, **140**, 140*f*
  nerve fiber/axon, 491–492, 493*f*
  neuronal, 141

Regeneration tube, 492, 493*f*

Regional anatomy, **2**

Regional terms in anatomy, 13*f*, **14**

Regular dense connective tissue, **129**, 129*f*, 134*t*

Regulatory functions of blood, 636

Regulatory T cells, 786, 787*f*, **792**, 795*t*
  autoimmune reactions inhibited by, 797

Relative refractory period, **404**, 404*f*

Relaxation
  receptive, of stomach muscles, **874**
  skeletal muscle fiber, 284, 284*f*, 293, 294*f*
  smooth muscle, 307

Relaxin, 1031, **1089**
  placental production of, 1078, **1089**

Relay(s), in spinal tracts, 470

Relay proteins, 598

Releasing hormones, hypothalamic, **603**

Remodeling (bone). *See* Bone remodeling

Remodeling units, 185

REM sleep. *See* Rapid eye movement (REM) sleep

Renal arteries, 725*f*, 730*f*, **732***t*, 733*f*, 961*f*, **963**, 964*f*

Renal autoregulation, **972**

Renal calculi, **986**

Renal calyces (major and minor), **962**, 963*f*

Renal clearance, **984**

Renal columns, **962**, 963*f*

Renal corpuscle, **964**, 965*f*, 966*f*, 967*f*

Renal cortex, **962**, 963*f*, 965*f*, 966*f*

Renal failure, 974, **984**

Renal fascia, **961**, 962*f*

Renal hilum, 961, 961*f*

Renal infarct, **992**

Renal medulla, **962**, 963*f*, 965*f*
  osmotic gradient in, 979*f*, 981

Renal pelvis, **962**, 963*f*, 985*f*

Renal physiology, 2, 969–984, 971*f*. *See also* Urine, formation of

Renal plexus, 964, 964*f*

Renal ptosis, 961–962

Renal (medullary) pyramids, **962**, 963*f*

Renal sinus, 961

Renal tubular acidosis, **1020**

Renal tubules, **964**, 965*f*, 966, 966*f*
  reabsorption in, 971*f*, **974**–978, 975*f*, 976*f*, 977*t*, **983***f*
    absorptive capabilities and, 976–978, 977*t*
    acid-base balance and, 1011, 1012*f*
    aldosterone affecting, 978, 983*f*, 1004, 1004*f*
    of bicarbonate, 1011, 1012*f*
    fluid balance and, 1000, 1000*f*
    of nutrients/water/ions, 975–976, 976*f*, 981–982, 982*f*, 983*f*
    passive, **975**, 976*f*, 983*f*
    of potassium, 1006
    of sodium, 974–975, 976*f*, 983*f*, 1004, 1004*f*
  secretion by, 971*f*, **978**, 983*f*
    acid-base balance and, 978, 983*f*, 1011, 1011–1014, 1013*f*
    of bicarbonate, 1014
    of potassium, 978, 1006

Renal veins, 736*f*, 737*f*, 742*f*, **742***t*, 743*f*, 961*f*, **964**, 964*f*

Renin, 615, 624, 625*t*, 710, 961, **972**
  blood pressure and, 710, 710*f*, 972, 1007*f*
  granular cells secreting, 968, 973*f*, 974
  sympathetic nervous system and, 539

Renin-angiotensin mechanism, 615, 616*f*, **710**, **972**–974, 973*f*, 1004, 1004*f*, 1007*f*
  sympathetic nervous system and, 539

Rennin, **871**, **897**

Repair
  bone fracture, 188–189, 189*f*
  tissue, 139–141, 140*f*

Replication fork, 96, 97*f*

Replisome, **96**

Repolarization, **288**, **402**
  ECG and, 679*f*, 680, 680*f*
  muscle contraction and, 287*f*, **288**, 288*f*
    in cardiac muscle, 675, 675*f*, 676, 676*f*
  neuron, action potential and, 399, 400–401*f*, **402**

Repressor genes, in cell division control, 100

Reproduction, **7**–8, 7*f*
  cellular, 7

Reproductive cloning, 1096–1097

Reproductive duct system
  embryologic/fetal development of, 1061*f*
  in females, 1040–1041, 1040*f*, 1042–1046, 1043*f*, 1045*f*
  in males, 1025, 1025*f*, **1028**–1030

Reproductive system, 7*f*, **1024**–1070. *See also* Female reproductive system; Male reproductive system
  accessory organs of, **1024**
  autonomic nervous system and, 542*b*
  cardiovascular system and, 746*b*
  developmental aspects of, 1059–1066, 1061*f*, 1062*f*
    embryologic/fetal events, 1059–1063, 1061*f*, 1062*f*
    menopause, **1063**–1066
    puberty, **1063**
  digestive system and, 902*b*
  endocrine system and, 628*b*, 629*b*
  in female, 7*f*. *See also* Female reproductive system
    anatomy of, 1040–1049, 1040*f*
    functions/physiology of, 7*f*, 1049–1058, 1050*f*, 1051*f*, 1053*f*, 1055*f*, 1057*t*
    pregnancy and, **1072**, 1089–1090, 1089*f*
  homeostatic relationships of, 1064*b*, 1065*b*
  integumentary system and, 166*b*
  lymphatic system and, 762*b*
  in male, 7*f*. *See also* Male reproductive system
    anatomy of, 1025–1031, 1025*f*
    functions/physiology of, 7*f*, 1031–1040, 1034*f*, 1035*f*, 1036*f*, 1037*f*, 1039*f*
  muscular system and, 314*b*
  respiratory system and, 844*b*
  sexually transmitted infections and, **1058**–1059
  skeletal system and, 192*b*
  thyroid hormone affecting, 612*t*
  urinary system and, 1018*b*

Residual volume, **824**, 825*f*

Resistance, **395**
  airway, 822–823, 823*f*
    flow/pressure relationship and, 822–823
  vascular/peripheral, **704**
    blood pressure and, 706, 710*f*, 711*f*
    in renal circulation, 968

Resistance exercise, **304**

Resistin, 624, 625*t*
  in insulin resistance, 627*b*

Resolution phase of sexual response, in male, 1032

Resonance, 580, 581*f*

Resorption, bone, 185
  in osteoporosis, 191

Respiration, **805**. *See also* Breathing
  cellular, 5, 83, 805, **919**, 920, 922*f*, 928, 934*t*

ATP for muscle activity and, 298*f*, 299, 299*f*, 300, 310*t*
  redox reactions in, 37

control of, 834–839, 835*f*, 836*f*, 837*f*, 838*f*

external, **805**, 828–830, 828*f*, 829*f*

fetal, 843

gas exchange and, 827–830, 827*t*, 828*f*, 829*f*

gas transport and, 637, 638, 717, 718*f*, 805, 830–834, 831*f*, 832*f*, 833*f*

internal, **805**, 828*f*, 830

muscles of, 340*t*, 341*f*, 820, 821*f*

neural control of, 835–836, 835*f*, 836*f*

volition (conscious control) and, 838–839

Respiratory acidosis (hypoventilation), **840**, 1011, **1014**, 1016*t*
  blood values in, 1017*b*
  renal compensations and, 1015

Respiratory alkalosis (hyperventilation), **837**, 1011, **1014**, 1016*t*
  blood values in, 1017*b*
  renal compensations and, 1015

Respiratory/lung alveoli, 807*t*, 814*f*, **815**, 816*f*
  developmental aspects of, 843
  gas partial pressures in, 827*t*, 828

Respiratory bronchioles, 814*f*, **815**

Respiratory burst, **644**, 768

Respiratory capacities, **824**, 825*f*

Respiratory cartilages, 173, 174*f*

Respiratory centers
  blood pH affecting, 1010
  medullary, 449, 835, 835*f*
    respiratory rate/rhythm affected by, 836–838, 836*f*, 837*f*, 838*f*
  pontine, **835**, 835*f*

Respiratory distress syndrome, infant (IRDS), **823**

Respiratory enzyme complexes, **926**

Respiratory gases. *See also under* Gas
  in plasma, 636*t*
  transport of, 637, 638, 717, 718*f*, **805**, 830–834, 831*f*, 832*f*, 833*f*

Respiratory membrane (air–blood barrier), **815**, 816*f*
  gas exchange at, 805, 815, 816*f*, 828–830, 828*f*, 829*f*
  thickness/surface area of, 830

Respiratory mucosa, **807**, 808*f*

Respiratory pressures, 819–820, 819*f*

Respiratory pump, venous return and, **706**, 707*f*

Respiratory rate/depth
  age affecting, 843
  factors affecting, 836–839, 836*f*, 837*f*, 838*f*

Respiratory rhythm, genesis of, 835–836

Respiratory system, 7*f*, 804–850, **805**, 805*f*, 807*t*, 808*f*. *See also specific organ or structure and under Pulmonary*
  in acid-base balance, 41, 834, 837*f*, 838, 1010–1011
    compensations for abnormalities and, 1014, 1014–1015

Respiratory system (*contd.*)
adjustments and, 839–840
autonomic nervous system and, 542*b*, 543*b*
breathing mechanics and, 819–826, 819*f*, 821*f*, 822*f*, 823*f*, 825*f*, 826*t*
cardiovascular system and, 746*b*, 805, 844*b*, 845*b*
developmental aspects of, 842–846, 843*f*
digestive system and, 902*b*
endocrine system and, 628*b*
functional anatomy of, 805–819, 805*f*, 807*t*, 808*f*
functions of, 6–7, 7*f*
gas exchange and, 827–830, 827*t*, 828*f*, 829*f*
gas transport and, 830–834, 831*f*, 832*f*, 833*f*
homeostatic imbalances and, 840–842
homeostatic relationships of, 5*f*, 844*b*, 845*f*
integumentary system and, 166*b*
lymphatic system and, 762*b*
muscular system and, 314*b*
pregnancy and, 1090
reproductive system and, 1064*b*
respiration control and, 834–839, 835*f*, 836*f*, 837*f*, 838*f*
skeletal system and, 192*b*
urinary system and, 1018*b*
Respiratory (bronchial) tree, 807*t*, 813–815, 813*f*, 814*f*, 818*f*. See *also* Bronchi
Respiratory volumes, 824, 825*f*
Respiratory zone, 806, 814*f*, 815
Respirometer, 947
Response to injury hypothesis, of atherosclerosis, 702*b*
Responsiveness (irritability), 5, 6*f*, 276
muscle cell, 276
neuron, 5, 6*f*, 395. See *also* Nerve impulse(s)
Restenoses, after angioplasty, 703*b*
Resting heart rate, 706
Resting membrane potential, 79–80, 79*f*, 396, 397*f*
in cardiac muscle cells, instability of, 676, 676*f*
in neurons, 396–398, 396*f*, 397*f*
Resting state, of action potential, 400–401*f*, 402
Resting (quiescent) zone (epiphyseal plate), 184, 184*f*
Restriction point, in cell cycle, 96*f*, 100
Restrictive pulmonary disorders, pulmonary function testing in, 825
Rete testis, 1026, 1027*f*
Reticular activating system (RAS), 453
Reticular cells, 128*f*, 129, 756, 756*f*
in bone marrow, 639
in lymphoid tissue, 756, 756*f*
Reticular connective tissue, 128*f*, 129, 134*t*, 756
lymph node/lymphoid organ, 756, 756*f*, 758

Reticular fibers, 125, 125*f*, 129
lymph node/lymphoid tissue, 756, 756*f*
Reticular formation, 447, 448*f*, 449*t*, 452–453, 453*f*
autonomic regulation by, 539*f*, 540
Reticular lamina, 115–116
Reticular layer of dermis, 149*f*, 152, 153*f*
Reticulocyte(s), 639, 639*f*
Reticulocyte count, 639
Reticulospinal tracts, 453, 471*f*, 474*t*, 476
Retina, 552*f*, 553, 554*f*, 555*f*
development of, 431, 431*f*
focusing light on, 557–559, 558*f*, 560*f*
photoreceptors in. See Photoreceptors
visual processing and, 567–568, 568*f*
Retinal (visual pigment), 562
Retinal artery, central, 552*f*, 553, 554*f*
Retinal detachment, 553
Retinal vein, central, 552*f*, 553, 554*f*
Retinitis pigmentosa, 566
Retinol. See Vitamin A
Retraction (body movement), 258*f*, 259
Retrograde amnesia, 459
Retrograde movement, 391
Retroperitoneal organs, 855*f*, 856
Retropulsion, 876, 876*f*
Retroverted uterus, 1043
Reuptake, neurotransmitter, 408, 409*f*
Reverberating (oscillating) circuits, 422, 422*f*
Reverse transcriptase, in HIV infection, 796
Reverse transcriptase inhibitors, for AIDS, 797
R group, amino acid, 47, 48*f*
Rh blood groups, 655
Rheumatic fever, 797
Rheumatism, 272
Rheumatoid arthritis (RA), 270–271, 271*f*, 797
Rh factor, 655
Rhinencephalon, 439, 452
Rhinitis, 809
Rhodopsin, 561*f*, 562, 563*f*
Rhombencephalon (hindbrain), 430, 431*f*
Rhomboid major muscle, 327*f*, 348*f*, 349*f*
Rhomboid minor muscle, 348*f*, 349*f*
Rhomboid muscles, 346*t*, 348*f*, 348*t*, 349*f*
Rhythm methods, of contraception, 1095*b*
Rib(s), 199*f*, 224–225, 225*f*
Riboflavin (vitamin B₂), 916*t*, 921
Ribonucleic acid. See RNA
Ribose, in RNA, 55
Ribosomal RNA (rRNA), 55, 84, 101
Ribosomes, 63*f*, 84, 84*f*, 94*t*
in translation, 104–105, 104*f*
Riboswitches, 105–106
RICE, 316

Rickets, 189
Right ascending lumbar vein, 740*t*, 742*f*
Right atrium, 664, 665–667*f*
Right brachiocephalic vein, 736*f*, 736*t*, 737*f*
Right bundle branch, 677
Right colic artery, 730*f*, 732*t*, 733*f*
Right colic (hepatic) flexure, 890, 891*f*
Right common carotid artery, 724*t*, 726*f*, 728*f*
Right common iliac artery, 724*t*, 733*f*
Right coronary artery, 665*f*, 666*f*, 669, 669*f*, 724*t*
Right gastric artery, 730*f*, 731*f*, 731*t*
Right gastroepiploic artery, 730*f*, 731*f*, 731*t*
Right hepatic duct, 878*f*
Right hypochondriac region, 17, 20*f*
Right iliac (inguinal) region, 17, 20*f*
Right lobe, of liver, 881, 882*f*
Right lower quadrant (RLQ), 17, 17*f*
Right lumbar region, 17, 20*f*
Right lymphatic duct, 754, 755*f*
Right main bronchus, 814
Right marginal artery, 669, 669*f*
Right pulmonary artery, 665–667*f*, 722*f*, 722*t*
Right pulmonary vein, 665–667*f*, 722*f*, 722*t*
Right subclavian artery, 724*t*, 726*f*, 728*f*, 729*f*
Right suprarenal vein, 736*f*, 742*t*, 743*f*
Right upper quadrant (RUQ), 17, 17*f*
Right ventricle, 665–667*f*, 669, 669*f*
Rigor mortis, 289
Ringer's solution, for volume restoration, 656
Risorius muscle, 330*t*, 331*f*
RNA (ribonucleic acid), 53, 55, 55*t*
in chromatin, 93
digestion of, 896*f*, 897
intron/junk NDA coding for, 105–106
messenger (mRNA), 55, 101, 102, 102*f*, 107*f*
processing of, 103
in translation, 103–105, 104*f*
micro (miRNAs), 55, 103, 105
single-stranded, 1108
in protein synthesis, 55, 101, 101*f*
ribosomal (rRNA), 55, 84, 101
short interfering, 1108
short-lived, 101
single stranded micro, 1108
small, 1108
transfer (tRNA), 55, 101, 107*f*
in translation, 103–105, 104*f*
RNA polymerase, 102, 102*f*
RNA primers, in DNA replication, 96
Rod, ATP synthase, 927, 928*f*
Rod(s), 553, 554*f*, 560–566, 561*f*. See *also* Photoreceptors
electromagnetic spectrum and sensitivities of, 557*f*
excitation of, 561*f*, 562, 563*f*
Rod inner segments, 560

Rod outer segments, 554*f*, 560, 561*f*
Roof
of nasal cavity, 212
of orbit, 212*f*
Root, 468, 505
brachial plexus, 505
hair, 149*f*, 157, 158*f*
of lung, 815, 817*f*
nail, 160, 160*f*
nerve, 468, 505. See *also specific type*
of nose, 806, 806*f*
of penis, 1028, 1029*f*
of tongue, 860
of tooth, 863, 863*f*
Root canal, 863, 863*f*
Root canal therapy, 863–864
Root hair plexus (hair follicle receptor), 149*f*, 157, 161, 486, 487*t*
Rooting reflex, 904
Rootlets, spinal nerve, 467*f*, 502, 503*f*
Rosacea, 168
Rotation (body movement), 256, 257*f*
of lower limb, 380*t*, 381*f*
of upper limb, 358*t*, 359*f*
Rotator cuff, 264–266
muscles of, 350*t*, 351–352*f*
Rotator muscles of thigh, lateral, 366–368*t*, 367–368*f*
Rotor, ATP synthase, 927, 928*f*
Rough endoplasmic reticulum, 63*f*, 84, 84*f*, 86*f*, 87*f*, 94*t*
Round ligament (ligamentum teres), 881, 882*f*, 1086*f*, 1093
Round ligament of uterus, 1040*f*, 1043*f*, 1044
Round (cochlear) window, 574, 575*f*
rRNA. See Ribosomal RNA
RU-486 (mifepristone), 1096*b*
Rubrospinal tract, 471*f*, 474*t*, 475*f*, 476
Ruffini endings, 487, 487*t*
Rugae, 867
of bladder, 986, 987*f*
gastric, 867, 868*f*
Rule of eights (octet rule), 31–32
Rule of nines, 163, 163*f*
Runner's reflux, 865
Ruptured eardrum, 583
RV. See Residual volume

S. See Sulfur
Saccule, 576, 577*f*, 584
Sacral artery, median, 730*f*, 732*t*, 733*f*
Sacral canal, 221*f*, 223
Sacral crests
lateral, 221*f*, 223
median, 221*f*, 223, 367*f*
Sacral curvature of spine, 217, 217*f*
developmental aspects of, 243
Sacral foramina, anterior and posterior, 221*f*, 223
Sacral hiatus, 221*f*, 223
Sacral nerves, 502*f*
Sacral outflow, parasympathetic, 530
Sacral plexus, 502*f*, 509–510
Sacral promontory, 220–223, 221*f*, 233*f*
Sacral splanchnic nerves, 532, 533*f*

Sacrificial bonds, in bone, 180
Sacroiliac joint, **220**, 233*f*, 235, 255*t*
Sacrospinalis (erector spinae) muscles, 336*t*, 338*t*, 339*f*, 367*f*
Sacrospinous ligament, 235
Sacrotuberous ligament, 235
Sacrum, 199*f*, **217**, 220–223, 221*f*
in male versus female, 236*t*
Saddle joints, **259**, 260*f*
Sagittal plane/section, **14**, 15*f*
Sagittal sinuses
inferior, 738*f*, **738***t*, 739*f*
superior, 460*f*, 461*f*, 738*f*, **738***t*, 739*f*
Sagittal suture, 200, **201**, 202*f*
Saline, for volume restoration, 656
Saliva, **860**
in body defense, 772*t*
composition of, 860–861
Salivary amylase, **895**, 896*f*
Salivary glands, 852*f*, **860–861**, 861*f*
autonomic innervation/effects and, 528*f*, 529*f*, 533*f*, 538*t*
Salivation, control of, 861
Salivatory nuclei, 529, **861**
Salpingitis, **1066**
Salt(s), **39**
Salt (table). *See* Sodium chloride
Saltatory conduction, 403, **405**, 405*f*
Salty taste, 571
SA node. *See* Sinoatrial (SA) node
Saphenous veins, great and small, 737*f*, 744*f*, **744***t*
Sarco (prefix), **276**
Sarcolemma, 276, **278**, 279*t*, 280*f*
in cardiac muscle, 674, 674*f*
generation of action potential across, 285–288, 287*f*, 288*f*
smooth muscle, 306
Sarcoma, **144**
Sarcomeres, 279*t*, **281**
cardiac muscle, 673
skeletal muscle, 279*t*, 280*f*, **281**
length-tension relationships in, **301**, 301*f*
in sliding filament model, 284, 284*f*
Sarcopenia, 312
Sarcoplasm, 276, **278**
Sarcoplasmic reticulum, **282**
in cardiac muscle, 310*t*, 673, 674–675, 674*f*
in skeletal muscle, **282–283**, 283*f*, 310*t*
in smooth muscle, 306, 310*t*
Sartorius muscle, 326*f*, **363***t*, 364*f*, 380*t*
Satellite cells, **389**
muscle, 311*f*, 312
neuroglia, 388*f*, 389
Satiety signals, food intake regulation and, 946, 946*f*
Saturated fats, **46**, 912
Saturation
of carrier proteins, 69
hemoglobin, 831–832, 831*f*, 832*f*
altitude affecting, 840
SCA. *See* Sickle-cell anemia
Scab, 139, 140*f*
Scalae, 577, 578*f*
Scala media, **577**, 578*f*
Scala tympani, **577**, 578*f*

Scala vestibuli, **577**, 578*f*
Scalene muscles, 336*t*, 337*f*
Scalp, muscles of, 329*f*, 331*f*
Scanning electron microscopy (SEM), 115
Scaphoid, **231**, 231*f*, 232*t*
Scapulae (shoulder blades), 199*f*, 225, **226–228**, 226*f*, 227*f*, 232*t*
muscles controlling movement of, 346–349, 347*f*, 348–349*f*
Scapular nerve, dorsal, 506*f*, 507*t*
Scapular spine, 228
Scar tissue, **139**, 141
Schleiden, Matthias, 62
Schlemm, canal of (scleral venous sinus), 552*f*, **555**, 555*f*
Schwann, Theodor, 62
Schwann cells (neurolemmocytes), 388*f*, **389**, 390*f*
myelin sheaths formed by, 388*f*, 389, 391, 392*f*
Sciatica, 510
Sciatic nerve, **509–510**, 509*f*, 510*t*
injuries to, 510
Sciatic notch
greater, 234*f*, **235**, 236*t*
lesser, 234*f*, **235**
SCID. *See* Severe combined immunodeficiency (SCID) syndromes
SC joint. *See* Sternoclavicular joint
Sclera, 548*f*, **551**, 552*f*, 554*f*
Scleral venous sinus (canal of Schlemm), 552*f*, **555**, 555*f*
Scleroses, in multiple sclerosis, 405
Sclerotherapy, **748**
Sclerotome, 1082*f*, **1084**, 1085*f*
Scoliosis, 217, 243
Scotoma, **589**
Scrotal septum, 1025, 1026*f*
Scrotum, **1025–1026**, 1025*f*, 1026*f*
embryologic/fetal development of, 1062*f*
SCT. *See* Sickle-cell trait
Scurvy, 144, 917*t*
Sebaceous (oil) glands, 122, 149*f*, **156–157**, 156*f*
Seborrhea, 157
Sebum, **156**
in acne, 157
Secondary active transport, 73, 75*f*, 77*t*, **975**
in tubular reabsorption, **975**, 976*f*, 983*f*
of sodium, 974, 976*f*, 983*f*
Secondary brain vesicles, **430**, 431*f*
Secondary (lobar) bronchi, 813*f*, **814**
Secondary capillary plexus, 602*f*, **603**
Secondary curvatures, **243**
Secondary follicle, **1042**, 1050*f*, 1051*f*, 1052
late, 1041*f*, **1042**, 1051*f*, 1052
Secondary humoral response, **781**, 781*f*, 782*f*
Secondary hypertension, **713**
Secondary immune response, **781**, 781*f*, 782*f*
Secondary lymphoid organs, **777**
Secondary oocyte, **1049**, 1050*f*, 1051*f*
fertilization of, 1025, **1072–1073**, 1072*f*, 1074*f*, 1075*f*, 1076*f*. *See also* Fertilization

Secondary ossification centers, 183*f*, **184**, 194
Secondary sensory endings, **515**, 515*f*
Secondary sex characteristics
female, 1056, 1057*t*
male, **1040**, 1057*t*
Secondary spermatocytes, 1036*f*, **1037**
Secondary structure of protein, 48–50, 49*f*
Second-class lever, 324, 325*f*
Second-degree burns, **164**, 164*f*
Second intention, healing by, **144**
Second messengers, 81, 82*f*, 420, **596**
in hormone mechanism of action, 596–598, 597*f*
Second-order neurons, in ascending pathways, 471, 472*f*
Second polar body, 1049, 1050*f*
Second (expulsion) stage of labor, **1091–1092**, 1092*f*
Secretin, 625*t*, **873**, 875*t*, 886–887, 887*f*
Secretion
glandular, 121
modes of, 122–124, 123*f*
renal tubular, 971*f*, **978**, 983*f*
acid-base balance and, 978, 983*f*, 1011, 1011–1014, 1013*f*
of bicarbonate, 1014
of potassium, 978, 1006
Secretory IgA, **784**
Secretory (postovulatory) phase of uterine (menstrual) cycle, 1055*f*, 1056
Secretory region of neuron, **391**
Secretory unit (acinus), of multicellular exocrine gland, 121, 122, 123*f*
Secretory vesicles/granules, **85**, 85*f*, 86*f*
Sectioning, tissue, for microscopy, **115**
Sections (body), 14, 15*f*, 18–19*b*
Segmental arteries, **963**, 964*f*
Segmental (tertiary) bronchi, 813*f*, **814**
Segmental level of motor control, **512**, 513*f*
Segmentation (digestive), **853–854**, 853*f*, 888*t*, 889, 889*t*
Segregation (chromosome), independent assortment and, 1103–**1104**, 1103*f*
Seizures, **454–455**
Selective estrogen receptor modulators, for osteoporosis, 191
Selective permeability, **68**. *See also* Membrane(s), permeability of; Membrane transport
Selenium, 919*t*
Self-antigens, **777**
autoimmune disease and, 797
development of tolerance to, 777–778
Self-propagating action potential, 403
Self-tolerance, **777**
development of, 777–778

Sella turcica, 203*f*, 204*f*, **207**, 214*t*
SEM. *See* Scanning electron microscopy
Semen, **1031**
Semicircular canals, 575*f*, **576**, 577*f*
in equilibrium, 585
Semicircular duct, **576**, 577*f*
Semiconservative replication (DNA), **96**, 97*f*
Semilunar cartilages (menisci of knee), **262–263**, 262–263*f*
injury of, 269
Semilunar valves, **670–672**, 671*f*, 673*f*. *See also* Aortic valve; Pulmonary valve
Semimembranosus muscle, 327*f*, 367*f*, 369*t*
Seminal vesicles/glands, 1025*f*, 1029*f*, **1030**
embryologic/fetal development of, 1061*f*
Seminiferous tubules, **1026**, 1027*f*
spermatogenesis in, 1032, 1033–1038, 1036*f*, 1037*f*
Semispinalis capitis/cervicis/thoracis muscles, 338*t*, 339*f*
Semitendinosus muscle, 327*f*, 367*f*, 369*t*, 380*t*
Sensation, 485, **488**. *See also under* Sensory
Sense organs, **486**. *See also* Sensory receptors
Sensible heat loss, 951
Sensible water loss, **1000**
Sensorineural deafness, **583**
Sensory areas, 436*f*, **437–439**, 438*f*
Sensory (afferent) division of peripheral nervous system, **386**, 387*f*, 485*f*
Sensory endings
primary, **515**, 515*f*, 516*f*
secondary, **515**, 515*f*
Sensory ganglia, **491**
cranial, **494**
Sensory input, **386**, 386*f*
Sensory integration, 488–491, 489*f*
pain perception and, 490–491
somatosensory system organization and, 488–490, 489*f*
Sensory (afferent) nerves, **491**
of synovial joint, 252
Sensory (afferent) neurons, 394, 394*t*
in reflex arc, 514, 514*f*
Sensory (ascending) pathways/tracts, 470, 471–473, 471*f*, 472*f*, 473*t*
Sensory receptors, **485–488**, 487–488*t*. *See also specific type*
classification of
by location, 486
by stimulus type, 485
by structure/function, 486–488, 487–488*t*
cutaneous, 149*f*, 150, 151*f*, **161**
peripheral, **485–488**, 487–488*t*
in reflex arc, 514, 514*f*
sensory integration at level of, 489, 489*f*
for special senses, 486. *See also* Special senses
Sentinel node, in cancer, **764**

Sepsis, 720, **800**
  burn injury and, 164
Septal cartilage, 212
Septal defects of heart, 689, 689f
Septal nuclei, 452
Septicemia, **658**
Septic shock, 720, **800**
  in burn injury, 164
Septum
  interatrial, **664**, 666f
  interventricular, **664**
  nasal, 212, **806**
    deviated, **846**
  scrotal, 1025, 1026f
  testicular, 1027f
Septum pellucidum, **432**, 433f
Serial processing, **423**
SERMs. *See* Selective estrogen receptor modulators
Seromucous glands, tracheal, 813
Serosa. *See* Serous membranes
Serotonin, 416t, 418, **650**, 870
  digestion/gastric secretion and, **870**, 875t
  platelet aggregation and, **650**
Serous cells
  in respiratory mucosa of nose, 807
  in salivary glands, **860**
Serous fluid, **16**–17, 17f, 139
Serous glands, in respiratory mucosa of nose, 807
Serous membranes (serosae), **16**, 17f, 138f, **139**
  of alimentary canal (visceral peritoneum), 17, 138f, **855**, 855f, 857, 857f, 892f
  inflammation of, 17
  of stomach, 868f, 869f
Serous pericardium, **663**, 663f
Serratus anterior muscle, 326f, **346t**, 347f
Sertoli (sustentacular) cells, 1036f, **1037**–1038, **1038**, 1039f
Serum, **652**
  immune, passive immunity and, 782, 782f
Sesamoid bones, **174**–175
Set point, in homeostasis, 9
Severe combined immunodeficiency (SCID) syndromes, **796**
Sex (gender), genetic, determination of, 1059–1060
Sex characteristics, secondary
  female, 1056, 1057t
  male, **1040**, 1057t
Sex chromosomes, **1059**, **1102**
  genetic sex determination and, 1059–1060
Sex hormones, 45t, 47, **1024**. *See also specific hormone*
  adrenal, 617t, 618
  bone growth and, 185
  gonadal secretion of, 623
  protein synthesis/growth and, 915
  terminal hair growth and, 159
Sex-linked inheritance, **1107**, 1107f
Sexual differentiation, 1060–1062, 1061f, 1062f
Sexually indifferent stage, **1060**, 1061f, 1062f

Sexually transmitted infections/diseases (STIs/STDs), **1058**–1059
  urinary infections and, 991
Sexual response
  female, **1058**
  male, 1031–1032
Shaft
  hair, 149f, 157
  long bone, 174
  of penis, 1028, 1029f
  rib, 224, 225f
Sharpey's (perforating) fibers, 176f, 178, 181f
Shell temperature, **950**
Shinbone (tibia), 199f, **237**–238, 239f, 242t
  in knee joint, 262, 262–263f
Shingles (herpes zoster), **425**
Shin splints, **382**
Shivering, 300, 952f, **953**
Shock
  anaphylactic, 719–720, 720f, **798**
  cardiogenic, **720**
  circulatory, **719**–721, 720f
    autonomic effects and, 537
    hypotension and, 712
  hypovolemic, **719**, 720f, 1001
  neurogenic, 720
  septic, 720, **800**
    in burn injury, 164
  spinal, 476, 514–515
  vascular, 719–720
Shock wave lithotripsy, for renal calculi, 986
Short bones, **174**–175, 175f, 179
Short interfering RNAs, 1108
Short-lived RNA, 101
Short reflexes, 854, 855f
Short-term (working) memory (STM), **457**, 458f
Shoulder blades. *See* Scapulae
Shoulder dislocation, 226, 266
Shoulder (pectoral) girdle, **225**
  bones of, 199f, **225**–228, 226f, 232t
  muscles of, 326f, 327f, 346–349t, 347f, 348–349f, 358t, 359f
Shoulder (glenohumeral) joint, 254t, 264–266, 265f
  muscles crossing/acting on, 326f, 327f, 350–352t, 351–352f, 358t, 359f
Sibutramine, 949b
Sickle-cell anemia, 642–643, **1106**
  genetic screening for, 1110
Sickle-cell crisis, 1106
Sickle-cell trait, 643, **1106**
  genetic screening for, 1110
Sickling gene(s), 1106
  genetic screening for, 1110
SIDS (sudden infant death syndrome), **847**
Sigmoidal artery, 730f, **732t**, 733f
Sigmoid colon, 852f, **890**, 891f
Sigmoid mesocolon, 892f
Sigmoid sinus, 738f, **738t**, 739f
Signaling chemicals, 81
Signaling pathways, in cancer, drugs targeting, 143b
Signal-recognition particle (SRP), 105, 106f

Signal sequence, **105**, 106f
Signal transduction, membrane proteins in, 64, 66f
Simple carbohydrates, 913t. *See also* Sugars
Simple diffusion, **69**, 69f, 72t
Simple epithelium, **116**, 116f, 117–119, 117–119f
  columnar, **117**–119, 118f
  cuboidal, **117**, 118f
  pseudostratified columnar, **119**, 119f
  squamous, **117**, 117f
Simple follicle retention cysts, 1066
Simple (closed) fracture, 188
Simple glands, **122**, 123f
Simple mastectomy, **1048**
Simple receptors, **486**
Simple sugars (monosaccharides), **43**, 43f, **895**, 912
Sine wave, 579, 579f
Single covalent bond, 33f, 34
Single stranded microRNAs, 1108
Single-unit (visceral) smooth muscle, 309–310t, **311**
Sinoatrial (SA) node, **677**, 677f, 678
Sinus (bone marking), 178t
Sinuses, paranasal, **216**, 216f, 807t, **809**
Sinus headache, 809
Sinusitis, **809**
Sinusoids/sinusoidal capillaries, 638, 697f, **699**, 699f
  in liver, 881, 883f
  in splenic pulp, 758, 759f
Sinus rhythm, **677**
Sinus venosus, **688**, 688f
Sister chromatids, 98f, 1033, 1034f, 1035f
Size principle of recruitment, 295, 296f
Skeletal cartilages, **173**, 174f
Skeletal muscle(s)/skeletal muscle tissue, **136**, 136f, **276**, **277**–305, 278f, 279t, 309–310t, **320**–384. *See also specific named muscle and* Muscular system; Skeletal muscle fibers/cells
  anabolic steroids affecting, 312, 313b
  attachments of, **277**–278
    naming muscles and, 321–322
  blood supply of, 277
  connective tissue sheaths in, 277, 278f, 279t
  contraction of, 276, 289–296, 293f, 294f, 295f, 296f
    action potential generation/propagation and, 285–288, 287f, 288f
    cross bridge activity and, 288–289, 292f
    energy for, 297–300, 298f, 299f
    excitation-contraction coupling and, 285, **288**, 290–291f
    fiber types affecting velocity/duration of, 302–303, 302f, 302t, 303f

  force of, 300–302, 301f
    frequency of stimulation affecting force and, 301, 301f
    graded responses and, 293–296, **294**, 294f, 295f, 296f
    heat production and, 276–277, 300, 952f, 953
    ion channels in, 286f, 288, 288f
    isotonic and isometric, 289, **296**, 297f
    motor unit and, 289–293, 293f
    muscle fatigue and, 295, **300**
    muscle stretch affecting force of, 301–302, 301f, 310t
    muscle tone and, 295–**296**
    muscle twitch and, **293**, 294f
    nerve stimulus/neuromuscular junction events and, 285, 285f, 286f
      stimulus frequency and, 294–295, 294f, 301, 301f
      stimulus strength and, 295, 295f, 296f
    number of stimulated fibers affecting force of, 300, 301f
    oxygen deficit and, **300**
    sarcoplasmic reticulum and T tubules in, 282–284, 284, 294
    of single muscle fiber, 284, 284–289, 284f, 285f, 286f, 287f, 288f
    size of fibers affecting force of, 301, 301f
    sliding filament model of, **284**, 284f
    velocity/duration of, 302–303, 302f, 302t, 303f, 304f
    of whole muscle, 289–296, 293f, 294f, 295f
  development of, 311–312, 312f
  exercise affecting, 304–305, 316
  glycogenolysis in, 939–940, 939f
  gross anatomy of, 277, 278f, 279t
  homeostatic imbalances and, 312
  homeostatic relationships of, 314b, 315b
  innervation of, 277, 512
    motor units, **289**–293, 293f
    nerve stimulus/neuromuscular junction events and, 285, 285f, 286f
  interactions of muscles in body and, 321
  metabolic fuel used by, 935t
  metabolism in, 296–300, 298f, 299f
    glycogenolysis and, 938–939, 939f
  microscopic anatomy of, 278–284, 279t, 280f, 282f, 283f
  movement and, 5, 6f, 276, 312
  naming, 321–322

perfusion (blood flow) of, 713, 713f, 716
skeletal system (bones) and, 192b, 193b, 314b, 315b
  lever systems and, 323–324, 323–324f, 325f
thyroid hormone affecting, 612t
Skeletal muscle fibers/cells, **136**, 136f, 276, 309t. See also Skeletal muscle(s)/skeletal muscle tissue
anatomy of, 278–284, 279t, 280f, 282f, 283f
in motor unit, 289–293, 293f
naming muscles and, 321
physiology/contraction of, 284, 284–289, 284f, 285f, 286f, 287f, 288f. See also Skeletal muscle(s)/skeletal muscle tissue, contraction of
  force of contraction and, 300–302, 301f
Skeletal system, 6f, **198**–247, 199f. See also Cartilage(s); Joint(s); Ligament(s); Skeleton
autonomic nervous system and, 542b
cardiovascular system and, 746b
digestive system and, 902b
endocrine system and, 628b
functions of, 6f
homeostatic relationships of, 192b, 193b
integumentary system and, 166b
lymphatic system and, 762b
movement and, 5, 6f, 175
muscular system and, 192b, 193b, 314b, 315b
  lever systems and, 323–324, 323–324f, 325f
reproductive system and, 1064b, 1065b
respiratory system and, 844b
thyroid hormone affecting, 612t
urinary system and, 1018b
Skeleton, **198**–247, 199f. See also Bone(s)/skeletal tissue
appendicular, 173, 174f, 199f, **225**–241
axial, 173, 174f, **199**–225, 199f
developmental aspects of, 242–244, 243f, 244f
homeostatic imbalances and, 244
hormones produced by, 624
thyroid hormone affecting, 612t
Skills (procedural) memory, **458**, 459f
Skin (cutaneous membrane/integument), 119, 138f, **139**, 149–155, 149f
aging affecting, 165
appendages of, 149f, **155**–160. See also specific structure
artificial/synthetic, for burn injury, 164
autonomic innervation/effects and, 528f
as blood reservoir, 161–162, 716
in body defense, 5, 5f, 6f, 149, 160–161, 767–768, 772t
in body temperature regulation, 161, 952–953, 952f

boundary maintenance and, 5, 5f, 6f, 149, 160–161
burn injury and, **163**–165, 163f, 164f
color of, 154–155
cutaneous sensation (receptors/sense organs) and, 149f, 150, 151f, **161**
developmental aspects of, 165
excretion via, 162
functions of, 6f, 149, 160–162
homeostatic imbalances of, 162–165, 162f, 163f, 164f
homeostatic relationships of, 5f, 165, 166b, 167b
hormones produced by, 624, 625t
innervation of, 510–511, 511f
metabolic functions of, 161
nervous structures in, 149f
perfusion (blood flow) of, 713f, 716–717
restriction of in thermoregulation, 952–953, 952f
permeability of, 161
protective secretions of, 160
sun damage and, 154, 162–163, 165
  melanin in protection from, 154
thick, **150**
thin, **150**
Skin cancer, 154, 162–163, 162f
Skin-fold test, **955**
Skin grafts, for burn injury, 164
Skin patch, for contraception, 1096b
Skin pigments, 154–155
Skin (decubitus) ulcers, **168**
Skull, 199f, **200**–216, 201f, 202f, 203–204f, 205f, 206f, 214–215t, 254t
congenital abnormalities affecting, 243, 243f
developmental aspects of, 242–243, 243f
SLE. See Systemic lupus erythematosus
Sleep, 455–457, 456f
Sleep apnea, **457**, 846
Sleep patterns, 455–456
Sleep-wake cycles, 455–457, 456f
hypothalamus and, 444
reticular activating system and, 453
Sliding filament model of contraction, **284**, 284f, 307, 307f
Slit diaphragm, 969, 970f
Slow block to polyspermy, 1073, 1074f
Slow Ca²⁺ channels, in cardiac muscle contraction, **675**
Slow fibers, **302**, 302t
Slow oxidative fibers, **302**, 302f, 302t, 303, 303f
Slow wave sleep, **455**, 456f
Small cardiac vein, 665f, 669f, **670**
Small cell carcinoma, of lung, **842**
Small cell (lateral) nuclear group, 448f, **452**
Small intestine, 852f, **877**–880, 878f, 879f, 880f, 888t
autonomic innervation/effects and, 529f, 533f, 889, 889t

bile and pancreatic juice secreted into, 886, 886f
  regulation of, 886–887, 887f
in calcium regulation, 1008
digestive processes occurring in, 887–890, 888t, 889t, 896f, 897
motility of, 889–890, 889f
Small RNAs, 1108
Small saphenous vein, 744f, **744t**
Smell, 569–571, 569f, 571f
cortical areas for, 436f, 438–439
development of sense of, 588
physiology of, 570, 571f
taste sensation and, 573
Smell (olfactory) cortex, primary, 436f, **438**–439
Smell transduction, 570, 571f
Smoking
COPD and, 840
hypertension and, 713
lung cancer and, 842
tracheal cilia affected by, 813
Smooth endoplasmic reticulum, 63f, **84**–85, 84f, 87f, 94t
Smooth muscle/smooth muscle tissue, **136**, 137f, **276**, 305–311, 305f, 309–310t
bronchial, 815
contraction of, 276, 307–311, 307f
development of, 311–312, 311f
innervation of, 306, 306f, 308, 310t
microscopic anatomy of, 305–307, 305f
multiunit, 309–310t, **311**
single-unit, 309–310t, **311**
Smooth muscle fibers/cells, 136, 137f, 276, 305–307, 305f, 309t
Smooth muscle tone, 308
Sneeze, 807, 826t
Sodium, 26t, 918t
absorption of, 900
  glucose/amino acid absorption and, 899, 900
action potential and, 287f, 400–401f
balance of
  abnormalities of, 1003t
  developmental aspects of, 1015
  regulation of, 1004–1006, 1004f, 1005f, 1007f
as chemically reactive element, 31f
dietary, 918t
in fluid and electrolyte balance, 1002–1004
  regulation and, 1004–1006, 1004f, 1005f, 1007f
in plasma/interstitial fluid/intracellular fluid, 997, 997f
resting membrane potential and, 80, 396, 397f
sodium chloride formation and, 32, 32f
in taste transduction, 573
tubular reabsorption of, 974–975, 976f, 983f, 1004, 1004f
Sodium bicarbonate. See Bicarbonate

Sodium channels
action potential and, 401f, 402
muscle contraction and, 286f, 287–288, 287f, 288, 288f
  in cardiac muscle, 674
voltage-gated fast, **674**
Sodium chloride, formation of, 32, 32f
Sodium-potassium pump (Na⁺-K⁺ ATPase), 73, **396**, 397f
action potential and, 402
in primary active transport, 73, 74f
  tubular reabsorption of sodium and, 974, 976f
resting membrane potential and, 80, **396**–398, **397**f
in secondary active transport, 73, 75f
  tubular reabsorption and, 975, 976f
of sodium, 974, 976f
Soft (fibrocartilaginous) callus, in bone repair, 188–**189**, 189f
Soft keratin, 157, 160. See also Keratin
Soft palate, **806**, 808f, **858**, 859f
Sole of foot, muscles on, 376–378, 377f, 379f
Soleus muscle, 326f, 327f, 372f, **373t** 374–375f, 380t
Sol-gel transformation, 29f, **30**
Solid(s), 24
Solitary nucleus, in gustatory pathway, 448f, **573**, 573f
Soluble fiber, 912
Solute(s), **29**
Solute pumps, 73
Solution(s), **29**–30, 29f
concentration of, 29–30
Solvent(s), **29**
universal (water), **38**–39
Soma (cell body), of neurons, 135f, **389**–390, 390f
Somatic afferent fibers/nerves, 386, 387f, 491
Somatic efferent nerves, 491
Somatic mesoderm, 1082f, **1084**, 1085f
Somatic (primary) motor cortex, **435**–437, 436f, 438f
homeostatic imbalances and, 437
Somatic motor (SM) neurons, 285, 310t, **470**, 470f. See also Motor (efferent) neurons
Somatic nervous system, **386**, 387f, 485f
autonomic nervous system compared with, 526–527, 527f
motor neurons of, 285, 310t, **470**, 470f. See also Motor (efferent) neurons
Somatic recombination, antigen receptor diversity and, **779**, 784
Somatic reflexes, 514. See also Spinal reflexes
Somatic sensory areas, 436f
Somatic sensory (SS) neurons, **470**, 470f
Somatomammotropin, human chorionic (hCS/human placental lactogen), 1078, **1090**
Somatosensory association cortex, 436f, **437**

Somatosensory cortex
   developmental aspects of, 478
   primary, 436*f*, **437**, 438*f*
Somatosensory homunculus, **437**, 438*f*
Somatosensory system, 488–490, 489*f*
Somatostatin, 417*t*, 419, **603**,
   604*f*, **870**
   digestion/gastric secretion and,
      870, 875*t*
Somatotopy, **435**, 470
Somatotrophs, **603**
Somatotropin/somatotropic hor-
   mone. *See* Growth hormone
Somites, 1082*f*, 1083*f*, **1084**, 1085*f*
Sonography (ultrasound), **18**–19*b*,
   1097
Sörensen, Sören, pH scale devised
   by, 40
Sound quality, **580**
Sounds of Korotkoff, 711–712
Sound/sound waves, **577**
   localization of, 583
   properties of, 577–580, 579*f*
   transmission of to internal ear,
      580, 581*f*
Sour taste, 571
SP-A. *See* Surfactant protein A
Spasm (muscle), **316**
Spastic paralysis, spinal cord damage
   causing, **476**
Spatial discrimination, **437, 490**
Spatial summation, by postsynaptic
   neuron, **412**, 413*f*
Special senses, **547**–593. *See also spe-
   cific sense and structure*
   chemical (taste and smell),
      569–574, 588
   developmental aspects of,
      588–589
   ear/hearing/balance, 574–588,
      575*f*, 588–589
   eye and vision, 548–569,
      548*f*, 588
Special sensory receptors, **547**–548.
   See also specific type
Specific gravity, of urine, **985**
Specific (adaptive) immune system,
   767, 767*f*, **775**–795, 794*f*, 795*t*
Spectrin, 51*t*
Spectroscopy, magnetic resonance
   (MRS), **19***b*
Speech, laryngeal voice production
   and, 811–812
Speech area, motor (Broca's area),
   436*f*, **437**
Speed lever, 323, 324*f*
Sperm (spermatozoa), 90, 1025,
   1036*f*, **1037**
   formation of, (spermatogenesis),
      1032, 1033–1038, 1036*f*, 1037*f*
   infertility and, 1038
   maturation/storage/ejaculation
      of from epididymis,
      1028, 1032
   penetration of oocyte by (fertil-
      ization), 1025, **1072**–1073,
      1072*f*, 1074*f*, 1075*f*, 1076*f*. *See
      also* Fertilization
   transport of, 1072–1073
Spermatic cord, 1026*f*, 1027*f*,
   1028, 1062

Spermatic fascia
   external, 1026*f*
   internal, 1026*f*
Spermatids, 1036*f*, **1037**
   differentiation of into sperm
      (spermiogenesis), 1036*f*,
      1037, 1037*f*
Spermatocytes
   formation of, 1033, 1036*f*
   meiosis of (spermatid forma-
      tion), 1036*f*, **1037**
   primary, 1033, 1036*f*, 1037
   secondary, 1036*f*, **1037**
Spermatogenesis, **1032**, 1033–1038,
   1036*f*, 1037*f*
   hormonal regulation and,
      1038–1039, 1039*f*
   sustentacular cells in, 1036*f*,
      1037–1038, **1038**, 1039*f*
Spermatogenic cells, **1033**, 1036*f*
Spermatogonia, **1033**
   mitosis of, 1033, 1036*f*
Spermatozoa. *See* Sperm
Sperm-binding receptors, 1073, 1074*f*
Spermicides, for contraception,
   1095–1096*b*
Spermiogenesis, 1036*f*, **1037**, 1037*f*
S (synthetic) phase, **96**
   of cell cycle, 96, 96*f*, 98*f*
   DNA replication during,
      96–97, 97*f*
Sphenoidal process, 211
Sphenoid bone, 202*f*, 203–204*f*, 205*f*,
   206*f*, **207**–208, 208*f*, 213*f*, 214*t*
Sphenoid sinuses, 203*f*, 204*f*,
   207, 216*f*
Sphincter(s), **322**. *See also specific
   type*
   in alimentary canal, 857
   laryngeal structures as, 812
Sphincter pupillae muscles, 552, 553*f*
Sphingolipids, in plasma
   membrane, 64
Sphygmomanometer, 711
Spina bifida, **245**, 477–478
Spina bifida cystica, 478
Spina bifida occulta, 478
Spinal (vertebral) cavity, **14**, 16*f*
Spinal column. *See* Spine
   (spinal/vertebral column)
Spinal cord, 386, 387*f*, **466**–477, 467*f*
   autonomic regulation by,
      539*f*, 540
   cross-sectional anatomy of,
      468–476, 469*f*
   embryonic development of, 466,
      466*f*, 1083
   gray matter of, 432*f*, 468–470,
      469*f*, 470*f*
   gross anatomy of, 466–468, 467*f*
   protection of, 466–468, 469*f*
   trauma/disorders of, 476–477
   white matter of, 469*f*, 470–471,
      471*f*
Spinal curvatures, 217, 217*f*
   developmental aspects of, 243, 243*f*
   primary and secondary, **243**
   vertebral collapse/osteoporosis
      and, 190*t*, 191, 244
Spinal dura mater, **466**, 467*f*
Spinal fusion, **245**

Spinal ganglion. *See* Dorsal root
   ganglion
Spinalis cervicis/thoracis muscles,
   338*t*, 339*f*
Spinal nerve(s), 386, 387*f*, 467*f*, 468,
   470, **502**–511, 502*f*, 503*f*
   development of, 503*f*, 520
Spinal nerve plexuses, **502**–504, 502*f*
Spinal reflexes, 466, **514**–520
Spinal rootlets, 467*f*, **502**, 503*f*
Spinal roots, 467*f*, 502
Spinal shock, **476**, 514–515
Spinal tap (lumbar puncture),
   468, 468*f*
Spindle, mitotic, 98*f*
Spindle equator, 97
Spine (bone marking), 178*t*
Spine (spinal/vertebral column),
   199*f*, **216**–223, 217*f*, 218*f*,
   219*f*, 220*f*, 221*f*, 222*t*
   developmental aspects of, 244
   muscles of, 336–338*t*, 339*f*
   osteoporotic fractures of,
      190*t*, 191
Spinocerebellar pathways/tracts,
   471–473, 471*f*, 472*f*, 473*t*, 490
Spinothalamic pathways/tracts, 471,
   471*f*, 472*f*, 473*t*, 490
Spinous process, vertebral, 217*f*,
   218*f*, **219**, 219*f*, 222*t*
   of vertebra prominens, **219**, 221*f*
Spiral (coiled) arteries, of uterus,
   1044, 1045*f*
Spiral fracture, 190*t*
Spiral ganglion, 499*t*, 578*f*, **582**, 582*f*
Spiral lamina, osseous, **577**, 578*f*
Spiral organ of Corti, **577**, 577*f*,
   578*f*, 582*f*
   excitation of hair cells in,
      580–582, 582*f*
Spirometer, for pulmonary function
   testing, **825**
Splanchnic circulation, **856**
Splanchnic mesoderm, 1082*f*,
   1084, 1085*f*
Splanchnic nerves, 530, 531*f*, **532**,
   533*f*
   lumbar, 532, 533*f*
   pelvic, 529*f*, **530**
   sacral, **532**, 533*f*
   thoracic, 531*f*, **532**
Spleen, **758**, 758*f*, 759*f*, 852*f*
   autonomic innervation/effects
      and, 533*f*
   enlargement of (splenomegaly),
      764
Splenectomy, 758
Splenic artery, 730*f*, 731*f*, **731***t*,
   758, 759*f*
Splenic cords, **758**, 759*f*
Splenic (left colic) flexure, **890**, 891*f*
Splenic vein, 737*f*, 742*f*, **742***t*, 743*f*,
   758, 759*f*
Splenius capitis/cervicis muscles,
   336*t*, 337*f*
Splenomegaly, **764**
Spliceosomes, 103
Spondylitis, ankylosing, **272**
Spongy bone, 134*t*, 176*t*, **177**, 179*f*
   microscopic anatomy of,
      179*f*, 180

Spongy (penile) urethra, **987**, 987*f*,
   1025*f*, 1029*f*, 1030
Spontaneous generation, theory
   of, 62
Spoon nail, 160
Sprain(s), **270**
Squamous cell carcinoma, **163**
   of lung, **842**
   of skin, 162*f*, **163**
Squamous cells/epithelium,
   116, 116*f*
   simple, **117**, 117*f*
   stratified, **119**, 120*f*
Squamous region, **204**
   frontal bone, 200, 202*f*
   temporal bone, **204**, 207*f*
Squamous (squamosal) suture, 200,
   201, 201*f*, 203*f*
SR. *See* Sarcoplasmic reticulum
SRY gene, 1060
Staging systems, for cancer, **143***b*
Stagnant (ischemic) hypoxia, **832**
Staining tissue, for microscopy, **115**
Stapedius muscle, **576**, 576*f*
Stapes (stirrup), 215*f*, 575*f*, **576**, 576*f*
Starch, 44, 895, 896*f*, 912, 913*t*. *See
   also* Carbohydrate(s)
Start codon, in translation, 104*f*, 105
Startle reflex, 446
Start point, in transcription,
   102, 102*f*
Static equilibrium, 584–585,
   584*f*, 585*f*
Statins, 703*b*, 944
   bone density affected by, 191
Stator, ATP synthase, 927, 928*f*
Steady state, 80, 935–936, 935*f*, 936*f*
Stem cell(s), 108, 144
   bone (osteogenic cells), **177**, 177*f*
   hematopoietic/pluripotent,
      125–126, **639**, 639*f*, 646,
      647*f*, 648*f*
   of immune system, 799
Stem region (antibody), **783**–784,
   783*f*
Stenosis, heart valve, 672, 681
Stents, coronary angioplasty and,
   703*b*
Stercobilin, 641, 884
Stereocilia
   of epididymis, 1028
   of hair cells, 578*f*, 581, 582*f*,
      584, 584*f*
Sterilization, for contraception,
   1096*b*
Sternal angle, **223**, 224*f*
Sternal end of clavicle, **226**, 226*f*
Sternoclavicular joint, 254*t*
Sternocleidomastoid muscle, 326*f*,
   327*f*, **336***t*, 337*f*
Sternocostal joint, 254*t*
Sternohyoid muscle, 326*f*, **334***t*,
   335*f*, 337*f*
Sternothyroid muscle, **334***t*,
   335*f*, 337*f*
Sternum, 199*f*, **223**–224, 224*f*
Steroid(s)/steroid hormones, 45*t*,
   46*f*, **47**, **596**
   anabolic, muscle affected by,
      312, 313*b*
   sex. *See* Sex hormones

Steroid diabetes, 618
Stimuli, **485**
    in homeostasis, 9, 9*f*, 10*f*
Stirrup (stapes), 215*t*, 575*f*, **576**, 576*f*
STIs/STDs. *See* Sexually transmitted
    infections/diseases
STM. *See* Short-term (working)
    memory
Stomach, 852*f*, **866–877**, 868*f*, 869*f*,
    888*t*. *See also under Gastric*
    autonomic innervation/effects
        and, 528*f*, 529*f*, 533*f*, 538*t*,
        868–869
    digestive processes occurring in,
        871–877, 872*f*, 874*f*, 875*t*,
        876*f*, 877*f*, 888*t*, 896*f*
    filling/emptying of, 874–876,
        876*f*, 877*f*
    gross anatomy of, 867–869, 868*f*
    hormones produced by, 625*t*
    microscopic anatomy of,
        869–871, 869*f*, 871*f*
Stomodeum, 901*f*, **904**
Stop codon, in translation, 104*f*, 105
Storage center, pontine, 988, 989*f*
Storage function, of bone, 176
Strabismus, 496*t*, **551**
Straight arteries, of uterus,
    1044, 1045*f*
Straight sinus, 738*f*, **738***t*, 739*f*
Straight tubule (tubulus rectus),
    1026, 1027*f*
Strain (muscle), **316**
Stratified epithelium, **116**, 116*f*,
    119–121, 120*f*
    columnar, **121**
    cuboidal, **119**
    squamous, **119**, 120*f*
    transitional, 120*f*, **121**
Stratum basale (stratum germina-
    tivum), **150**, 151*f*
Stratum basalis of endometrium,
    1044, 1045*f*
Stratum corneum, 151*f*, **152**
Stratum functionalis of en-
    dometrium, **1044**, 1045*f*
    lacunae (intervillous spaces) in,
        1078, 1079*f*, 1080*f*
Stratum granulosum, **150–152**, 151*f*
Stratum lucidum, **152**
Stratum spinosum, **150**, 151*f*
Streamlining (laminar flow), 704
Stress (mechanical), bone remodel-
    ing and, 187–188, 187*f*, 188*f*
Stress, metabolic rate and, 947–948
Stress incontinence, 988
    pregnancy and, 988, 1090
Stress proteins, 51
    antibodies against, in diabetes
        mellitus, 626*b*
Stress-relaxation response, **308**, 310*t*
Stress response, 619, 619*f*
    adrenal gland in, 617, 619, 619*f*
    glucocorticoids in, 617, 619*f*
    sympathetic nervous system
        in, 619
Stretch receptors
    in food intake regulation,
        945, 946*f*
    smooth muscle contraction and,
        308, 310*t*

Stretch reflex, **515–516**, **517***f*
Stria(e), 153
    vascularis, **577**, 578*f*
Striate (visual) cortex, primary, 436*f*,
    437–438, **566**, 567*f*, **568–569**
    homeostatic imbalance and, 439
Striations, **281**
    cardiac muscle, 136, 137*f*, 276,
        309*t*, 673
    skeletal muscle, 136, 136*f*, 276,
        280*f*, **281**, 309*t*
Stroke (cerebrovascular accident),
    464–465
    diagnosis of, 477
Stroke volume, **682–683**, 706, 707*f*
    regulation of, 684–685, 685*f*,
        686*f*, 707*f*
Stroma, **129**
    of lung, **818**
    reticular tissue forming, 128*f*,
        129, 756*f*
Strong acids, **41**, 1009
Strong bases, **41**
Structural (fibrous) proteins, **50**, 51*t*
S-T segment, 679*f*, **680**
Stuart factor, 651*t*
Student's elbow, 270
Stupor, 455
Stuttering, **847**
Sty, 549
Styloglossus muscle, 332*t*, 333*f*
Stylohyoid ligaments, 211
Stylohyoid muscle, 334*t*, 335*f*
Styloid process, 204, 214*t*, **229**, **230**
    of radius, **230**, 230*f*
    temporal bone, 204, 205*f*,
        207*f*, 214*t*
    of ulna, **229–230**, 230*f*
Stylomastoid foramen, **204**,
    205*f*, 214*t*
Stylopharyngeus, glossopharyngel
    nerve supplying, 500*t*
Subacromial bursa, 253*f*
Subacute hypersensitivities, **798–799**
Subarachnoid hemorrhage, **464**
Subarachnoid space, **461**
    of brain, 460*f*, **461**
    spinal, 469*f*
Subcapsular sinus, **757**, 757*f*
Subclavian arteries, 725*f*, 727*f*, 728*f*,
    728*t*
    left, **724***t*, 726*f*, 729*f*
    right, **724***t*, 726*f*, 728*f*, 729*f*
    upper limb arteries arising from,
        728*f*, 728*t*, 729*f*
Subclavian trunks, 754, 755*f*
Subclavian vein, 736*f*, **736***t*, 737*f*,
    738*f*, 739*f*, 740*f*, **740***t*, 741*f*
Subclavius muscle, 346*t*, 347*f*
Subcostal arteries, **729***t*
Subcostal nerve, **504**
Subcutaneous prepatellar bursa,
    262*f*, 263
Subcutaneous tissue
    (hypodermis/superficial fas-
    cia), 149–150, 149*f*
    development of, 165
Subdural hemorrhage, **464**
Subdural space, **461**
    of brain, 460*f*, **461**
    spinal, 469*f*

Subendothelial layer, blood vessel,
    695, 696*f*
Sublingual glands, 852*f*, **860**
Subluxation, 270
Submandibular ganglia, 498*t*,
    529, 529*f*
Submandibular gland, 852*f*, **860**
Submucosa
    of alimentary canal, **856–857**,
        857*f*
    of esophagus, 865, 865*f*
    of small intestine, 880
    of stomach, 869*f*
    tracheal, 812, 812*f*, **813**
Submucosal nerve plexus, **857**, 857*f*
Subpapillary plexus, 149*f*, 152
Subpubic angle (pubic arch), 233*f*,
    235, 236*t*
Subscapular artery, 728*f*, **728***t*, 729*f*
Subscapular fossa, 227*f*, 228
Subscapularis muscle, **350***t*, 352*f*,
    352*t*, 358*t*
Subscapular nerves, 506*f*, 507*t*
Substance P, 417*t*, **418**
    in pain perception, 490
Substance trafficking, 75
Substantia nigra, 441, **446**, 448*f*
    in memory, 459*f*
    in Parkinson's disease, 465
Substrate, **52**, 52–53, 53*f*
Substrate level phosphorylation,
    921–922, 921*f*, 924, 929*f*
Subthalamic nuclei, 441
Subthreshold stimuli, **295**, 403
Sucking reflex, 904
Sucrase, 896*f*, **897**
Sucrose, 43, 44*f*, 895, 896*f*
    dehydration synthesis of, 42*f*
    hydrolysis of, 42*f*
Sudden infant death syndrome
    (SIDS), **847**
Sudoriferous glands. *See* Sweat (su-
    doriferous) glands
Sugars, 912, 913*t*. *See also* Carbohy-
    drate(s); Fructose; Galactose;
    Glucose; Sucrose
    double, 43
    simple, 43, 44*f*, 895
Sulci (sulcus), **433**, 434*f*
Sulfate, in plasma/interstitial
    fluid/intracellular fluid, 997*f*
Sulfur, 26*t*, 918*t*
    dietary, 918*t*
Summation, **295**, **412**
    multiple motor unit (recruit-
        ment), **295**, 295*f*, 296*f*
    contraction duration/velocity
        affected by, 303
    by postsynaptic neuron, **412**, 413*f*
    temporal (wave), **294–295**, 294*f*,
        412, 413*f*
Sun exposure/sunlight. *See* Ultravio-
    let radiation
Superficial (term), 12*t*. *See also under*
    External
Superficial fascia (hypodermis),
    149–150, 149*f*
    development of, 165
Superficial fibular (peroneal)
    nerve, 509*f*
    leg muscles supplied by, 373*t*

Superficial palmar arch, 725*f*, 728*f*,
    728*t*, 729*f*
Superficial palmar venous arch, 740*f*,
    740*t*, 741*f*
Superficial reflexes, **519–520**
Superficial temporal artery, 726*f*,
    726*t*, 727*f*
    pulse at, 712*f*
Superficial temporal vein, 738*f*,
    738*t*, 739*f*
Superficial transverse perineal mus-
    cle, **344***t*, 345*f*
Superficial veins
    of lower limbs, 744*t*
    of upper limbs, 740*t*
Superior (term), 12*t*
Superior angle of scapula, 227*f*, 228
Superior articular process, vertebral,
    219, 219*f*, **220**, 222*t*
Superior border of scapula, 227*f*, 228
Superior cerebellar peduncles, 445,
    446–447*f*, 448*f*, **450**, 451*f*
Superior cervical ganglion, **532**, 533*f*
Superior colliculi, 446, 446–447*f*,
    476, **566**, 567*f*
Superior costal facet, 220, 225*f*
Superior ganglion, 500*t*
Superior gemellus muscle, 368*f*, 368*t*
Superior gluteal artery, 734*f*,
    734*t*, 735*f*
Superior gluteal nerve, 509*f*,
    510, 510*t*
Superior iliac spines, 233*f*, 234*f*, 235
Superior mesenteric artery, 725*f*,
    730*f*, 731*f*, 733*f*
Superior mesenteric ganglion,
    532, 533*f*
Superior mesenteric vein, 737*f*, 742*f*,
    742*t*, 743*f*
Superior nasal conchae, **209**, 215*t*,
    807–809, 808*f*
Superior nasal meatus, 808*f*
Superior nuchal line, 202*f*, 204, 205*f*
Superior oblique muscle, **550**, 550*f*
Superior olivary nuclei, in auditory
    pathway, 582, 582*f*
Superior orbital fissure, 202*f*, **208**,
    208*f*, 214*t*
Superior pharyngeal constrictor
    muscle, 335*f*, 335*t*
Superior phrenic arteries, 729*t*
Superior pubic ramus, 234*f*, **235**
Superior rectal arteries, 730*f*,
    732*t*, 733*f*
Superior rectus muscle, **550**, 550*f*
Superior sagittal sinus, 460*f*, 461*f*,
    738*f*, **738***t*, 739*f*
Superior salivatory nuclei, 529
Superior suprarenal artery, 732*t*
Superior thyroid artery, 608, 609*f*,
    726*f*, **726***t*, 727*f*
Superior vena cava, 664, 665–667*f*,
    736–737*f*, **736***t*
    veins draining into, 736–737*f*,
        736*t*
Superior vesical artery, 1093
Superior vestibular ganglion,
    577*f*, **584**
Supination (body movement),
    256, 258*f*
    of upper limb, 358*t*, 359*f*

Supinator muscle, 354t, 355f, 356t, 357f, 358t
Support function, of bone, 175
Supporting cells, 570, 584
    in cochlea, 578f
    in maculae, 584, 584f
    nervous tissue (neuroglia), 388–389, 388f
    olfactory receptor, 569f, 570
Suppressor factors, 790t
Suprachiasmatic nucleus, 444, 444f, 456, 566, 620
    in visual pathway, 566, 567f
Supraclavicular nerves, 504f, 504t
Supracondylar lines, medial and lateral, 237, 238f
Supracondylar ridges, medial and lateral, 228, 229f
Suprahyoid muscles, 334t, 335f
Supraoptic nuclei, 444, 444f, 603
Supraorbital foramen/notch, 200, 202f, 214t
Supraorbital margins, 200, 202f
Suprarenal arteries, 732t
    inferior, 732t
    middle, 730f, 732t, 733f
    superior, 732t
Suprarenal gland(s), 614. See Adrenal (suprarenal) gland(s)
Suprarenal veins, 736f, 742f, 742t, 743f
Suprascapular artery, 728f, 729f
Suprascapular nerve, 506f, 507t
Suprascapular notch, 227f, 228
Supraspinatus muscle, 350t, 351f, 352t, 358t
Supraspinous fossa, 227f, 228
Supraspinous ligament, 218f
Suprasternal (jugular) notch, 223, 224f
Sural nerve, 509f, 510, 510t
Surface anatomy, 2
Surface tension, 823
    alveolar, 823
    intrapleural pressure and, 819–820
    of water, 35, 35f
Surface-volume relationships, cell division control and, 100
Surfactant, 815, 823
    first breath and, 1093
Surfactant protein A, 1091
Surgery, for obesity, 949b
Surgical neck of humerus, 228, 229f
Survival needs, 8
Suspension(s), 29f, 30
Suspensory ligament, 1041, 1047
    of breast, 1047, 1047f
    of lens of eye (ciliary zonule), 551, 552f, 555f
    of ovary, 1040f, 1041, 1043f
Sustentacular (Sertoli) cells, 1036f, 1037–1038, 1038, 1039f
Sustentaculum tali, 240, 240f
Sutural bones, 202f, 209
Sutures (cranial), 200, 200–201, 201f, 249, 249f
Swallowing, 853, 853f, 866, 867f, 888t
    difficulty with (dysphagia), 905
    epiglottis in, 811
    muscles controlling, 334–335t, 335f
Sweat, 155, 162

Sweat (sudoriferous) glands, 155–156
    apocrine, 156
    autonomic innervation/effects and, 533f, 538t
    eccrine (merocrine), 149f, 155–156, 156f
Sweating, 155–156
    heat loss and, 951, 952f, 953
Sweat pores, 155
Sweet taste, 571
Sympathectomy, for Raynaud's disease, 541
Sympathetic (thoracolumbar) division of autonomic nervous system, 387, 387f, 485f, 526f, 528, 528f, 531f, 533f, 534t
    adrenal medulla and, 532, 533f
    anatomy of, 530–533, 531f, 533f
    glomerular filtration regulated by, 972, 973f
    heart regulation and, 678f, 679, 685, 686f, 707f
    parasympathetic division differentiated from, 534t
    in postabsorptive state regulation, 941
    role of, 528, 528f, 534t, 538–539
    somatic nervous system compared with, 527f
    in stress response, 619
Sympathetic fibers, 530
Sympathetic pathways, 530–533, 531f, 533f
    with synapses in adrenal medulla, 532, 533f
    with synapses in collateral ganglia, 532, 533f
    with synapses in trunk ganglia, 531f, 532, 533f
Sympathetic (vasomotor) tone, 537, 707
Sympathetic trunk (chain), 530, 531f
Sympathetic trunk (paravertebral) ganglia, 503f, 530, 531f
    pathways with synapses in, 531f, 532, 533f
Sympatholytic agents, autonomic activity and, 537t
Sympathomimetic agents, autonomic activity and, 537t
Symphyses, 250, 250f, 251
Symport system, 73
Synapse(s), 406–413, 407f
    chemical, 407–408, 409f
    electrical, 406
    en passant, 512
    integration/modification of events at, 412–413, 413f
Synapsis, 1033
Synaptic cleft, 285, 407, 409f
    neuromuscular junction, 285, 286f
Synaptic delay, 408
Synaptic integration, 408–413
Synaptic knobs (axon terminals), 390f, 391
    in motor unit, 289, 293f
Synaptic potentiation, 412–413
    long-term (LTP), 413, 460
    in memory, 460
Synaptic terminals, rod and cone, 560, 561f

Synaptic vesicles, 285, 407
Synaptotagmin, 408
Synarthroses, 249
Synchondroses, 250, 250–251, 250f
Syncope, 455, 716
    vasovagal (neurocardiogenic), 544
Syncytiotrophoblast (syncytial trophoblast), 1077, 1077f, 1079f
Syncytium, functional, cardiac muscle as, 673
Syndesmoses, 249, 249–250, 249f
Syndrome of inappropriate ADH secretion (SIADH), 608, 1020
Synergism, hormone, 600
Synergist (muscle), 321
Synostoses, 249
Synovial (joint) cavities, 20, 251, 251f
Synovial fluid, 251–252, 251f
    in bursae, 252
Synovial joints, 249, 251–269, 251f, 252t, 260f, 261b. See also specific joint
    blood supply of, 252
    bursae and tendon sheaths and, 252, 253f
    factors affecting stability of, 252–253
    general structure of, 251–252, 251f
    innervation of, 252
    movements allowed by, 253–259, 256–258f
    types of, 259, 260f
Synovial membrane, 251, 251f
Synovitis, 271, 272
Synthesis reactions, 36, 36f
Synthetic growth hormone, 604–605
Synthetic skin, for burn injury, 164
Syphilis, 1058
System(s), organ. See Organ systems
Systemic anatomy, 2
Systemic circuit/circulation, 668, 668f, 721, 723f, 723t
    arteries of, 721, 724–725f, 724t
    veins of, 721, 736–737f, 736t
Systemic lupus erythematosus (SLE), 797, 800
Systole, 682, 683f
Systolic pressure, 705, 705f

T₁. See Monoiodotyrosine
T₂. See Diiodotyrosine
T₃. See Triiodothyronine
T₄. See Thyroxine
Tabes dorsalis, 520
Table sugar. See Sucrose
Tachycardia, 687
    paroxysmal atrial, 690
    ventricular, 690
Tachykinin(s), 417t
Tactile (Merkel) cells, 150, 151f, 486
Tactile (Meissner's) corpuscles, 152, 161, 486, 487t
Tactile (Merkel) discs, 150, 151f, 161, 486, 487t
Tailbone. See Coccyx
Tail of epididymis, 1028
Tail of sperm, 1037, 1037f
Talar shelf (sustentaculum tali), 240, 240f
Talus, 240, 240f, 242t

Tamponade, cardiac, 663
Target cells, hormone, 596
    interaction at, 600
    specificity of, 598
Target-SNAREs, in exocytosis, 78f, 79
Tarsal bones/tarsus, 199f, 240, 240f, 242t
Tarsal (Meibomian) glands, 548f, 549
Tarsal plates, 548–549, 548f
Tarsometatarsal joint, 255t
Tarsus, bones of (tarsals), 199f, 240, 240f, 242t
Tastant, 572
Taste, 571–573, 572f
    cortical areas for, 436f, 439, 573, 573f
    development of sense of, 588
    physiology of, 572–573
    smell sensation and, 573
Taste buds, 571–573, 572f, 859
    activation of, 572
Taste (gustatory) cells, 571, 572f
    activation of, 572
Taste (gustatory) cortex, 436f, 439, 573, 573f
Taste pore, 571, 572f
Taste receptors. See Taste buds
Taste sensations, 571–572
Taste transduction, 573
Tay-Sachs disease, 87, 1106
TB. See Tuberculosis
TBGs. See Thyroxine-binding globulins
T_C cells. See Cytotoxic T cells
T cell antigen receptors (TCRs), 777, 787f, 789
T cell-dependent antigens, 791
T cell-independent antigens, 791
T cells. See T lymphocytes
TCRs. See T cell antigen receptors
Tears, 549
    in body defense, 772t
Tectorial membrane, 578f, 581
Tectospinal tract, 471f, 474t, 476
Tectum, of midbrain, 446, 448f
Teeth, 862–864, 862f, 863f
    disease of, 864
    sockets for (alveoli), 209, 215t
    articulation of tooth with (gomphosis), 249f, 250, 863
    structure of, 863, 863f
Telencephalon, 430, 431f, 432f
Telodendria (terminal branches), 390f, 391
Telomerase, 109
Telomere(s), 108–109
Telomere clock, 108
Telophase
    in meiosis, 1035f
    in mitosis, 96f, 97, 99f
TEM. See Transmission electron microscopy
Temperature
    body. See Body temperature
    chemical reaction rate affected by, 38
    hemoglobin saturation affected by, 831–832, 832f
Temperature receptors. See Thermoreceptors

Template, in DNA replication, 96, 97f
Template strand, in transcription, 102, 102f
Temporal artery, superficial, 726f, **726t**, 727f
pulse at, 712f
Temporal bones, 202f, 203f, **204–207**, 205f, 206f, 207f, 214t
Temporal branch of facial nerve, 498t, 499t
Temporalis muscle, 326f, **332t**, 333f
Temporal lobe, 433, 434f, 435f, 436f
in memory, 458, 459f
Temporal (wave) summation, 294–295, 294f, **412**
by postsynaptic neuron, 412, 413f
Temporal vein, superficial, 738f, **738t**, 739f
Temporomandibular joint (TMJ), 204, 209, 210f, 254t, **268–269**, 268f
disorders/dislocation of, 269
Tendon(s), 129, **278**. See also specific named tendon
of long head of biceps brachii muscle, 264
muscle attachment to, **278**
Tendonitis, 270
Tendon sheaths, 252, 253f
Teniae coli, **890**, 891f
Tennis elbow, **382**
Tension (muscle)
skeletal muscle contraction and, 289
smooth muscle contraction and, 308
Tension (cleavage) lines, 152–153, 154f
Tensor fasciae latae muscle, 326f, **363t**, 364f, **366t**, 380t
Tensor tympani muscle, **576**, 576f
Tentorium cerebelli, **461**, 461f
Teratogens, **1085**
Teres major muscle, 327f, **350t**, 351f, **352t**, 358t
Teres minor muscle, **350t**, 351f, **352t**, 358t
Terminal arteriole, 697f, **700**, 700f
Terminal branches (telodendria), 390f, **391**
Terminal bronchioles, **814**, 814f
Terminal cisternae, of sarcoplasmic reticulum, **283**, 283f
Terminal ganglia, **529**
Terminal hair, **159**
Terminal sulcus, of tongue, **859–860**, 860f
Terminal web, 88, 91
Termination, in transcription, **102**, 102f
Termination signal, **102**, 102f
Terminology (anatomical), 2. See also Anatomy, terminology used in
Tertiary (segmental) bronchi, 813f, **814**
Tertiary (vesicular/Graafian) follicles, 1041f, **1042**, 1050f, 1051f, **1052**
Tertiary structure of protein, 49f, 50

Tertiary syphilis, 1058
Testes, 595f, 623, 1024, **1025**, 1025f, 1026–1028, 1026f, 1027f, 1029f
anatomy of, 1026–1028, 1026f, 1027f
cancer of, 1028
descent of, 1062
embryologic/fetal development of, 1061f
failure to descend, 1028, 1063
hormones of, 623
rete, **1026**, 1027f
Testicular arteries, **732t**, 1026, 1026f
Testicular cancer, 1028
Testicular fluid, **1038**
Testicular veins, **742t**, 1026–1027
Testis. See Testes
Testosterone, **623**, **1038**, 1057t
adrenal, 618
aging affecting production of, 1066
in embryos, 1040
erythropoietin affected by, 640
gonadal development and, 1039
interstitial (Leydig) cell production of, 1026, 1039, 1039f
in male reproductive function, **1038**, 1039, 1039f, 1057t
mechanism/effects of activity of, 1039–1040
metabolism and, 941t
muscle mass affected by, 312
somatic effects of, 1040
in spermatogenesis, 1038, 1039, 1039f
terminal hair growth affected by, 159
Tetanus (infection), **316**
Tetanus (tetanic muscle contraction), 294f, 295, 301, **316**
Tetany, 613
Tetrads, **1033**, 1034f, 1035f
chromosome segregation in, 1103–1104, 1103f
Tetralogy of Fallot, 689, 689f
TF. See Tissue factor
TGF-β. See Transforming growth factor beta
TH. See Thyroid hormone
T$_H$ (helper T cells) cells, **786**, 787f, **791–792**, 791f, 794f, 795t
CD4 cell activation into, 786, 787f, 789, 791, 791f, 794f
cytotoxic T cell activation and, 791, 791f
HIV infection and, 796
vaccines and, 782
T$_H$1 cells, 792
T$_H$2 cells, 792
vaccines and, 782
T$_H$17 cells, 792
Thalamic nuclei, 441–443, 444f, **449t**
limbic system and, 452, 452f
Thalamus, 440f, **441–443**, 443f, 444f
development of, 431, 431f, 478
in memory, 458, 459f
in visual processing, 568
Thalassemias, 642
Thalidomide, **1085**
for autoimmune disease, 797
birth defects caused by, **1085**

Theca folliculi, 1041f, 1051f, **1052**
Thenar eminence, muscles of, 360t, 361f
Theory of spontaneous generation, 62
Thermodynamics, first law of, 944
Thermogenesis
chemical (nonshivering), **953**
food-induced, **949**
Thermoreceptors, **485**, 487t
peripheral and central, 951–952
Thermoregulation, 10, 10f, 950–954, 950f, 951f, 952f
energy conversions and, 25
hypothalamus in, 10, 10f, 444, 951
muscles in, 276–277, 300, 952f, 953
skin in, 161, 952–953, 952f
sympathetic nervous system and, 539
thyroid hormone/thyroxine in, 612t, 948
Thermoregulatory centers, **951**
Theta waves, **454**, 454f
Thiamine (vitamin B$_1$), 916t
Thiazide diuretics, 982
Thick (myosin) filaments, 88, 136, **281**
in cardiac muscle, 673
in skeletal muscle, 280f, **281**, 282f
in sliding filament model, 284, 284f, 307, 307f
in smooth muscle, 306, 307, 307f, 310t
Thick segment of loop of Henle, 965f, **966**, 967f. See also Loop of Henle
Thick skin, **150**
Thigh
bones of, 237, 238f, 242t
deep artery of, **734t**, 735f
muscles of/muscles controlling movement of, 326f, 327f, 363–369t, 364f, 367–368f, 380t, 381f
Thin (actin) filaments, 88, 136, **281**
in cardiac muscle, 310t, 673
in cytokinesis, 97, 99f
in microvilli, 91
in skeletal muscle, 279t, 280f, **281**, 282f, 310t
in sliding filament model, 284, 284f, 307, 307f
in smooth muscle, 306, 307, 307f
Thin segment of loop of Henle, 965f, **966**, 967f. See also Loop of Henle
Thin skin, **150**
Third-class lever, **324**, 325f
Third-degree burns, 164, 164f
Third-order neurons, in ascending pathways, **471**, 472f
Third (placental) stage of labor, **1092**, 1092f
Third ventricle of brain, 431f, **432**, 433f
Thirst mechanism, **999**, 999f
Thirst/thirst center, hypothalamus in regulation of, 444, 999, 999f
Thoracic (descending) aorta, **724t**
branches of, 724f

Thoracic arteries
internal (internal mammary artery), 727f, 728f, **728–729t**, 729f
lateral, 728f, **728t**, 729f
Thoracic cage/thorax, 199f, **223–225**, 224f, 225f
aging affecting, 244
anatomical relationships of organs in, 817f
arteries of, 728–729f, 728–729t
bones of, 199f, 223–225, 224f, 225f
bony, 199f, **223–225**, 224f, 225f
compliance of wall of, 824
innervation of, 504. See also Thoracic nerves
muscles of, 326f, 340t, 341f
deep (breathing), 340t, 341f
superficial (scapular movements), 346–349t, 347f, 348–349f
sympathetic pathways to, 532, 533f
veins of, 740–741f, 740–741t
Thoracic cavity, **16**, 16f
pressure relationships in, 819–820, 819f
Thoracic curvature of spine, **217**, 217f
developmental aspects of, 243
Thoracic duct, **754**, 755f
Thoracic nerves, 502f
long, 506f, 507t
Thoracic splanchnic nerves, 531f, **532**
Thoracic vertebrae, **216**, 217f, 220, 221f, 222t
Thoracic visceral organs, arteries of, 729f
Thoracoacromial artery, 728f, **728t**, 729f
Thoracolumbar division of autonomic nervous system. See Sympathetic (thoracolumbar) division of autonomic nervous system
Thorax wall. See Thoracic cage/thorax
Thoroughfare channel, 697f, **700**, 700f
Three-dimensional vision (depth perception), **566**
Threshold (anaerobic), **299**
Threshold/threshold stimulus, **295**, **402**
for action potential, 400f, **402**, 403–404
for muscle cell, 288, **295**, 295f
Throat. See Pharynx
Thrombin, 650, 650f, 651
Thrombocytopenia, **653**
Thromboembolic disorders, **653**
Thrombolytic agents, 703b
Thrombophlebitis, **748**
Thrombopoietin, **648**
Thromboxane(s), 45t
Thromboxane A$_2$, platelet aggregation and, **650**
Thrombus, **653**
Thumb (pollex), **233**
carpometacarpal joint of, 254t
muscles controlling movement of, 360t, 361f
opposition of, 258f, **259**

Thymic aplasia, congenital, **800**
Thymic (Hassall's) corpuscles, **759**, 760*f*
Thymic lobules, 759, 760*f*
Thymine (T), **53**, 54*t*
Thymopoietin, **624**, 625*t*
Thymosins, **624**, 625*t*
Thymulin, **624**, 625*t*
Thymus, 595*f*, **624**, 625*t*, 758*f*, **759**–760, 760*f*
  developmental aspects of, 761
  failure of development of (congenital thymic aplasia), **800**
  hormones produced by, 624, 625*t*
  in lymphocyte differentiation/maturation, 624, 625*t*, 759, 777–778, 779*f*, 787*f*
Thyrocervical trunk, 727*f*, **727***t*, 728*f*, 729*f*
Thyroglobulin, **608**, 609, 610, 610*f*
Thyrohyoid membrane, 810*f*
Thyrohyoid muscle, **334***t*, 335*f*
Thyroid arteries
  inferior, 608, 609*f*
  superior, 608, 609*f*, 726*f*, **726***t*, 727*f*
Thyroid cartilage, 808*f*, **810**–811, 810*f*
Thyroid crisis/storm, **627**
Thyroid follicles, **608**, 609*f*
Thyroid gland, 595*f*, **608**–612, 609*f*, 610*f*, 611*f*, 612*t*
  homeostatic imbalances and, 611
  metabolism and, 612*t*, 941*t*, 948
Thyroid hormone (TH), 608, **609**–611, 612*t*
  age affecting synthesis of, 626
  bone growth and, 185
  hyper-/hyposecretion of, 612*t*
  metabolism and, 611, 612*t*, 941*t*, 948
  synthesis of, 609–610, 610*f*
  thermoregulation and, 953
  transport and regulation of, 605, 610–611
Thyroiditis, Hashimoto's, **800**
Thyroid-stimulating hormone (thyrotropin/TSH), 602*f*, **605**, 605*f*, **606***t*
  thermoregulation and, 953
  in thyroid hormone release, 610
  in thyroid hormone synthesis, 609
Thyroid storm/crisis, **627**
Thyroid vein
  middle, 738*f*, 739*f*
  superior, 739*f*
Thyrotrophs, **605**
Thyrotropin, **605**. *See also* Thyroid-stimulating hormone
  human chorionic (hCT), 1078, **1090**
Thyrotropin-releasing hormone (TRH), 605, 605*f*, 610–611
  thermoregulation and, 953
Thyroxine (T₄), **609**, 612*t*, **948**. *See also* Thyroid hormone
  heart rate and, 686
  metabolism and, 612*t*, 941*t*, **948**
  thermoregulation and, 953

Thyroxine-binding globulins (TBGs), 610
TIA. *See* Transient ischemic attack
Tibia, 199*f*, **237**–238, 239*f*, 242*t*
  in knee joint, 262, 262–263*f*
Tibial arteries
  anterior, 725*f*, 734*f*, **734***t*, 735*f*
  posterior, 725*f*, 734*f*, **734**–735*t*, 735*f*
  pulse at, 712*f*
Tibial collateral ligament, 262–263*f*, **263**
Tibialis anterior muscle, 326*f*, **370***t*, 371*f*, 372*f*, 380*t*, 381*f*
Tibialis posterior muscle, **373***t*, 375*f*, 380*t*
Tibial nerve, 509, 509*f*, **510**, 510*t*
Tibial tuberosity, **238**, 239*f*
Tibial veins, anterior and posterior, 744*f*, **744***t*
Tibiofemoral joint, 255*t*, **262**, 263. *See also* Knee joint
Tibiofibular joints, 237
  distal, 238, 239*f*, 255*t*
  proximal, 238, 239*f*, 255*t*
Tic douloureux (trigeminal neuralgia), 497*t*
Tidal volume, **824**, 825*f*
Tight junctions, **66**
  blood–brain barrier and, 464
  in capillaries, 699, 699*f*
  of brain, 464
  epithelial, 115
  of sustentacular cells (blood-testis barrier), **1038**
Tine test, 799
Tinnitus, **583**
Tip-links, 581, 582*f*
Tissue(s), 3, 4*f*, 113–147, **114**, 114*f*. *See also specific type*
  blood flow through (tissue perfusion), **713**–721, 714*f*, 715*f*, 718*f*, 719*f*, 720*f*
  connective, 114*f*, **124**–134, 125*f*, 127–135*f*, 134*t*
  covering/lining membranes, 115, 138–139, 138*f*
  developmental aspects of, 141–144, 141*f*
  epithelial, 114*f*, **115**–124, 116*f*, 117–120*f*, 122*f*, 123*f*
  muscle, 114*f*, **136**, 136–137*f*
  nervous, 114*f*, 134–135, 135*f*
  preparation of for microscopy, 114–115
  regenerative capacity of, 141
  repair and, 139–141, 140*f*
  structural organization at level of, 3, 4*f*
Tissue factor (TF/factor III), 650*f*, **651**, 651*t*
Tissue fluid. *See* Interstitial (tissue) fluid
Tissue perfusion, **713**–721, 714*f*, 715*f*, 718*f*, 719*f*, 720*f*
Tissue plasminogen activator (tPA), **652**, 703*b*
  for stroke, 465
Tissue repair, 139–141, 140*f*
  first/second intention, **144**
Tissue typing, transplantation and, 792–793

Titin, 51*t*, 280*f*, **281**–282
Titin (elastic) filaments, in skeletal muscle, 280*f*, **281**–282
TLC. *See* Total lung capacity
TLRs. *See* Toll-like receptors
T lymphocytes (T cells), **646**, **756**, **777**, 786
  activation of, 789–790, 789*f*
    MHC proteins and, 779, 786–789, 787*f*, 788*f*
  clonal selection/differentiation of, 786–791, 787*f*, 788*f*, 789*f*
  cytotoxic, 786, 787*f*, **792**, 793*f*, 794*f*
  education of in thymus, 624, 625*t*, 759, 777–778, 779*f*
  effector roles of, 791–792
  helper, 786, 787*f*, **791**–792, 791*f*, 794*f*, 795*t*
    CD4 cell activation into, 786, 787*f*, 789, 791, 791*f*, 794*f*
    cytotoxic T cell activation and, 791, 791*f*
    HIV infection and, 796
    vaccines and, 782
  memory, 787*f*, 794*f*
  receptors on, 777, 787*f*, **789**
  regulatory, 786, 787*f*, **792**
T$_m$. *See* Transport maximum
TMJ. *See* Temporomandibular joint
TMR. *See* Total metabolic rate
TNF. *See* Tumor necrosis factor
Tocopherol (vitamin E), 45*t*, 917*t*
Toe(s)
  bones of (phalanges), 199*f*, 240, 240*f*, 241, 242*t*
  joints of (interphalangeal joints), 255*t*
  muscles controlling movements of, 370–373*t*, 371*f*, 372*f*, 374–375*f*, 376–378*t*, 377*f*, 379*f*, 380*t*, 381*f*
Tolerance, immune. *See also* Self-tolerance
  transplantation and, 795
Toll-like receptors (TLRs), **769**
Tongue, 852*f*, **859**–860, 859*f*, 860*f*
  muscles of
    extrinsic, 332*t*, 333*f*, 859
    intrinsic, 332*t*, 859
  papillae of, 571, 859, 860*f*
  taste buds on, **571**
"Tongue-tied," 859
Tonic-clonic (grand mal) seizures, 454
Tonicity, **71**–72, 71*f*
Tonic receptors, **489**
Tonsil(s), 758*f*, **760**, 760*f*
  inflammation of (tonsillitis), 764
  lingual, **760**, 760*f*, 808*f*, **809**, 859*f*, 860, 860*f*
  palatine, **760**, 760*f*, 808*f*, **809**
  pharyngeal, **760**, 760*f*, 808*f*, **809**
  tubal, **760**, 808*f*, 809
Tonsillar crypts, **760**, 760*f*
Tonsillitis, **764**
Tooth. *See* Teeth
Tooth sockets (alveoli), 209, **215***t*
  articulation of tooth with (gomphosis), 249*f*, **250**, 863
Torticollis, **382**

Total dead space, **824**
Total lung capacity, **824**, 825*f*
Total metabolic rate, **949**
Touch, discriminative, 471
Touch receptors
  tactile/Meissner's corpuscles, 152, 161, **486**, 487*t*
  tactile/Merkel discs, 150, 151*f*, 161, **486**, 487*t*
tPA. *See* Tissue plasminogen activator
Trabeculae, **177**
  carneae, 667*f*, **668**
  in intramembranous ossification, 182*f*
  lymph node, **757**, 757*f*
  in spongy bone, **177**, 179*f*, 180
Trace elements, 26*t*
Trace minerals, 917, 918–919*t*
Trachea, 805*f*, 807*t*, 808*f*, **812**–813, 812*f*
  obstruction of, 813
Tracheal cartilages, 810*f*, 813
Trachealis muscle, 812*f*, **813**
Tracheoesophageal fistula, 904
Tracheotomy, **847**
Trachoma, **589**, 1059
Traction, **195**
Tracts, **390**
Transamination, **933**, 933*f*, 934*t*
Transcellular route, of tubular reabsorption, 974, 975*f*
  sodium reabsorption and, 974, 976*f*
Transcription, 101, **101**–102, 101*f*, 102*f*, 107*f*
Transcription factors, 101
Transcytosis, 75, 898*f*
Transducin, **563**, 564*f*
Transduction, **489**
  light (phototransduction), 559, 563–564, 564*f*, 565*f*
  in sensory integration, **489**
  signal, membrane proteins in, 64, 66*f*
  smell, 570, 571*f*
Trans face, of Golgi apparatus, 85, 85*f*
Trans fats/trans fatty acids, 47, 913*t*, **944**
Transferrin, **640**, 900
  erythropoiesis and, **640**, 641*f*
Transfer RNA (tRNA), 55, **101**, 107*f*
  aminoacyl, 104, 104*f*, 105
  initiator, **105**
  in translation, 103–105, 104*f*
Transformation, in cancer, 142*b*
Transforming growth factor beta (TGF-β), 790*f*, 792
Transfusion (blood), **654**–657
  blood groups and, 654–655, 655*t*, 656*f*
Transfusion reactions, **656**
  Rh incompatibility and, 655
Transient ischemic attack, **464**–465
Transitional epithelium, 120*f*, **121**
  of bladder wall, 986
  in ureters, 986, 986*f*
Transitional period, of newborn, **1093**
Translation, 101, 101*f*, **103**–105, 103*f*, 104*f*, 105*f*, 107*f*

Transmission electron microscopy (TEM), 115
Transplants (organ), 792–795, 795t
Transport, membrane. See Membrane transport
Transport maximum, in tubular reabsorption, **975**
Transport medium, water as, 38–39
Transport proteins, 51t
Transport vesicles, 85, 85f, 87f
Transposons, 1108
Transpulmonary pressure, 819f, **820**, 822f
Transverse arch of foot, **241**, 241f
Transverse cerebral fissure, **433**, 434f
Transverse cervical nerve, 504f, 504t
Transverse colon, 852f, **890**, 891f
Transverse costal facets, 220, 225f
Transverse foramen, **219**
Transverse fracture, 188
Transverse mesocolon, 891f, 892f
Transverse perineal muscle
    deep, **344**t, 345f
    superficial, **344**t, 345f
Transverse (horizontal) plane/section, **14**, 15f
Transverse processes, vertebral, 217f, 218f, **219**, 219f, 222t
Transverse ridges, in sacrum, 221f, **223**
Transverse sinuses, 461f, 738f, **738**t, 739f
Transversus abdominis muscle, 326f, **342**t, 343f
Trapezium, **231**, 231f, 232t
Trapezius muscle, 326f, 327f, **346**t, 348f, **348**t, 349f
Trapezoid, **231**, 231f, 232t
Trapezoid line, 226, 226f
Trastuzumab, 143b
T$_{Reg}$ cells. See Regulatory T cells
Treponema pallidum, 1058
TRH. See Thyrotropin-releasing hormone
Triad(s), **283**, 283f, 284
Triceps brachii muscle, 326f, 327f, 351f, **353**t, 358f, 359f
Triceps surae muscle, **373**t
Trichomoniasis, **1059**
Trichosiderin, 157
TRICOM. See Cancer vaccine
Tricuspid valve, 666f, 667f, **670**, 671f
Trigeminal ganglion, 497t
Trigeminal nerve (cranial nerve V), 446f, 447, 448f, **493**, 494f, **497**t
    mandibular division of (cranial nerve V$_3$), **497**t
        muscles of mastication supplied by, 332t
    maxillary division of (cranial nerve V$_2$), **497**t
    ophthalmic division of (cranial nerve V$_1$), **497**t
    postganglionic fibers and, 530
Trigeminal neuralgia (tic douloureux), **497**t
Trigger zone, 391, 393t
Triglycerides, **45–47**, 45t, 46f, 897, 912
    in absorptive state, 936–937
    storage of in bone, 176
    transport of, 943, 943f
Trigone (bladder), **986**, 987f

Triiodothyronine (T$_3$), **609**, 612t
Tripeptide, 47
Triple covalent bond, 33f, 34
Triplet (nucleotide base), **100**, 107f
Triplets (microtuble), 89, 90
Triquetrum, **231**, 231f, 232t
Tritium, 28f
tRNA. See Transfer RNA
Trochanter (bone marking), 178t
    greater and lesser, **237**, 238f
Trochlea, **228**, **550**
    of eye, **550**, 550f
    of humerus, **228**, 229f
    of talus, 240, 240f
Trochlear nerve (cranial nerve IV), 446–447f, **493**, 494f, **496**t
    extrinsic eye muscles supplied by, 496t, 551
    trauma/paralysis of, 496t
Trochlear notch, **229**, 230f
Trochlear nuclei, 446
Trophoblast
    cellular (cytotrophoblast), **1077**, 1077f, 1079f
    syncytial (syncytiotrophoblast), **1077**, 1077f, 1079f
Trophoblast cells, **1075**, 1076–1077, 1076f, 1077f, 1079f
Tropic hormones/tropins, **603**
Tropomyosin, **281**, 282f, 291f
    in excitation-contraction coupling, 291f
Troponin, **281**, 282f, 291f, 310t
    in excitation-contraction coupling, 291f
True capillaries, **700**, 700f
True pelvis, **235**
    childbearing and, 235–237
True (vertebrosternal) ribs, **224**, 224f, 225f
True solutions, 29
    concentration of, 29–30
True vocal cords (vocal folds), 808f, 810f, **811**, 811f
    inflammation of (laryngitis), **812**
    voice production and, 811–812
Truncus arteriosus, 688, 688f
Trunk(s), brachial plexus, **505**, 506f
Trunk movements, muscles controlling, **342**t, 343f
    extension, 336–338t, 339f
Trunk region
    arteries supplying, 725f
    veins of, 736f, 737f
Trypsin, **886**, 886f, 896f, 897, 898f
Trypsinogen, 886, 886f
TSH. See Thyroid-stimulating hormone
t-SNAREs, in exocytosis, 78f, 79
T tubules, **283**
    in cardiac muscle, 309t, 673, 674, 674f
    in excitation-contraction coupling, 291f
    in skeletal muscle, **283–284**, 283f, 309t
Tubal ligation, 1096b
Tubal tonsils, **760**, 808f, 809
Tubercle (bone marking), 178t
    adductor, **237**, 238f
    articular, **268**, 268f

conoid, 226, 226f
    of humerus, 228
    pubic, 233f, 234f, **235**
    of rib, 225, 225f
Tuberculosis (TB), **841**–842
    skin tests for, 799
Tuberosity (bone marking), 178t
Tubular glands, **122**, 123f
Tubular reabsorption, 971f, **974**–978, 975f, 976f, 977t, **983**f
    absorptive capabilities of tubules/collecting ducts and, 976–978, 977t
    acid-base balance and, 1011, 1012f
    aldosterone affecting, 978, 983f, 1004, 1004f
    of bicarbonate, 1011, 1012f
    fluid balance and, 1000, 1000f
    of nutrients/water/ions, 975–976, 976f, 981–982, 982f, 983f
    passive, **975**, 976f, 983f
    of potassium, 1006
    of sodium, 974–975, 976f, 983f, 1004, 1004f
Tubular secretion, 971f, **978**, 983f
    acid-base balance and, 978, 983f, 1011, 1011–1014, 1013f
    of bicarbonate, 1014
    of potassium, 978, 1006
Tubulin(s), 88
Tubuloalveolar glands, **122**, 123f
Tubuloglomerular feedback mechanism, **972**, 973f, 974
Tubulus rectus (straight tubule), **1026**, 1027f
Tumor. See Neoplasm
Tumor necrosis factor (TNF), 790f, 791
    in insulin resistance, 627b
Tumor suppressor genes (antioncogenes), **142**b, 143f
Tunic(s), of blood vessels, 695, 696f
Tunica albuginea, **1026**, **1041**
    of ovary, **1041**, 1041f
    of testis, **1026**, 1026f, 1027f, 1029f
Tunica externa (tunica adventitia), **695**, 696f
    in veins, 696f, 700–701
Tunica intima, **695**, 696f
    in atherosclerosis, 702b
Tunica media, **695**, 696f
    in veins, 696f, 700
Tunica vaginalis, **1026**, 1026f, 1027f, 1062
Turbulent flow, 704
Turner's syndrome, 1060
TV. See Tidal volume
T wave, 679f, **680**, 680f
Twins
    fraternal, 1052
    identical, 1052
Twitch, muscle, **293**, 294f
Two-neuron chain, 526, 527f
Two-point discrimination test, **490**
Tympanic cavity (middle ear), **20**, **574**–575, 575f, 576f
Tympanic membrane (eardrum), **574**, 575f
    perforated/ruptured, 583
Tympanic region, temporal bone, **204**, 207f

Type I cells, alveolar, **815**, 816f
Type 1 (insulin-dependent) diabetes mellitus, **626–627**b, 797, 954
Type Ia fibers, **515**, 515f, 516f
Type I (immediate/acute) hypersensitivity, **798**, 798f
Type II cells, alveolar, **815**, 816f
Type 2 (non-insulin-dependent) diabetes mellitus, **627**b, 954
Type II fibers, **515**, 515f
Type II (cytotoxic) hypersensitivity, **799**
Type III (immune complex) hypersensitivity, **799**
Type IV (delayed) hypersensitivity, **799**
Type A blood, 654, 655t, **656**f
Type AB blood, 654, 655t, **656**f
Type A daughter cells, **1033**, 1036f
Type A intercalated cells
    hydrogen secretion by, in acid base balance, 1011
    in potassium regulation, 1006
Type B blood, 654, 655t, **656**f
Type B daughter cells, **1033**, 1036f
Type O blood, 654, 655t, **656**f
Tyrosinase/tyrosine
    in melanin production, 154
    in thyroid hormone synthesis, 610, 610f
Tyrosine kinase, as insulin receptor, 598

Ubiquitins, **106**
Ulcer(s)
    decubitus (skin), **168**
    duodenal, 880
    esophageal, 865
    gastric, **870–871**, 871f
    peptic, **870–871**, 871f, **905**
Ulcerative colitis, 905
Ulna, 199f, **229–230**, 229f, 230f, 232t
Ulnar artery, 725f, 728f, **728**t, 729f
Ulnar collateral ligament, of elbow, **266**, 266f
Ulnar nerve, **505**, 506f, 507t
Ulnar notch, **230**, 230f
Ulnar vein, 737f, 740f, **740**t
Ultrasound imaging (ultrasonography/sonography), **18–19**b, **1097**
Ultraviolet radiation, 154
    melanin response to, 154
    as radiant energy, 24
    skin damage/cancer caused by, 154, 162–163, 165
        aging and, 165
        melanin in protection from, 154
Umami, 572
Umbilical arteries, 745, 1080f, **1084**, 1086f
Umbilical cord, 1079f, **1080**, 1080f
    blood vessels in, 745, 1080f, 1084–1085, 1086f
Umbilical ligaments, medial, 1086f, **1093**
Umbilical region, **17**, 20f
Umbilical vein, 745, 1080f, **1084**–1085, 1086f

Umbilicus, 17, 1086*f*
Uncinate fits, 573
Unconventional myosin, 88
"Uncouplers," poisons as, 928
Uncus, 436*f*, 438
Undershoot (after-hyperpolariza-
    tion), **402**
Undescended testis (crypt-
    orchidism), 1028, 1063
Unencapsulated nerve endings,
    486, 487*t*
Unfused (incomplete) tetanus,
    294*f*, **295**
Uniaxial movement, **253**
Unicellular glands, **121**
    exocrine (mucous/goblet cells),
    121, 122*f*
Unipennate fascicle pattern/muscles,
    322*f*, 323
Unipolar neurons, 392–394, 393–394*t*
Universal donor, **656**
Universal recipient, **656**
Universal solvent (water), **38**–39
Unmyelinated fibers, **391**, 392
    action potential conduction
    velocity and, 404, 405*f*
Unsaturated fats, **46**–47, 912
Upper limbs. *See also* Arm; Forearm;
    Hand
    arteries of, 725*f*, 728–729*f*,
    728–729*t*
    bones of, 199*f*, 228–233, 229*f*,
    230*f*, 231*f*, 232*t*
    innervation of, 505–507, 506*f*, 507*t*
    veins of, 736*f*, 737*f*, 740–741*f*,
    740–741*t*
Upper motor neurons, 474, 512
Upper trunk, brachial plexus,
    505, 506*f*
Up-regulation, **598**
Uracil (U), **53**
Urea, **933**, 933*f*, 985
    recycling, 981, 982*f*
    tubular secretion of, 978
Urea cycle, **934**
Ureter(s), 961, 961*f*, **985**–986, 985*f*,
    986*f*, 987*f*
    autonomic innervation/effects
    and, 529*f*
Ureteral orifices, 986, 987*f*
Ureteric buds, **989**, 990*f*
Ureteric ducts, **989**
Urethra, 961, 961*f*, **987**–988,
    987*f*, **1030**
    autonomic innervation/effects
    and, 538*t*
    embryologic/fetal development
    of, 1061*f*
    in female, 987, 987*f*, 988, 1040*f*
    hypospadias and, 990
    in male, 987, 987*f*, 1025*f*,
    1029*f*, **1030**
Urethral folds, **1060**, 1062*f*
Urethral glands, 1030
Urethral groove, **1060**, 1062*f*
Urethral orifice, external, **987**, 987*f*,
    1025*f*, 1029*f*, 1030,
    1046*f*, 1060
Urethral sphincters
    external, **344***t*, 345*f*, 987, 987*f*
    internal, **987**, 987*f*

Urethritis, 988, 1058
Urgency, urinary, infection and, 988
Uric acid, 985
    in gout, 271
    tubular secretion of, 978
Urinalysis, **992**
Urinary bladder, 961, 961*f*, 985*f*,
    986–988, 987*f*
    atonic, 544
    autonomic innervation/effects
    and, 528*f*, 529*f*, 533*f*, 538*t*
    cancer of, **991**
    developmental aspects of,
    990–991, 990*f*
    embryologic/fetal development
    of, 1061*f*
    infection of (cystitis), 988
Urinary incontinence, **988**
    pregnancy and, 988, 1090
Urinary retention, **988**
Urinary system, 7*f*, 960–994, **961**,
    961*f*. *See also specific structure
    and* Kidneys
    autonomic nervous system
    and, 542*b*
    cardiovascular system and,
    746*b*, 747*b*
    congenital abnormalities of,
    989–990
    developmental aspects of,
    988–991, 990*f*
    digestive system and, 902*b*
    endocrine system and, 628*b*
    homeostatic relationships of, 5*f*,
    1018*b*, 1019*b*
    integumentary system and, 166*b*
    lymphatic system and, 762*b*
    muscular system and, 314*b*
    physiology/functions of, 2, 7*f*
    pregnancy and, 1090
    reproductive system and, 1064*b*
    respiratory system and, 844*b*
    skeletal system and, 192*b*
Urinary tract infections, 963, 988
Urination (micturition), **988**, 989*f*
    development of control of,
    990–991
Urine, **970**, 984–985
    abnormal constituents in,
    985, 985*t*
    in body defense, 772*t*
    chemical composition of, 985
    concentration/volume regulation
    and, 978–982, 979*f*, 980*f*, 982*f*
    countercurrent exchanger
    and, 979, 980*f*, **981**
    countercurrent multiplier
    and, 979, **979**–981, 980*f*
    diuretics and, **982**
    formation of dilute/
    concentrated urine
    and, 981–982, 982*f*
    renal clearance and, 984
    urea recycling/medullary
    osmotic gradient and,
    981, 982*f*
    formation of, 969–984, 971*f*
    concentrated urine and,
    981–982, 982*f*
    dilute urine and, 981, 982*f*
    fetal, 989

    glomerular filtration in,
    969–974, 971*f*, 973*f*
    tubular reabsorption in, 971*f*,
    974–978, 975*f*, 976*f*, 977*t*,
    983*f*. *See also* Tubular
    reabsorption
    tubular secretion in, 971*f*,
    978, **983***f*
    physical characteristics of,
    984–985
    ureters in transport of, 985–986
    urethra in transport of, 987
    water loss in, 999, 999*f*, 1000
Urine output
    low
        anuria, 974
        oliguria, 1001
    water loss and, 999, 999*f*, 1000
Urobilinogen, 641
Urochrome, **984**
Urogenital diaphragm, 987, 987*f*,
    1029*f*, 1040*f*
    muscles of, **344***t*, 345*f*
Urogenital ridges, 988–989, 990*f*
Urogenital sinus, **989**, 990*f*,
    1061*f*, 1062*f*
Urologist, **992**
Uterine arteries, 1043*f*, **1044**, 1045*f*
    ovarian branches of, 1041
Uterine contractions
    Braxton Hicks, 1091
    in labor, 1091, 1092
Uterine (menstrual) cycle,
    1054–1057, 1055*f*, 1057*t*
Uterine glands, 1044, 1045*f*
Uterine (fallopian) tubes, 1040*f*,
    1042, 1043*f*
    embryologic/fetal development
    of, 1061*f*
    fertilization in, 1042, 1076*f*
    inflammation of (salpingitis),
    1066
    resection of (tubal ligation), 1096*b*
Uterosacral ligaments, 1040*f*, 1043*f*,
    1044
Uterus, 1040*f*, **1042**–1044, 1043*f*
    autonomic innervation/effects
    and, 533*f*
    cancer of (endometrial cancer),
    1066
    embryologic/fetal development
    of, 1061*f*
    pregnancy affecting, 1089, 1089*f*
    prolapse of, **1044**
    surgical removal of (hysterec-
    tomy), **1066**
    vascular supply of, 1043*f*,
    1044, 1045*f*
Utricle, **576**, 577*f*, 584
Utrophin, for muscular dystrophy,
    312
Uvea, 551–553, 552*f*
Uvula, 808*f*, 809, **858**, 859*f*

VAC (vacuum-assisted closure), **144**
Vaccines, **782**, 782*f*
Vacuum-assisted closure (VAC), **144**
Vagal tone, of heart, **686**
Vagal trunks, anterior and poste-
    rior, **530**

Vagina, 1040*f*, 1043*f*, **1044**–1046
    autonomic innervation/effects
    and, 533*f*, 538*t*
    embryologic/fetal development
    of, 1061*f*
Vaginal fornix, 1040*f*, **1045**
Vaginal orifice, **1045**, 1046*f*
Vaginal process, 1062
Vaginal ring, for contraception,
    1096*b*
Vagotomy, **544**, **906**
Vagus nerve (cranial nerve X),
    446–447*f*, 448, 448*f*, **493**, 494*f*,
    500*t*, 573
    in food intake regulation,
    945–946, 946*f*
    in gustatory pathway, **573**, 573*f*
    injury/paralysis of, 500*t*
    parasympathetic fibers of,
    529*f*, 530
    resection of (vagotomy), **544**, **906**
Vagus nerve stimulator, in seizure
    prevention, 454
Valence shell, **31**, 31*f*
Vallate (circumvallate) papillae, **571**,
    572*f*, **859**, 860*f*
Valsalva's maneuver, **812**, 895
Valves
    heart, 667*f*, 670–672, 671*f*,
    672*f*, 673*f*
        aging and, 689
        heart murmurs and, **681**
        homeostatic imbalances
        and, 672
    lymphatic capillary, 753*f*, 754
    venous, 696*f*, **701**
Valvular heart disease
    aging and, 689
    incompetence/stenosis, 672, 681
    murmurs and, 681
Vanilloid receptor, 486
Vaporization, heat of, of water,
    38, **951**
Variability/variations, anatomical, 14
Variable, in homeostasis, 9
Variable (V) region, **783**, 783*f*
Variation, genetic, sexual sources of,
    1103–1105, 1103*f*, 1104*f*
Varicocele, 1038
Varicose veins, **701**
    pregnancy and, 1090
Varicosities, autonomic nerve fiber,
    306, **512**
    in smooth muscle, 306, 306*f*
Vasa recta, 967*f*, **968**
Vasa vasorum, **695**
Vascular anastomoses, **701**
Vascular dilation. *See* Vasodilation
Vascular disorders, 745
Vascular endothelial growth factor
    (VEGF), hepatocyte secretion
    of, 881
Vascular layer of eye, 551–553, 552*f*
Vascular permeability, inflammation
    and, 769–771
Vascular plexus
    cutaneous, 149*f*, 152
    subpapillary, 149*f*, 152
Vascular resistance. *See* Peripheral
    (vascular) resistance
Vascular shock, **719**–720

Vascular shunts
 in capillary bed, 699–700, 700*f*
 in fetal circulation, 1084–1085,
  1086*f*
 occlusion of, 1086*f*, 1093
Vascular spasm, in hemostasis,
 649, 649*f*
Vascular system, **714**–744. *See also*
  Blood vessels; Circulation
Vascular tissue. *See* Blood
Vas (ductus) deferens, 1025*f*, 1026*f*,
  1027*f*, 1028, **1029**–1030, 1029*f*
 ampulla of, 1025*f*, **1029**, 1029*f*
 embryologic/fetal development
  of, 1061*f*
 resection of (vasectomy),
  1030, 1096*b*
Vasectomy, **1030**, 1096*b*
Vasoactive intestinal peptide,
  873, 875*t*
Vasoconstriction, **695**
 blood pressure and, 540, 707*f*,
  708, 1007*f*
 heat promotion and, 952, 952*f*
 Raynaud's disease and, 541
Vasodilation, **695**
 heat loss and, 952*f*, 953
 in inflammation, 769–771
Vasomotion, **717**
Vasomotor center, 449, 540, **707**
 blood pressure control and, 707
Vasomotor fibers, **537**, **707**
 blood pressure and, **707**
 vasoactivity and, 695
Vasomotor (sympathetic) tone,
  537, **707**
Vasopressin (antidiuretic hor-
  mone/ADH), 602*f*, **607***t*, **608**,
  709, **981**, 1000–1001, 1000*f*
 blood pressure and, **709**, 709*t*,
  710*f*, 711*f*, 1001, 1007*f*
 in blood volume control, 10
 syndrome of inappropriate secretion of (SIADH), 608, **1020**
 tubular reabsorption and, 978,
  981, 983*f*, 1000, 1000*f*
 urea recycling and, 981
 in water balance regulation,
  1000–1001, 1000*f*
Vasovagal (neurocardiogenic) syncope, **544**
Vastus muscles, 380*t*
 intermedius, 364*f*, **366***t*, 381*f*
 lateralis, 326*f*, 364*f*, **365***t*, 381*f*
 medialis, 326*f*, 364*f*, **365***t*, 381*f*
VC. *See* Vital capacity
VEGF. *See* Vascular endothelial
  growth factor
Veins, **695**, 696*f*, 697*f*, 698*t*, 700–701.
  See also specific named vein
 blood flow velocity and, 714*f*
 blood pressure in, 705–706,
  705*f*, 706*f*
 blood volume in, 701, 701*f*
 pulmonary, **664**, 665–667*f*, 722*f*,
  722–723*t*, 817*f*, **818**
 structure of, 696*f*, 698*t*
 systemic, 721, 736–737*f*, 736*t*
 valves in, 696*f*, **701**
 varicose, **701**
  pregnancy and, 1090

Vellus hair, **159**
Venae cavae, 700–701, 736–737*f*,
  736*t*
 blood flow velocity and, 714*f*
 blood pressure in, 705*f*
 inferior, **664**, 665–667*f*, 731*f*,
  736–737*f*, **736***t*, **742***t*
 superior, **664**, 665–667*f*,
  736–737*f*, **736***t*
 veins draining into, 736–737*f*,
  736*t*
Venereal disease (VD/sexually transmitted infections),
  1058–1059
Venous anastomoses, **701**
Venous blood pressure, 705–706,
  705*f*, 706*f*
Venous plexuses, 716
Venous return, **684**
 muscular/respiratory pumps
  and, **706**, 706*f*, 707*f*
 stroke volume and, **684**, 707*f*
Venous sinuses, **701**
 dural, **461**, 461*f*, 701, 721, 736*f*,
  737*f*, **738***t*
 scleral (canal of Schlemm), 552*f*,
  555, 555*f*
 in splenic pulp, 758, 759*f*
Venous system, 700–701
Venous valves, 696*f*, **701**
Ventilation, 829
 alveolar, **826**, 826*t*
 minute, **825**
 pulmonary. *See* Pulmonary
  ventilation
Ventilation-perfusion coupling,
  829–830, 829*f*
Ventral (term), 12*t*. *See also under
  Anterior*
Ventral body cavity, **16**–20, 16*f*,
  17*f*, 20*f*
 membranes of, 16–17, 17*f*
Ventral (anterior) funiculi, 469*f*, **470**
Ventral (anterior) horns, 433*f*, **468**,
  469*f*, 470*f*
Ventral (anterior) median fissure,
  468, 469*f*
Ventral mesentery, 855, 855*f*
Ventral posterolateral nuclei,
  442, 444*f*
Ventral ramus/rami, **502**, 503*f*, 504,
  504*f*, 504*t*
 brachial plexus, 505, 506*f*
 lumbar plexus, 508*f*
Ventral respiratory group, **835**, 835*f*.
  See also Medullary respiratory
  centers
Ventral root(s), **468**, 469*f*, 470*f*, **502**
 brachial plexus, 505, 506*f*
 lumbar plexus, 508*f*
Ventral rootlets, 468, 469*f*, 503*f*
Ventral (anterior) spinocerebellar
  tract, **471**–472, 471*f*, 473*t*
Ventral (anterior) spinothalamic
  tracts, **471**, 471*f*, 473*t*
Ventral white commissure, 471*f*
Ventricles
 of brain, 431, **431**–433, 431*f*, 433*f*
 of heart, **664**, 665–667*f*, 668, **688**
  development of, 688, 688*f*
Ventricular ejection phase, **682**, 683*f*

Ventricular septal defect, 689*f*
Ventricular systole, 682, 683*f*
Ventricular tachycardia, **690**
Ventromedial nucleus, food intake
  regulation and, 945, 946*f*
Venules, 697*f*, 698*t*, **700**
 blood flow velocity and, 714*f*
 blood pressure in, 705*f*
 postcapillary, **700**, 700*f*
Vermiform appendix, 852*f*, **890**, 891*f*
Vermis, **450**, 451*f*
Vernix caseosa, 165
Vertebrae, 199*f*, **216**, 217*f*, 219, 219*f*
 cervical, **216**, 217*f*, 219–220, 220*f*,
  221*f*, 222*t*
 compression fractures of, in osteoporosis, 190*t*, 191, 244
 lumbar, **216**, 217*f*, 220, 221*f*, 222*t*
 regional characteristics of,
  219–223, 222*t*
 structure of, 219, 219*f*
 thoracic, **216**, 217*f*, 220, 221*f*, 222*t*
Vertebral arch, 219, 219*f*
Vertebral arteries, 725*f*, 726*f*,
  726–727*t*, 727*f*, 728*f*, 729*f*
Vertebral (medial) border of scapula,
  228
Vertebral canal, **219**
Vertebral (spinal) cavity, **14**, 16*f*
Vertebral column (spine/spinal column), 199*f*, **216**–223, 217*f*,
  218*f*, 219*f*, 220*f*, 221*f*, 222*t*
 developmental aspects of, 244
 muscles of, 336–338, 339*f*
 osteoporotic fractures of, 190*t*, 191
Vertebral foramen, 217*f*, 218*f*, **219**,
  219*f*, 222*t*
Vertebral (floating) ribs, **224**, 224*f*
Vertebral spine (spinous process),
  217*f*, 218*f*, **219**, 219*f*, 222*t*
 of vertebra prominens, 219, 221*f*
Vertebral vein, 737*f*, 738*f*, **738***t*, 739*f*
Vertebra prominens, **219**, 221*f*
Vertebrochondral (false) ribs,
  224, 224*f*
Vertebrocostal joint, 254*t*
Vertebrosternal (true) ribs, **224**,
  224*f*, 225*f*
Vertex presentation, 1092, 1092*f*
Vertical (perpendicular) plate, 202*f*,
  203*f*, 204*f*, **209**, 209*f*, 211
Very low density lipoproteins
  (VLDLs), 935, **943**, 943*f*
Vesical artery, superior, 1093
Vesicle(s), **78**
 brain, 1083
  primary, **430**, 431*f*
  secondary, **430**, 431*f*
 clathrin-coated, **75**, 76*f*, 80*t*
 in exocytosis, **78**, 78*f*
 lens, **588**
 optic, **588**
 otic, **588**
 secretory, **85**, 85*f*, 86*f*
 transport, 85, 85*f*, 87*f*
Vesicle SNAREs, in exocytosis, 78, 78*f*
Vesicouterine pouch, 1040*f*, **1044**
Vesicular (Graafian/tertiary) follicles,
  1041*f*, **1042**, 1050*f*, 1051*f*,
  1052
Vesicular trafficking, 75, 77, 77*t*

Vesicular transport, **73**–79, 76*f*,
  77*t*, 78*f*
Vesiculase, 1030
Vestibular apparatus, **584**
Vestibular (equilibrium) cortex, 439
Vestibular folds (false vocal cords),
  808*f*, 810*f*, **811**
Vestibular ganglia, 499*t*, 577*f*, **584**
Vestibular glands, greater (Bartholin's),
  1040*f*, **1046**, 1046*f*
Vestibular membrane, 577, 578*f*
Vestibular nerve, 499*t*, 575*f*, **584**, 584*f*
Vestibular nuclear complex/vestibular
  nuclei, **448**, 448*f*, **587**, 587*f*
Vestibular nystagmus, **585**
Vestibular (oval) window, **574**, 575*f*
Vestibule, **1044**
 of bony labyrinth, 575*f*, **576**
 of mouth, **858**, 859*f*
 of nose, **806**, 808*f*
 of vagina, **1046**, 1046*f*
  bulbs of, 1046*f*, **1047**
  embryologic/fetal development
   of, 1061*f*
Vestibulocochlear nerve (cranial
  nerve VIII), 446–447*f*, 448,
  493, 494*f*, 499*t*, 577, 578*f*, 580,
  582*f*. *See also* Cochlear nerve;
  Vestibular nerve
 lesions of, 499*t*
Vestibulospinal tract, 471*f*, 474*t*, **476**
Viagra, 1032
Vibrissae (nose hairs), **806**
Villi, **878**
 arachnoid, 460*f*, 461
 chorionic, **1078**, 1079*f*, 1080*f*
  testing (chronic villus sampling), **1110**, 1111*f*
 in small intestine, **878**, 879*f*, 880*f*
VIP. *See* Vasoactive intestinal peptide
Viral load, in HIV infection/AIDS, 797
Virchow, Rudolf, 62
Viruses, interferon mechanism
  against, 773–774, 773*f*
Viscera/visceral organs, **16**, 16*f*. *See
  also specific organ*
 musculature of, 342*t*, 343*f*
 thoracic, arteries of, 729*t*
Visceral afferent fibers/nerves, 386,
  387*f*, 491
Visceral efferent nerves, 491
Visceral layer, **663**
 of glomerular capsule, 965*f*, 966,
  969, 969*f*
 of serous pericardium (visceral
  pericardium/epicardium), 17,
  17*f*, 138*f*, **663**, 663*f*
Visceral motor (VM) neurons, **470**,
  470*f*. *See also* Autonomic
  nervous system
Visceral motor zones (lateral horns),
  468, 469*f*, 530, 531*f*
Visceral muscle, 276, **311**. *See also*
  Smooth muscle
 innervation of, 512
Visceral peritoneum, 17, 138*f*, **855**,
  855*f*, 857, 857*f*, 892*f*
Visceral (pulmonary) pleura, 17,
  138*f*, 817*f*, **818**
Visceral (autonomic) reflexes, **514**,
  534–535, 534*f*, 535*f*

Visceral reflex arc, **534**
Visceral sensory area, 439
Visceral (autonomic) sensory (VS) neurons, **470**, 470*f*, **534**
Visceral serosa, **16**, 17*f*
Visceroceptors (interoceptors), **486**, 487*t*
Viscosity (blood), 704
Visible light, **556–557**, 557*f*
Visible spectrum, **556–557**, 557*f*
Vision, **556–569**. *See also under Visual and* Eye
  cortical areas in, 436*f*, 437–438, 566, 567*f*, 568–569
  developmental aspects of, 588
  focusing of light on retina in, 557–559, 558*f*, 560*f*
  light and optics in, 556–557, 557*f*, 558*f*
  pathway to brain and, 566, 567*f*
  photoreceptors/phototransduction in, 559–566, 561*f*, 563*f*, 564*f*, 565*f*
  visual processing and, 566–569, 568*f*
Visual acuity, developmental aspects of, 588
Visual areas, 436*f*, 437–438
Visual association areas, 436*f*, **438**, 568
  homeostatic imbalance and, 439
Visual (striate) cortex, primary, 436*f*, **437–438**, **566**, 567*f*, **568–569**
  homeostatic imbalance and, 439
Visual fields, 566, 567*f*
Visual pathways, 566, 567*f*
Visual pigments (photopigments), **560**, 561*f*, 562, 564*f*
  bleaching of, **562**, 563*f*
Visual processing, 566–569, 568*f*
Visual receptor cells. *See* Photoreceptors
Vital capacity, **824**, 825*f*
Vital signs, **710**
Vitamin(s), 8, **915–916**, 916–917*t*
  absorption of, 900
  fat-soluble, 45*t*, 897, 900, **916**, 917*t*
  storage of in liver, 942*t*
  water-soluble, 900, **916**, 916–917*t*
Vitamin A (retinol), 45*t*, 917*t*
  deficiency of, night blindness and, 566
  in vision, 562, 563*f*
Vitamin B_1 (thiamine), 916*t*
Vitamin B_2 (riboflavin), 916*t*, 921
Vitamin B_3 (niacin), 916*t*, 921
Vitamin B_5 (pantothenic acid), 916*t*
Vitamin B_6 (pyridoxine), 916*t*
Vitamin B_9 (folic acid/folacin), 916*t*
Vitamin B_{12} (cyanocobalamin), 900, 916*t*
  intrinsic factor and, 872, 900
Vitamin C (ascorbic acid), 917*t*
  deficiency of (scurvy), **144**, 917*t*
Vitamin D, 45*t*, 917*t*, **900**
  calcium regulation and, 186, **900**
  deficiency of, osteomalacia and rickets and, **189**
  for osteoporosis, 191
  synthesis of in skin, 161, 624
Vitamin E (tocopherol), 45*t*, 917*t*

Vitamin K (phylloquinone), 45*t*, 917*t*
Vitiligo, **168**
Vitreous humor, 552*f*, **555**
VLDLs. *See* Very low density lipoproteins
VMN. *See* Ventromedial nucleus
$\dot{V}_{O_2max}$, aging affecting, 846
Vocal cords
  false (vestibular folds), 808*f*, 810*f*, **811**
  true. *See* Vocal folds
Vocal folds (true vocal cords), 808*f*, 810*f*, **811**, 811*f*
  inflammation of (laryngitis), **812**
  voice production and, 811–812
Vocal ligaments, **811**
Voice box. *See* Larynx
Voice production, 811–812
Voiding (micturition), **988**, 989*f*
  development of control of, 990–991
Volatile acid, **1011**
Volkmann's (perforating) canals, **180**, 181*f*
Volt(s), 395
Voltage, 79, **395**
Voltage-gated channel(s), 81, **395**, 396*f*
  action potential and, 401*f*, 402
  fast sodium, **674**
  information transfer at chemical synapse and, 408, 409*f*
  muscle contraction and, 288, 288*f*
    in cardiac muscle, 674
Volume–pressure relationships, pulmonary ventilation and, 820, 821*f*, 822*f*
Voluntary muscle, **136**, **276**. *See also* Skeletal muscle(s)
Voluntary nervous system, **386**. *See also* Somatic nervous system
Vomer, 202*f*, 203*f*, 205*f*, **211**, 215*t*
Vomiting (emesis), **876**
von Willebrand factor, 649–650
V (variable) region, **783**, 783*f*
VRG. *See* Ventral respiratory group
v-SNAREs, in exocytosis, 78, 78*f*
VT/V-tac. *See* Ventricular tachycardia
Vulva (external genitalia), **1041**, **1046–1047**, 1046*f*
  embryologic/fetal development of, 1062*f*

Wallerian degeneration, **491–492**, 493*f*
Warfarin, **653**
Warton's jelly, 1080
Warts, genital, **1059**
Water, 8, 34, 34*f*, 38–39
  absorption of, in digestion, 900–901
  body, 996, 997*f*
    developmental changes in, 1015. *See also* Water balance
  exchanges of among fluid compartments, 998, 998*f*
  facultative reabsorption of, **981**
  hydrogen bonding and, 35, 35*f*
  intake of, 998, 999–1000, 999*f*
  loss of

  insensible, **951**, **998**, 999*f*
  obligatory, **1000**
  sensible, **1000**
  metabolic (water of oxidation), **998**
  obligatory reabsorption of, **975**
  output of, 998–999, 999*f*, 1000
  polarity of, 38
  as solvent, 29, 38–39
  as survival requirement, 8, 38–39
  tubular reabsorption of, 975–976, 976*f*, 981–982, 982*f*, 983*f*
  in urine, 985
Water balance, 998–1002, 999*f*, 1000*f*, 1001*f*
  antidiuretic hormone in, 1000–1001, 1000*f*
  developmental aspects of, 1015
  disorders of, 1001–1002, 1001*f*
  hypothalamus in, 444, 999, 999*f*
  kidneys in, 975, 976*f*, 1000, 1000–1001, 1000*f*
  sodium in, 1002–1004
    regulation and, 1004–1006, 1004*f*, 1005*f*, 1007*f*
  water intake regulation and, 999–1000, 999*f*
  water output regulation and, 1000
Water intake, 998, 999–1000, 999*f*
Water on the knee, 270
Water output, 998–999, 999*f*, 1000
Water-soluble vitamins, 900, **916**, 916–917*t*
Wavelength
  light, 556–557, 557*f*
  sound, **579**
Wave (temporal) summation, **294–295**, 294*f*, **412**
  by postsynaptic neuron, **412**, 413*f*
WBCs. *See* White blood cell(s)
Weak acids, 41, 1009, 1009*f*
Weak bases, **41**
Wear-and-tear theory of aging, 108
Weber's test, **589**
Weeping lubrication, 251–252
Weight, regulation of, 945–947, 946*f*
Weight gain, during pregnancy, 1089
Weight-loss supplements, 949*b*
Weight training
  anabolic steroid abuse and, 313*b*
  energy balance and, 945
Wernicke's area, 436*f*, **457**
  language and, **457**
White blood cell(s) (leukocytes), **126**, 133, 134*t*, 135*f*, 635, 635*f*, 637, **643–648**, 644*f*, **645***t*. *See also specific type*
  disorders of, 646–648
  granular (granulocytes), 643, **644–646**, 644*f*, 645*t*
  nongranular (agranulocytes), 643, 644*f*, 645*t*, **646**
  production/life span of, 645*t*, 646
  in urine, 985*t*
White blood cell count, 643, 644*f*, 657
  differential, **657**
White columns/funiculi, 469*f*, **470**, 471*f*
White fat (white adipose tissue), 127
White fibers, 124, 125*f*
Whitehead, 157

White matter, **392**
  of brain
    cerebellar, 450
    cerebral, 434*f*, 435, **440–441**, 440*f*
    midbrain, 446
  development of, 431
  of spinal cord, 469*f*, 470–471, 471*f*
White pulp, **758**, 759*f*
White ramus communicans/rami communicante, **530**, 531*f*, 533*f*
Whole blood transfusions, **654**
Willis, circle of (cerebral arterial circle), 726*f*, 727*f*, **727***t*
Window of implantation, 1076
Windpipe. *See* Trachea
Wisdom teeth, 862, 862*f*
Withdrawal (coitus interruptus), 1095*b*
Withdrawal (flexor) reflex, 5, 10, **518–519**, 519*f*
Wolffian (mesonephric) ducts, **989**, **1060**
  in gonadal development, **1060**, 1061*f*
  in kidney development, **989**, 990*f*
Wolff's law, 187
Working (short-term) memory, **457**, 458*f*
Wound healing/repair, 139–141, 140*f*
  by first/second intention, **144**
Woven bone
  in intramembranous ossification, 182*f*
  in longitudinal bone growth, 184
Wrist (carpus)
  bones of (carpals), 199*f*, **231**, 231*f*, 232*t*
  muscles controlling movement of, 354*t*, 356*t*, 357*f*, 358*t*, 359*f*
Wrist drop, 507
Wrist (radiocarpal) joint, 254*t*

X chromosome, **1059**, 1102, 1107*f*
  genetic sex determination and, 1059–1060
  sex-linked inheritance and, **1107**, 1107*f*
Xenical. *See* Orlistat
Xenobiotics, male infertility and, 1038
Xenografts, **792**
Xenon CT, **18***b*
Xerostomia, 861, **906**
Xiphisternal joint, **223–224**, 224*f*
Xiphoid process, 223, 224*f*
X-linked inheritance, **1107**, 1107*f*
X ray imaging, **18***b*

Yawn, 826*t*
Y chromosome, **1059**, 1102, 1107*f*
  genetic sex determination and, 1059–1060
  sex-linked inheritance and, 1107, 1107*f*
Yellow bone marrow, 177
Yellow bone marrow cavity, **177**
Yellow fibers, 125, 125*f*
Yolk sac, 1079*f*, **1080**, 1081*f*, 1082*f*, 1083*f*, 1084

Z discs/lines, **281**
in cardiac muscle, 673, 674*f*
in skeletal muscle, 280*f*, **281**
in sliding filament model of contraction, 284, 284*f*
ZIFT. *See* Zygote intrafallopian transfer

Zinc, 919*t*
ZIPs. *See* Zonal inhibiting proteins
Zona fasciculata, **614**, 615*f*
Zona glomerulosa, **614**, 615*f*
Zonal inhibiting proteins, 1073
Zona pellucida, 1041*f*, 1051*f*, **1052**
Zona reticularis, **614**, 615*f*

Zygomatic arch, **204**, 205*f*
Zygomatic bones, 202*f*, 203*f*, 205*f*, **211**, 215*t*
Zygomatic branch of facial nerve, 498*t*, 499*t*
Zygomatic process, 203*f*, **204**, 205*f*, 207*f*, **210**, 210*f*, 211, **214***t*, **215***t*

Zygomaticus muscles, 326*f*, **330***t*, 331*f*
Zygote, **1072**, 1073, 1075*f*, 1076*f*
cleavage of, **1075**–1076, 1076*f*
Zygote intrafallopian transfer (ZIFT), 1096
Zymogen granules, **885**, 885*f*

Word Roots, Prefixes, Suffixes, and Combining Forms

Prefixes and Combining Forms

a-, an- *absence or lack*; acardia, lack of a heart, anaerobic, in the absence of oxygen

ab- *departing from, away from*; abnormal, departing from normal

acou- *hearing*; acoustics, the science of sound

ac-, acro- *extreme or extremity, peak*; acrodermatitis, inflammation of the skin of the extremities

ad- *to or toward*; adorbital, toward the orbit

aden-, adeno- *gland*; adeniform, resembling a gland in shape

adren- *toward the kidney*; adrenal gland, adjacent to the kidney

aero- *air*; aerobic respiration, oxygen-requiring metabolism

af- *toward*; afferent neurons, which carry impulses to the central nervous system

agon- *contest*; agonistic and antagonistic muscles, which oppose each other

alb- *white*; corpus albicans of the ovary, a white scar tissue

aliment- *nourish*; alimentary canal, or digestive tract

allel- *of one another*; alleles, alternative expressions of a gene

amphi- *on both sides, of both kinds*; amphibian, an organism capable of living in water and on land

ana- *apart, up, again*; anaphase of mitosis, when the chromosomes separate

anastomos- *come together*; arteriovenous anastomosis, a connection between an artery and a vein

aneurysm *a widening*; aortic aneurysm, a weak spot that causes enlargement of the blood vessel

angi- *vessel*; angiitis, inflammation of a lymph vessel or blood vessel

angin- *choked*; angina pectoris, a choked feeling in the chest due to dysfunction of the heart

ant-, anti- *opposed to, preventing or inhibiting*; anticoagulant, a substance that prevents blood coagulation

ante- *preceding, before*; antecubital, in front of the elbow

aort- *great artery*; aorta

ap-, api- *tip, extremity*; apex of the heart

append- *hang to*; appendicular skeleton

aqua-, aque- *water*; aqueous solutions

arbor- *tree*; arbor vitae of the cerebellum, the treelike pattern of white matter

areola- *open space*; areolar connective tissue, a loose connective tissue

arrect- *upright*; arrector pili muscles of the skin, which make the hairs stand erect

arthr-, arthro- *joint*; arthropathy, any joint disease

artic- *joint*; articular surfaces of bones, the points of connection

atri- *vestibule*; atria, upper chambers of the heart

auscult- *listen*; auscultatory method for measuring blood pressure

aut-, auto- *self*; autogenous, self-generated

ax-, axi-, axo- *axis, axle*; axial skeleton, axis of vertebral column

azyg- *unpaired*; azygous vein, an unpaired vessel

baro- *pressure*; baroreceptors for monitoring blood pressure

basal *base*; basal lamina of epithelial basement membrane

bi- *two*; bicuspid, having two cusps

bili- *bile*; bilirubin, a bile pigment

bio- *life*; biology, the study of life and living organisms

blast- *bud or germ*; blastocyte, undifferentiated embryonic cell

brachi- *arm*; brachial plexus of peripheral nervous system supplies the arm

brady- *slow*; bradycardia, abnormally slow heart rate

brev- *short*; peroneus brevis, a short leg muscle

broncho- *bronchus*; bronchospasm, spasmodic contraction of bronchial muscle

bucco- *cheek*; buccolabial, pertaining to the cheek and lip

calor- *heat*; calories, a measure of energy

capill- *hair*; blood and lymph capillaries

caput- *head*; decapitate, remove the head

carcin- *cancer*; carcinogen, a cancer-causing agent

cardi-, cardio- *heart*; cardiotoxic, harmful to the heart

carneo- *flesh*; trabeculae carneae, ridges of muscle in the ventricles of the heart

carot- *(1) carrot, (2) stupor*; (1) carotene, an orange pigment, (2) carotid arteries in the neck, blockage causes fainting

cata- *down*; catabolism, chemical breakdown

caud- *tail*; caudal (directional term)

cec- *blind*; cecum of large intestine, a blind-ended pouch

cele- *abdominal*; celiac artery, in the abdomen

cephal- *head*; cephalometer, an instrument for measuring the head

cerebro- *brain, especially the cerebrum*; cerebrospinal, pertaining to the brain and spinal cord

cervic-, cervix *neck*; cervix of the uterus

chiasm- *crossing*; optic chiasma, where optic nerves cross

chole- *bile*; cholesterol, cholecystokinin, a bile-secreting hormone

chondr- *cartilage*; chondrogenic, giving rise to cartilage

chrom- *colored*; chromosome, so named because they stain darkly

cili- *small hair*; ciliated epithelium

circum- *around*; circumnuclear, surrounding the nucleus

clavic- *key*; clavicle, a "skeleton key"

co-, con- *together*; concentric, common center, together in the center

coccy- *cuckoo*; coccyx, which is beak-shaped

cochlea *snail shell*; the cochlea of the inner ear, which is coiled like a snail shell

coel- *hollow*; coelom, the ventral body cavity

commis- *united*; gray commissure of the spinal cord connects the two columns of gray matter

concha *shell*; nasal conchae, coiled shelves of bone in the nasal cavity

contra- *against*; contraceptive, agent preventing conception

corn-, cornu- *horn*; stratum corneum, outer layer of the skin composed of (horny) cells

corona *crown*; coronal suture of the skull

corp- *body*; corpse, corpus luteum, hormone-secreting body in the ovary

cort- *bark*; cortex, the outer layer of the brain, kidney, adrenal glands, and lymph nodes

cost- *rib*; intercostal, between the ribs

crani- *skull*; craniotomy, a skull operation

crypt- *hidden*; cryptomenorrhea, a condition in which menstrual symptoms are experienced but no external loss of blood occurs

cusp- *pointed*; bicuspid, tricuspid valves of the heart

cutic- *skin*; cuticle of the nail

cyan- *blue*; cyanosis, blue color of the skin due to lack of oxygen

cyst- *sac, bladder*; cystitis, inflammation of the urinary bladder

cyt- *cell*; cytology, the study of cells

de- *undoing, reversal, loss, removal*; deactivation, becoming inactive

decid- *falling off*; deciduous (milk) teeth

delta *triangular*; deltoid muscle, roughly triangular in shape

den-, dent- *tooth*; dentin of the tooth

dendr- *tree, branch*; dendrites, telodendria, both branches of a neuron

derm- *skin*; dermis, deep layer of the skin

desm- *bond*; desmosome, which binds adjacent epithelial cells

di- *twice, double*; dimorphism, having two forms

dia- *through, between*; diaphragm, the wall through or between two areas

dialys- *separate, break apart*; kidney dialysis, in which waste products are removed from the blood

diastol- *stand apart*; cardiac diastole, between successive contractions of the heart

diure- *urinate*; diuretic, a drug that increases urine output

dors- *the back*; dorsal, dorsum, dorsiflexion

duc-, duct *lead, draw*; ductus deferens which carries sperm from the epididymis into the urethra during ejaculation

dura *hard*; dura mater, tough outer meninx

dys- *difficult, faulty, painful*; dyspepsia, disturbed digestion

ec-, ex-, ecto- *out, outside, away from*; excrete, to remove materials from the body

ectop- *displaced*; ectopic pregnancy, ectopic focus for initiation of heart contraction

edem- *swelling*; edema, accumulation of water in body tissues

ef- *away*; efferent nerve fibers, which carry impulses away from the central nervous system

ejac- *to shoot forth*; ejaculation of semen

embol- *wedge*; embolus, an obstructive object traveling in the bloodstream

en-, em- *in, inside*; encysted, enclosed in a cyst or capsule

enceph- *brain*; encephalitis, inflammation of the brain

endo- *within, inner*; endocytosis, taking particles into a cell

entero- *intestine*; enterologist, one who specializes in the study of intestinal disorders

epi- *over, above*; epidermis, outer layer of skin

erythr- *red*; erythema, redness of the skin, erythrocyte, red blood cell

eso- *within*; esophagus

eu- *well*; euesthesia, a normal state of the senses

excret- *separate*; excretory system

exo- *outside, outer layer*; exophthalmos, an abnormal protrusion of the eye from the orbit

extra- *outside, beyond*; extracellular, outside the body cells of an organism

extrins- *from the outside*; extrinsic regulation of the heart

fasci-, fascia- *bundle, band*; superficial and deep fascia

fenestr- *window*; fenestrated capillaries

ferr- *iron*; transferrin, ferritin, both iron-storage proteins

flagell- *whip*; flagellum, the tail of a sperm cell

flat- *blow, blown*; flatulence

folli- *bag, bellows*; hair follicle

fontan- *fountain*; fontanelles of the fetal skull

foram- *opening*; foramen magnum of the skull

foss- *ditch*; fossa ovalis of the heart, mandibular fossa of the skull

gam-, gamet- *married, spouse*; gametes, the sex cells

gangli- *swelling, or knot*; dorsal root ganglia of the spinal nerves

gastr- *stomach*; gastrin, a hormone that influences gastric acid secretion

gene *beginning, origin*; genetics

germin- *grow*; germinal epithelium of the gonads

gero-, geront- *old man*; gerontology, the study of aging

gest- *carried*; gestation, the period from conception to birth

glauc- *gray*; glaucoma, which causes gradual blindness

glom- *ball*; glomeruli, clusters of capillaries in the kidneys

glosso- *tongue*; glossopathy, any disease of the tongue

gluco-, glyco- gluconeogenesis, the production of glucose from noncarbohydrate molecules

glute- *buttock*; gluteus maximus, largest muscle of the buttock

gnost- *knowing*; the gnostic sense, a sense of awareness of self

gompho- *nail*; gomphosis, the term applied to the joint between tooth and jaw

gon-, gono- *seed, offspring*; gonads, the sex organs

gust- *taste*; gustatory sense, the sense of taste

hapt- *fasten, grasp*; hapten, a partial antigen

hema-, hemato-, hemo- *blood*; hematocyst, a cyst containing blood

hemi- *half*; hemiglossal, pertaining to one-half of the tongue

hepat- *liver*; hepatitis, inflammation of the liver

hetero- *different or other*; heterosexuality, sexual desire for a person of the opposite sex

hiat- *gap*; the hiatus of the diaphragm, the opening through which the esophagus passes

hippo- *horse*; hippocampus of the brain, shaped like a seahorse

hirsut- *hairy*; hirsutism, excessive body hair

hist- *tissue*; histology, the study of tissues

holo- *whole*; holocrine glands, whose secretions are whole cells

hom-, homo- *same*; homeoplasia, formation of tissue similar to normal tissue; homocentric, having the same center

hormon- *to excite*; hormones

humor- *a fluid*; humoral immunity, which involves antibodies circulating in the blood

hyal- *clear*; hyaline cartilage, which has no visible fibers

hydr-, hydro- *water*; dehydration, loss of body water

hyper- *excess*; hypertension, excessive tension

hypno- *sleep*; hypnosis, a sleeplike state

hypo- *below, deficient*; hypodermic, beneath the skin, hypokalemia, deficiency of potassium

hyster-, hystero- *uterus or womb*; hysterectomy, removal of the uterus, hysterodynia, pain in the womb

ile- *intestine*; ileum, the last portion of the small intestine

im- *not*; impermeable, not permitting passage, not permeable

inter- *between*; intercellular, between the cells

intercal- *insert*; intercalated discs, the end membranes between adjacent cardiac muscle cells

intra- *within, inside*; intracellular, inside the cell

iso- *equal, same*; isothermal, equal, or same, temperature

jugul- *throat*; jugular veins, prominent vessels in the neck

juxta- *near, close to*; juxtaglomerular apparatus, a cell cluster next to a glomerulus in the kidneys

karyo- *kernel, nucleus*; karyotype, the assemblage of the nuclear chromosomes

kera- *horn*; keratin, the water-repellent protein of the skin

kilo- *thousand*; kilocalories, equal to 1000 calories

kin-, kines- *move*; kinetic energy, the energy of motion

labi-, labri- *lip*; labial frenulum, the membrane which joins the lip to the gum

lact- *milk*; lactose, milk sugar

lacun- *space, cavity, lake*; lacunae, the spaces occupied by cells of cartilage and bone tissue

lamell- *small plate*; concentric lamellae, rings of bone matrix in compact bone

lamina *layer, sheet*; basal lamina, part of the epithelial basement membrane

lat- *wide*; latissimus dorsi, a broad muscle of the back

laten- *hidden*; latent period of a muscle twitch

later- *side*; lateral (directional term)

leuko- *white*; leukocyte, white blood cell

leva- *raise, elevate*; levator labii superioris, muscle that elevates upper lip

lingua- *tongue*; lingual tonsil, adjacent to the tongue

lip-, lipo- *fat, lipid*; lipophage, a cell that has taken up fat in its cytoplasm

lith- *stone*; cholelithiasis, gallstones

luci- *clear*; stratum lucidum, clear layer of the epidermis

lumen *light*; lumen, center of a hollow structure

lut- *yellow*; corpus luteum, a yellow, hormone-secreting structure in the ovary

lymph *water*; lymphatic circulation, return of clear fluid to the bloodstream

macro- *large*; macromolecule, large molecule

macula *spot*; macula lutea, yellow spot on the retina

magn- *large*; foramen magnum, largest opening of the skull

mal- *bad, abnormal*; malfunction, abnormal functioning of an organ

mamm- *breast*; mammary gland, breast

mast- *breast*; mastectomy, removal of a mammary gland

mater *mother*; dura mater, pia mater, membranes that envelop the brain

meat- *passage*; external acoustic meatus, the ear canal

medi- *middle*; medial (directional term)

medull- *marrow*; medulla, the middle portion of the kidney, adrenal gland, and lymph node

mega- *large*; megakaryocyte, large precursor cell of platelets

meio- *less*; meiosis, nuclear division that halves the chromosome number

melan- *black*; melanocytes, which secrete the black pigment melanin

men-, menstru- *month*; menses, the cyclic menstrual flow

meningo- *membrane*; meningitis, inflammation of the membranes of the brain

mer-, mero- *a part*; merocrine glands, the secretions of which do not include the cell

meso- *middle*; mesoderm, middle germ layer

meta- *beyond, between, transition*; metatarsus, the part of the foot between the tarsus and the phalanges

metro- *uterus*; endometrium, the lining of the uterus

micro- *small*; microscope, an instrument used to make small objects appear larger

mictur- *urinate*; micturition, the act of voiding the bladder

mito- *thread, filament*; mitochondria, small, filament-like structures located in cells

mnem- *memory*; amnesia

mono- *single*; monospasm, spasm of a single limb

morpho- *form*; morphology, the study of form and structure or organisms

multi- *many*; multinuclear, having several nuclei

mur- *wall*; intramural ganglion, a nerve junction within an organ

muta- *change*; mutation, change in the base sequence of DNA

myelo- *spinal cord, marrow*; myeloblasts, cells of the bone marrow

myo- *muscle*; myocardium, heart muscle

nano- *dwarf*; nanometer, one-billionth of a meter

narco- *numbness*; narcotic, a drug producing stupor or numbed sensations

natri- *sodium*; atrial natriuretic peptide, a sodium-regulating hormone

necro- *death*; necrosis, tissue death

neo- *new*; neoplasm, an abnormal growth

nephro- *kidney*; nephritis, inflammation of the kidney

neuro- *nerve*; neurophysiology, the physiology of the nervous system

noci- *harmful*; nociceptors, receptors for pain

nom- *name*; innominate artery, innominate bone

noto- *back*; notochord, the embryonic structure that precedes the vertebral column

nucle- *pit, kernel, little nut*; nucleus

nutri- *feed, nourish*; nutrition

ob- *before, against*; obstruction, impeding or blocking up

oculo- *eye*; monocular, pertaining to one eye

odonto- *teeth*; orthodontist, one who specializes in proper positioning of the teeth in relation to each other

olfact- *smell*; olfactory nerves

oligo- *few*; oligodendrocytes, neuroglial cells with few branches

onco- *a mass*; oncology, study of cancer

oo- *egg*; oocyte, precursor of female gamete

ophthalmo- *eye*; ophthalmology, the study of the eyes and related disease

orb- *circular*; orbicularis oculi, muscle that encircles the eye

orchi- *testis*; cryptorchidism, failure of the testes to descend into the scrotum

org- *living*; organism

ortho- *straight, direct*; orthopedic, correction of deformities of the musculoskeletal system

osm- *smell*; anosmia, loss of sense of smell

osmo- *pushing*; osmosis

osteo- *bone*; osteodermia, bony formations in the skin

oto- *ear*; otoscope, a device for examining the ear

ov-, ovi- *egg*; ovum, oviduct

oxy- *oxygen*; oxygenation, the saturation of a substance with oxygen

pan- *all, universal*; panacea, a cure-all

papill- *nipple*; dermal papillae, projections of the dermis into the epidermal area

para- *beside, near*; paranuclear, beside the nucleus

pect-, pectus *breast*; pectoralis major, a large chest muscle

pelv- *a basin*; pelvic girdle, which cradles the pelvic organs

peni- *a tail*; penis; penile urethra

penna- *feather*; unipennate, bipennate muscles, whose fascicles have a feathered appearance

pent- *five*; pentose, a 5-carbon sugar

pep-, peps-, pept- *digest*; pepsin, a digestive enzyme of the stomach; peptic ulcer

per-, permea- *through*; permeate, permeable

peri- *around*; perianal, situated around the anus

phago- *eat*; phagocyte, a cell that engulfs and digests particles or cells

pheno- *show, appear*; phenotype, the physical appearance of an individual

phleb- *vein*; phlebitis, inflammation of the veins

pia *tender*; pia mater, delicate inner membrane around the brain and spinal cord

pili *hair*; arrector pili muscles of the skin, which make the hairs stand erect

pin-, pino- *drink*; pinocytosis, the engulfing of small particles by a cell

platy- *flat, broad*; platysma, broad, flat muscle of the neck

pleur- *side, rib*; pleural serosa, the membrane that lines the thoracic cavity and covers the lungs

plex-, plexus *net, network*; brachial plexus, the network of nerves that supplies the arm

pneumo- *air, wind*; pneumothorax, air in the thoracic cavity

pod- *foot*; podiatry, the treatment of foot disorders

poly- *multiple*; polymorphism, multiple forms

post- *after, behind*; posterior, places behind (a specific) part

pre-, pro- *before, ahead of*; prenatal, before birth

procto- *rectum, anus*; proctoscope, an instrument for examining the rectum

pron- *bent forward*; prone, pronate

propri- *one's own*; proprioception, awareness of body parts and movement

pseudo- *false*; pseudotumor, a false tumor

psycho- *mind, psyche*; psychogram, a chart of personality traits

ptos- *fall*; renal ptosis, a condition in which the kidneys drift below their normal position

pub- *of the pubis*; puberty

pulmo- *lung*; pulmonary artery, which brings blood to the lungs

pyo- *pus*; pyocyst, a cyst that contains pus

pyro- *fire*; pyrogen, a substance that induces fever

quad-, quadr- *four-sided*; quadratus lumborum, a muscle with a square shape

re- *back, again*; reinfect

rect- *straight*; rectus abdominis, rectum

ren- *kidney*; renal, renin, an enzyme secreted by the kidney

retin, retic- *net, network*; endoplasmic reticulum, a network of membranous sacs within a cell

retro- *backward, behind*; retrogression, to move backward in development

rheum- *watery flow, change, or flux*; rheumatoid arthritis, rheumatic fever

rhin-, rhino- *nose*; rhinitis, inflammation of the nose

ruga- *fold, wrinkle*; rugae, the folds of the stomach, gallbladder, and urinary bladder

sagitt- *arrow*; sagittal (directional term)

salta- *leap*; saltatory conduction, the rapid conduction of impulses along myelinated neurons

sanguin- *blood*; consanguineous, indicative of a genetic relationship between individuals

sarco- *flesh*; sarcomere, unit of contraction in skeletal muscle

saphen- *visible, clear*; great saphenous vein, superficial vein of the thigh and leg

sclero- *hard*; sclerodermatitis, inflammatory thickening and hardening of the skin

seb- *grease*; sebum, the oil of the skin

semen *seed, sperm*; semen, the discharge of the male reproductive system

semi- *half*; semicircular, having the form of half a circle

sens- *feeling*; sensation, sensory

septi- *rotten*; sepsis, infection, antiseptic

septum *fence*; nasal septum

sero- *serum*; serological tests, which assess blood conditions

serrat- *saw*; serratus anterior, a muscle of the chest wall that has a jagged edge

sin-, sino- *a hollow*; sinuses of the skull

soma- *body*; somatic nervous system

somn- *sleep*; insomnia, inability to sleep

sphin- *squeeze*; sphincter

splanchn- *organ*; splanchnic nerve, autonomic supply to abdominal viscera

spondyl- *vertebra*; ankylosing spondylitis, rheumatoid arthritis affecting the spine

squam- *scale, flat*; squamous epithelium, squamous suture of the skull

steno- *narrow*; stenocoriasis, narrowing of the pupil

strat- *layer*; strata of the epidermis, stratified epithelium

stria- *furrow, streak*; striations of skeletal and cardiac muscle tissue

stroma *spread out*; stroma, the connective tissue framework of some organs

sub- *beneath, under*; sublingual, beneath the tongue

sucr- *sweet*; sucrose, table sugar

sudor- *sweat*; sudoriferous glands, the sweat glands

super- *above, upon*; superior, quality or state of being above others or a part

supra- *above, upon*; supracondylar, above a condyle

sym-, syn- *together, with*; synapse, the region of communication between two neurons

synerg- *work together*; synergism

systol- *contraction*; systole, contraction of the heart

tachy- *rapid*; tachycardia, abnormally rapid heartbeat

tact- *touch*; tactile sense

telo- *the end*; telophase, the end of mitosis

templ-, tempo- *time*; temporal summation of nerve impulses

tens- *stretched*; muscle tension

terti- *third*; fibularis tertius, one of three fibularis muscles

tetan- *rigid, tense*; tetanus of muscles

therm- *heat*; thermometer, an instrument used to measure heat

thromb- *clot*; thrombocyte, thrombus

thyro- *a shield*; thyroid gland

tissu- *woven*; tissue

tono- *tension*; tonicity, hypertonic

tox- *poison*; toxicology, study of poisons

trab- *beam, timber*; trabeculae, spicules of bone in spongy bone tissue

trans- *across, through*; transpleural, through the pleura

trapez- *table*; trapezius, the four-sided muscle of the upper back

tri- *three*; trifurcation, division into three branches

trop- *turn, change*; tropic hormones, whose targets are endocrine glands

troph- *nourish*; trophoblast, from which develops the fetal portion of the placenta

tuber- *swelling*; tuberosity, a bump on a bone

tunic- *covering*; tunica albuginea, the covering of the testis

tympan- *drum*; tympanic membrane, the eardrum

ultra- *beyond*; ultraviolet radiation, beyond the band of visible light

vacc- *cow*; vaccine

vagin- *a sheath*; vagina

vagus *wanderer*; the vagus nerve, which starts at the brain and travels into the abdominopelvic cavity

valen- *strength*; valence shells of atoms

venter, ventr- *abdomen, belly*; ventral (directional term), ventricle

vent- *the wind*; pulmonary ventilation

vert- *turn*; vertebral column

vestibul- *a porch*; vestibule, the anterior entryway to the mouth and nose

vibr- *shake, quiver*; vibrissae, hairs of the nasal vestibule

villus *shaggy hair*; microvilli, which have the appearance of hair in light microscopy

viscero- *organ, viscera*; visceroinhibitory, inhibiting the movements of the viscera

viscos- *sticky*; viscosity, resistance to flow

vita- *life*; vitamin

vitre- *glass*; vitreous humor, the clear jelly of the eye

viv- *live*; in vivo

vulv- *a covering*; vulva, the female external genitalia

zyg- *a yoke, twin*; zygote

Suffixes

-able *able to, capable of*; viable, ability to live or exist

-ac *referring to*; cardiac, referring to the heart

-algia *pain in a certain part*; neuralgia, pain along the course of a nerve

-apsi *juncture*; synapse, where two neurons communicate

-ary *associated with, relating to*; coronary, associated with the heart

-asthen *weakness*; myasthenia gravis, a disease involving paralysis

-bryo *swollen*; embryo

-cide *destroy or kill*; germicide, an agent that kills germs

-cipit *head*; occipital

-clast *break*; osteoclast, a cell that dissolves bone matrix

-crine *separate*; endocrine organs, which secrete hormones into the blood

-dips *thirst, dry*; polydipsia, excessive thirst associated with diabetes

-ectomy *cutting out, surgical removal*; appendectomy, cutting out of the appendix

-ell, -elle *small*; organelle

-emia *condition of the blood*; anemia, deficiency of red blood cells

-esthesi *sensation*; anesthesia, lack of sensation